HUMIDITY AND MOISTURE

Measurement and Control
in Science and Industry

HUMIDITY AND MOISTURE

Measurement and Control in Science and Industry

Arnold Wexler, Editor-in-Chief
National Bureau of Standards

Volume One

Principles and Methods of Measuring Humidity in Gases
Robert E. Ruskin, Editor
Naval Research Laboratory

Volume Two

Applications
Elias J. Amdur, Editor
Honeywell, Inc.

Volume Three

Fundamentals and Standards
Arnold Wexler and William A. Wildhack, Editors
National Bureau of Standards

Volume Four

Principles and Methods of Measuring Moisture in Liquids and Solids
Paul N. Winn, Jr.
University of Maryland

HUMIDITY
and
MOISTURE

Measurement and Control in Science and Industry

ARNOLD WEXLER
Editor-in-Chief
National Bureau of Standards

VOLUME ONE
PRINCIPLES AND METHODS OF MEASURING HUMIDITY IN GASES

ROBERT E. RUSKIN, Editor
Naval Research Laboratory

---

*Based on papers presented at the
1963 International Symposium on Humidity and Moisture
Washington, D.C.*

Sponsored by

National Bureau of Standards
U.S. Weather Bureau
American Society of Heating, Refrigerating and Air-Conditioning Engineers
American Meteorological Society
Instrument Society of America

REINHOLD PUBLISHING CORPORATION, NEW YORK
Chapman & Hall, Ltd., London

Symposium Committees

General Committee

W. A. Wildhack, *Chairman*
National Bureau of Standards
Washington, D. C.

Arnold Wexler
National Bureau of Standards
Washington, D.C.

A. K. Showalter
U.S. Weather Bureau
Washington, D.C.

Lester Machta
U.S. Weather Bureau
Washington, D.C.

A. S. Gates, Jr.
ASHRAE, National Institutes of Health
Bethesda, Md.

J. L. Threlkeld
ASHRAE, University of Minneapolis
Minneapolis, Minn.

G. O. Haglund
ISA, Vitro Corporation
New York, N.Y.

H. S. Kindler
Instrument Society of America
Pittsburgh, Pennsylvania

K. C. Spengler
American Meteorological Society
Boston, Massachusetts

Program Committee

Arnold Wexler, *Chairman*
National Bureau of Standards
Washington, D.C.

B. R. Bean
National Bureau of Standards
Boulder, Colorado

D. M. Gates
National Bureau of Standards
Boulder, Colorado

Christos Harmantas
U.S. Weather Bureau
Washington, D.C.

N. B. Hutcheon
Division of Building Research
National Research Council
Ottawa, Canada

D. A. Mazzarella
Science Associates
Princeton, N.J.

P. E. McNall, Jr.
Minneapolis-Honeywell Regulator Co.
Minneapolis, Minn.

H. D. Parry
U.S. Weather Bureau
Washington, D.C.

C. L. Roberson
Owen-Corning Fiberglass Corporation
Granville, Ohio

R. E. Ruskin
Naval Research Laboratory
Washington, D.C.

P. N. Winn, Jr.
University of Maryland
College Park, Maryland

Assisted by:

E. J. Amdur
Minneapolis-Honeywell Regulator Co.
Minneapolis, Minn.

Calvin Golumbic
Agricultural Marketing Service, USDA
Beltsville, Maryland

Anthony Haas
Dryomatic Division
Alexandria, Va.

R. M. Marchgraber
U.S. Army Electronics Research and
Dev. Laboratory
Fort Monmouth, N.J.

R. G. Nevins
Kansas State University
Manhattan, Kansas

K. H. Norris
Agricultural Marketing Service
USDA, Beltsville, Maryland

Edward Penner
Division of Building Research
National Research Council
Ottawa, Canada

P. J. Sereda
Division of Building Research
National Research Council
Ottawa, Canada

Norman Sissenwine
Air Force Cambridge Research Laboratories
Bedford, Massachusetts

H. K. Weickmann
U.S. Army Research and
Development Laboratory
Fort Monmouth, N.J.

R. G. Yeck
Agricultural Research Service
USDA, Beltsville, Maryland

Local Committee on Arrangements

J. W. Morgan, *Chairman*
Johnson Service Co.
Arlington, Va.

R. J. Dillard
York Corporation
Washington, D.C.

G. F. Guenterberg
Harvey W. Hottel Incorporation
Silver Spring, Maryland

Kirby Hanson
U.S. Weather Bureau
Washington, D.C.

F. A. Leser
ILG Electric Ventilating Co.
Washington, D.C.

F. C. Quinn
Hygrodynamics
Silver Spring, Maryland

W. C. Reamy
Meleney Engineering Co.
Washington, D.C.

B. F. Remington
U.S. Weather Bureau
Washington, D.C.

W. R. Tilley
National Bureau of Standards
Washington, D.C.

Julia I. Szabo
ASHRAE
New York, N.Y.

J. H. Cansdale
ASHRAE
New York, N.Y.

Foreword

Humidity is an attribute of the human environment most generally recognized by its important role as a determinant in climate, weather, and personal comfort—"It's not the temperature, it's the humidity!" It is also frequently apparent by its effect on common hygroscopic materials such as wood, textiles, paper and foodstuffs.

Like the other climatic variables—temperature, pressure and precipitation—humidity has long been regularly measured and recorded as a part of the synoptic history which provides some basis for weather prediction and some measure of the problem of climate or weather control. On a small scale, humidity control has long been feasible in the laboratory test chamber, and with the first advent of mechanical refrigeration it was rapidly extended to the whole laboratory as well. On a large scale, dams and reservoirs, irrigation projects and reforestation belts, film-covered or blackened ponds, have some effect on local climate. Proposals for shifting the course of the ocean currents, blocking or widening the ocean straits, and blackening the polar ice caps, envisage man's widespread "control" of climatic humidity. To the extent that these programs progress beyond the proposal stage, more precise and careful measurement of humidity over wide areas will be necessary in order to assess the effects.

Techniques for making these measurements at the National Bureau of Standards have progressed from less to greater precision with perhaps an occasional side trip. I recall one such journey, when one of my first assignments at NBS was calibrating aerographs (time-recorders of temperature, pressure, humidity) for the Aerology Branch of the Navy. The "precision" hygrometric element was a bundle of human hairs, transmitting its variation in length to a pen recorder. To lessen the tedium of many observations of dew point in the test chamber—using an airstream bubbling through ether to cool a metallic mirror and reading a liquid-in-glass thermometer immersed in the ether both when the mist appeared and when it disappeared—I proposed to use the "well-known" fact that the humidity is roughly constant with temperature over saturated salt solutions. I consulted the International Critical Tables, selected four or five salts to cover the relative humidity range of 15 to 95 per cent, visited the storeroom for salts and trays—and cut calibration times to a small fraction! My pride in this achievement was considerably abated when I found, on finally reading in detail the references given in the I.C.T. that the salts had been "calibrated" by use of a hair hygrometer!

It was a long and tedious job to check—or "re-calibrate"—the salt solutions from 0 to 40°C using the dew-point apparatus. Although the results were well within 1 per cent of presently accepted values (except for the saturated solution of LiCl), and the method was routinely used thereafter, publication of the results was postponed for still better accuracy; it was finally redone by Wexler and Hasegawa [*J. Res. Natl. Bur. Std.*, **53**, 19 (1952)]

Some years later, when exploring the utility of the critical flow principle in a variety of devices, including a gas analyzer, it seemed natural to try it in a hygrometer (Wildhack, Perls, Kissinger and Hayes, Vol. I). It worked quite well; but again waited some years to be refined for greater precision as a laboratory standard (Greenspan, Vol. III).

The central province of the National Bureau of Standards is precision physical measurements and measurement standards; its national role is to provide measurement services and data to science, engineering and technology. These services include not only calibrations performed on precision instruments, which are to be used further in the laboratory or in calibration of working instruments for field or factory, but also the publication of research on methods of measurement, or of results of measurement, and the collection and dissemination of information on all areas of measurement science.

A particularly appropriate service is the compilation of papers on the state of the art in the measurement of physical quantities important to science and industry. One of the best ways to achieve a definitive coverage is to get experts in the field to present papers describing both old techniques and new discoveries and developments. Thus, NBS frequently sponsors symposia or conferences, in a variety of fields, usually in cooperation with other organizations having allied interests in particular fields. As an example, NBS has sponsored several Temperature Symposia over the years: in 1938, with the American Institute of Physics; in 1954, with the American Institute of Physics and the Office of Aerospace Research; and in 1961, with the American Institute of Physics and the Instrument Society of America. Thus when it appeared that a Symposium on Humidity would be of value to the technical community, NBS proposed that the Weather Bureau, the American Meteorological Society, the Instrument Society of America, and the American Society of Heating, Refrigerating, and Air-Conditioning Engineers join in planning and arranging the Symposium.

The result of the jointly sponsored Symposium, in which 306 authors presented 229 papers during four days to 850 people, is not only this four-volume definitive record of the present state of humidity measurement and control; it was for the participants—and hopefully will be for our readers—an inspiration and impetus to more extensive work in this area, and it gave them a better appreciation of the many techniques available for application to a host of practical problems.

The Symposium General Committee, composed of representatives of each of the sponsoring organizations, worked harmoniously to achieve a well-planned and well-operated symposium (with an exhibit!) and to publicize it to interested persons. To select papers of high quality, the Committee appointed my colleague, Mr. Arnold Wexler, Chief of the Humidity Measurements Section, to serve as Program Chairman and as Editor-in-Chief for the publication. On his committee also were representatives of each of the sponsors.

After selecting a publisher, Reinhold Publishing Corporation, who had also published the Temperature Symposia volumes, the General Committee has gone into a state of hibernation, to bestir itself some few years hence when further advances in the measurement and control of humidity and moisture make appropriate a return engagement.

My official and personal thanks go to all participants.

W. A. WILDHACK
Chairman, General Committee
1963 *International Symposium*
on Humidity and Moisture.

General Preface

On May 20-23, 1963, over 850 scientists and engineers from around the world attended the 1963 International Symposium on Humidity and Moisture in Washington, D.C. The Symposium was sponsored by two U.S. Government agencies, the National Bureau of Standards and the U.S. Weather Bureau, and three technical societies, the American Society of Heating, Refrigerating and Air-Conditioning Engineers, the American Meteorological Society and the Instrument Society of America. "Humidity and Moisture" contains most of the papers that were presented at the Symposium, as well as several other papers that were subsequently added to augment the coverage in certain areas.

The measurement and control of humidity —water in the vapor phase—and moisture— water in the adsorbed or absorbed phase— play an important role in such scientific disciplines as physics, chemistry, biology and medicine, in many branches of engineering, in meteorology and in agriculture, and in such diverse industrial fields as air conditioning, drying, refrigeration, cryogenics, storage, food processing, packaging, materials manufacturing and processing, gas transmission, and electronics. The Symposium provided an unique opportunity for representatives from the scientific, engineering and industrial communities to meet at a common forum to exchange information on the latest research and developments and to review the current state of the art.

The organization of the sessions, the invitation of contributions on special topics, and the selection of papers were arranged by the Program Committee. Dr. J. Herbert Holloman, Assistant Secretary of Commerce for Science and Technology, delivered the keynote address. Over 200 papers were presented at 32 meetings in four parallel sessions. Because of the large number of papers and the broad subject matter, there are both duplications and omissions. No attempt was made to edit the written papers so that definitions, terminology and mathematical symbols would be uniform and consistent.

It was impractical to encompass all the papers within one set of covers. The contents were therefore divided into the following four volumes, each under the cognizance of a separate volume editor:

Volume One. Principles and Methods of Measuring Humidity in Gases. Editor, Robert E. Ruskin, Naval Research Laboratory.

Volume Two. Applications (measurements unique or special to various fields or disciplines; studies and investigations in which humidity or moisture is the critical parameter). Editor, Elias J. Amdur, Honeywell, Inc.

Volume Three. Fundamentals and Standards. Editors, Arnold Wexler and William A. Wildhack, National Bureau of Standards.

Volume Four. Principles and Methods of Measuring Moisture in Liquids and Solids. Editor, Paul N. Winn, Jr., University of Maryland.

I would like to express my appreciation and acknowledgment to the members of the General Committee, the members of the Program Committee, the members of the Local Committee on Arrangements, the headquarters staff of the American Society of Heating, Refrigerating and Air-Conditioning Engineers, particularly Miss Julia Szabo, the Office of Technical Information of the National Bureau of Standards, especially Messrs. W. R. Tilley and R. T. Cook, and to Mrs. Rosemary Soler of NBS. Their enthusiastic cooperation and diligent work contributed materially to the success of the Symposium.

ARNOLD WEXLER,
Editor-in-Chief

Preface to Volume One

Humidity measurement has been important in instrumentation endeavors throughout a long history. Both the capabilities and the number of types of humidity instruments have expanded steadily to the present time. The 1963 International Symposium on Humidity and Moisture was planned to bring up to date the state of the art; and this volume was planned to form a quite complete reference work on instrumentation for water vapor measurement. An unexpected bonus from the Symposium has been an apparently increased interest among workers in the humidity field, resulting in more rapid improvements in instrumentation and more difficulty in keeping informed of the latest developments. Among the promising new developments are simplified automatic dew-point hygrometers which increase the possibility of their eventual use in radiosondes for network observations. Other possibilities for improved expendable humidity instrumentation are almost certain to result from progress being made in aluminum oxide, barium fluoride, and piezoelectric crystal developments.

In this volume the principles and methods of measuring the humidity of gases are divided into several general categories, as shown in the Table of Contents, each category starting with the papers of more fundamental or general nature, followed by more specific embodiments of these principles in instruments. A final miscellaneous section contains those papers which either do not fit any of the main sections or which discuss instruments of more than one of the categories.

I wish to thank the authors who have all cooperated in every way to make a maximum contribution, both to the Symposium and to this volume, especially in checking the galley proofs. I also thank the reviewers, particularly Mr. Christos Harmantas and Mr. D. A. Mathews of the U.S. Weather Bureau for their assistance. It has been a pleasure working with the publishers, Reinhold Publishing Corporation, and their technical representatives, Mr. C. G. Hawley and Mrs. Alberta Gordon. I further wish to acknowledge the considerable effort made on this volume by Mr. Arnold Wexler, Editor-in-Chief of the four volumes.

My editing of this volume would also not have been possible without the cooperation of Dr. J. E. Dinger and the indexing, editing, and secretarial aid of Mrs. Ruth K. McNamee, both of the Naval Research Laboratory.

ROBERT E. RUSKIN,
Editor, Volume One

Contents

CONTENTS

SECTION III: ELECTRIC HYGROMETRY

SECTION IV: SPECTROSCOPIC HYGROMETRY

SECTION V: COULOMETRIC HYGROMETRY

SECTION VI: MISCELLANEOUS METHODS

SECTION I

PSYCHROMETRY

I. A Critical Review of Tables and Charts used in Psychrometry

H. H. Bindon

Department of Transport, Toronto, Canada

ABSTRACT

The equations defining the thermodynamic wet-bulb temperature of moist air are compared with the theoretical-empirical equations used in describing the phenomena of the real wet-and-dry-bulb psychrometer. The normal form of the theoretical-empirical psychrometer equation is discussed and the important effect of ventilation rates on the psychrometric constant is evaluated.

A comparative tabulation of the constants and ventilation rates used in the construction of various standard Meteorological Tables used in meteorology is given. Attention is directed to the practice when the wet bulb is ice covered. The various sources of error arising in practical psychrometry are discussed and their magnitude estimated.

The normal methods of construction and layout of psychrometric tables, charts and slide rules are discussed and examples of the methods used in specific Standard Tables are given. A bibliography of relevant literature on the theory of the psychrometer and source information on the various standard charts, slide rules and nomograms is appended.

BASIC PSYCHROMETRY

Cooling by the evaporation of water into air has been known and applied throughout recorded history. The specific use of the wet bulb depression as a measure of humidity in the atmosphere was first mentioned in the mid 18th century and subsequently gave rise to the well-known psychrometer. This instrument, even today, is the most practicable and widely used method of humidity measurement. It is not surprising, therefore, that an extensive literature has been developed on the subject. Repeated theories have been put forward to explain the operation of the psychrometer, and a great variety of tables, charts, slide rules and nomograms have been devised to convert the readings into desired humidity parameters.

Psychrometric apparatus has been devised in many forms, but all instruments of this type consist essentially of a temperature sensor (wet bulb) covered with cloth which is wetted and kept supplied with water by means of a wicking. The ambient temperature of the air under examination is simultaneously measured with a temperature sensor similar to the wet bulb sensor but without a wetted surface. It is generally recommended that both bulbs be ventilated, and shielded as far as possible from radiational heating or cooling from external sources. The precise construction of various instruments will not be discussed here.

THERMODYNAMIC THEORY

The basic thermodynamic approach to a theory for the wet bulb phenomenon envisages an isenthalpic process (i.e., adiabatic, isobaric and irreversible). The joint committee on Psychrometric Data and the World Meteorological Organization recommended that the thermodynamic wet bulb temperature (T_w) be defined by solving for $T_w(p,T,r)$ from the equation

$$h(p,T,r) + [r_w(p,T_w) - r]h_w(p,T_w)$$
$$= h[p,T_w,r_w(p,T_w)] \quad (1)$$

where

$\quad h(p,T,r)$ = enthalpy of $1 + r$ grams of moist air

$\quad h(p,T_w)$ = enthalpy of 1 gram of pure water

$\quad h[p,T_w,r_w(p,T_w)]$ = enthalpy of $1 + r_w$ grams of saturated air at temperature T_w.

This definition refers to a process of injecting pure compressed liquid (or solid) water at pressure p and temperature T_w into a stream of moist air at pressure p, temperature T and mixing ratio r to bring the air adiabatically to saturation, at pressure p and temperature T_w. The process refers to an ideal case and is successful in describing a property of the atmosphere operating in accordance with the constraints of classical thermodynamics. To what extent this idealized theory may be related to the phenomenon occurring in the vicinity of a real wet bulb is a moot point.

A simplification of the above equation with reference to the behavior of the moist air when treated as a perfect gas and neglecting certain second order terms leads to the following equations

For water:

$$e = e_w(T_d) = e_w(T_w) - \frac{pC_p}{\epsilon L_v(T_w)}$$
$$\left[1 - \frac{e_w(T_w)}{p}\right](T - T_w) \quad (2)$$

For ice:

$$e = e_w(T_d) = e_i(T_i) - \frac{pC_p}{\epsilon L_s(T_i)}$$
$$\left[1 - \frac{e_i(T_i)}{p}\right](T - T_i) \quad (3)$$

The symbols used in the above equations are in accordance with the definitions and specifications for water vapor in the atmosphere (Resolution 166, W.M.O. Conference of Directors, Washington, 1947). It should be noted that in meteorological practice, the dew point with respect to water is the derived humidity parameter even though, in psychrometric use, the wet bulb is covered with ice. This particular convention has been adopted in meteorology and may be justified on several theoretical and practical grounds. Users of psychrometric tables should ascertain whether the dew point or frost point is being used since many of the older tables refer to the frost point and relative humidity with respect to ice.

The formal similarity between Eqs. (2) and (3) and the theoretical empirical psychrometric Eqs. (6) and (7) below may be noted. It is possible to define a thermodynamic psychrometric constant in the following manner, neglecting the factor $[1 - e_w(T_w)/p]$.

For water:

$$A(T_w) = \frac{C_p}{\epsilon L_v(T_w)} = 6.5295 \times 10^{-4}(°C)^{-1}$$
$$\text{or } 3.631 \times 10^{-4}(°F)^{-1} \quad (4)$$

where C_p is taken at 0°C and L_v at 10°C.

For ice:

$$A(T_i) = \frac{C_p}{\epsilon L_s(T_i)} = 5.703 \times 10^{-4}(°C)^{-1}$$
$$\text{or } 3.168 \times 10^{-4}(°F)^{-1} \quad (5)$$

where C_p is taken at 0°C and L_s at −10°C.

The above derivation is approximate but is useful in providing basic reference values against which various accepted psychrometric constants may be compared. The form of the constant is similar to the constant in the August-Apjohn[1, 3] psychrometric formula.

When an attempt is made to provide a satisfactory theory for the real wet bulb process, it becomes obvious that classical thermodynamics cannot be directly applied. This theory is generally applicable only to closed systems in equilibrium, whereas the real wet bulb process is an open system in a stationary state rather than in thermodynamic equilibrium in the classical sense. To solve the real problem, it is necessary to make a detailed accounting of the heat and mass exchange between the wet bulb and the ambient atmosphere. The most satisfactory theoretical attempt to follow along these lines was made by Arnold. Other writers have extended the Arnold theory, and it is possible that further work might be done if all the resources of modern heat and mass exchange theory were applied to the problem. In view, however, of the many sources of error in the real psychrometer, it is doubtful if any appreciable gain in accuracy would result from a more detailed theory.

THE THEORETICAL-EMPIRICAL FORM OF THE PSYCHROMETRIC EQUATION

The following is the generally accepted form of the psychrometric equation as used in humidity computations and the construction of psychrometric charts.

For a water bulb:

$$e = e_w(T_d) = e_w(T_w) - pA_w(T - T_w) \qquad (6)$$

For an ice bulb:

$$e = e_i(T_i) = e_w(T_d) \\ = e_i(T_i) - pA_i(T - T_i) \qquad (7)$$

where

e = vapor pressure

$e_w(T)$ = the saturated vapor pressure with respect to water of moist air at pressure p and temperature T

$e_i(T)$ = the saturated vapor pressure with respect to ice of moist air at pressure p and temperature T

T_d = dew-point temperature

T_f = frost-point temperature

T = ambient temperature

T_w = wet bulb temperature

T_i = ice bulb temperature

A_w = the psychrometric constant with respect to water

A_i = the psychrometric constant with respect to ice (with ice covered bulb).

Some Remarks on the Theoretical-Empirical Psychrometric Constant

The so-called psychrometric constant is constant in a formal sense only. When the constant is derived from purely thermodynamic assumptions [e.g., Eqs. (4) and (5)], the specific heat and latent heats of vaporization and sublimation are functions of temperature. Furthermore, the thermodynamic derivation indicates that the "constant" involves a factor dependent upon the wet bulb temperature and pressure which may cause a variation in the thermodynamic constant of 3 per cent at high temperatures and humidity.

In the case of the theoretical-empirical constant, it is well known that the value is strongly dependent upon ventilation and is also affected by radiational heat exchange with the surroundings which are generally held near the temperature of the ambient air by shieldings.

Ventilation is by far the most important parameter that affects the value of the constant. The rate with which heat is transferred to the wet bulb and water substance removed by evaporation depends chiefly upon forced convective processes which are largely governed by the ventilation rate over the wetted surface of the bulb. This matter was investigated by Arnold,[2] Powell, Wylie,[7] etc. Arnold in his treatment gave the following formulation for the psychrometric constant

$$A_w = \frac{1}{\epsilon} \frac{C_p}{L_v(T_w)} \left\{ \frac{(1 - r)/r + Z/D\rho_a}{(1 - r)/r + C_pZ/K} \right\} \qquad (8)$$

where

$r = \dfrac{u_a}{u_b} = \dfrac{\text{velocity of the general airstream}}{\text{velocity at film boundary}}$

Z = The viscosity within the film on the wet bulb

D = vapor diffusivity

K = thermal conductivity.

Arnold pointed out that the quantity in brackets will approach unity at high velocities and will also tend to unity at all speeds if $K = D$. In the case of water, unlike other volatile liquids, K is approximately equal to D, and as a result, the thermodynamic psychrometric equation (August–Apjohn equation) is very nearly correct at high ventilation rates and also gives a reasonably correct result at low ventilation. This would not be the case if psychrometric methods were used to determine the atmospheric content of most other volatile liquids.

Wylie has also shown in a series of experiments that the wet bulb depression depends both upon the wind speed and the dimensions of the wet bulb. This clearly indicates that the problem must be understood in the context of modern heat and mass exchange theory. If great accuracy is to be achieved, it is necessary to carry out a specific experimental investigation on each type of psychrometer in

TABLE 1. PSYCHROMETERS WITH ADEQUATE VENTILATION

Psychrometric Constants A_w	A_i	Ventilation	$\dfrac{A_w - A_{wt}}{A_{wt}} \times 100$	Table or Slide Rule	U and T_d below 0°C
$6.530 \times 10^{-4}(°C)^{-1}$ $3.631 \times 10^{-4}(°F)^{-1}$	$5.703 \times 10^{-4}(°C)^{-1}$ $3.168 \times 10^{-4}(°F)^{-1}$		0	Thermodynamic (August–Apjohn) ($A_w t$)	W.R.T. Ice
$3.7 \times 10^{-4}(°F)^{-1}$	$3.3 \times 10^{-4}(°F)^{-1}$	7 kts	1.9	British M.O. Slide Rule (Bilham) British M.O. Tables	W.R.T. Water
$6.60(1 + 0.00115 T_w) \times 10^{-4}(°C)^{-1}$	$A_i = A_w$	Greater than 15 fps less than 100 fps based on Ferrel's Work (1886) with the Sling Psychrometer	1.2	U.S. Weather Bureau W.B. No. 235, 1941, C. F. Marvin (Frost Points Valid) Table for various pressures	W.R.T. Ice
$3.67\left(1 + \dfrac{T_w - 32}{1571}\right) \times 10^{-4}$ $(°F)^{-1}$				Relative humidity tables—Psychrometric Celsius—U.S.W.B.	
				Smithsonian Meteorological Tables (6th ed.)	
$3.724 \times 10^{-4}(°F)^{-1}$	$3.628 \times 10^{-4}(°F)^{-1}$	Based on Ferrels Formulas for Sling Psychrometer	1.9	Weather Bureau Circular Slide Rule, 1947—rule for 30, 29, 28, 27, 25, 23 inches mercury	W.R.T. Water
$3.5727 \times 10^{-4}(°F)^{-1}$	$3.1533 \times 10^{-4}(°F)$	Sufficient ventilation, derived from thermodynamic theory	−1.7	Psychrometric tables—Canada—Met. Branch, Dept. of Transport 1962 (Tables for various heights)	W.R.T. Water
$3.726 \times 10^{-4}(°F)^{-1}$	$3.628 \times 10^{-4}(°F)$ when supercooled water on bulb $3.17 \times 10^{-4}(°F)^{-1}$ when ice on bulb	Ventilation adequate	1.9	Psychrometric tables—Canada—Met. Branch, Dept. of Transport, 1953 (Godson)	W.R.T. Water
$\dfrac{1}{1510} = 6.62 \times 10^{-4}(°C)^{-1}$		Based on the Assmann Psychrometer	1.4	Aspirations Psychrometer-Tafeln Preussischen Meteorologischen Inst. 1930	W.R.T. Ice
$6.56 \times 10^{-4}(0°C)^{-1}$	$5.79 \times 10^{-4}(°C)^{-1}$	Greater than 2.5 m/sec	0.45	Jelineks Psychrometer—Tafeln 1929	W.R.T. Ice
$6.5 \times 10^{-4}(°C)^{-1}$	$5.8 \times 10^{-4}(°C)^{-1}$	Greater than 5.5 m/sec	0.45	Meteorologie Nationale France, Nouvelles Tables (1956)	W.R.T. Water

TABLE 2. PSYCHROMETERS WITH INADEQUATE VENTILATION

Psychrometric Constants A_w	A_i	Ventilation	Table or Slide Rule	U and T_d below 0°C
$4.44 \times 10^{-4}(°F)^{-1}$	$4.00 \times 10^{-4}(°F)^{-1}$	Screen ventilation 2.4 kts	British M.O. Slide Rule (Bilham)	W.R.T. Water
$4.2872 \times 10^{-4}(°F)^{-1}$	$3.7840 \times 10^{-4}(°F)^{-1}$	Natural movement of air relied on for ventilation	Psychrometric table—Canada—Met. Branch, Dept. of Transport, 1962	W.R.T. Water
$12.00 \times 10^{-4}(°C)^{-1}$ $8.00 \times 10^{-4}(°C)^{-1}$	$10.60 \times 10^{-4}(°C)^{-1}$ $7.06 \times 10^{-4}(°C)^{-1}$	0—m/sec 1-1.5 m/sec	Jelinek—Psychrometric tables, 1929	W.R.T. Ice
$7.9 \times 10^{-4}(°C)^{-1}$	$6.9 \times 10^{-4}(°C)^{-1}$	Natural ventilation	Meteorologie Nationale France, Nouvelles Tables (1956)	W.R.T. Water

order to derive a psychrometric constant valid for the particular instrument.

It has been experimentally established, however, that at speeds in excess of 3 m/sec, the wet bulb depression approaches a limiting value and above this speed, the psychrometric constant becomes virtually independent of the ventilation rate and of the geometry of the wet bulb. For this reason, a ventilation rate of greater than 3 m/sec is recommended for accurate psychrometry. It should, however, be mentioned that too high a ventilation rate will introduce other errors which may become serious. A velocity of 3 to 4 m/sec has been found ideal for most purposes.

There are, however, certain important applications of the psychrometer where humidity measurements must be made with minimum disturbance of the ambient environment and hence low ventilation rates must be used. In this case, it may be necessary to modify the design of the psychrometer (by reducing the size of the wet bulb) and to determine a psychrometric equation appropriate to the ventilation speed and construction of the instrument.

EQUATIONS USED IN THE CONSTRUCTION OF STANDARD PSYCHROMETRIC TABLES, CHARTS AND SLIDE RULES

It is desirable at this point to examine constants used in the construction of certain well-known psychrometric tables and devices. Tables 1 and 2 give the values for the various constants used. The percentage difference between selected constants and the thermodynamic constant is tabulated as a measure of the agreement of one constant with another. It should be noted that only one formula takes into account the variation of the so-called constant with temperature. It seems unlikely that the overall accuracy of the results will make a variation of this order significant although some increased accuracy may be obtained by assuming different values over specific temperature ranges.

The value of the psychrometric constant when the "wet" bulb is known to be covered with ice is not too well established by experimental work. It would appear from thermodynamic considerations that $A_i/A_w = 0.882$. However, opinion is divided as to whether such a difference does exist in practice. The U.S. Weather Bureau and the Smithsonian Institution have adopted a universal constant which is to a small degree temperature sensitive. In the construction of the U.S. Weather Bureau circular slide rule, a mean value of $3.628 \times 10^{-4}(°F)^{-1}$ is assumed when temperatures are below 32°F. The value adopted by other services for an ice covered bulb is approximately $3.2 \times 10^{-4}(°F)^{-1}$ There is a requirement, therefore, for some further work in the area of low-temperature psychrometry. It would appear that the results will depend upon whether the ice bulb is covered by a frozen muslin or with a thin layer of ice. It is obvious that the roughness coefficient will vary in these two cases and the convective heat and mass transfer will be different for this reason. It should be pointed out that errors due to other causes also become acute at low temperatures and join to reduce the accuracy of low-temperature psychrometry.

ERRORS IN PSYCHROMETRIC PRACTICE

It is appropriate to examine some of the more important sources of error that arise in psychrometric practice.

Temperature Errors

Errors in humidity occur when the wet or dry bulb have a calibration error, but the most serious defect will occur when these errors combine to cause an appreciable error in the depression. Errors of this type may be minimized by matching the thermometers or applying calibration corrections to the indicated temperature values. Table 3 indicates the magnitude of relative humidity errors caused by temperature errors.

TABLE 3. ERROR IN THE RELATIVE HUMIDITY (PER CENT) DUE TO ERRORS IN THE DEPRESSION

Temperature (°C)					Error in
−20	−10	0	+10	+20	Depression (°C)
5	3	2	1	1	0.1
11	6	4	3	2	0.2

Incorrect Psychrometric Constant

Errors due to the use of incorrect psychrometric constants will cause errors in the derived humidity parameters. Table 4 indicates the effect on the percentage relative humidity due to percentage difference in the constant used.

It may be noted from Table 2 and Table 4 that the errors due to lack of agreement between the psychrometric constants used in various tables under ventilated conditions cause insignificant errors in the derived parameters of dew point and relative humidity. The position is different, however, when low or inadequate ventilation prevail, and the errors may be quite serious, if the incorrect constant is used. This is one of the reasons that psychrometers with inadequate ventilation are not recommended for normal use.

TABLE 4. ERROR IN THE RELATIVE HUMIDITY DUE TO AN ERROR IN THE PSYCHROMETRIC CONSTANT

Error in Psychrometric Constant A_w (%)	Depression (°C)					
	T(°C)	2°	4°	6°	8°	10°
1%	0	0	1			
	10	0	0	0	1	2
	20	0	0	0	1	2
2%	0	0	1			
	10	0	1	1	1	2
	20	0	1	1	1	2

Pressure Errors

Large errors will arise if the pressure corrections are not applied or if tables for inappropriate pressures are used. In the case of a table valid at 1000 mb, a correction of 10 per cent must be applied to the depression values for 900 mb, etc.

Radiational Errors

Errors due to radiational heat exchange between the surroundings and the wet bulb have been discussed by various authors.[2, 11] Errors from this cause are generally independent of the ventilation speed. In the normal psychrometer, precautions are taken to shield the wet bulb from external sources of radiation, but the shielding is at or near the ambient temperature. The radiation correction will, therefore, be a function of the depression and will be a maximum in dry warm conditions when the depressions are large. The effect of radiation must be determined by theoretical-empirical considerations for a specific psychrometer.

Errors Arising from Other Sources

The errors mentioned above are the most important in normal psychrometric practice. However, conduction of heat into the wet bulb along the sensing element may cause large errors when metallic sensing elements are used and particularly in the case of thermocouple elements unless precautions are taken to insulate the sensing element from its supports or cool the apparatus to the wet bulb temperature.

THE CONSTRUCTION AND USE OF PSYCHROMETRIC TABLES

The form and construction of meteorological tables depend upon the ultimate use to which they will be put.

The primary humidity parameters used in meteorology are the dew point, vapor pressure and relative humidity.

Dewpoint

The thermodynamic dew-point temperature (T_d) of moist air at temperature T, pressure p and mixing ratio r is the temperature to which the air must be cooled in order that it shall be saturated with respect to water at the initial p and mixing ratio r. A similar definition serves for the thermodynamic frost point T_f. In present day meteorological practice, the computed dew point is defined as the dew point with respect to water. At temperatures below 0°C, this value will differ appreciably from the frost point. It is necessary, therefore, to ascertain whether the dew point or the frost point is given by a specific set of tables. It is also necessary to know precisely which is being used in the calibration of certain humidity devices such as the Foxboro dewcel.

Relative Humidity

The relative humidity with respect to moist air at pressure p and temperature T is defined as

$$U_w = 100\left(\frac{Nv}{Nvw}\right)_{P,T} = 100\left(\frac{e}{e_w}\right)_{p,T} \quad (9)$$

where Nv is the vapor mole fraction and Nvw is the vapor mole fraction for saturated air at pressure p and temperature T

$$U_w = 100\,\frac{r}{r_w}\left(\frac{0.62197 + r_w}{0.62197 + r}\right)$$

where r_w is the saturated mixing ratio at p and T.

In meteorology, the relative humidity at temperatures less than 0°C is evaluated with respect to water and not with respect to ice. This was not always the case and the method used in a specific psychrometric table must be known.

Saturated Vapor Pressure

Resolution 164 of the Twelfth Conference of Directors of W.M.O. (Washington 1947) adopted the Goff–Gratch formulation for the saturation vapor pressure in pure phase over plane surfaces of pure water or pure ice. Tables of these values are given in the Smithsonian Meteorological Tables (sixth revised edition).

For ease of construction, the most satisfactory basic parameters for use in psychrometric tables, slide rules and nomograms are the wet bulb temperature T_w and the depression $(T - T_w)$. When these parameters are used, the dew point and vapor pressure may be directly computed. It is also comparatively easy to adjust a master table (e.g., prepared for a pressure of 1000 mb) for utilization at other pressures or to allow for different values of the psychrometric constant appropriate to different ventilation rates. The Smithsonian Tables (6th edition), Tables 98 and 99 are constructed in this manner.

An interesting table along these lines was prepared for use in the Canadian Meteorological Service by W. L. Godson, 1953. This table consists of a master dew point table which used the basic parameters T_w and $T - T_w$ and is valid for the pressure of 1016 mb (30.00 in. of mercury). A_w for $T_w > 32°F$ was 3.726×10^{-4} and 3.17×10^{-4} when $T_i < 32°F$ and the bulb was ice covered. Supplementary tables were supplied that allowed the depression $(T - T_w)$ to be adjusted to take care of pressures from 700 to 1036 mb for a ventilated psychrometer and for a similar pressure range on a nonventilated psychrometer. This type of table may be compressed to a very manageable size. Unfortunately, in practice, it was found too complex for use by normal meteorological observers carrying out routine observations and has been superseded with a series of tables valid at fixed heights and using the basic parameters of air temperature T and the depression $(T - T_w)$. The original Godson table, however, provides considerable flexibility and is very useful for workers making a variety of humidity measurements. The relative humidity was computed by means of a separate table from the parameters of dry bulb T and dew point T_d.

A somewhat similar approach has been used in a set of tables prepared by National Meteorological Service of France. The basic parameters used in the construction of the charts are $P/1000(T - T_w)$ and T_w. T_d and U may be derived directly. A supplementary graph is provided to correct for pressure, and a method for use under ventilated conditions is incorporated. Two sheets of tables and a supplementary graph are sufficient to cover a considerable range of conditions.

For routine work where constant pressure may be assumed and specific parameters such as the dew point and relative humidity are to be determined, simplicity is achieved in utilization of the tables by the use of the dry bulb temperature and depression as basic parameters. This system is followed in the U.S. Weather Bureau Psychrometric Tables, U.S. No. 235, 1941. A series of these tables are produced to various pressures (i.e., 29.00 in.) and are broken into separate sections, one for the dew point and one for the relative humidity. The parameters are with respect to ice when temperatures are below 32°F.

A similar set of tables have been computed and are currently used by the Meteorological Branch of the Canadian Department of Transport. These tables are prepared for various pressure heights (i.e., less than 1000 ft), and the basic reference parameters are temperature and depression in degrees Fahrenheit. The dew point appears in black and the relative humidity in red opposite a specific temperature and depression. These tables probably are the ultimate in operational simplicity when these two humidity parameters are required. It has been Canadian experience that by the use of relatively simple

and straightforward tables such as these, the percentage of routine errors on the part of meteorological observers may be kept to a desirable minimum.

In some European tables, the basic parameters used are the dry bulb and wet bulb temperatures. This arrangement also leads to a rather simple form of table but is not so easy to use as the tables utilizing temperature and depression. It has some advantage, however, in that it is not necessary to compute the depression.

CHARTS

Humidity charts for psychrometric purposes find only limited use in general meteorological practice. However, a number of charts have been devised and are used chiefly for converting from one parameter to another, e.g., from dewpoint to relative humidity at constant pressure. By the proper selection of scales, it is possible to have one set of parameter isolines straight.

While charts have limited use in meteorology, they are extensively used in air conditioning and other engineering fields. A large variety of charts have been devised for various purposes. These charts frequently use the specific humidity as major axis and some charts may be used to determine the entropy of dry air. The charts are generally valid at one pressure only. In North America, the engineering units of inches, pounds, degrees Fahrenheit, etc., are used except in cases where the charts are specifically designed for meteorological purposes.

SLIDE RULES

The form of the psychrometric equation allows excellent slide rules to be devised for the rapid determination of the psychrometric parameters. From Eqs. (6) and (7), it is obvious that the vapor pressure (and from this dew point) may be calculated by the addition of $e_w(T_w)$ to the term $pA_w(T - T_w)$. The slide rule, therefore, is designed to perform this simple addition with the basic parameters T_w and $(T - T_w)$. The term pA_w is usually chosen at 1000 millibars, and the value of $pA_w(T - T_w)$ is in a linear scale and marked in values of $(T - T_w)$.

A useful type of circular slide rule devised by L. P. Harrison and presently in operational use at U.S. Weather Bureau Observing Stations is valid for a fixed pressure. A series of slide rules are available and in use, and it is necessary to select the one nearest to the mean station pressure. The British Meteorological Office uses a straight humidity slide rule devised by Bilham. This rule has a provision whereby the existing depression may be adjusted for all pressure down to 500 mb. Both of these rules have been successfully used in regular observing programs which indicates the basic simplicity of the designs.

The relative humidity as defined by Eq. (9) requires a graphical division of e by e_w. These values are expressed in terms of the dewpoint and dry bulb temperatures. This requires that the dew point be computed first and the relative humidity obtained by a second calculation.

The humidity slide rule is probably the most versatile and compact method for computing dew point and relative humidity. The method may be very easily extended to allow for the computation of the mixing ratio and the vapor pressure when these values are required.

NOMOGRAMS

The form of the psychrometric equation lends itself to the construction of rather simple nomograms. Psychrometric nomograms have been devised in a number of forms. Figure 2 illustrates a rather useful form of nomogram devised by W. G. Godson for computing the dew point and relative humidity. It is obvious that it is not possible

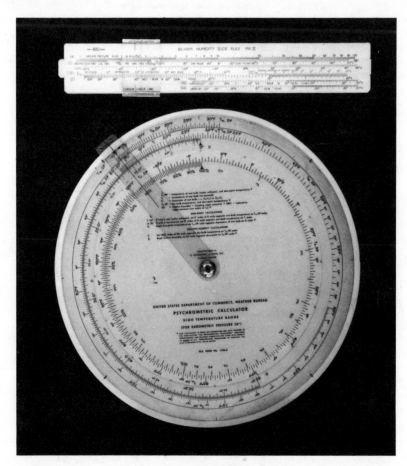

FIG. 1. Slide rules.

to devise a nomogram that will allow the determination of the dew point and relative humidity with a single alignment. However, in the form devised by Godson, it is possible to utilize one scale (T_d) for dual use in the nomogram, for determination of T_d from T_w and the depression, and for the determination of the relative humidity. The nomogram illustrated is valid for 1000 mb. It is possible, however, to supply a grid of T_w scales, so that the graph may be used for a range of pressures.

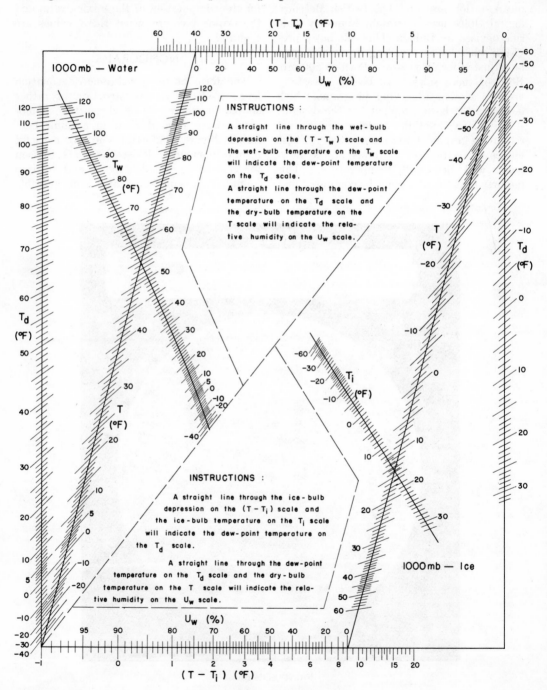

FIG. 2. Psychrometric nomogram.

CONCLUSIONS

The values of the psychrometric constant deemed valid for ventilated psychrometers and used in the computation of various psychrometric tables in general use, do not differ from the so-called thermodynamic psychrometric constant by more than 1.9 per cent. Table 4 would indicate that this divergence will not cause more than 2 per cent difference between the relative humidity as derived from tables using accepted constants based on theoretical-empirical data and thermodynamic constant. The constants used in the standard tables have been selected by a variety of methods, and in some cases, they have been based on experimental determinations with specific psychrometers. The validity of the experimental procedures and methods used, which in most cases were carried out many years ago, should be critically reviewed in the light of modern techniques and the latest values of the humidity constants. In view of the differences that exist between the various accepted tables, some consideration might be given to the use of a standard value for the so-called thermodynamic psychrometric constant that could be used to form a master or basic psychrometric table. As indicated above, such a table would give acceptable results with most existing ventilated psychrometers. An attempt might also be made to devise a psychrometer that would read in the thermodynamic wet bulb temperature. A course of action along these lines was recommended by the Working Group on Psychrometry of the World Meteorological Organization, II Session, Paris, 1957.

An examination of the tables which are being used for observations from non-ventilated psychrometers indicates that a wide variety of constants are used. It is obvious that the use of unventilated or naturally ventilated psychrometers may lead to large absolute errors in the determination of the humidity parameters. It is necessary, therefore, when using psychrometers without ventilation, to critically examine the tables used and make certain that they are appropriate to the particular psychrometric apparatus to be used. In many experiments where psychrometers without forced ventilation are used, the main requirement is to determine space gradients or time gradients of humidity. Fortunately, it may turn out that in these cases, the results may be reasonably satisfactory in a relative sense, but contain considerable errors in an absolute sense.

The overall accuracy that may be expected from a ventilated psychrometer of adequate design, when careful attention is given to the various sources of error, is of the order of ± 2 per cent when temperatures are above freezing. At temperatures below freezing, the errors will increase as the temperature lowers.

The accuracy to be expected from non-ventilated psychrometers may only be estimated or determined by experimental comparisons with a standard. In general, the results are much less reliable than in the case of a ventilated instrument.

Appendix

SOURCE INFORMATION

Humidity Parameters, Definitions, etc.

(1) For accepted meteorological definitions and specifications for the water vapor parameters, see Resolution 166, I.M.O. Conference of Directors, Washington, 1947; also, Guide to Meteorological Instrument and Observing Practices, WMO No. 8, TP. 3 and Smithsonian Tables (6th ed.), Table 93.

(2) Saturation Vapour Pressure Tables, Resolution 164 of the 12th Conference of Directors of the International Meteorological Organization (now World Meteorological Organization), Washington,

1947, adopted a formulation by Goff–Gratch (Goff, J. A. and Gratch, S., *Trans. Amer. Soc. Heat Vent. Eng.*, **52**, 95 (1946).

Psychrometric Tables

Meteorological. (1) Meteorological Office, Hygrometric Tables (M.O. 265) (London H.M. Stationery Office 1940) (Fahrenheit).

(2) Smithsonian Meteorological Tables, 6th ed., Fahrenheit and Celsius.

(3) Marvin, C. E., Psychrometric Tables for Obtaining the Vapour Pressure, Relative Humidity and Temperature of the Dewpoint from readings of

the wet and dry bulb thermometer, No. 235, Reprint 1941, for sale by Superintendent of Documents, U.S. Government Printing Office. Fahrenheit, Produced for barometric pressures of 23, 25, 27, 29, 30 in. of Hg.

(4) Relative Humidity Psychrometric Tables—Celsius, revised 1953—Superintendent of Documents, U.S. Government Printing Office, Washington, D.C.

(5) Preussischen Meteorologishen Institut, "Aspirations - Psychrometer - Tafeln," III Aufl. Braunschweig, 1927.

(6) Psychrometer—Tafeln—Jelineks VII Aufl. Leipzig, 1929.

(7) Psychrometric Tables—Ventilated Psychrometer—Canada, Department of Transport, Meteorological Branch. Separate books for less than 1000, 1000 to 2500, or more than 2500 ft.

(8) Psychrometer Tables—nonventilated—separate books for less than 1000, 1000 to 2500, or greater than 2500 ft.

(9) Psychrometric Tables (Form 2240), prepared by W. L. Godson, 1953, Department of Transport, Meteorological Branch, Canada.

(10) Publication of the National Meteorological Service, France, Notice D'exploitation due S.M.M.A. Fasicule E Piece No. 21, No. 27/55 Nouvelles Tables Psychrometrique, January 1956.

Engineering. National Physical Laboratory (Teddington), report for the year 1932, p. 70, London, 1933. This reference gives the relative humidity as a function of the wet and dry bulb temperature from 30 to 100°C.

Slide Rules. (1) U.S. Weather Bureau Psychrometric Calculators. Circular plastic slide rule used at U.S. Weather Bureau Observing Stations. For details, see "Manual of Surface Observations (WBAN)," Circular N, 7th ed., 1957, for sale by Superintendent of Documents, U.S. Government Printing Office, Washington 25, D.C. These slide rules are available for 30, 29, 28, 27, 25, 23 in. of Hg. (These rules are stocked by the American Instrument Company, Inc., 8030 Georgia Avenue, Silver Springs, Maryland.)

(2) E. G. Bilham, "New Version of the Humidity Slide Rule," *The Meteorological Magazine*, **79**, No. 933 (1950).

Charts

Meteorological. (1) U.S. Weather Bureau Form No. 1186-A, 1186-B for use with W.B. Circular N—relate dry bulb, wet bulb and dew point at constant pressure—prepared by L. P. Harrison.

(2) U.S. Weather Service of the U.S. Air Force (elaborate charts relating dry bulb, wet bulb, dew point and relative humidity at constant pressure—30, 29, 27, 25, 23 in. of Hg).

(3) Horton, R. E., "Vapour Pressure and Humidity Diagram," *Monthly Weather Rev.*, **49**, 285–287 (May 1921).

(4) Smith, R. B., "A Psychrometric Chart for Determining the Dewpoint and Relative Humidity," *Monthly Weather Rev.*, **49**, 287–288 (May 1921).

(5) Albright, J. G., "Psychrometric Charts," *Monthly Weather Rev.*, **66**, 178–181 (June 1938).

Engineering. (1) The Bulkeley Psychrometric Chart, copyright 1926 by the American Society of Heating and Ventilating Engineers, 51 Madison Avenue, New York 10, N.Y. (for standard pressure 29.92 in. Hg, dry bulb temperature range 0 to 170°F., and wet bulb temperature range 0 to 140°F) *ASHVE Transactions*, **32**, 1926.

(2) Psychrometric Charts for High and Low Pressures by Donald B. Brooks, National Bureau of Standards Miscellaneous Publication M-146, January 1935 (pressure range 5 in. Hg to 10 atmospheres; dry bulb temperature range 0 to 212°F, wet bulb temperature range −40 to 114°F).

(3) Brooks, Donald B., "Psychrometric Chart High Range" *Metal Progr.*, 1942 Reference Issue, **42**, 689. (Pressure range 5 in. Hg to 10 atm, dry bulb temperature range 32 to 212°F).

(4) "Psychrometric Chart High Range," *Metal Progr.*, **42**, No. 4, 689 (October 1942).

(5) Zimmerman, O. T., and Lavine, I., "Psychrometric Tables and Charts," 1st ed., p. 162, published by Industrial Research Service, cloth bound, 1945.

(6) American Society of Heating and Air Conditioning Engineers—Heating, Ventilating, Air Conditioning Guide.

(7) American Society of Heating and Air Conditioning Engineers, Inc.

(8) The Bulkeley Psychrometric Chart (a) The American Society of Heating and Ventilating Engineers (ASHVE), Guide 1937, see Ch. 1, Air, Water and Steam; (b) *ASHVE Transactions*, **32**, 1926.

(9) Deverall, C. N., "Deverall Psychrometric Chart," −40 to +50°F, published by the Niagara Blower Company, 6 East 45th Street, New York City (price, 50 cents).

(10) Carrier Corporation, Syracuse, New York, published a Psychrometric Chart, copyright 1945.

(11) H. B. Nottage, "A Proposed Psychrometric Chart," *ASHVE Journal*, section on Heating, Piping and Air Conditioning (1950).

References

General Theory

1. Apjohn, J., "Formula for Inferring the Dewpoint from Indications of the Wet-bulb Hygrometer," *Phil. Mag.*, **6**, 182 (1835).

2. Arnold, J. H., "The Theory of the Psychrometer," *Physics*, 4, 255 and 334 (1933).

3. August, E. F., "Uber die Verdunstungskälte und deren Anwendung auf Hygrometrie," *Ann. Physik*, **5**, 69 (1825).

4. Bouman, D. J., "A Theory of the Ventilated Psychrometer Based on the Thermodynamics of Irreversible Processes," *Tellus*, 6, 399 (1954).

5. Maxwell, J. C., "Diffusion," "Encyclopedia Britannica," 9th ed., Vol. 7, p. 218, Edinburgh, 1877.

6. Regnault, V., "Étude sur l'Hygrometrie," *Annales de Chimie et de Physique*, **15**, 201 (1845).

Regnault, V., "Étude sur l'Hygrometrie (Deuxieme Memoire)," *Annales de Chimie et de Physique*, **37**, 257 (1853).

7. Wylie, R. G., "Psychrometry," National Standards Laboratory, PA-4. Com. of Australia, Scientific and Industrial Research Organization, 1949.

Psychrometry Under Special Conditions

8. Awbery, J. H., and Griffiths, E., "The Basic Law of the Wet and Dry Bulb Hygrometer at Temperatures from 40° to 100°C," *Proc. Phys. Soc. London*, **44**, 132 (1932).

9. Ebert, H., "On the Conception of Relative Humidity at High Temperatures," *Zeit. Physik*, **76**, Heft 3-4, 163–171 (1932).

10. Wexler, A., and Brombacher, W. G., "Methods of Measuring Humidity and Testing Hygrometers," National Bureau of Standards Circular 512, 1951.

11. Wile, D. D., "Psychrometry in the Frost Zone," *Refrig. Eng.* **48**, 291 (1944).

2. Calculation of the Temperature of a Flat-plate Wet Surface under Adiabatic Conditions with Respect to the Lewis Relation

Tamami Kusuda

National Bureau of Standards, Washington, D.C.

ABSTRACT

The state of development of the wet-bulb psychrometric theory is reviewed in conjunction with the Lewis relation of heat- and water-vapor-transfer coefficients.

A theoretical calculation of the wet surface temperature profile under the condition of adiabatic evaporation was performed to investigate the influence of heat from the water supply reservoir upon a thin flat plate wet-bulb element. Several pertinent factors essential for calculating the Lewis relation are studied. An exact solution to the laminar boundary layer equations is incorporated into the convective Lewis relation to study the influence of evaporation velocity for both forced and natural convection.

The ratio of thermal diffusivity to the diffusion coefficient is evaluated using moist air properties calculated by Cheung's empirical formulation for transport properties of gas mixtures.

INTRODUCTION

The major purpose of this paper is to explore several subjects that have been customarily neglected from the theory of wet-bulb psychrometry. Subjects, such as evaporation velocity, air transport property change due to moisture, and heat flow from or to the water supply reservoir are usually not included in conventional heat and mass transfer calculation involved in the evaporating

surface temperature determination. However, since the use of psychrometric theory requires very rigorous evaluation of heat and mass transfer parameters, a refinement of the existing knowledge is clearly needed.

A paper of Arnold[1] described two historical theories of wet-bulb psychrometry, namely, the diffusion theory of Maxwell and the convection theory of August. The diffusion theory correlates energy and mass transports with random molecular motion; whereas, the convection theory treats the transport processes entirely in terms of turbulent or macroscopic mixing of ambient moist air and moisture-saturated air over a wet surface. Arnold developed a modified theory combining the diffusion and convection principles. This theory utilizes both the Prandtl analogy of heat and momentum transfer in a boundary layer and the similarity relation between heat- and mass-transfer processes. An excellent review of the Arnold theory as well as the correlation of experimental wet-bulb temperatures and adiabatic saturation temperature was presented by Carrier and Mackey in 1937.[2] Other notable contributions to the theory of wet-bulb psychrometry were made by Muller-Cosna and Mainer-Leibnitz,[3] and Monteith[4] who made extensive studies of fine wire thermocouple psychrometers.

As recently as 1962, Wentzel[5] presented a thorough summary of the so-called psychrometric constants derived from several past studies. The most comprehensive treatment on wet-bulb psychrometry, however, has been

16

given by Threlkeld.[6] Threlkeld not only pointed out the importance of the Lewis relation of heat- and mass-transfer coefficients for wet-bulb thermometry, but also correlated the ordinary wet-bulb temperature with the thermodynamic wet-bulb temperature. The theory of wet-bulb psychrometry depends entirely on the Lewis relation. Because of recent advances in the knowledge of heat and mass transfer, the numerical evaluation of the Lewis relation still requires refinement from the standpoint of rigorous thermodynamic and transport properties of moist air.

The Lewis relation of heat- and water-vapor-transfer coefficients is extensively reviewed in this paper for various flow configurations over a flat plate. The flat plate was chosen since theoretical treatments are possible, particularly for laminar boundary layer flow.

This paper also includes an extensive analytical study of reservoir heat flow effects upon the wet-bulb temperature measurement, which is obtained by developing and solving a differential equation for the temperature profile from the reservoir to the tip of the wet-bulb element.

SIMULTANEOUS TRANSFER OF HEAT AND WATER VAPOR FROM A WET SURFACE

The sensible heat transfer from well-mixed moist air of temperature t_∞ to a unit area of wet surface of temperature t_w is described by overall surface heat conductance f in the following manner:*

$$q = f(t_\infty - t_w) \tag{1}$$

Water vapor exchange between the wet surface and surrounding moist air is expressed in various forms depending upon the purpose of investigation or upon the type of water vapor concentration parameters.

Three basic formulations for mass transfer rate that appear in the literature are

$$\dot{m} = M_w f_f (y_w - y_\infty) \tag{2}$$
$$= \rho h_D (W_w - W_\infty) \tag{3}$$
$$= \sigma(S_w - S_\infty) \tag{4}$$

* All the symbols used in this paper are summarized in the section on Nomenclature. A unit conversion table is also provided in Table 5.

where

$y =$ mole fraction of water vapor in moist air

$W =$ mass fraction of water vapor in moist air

$S =$ humidity ratio or specific humidity, weight of water vapor per unit weight of dry air

$\rho =$ mixture density.

Equation (2) is favored by chemists and chemical engineers, whereas Eq. (4) is familiar to air-conditioning engineers who customarily use the humidity ratios tabulated in the moist air table of Goff and Gratch.[7]

Equation (3) is sometimes expressed in the following form:

$$\dot{m} = h_D(C_w - C_\infty) \tag{3a}$$

which incorporates the partial density of water vapor, $C = \rho W$. Equations (3) and (3a) are frequently used in theoretical heat-transfer calculations.

The familiar form of vapor-transfer equation, correlating the partial vapor pressure difference, can be obtained directly from Eq. (2) by noting that $y = e/P_t$ for the perfect gas, or

$$\dot{m} = f_f \frac{M_w}{P_t}(e_w - e_\infty) \tag{2a}$$

Relations among the three different transfer coefficients, f_f, h_D, and σ, can be derived as follows:

$$W = \frac{S}{S+1} \tag{5}$$

$$y = \frac{S}{S + M_w/M_a} \tag{6}$$

hence

$$\sigma = \frac{\rho h_D}{(1 + S_w)(1 + S_\infty)}$$
$$= \frac{M_w(M_w/M_a)f_f}{[(M_w/M_a) + S_\infty][(M_w/M_a) + S_w]} \tag{7}$$

If S_w and S_∞ are very small, an approximate relation for σ is

$$\sigma \approx \rho_a h_D \approx M_a f_f \tag{8}$$

where $\rho_a =$ partial density of dry air in moist air.

When the latent heat dissipated from the surface by evaporation and the sensible heat transferred to the surface are balanced to yield zero net heat exchange, an adiabatic relation can be expressed by

$$q = \dot{m}\lambda \qquad (9)$$

which serves as a starting point for the wet-bulb theory.

The heat balance relation [Eq. (9)] of an adiabatically evaporating surface would result in either

$$A' = \frac{e_w - e_\infty}{P_t(t_\infty - t_w)} \approx \frac{y_w - y_\infty}{t_\infty - t_w} = \frac{f}{M_w \lambda f_f} \qquad (10)$$

the psychrometric relation, or

$$N_L = \frac{\lambda(S_w - S_\infty)}{C_P(t_\infty - t_w)} = \frac{f}{\sigma C_P} \approx \frac{f}{h_D \rho C_P} \qquad (11)$$

the Lewis relation, where C_P is the specific heat of moist air. In Eq. (10), λ is evaluated at the surface temperature, whereas the value for ρC_P in Eq. (11) is taken as a mean between the surface and stream values.

The two relations of Eqs. (10) and (11) are essentially compatible except that the latter may be more useful from the standpoint of present-day thermodynamics of moist air, which employs humidity ratio in place of vapor pressure.

The Lewis relation is a dimensionless entity, whereas the psychrometric constant A' possesses a dimension of $[°F]^{-1}$. The formulation of the psychrometric constant [Eq. (10)] does not completely separate the thermodynamic terms from the transport process terms. Consequently the value of A' depends upon the temperature level.

THE LEWIS RELATION WITH RESPECT TO THE THERMODYNAMIC WET-BULB TEMPERATURE

The Lewis relation N_L obtained from rigorous thermodynamic theory of moist air can be investigated by replacing t_w and S_w in Eq. (11) by t^* and S^* which are the thermodynamic wet-bulb temperature and corresponding saturated air humidity ratio. The thermodynamic wet-bulb temperature is expressed implicitly in the following relation:[7]

$$\frac{S^* - S_\infty}{h^* - h_\infty} = \frac{1}{h_L^*} \qquad (12)$$

where

$h^* =$ enthalpy of moisture-saturated air
$S^* =$ humidity ratio of moisture-saturated air
$h_L^* =$ enthalpy of liquid water,

all of which are functions of the thermodynamic wet-bulb temperature t^*. If Eq. (12) can be converted explicitly into the form of the Lewis relation [Eq. (11)], the thermodynamic wet-bulb temperature relation can be compared with the transfer coefficient relation $f/\sigma C_P$.

A rigorous analytical treatment of this conversion is rather difficult in view of the complex nature of the thermodynamic properties of moist air with respect to the temperature and humidity ratios. But an approximate formulation of h suggested in the ASHRAE Guide,[7] with an accuracy of 0.1 per cent over the range 32 to 100°F at $P_t = 1$ atm, enables us to write

$$h = (0.2402 + 0.44S_\infty)t_\infty + 1061S_\infty$$
$$\text{Btu/lb of dry air}$$
$$\qquad (13)$$
$$h^* = (0.2402 + 0.44S^*)t^* + 1061S^*$$
$$\text{Btu/lb of dry air}$$

Noting further that

$$0.2402 + 0.44S_\infty \approx 0.2402 + 0.44S^* \approx C_P \qquad (14)$$

and that

$$\lambda \approx 1061 \text{ Btu/lb}$$

it is possible to derive

$$N_L^* = \frac{(S^* - S_\infty)\lambda^*}{C_P(t_\infty - t^*)} \approx 1 + \frac{h_L^*}{\lambda^*} \qquad (15)$$

which yields essentially $N_L^* \approx 1$, since h_L^*/λ^* is very small.

Extensive calculations incorporating the Goff and Gratch data[7] for moist air have been performed to check Eq. (15) with respect to the basic relation of Eq. (12). For the range of thermodynamic wet-bulb temperature from 50 to 120°F, humidity ratio from 0 to 0.12, and dry-bulb temperature from 60 to 200°F, N_L^* is again found to be very nearly unity when C_P is computed from Eq. (14).

We may then conclude that, at least in the range investigated above, the thermodynamic wet-bulb temperature derived from the present Goff and Gratch moist-air table demands that $N_L = f/\sigma C_P \approx 1$.

The Lewis relation N_L is, therefore, much more convenient and meaningful than the psychrometric constant A' for the analysis of the wet-bulb psychrometry.

EFFECT OF WATER RESERVOIR ON THE TEMPERATURE OF ADIABATIC EVAPORATION ON A THIN-PLATE WETTED SURFACE

The heat transfer coefficient f used in the previous discussion is a combination of the convective coefficient f_c and radiative coefficient K_R. In formulating the Lewis relation [Eq. (11)], the surface temperature was assumed to be uniform. This assumption is usually not valid if the liquid water is supplied from a reservoir that is attached to the end of the wet-bulb element.

A more descriptive formulation of the heat and vapor transfer phenomena on the actual wet-bulb element is as follows:

$$(f_c + K_R)(t_\infty - t_w) + Q_K = \sigma(S_w - S_\infty)\lambda \quad (16)$$

or

$$N_L = \frac{(S_w - S_\infty)\lambda}{(t_\infty - t_w)C_P}$$
$$= \frac{f_c}{\sigma C_P}\left(1 + \frac{K_R}{f_c}\right) + \frac{Q_K}{\sigma C_P(t_\infty - t_w)} \quad (17)$$

where Q_K is the heat flux due to the temperature gradient along the wet-bulb element.

In Eq. (17) $f_c/\sigma C_P$ is factored out to designate it as the convective Lewis relation $N_L^{(c)}$ in order to separate the convective contribution from the overall Lewis relation N_L, which is influenced by the radiation heat and by the heat from the reservoir. Equation (17) can then be written as

$$N_L = N_L^{(c)}\left(1 + \frac{K_R}{f_c}\right) + \frac{Q_K}{\sigma C_P}\frac{1}{t_\infty - t_w} \quad (18)$$

Extensive analysis of the radiative heat transfer upon the wet-bulb psychrometry is available,[2,6] but the influence of the supply water reservoir has rarely been discussed except in an experimental work of Brooks and Allen.[8] Brooks and Allen recognized that an error in the wet-bulb temperature could be caused by a large temperature difference between the supply water reservoir and the wet-bulb element. They successfully minimized the error by cooling the reservoir wall with a wet wick.

Theoretical study of the reservoir heat flow effect, however, merits further attention. In this section, temperature profile along a thin hygroscopic element, which is exposed to the ambient air and attached to the water supply reservoir at one end, will now be discussed in detail.

The entire device including the reservoir is assumed to be surrounded by an ambient of dry-bulb temperature t_∞ and humidity ratio S_∞. The model of such a system is illustrated in Fig. 1, for which it is also assumed that

(1) The plate is homogeneously porous and so thin that no transverse temperature gradient exists; in other words, the heat conduction is only along the longitudinal axis.

(2) The reservoir feeds water to the element at a rate such that the capillary pores over the entire length of the plate are filled with liquid water and that the plate surface is completely covered by a liquid water film; and no water leaves the plate surface except by surface evaporation to the surrounding medium. (This assumption is usually satisfied by hygroscopic and porous materials.)

(3) Heat conduction due to the presence of a temperature sensing element in the system is not considered.

Using the scheme illustrated in Fig. 1 and referring to the nomenclature, heat- and mass-balance relationships are established for an elementary plate segment between x and $x + \Delta x$ as follows:

(a) Heat flowing out of the segment at the x plane

$$Q_x = k'\frac{dt}{dx}A + mC_Lt$$

(b) Heat flowing into the segment at the $x + \Delta x$ plane

$$Q_{x+\Delta x} = k'\frac{dt}{dx}A + k'\frac{d^2t}{dx^2}A\Delta x +$$
$$\left(m + \frac{dm}{dx}\Delta x\right)\left(t + \frac{dt}{dx}\Delta x\right)C_L$$

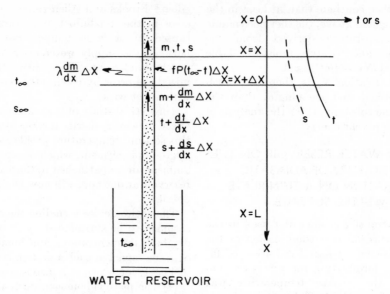

FIG. 1. Schematic view of the wet hygroscopic plate with water supply reservoir under simultaneous transfer of heat and water vapor.

(c) Sensible heat input to the segment surface from the surrounding air

$$Q_S = f(t_\infty - t)P\Delta x$$

(d) Latent heat transferred from the segment surface to the surrounding air

$$Q_L = \sigma\lambda(S - S_\infty)P\Delta x \qquad (19)$$

Combining all the heat flows for the adiabatic system, we have the heat-balance equation

$$Q_x + Q_S = Q_{x+\Delta x} + Q_L \qquad (20)$$

which results in a differential equation

$$Ak'\frac{d^2t}{dx^2} + mC_L\frac{dt}{dx} + C_Lt\frac{dm}{dx} +$$
$$f(t_\infty - t)P = \sigma(S - S_\infty)P\lambda \qquad (21)$$

The mass-balance relation must satisfy

$$\frac{dm}{dx} = \sigma(S - S_\infty)P \qquad (22)$$

Substituting Eq. (22) into Eq. (21) and dividing Eq. (21) by Ak' gives

$$\frac{d^2t}{dx^2} + \left(\frac{mC_L}{Ak'}\right)\frac{dt}{dx} = \left(\frac{fP}{Ak'}\right)(t - t_\infty) +$$
$$\left(\frac{C_L\sigma P}{Ak'}\right)\left(\frac{\lambda}{C_L} - t\right)(S - S_\infty) \qquad (23)$$

New variables ξ, V, and M are now introduced.

$$\xi = x\sqrt{\frac{Pf}{k'A}}, \quad V = \frac{m}{\sigma}\sqrt{\frac{f}{PAk'}},$$
$$M = \frac{C_L\sigma}{f} = \frac{C_L}{C_PN_L} \qquad (24)$$

Equations (22) and (23) can be resolved into the following simple forms:

$$\frac{d^2t}{d\xi^2} + MV\frac{dt}{d\xi} = (t - t_\infty) +$$
$$M\left(\frac{\lambda}{C_L} - t\right)(S - S_\infty) \qquad (25)$$
$$\frac{dV}{d\xi} = S - S_\infty \qquad (26)$$

The saturated air humidity ratio in Eqs. (25) and (26) is a function of temperature,

$$S = G(t) \qquad (27)$$

which can be found in the Goff and Gratch Table.[7] Three boundary conditions are required for solving the above set of simultaneous differential equations. The most obvious boundary condition is

$$t = t_\infty \text{ at } \xi = \xi_0 = l\sqrt{\frac{Pf}{k'A}} \qquad (28)$$

The other two conditions are arbitrarily selected for two different cases at $x = 0$:

Case 1: $V = 0, \dfrac{dt}{d\xi} = 0$

Case 2: $V = 0, t = t^*$ (thermodynamic wet-bulb temperature)

Case 1 corresponds to a situation in which the tip of the wet plate is perfectly insulated from heat and water flow. A preliminary experimental study of temperature distribution along the hygroscopic plate with one end immersed in the water revealed that the temperature gradient becomes negligible at some distance from the reservoir. Thus, the origin of the x-coordinate system can be located where $dt/dx = 0$ for the purpose of this analysis.

Case 2 is somewhat arbitrary and represents the case where a blunt plate leading edge is exposed to the moist air stream. If the radiation error were compensated and a barrier to water flow were placed at the tip, it could be assumed that the tip temperature should be the thermodynamic wet-bulb temperature, since turbulent mass-exchange systems such as described on p. 22 would be expected.

An analytical solution satisfying a nonlinear system of Eqs. (25), (26) and (27) is impossible. Sample calculations at a moist-air condition of $t_\infty = 80°F$, $S_\infty = 0.0112$ were performed by the Runge-Kutta numerical integration method.

Figures 2 and 3 show the temperature profiles over the wet-plate from the tip to the reservoir for various ξ_0 at $M = 4.11$ and $\lambda/C_L = 1055.4$ for Cases 1 and 2, respectively. The temperature at $x = 0$ is superimposed on Fig. 2, and $dt/d\xi$ at $x = 0$ is superimposed on Fig. 3.

In these calculations λ/C_L is assumed constant, because its change with respect to temperature is relatively small. A value $M = 4.11$ corresponds to the Lewis relation of unity for $C_P = 0.243$ and $C_L = 1.0$. The Lewis relation of unity is chosen to isolate the effect of the reservoir for this study from the overall problem.

Figures 2 and 3 illustrate that the tip temperature rapidly decreases with increase in plate length. Also, the plate temperature

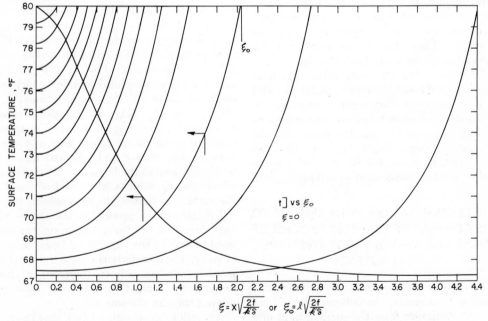

FIG. 2. Calculated temperature distribution along the wet hygroscopic plate and tip temperature for various ξ_0, for $dt/d\xi = 0$ at $\xi = 0$, and for $t = 80°F$ at $\xi = \xi_0$ ($t_\infty = 80°F, S_\infty = 0.01120, M = 4.11$ and $\lambda/C = 1055.4$).

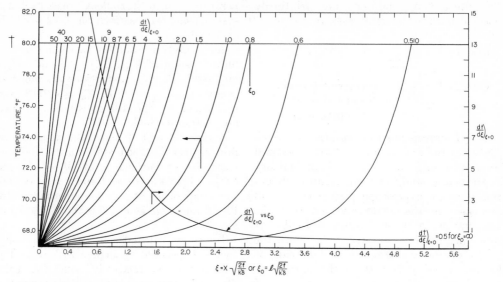

FIG. 3. Calculated temperature distribution along the wet hygroscopic plate and tip temperature gradient for various ξ_0 for $t = 67°F$ at $\xi = 0$ and for $t = 80°F$ at $\xi = \xi_0$ ($t_\infty = 80°F$, $S_\infty = 0.01120$, $M = 4.11$ and $\lambda/C_L = 1055.4$).

remains very nearly constant over 50 per cent of the length from the tip for a plate length $\xi_0 \geqq 4$. In Case 1 the tip temperature asymptotically approaches 67.3°F instead of the expected thermodynamic wet-bulb temperature of 67°F as ξ_0 increases. Figure 2 also illustrates the wet-bulb temperature measurement error due to the heat flow from the reservoir when the temperature sensing element is placed away from the tip.

In Case 2, the tip temperature gradient approaches 0.5 as ξ_0 increases. In Cases 1 and 2, it is apparent that serious error can be avoided if the surface temperature is measured at a distance away from the reservoir—the distance corresponding to $\xi_0 \geqq 4$. This has been confirmed also for the case of a much higher wet-bulb depression by setting $S_\infty = 0$.

THE LEWIS RELATION WITH RESPECT TO THE CONVECTIVE TRANSFER PROCESS OF HEAT AND WATER VAPOR OVER THE FLAT SURFACE

By proper instrumentation design, it is possible to eliminate the influence of the heat flow by radiation from the surroundings and that from the reservoir. There remains, however, consideration of whether the expression

$$N_L^{(c)} = \frac{f_c}{\sigma C_P} = 1$$

accurately expresses the convection heat transfer phenomena at the wet-bulb surfaces. In order to simplify the discussion, the flat-plate wet-bulb element is used in this section to explore the convection process in detail.

Velocity profiles for moist air flowing over a flat plate are described in Fig. 4. Figures 4.1 and 4.2 show simplified profiles which are essential parts of the August convection theory and the Maxwell diffusion theory, respectively. The August convection theory relies on turbulent mixing of heat and vapor between the surface and adjacent moist air without regard to the boundary layer through which the air velocity changes from zero at the surface to that of the free stream, U_∞.

Eckert[9] gives a proof that the Lewis relation, based on the turbulent mixing process, would result in the convective Lewis relation of unity. The thermodynamics of the wet-bulb psychrometry (p. 18) is, therefore, at least numerically compatible with the turbulent mixing transfer phenomena.

Assuming, on the other hand, that the temperature and humidity changes from the surface to the free stream are linear, and also

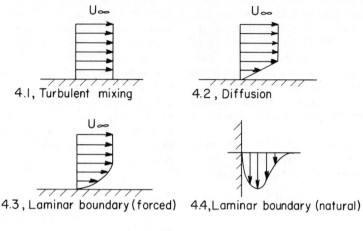

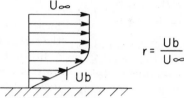

4.5 Turbulent boundary (forced)

Fɪɢ. 4. Various velocity profiles along the flat plate considered for the Lewis relation calculation.

assuming that the boundary layer thicknesses for temperature and humidity gradients are equal,

$$\frac{f}{\sigma C_P} \approx \frac{f_c}{h_D \rho C_p} \approx \frac{\alpha}{D} \qquad (29)$$

which is the essence of the Maxwell diffusion theory.

Actual convection phenomena are described neither by the turbulent mixing nor by the simple boundary profiles of Figs. 4.1 and 4.2. There are three basic patterns of the boundary layer velocity profile that are commonly cited in the heat-transfer literature. They are depicted schematically in Figs. 4.3, 4.4, and 4.5 corresponding, respectively, to the cases of forced laminar flow, natural convection flow, and forced turbulent flow with laminar sublayer.

Generally speaking, the empirical Lewis relation of heat and vapor over the wet evaporating surface of many geometrical configurations (flat-plate, cylinder, sphere, and packed beds) is usually expressed by the following relations:

$$N_L^{(c)} = \frac{f_c}{h_D \rho C_P} \approx \frac{f_c}{\sigma C_P} \approx \left(\frac{\alpha}{D}\right)^{2/3} \qquad (30)$$

for the forced-convection transfer phenomena[6, 9] and for the entire range of the Reynolds number $Re_x = U_\infty x/\nu$.

Eckert[9] implied that Eq. (30) is not valid for very high evaporation rates. Rigorous laminar boundary layer calculations have been applied for studying the Lewis relation for a range of evaporation rates that is experienced in air conditioning wet-bulb psychrometry. These computations used the forced-convection calculation of Hartnett and Eckert[10] (corresponding to Fig. 4.3) and the natural convection calculation of Nakamura (corresponding to Fig. 4.4).[11]

Although the study of the laminar boundary layer is restricted to idealized conditions, it will nevertheless provide a good understanding of the gap between the diffusion theory of Maxwell and the completely turbulent mixing transfer theory advocated by August. The actual heat- and vapor-transfer processes over a wet evaporating surface, even for the turbulent flow condition, must include the resistance of the laminar sublayer. Moreover, the very small geometrical factor associated with conventional wet-bulb elements results in a low Reynolds number even at a higher stream velocity; so that influence of the laminar boundary layer still predominates the entire process.

The basic relations of heat and mass transfer across the evaporating surface boundary layer can be written as follows:-

$$f_c(t_\infty - t_w) = \left[k \frac{\partial t}{\partial Y} \right]_w \qquad (31)$$

$$\rho h_D(W_\infty - W) = \left[\frac{-CD}{W(1-W)} \frac{\partial W}{\partial Y} \right]_w \qquad (32)$$

By proper transformation of the variables for temperatures and mass fractions as well as for the length element, it is possible to derive the transfer coefficient ratio in the following form:

$$\frac{f}{\rho h_D} = \left[\frac{k}{D} \frac{(1-W)}{\rho} \frac{\psi(Pr, F_w)}{\psi(Sc, F_w)} \right]_w \qquad (33)$$

where ψ is the dimensionless gradient function and F_w is the dimensionless evaporation velocity.*

Equations (5), (6) and (7) can be utilized to reduce the above expression to the following form:

$$\frac{f_c}{\sigma} = (1 + S_\infty) \left[\frac{k}{D\rho} \frac{\psi(Pr, F_w)}{\psi(Sc, F_w)} \right]_w \qquad (34)$$

* The reader who is interested in carrying out the derivation of this equation will find the papers by Hartnett[10] and Eckert[9] and Nakamura[11] useful in general.

It should be noted that the thermal conductivity, diffusion coefficient, and mixture density are all to be evaluated at the surface or at the saturated moist-air condition at the surface temperature.

The specific heat of the Lewis relation, however, should be an integrated mean of the values across the boundary layer as indicated in Eq. (11). The exact formulation of the Lewis relation for the boundary layer calculation can be expressed by the following relation:

$$N_L^{(c)} = \frac{f_c}{\sigma C_P}$$

$$= (1 + S_\infty)\left(\frac{C_{P,w}}{C_P}\right)\left[\frac{\alpha\psi_j(Pr, F_w)}{D\psi_j(Sc, F_w)}\right]_w \qquad (35)$$

for $j = 1$ and 2, corresponding respectively to the cases of forced and natural convection.

In Eq. (35), $C_{P,w}$ is the specific heat of the water vapor in saturated air at the surface temperature; the dimensionless evaporation velocity F_w is expressed implicitly as

$$F_w = \frac{2}{Sc} \Gamma\psi_1(Sc, F_w) \quad \begin{array}{l}\text{for forced}\\\text{convection}\end{array} \qquad (36)$$

and

$$F_w = \frac{1}{3Sc} \Gamma\psi_2(Sc, F_w) \quad \begin{array}{l}\text{for natural}\\\text{convection}\end{array} \qquad (37)$$

where

$$\Gamma = \frac{S_w - S_\infty}{1 + S_\infty} \qquad (38)$$

There are no explicit functional forms available for ψ_1 and ψ_2. The numerically computed values of ψ_1 and ψ_2 are listed in Tables 1 and 2 for several combinations of F_w and Pr or Sc. The values for Table 1 were calculated using a digital computer, and the values for

TABLE 1. NUMERICAL EVALUATION OF ψ_1 FOR EQ. (35)

F_w	Pr or Sc						
	1.0	0.9	0.8	0.7	0.6	0.5	0.4
−0.020	0.3255	0.3140	0.3016	0.2879	0.2728	0.2558	0.2361
−0.015	0.3273		0.3030		0.2740		0.2369
−0.010	0.3291	0.3173	0.3045	0.2906	0.2751	0.2577	0.2377
−0.008	0.3298		0.3051		0.2756		0.2381
−0.005	0.3309		0.3060		0.2763		0.2385
−0.004							
−0.002	0.3320		0.3069		0.2770		0.2390
−0.000	0.3327	0.3206	0.3075	0.2932	0.2774	0.2597	0.2393

Table 2 are taken from Nakamura's paper.[11] In order to evaluate Eq. (35), $\psi_j(j = 1,2)$ must be calculated for the evaporation velocity F_w which is also a function of ψ_j and Γ which is a function of the humidity ratio difference. Theoretically, the Lewis relation is related to the humidity ratio difference between the wet surface air and the stream air, which, to the author's knowledge, has not been mentioned in previous literature.

TABLE 2. NUMERICAL EVALUATION OF ψ_2 FOR EQ. (35)

F_w	Pr or Sc		
	0.72	0.6	0.5
-0.030	0.4707	0.4318	0.3942
-0.015	0.4876	0.4455	0.4053
0	0.5046	0.4592	0.4164
0.015	0.5218	0.4734	0.4279
0.03	0.5393	0.4876	0.4395

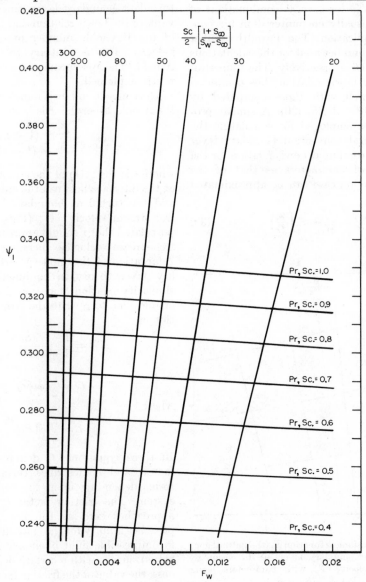

FIG. 5. Dimensionless function ψ_1 (the forced convection laminar boundary layer) vs the dimensionless evaporation velocity F_w with parameters being (Pr, Sc) and $Sc/2 \, (1 + S_\infty)/(S_w - S_\infty)$.

Figure 5 illustrates the solution of ψ_1 from Eq. (36) by two families of curves: one for $\psi_1(F_w)$ and the other for $ScF_w/2\Gamma$; both are plotted against F_w. For a given set of S_∞ and S_w, Γ is computed and the intersection of curves $ScF_w/2\Gamma$ and $\psi_1(Sc, F_w)$ would yield the evaporation velocity F_w. This evaporation velocity then gives $\psi_1(Pr, F_w)$ and $\psi_1(Sc, F_w)$ for the evaluation of the convective Lewis relation, Eq. (35). This procedure is used in calculating $N_L^{(c)}$ for several combinations of S_w and S_∞ usually encountered in air conditioning application. The Prandtl number and Schmidt number used for the calculations are 0.7 and 0.6, respectively. The numerical values of the Lewis relation thus computed agree very well with those computed by relation $(\alpha/D)^{2/3}$ of Eq. (30). A similar procedure can be employed for calculating the laminar natural convection boundary layer (Fig. 6). The computed Lewis relation for the same range of parameters as that of the forced convection case can be approximated by

$$N_L^{(c)} = \frac{f_c}{\sigma C_P} \approx \left(\frac{\alpha}{D}\right)^{0.48} \quad (39)$$

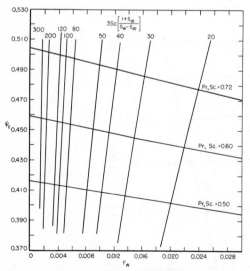

FIG. 6. Dimensionless function ψ_2 (the natural convection laminar boundary layer) *vs* dimensionless evaporation velocity F_w with parameters being (Pr, Sc) and $3Sc(1 + S_\infty)/(S_w - S_\infty)$.

Unfortunately, no rigorous analytical calculation for the turbulent boundary transfer

process (Figs. 4, 5) is available at present. The author, however, feels that, judging from the laminar boundary layer calculation, the evaporation velocity influence upon the Lewis relation can also be ignored for the case of turbulent boundary layer transfer processes.

It is very interesting to note that the theoretical analysis of the laminar boundary layer calculation and the experimental studies of the heat and vapor transfer for the turbulent boundary layer range, result in a value of the Lewis relation that is independent of the Reynolds number or of the stream velocity. This is contrary to the theory of Arnold. The discrepancy, however, may be partly explained.

The convective Lewis number derived from the Arnold theory[1, 2, 6] is

$$N_L^{(c)} = \frac{Sc + (1 - r)/r}{Pr + (1 - r)/r} \quad (40)$$

where r is the ratio of the stream velocity U_b at the interface between the laminar sublayer and the turbulent boundary layer and the free-stream velocity, U_∞ (Figs. 4, 5). Arnold postulated that r should approach zero as the free-stream velocity increases to infinity. Adaptation of the modern turbulent boundary layer theory in conjunction with the similarity relation of heat and mass transfer enables one to rewrite the Arnold's formulation as

$$N_L^{(c)} = \frac{1 + r'(Sc - 1)}{1 + r(Pr - 1)} \quad (41)$$

$$r' = \frac{f_p}{2}\,\phi(Sc)$$

where $\quad (42)$

$$r = \frac{f_p}{2}\,\phi(Pr)$$

In these equations, f_p denotes the friction factor, and ϕ describes certain functional forms depending upon the type of transfer system. The friction factor f_p theoretically approaches zero as the flow velocity approaches infinity for the smooth surface of the incompressible fluid boundary layer. For an actual surface with a certain degree of roughness, the value of the friction factor asymptotically approaches a nonzero constant as the Reynolds number becomes very large.[12] The numerical value of $N_L^{(c)}$ therefore tends to become a constant different from unity and independent of the flow velocity above certain Reynolds number.

IMPORTANCE OF THE MOIST AIR PROPERTIES

Even when the simple relation of Eq. (30) or (39) is employed, accurate numerical evaluation of $N_L^{(c)}$ is hindered by the lack of reliable transport properties associated with moist air. In the past, α/D has been evaluated on the basis of dry air properties. The author felt it necessary to investigate the value of α/D for moist air. The thermal conductivity of the moist air was computed from a semi-empirical formula of Cheung and Bromely,[13, 14]

which is currently considered to be the best available formulation and shows a remarkable agreement with various experimental data on several other polar-nonpolar gas mixtures (average deviation, 2.1 per cent for a temperature range of 0 to ∼774°F). The results for moist air thermal conductivity computed from the semiempirical formula are illustrated in Fig. 7. The effect of water vapor upon the thermal conductivity of dry air becomes significant at higher temperatures. The results of a similar calculation for moist air viscosity are shown in Fig. 8. Although moist air viscosity has no direct bearing upon the calculation of α/D, it is required for the evaluation of ψ_1 and ψ_2.

The specific heat of moist air was obtained from the Smithsonian Meteorological Table,[15]

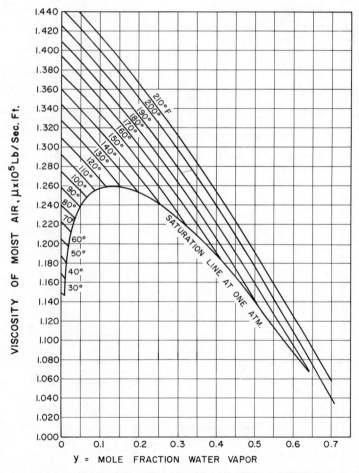

FIG. 7. Computed thermal conductivity of moist air based on the empirical formulation of Cheung.

and its density was computed from the ASHRAE Guide Table.[7] Experimental diffusion coefficients of water vapor in air from literature are shown in Fig. 9.[16] The value for D was computed with Spalding's formula,[7] and appears to closely approximate the experimental data.[16] All the other available empirical formulations[15] for the diffusion coefficients also fail to take into account the effect of the moisture content. Although, according to rigorous kinetic theory, D for a gas mixture is actually a function of composition,[17] the composition influence factor on D is usually very small (in the range from 1.0 to 1.03).

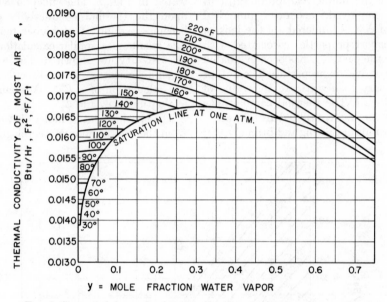

FIG. 8. Computed dynamic viscosity of moist air based on the empirical formulation of Cheung.

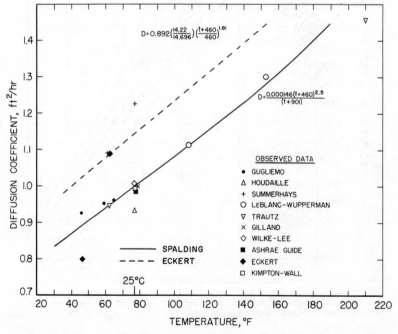

FIG. 9. Diffusion coefficients of water vapor in air observed by various investigators.

Table 3 shows pertinent properties of dry and saturated air for several temperatures on the assumption that D is independent of the moisture content. The values of α and α/D for the unsaturated moist air may have a higher value than those for the dry and saturated air since the thermal conductivity reaches a maximum at an intermediate degree of saturation as shown in Fig. 8.

The effect of water vapor upon α/D is not significant below 100°F. It may become significant above 140°F, but this study does not cover the higher temperature range.

Table 3 indicates that Pr and Sc are only slightly affected by moisture in the air within the temperature range.

Using the value of α/D in Table 3, the convective Lewis relation is computed for the forced convection flow cases by $(\alpha/D)^{2/3}$. For dry air, this value is approximately 0.90 for the temperature range from 50 to 140°F, decreasing slightly with temperature increase. For saturated moist air the value is 0.9 at 50°F and 0.87 at 140°F. The Lewis relation

computed by Kern,[18] showed that $(\alpha/D)^{2/3}$ for air increases with temperature increase (approximately 0.87 at 0°F and 0.9 at 140°F).*

DEVIATION OF THE SURFACE TEMPERATURE OF THE ADIABATIC EVAPORATION PROCESS FROM THE THERMODYNAMIC WET-BULB TEMPERATURE

According to Eq. (17) and the forced convection Lewis relation investigated above, the overall Lewis relation N_L would seldom satisfy the condition of being unity for the actual heat and vapor transfer processes

* E. A. Mason and L. Monchick[19] have presented transport properties of moist air based on their rigorous kinetic theory calculations simultaneously with the author's paper at the 1963 International Symposium on Humidity and Moisture. The values of α/D calculated from transport properties of Mason and Monchick are slightly different from those shown in Table 3. For instance, it is 0.863 for dry air and 0.828 for saturated moist air at 140°F.

TABLE 3. TRANSPORT PROPERTIES OF DRY AND MOISTURE-SATURATED AIR

t (°F)	Degree of Saturation	$\left(\dfrac{k/\text{Btu}}{\text{hr, ft, °F}}\right)$	α (ft²/hr)	D (ft²/hr)	ν (ft²/hr)	α/D	$Pr = \dfrac{\nu}{\alpha}$	$Sc = \dfrac{\nu}{D}$
50	0	0.01441	0.770	0.901	0.548	0.855	0.712	0.609
	1	0.01442	0.769		0.549	0.854	0.713	0.609
60	0	0.01466	0.799	0.936	0.568	0.854	0.711	0.607
	1	0.01467	0.797		0.568	0.852	0.713	0.607
70	0	0.01491	0.828	0.971	0.587	0.853	0.709	0.605
	1	0.01493	0.826		0.588	0.850	0.712	0.606
80	0	0.01516	0.858	1.007	0.607	0.852	0.708	0.603
	1	0.01519	0.854		0.608	0.848	0.712	0.604
90	0	0.01541	0.888	1.044	0.627	0.851	0.706	0.601
	1	0.01545	0.883		0.629	0.846	0.712	0.602
100	0	0.01566	0.919	1.081	0.647	0.850	0.705	0.599
	1	0.01571	0.911		0.650	0.843	0.713	0.601
110	0	0.01590	0.949	1.119	0.668	0.848	0.704	0.597
	1	0.01596	0.938		0.671	0.838	0.715	0.600
120	0	0.01615	0.981	1.157	0.689	0.848	0.702	0.595
	1	0.01620	0.963		0.693	0.832	0.719	0.598
130	0	0.01639	1.012	1.196	0.710	0.846	0.701	0.593
	1	0.01642	0.985		0.714	0.823	0.725	0.597
140	0	0.01663	1.044	1.235	0.731	0.845	0.700	0.592
	1	0.01661	1.003		0.736	0.812	0.734	0.596

unless the radiation and reservoir effect exactly compensates for the convective Lewis relation. In actual practice, the overall Lewis relation may vary from 0.8 to 1.2. It is interesting, therefore, to investigate the discrepancy between the temperature of the adiabatically evaporating surface and the thermodynamic wet-bulb temperature for various values of the overall Lewis relation N_L.

Combining the thermodynamic Lewis relation [Eq. (15)] and the overall transfer process relation [Eq. (17)], we obtain an approximate relation between the thermodynamic wet-bulb temperature and the adiabatic evaporating temperature

$$\frac{S^* - S_\infty}{t_\infty - t^*} \approx \frac{1}{N_L} \frac{S_w - S_\infty}{t_\infty - t_w} \qquad (43)$$

Since S^* and S_w are functions of t^* and t_w, respectively, Eq. (17) can be used to compute $t^* - t_w$ as a function of N_L for given t_∞ and S_∞.

Table 4 illustrates adiabatic wet surface temperature deviations from the thermodynamic wet-bulb temperature for various N_L, which is obtained by solving Eq. (43). The wet-bulb temperature error caused by a

given N_L becomes greater as S_∞ becomes smaller and t_∞ becomes larger.

DISCUSSIONS AND CONCLUSIONS

The Lewis relation was examined in the light of recent empirical as well as theoretical findings on the simultaneous transfer of heat and water vapor under an adiabatic condition. The Lewis relation, rather than the conventional psychrometric constant, was chosen as a basis for the psychrometric calculation because of its dimensionless character and feasibility of correlating the ordinary wet-bulb temperature with thermodynamic wet-bulb temperature. At least for the temperature and humidity range of air conditioning, the thermodynamic wet-bulb temperature formulation corresponds to a heat- and vapor-transfer condition where the overall Lewis relation is unity. The Lewis relation is near unity, however, only when the transfer of heat and vapor is accomplished by perfect turbulent mixing without the influence of radiation and reservoir heat flow.

Although the radiation heat exchange between the wet surface and the surroundings has been included in previous studies,[1, 2, 4] study of the reservoir influence has been

TABLE 4. ADIABATICALLY EVAPORATING SURFACE TEMPERATURE DEVIATION FROM THE THERMODYNAMIC WET-BULB TEMPERATURE, $t^*\text{-}t_w$, FOR VARIOUS LEWIS RELATION N_L

S_∞	t_∞ (°F)		60	80	100	120	140	160
	t^* (°F)		38.28	48.24	56.68	63.92	70.20	75.74
		0.8	2.68	3.27	3.77	4.19	4.54	4.84
		0.9	1.25	1.53	1.77	1.97	2.14	2.29
0.000	N_L	1.0	0.00	0.00	0.00	0.00	0.00	0.00
		1.1	−1.10	−1.36	−1.59	−1.78	−1.92	−2.06
		1.2	−2.08	−2.58	−3.02	−3.38	−3.68	−3.94
	t^* (°F)		58.27	65.30	71.45	76.93	81.69	86.04
		0.8	0.14	1.05	1.77	2.38	2.87	3.30
		0.9	0.07	0.50	0.85	1.14	1.38	1.58
0.0100	N_L	1.0	0.00	0.00	0.00	0.00	0.00	0.00
		1.1	−0.06	−0.46	−0.79	−1.06	−1.28	−1.45
		1.2	−0.12	−0.89	−1.52	−2.04	−2.46	−2.81
	t^* (°F)		—	77.59	82.39	86.79	90.61	94.18
		0.8	—	0.13	0.85	1.46	1.96	2.39
		0.9	—	0.06	0.41	0.70	0.94	1.15
0.0200	N_L	1.0	—	0.00	0.00	0.00	0.00	0.00
		1.1	—	−0.06	−0.39	−0.66	−0.89	−1.09
		1.2	—	−0.12	−0.76	−1.30	−1.74	−2.11

incomplete. The reservoir effect therefore was extensively treated in this paper by solving a differential equation that includes the heat inputs due to the conduction and the water flow. The temperature gradient effect along the evaporating surface caused by the reservoir can be eliminated by placing the temperature probe away from the reservoir, so that $\xi_0 = l\sqrt{Pf/k'A} \approx l\sqrt{2f/k'\delta}$ (for the thin element) is greater than 4. Equation (18) indicates that the overall Lewis relation can be reduced to the convective Lewis relation, a multiplier that comprises the influence of radiation, and an added term that comprises heat conduction and reservoir water flow. Theoretically, the multiplier could be reduced to unity by taking suitable precautions, such as placing a radiation shield around the temperature probe, and the added term can be reduced to zero by placing the probe far away from the reservoir ($\xi_0 > 4$).

The convective Lewis relation differs from unity and is nearly equal to $(\alpha/D)^{2/3}$ for forced convection, as has been shown somewhat intuitively in the past from the similarity relation between the mass transfer and the heat transfer. A rigorous laminar boundary layer calculation was applied in this paper to study the evaporation velocity effect on the convective Lewis relation. At least for the range of air-conditioning wet-bulb psychrometry, it was found that the convective Lewis relation is still nearly $(\alpha/D)^{2/3}$ for forced convection, and that it is closely estimated by $(\alpha/D)^{0.48}$ for natural convection. In this paper, α/D was evaluated using the properties of moist air rather than those of dry air. Although the diffusion coefficient was not taken as a function of the humidity ratio, α/D appears to depend upon moisture content at higher temperature.

Further studies on the transport properties of moist air may help to clarify the differences between the thermodynamic wet-bulb relation and the convective Lewis relation.

The overall Lewis relation can be evaluated by the convective Lewis relation with corrections due to heat flow from the radiating ambient and that from the water reservoir.

Deviations of the ordinary wet-bulb temperatures from the thermodynamic wet-bulb temperatures are shown in Table 4 for several values of the overall Lewis relation.

NOMENCLATURE

Unless otherwise defined in the text, the following notations are used:

A	Cross-sectional area	ft^2
A'	Psychrometric constant	°F^{-1}
C	Partial water density	lb/ft^3
C_L	Liquid water specific heat	Btu/lb, °F
C_P	Moist air specific heat	Btu/lb, °F
$C_{P,w}$	Moist air specific heat at the surface	Btu/lb, °F
D	Coefficient of diffusion of moist air	ft^2/hr
e	Partial vapor pressure	in. of Hg
F_w	Evaporation velocity	dimensionless
f	Overall heat-transfer coefficient	Btu/hr, ft^2, °F
f_f	Molar mass-transfer coefficient	Mole/(hr)(ft^2) (mole fraction)
f_c	Convective heat-transfer coefficient	Btu/hr, ft^2, °F
f_p	Friction coefficient	dimensionless
h	Enthalpy of moist air	Btu/lb of dry air
h_D	Mass-transfer coefficient	lb/hr, ft^2
k	Thermal conductivity of moist air	Btu/hr, ft, °F
k'	Thermal conductivity of wet hygroscopic plate	Btu/hr, ft^2, °F
K_R	Radiation coefficient	Btu/hr, °F, ft^2
l	Length of thin plate	ft
M_a	Molecular weight of air	lb mole
M_w	Molecular weight of water	lb mole
m	Liquid water flow rate along a thin plate	lb/hr
$\dot{m}$	Mass-transfer rate	lb/hr, ft^2
M	A factor defined in the text [Eq. (24)]	
N_L	The Lewis relation or the Lewis number	dimensionless
$N_L^{(c)}$	Convective Lewis number	dimensionless
P	Perimeter	ft
P_t	Total pressure	in. of Hg
Pr	Prandtl number $= \nu/\alpha$	dimensionless
Q	Heat exchanged	Btu/hr
Q_K	Heat flow from reservoir	Btu/hr, ft^2
q	Heat flux	Btu/hr, ft^2
R_e	Reynolds number $= U_\infty x/\nu$	dimensionless
Sc	Schmidt number $= \nu/D$	dimensionless
S	Humidity ratio	lb/lb of dry air
t	Temperature	°F
U_∞	Stream velocity	ft/hr
U_b	Interfacial velocity between the laminar sublayer and turbulent boundary layer	ft/hr
V	A variable defined in the text [Eq. (24)]	
W	Mass fraction of water vapor	lb/lb of moist air
x	Coordinate along the surface	ft
Y	Coordinate perpendicular to the surface	ft

y	Mole fraction of water vapor	
α	Thermal diffusivity of moist air	ft²/hr
ν	Kinematic viscosity of moist air	ft²/hr
ρ	Mixture density	lb/ft²
λ	Latent heat of evaporation of water	Btu/lb
ξ, ξ_0	Dimensionless length defined in the text [Eq. (24)]	
Γ	Factor defined in the text [Eq. (38)]	
ψ_j, ψ	Dimensionless gradient function [ψ_1 for the forced convection, ψ_2 for the natural convection, Eq. (33)]	
σ	Evaporation coefficient	lb/(hr), (ft²), (lb/lb of dry air)
δ	Plate thickness	ft
ϕ	A function of Pr or Sc [Eq. (42)]	

Subscripts

∞	Well mixed airstream properties
w	Wet evaporating surface properties
a	Pure air properties
v	Pure vapor properties

Superscripts

*	Properties at the thermodynamic wet-bulb temperature
(c)	Convection properties

UNIT CONVERSION TABLE

Symbol	To Convert From	To	Multiply By
α, D, ν	$\dfrac{\text{ft}^2}{\text{hr}}$	$\dfrac{\text{cm}^2}{\text{sec}}$	0.2581
μ	$\dfrac{\text{lb}}{\text{sec, ft}}$	centipoises	1488
k	$\dfrac{\text{Btu}}{\text{hr, ft}^2, °F/ft}$	$\dfrac{\text{g-cal}}{\text{sec, cm}^2, °C/cm}$	0.004134
C_P	$\dfrac{\text{Btu}}{\text{lb, °F}}$	$\dfrac{\text{g-cal}}{\text{g, °C}}$	1
ρ	$\dfrac{\text{lb}}{\text{ft}^3}$	$\dfrac{\text{g}}{\text{cm}^3}$	0.0160184

References

1. Arnold, J. H., "The Theory of the Psychrometer Physics," Vol. 4, pp. 255–261, July 1933.
2. Carrier, W. H., and Mackey, C. O., "A Review of Existing Psychrometric Data in Relation to Practical Engineering Problems," *ASME Transactions*, **59**, 33–47 (January 1937).
3. Muller-Cosna, C., and Mainer-Leibnitz, H., "Zur Formil des Aspirationspsychrometers," *Z. Angew. Phys.*, **3**, 343 (1951).
4. Monteith, J. L., "Error and Accuracy in Thermocouple Psychrometry," *Proc. Phys. Soc.*, **67**, Part 3, 217–226 (March 1954).
5. Wentzel, J. C., "An Instrument for the Measurement of the Humidity of Air," Paper presented in ASHRAE St. Louis meeting, January 29, 1962.
6. Threlkeld, J. L., "Thermal Environmental Engineering," pp. 190–213, New York, Prentice Hall, Inc., 1962.
7. Guide and Data Book: The American Society of Heating, Refrigerating and Air-Conditioning Engineers, Fundamentals and Equipment, Chapters 3 and 5, pp. 27–48 and 67–78, 1961.
8. Brooks, D. B., and Allen, H. H., "Some Improvements in Psychrometry," *J. Wash. Acad. Sci.*, **23**, 121–134, March 15, 1933.
9. Eckert, E. R. G., "Heat and Mass Transfer," pp. 440–476, New York, McGraw-Hill Book Company, Inc., 1959.
10. Hartnett, J. P., "Recent Advances in Heat and Mass Transfer," pp. 142–160, New York, McGraw-Hill Book Company, 1961.
11. Nakamura, H., "Heat Transfer by Laminar Free-Convection on a Vertical Flat Plate Accompanied by Vapor Transfer," *Bull. JSME*, **5**, No. 1B, 311 (1962).
12. Sato, T., Kadono, A., and Ando, M., "Experimental Researches on Heat Transfer on the Surface of Flat Plate in Forced Flow," *Transactions of the Japanese Society of Mechanical Engineers*, **17**, No. 62, 130–136 (1951).
13. Cheung, H., Bromley, L. A., and Wilke, C. R., "Thermal Conductivity of Gas Mixtures," *A.I.Ch.E. J.*, 8, No. 2, 221–228 (May 1962).
14. Cheung, H., Thermal Conductivity and Viscosity of Gas Mixture, UCRL–8230, University of California Radiation Laboratory, Berkeley, California, 1958.
15. Smithsonian Meteorological Tables, 6th ed., p. 339, Washington, D.C., 1951.
16. Lee, C. Y., and Wilke, C. R., "Measurement of Vapor Diffusion Coefficients," *Ind. Eng. Chem.*, **46**, 2381 (1954); **47**, 1253 (1955).
17. Hirschfelder, J. O., *et al.*, "Molecular Theory of Gases and Liquids," p. 539, New York, John Wiley & Sons, Inc., 1954.
18. Kern, D. O., "Process Heat Transfer," p. 575, New York, McGraw-Hill Book Company, Inc., 1950.
19. Mason, E. A., and Monchick, L., "Survey of the Equation of State and Transport Properties of Moist Gases," Paper presented at the 1963 International Symposium on Humidity and Moisture, Washington, D.C., May 20–23, 1963.

3. Proposal for an Experimental Triple-tubed Adiabatic Saturator to Measure Thermodynamic Wet-bulb Temperature as a Limit Approached During the Saturation Process

Louis P. Harrison

U.S. Weather Bureau, Washington, D.C.

ABSTRACT

Three different designs are proposed for adiabatic saturators to be used with gas samples (such as air containing water vapor) in the hope that they might lead eventually to the experimental attainment of the relevant "thermodynamic wet-bulb temperature" T_w^* to a close degree of approximation, irrespective of the chemical species of the liquid and the carrier gas used for the entrainment of its vapor. Each of the designs involves the employment of three concentric tubes, because of the fact that with such arrangements one can more closely approach adiabatic processes than with fewer tubes. Since successful operation requires the evaporation of the liquid at temperature T_w^* into the gas under adiabatic conditions, use of thermostatically controlled means is indispensable for supplying the liquid at the proper value of T_w^* which depends upon the pressure P, temperature T, and mixing ratio r pertinent to the sample of carrier gas admixed with the vapor of the liquid under consideration. Equation (2) gives a mathematical definition of T_w^* in terms of these variables.

Paired temperature-measuring devices exposed to the vapor-containing gas and the liquid, respectively, will be required at a number of stations along the path of contact between the two media continuously flowing through the apparatus. Feedback from their readings at the outlet can be used to control the temperature of the liquid at the inlet which should be effectively equal to T_w^*. When saturation is attained in the apparatus, it should be indicated by agreement of the readings of the pairs of temperature-measuring devices at two or more consecutive stations working backward from the last station (outlet point).

INTRODUCTION

There is clearly a need for a device which, based on sound thermodynamic principles, is capable of yielding indications that are directly related to the water vapor content of moist air or other carrier gas involved. A fairly close approximation to this objective is secured by the use of the well-known psychrometer when this instrument consists of separately shielded, matching thermometers having relatively small bulbs, one of which is wetted by means of a moistened wick of suitable material. Consistent results may be secured provided that the thermometers are given adequate ventilation within a range of the order of 3 to 7 m/sec under normal conditions regarding density and temperature, calculated to assure the obtainment of a stable minimum wet-bulb temperature.[1-7] Under these circumstances the minimum wet-bulb temperature, taken in conjunction with the dry-bulb temperature and the existing barometric pressure, serves as a useful index of the amount of water vapor present in the sample of moist air or other carrier gas under consideration, but the actual value of the minimum wet-bulb temperature reading may vary with the design of the specific psychrometer being used, the size of the thermometer bulbs, the ventilation rate (especially if less than 3 m/sec), the radiation conditions, and other factors independent of the hygrometric state of the moist air. From this, the inference is clear that the psychrometer is not an absolute instrument, for the indications which it gives directly are not independent of the design. Therefore, its immediate indications cannot be regarded to be universally valid as a representation of the hygrometric state of the moist air.

Various well-designed psychrometers, however, when operated at suitable ventilation rates to produce maximum cooling of the wick by evaporation, yield minimum wet-bulb thermometer readings that are relatively coherent in a statistical sense. The readings in the shielded types of psychrometer appear to approach asymptotically a limit. This limit may be assumed to be like the minimum wet-bulb temperature but to be a thermodynamic counterpart which truly represents the hygrometric state of the moist air and is capable of being defined without reference to the psychrometer as the appropriate type of instrument for measuring it. The matter of defining the limit mentioned above is dealt with in the discussion of the theory of psychrometers, but we shall be primarily concerned with the problem of developing some kind of apparatus which would permit a direct measurement of the asymptotic limit approached by the readings of the psychrometer whose bulbs are shielded or, better still, a thermodynamically defined counterpart of the limit independent of the dynamics of the psychrometer.

In the utilization of any actual ventilated psychrometer it is generally the practice to moisten the wick surrounding the wet bulb by dipping it in a small cistern containing water at approximately ambient temperature. When employing such a procedure the water supply is thus usually provided at an initial temperature higher than the minimum wet-bulb thermometer reading attainable with the given psychrometer under the existing ventilation. Clearly, if the moist air current employed to ventilate the instrument has a low relative humidity, the wick may dry out before the minimum attainable wet-bulb reading is reached for the existing hygrometric state of the air. On these grounds it follows that a system involving a water supply at an initial temperature different from that of the potentially lowest wet-bulb reading may not yield a final result having a unique value dependent upon the actual hygrometric state of the sample of moist air involved. In the light of this fact, Carrier[8, 9] suggested that one should idealize the processes which occur in connection with the evaporation of water from the wet-bulb wick by assuming that the water is supplied at the final minimum temperature of equilibrium reached by the wet bulb. Under these circumstances one could hope that a stable minimum would be attained and that this would be at least closer to the asymptotic limit previously mentioned than was reached by means of the conventional procedures.

THEORY

The earliest theory of the mode of operation of the psychrometer was based on the idea that is expressed simply by one of its pioneers, Ivory,[10] in the following words: "... all the air that comes in contact with the wet bulb is continuously saturated with vapor, and likewise that all the heat necessary for feeding the evaporation is furnished by the same air." This underlying principle, called the "convection theory of the psychrometer" was shown to be inadequate as a basis of explanation for all of the processes occurring in connection with the wet bulb, according to a theory given by Arnold.[11, 12]

Carrier[8, 9] and Carrier and Lindsay[13] endeavored to rationalize the convection theory in its application to the psychrometer by making use of essentially the following steps of reasoning on the basis of the assumption of perfect-gas theory and classical thermodynamics as developed before the modern concept of "enthalpy" was born: Consider moist air which has a pressure P, temperature T, and mixing ratio r, interacting with a wet bulb by being convected across the wick at a suitable ventilation rate such that the final minimum temperature of equilibrium reached by the wet bulb is T'_w. For simplicity let us fix our attention on such an interacting quantity of moist air having a mass of $(1 + r)$ grams, consisting of one gram of dry air and r gram of water vapor associated with the dry air. (It will be recognized that r represents the mixing ratio of the moist air, in accordance with the definitions presented by Harrison.[14]) On the basis of the convection theory it is assumed that the heat yielded by the $(1 + r)$ grams of moist air in cooling from dry-bulb temperature T to the wet-bulb temperature T'_w is exactly the right amount to provide the heat necessary for the evaporation of water from the moistened wick at the latter temperature just sufficient in quantity to produce saturation of the interacting air at the temperature T'_w. If C_{pa} denotes the specific heat at constant pressure of the dry air, and C_{pv} denotes the specific heat at constant pressure of the water vapor, the heat yielded by the one gram of dry air in cooling from T to T'_w is represented by $C_{pa}(T - T'_w)$, while the heat yielded by the associated r gram of water vapor is represented by $rC_{pv}(T - T'_w)$. Therefore, the sum of these two contributions is $(C_{pa} + rC_{pv})(T - T'_w)$, provided the moist air behaves as a perfect gas. Suppose that L'_w denotes the latent heat of vaporization of water at the wet-bulb temperature T'_w and that r'_w denotes the mixing ratio of moist air saturated with water vapor at pressure P and temperature T'_w. Then, if the moist air becomes saturated at these conditions during its contact and interaction with the wet bulb, its mixing ratio has changed from r to r'_w, thus undergoing an increase of $(r'_w - r)$. Therefore, the latent heat required to evaporate this amount of water at temperature T'_w is represented by $(r'_w - r)L'_w$. Finally, when the heat yielded by the original moist air in cooling from T to T'_w is equated to the latent heat required to saturate the moist air at the equilibrium wet-bulb temperature T'_w under constant pressure conditions, one obtains the relationship

$$(C_{pa} + rC_{pv})(T - T'_w) = (r'_w - r)L'_w \quad (1)$$

This represents a process of adiabatic saturation for an ideal gas.

It is important to note in regard to this classical derivation that the evaporation of the water is supposed to take place at wet-bulb temperature T'_w and that there is no question with regard to the temperature of the water supply to the wick. Since C_{pa} and C_{pv} are functions of the moist-air temperature, the magnitudes of these parameters pertinent in Eq. (1) ought to be integral mean values in the range between the temperature limits T and T'_w.

Even if we should for the moment consider that the convection theory is adequate, we must still be forced to the conclusion that Eq. (1) suffers from the fact that it does not take into account the imperfect-gas interactions between the dry air and the water vapor associated with it. Certain effects relating to real gases and their mixtures are neglected in the simple perfect-gas theoretical and classical thermodynamic approach to the problem outlined above, as indicated by Keyes and Smith,[15] Goff and Gratch,[16] and Goff.[17]

Owing to the fact that in the development of Eq. (1), the underlying assumption was made that no heat was added to or removed from the system involved during the interaction between the moist air and the wet bulb, Carrier[8, 9] suggested that the minimum theoretical wet-bulb temperature T'_w be termed the "temperature of adiabatic saturation." This concept did not, of course, take into account the role of diffusion in governing the rate of vapor transfer through the thin film of nearly stagnant moist gas surrounding the wet bulb, as indicated in the theory of the wet-bulb thermometer due to Maxwell.[18]

Not many years elapsed after Carrier's suggestion relative to the "temperature of adiabatic saturation" before evidence was forthcoming to the effect that this entity was, in general, different from the observed wet-bulb temperature yielded by actual psychrometers, for the given values of P, T, and r. This evidence stemmed from the analyses and research of various investigators, among whom we may list in roughly chronological order Carrier,[8, 9] Carrier and Lindsay,[13] Skinner,[19] Lewis,[20, 21] Sherwood and Comings,[22] Arnold,[11, 12] Whipple,[23] Dropkin,[24, 25] Carrier and Mackey,[26] and Wile.[27]

Admitting the usefulness of the concept of adiabatic saturation and the related parameter "temperature of adiabatic saturation," it was strongly emphasized by Goff[17] and others that one should employ real-gas properties and consistent, modern thermodynamic definitions and specifications with regard to the problem under consideration. In order to make a clear distinction between the "temperature of adiabatic saturation" as defined by Carrier[8] and a corresponding, somewhat similar entity properly defined in accordance with these more realistic, modern methods of approach to the problem, it was proposed by various authorities[28] that the term "thermodynamic wet-bulb temperature" be employed in referring to such an entity. The suggestion was made by Goff[17] that the *thermodynamic wet-bulb temperature* be defined essentially in accordance with the specifications given below: The thermodynamic wet-bulb temperature T_w^* of moist air characterized by pressure P, temperature T, and mixing ratio r, is a function of these variables $T_w^* = T_w^*(P,T,r)$, determined as the solution T_w^* of the following equation:

$$h(P,T,r) + [r_w(P,T_w^*) - r]h_w(P,T_w^*)$$
$$= h_s(P,T_w^*,r_w(P,T_w^*)) \quad (2)$$

where

$r_w(P,T_w^*) = r_w =$ the mixing ratio of moist air saturated with respect to a plane surface of clean liquid water at pressure P and temperature T_w^*;

$h_w(P,T_w^*) =$ the enthalpy of one gram of pure water at pressure P and temperature T_w^*;

$h(P,T,r) =$ the enthalpy of $(1 + r)$ grams of the original moist air, composed of one gram of dry air and r gram of water vapor, at the pressure P and temperature T which characterized the moist air initially;

$h_s(P,T_w^*,r_w(P,T_w^*)) =$ the enthalpy of $(1 + r_w)$ grams of saturated air, composed of one gram of dry air and $r_w(P,T_w^*)$ gram of water vapor, such that the moist air

under consideration in this case exists in a state of saturation with respect to a plane surface of clean water at pressure P and temperature T_w^*.

To avoid ambiguity we may add a definition of enthalpy: Consider unit mass of a substance which consists of a single homogeneous phase in equilibrium at uniform pressure P, temperature T, and composition, e.g., constant mole fractions, say, $x_1, x_2, \ldots, x_n$, if there are n components in the substance.[14] Let $U_1 =$ the internal energy, and $V_1 =$ the volume, both of these pertaining to unit mass of the given homogeneous phase of the substance, where U_1 and V_1 are each functions of the parameters $P, T, x, x_2, \ldots, x_n$. The enthalpy per unit mass of the homogeneous phase of the substance is defined by the relationship

$$h_1 = (U_1 + PV_1) \quad (3)$$

On letting U, V, and h denote the internal energy, volume and enthalpy, respectively, of mass m of the given homogeneous phase of the substance at the same uniform pressure P, temperature T, and mole fractions $x_1, x_2, \ldots, x_n$, it follows, because these functions are extensive thermodynamic properties,[29] that

$$U = mU_1 \quad (4)$$

$$V = mV_1 \quad (5)$$

and

$$h = mh_1 = m(U_1 + PV_1) = (U + PV) \quad (6)$$

Tables which facilitate the evaluation of Eq. (2) for standard atmospheric pressure have been published by Goff and Gratch,[16, 17] and by the American Society of Heating, Refrigerating, and Air-Conditioning Engineers.[30]

It will be clear from the context that r_w is a function of P and T_w^*; hence the expression on the right-hand side of Eq. (2) is a function of P and T_w^*. Since the parameter P is intended to refer to the same value in every term of Eq. (2), whether explicitly indicated or implicitly, one will understand that a constant-pressure process is specified in the definition of thermodynamic wet-bulb temperature. Figure 1 illustrates schematically an appara-

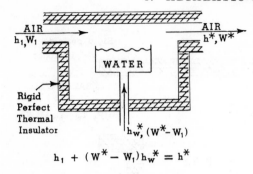

$$h_1 + (W^* - W_1)h_w^* = h^*$$

where

h_w^* = enthalpy of water at T_w^* and pressure P

h^* = enthalpy of <u>saturated air</u> at T_w^* and pressure P

h_1 = enthalpy of <u>unsaturated air</u> at original temperature T, pressure P, and mixing ratio W_1

W^* = mixing ratio of saturated air at temperature T_w^* and pressure P

$*$ Refers to conditions at thermodynamic wet-bulb temperature (T_w^*)

Fig. 1. Schematic form of adiabatic saturator as commonly presented in handbook treatments of the subject.

tus such as that usually depicted in handbooks[30] for visualizing the steady-flow, isobaric thermodynamic process underlying Eq. (2), whereby one may hope to realize the temperature of adiabatic saturation (which ideally may now be regarded as equivalent to the thermodynamic wet-bulb temperature defined by this equation). The equation implies that for every $(1 + r)$ grams of moist air that enters the apparatus, there is an initial input of one gram of dry air and r gram of water vapor, to which there is added by evaporation at temperature T_w^* an amount of water vapor $(r_w - r)$, hence the corresponding quantity of saturated moist air emerging from the apparatus after the completion of the process of adiabatic saturation consists of one gram of dry air admixed with r_w gram of water. In other words, a material balance is demanded in accordance with the principle of conservation of mass as evidenced by the fact that as much dry air and water substance, respectively, leave the apparatus as enter it. Similarly, the assumption is made that there will be maintained an energy balance involv-

ing as much energy output as input. In order to assure that energy is conserved in the processes which occur within the apparatus, the walls of the apparatus are assumed to be rigid and impervious to heat, preventing the accumulation of energy within the system or net loss of energy by the system, thus providing an adiabatic enclosure. On the basis of these conditions, no work can be done on or by the material within the apparatus due to contraction or expansion of its walls, while no heat can flow into or out of its walls because of their assumed perfect thermal insulating qualities. If these conditions are fulfilled exactly, the processes occurring within the apparatus should be adiabatic.

With a view to obtaining conformance to the underlying assumptions, the rate of input of total kinetic energy into the apparatus from all sources must always be maintained the same as the rate of total kinetic energy output at the exit where the stream of saturated air emerges. For similar reasons, it is demanded that there should not be any net variation in the total potential energy of the materials involved between their entrance and exit points. Likewise, it is assumed that negligible energy losses or inputs occur due to effects that stem from factors not immediately involved in the thermal and flow-work processes pertaining to the adiabatic saturation; that is, such extraneous factors as losses due to radiation of sound energy, and the influence of surface tension, electrical or magnetic phenomena, chemical changes, etc.

Figure 2, essentially like Fig. 1, illustrates an open system involving steady flow through an apparatus which, after equilibrium conditions are attained, is intended ideally to produce adiabatic saturation in conformity with Eq. (2). The term "steady flow" here refers to the flow through a system in such a manner that all of the properties of the substances and components at each point within the system remain constant with time. In order that this definition of *steady flow* be realizable the following four conditions must be satisfied:[31]

(a) The chemical and physical properties of the fluids which cross the boundary of the system must remain constant with time at each point on the boundary.

(b) The rate of mass flow of material at each

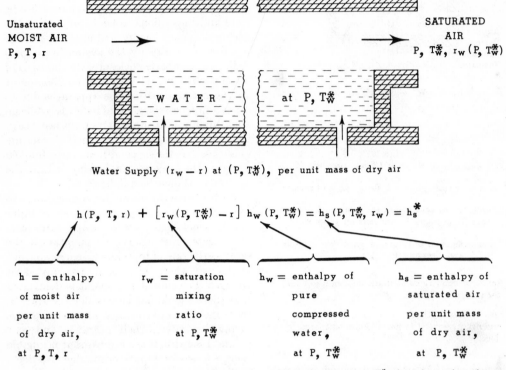

FIG. 2. Equation defining the thermodynamic wet-bulb temperature T_w^* given in conjunction with a schematic view of idealized adiabatic saturator to obtain saturation by prolonged contact of injected moist air with water at temperature T_w^* where the pressure P is held constant.

boundary section where mass enters or leaves the system must be constant.

(c) The rate at which mass from all sources enters the system must be precisely equal to the rate at which mass leaves the system through all exit points; in other words, the total mass content of material within the boundary of the system must remain constant. Under many types of situations, the latter conclusion leads to the inference that the instantaneous density of the fluids at each fixed point within the system must hold unchanged during the operation of the process, and in any case, it enables one to infer that the mean density with respect to time of the fluids at each fixed point must remain uniform during the process. (This statement should not be interpreted as signifying that the density of a given particle of fluid does not change with location of the particle; in other words variations in density attending dis-placement of a particle do *not* violate the underlying assumptions regarding steady flow.)

(d) Interactions between the environment of the system and the system, including the materials, must take place at a constant rate; for example, in relation to the rate of kinetic energy input and output, and in regard to the rate of doing work required to force the various substances into the system and the rate of doing work to force the various materials out of the system against the pressure exerted by the surrounding atmosphere.

The basic theory underlying Eq. (2), which depends upon the assumptions of mass balance and total energy balance for the streams of materials entering and emerging from the open system, has been presented in a number of textbooks; for example, those by Jones and Hawkins,[31] McAdams,[32] Knudson and Katz,[33] and Faires.[34] In view of this, it is unnecessary to give the complete details of the basic theory, but we may indicate that its essential result can be epitomized by the following statement: the sum of the differences between the emerging and entering values of the aggregate of enthalpy, kinetic energy, and potential energy pertaining to all streams of substances which are introduced into and are forced to leave the open system will be equal to the energy in the form of heat added to the system *minus* the energy in the form of external work done by the fluids involved. It follows from this result that if the sum of the kinetic and potential energies do not change, and if no heat is added to the system while none of the fluids do any net external work on the environment, the enthalpies must be conserved. This conclusion gives rise to Eq. (2).

EXAMPLES OF NON-ADIABATIC SATURATORS

Because of the need to produce saturation of the air or other carrier gases with water vapor in order to realize the temperature of adiabatic saturation, it is worthwhile at this point to review briefly the various methods that have been employed in the past to secure saturation of gases even though the techniques used were not in strict accordance with the assumptions underlying Eq. (2). In essence, the various techniques of obtaining saturation of any given carrier gas (such as dry air or nitrogen) involve the passage of the gas over or through the humidifying substance (water or ice) so that intimate contact between the two is maintained over suitable intervals of space and time as found adequate to yield a saturated end state of the gas. A short list descriptive of saturation methods, with pertinent references to some investigators who have employed these methods, now follows:

Bubbling

This involves bubbling of the gas at a suitably slow rate through water in bulk, maintained at uniform temperature in a vessel (termed a "saturator") which is itself immersed in a thermostatically controlled bath. As an improvement on this technique, it is common practice to use two similar saturators in series, with arrangements permitting the temperature of each to be controlled separately. Under these circumstances the temperature of the first saturator may be held either higher or lower than the temperature of the second saturator. When it is higher, the processes that occur in the attainment of saturation under equilibrium at the temperature of the second device will involve condensation; and when it is lower, the processes will involve evaporation. Thus, if the same final results (e.g., by means of gravimetric determinations of vapor content) are obtained with both of these temperature combinations, it is usually considered that saturation was actually secured at least in the case of the second saturator in series. This technique of alternating the temperature difference between the two saturators was used by Bartlett.[35] Most commonly, it is considered to be sufficient to hold the temperature of the first saturator about 5 to 10°C higher than that of the second in order to obtain precise saturation in the latter device. This method was employed by Pollitzer and Strebel,[36] and by Saddington and Krase.[37] For good results, the bubbles of carrier gas released at the bottom of the saturator by means of a bubbling tube must be of small dimensions relative to the height of the column of water through which they will rise. In view of this consideration, Smith and Eiseman[38] made use of a sintered glass frit at the lower end of the bubbling tube so that when air was forced through the pores of the frit a large number of very small bubbles were produced, thereby assuring complete saturation.

Flow Through Wetted Porous Medium

This involves upward passage of the gas through a wetted column of granulated solid material of chemically neutral character, such as clean quartz sand or small glass beads standing in distilled water within a container at the bottom of which the gas is released in a steady stream. This method has been outlined by Wexler and Brombacher.[39] The granulated material serves the purpose of breaking up the bubbles into minute packets of irregular form and providing intimate contact of the gas and the water as the gaseous filaments undergo streaming motion through the interstices.

Passage of Gas over Humidifying Substance

This method consists of flowing contact of the gas with water substance over a distance during an adequate time interval. An example of this technique was given by Wexler,[40] who employed it to secure saturation of the air with respect to ice by causing air to flow over a series of trays containing the frozen water held at uniform temperature. The trays were arranged in the form of a vertical stack of shelves with openings at alternate ends so that the air passed in sequence over the trays from the top down. By immersing three similar saturators in a thermostatically-controlled, constant-temperature bath and conveying the air from one to another in tandem, it was apparently possible to obtain saturation at least for the air emerging from the last saturator of the three. A different arrangement for securing saturation was employed by McHaffie[41] who made use of a large-bore vertical steel cylindrical tube divided into six equal compartments by brass plugs soldered into the tube at uniform intervals of height. A small-bore tube of short length extended from the central point of the bottom of each plug and the uppermost part of each such short length of tube was bent into the form of an inverted U. Water was placed in the five upper compartments so that the surface level of the liquid was just below the opening of the inverted U of the small tube in each case. When air was introduced under pressure into the lowest compartment of the large steel tube, it passed by way of the small-bore tubes through the succession of compartments so that as the air emerged from the opening of the inverted U in each compartment, it came in intimate contact with the water. Inasmuch as the opening of the inverted U was off center in the large-bore steel tube, the impingement of the stream of air on the water surface as the air issued from the nozzle of the inverted U of the small-bore tube in the various compartments must have caused the water to swirl, thereby enhancing the extent of contact of the air with the water. This would clearly improve the efficiency of the apparatus as a saturator. Thermal equilibrium was maintained by having the apparatus immersed in a constant temperature bath.

Vortex System of Contact

This technique involves centrifugal action of the carrier gas over water substance in a cylindrical container. It was employed by Wexler,[42] and by Wexler and Daniels.[43] The saturator in this design may be used for temperatures either above or below the freezing point of water. First of all, the water is added to a convenient depth in the cylindrical chamber and is brought to the desired temperature by means of a thermostatically controlled bath in which the chamber is immersed. The operation of the saturator has been described by Wexler[42] as follows:

"Air is discharged through a nozzle into the chamber above the water surface and tangential to the vertical walls and is exhausted through a central port in the top. The centrifugal action creates a whirlpool and thoroughly mixes water vapor with the air. Spray and liquid droplets are forced to the walls by centrifugal force, with the result that there is little tendency for liquid water to emerge through the exit port, except at very low air flows. A multi-layer fine wire screen baffle is used at the exit to trap and prevent water from passing out of the saturator at the low flows. As the air does not bubble through the water but only passes over its exposed surface, the water may be frozen without impairing the functioning of the saturator. The saturation pressure of the water vapor in the saturator is taken, then, with respect to ice."

In order to accomplish saturation, Wexler and Daniels arranged their apparatus in four stages. The first stage consisted of a centrifugal saturator maintained at a higher temperature than the last three saturators which were themselves held at a uniform temperature by being immersed in a thermostatically controlled bath. Between and following each of the four saturators was a heat exchanger also immersed in this bath. Because of the higher temperature prevailing in the first saturator, an amount of water vapor was introduced in excess of that required to secure saturation at the temperature which existed in the other three saturators and the heat exchangers in the bath. This excess vapor was precipitated within these latter devices so that just complete saturation was secured within the last saturator in the sequence of four.

Flow Through Moistened Wicking

Here, the carrier gas passes over a long tape made of suitable fabric cloth and wetted with water. In this method, as used by Webster,[44] the saturator consisted of a mild steel coil ($3/16$-in. i.d. and 8 ft long) fitted internally with a cotton tape moistened with water. In his design, the above-mentioned coil was followed by a mild-steel tube ($1/2$-in. i.d. and 6 in. long) packed with copper rivets to ensure temperature equilibrium and also to separate entrained water. Both the coil and the filter were immersed in a constant temperature bath.

Saturator Used by Washburn and Heuse

Washburn and Heuse[45] employed a saturator consisting of horizontal tubes which were filled about half full of the liquid involved (e.g., water) and mounted on a platform arranged to rock slowly back and forth. As the platform was thus rocked, the liquid flowed from one end of the horizontal tubes to the other, thereby increasing the contact of the liquid with the carrier gas (e.g., air) that was passing over the liquid. A given saturator was formed of four parallel pairs of horizontal tubes, and the two members of each pair were connected at both neighboring ends by means of vertical inverted U-shaped tubes. Excluding the first and last tubes in the sequence of eight tubes, the even- and odd-numbered ones (that is, No. 2–3, 4–5, and 6–7) were connected by means of inverted U-shaped tubes joining the specified horizontal members on top in a vertical plane midway between their ends. The entrance pipe was installed in this plane on top of the first horizontal member of the sequence of eight tubes, while the exit pipe was also located in the same plane on top of the eighth tube in the sequence. When air was introduced through the entrance pipe and the saturator was rocked back and forth by the platform, the air passed around through first one vertical inverted U-tube at the end and then the other as the saturator tipped each way. The inverted U-shaped tubes connecting the even and odd numbered horizontal members along the central vertical plane permitted the air to pass from one pair to the next.

Generally three saturators were used in a train with hygroscopic absorbers or cold traps installed at intermediate points. If the temperatures of the saturators were maintained first in descending and then in ascending order, it was possible to approach saturation both from above and from below, thus permitting the results to be compared. When the results agreed, it was inferred that the saturation was complete in each case. This method of attaining saturation was utilized by Goff and Bates.[46]

DEVICES OF OTHER AUTHORS TO ACHIEVE ADIABATIC SATURATION

The earliest known attempt to achieve adiabatic saturation was made by Carrier,[8] who first passed the air under test through two layers of moistened sponge, thus bringing it very close to the desired temperature.

Carrier and Lindsay[13] constructed an elaborate apparatus for the purpose of securing adiabatic saturation. The essential component of this apparatus consisted of two ducts arranged concentrically with provisions for the axial flow of air. Each of these ducts was constructed of cork, 2 in. thick, encased in copper. Both the inside and the outside walls of the inner duct were covered with cloth which was kept wet during the experiment. In addition, the cylindrical space within the inner duct contained a cloth strip arranged in a number of vertical planes parallel to the flow of air. The strip was fastened by winding the cloth over and under $1/4$-in. diameter brass tubes mounted parallel to the duct axis. By sealing the upper tubes at one end and connecting them at the other end to a header which led from a gear pump, a steady stream of circulating water was caused to flow through the tubes. The upper part of each tube had holes of $1/32$-in. diameter spaced at 2-in. intervals, which provided openings for the circulating water to run out and trickle over the cloth, thus keeping it wet. The lower part of the inner duct contained a shallow reservoir (sump) from which the gear pump drew water for circulation through the brass tubes. A water tank installed atop, on the outside of the leading end of the outer duct, was connected by a small tube to a point close to the water surface in the sump, and arrangements were provided to admit automatically a certain amount of water into the sump from the tank whenever the water in the shallow reservoir went down to a pre-established level.

In order to produce stable conditions for the performance of the experiments, a special room was prepared for installation of the apparatus, the room being furnished with air-conditioning equipment to supply air within desired practical limits regarding temperature and humidity. The temperature within the room was usually maintained at a value within several degrees F of the temperature in the water tank. With a further view to minimizing heat exchanges, the supply pump and all pipings were insulated.

The apparatus used in the experiments consisted of the following components in series:

(a) First there was a centrifugal-type blower fan which took air from the constant-temperature room and delivered it at a controlled rate to the next component. The velocity of the air flow ranged up to 2000 fpm at a standard temperature of 70°F.

(b) Second there was a humidifier in the form of a well-insulated tunnel, 3 ft long, 1 ft high and 9 in. wide, provided with a bank of staggered, vertically positioned, brass tubes. These brass tubes of ½-in. diameter were spaced at about ¼-in. intervals and were wound with thin wicking material. The lower ends of the tubes were connected to a source of flowing water, while the upper ends were left open to permit circulation of water from the sump at the bottom of the tunnel over the wicking, thereby enabling the wicking to be kept wet.

(c) Third in the series was a tunnel containing a heater system formed of four electric resistance heating elements whose current was controlled to yield air flow of the desired temperature.

(d) Fourth in the series was a heat accumulator designed to minimize any air temperature fluctuations that might occur. It consisted of about 1000 pounds of copper plates, 10 in. wide and 60 in. long mounted in a thermally insulated duct. These plates were laid in horizontal planes arranged to form a vertical stack of the plates in parallel with wire spacers having a diameter equal to the thickness of a plate installed between each plate. Air driven from the heater system [see item (c) above] into the heat accumulator flowed through the spaces between the plates and attained temperature equilibrium by contact with the mass of copper.

(e) Finally, the air was passed into the adiabatic saturator previously described. Moving first into the leading end (entrance section) of the adiabatic saturator, the air flowed axially through the central part of the inner duct, and at the other end it was deflected so that the air flowed through the annular space between the inner and the outer ducts back toward the leading end. Since the air came into flowing contact with the wetted cloths and the surface of the sump water in the adiabatic saturator, it was to be expected that the air would become saturated and would cool due to evaporation of water, thereby attaining a minimum wet-bulb temperature. As the moist air came through the annular space between the inner and outer ducts, the air finally reached the water tank mounted over the leading end of the device and flowed in a casing around it, thus bringing the tank nearly to equilibrium with the minimum wet-bulb temperature of the air which emerged from the apparatus. In this manner, the water supply provided from the tank was very close to the desired temperature equal to the final wet-bulb reading. Because of the fact that wetted cloth or water was present along the path of the flowing air on both the inside and the outside of the inner duct, it was assumed by Carrier and Lindsay that the conductive heat transfer through the walls of this duct was negligible and that the processes within the device would therefore be essentially adiabatic. On these grounds, Carrier and Lindsay concluded that when the wet- and dry-bulb thermometers installed at the terminus of the device farthest removed from the leading end yielded equal readings of temperature, those readings could be regarded as equivalent to the "temperature of adiabatic saturation." They applied corrections to compensate for the mechanical heat supplied to the liquid by the pump, and corrections to allow for the effect of the difference in pressure between the entrance and outlet of the saturator. In order to establish constant conditions preparatory to the taking of temperature observations in the apparatus, Carrier and Lindsay operated the equipment for about four or five hours before readings were begun.

There is some doubt whether the Carriee-Lindsay apparatus actually would yield thr temperature of adiabatic saturation in all cases, for example if liquids other than water were employed. It is problematical whether adiabatic conditions were achieved, partly due to the fact that a radial temperature gradient may have existed within the wall of the inner duct, near the leading end of the device. This type of gradient seems possible because the entering air at the leading end of the inner duct was at the dry-bulb temperature, whereas the air emerging from the annular space just outside the inner duct was practically at the wet-bulb temperature, hence there could have been some heat conduction through the wall of this duct even though the both surfaces had a covering of wet cloth. It may be noted that the wet-bulb depression of the air leaving the device did not fall precisely to zero when the entering air had a large wet-bulb depression and the ventilation velocity was of the order of 2000 fpm. On these grounds, it would appear that the distance and duration of contact between the air and the wetted cloth may not have been sufficient within the inner duct to have caused saturation of relatively dry air introduced at high ventilation rates. Finally, it is likely that unshielded thermometers experienced some radiation effects for which corrections were not applied.[13]

On the basis of a comparison of the description given by Carrier and Lindsay of the equipment which they used in an effort to produce adiabatic saturation and the description given by Dropkin[24] of the equipment which he employed for that specified purpose, it may be concluded that Dropkin made use of the principal components of the very same apparatus which had been developed by Carrier and Lindsay. A few minor differences with respect to the descriptions may be noted, however, such as the statement by Dropkin that the heat accumulator consisted of about 700 pounds of copper plates, whereas Carrier and Lindsay indicated 1000 pounds. Dropkin was also specific in pointing out that the cloth placed in vertical planes in the adiabatic saturator was a continuous strip about 17 yards in length, wound

over and under $\frac{1}{4}$-in. diameter brass tubes. He studied three methods of wetting the wet bulb, being careful that the wicking covered the entire length of the immersion stem and that the cloth was kept wet throughout this length by first dipping the wick into distilled water whose temperature was approximately that of the final wet-bulb reading. In the experiments performed by Dropkin, he adjusted the apparatus to give the desired ventilation velocity, temperature, and wet-bulb depression, and then allowed the apparatus to run from 8 to 14 hours until equilibrium conditions were established. The air velocity was varied in steps of 250 fpm, to cover the range from 750 to 2000 fpm. In addition to the two corrections applied by Carrier and Lindsay, Dropkin applied a correction to allow for the effect of the difference in temperature between the water in the supply tank and the wet-bulb temperature at the outlet of the saturator.

The questions which we have raised regarding the correctness of the assumption that adiabatic saturation was truly realized in the Carrier-Lindsay apparatus are equally pertinent with reference to the apparatus used by Dropkin. He found that with small to moderate ventilation rates and inlet wet-bulb depressions, it was possible to secure essentially zero wet-bulb depressions at the outlet of the apparatus, thus implying that saturation was indeed obtained. In the light of the experiments conducted by Arnold[11,12] and the theory which he developed with regard to the operation of the psychrometer, it seems fair to ask whether Dropkin would have found similar zero wet-bulb depressions at the outlet if he had used various liquids instead of water.

Finally, we turn to the new instrument developed by Wentzel[47] for the purpose of determining the temperature of adiabatic saturation. It was formed basically of a well-insulated vertical tube within which air and water were mixed adiabatically when air was introduced at the bottom of the tube. The tube was constructed in such a manner that it had a hollow between its inner and outer walls, like a Dewar flask or vacuum Thermos bottle, and this hollow space was evacuated while the inner walls were silvered, thereby reducing the heat flow. A quantity of natural sponge moistened with water was squeezed into the upper half of the cylindrical region within the tube surrounding the axis. In order to measure the dry-bulb temperature, a thermocouple was installed in an axial position within the tube a short distance below the bottom of the sponge. Similarly, in order to measure the equilibrium temperature attained in the moistened sponge a thermocouple was embedded in the sponge in an axial position a short distance below its top. With a view to minimizing the heat exchange between the entire tube and the environment, Wentzel fastened the tube coaxially inside a cylindrical hollow of larger diameter which existed in a container formed of plastic insulating material enclosed by aluminum foil. Thus an annular space was present between the outer wall of the tube and the inner wall of the container. The top of the container was closed, but its inner surface was shaped like a hollow hemisphere. This allowed some room for air to flow out from the top of the tube and then be deflected so that the air could pass downward through the annular space between the outer wall of the tube and the inner wall of the container. Because of this arrangement, the radially directed temperature gradient through the walls of the tube near the upper portion of the sponge was reduced, thereby limiting the heat flow.

An inlet was furnished for the axial inflow of air into the bottom of the tube, while an outlet for the air was provided by means of a hole near the bottom of the apparatus connecting with the annular space between the outer wall of the tube and the inner wall of the container. Use was made of an air-ejector pump to yield an air-flow velocity of at least 50 fpm at the inlet. The air then advanced up the tube so that on encountering the sponge it passed through the interstices of this porous medium. Contact of the flowing air with the water present in the sponge gave rise to evaporation of some of the liquid and, therefore, produced evaporative cooling. It seems likely that the air emerging from the top of the sponge was either saturated or very nearly saturated at the temperature reached in the uppermost layer of sponge.

Wentzel found that the equilibrium temperature indicated by the thermocouple em-bedded near the upper part of the sponge depended on the following principal factors: barometric pressure, dry-bulb temperature, and mixing ratio (or dew-point temperature) of the air injected at the inlet of the apparatus, together with the temperature and rate of delivery of the water supplied to the sponge, provided that the ventilation rate of the air inflow exceeded a certain critical limit, namely, about 50 fpm under normal operating conditions with respect to temperature and pressure. (Note: Wentzel's experiments were conducted at Pretoria, South Africa, where the normal barometric pressure is 873 mb.)

With a view to checking whether the embedded thermocouple in his apparatus yielded the temperature of adiabatic saturation, Wentzel constructed equipment which supplied moist air characterized by closely controlled and known values of the dry-bulb and dew-point temperatures. When this controlled air was introduced at the inlet of his saturation apparatus described above, Wentzel measured the dry-bulb temperature indicated by the thermocouple mounted below the sponge and he measured the temperature given simultaneously by the thermocouple embedded near the top of the sponge under conditions of equilibrium. Wentzel was able to compute essentially on the basis of Eq. (1) what the dew-point temperature of the original moist air supply had to be in order that its temperature of adiabatic saturation be equal to the equilibrium temperature indicated by the embedded thermocouple. In a series of tests carried out in this manner, he found that the controlled dew-point temperature of the input air agreed within 0.1°F with the dew-point temperature as thus calculated. On these grounds, Wentzel concluded that the apparatus which he had developed was capable of measuring the adiabatic saturation temperature to a high degree of accuracy.

Owing to the fact that Wentzel did not make similar tests involving liquids other than water as had been done by Arnold,[11,12] it remains uncertain whether his apparatus would have given as good agreement for such liquids as he observed for water. He did not apply corrections for the effects due to the pressure difference between the air at the inlet and outlet. Proper allowances for possible changes in kinetic energy of the fluids caused by the apparatus would have to be considered, especially in view of the resistance to flow offered by the sponge. It was established by Arnold[11,12] that the close agreement of the wet-bulb temperature reading of the typical ventilated psychrometer with the temperature of adiabatic saturation depends on the fortuitous circumstance that the thermal diffusivity of air is nearly equal to the vapor diffusivity of water vapor. In the light of these facts, it is worthwhile to investigate the problem of measuring the temperature of adiabatic saturation in a variety of ways and to study the results when using various liquids.

GENERAL CONSIDERATIONS LEADING TO DESIGNS OF ADIABATIC SATURATORS

Before entering into any detailed plans for an adiabatic saturator, it would be worthwhile to consider the qualities which are demanded of such a device in the light of the theory underlying Eq. (2). This will provide some guidelines for the design. As may be visualized with the aid of Fig. 2, the fluids injected into the adiabatic saturator consist of a water-vapor bearing carrier gas (e.g., moist air) and water substance, the state of which will depend upon the temperature of adiabatic saturation. In this paper we will restrict our attention to values of temperature above the freezing point. On this basis we present below some brief indications of the criteria which we consider should govern the design and operation of the device.

Control of Input Water Temperature

The input water temperature should be the same as the temperature of adiabatic saturation in order to secure perfect agreement with the provisions of Eq. (2).

Maintenance of Adiabatic Conditions

It is necessary that the walls of the device be rigid in order that no work be done by the fluids involved in expanding against any surrounding medium and that no work be done on the fluids by the surrounding medium (e.g., atmosphere). The walls of the device should be so contrived that the heat exchange

with the environment is nil; that is, the fluids involved should neither lose heat to, nor gain heat from, the environment. The rate of flow of kinetic energy of all fluids into the device for any interval of time must always be equal to the rate of flow of kinetic energy of all fluids out of the device for the same interval of time. No net gain or loss of total potential energy of the fluids involved should occur between the inlet and discharge orifices of the apparatus. With a view to rendering as small as possible the heat and energy transfer between the environment and the fluids while they are in the device, the apparatus must have an optimum amount of good thermal insulating material strategically placed, and/or a double-walled vacuum vessel enclosure, with highly reflecting surfaces to minimize radiative heat exchanges. Inward or outward directed temperature gradients should be brought as closely as possible to zero. This may be accomplished by employing for the device and its connections various suitable jackets which carry some fluid medium in annular passages at the same temperature as the fluid contents involved in the process of adiabatic saturation.

Maintenance of Constant Pressure

A uniform absolute pressure should be maintained with regard to the conditions under which all materials are supplied to and removed from the adiabatic saturator. That is, the moist carrier gas as it enters the inlet and the water substance injected into the device should be subject to the same barometric pressure as the saturated carrier gas which emerges from the adiabatic saturator.

Mass-flow Balance

The mass rate of flow of the moist input carrier gas, when added to the mass rate of flow of the input water substance, must be precisely equal to the mass rate of flow of the saturated output carrier gas at the temperature of adiabatic saturation pertinent to the conditions which relate to the moist input carrier gas. (By "moist input carrier gas," we mean the specified carrier gas such as air containing water vapor at the given mixing ratio r, temperature T, and pressure P, which is supplied at the inlet of the device. (See Fig. 2.)

By "saturated output carrier gas" in the present context we signify the carrier gas saturated with respect to water at the temperature of adiabatic saturation which applies to the moist input carrier gas when the pressure is maintained constant. The term "input water substance" relates to the water or ice evaporated into the moist input carrier gas at the temperature of adiabatic saturation of the latter.) When the foregoing conditions are satisfied, the adiabatic saturator constitutes a steady-flow system.

CRITERIA AND CHARACTERISTICS BASED ON EXPERIMENTAL REQUIREMENTS

A number of different tests would have to be carried out during the course of development of any device as complex as the adiabatic saturator, with a view to checking its performance. Because of this, it is worthwhile to formulate a list of questions that might be posed with respect to the operation of the equipment and to draw up plans as to how crucial tests or experiments could be performed with the object of providing answers to the questions. On this basis, one can envisage certain features which would have to be embodied in the apparatus in order to permit the conduct of such experiments and tests. Among the pertinent questions that might be asked there are likely to be some of the following character:

(a) How does one know that saturation has been achieved by means of the apparatus?

(b) How closely is the process adiabatic?

(c) Is a uniform pressure maintained in the system?

(d) Is an accurate mass balance of fluid flow in the device obtained?

(e) How long and over what distance or area must the carrier gas remain in contact with the water in order to bring the gas to a saturated state?

(f) How do the results vary when different combinations of various carrier gases and liquids (apart from air and water) are employed?

In the light of the foregoing criteria the following characteristics are deemed essential for embodiment in the experimental design of an adiabatic saturator:

(1) A number of temperature- and pressure-determination stations should be installed at various strategic points within the apparatus.

(2) Several methods should be provided to permit checking the degree of saturation of the moistened carrier gas emitted from the exhaust outlet of the apparatus.

(3) The temperature of the input liquid (e.g., water) should be subject to close control at will, while arrangements should also be included so that the temperature of the input liquid can be automatically controlled, if desired, by the temperature of the moistened carrier gas emitted from the exhaust outlet.

(4) The capability should be provided of carefully controlling and measuring the flow rates of the gaseous and liquid substances injected into or exhausted from the apparatus.

(5) Provisions should be made for varying and controlling the path length of contact of the carrier gas with the liquid in respect to which the gas is to be saturated.

(6) Arrangements should be such that it is readily possible to check the performance of the apparatus with either intermittent or continuous influx of controlled samples of various carrier gases containing known mole fractions of vapor content derived from any selected liquid (not merely water). Combinations giving different ratios of thermal diffusivity of the carrier gas to the vapor diffusivity should be tested.

(7) Means should be available to supply the apparatus with a steady flow of samples of any chosen carrier gas having accurately controlled proportions of any selected vapor at a pre-established temperature and pressure.

(8) Several different designs of adiabatic saturator should be contemplated in order to compare their relative performances.

(9) Equipment should be provided to enable the calibration of the apparatus. This should include means for checking the controlled samples and the gas emitted by the exhaust with reference to a gravimetric standard, employing secondary standards for auxiliary purposes, if found satisfactory.

(10) The apparatus should be installed in a suitable air-conditioned room where the conditions are maintained with the aim of keeping heat exchanges between the adiabatic saturator and its environment at a minimum.

GENERAL DESIGN OF ADIABATIC SATURATORS TO BE OPERATED IN TANDEM

Because of the fact that we do not know *a priori* how long a contact is necessary between the carrier gas and the liquid to obtain precise saturation under adiabatic conditions, it is desirable that we have the capability of allowing the liquid to evaporate into the gas over progressively longer and longer paths while contact of the gas with the liquid is maintained until the saturated state is realized. This objective might be accomplished by means of two of the devices (saturators) connected in series so that the gas can be circulated from one to the other and back again until the desired end is achieved. Evaporation carried out under adiabatic conditions during successive passages of the gas through the devices might be termed "sequential processing."

Figure 3 gives a schematic presentation of the general arrangement of two adiabatic saturators so connected that they may be operated for sequential processing of the carrier gas when two suffice. Thus, if saturation of the gas is not complete in the first device (upper part of Figure), the gas may be transferred to the second device (lower part of the Figure) for further contact of the gas with the liquid (water), with the aim of attaining saturation. Finally, if saturation is not yet achieved in the second device, it would be possible to transfer the moistened gas back to the inlet (air source at the upper left-hand side) of the first device and thereby continue the processing of the gas by further contact of the gas with the liquid; and so on. In this manner the flow of the gas can be carried forward from one device to the other in a cyclical manner until saturation of the gas is finally reached.

Several proposed designs of the interior mechanism of the adiabatic saturator are submitted on pp. 49, 52 and 54.

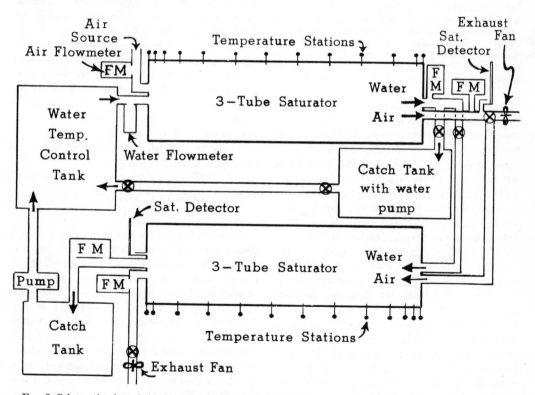

Fig. 3. Schematic plan view of two triple-tubed adiabatic saturators arranged for their possible operation in sequence involving moist air. (Note: FM denotes flowmeter, and Sat. Detector denotes saturation detector. For cross-sectional views of the saturator, see the proposed designs in Figs. 5 through 7.)

A water temperature control tank, shown schematically at the left of Fig. 3 and in greater detail in Fig. 4, is intended to provide a supply of water (or other liquid, if chosen) at any closely controlled temperature. The liquid may be introduced into the saturators at one or more inlets, depending on the requirements.

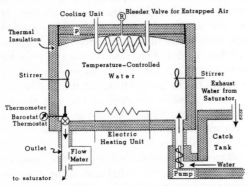

FIG. 4. Schematic vertical cross-sectional view of thermostatically controlled tank for the supply of the liquid (in this case, water) with respect to which the sample gas is to be saturated. (Under ideal conditions, the contents of the tank would be so controlled as to supply the liquid at the temperature $T-$ pertinent to the injected sample of gas at the given value of pressure P, temperature T, and mixing ratio r.)

By making observations at the numerous temperature stations located at points along the path taken by the fluids involved, it would be possible to determine the temperatures of both the liquid and the carrier gas moistened by evaporation of the liquid into it. Due to evaporative cooling of the gas, the reading should approach a lower limit asymptotically along the path. If one then takes the temperature reading at the last station in the sequence as a basis for the thermal control of the liquid in the temperature control tank (Fig. 4), one can supply the liquid very nearly at the final temperature which would be reached when saturation is attained. The temperature selected for use in the initial setting of the thermostat governing the temperature control tank could be based on an approximate solution of Eq. (2) for T_w^*, when the pressure P, temperature T, and mixing ratio r of the given sample of moist gas are known. In this case, it would require a very slight adjustment of the control tem-

perature to bring it into agreement with the final temperature reached by the gas as a result of evaporative cooling when the supply of liquid is provided at the same temperature. If the processes occurring in the saturator are adiabatic and the other required conditions are satisfied (see p. 45), one might then expect the final equilibrium reading to be essentially at the temperature of adiabatic saturation (or "thermodynamic wet-bulb temperature" T_w^*) in accordance with the definition based on Eq. (2).

Arrangements are contemplated which would permit the adiabatic saturators to be employed either singly or in tandem, for cyclical application. Any liquid exhausted at the outlet of a saturator would be run into a catch tank from which the liquid could be transferred by means of pumps to the temperature control tank for further use. Corrections for the energy input of the pumps would have to be applied. Flowmeters (designated by the symbol FM) are considered as necessary adjuncts for measuring the mass rate of flow of the gases and liquid involved. At the exhaust outlet of the adiabatic saturator, suitable means of detecting saturation and measuring the degree of saturation would be required (see saturation detector in Fig. 3). Devices of this character would permit determination of the dew-point temperature, relative humidity, or other parameters which yield indications of the closeness to saturation reached by the gases emitted through the exhaust.

TEMPERATURE CONTROL OF WATER SUPPLY

Figure 4 illustrates schematically a design conceived for the tank in which the temperature of the liquid would be controlled. It should, of course, have cooling and heating elements whose outputs are controlled by means of a thermostat. A barostat is also required to maintain the liquid at the pressure desired for introduction of the liquid into the saturator. Stirrers are needed to keep the liquid in the tank in a homogeneous condition. A flowmeter to measure the outflow rate of the liquid and suitable valves to control the rate at a desired level are necessary. Impetus for the circulation of the liquid through the saturator system would be provided by pumps operated at an appropriately controlled speed. Any liquid which is exhausted from a saturator into a catch tank would be pumped back into the temperature-controlled tank. Good thermal insulation would be called for to keep the heat exchanges between the equipment and the environment as nearly zero as practicable, and if necessary to fulfill this objective, the temperature-control tank and the catch tank could be jacketed so that a circulating flow of liquid would be provided around their exterior walls at the same temperature as that which exists within their liquid contents. It is envisioned that the upper component of the temperature-control tank might consist of a piston (p) furnished with a bleeder valve to eliminate entrapped gases and keep the tank always full of the liquid at the desired pressure. The thermostat will have to be connected by means of suitable wiring, switches, and control mechanisms with the element at the last temperature station employed in the saturators. Such an arrangement would enable the indication at the last temperature station to operate as a basis for the automatic control of thermal conditions within the tank. It would be essential also for experimental purposes to permit the control of the temperature in the tank at will.

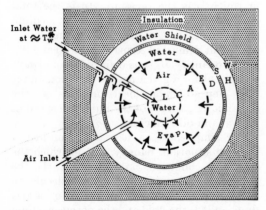

FIG. 5. Cross-sectional view of triple-tubed adiabatic saturator involving the use of two porous tubes through the interstices of which water vapor may pass, but not liquid water in bulk. (*Note:* Operations using air as the carrier gas are indicated; while it is contemplated that the inlets should, in general, be located at the ends of the tubes, not at the sides, as shown.)

SATURATOR CONSTRUCTED OF CONCENTRIC POROUS TUBES WITH WATER JACKET

In Fig. 5 there is depicted a schematic view of a cross section of the first proposed design of the adiabatic saturator. It consists of several concentric components. Beginning with the innermost component, one sees a porous tube C within which (at L) water flows at a temperature equal to or very closely in agreement with the thermodynamic wet-bulb temperature T_w^* of the moist air introduced into the adiabatic saturator. (Other liquids and carrier gases may be substituted if desired.) The material and pores of tube C must be of such character as to permit the passage of water vapor molecules but to inhibit the flux of liquid water in bulk. Next in the sequence of tubes, going outward from the center, will be noted the concentric porous tube E, which must have the same characteristics as porous tube C. Air (or other gas, if desired) will flow through the annular space A between tubes C and E. The third concentric tube, designated by S, will consist of impermeable thermal insulating material. At a radial distance somewhat greater than the outside radius of tube S will be the inside wall W of the thermal insulation which forms the outermost component of the cross section shown. It will be required that water (or other liquid, if desired) flow through the annular passage D between components E and S, while water (or other liquid, if desired) will be required to flow through the annular passage H between component S and wall W. In every instance, the water (or other liquid) will have to be injected at the same temperature, preferably at T_w^*, in accordance with the need to satisfy Eq. (2). One may contemplate that the inlet for the gas (e.g., air) and the inlets for the liquid (e.g., water) will be located at the leading end of the adiabatic saturator (see, for example, the left-hand side of the upper part of Fig. 3).

The "water shield" represented by H is intended to serve as a conduit for water (or other chosen liquid) at a temperature in equilibrium with that of water (or other liquid) passing through the annular space D. Owing to the agreement of the two temperatures on opposite sides of the thermal insulating tube S, the heat flux through S should be negligibly small, and this complete lack of radial heat flux should contribute to the obtainment of adiabatic processes at radii less than the radius of the inside cylindrical surface of S. By virtue of the fact that the pores of tubes C and E will permit the passage of water vapor molecules, there will occur evaporation of water into the air (or other gas) present within the annular space designated by A. In order to provide for the latent heat equivalent of the quantities of water thus evaporated through the pores of C and E, heat will flow from the gas within space A both radially inward through the walls of C and radially outward through the walls of E. Any energy lost by water (or other liquid) molecules during their passage through the pores of tubes C and E will be communicated to the material of which these tubes are composed. The heat thus added to the material of the porous tubes will at first produce a temperature rise, and this will be attended by an increased rate of heat transfer from the porous tubes to all substances with which the tubes have contact and to bodies in their surroundings capable of receiving heat from them by radiation. Due to these mechanisms, the gain of internal energy of the porous tube material will finally reach a limit when a balance between the rates of energy input and energy output occurs, which will bring about an equilibrium condition at a temperature somewhat higher than that which would obtain if there had been no effect due to the porous medium. So long as such an equilibrium persists, the equivalent of the energy yielded up to the tube material by the vapor molecules during their passage through the pores of components C and E in a given time interval will be transferred during the same period in a steady-rate process to other vapor molecules which are in the pores, or to any other substances which are present on both sides of the walls of C and E. While such a process is going on, the rate of total enthalpy input is precisely the same as the rate of total enthalpy output after steady-flow, equilibrium conditions have been established, provided that the rate of input of kinetic energy into the system is kept equal to the rate of output of kinetic energy and further, provided that the total potential energy of all mass fluxes into and out of the system are held equal.

Vapor molecules will pass steadily through the pores of components C and E only under a motive power furnished by properly oriented radial pressure gradients of the requisite magnitudes. That is, a pressure gradient is necessary across (through) the walls of tube C directed radially outward, while another pressure gradient is required across (through) the walls of tube E directed radially inward as indicated by the arrows in Fig. 5, for the purpose of driving the vapor molecules at the desired rates through the pores of the materials of which tubes C and E are composed. We may gain some idea of the problem from the following theoretical considerations. Let Q = the volume of vapor (or fluid) which flows through a cross-sectional area A in time t, and u = the apparent linear speed of the flow. Then it follows that

$$u = \frac{Q}{At} \qquad (7)$$

The value of u for flow through a porous medium will be determined by Darcy's law which, as indicated by Carman,[48] may be expressed, for cases where the flow is parallel to the x-axis, by the relationship

$$u = -B_1 \frac{\partial p}{\partial x} = B_1 \frac{\Delta p}{L} \qquad (8)$$

in which p is the pressure, Δp is the total pressure drop across a sample of the medium whose length is L, and B_1 is a permeability coefficient defined in terms of Eqs. (7) and (8).

The quantity B_1 thus defined is not always a constant for a given porous medium, and it may depend upon local pressure p, the dynamic viscosity η of the fluid, the speed of flow u, and other factors.

For simplicity, we may first consider a limiting situation, namely, one in which the following conditions are satisfied: (1) the resistance to flow of the gaseous molecules in the porous medium is wholly due to viscous drag, and (2) the fluid and the porous medium are inert with respect to one another, that is, no reactions occur due to chemical processes, adsorption of the fluid particles on the surface of the medium and within its pores, electrical or electrochemical phenomena, and capillary effects.

Now let

$G =$ the mass rate of flow of the gaseous fluid through the porous medium along the direction of the x-axis;

$\rho =$ the density of the gaseous fluid;

$\eta =$ the dynamic viscosity of the fluid; and

$B_0 =$ the specific permeability coefficient for the porous medium pertaining to flow of the specified gaseous fluid through it under the conditions (1) and (2) stipulated above.

Then, for steady flow

$$G = \rho u = - \frac{B_0 \rho}{\eta} \frac{\partial p}{\partial x} \qquad (9)$$

In actual practice the opposition to the flow of the gaseous molecules through the pores of the medium depends at least to a great extent on a combination of viscous resistance and inertial resistance, where the latter is largely due to eddy formation and turbulent motions within the pores. To a certain degree of approximation, the inertial resistance will be proportional to the kinetic energy per unit volume of the fluid, namely $(1/2)\rho u^2$.

Let us consider conditions of steady flow of a gaseous substance through a length L of a porous medium under this assumption. If there were a balance between the pressure gradient which provides the driving force and the sum of the two viscous and inertial resistances to the flow, then neglecting other considerations such as capillary effects previously mentioned, one would have approximately[48]

$$\frac{\Delta p}{L} = \frac{\eta}{B_0} u + b\rho u^2 \qquad (10)$$

where b is a coefficient which is generally a function of u, the porosity and pore texture of the porous medium, and some other parameters.

It follows from a comparison of the foregoing equations that the pressure gradient through the walls of the porous tubes C and E will vary depending upon whether the flow of the gaseous fluid through the pores of the medium is primarily viscous or turbulent.

Work would have to be done by the pumps connected with the saturator in driving fluids through the various conduits of the apparatus against the resistances to the flow in those channels. One may distinguish three separate work contributions involving the action of the pumps, as follows: (1) work exerted in forcing the moist carrier gas through annular space A between the porous tubes C and E; (2) work done in impelling the liquid through the cylindrical channel L within tube C and through the annular space D between tubes E and S; and (3) energy contributed to provide impetus for the flux of gaseous molecules through the pores of tubes C and E in overcoming any reactions or resistances which operate in opposition to the passage of the molecules. When these three contributions of work are combined per unit time, the sum total represents power expended by the pumps yielding an energy increment to the saturator which becomes available for the augmentation of the enthalpy within the system, beyond the amount introduced by the injection of the liquid (water) or unsaturated carrier gas (moist air). The energy equivalent of this input by all the pumps acting on the system per unit mass of dry carrier gas must be added to the left-hand side of Eq. (2) as a correction in computing the effective value of the "thermodynamic wet-bulb temperature," T_w^*.

It is intended that the input of moist air and liquid water be injected at one end of the saturator tubes and that the output of saturated air be exhausted at the other end. Note must be taken of the fact that the pressure at which the water is injected before its passage through the porous medium will be higher than that at which the moist air will be introduced or exhausted. This means that the enthalpy of the injected water will be greater than that of water at a pressure equal to that of the input moist air or the output saturated air. A difference may also be expected to occur between the input and output sum of kinetic and potential energies pertaining to the materials introduced into and exhausted from the apparatus while a mass balance exists. In addition, the energy which enters the system due to the working of the pumps used for driving the water and air through the apparatus, when combined with the energy which enters the system from its surroundings due to imperfect isolation of the apparatus (i.e., departure from adiabatic enclosure) will yield contributions.

Thus, it is clear that in the actual operation of the apparatus, we will not simply satisfy Eq. (2), but rather there will be increments of energy input which augment the left-hand side of the equation so that the observed value (T_{wx}) of the temperature of the saturated air exhausted from the apparatus will be greater than the value of the thermodynamic wet-bulb temperature T_w^* defined by Eq. (2). If one could make an accurate determination of the excess energy inputs from these sources, it would be possible to calculate a correction to the observed value of the temperature specified above in order to reduce it to the pertinent quantity T_w^*.

Such a correction can be computed essentially as follows:
Let

$\Delta E =$ the algebraic sum, per unit mass of dry air, of the energy increments contributed to the system in excess of the amounts of enthalpy inputs given in the left-hand side of Eq. (2); i.e., the sum of the enthalpy excess of the injected water due to its pressure being greater than the value P pertaining to the moist air, the energy used for operating the pumps which drive the various materials through the apparatus, the energy increment measured as the difference between the input and output sum of the kinetic and potential energies pertaining to the materials introduced into and exhausted from the apparatus, and the energy entering the system from the surroundings due to imperfect insulation of the apparatus (departure from adiabatic conditions), all measured per unit mass of dry air;

$h_s =$ the enthalpy of air saturated with respect to water at pressure P and thermodynamic wet-bulb temperature T_w^* [see Eq. (2)];

$\Delta T_w^* =$ the difference ($T_{wx} - T_w^*$), where T_{wx} is the actual temperature at which the saturated air is exhausted from the system at pressure P, and T_w^* is the thermodynamic wet-bulb temperature defined in accordance with Eq. (2).

Then, when ΔE is relatively small, we shall have to a close degree of approximation

$$\frac{\partial h_s}{\partial T_w^*} \Delta T_w^* = \Delta E \qquad (11)$$

By computing ΔT_w^* on the basis of Eq. (11), one can determine the negative of the correction which must be applied to T_{wx} in order to obtain the desired value of T_w^* defined in accordance with Eq. (2).

SATURATOR WITH PARALLEL AIR AND WATER JACKETS—INLETS AT ONE END

Figure 6 shows the schematic view of a cross section of the second proposed design of the adiabatic saturator. It is intended for operation similar to that illustrated in Fig. 5, where both air and water inlets as well as the saturated air outlet are to be at the ends of the tubes, consistent with the arrangements presented in Fig. 3. The three concentric tubes depicted in Fig. 6 are, by design, to be formed of thermal insulating material. The lower half of the innermost concentric tube is supplied with water through an inlet located at the end of the tube. The lower half of the annular space between the innermost tube and the second tube (shown dotted) will also be supplied with water through the same inlet at the end. With such an arrangement, the water supply should be introduced at a tem-

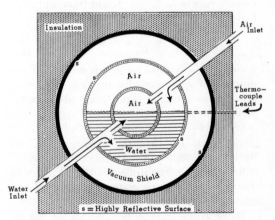

FIG. 6. Cross-sectional view representing a triple-tubed adiabatic saturator that involves the use of materials impervious to the water vapor. (See Note for Fig. 5, which applies here.)

perature as nearly as practicable equal to the thermodynamic wet-bulb temperature, T_w^*. Moist air (or other carrier gas) is to be introduced at the same end of the two inside tubes where the water supply is injected, but in each case the moist air will flow above the surface of the water located in the lower half of the tubes. Contact between the air (or other carrier gas) and the water will cause evaporation of some of the liquid. If this contact is sufficiently prolonged, the air will approach saturation as it moves over the water surface.

The annular space s-s between the second and third tubes from the center is intended to be evacuated for the purpose of reducing the transfer of heat by conduction and convection between the inside tubes and the outermost tube. The latter tube (heavy black ring in Fig. 6) is itself to be enclosed with layers of thermal insulating material to such an extent as will minimize the conductive heat transfer between the surroundings of the apparatus and the outer surface of the vacuum shield (outer boundary of the outermost of the three tubes). The outside surface s of the second tube and the inside surface s of the third tube should be composed of some material which is highly reflective in order to reduce radiative heat exchange across the annular space designated as "Vacuum Shield."

With regard to the lower half of the innermost tube, it will be noted that both the inside radius and the outside radius of the tube are bathed in water at substantially the same temperature. This condition should render practically negligible the heat transfer by radial conduction through the lower half of the tube wall. Similarly, with regard to the upper half of the innermost tube, one may note that both the inside radius and the outside radius are in contact with moist air at substantially the same temperature (and humidity) measured radially. Therefore, the heat transfer by radial conduction should be very small, if not negligible, through the upper half of the tube wall. We may expect this condition to exist with respect to the two inner tubes because the evaporative cooling of the air occurs in parallel above the two separate water surfaces and because this process should yield substantially the same temperature distributions radially in both air passages when fully developed turbulent flow

exists in the air moving through the upper halves of the two inside tubes.

A small rate of conductive heat transfer will exist, however, directed tangentially downward within the two inside tube walls in the neighborhood of the air-water line of contact, wherever the temperature of the moist air in touch with the upper half of the tube wall is greater than the temperature of the water in which the lower half of the tube is bathed. It should be noted that the heat thus transferred downward through the inside tube walls is not necessarily lost to the system after equilibrium and steady-flow conditions are attained, since the sensible heat which the water may gain indirectly from the moist air can be used to supply latent heat absorbed when an appropriate corresponding quantity of water is evaporated.

Furthermore, it should be noted that any radiant energy reflected back and forth between the highly reflective surfaces s-s within the evacuated annular space between the second and third tubes will also be energy *not* lost to the system. Some small fraction of the radiant heat transfer from the upper half of the middle tube will be absorbed by the lower half, and this component of the energy within the system may then become available to provide a small heat flux by conduction into the water contained in the annular space between the two inner tubes. The heat from this source can then give rise to evaporation of an appropriate quantity of water by using it as a latent heat equivalent. One may therefore envision that the corresponding heat which originated in the moist air has reached the water by a circuitous route, and again is not lost to the system.

It is conceivable that heat could be transferred by conduction through the outer wall of the third tube (heavy black ring in Fig. 6), but the rate of such heat transfer can be held very low by maintaining the ambient room temperature at a value equal to the mean absolute temperature which characterizes the heat radiation within the evacuated space (labeled "Vacuum Shield" in Fig. 6), and by employing a suitable quantity of good thermal insulating material to envelop the outer wall of the third tube.

When all of the measures outlined above are taken, the heat exchange rate between the apparatus and its surroundings can be reduced to a relatively low level; in fact so low that the system may be regarded as practically an adiabatic one while equilibrium and steady-flow conditions prevail.

Finally, a correction may be computed, if necessary, in a manner similar to that indicated by Eq. (11). Such a correction would be intended to take account of the effects of all known causes of departure from the ideal conditions postulated in connection with the definition of T_w^* represented by Eq. (2).

The temperature of the saturated air which is to be exhausted from the outlet of the apparatus will be measured within the air both in the upper half of the innermost tube and in the annular space between the two inner tubes. If the desired equilibrium conditions are achieved, the two temperature readings should be equal; but in any case preference and priority would seem to fall to the reading obtained within the innermost tube. Similarly, the temperature of the water would be observed at a number of points along the paths of contact between the air and water. Again, if the desired equilibrium conditions are attained and Eq. (2) were satisfied identically, the water temperature readings should be alike and equal to the temperature of the saturated air exhausted from the outlet of the apparatus. Any departure from these ideal results would be revealed by disparities between the various temperature readings, both for the air and water. If such disparities were to appear, they would have to be investigated until their causes were discovered, and this would provide a basis for remedial action.

Any struts employed in the construction of the apparatus to furnish support for the innermost tube with respect to the second tube can be composed of thermally conducting materials, provided that the struts are entirely immersed either in the water or in the moist air. Struts used to furnish support for the second tube with respect to the outermost tube should be composed of thermally insulating material coated with a highly reflective film, in order to minimize heat transfer between those tubes.

It will be noted that in the operation of the apparatus depicted in Fig. 3, moist air and water are to be introduced at one end of the two innermost tubes while the moist air and water have, generally speaking, different initial temperatures, that is T and very nearly T_w^*, respectively. Because of the heat transfer from the air to the water, it is possible that the water temperature may depart from the initial value during passage of the liquid through the lower half of the two innermost conduits as indicated in Fig. 6. In case such a difference should appear, it would constitute a departure from the ideal conditions to which Eq. (2) was intended to apply (see Fig. 2). If the temperature departure were to turn out experimentally to be more than could be tolerated, it might be necessary to consider the employment of a different design of adiabatic saturator, which would perhaps be capable of overcoming the cause of the departure, for example, as indicated in the next section.

SATURATOR INVOLVING USE OF PARALLEL AIR AND WATER SHIELDS, WHERE WATER IS SUPPLIED ISOTHERMALLY IN LOCAL SIDE AND BOTTOM INLETS

Figure 7 illustrates a design which could be employed to replace the two inner tubes shown in Fig. 6, for the purpose of supplying the water through a number of local inlets (such as M, L, and K placed at the sides, together with E placed at the bottom) distributed along the length of the apparatus. Tubes shown dotted in Fig. 7 are characterized by material of very low thermal conductivity, hence their insulating properties and multiple layers should tend to minimize heat transfer to contiguous components. The water jets E-B which emerge from the bottom conduit F into tube D, when combined with the water jets which impinge upon the above-specified jets (near B) after injection of water through the side inlets L, should tend to provide a fresh water supply at many inlet points along the length of the apparatus. In this manner, the temperature of the water may be kept in very close agreement with the pertinent value of T_w^* along the entire length of the apparatus.

Owing to the action of the impinging jets, the surface of the water near B in Fig. 7 should be fairly rough, and this would be

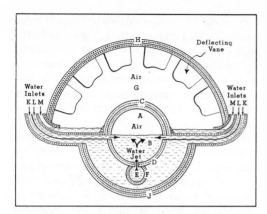

Fig. 7. Cross-sectional view relating to a triple-tubed adiabatic saturator designed for the continuous supply of the liquid by inflow at numerous orifices distributed along the length of the tubes. In order to secure a more nearly perfect degree of adiabatic operation than is possible with this design as shown, its outer surface should be provided with a highly reflective coating, and the entire ensemble may be enclosed in a vacuum shield as illustrated by Fig. 6.

expected to enhance the rate of approach to saturation affecting the air passing over the water in the channel marked A in Fig. 7. Care would have to be taken to avoid entrainment of liquid droplets in the air.

The water at the foot of the space marked G in Fig. 7 will have to be maintained at a suitable, optimum height by means of a controlled rate of injection of water through the side inlets marked M in the Figure. Deflecting vanes are envisaged as necessary to create turbulence in the air moving through the channel marked G and thus to keep the air stirred up for the purpose of obtaining a more homogeneous mixture as well as accelerating the evaporative processes that take place at the water surface.

Since air will be flowing both in channels marked A and G in Fig. 7, the air in the two channels will tend to approach saturation and temperature equilibrium in parallel. Therefore, the radially directed temperature gradient from A to G through the tube wall marked C in Fig. 7 will tend to be close to zero, hence the conductive heat transfer from A to G through the tube wall C should be very small and perhaps negligible.

By virtue of the fact that the water on both sides of the lower half of tube D in Fig. 7 will be virtually isothermal, having a temperature

at or very nearly equal to the pertinent value of T_w^*, the heat transfer through the wall of tube D where water contact exists on both sides should be essentially negligible. On this account, the water marked B in Fig. 7 should experience little gain or loss by conduction with reference to the water on the outside of D, such as the water marked E in tube F or the water contained in the half-annular space between tubes D and J in the Figure.

If the outside surfaces of tubes H and J in Fig. 7 were provided with a highly reflective coating, and this ensemble shown in the diagram were placed inside a vacuum shield with suitable outer thermal insulation as illustrated by Fig. 6, the net heat transfer between the inner ensemble and the ambient room could be kept extremely low. Finally, if the ambient room in which the apparatus is installed be maintained at a temperature equal to the mean temperature characterizing the thermal radiation within the "vacuum shield," the net heat transfer would be minimal.

When all of the measures outlined above are taken while the water is continuously supplied at the proper temperature, to within a narrow tolerance, one may expect that the evaporative processes that occur inside tube D, involving the interaction of the air A and the water B, will be essentially adiabatic. By these means it should be possible to determine finally at least a close approximation of the thermodynamic wet-bulb temperature T_w^* upon attainment of saturation of the air A moving through the channel in the upper half of tube D. Precise saturation of the air should be attended by perfect agreement between the temperatures of the air A and the water B along their surface of contact after flowing air has reached a point at which it is saturated. It will be clear for this and other reasons, that the making of temperature measurements at a number of points both within the air and the water moving through the apparatus will be necessary. On the basis of such parallel measurements in the two moving media, it will be possible to determine experimentally how long a path of contact between the air and water is required for the air to reach saturation.

It is quite probable that as a result of the

frictional effects of the deflecting vanes and the attendant turbulence generated in G, the temperature will become slightly higher in channel G than in channel A at the same longitudinal position. Energy for this temperature increase will, of course, be derived from the pump or fan which is employed to drive the air, and the kinetic energy of the air will, in part, be converted to heat by the action of friction and viscosity. Owing to these effects, there is likely to be a small, radially inward heat flux by conduction from G to A through the walls of tube C, shown in Fig. 7. The rate of this heat flux could be calculated on the basis of measured values of the temperature on the inside and outside surfaces of the wall of tube C, when the overall thermal resistance of the composite tube C is known. This resistance can be determined experimentally.

To generalize, allowances can be made for all energy inputs which tend to produce departures from the ideal adiabatic conditions assumed as the underlying foundation for Eq. (2). Thus, in order to obtain the most accurate results by means of the apparatus, it is advisable to compute the correction $-\Delta T_w^*$ as defined in terms of Eq. (11).

CALIBRATION

In order to test the apparatus, it would be desirable to conduct a number of experiments with various combinations of carrier gases and liquids at several flow speeds and temperatures. This would permit operation of the equipment over wide ranges of the relevant dimensionless parameters, such as the Reynolds number, Prandtl number, and Schmidt number, which play a crucial role in regard to the flow characteristics, heat transfer, and mass transfer. When a gravimetric or other fundemental method of measuring the mixing ratio of the injected moist gas is employed and the pertinent thermodynamic functions involved in Eq. (2) are known, it is possible to compute by means of that equation the appropriate value of the thermodynamic wet-bulb temperature T_w^* for the given moist gas, making use of its observed temperature T, pressure P, and mixing ratio r. The computed value of T_w^*

may then be compared with the observed value of the temperature T_{wx} at which the saturated gas is exhausted from the apparatus, and also with the corrected value, namely $(T_{wx} - \Delta T_w^*)$, which should agree in principle with the theoretical value of T_w^*, where the correction $-\Delta T_w^*$ is defined in terms of Eq. (11).

Another method of determining the thermodynamic wet-bulb temperature T_w^* from the data obtained by means of the apparatus can be based on the consideration of T_w^* as a limit which will be approached by T_{wx} when the variables which depend on the flow approach zero as a limit. In this method the quantity $(T_{wx} - T_w^*)$ will be regarded as a function of three variables, namely, (1) the energy input due to the action of the pumps employed to drive the carrier gas and water through the system, (2) the difference between the input and output sums of the kinetic and potential energies of all the moving materials involved, and (3) the energy transferred to the system from its surroundings due to non-adiabatic conditions, i.e., heat flux from the environment of the apparatus to its interior. Each of the terms (1), (2), and (3) should be expressed with respect to unit mass of the dry carrier gas. On this basis, it follows that T_{wx} approaches T_w^* as a limit when each of the above-mentioned variables (1), (2), and (3) approaches zero as a limit. Therefore, in order to apply this method, it is necessary to obtain readings of T_{wx} pertinent to different values of these variables when they form sequences that approach zero as a limit. Investigation of the variation of $(T_{wx} - T_w^*)$ with respect to the specified variables in turn, when each of the others is kept constant but in the vicinity of zero, will permit one to compute approximately the value which T_{wx} would assume if those variables were brought to their potentially limiting values of zero. The quantity thus evaluated for the limit of T_{wx} as the three above-mentioned variables approach this limit should be very closely in agreement with the desired value of T_w^* pertinent to the given sample of moist carrier gas under consideration.

It is to be expected that $(T_{wx} - T_w^*)$ will also be a function of the Reynolds numbers (Re) which characterize the flow of moist carrier gas and water through the apparatus, and that $(T_{wx} - T_w^*)$ will approach zero as a limit as Re approaches zero as a limit in each case.

Finally, a correction would also be required in principle whenever the pressure of the water or gas is not everywhere uniform [see Eq. (11)].

CONTEMPLATED OPERATION WHEN INLET WATER IS COLDER THAN INJECTED MOIST AIR (OR OTHER CARRIER GAS)

As indicated by Fig. 3, it is deemed essential to have temperature measuring devices installed at a number of positions longitudinally in the saturator to measure both the temperature of the moist carrier gas and that of the water (or other liquid involved). For any given values of P, T, and r, pertaining to a sample of injected moist carrier gas, one would not necessarily know, *a priori*, the value of T_w^* which would satisfy Eq. (2) relating to the sample. Therefore, at the commencement of an experiment it would not be known what temperature should be employed for the injected water controlled by means of the device illustrated schematically in Fig. 4. An estimate of the proper temperature can be obtained by use of a psychrometer, whose wet-bulb reading would be nearly equal to the proper value of T_w^* when the liquid involved is water.

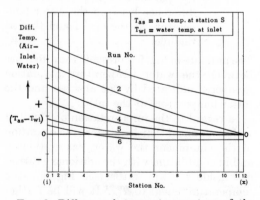

FIG. 8. Difference between temperature of the moist air at station S in the adiabatic saturator and the temperature of the water as it is initially injected at the inlet, plotted as a function of S, for various hypothetical trial runs of the apparatus.

Still a different manner in which to secure a closer approximation to the proper value of T_w^* is to determine it by successive trial experiments with the saturator apparatus. This procedure may be illustrated by means of Fig. 8. In Fig. 8 the various temperature stations are numbered seriatim, say from 0 to 12, and the general temperature station is designated by subscript s, while the initial temperature station at the inlet is designated by number 0 and subscript i. The last temperature station at which the saturated carrier gas is to be exhausted from the outlet is designated by number 12 and subscript x. As shown in Fig. 8, the symbol T_{as} denotes the temperature of the moist air (or other carrier gas) at the temperature station whose number is S, and T_{wi} denotes the temperature of the water (or other liquid) injected at the inlet.

In accordance with this notation, the quantity $(T_{as} - T_{wi})$ shown as the ordinate of Fig. 8 represents the difference between the temperature of the moist air (or other carrier gas) at the indicated temperature station and the temperature at which the water (or other liquid) is injected at the inlet (station 0). The station number is represented by the abscissa. By starting, for example, an experiment with water injected at a temperature very much lower than that of the injected moist air, one might expect to obtain results such as those indicated by run No. 1 as assumed in Fig. 8, which reveals that temperature of the moist air exhausted near station 12 was much higher than the temperature at which the water was initially injected at station 0. It would appear that a result of this character points immediately to the conclusion that the moist air emitted from the outlet had not yet attained a state of saturation with respect to the water, as will be evident from the fact that the conditions underlying Eq. (2) have not been satisfied. It is important to observe that the satisfaction of that equation demands that the moist gas emerge from the outlet in a saturated state at the same temperature as that of the injected water. Clearly then, run No. 1 as depicted in Fig. 8 violates this condition. (See also p. 58.)

By progressively adjusting the water temperature at the inlet, T_{wi}, for a steadily flowing sample of moist air (or other carrier gas) characterized by fixed values of pressure, temperature, and mixing ratio, it is possible to secure different results with the apparatus as illustrated by hypothetical run No. 2, 3, 4, 5, and 6. We have made the assumption with respect to run No. 2, 3, 4, and 5 that the water temperature at the inlet T_{wi} had been so adjusted that the gas emerging from the outlet was at precisely the same temperature. That is, if $T_{ax} =$ the temperature of the moist gas emitted from the exhaust (say at the location of temperature station No. 12) then in the cases of run No. 2, 3, 4, and 5, we would have $T_{wi} = T_{ax}$, which is in harmony with the condition required to satisfy Eq. (2). Run No. 5 differs significantly from run No. 2, however, because the readings of the moist gas temperature at station No. 7, 8, 9, 10, 11, and 12 were all in agreement with T_{wi}, the water temperature at the inlet, whereas this agreement was presumably found in the case of run No. 2 only at station No. 12. Results such as those indicated for run No. 5 may be interpreted as signifying that saturation of the moist gas had occurred by the time the sample reached station No. 7 and that the moist gas had remained in a state of saturation during the remainder of its passage from station No. 7 to station No. 12, while it was in equilibrium with the water at the temperature T_{wi} over this interval. Operations yielding results such as those shown for hypothetical run No. 5 would be considered ideally in agreement with the requirements of Eq. (2), provided that there was independent evidence that the moist air emerging from the apparatus was precisely saturated and that the water temperatures observed at all of the stations were alike and had exactly the same value as the temperature of the saturated gas emitted from the exhaust.

Hypothetical run No. 6 whose results are depicted in Fig. 8 constitutes an exception, for which it was assumed that the temperature of the water injected at the inlet was only slightly lower than the temperature of the gas introduced at station No. 0 for given values of pressure and mixing ratio in the case of low relative humidity so that the moist gas came out of the exhaust at a temperature lower than T_{wi}.

If, in run No. 1 also, the sample of moist gas was initially saturated or nearly saturated while the temperature of the injected water was significantly lower than that of the gas originally, the result shown by run No. 1 might be attributed partially to the effects of supersaturation developed in the moist gas and the release of latent heat of condensation at the water surface.

THEORETICAL INITIAL EFFECTS OF INJECTION OF CARRIER GAS OVER WATER

When a carrier gas is initially injected into a tube above a surface of water, the thermal interaction between the two depends greatly upon a number of parameters, principally upon the relative humidity of the gas, the original temperatures of the two fluids, and their respective forward speeds. The theoretical curves presented in Fig. 9 may be considered in order to obtain some idea of the various possible interactions along the path of contact between the gas and the water within the adiabatic saturator of the type shown in Fig. 6 when the gas and the water are first introduced into one end of the tubes (say, the left-hand end, as in Fig. 3).

The following notation is employed in Fig. 9:

$T_{ws} =$ the water temperature at station No. S

$T_{wi} =$ the water temperature as introduced at the inlet (station 0 or i)

$T_{wx} =$ the water temperature as the water emerges from the outlet (at station 12 or x)

$\Delta T_w =$ the parameter $(T_{wx} - T_{wi}) =$ the difference between the water temperature at the outlet and that at the inlet.

The ordinate in Fig. 9 represents the difference between the water temperature at station number S indicated by the abscissa and the water temperature at the inlet.

In regard to the interpretation of Fig. 9, it will be assumed that just before the operation of the equipment the water was stationary and in equilibrium with the stationary carrier gas inside the apparatus (see Fig. 6) at a temperature equal to T_{wi}. It will be further assumed that a fresh sample of carrier gas characterized by definite values of pressure (P), temperature (T_{ai}), and mixing ratio (r_i), is then injected into the inlet at the left-hand side with a greater forward speed than that at which the water is injected at the same pressure but at temperature T_{wi}. Under these conditions, the changes which occur in the carrier gas as a result of its interaction with the water will affect the water downstream because of the forward transport of the properties of the gas relative to the underlying liquid.

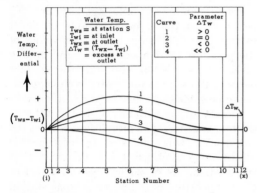

FIG. 9. Difference between temperature of the water at station S and the temperature of the water as it is initially injected at the inlet of the adiabatic saturator, plotted as a function of S, for various hypothetical operations in which the injected sample of air has just reached the last station for the first time.

Suppose that we wish to study the temperature distribution in the water along the entire length of the adiabatic saturator immediately after the injected gas has reached the right-hand outlet for the first time. Under the stipulated circumstances, the water temperature at points along the path of contact between the gas and water surface will depend on the speed of response of the two components to the various physical processes involved, such as heat conduction and convection, vapor diffusion and convection, evaporative cooling, etc. Since vapor diffusion is a relatively slow process in close proximity to the boundary surface between the gas and water, this will serve to limit the speed of response to the evaporating cooling. On the other hand, the heat conduction and convection in the rapidly moving gas will entail a faster process of heat transfer which will give rise to a fairly high speed of response of

the boundary layer in the vicinity of the inlet region. We can therefore infer that the temperature of the water surface will react quickly to the temperature of the superincumbent gas in that region at the first stage of the injection of gas over the water. Then, as the gas passes over the water downstream in the adiabatic saturator the temperature contrast between the two will be different from what it originally was upstream. As a consequence, the heat conduction into or out of the water surface will vary with longitudinal position along the surface in the saturator, and the effect of these different rates of heat transfer with position will be reflected in corresponding different rates of evaporation of the water (or condensation upon its surface), depending upon the existing relative humidity, speed of response of the various processes involved, etc.

The theoretical curves presented in Fig. 9 are intended to show the resulting temperature distribution in the water surface under various hypothetical combinations of conditions in regard to the initial relative humidity and gas-water temperature differences. For brevity regarding materials as *initially injected*, we denote by T_{wi} the temperature of the water, and by T_{ai} and RH$_i$ the temperature and the relative humidity, respectively, of the gas. The following conditions have been assumed regarding the four curves shown in Fig. 9.

Curve 1: RH$_i$ = 100 per cent; $T_{ai} \gg T_{wi}$

The abrupt injection of the warmer, saturated gas over the water surface will cause the gas to become supersaturated near the surface. At first, heat transfer from the gas to the water will cause the temperature of the water surface to rise. Flow of the supersaturated gas downstream will lead to condensation on the colder water surface, and this process will enhance the heating of the water surface. The gas will cool progressively as it moves forward over the colder water, but at the same time its moisture content will have been somewhat decreased due to condensation on the water upstream. Finally, towards the end of its passage, the total effects of these changes in the gas will tend to produce a slowing down in the heat and vapor exchange between the gas and underlying water, until in the last stages a balance may be reached as reflected by the leveling off of the curve at the right.

Curve 2: $RH_i = 70$ per cent, say; $T_{ai} > T_{wi}$

Under these conditions, the gas does not become supersaturated and the temperature rise in the early stages of the gas flow over the water is smaller than that shown for curve 1. It is assumed in regard to curve 2 that the gas becomes saturated by the time it reaches station No. 10, and that equilibrium between the gas and water will be maintained during the remainder of the passage of the gas covering the range from station No. 10 to No. 12, so that $T_{as} = T_{ws} = T_{wi}$ in this range.

Curve 3: $RH_i = 40$ per cent, say; T_{ai} slightly greater than T_{wi}

This case is somewhat similar to that presented for curve 2, except that the effect of the evaporative cooling causes a greater dip in the curve as the gas progresses to the right, and may finally lead to equilibrium temperature lower than T_{wi}.

Curve 4: $RH_i = 0$, say; $T_{ai} < T_{wi}$

Because the evaporative cooling will be very intense and the heat transfer will be directed from the water to the gas under these specified conditions, the water surface will manifest immediate falls of its temperature as the gas passes over the liquid. Finally, however, due to the evaporation into it, the gas reaching the last stages of the passage will have become saturated, provided that the surface of contact is sufficiently long. The gas may also have gained enough heat by conduction from the initially warmer water to permit it to be in equilibrium with the water on closely approaching the outlet at the right.

The intercept of the curves on the ordinate scale at the right-hand side of Fig. 9 shows the value of the parameter ΔT_w pertaining to the several curves given. One may measure the value of this parameter relating to any experimental situation by means of a thermocouple which indicates the difference between the outlet and inlet values of the water temperatures. It is possible to employ this parameter as a basis for the thermal regulation of the water temperature control tank (see Figs. 3 and 4). A necessary, but not sufficient, condition for the proper regulation of this tank is that the parameter be equal to zero, that is, $\Delta T_w = (T_{wx} - T_{wi}) = 0$.

NECESSARY AND SUFFICIENT CONDITIONS FOR OPERATION

In accordance with the provisos on whose basis Eq. (2) was developed, the water must be supplied everywhere in the adiabatic saturator at the same temperature as the thermodynamic wet-bulb temperature T_w^* pertinent to the injected sample of moist carrier gas characterized by given values of the pressure P, temperature T, and mixing ratio r. One should also like the contact between flowing gas and water in the apparatus to be sufficiently long to permit the gas to attain saturation with respect to the water at the temperature T_w^* before the gas reaches the outlet where it is exhausted. In order for this condition to be satisfied, it is necessary that the temperature of the gas become equal to the temperature of the water at some station before the outlet is reached and that both of these temperatures must remain the same at all stations farther downstream. Finally, the carrier gas which is emitted from the outlet must be in a saturated state at the initial pressure P and at temperature T_w^*, in harmony with the foregoing specifications and in agreement with the provisions of Eq. (2).

Using the notation for T_{wi}, T_{ws}, T_{wx}, and T_{as} previously introduced (see Figs. 8 and 9), and employing the symbol RH_s to denote the relative humidity with respect to water at the pressure P and temperature T_{ws} at the station designated by S, we may therefore express the necessary and sufficient conditions for the *ideal* steady-flow operation of an adiabatic saturator by the following relationships:

$$T_{wi} = T_{ws} = T_{wx} \tag{12}$$

for all $S = 0, 1, 2, 3, \ldots, x$;
and

$$T_{as} = T_{ws} \tag{13}$$

$$RH_s = 100 \text{ per cent} \tag{14}$$

where S assumes all values in the sequence $S_1, (S_1 + 1), (S_1 + 2), (S_1 + 3), \ldots, x$, for some value of the parameter S_1 which satisfies the condition

$$0 \leq S_1 < x$$

If Eq. (2) is satisfied, then we have also in conjunction with Eqs. (12) and (13)

$$T_{wx} = T_w^* \tag{15}$$

For a non-ideal operation of the apparatus, the correction $-\Delta T_w^*$ indicated by Eq. (11) would have to be taken into consideration.

If a close approximation of the conditions specified by Eqs. (12) through (14) is not achieved in a single passage of a given sample of gas through the apparatus, it is deemed necessary to operate the equipment in tandem as illustrated by Fig. 3 until the required conditions are essentially satisfied after an adequate sequence of such passages by successive transfers of the gas from one apparatus to another.

When a steady-flow condition is attained, involving the continuous supply of the sample gas via the inlet at given pressure P, temperature T, and mixing ratio r, the temperature distribution along the water surface will not be like that indicated by curves 1, 3, or 4 in Fig. 9. On the other hand it may be somewhat similar to that indicated by curve 2, or when the ideal is reached, it may be even represented by the horizontal line 0-0 in Fig. 9, since the water should be supplied in such a manner that $T_{wi} = T_{wx}$, while T_{wi} in practice must always be less than T if the sample gas was initially unsaturated.

By studying the results provided by the temperature probes employed at the various stations for giving temperatures of gas and water, respectively, it is possible to determine whether the conditions specified by Eqs. (12) through (14) are satisfied. The problem of verifying the satisfaction of the conditions stipulated by Eq. (14) must be solved in another manner as indicated by the discussion in the next section.

CHECKING SATURATION AT THE OUTLET

As a matter of precaution it is deemed advisable to make use of two or more devices for determining independently whether the gas emitted from the exhaust outlet is actually saturated at the temperature and pressure observed in the exit region.

Several methods are available for this purpose. One of the most promising of these involves the employment of a thermocouple for the wet bulb of a psychrometer, as described by Monteith and Owen.[49] These authors indicate that at high relative humidities, a current of 30 mA through a 38 SWG "chromel-P" constantan thermocouple yields sufficient Peltier cooling to enable formation of a film of water on the junction which can then be used as a wet bulb. Owing to the fact that the wet-bulb depression can be read to $0.001°C$, changes in the relative humidity of the order of 0.01 per cent can be detected when the relative humidity is in the range 97 to 100 per cent at temperatures above freezing.

A dew-point meter may also be used separately. Care would be necessary in such designs to preclude the ingestion into the apparatus of foreign vapors which can form condensation before the water vapor does at the same pressure and temperature. Furthermore, it would be essential to install a fine filter at the inlet of the space from which the gas is sampled in order to remove dust particles and condensation nuclei so that condensation will not occur at any relative humidity below 100 per cent. The filter employed at the inlet would have to be one which did not serve as a long-time source or sink of water molecules.

CONCLUSIONS WITH REGARD TO CHOICE OF DESIGN OF ADIABATIC SATURATOR

Several criteria have been presented to provide bases by means of which one may choose an optimum design for an adiabatic saturator. It will be clear from the information given previously (see p. 51) that the porous-tube design (Fig. 5) is likely to require somewhat larger corrections than the others. One may also infer that the second design, as described on p. 52 (see Fig. 6), is of such character that without unduly long tubes, one would find it extremely difficult to satisfy the conditions specified in Eqs. (12) through (14), in the light of the general considerations laid down on p. 45. In view of the consideration that the above-mentioned objections and difficulties should be largely overcome by the third design (see Fig. 7), we conclude that the design described on p. 54 is likely to enable one to attain the desired objectives most closely. In this regard, we may recall that saturation can be more readily achieved in this design by virtue of the action of the water jets and the turbulence engendered by the flow of the moist gas over the roughened water surface. Finally, we still envision the possible need for tandem operation of the apparatus in sequence until saturation is reached (see Fig. 3).

Because of the special difficulties which attend the development and use of an adiabatic saturator operated under conditions where freezing of the liquid will occur, it must be emphasized, in closing, that the designs described on pp. 47–56 cannot be employed when the temperature in the apparatus falls below the freezing point. Therefore, the experimental determination of the thermodynamic frost-point temperature, T_f^*, must be undertaken in some other manner. T_f^* may be understood as defined in terms of Eq. (2), provided that one substitutes in that relationship, for the thermodynamic functions relating to water, the corresponding functions which are pertinent to ice.

References

1. Sworykin, N., "Die Bestimmung der Feuchtigkeit der Luft mit dem Psychrometer," *Wild, Repertorium für Meteorologie*, 7, No. 8, 28 (1881).
2. Ferrel, Wm., "Recent Advances in Meteorology," Annual Report of the Chief Signal Officer, 1885, Part II, Appendix 71, pp. 380–391, Washington, 1886.
3. Bongards, H., "Feuchtigkeitsmessung," 322 pp. Munich and Berlin, R. Oldenburg, 1926.
4. Brooks, D. B., and Allen, H. H., "Some Improvements in Psychrometry," *J. Wash. Acad. Sci.*, 23, 121 (1933).
5. Wylie, R. G., "Psychrometry," Report PA-4, Commonwealth of Australia, Commonwealth Scientific and Industrial Research Organization, National Standards Laboratory, Division of Physics, University Grounds, Sydney, Australia, July 1949.
6. Kopcewicz, Teodor, "On the Influence of Wind Velocity on the Psychrometric Constant," *Acta Geophys. Polon.*, 1, 82 (1953).
7. Spencer-Gregory, H., and Rourke, E., "Hygrometry," 254 pp. London, Crosby Lockwood & Son, Ltd., 1957.
8. Carrier, W. H., "Rational Psychrometric Formulas," *Trans. ASME*, 33, 1005 (1911).
9. Carrier, W. H., "The Temperature of Evaporation," *Trans. Am. Soc. Heat. Vent. Engrs.*, 24, 25 (1918).
10. Ivory, J., "On the Hygrometer by Evaporation," *Phil. Mag.*, 60, 81 (1822).
11. Arnold, J. Howard, "The Theory of the Psychrometer. I. The Mechanism of Evaporation," *Physics*, 4, 255 (July 1933).
12. Arnold, J. Howard, "The Theory of the Psychrometer. II. The Effect of Velocity," *Physics*, 4, 334 (September 1933).
13. Carrier, W. H. and Lindsay, D. C., "The Temperatures of Evaporation of Water into Air," *Trans. ASME*, 46, 36 and 739 (1924).
14. Harrison, Louis P., "Fundamental Concepts and Definitions Relating to Humidity," in "Humidity and Moisture," Vol. III, New York, Reinhold Publishing Corp., 1964.
15. Keyes, F. G. and Smith, L. B., "The Present State of Psychrometric Data," *Refrig. Eng.*, 27, 127 (1934).
16. Goff, J. A., and Gratch, S., "Thermodynamic Properties of Moist Air," *Trans. Am. Soc. Heat. Vent. Engrs.*, 51, 125 (1945).
17. Goff, J. A., "Standardization of Thermodynamic Properties of Moist Air—Final Report of Working Subcommittee, International Joint Committee on Psychrometric Data," *ASHVE Journal* Section Heating, Piping & Air Conditioning, 55, 118 (1949).
18. Maxwell, J. C., "Diffusion," in "Encyclopedia Britannica," 9th ed., Vol. 7, p. 218, Edinburgh, 1877. (This article contains Maxwell's "Theory of the Wet-Bulb Thermometer.")
19. Skinner, S., Article on "Humidity" in R. Glazebrook, "Dictionary of Applied Physics," Vol. III, p. 423, London, Macmillan and Co., Ltd., 1923.
20. Lewis, W. K., "The Evaporation of a Liquid into a Gas," *Trans. ASME*, 44, 325 (1922).
21. Lewis, W. K., "The Evaporation of a Liquid into a Gas—A Correction," *Mech. Eng.*, 55, 567 (September 1933).
22. Sherwood, T. K., and Comings, E. W., "An Experimental Study of the Wet-Bulb Hygrometer," *Trans. A.I.Ch.E.*, 28, 88 (1932).
23. Whipple, F. J. W., "The Wet- and Dry-Bulb Hygrometer: The Relation to Theory of the Experimental Researches of Awbery and Griffiths," *Proc. Phys. Soc. London*, 45, 307 (1933).
24. Dropkin, David, "The Deviation of the Actual Wet-Bulb Temperature from the Temperature of Adiabatic Saturation," Ithaca, New York, Cornell University, Engineering Experiment Station, Bulletin No. 23, 45 pp. July 1936.
25. Dropkin, David, "The Effect of Radiation on Psychrometric Readings," Ithaca, New York, Cornell University, Engineering Experiment Station, Bulletin No. 26, 60 pp. October 1939.
26. Carrier, W. H., and Mackey, C. O., "A Review of Existing Psychrometric Data in Relation to Practical Engineering Problems," *Trans. ASME*, 59, 33 (1937).
27. Wile, D. D., "Psychrometry in the Frost Zone," *Refrig. Eng.*, 48, 291 (1944).
28. International Meteorological Organization, "Values of Some Physical Functions and Constants Used in Meteorology. Definitions

and Specifications of Water Vapour in the Atmosphere," IMO Publication No. 79, Imprimerie la Concorde-Lausanne, Switzerland, 1951.

29. Guggenheim, E. A., "Thermodynamics," 476 pp. 3rd ed., New York: Interscience Publishers, Inc., 1957.

30. American Society of Heating, Refrigerating, and Air-Conditioning Engineers, "ASHRAE Guide and Data Book 1961, Fundamentals and Equipment," Ch. 3, New York, 1961.

31. Jones, J. B., and Hawkins, G. A., "Engineering Thermodynamics," 724 pp. New York, John Wiley & Sons, Inc., 1960.

32. McAdams, William H., "Heat Transmission," 3rd ed., 532 pp. New York, McGraw-Hill Book Co., Inc., 1954.

33. Knudsen, J. G., and Katz, D. L., "Fluid Dynamics and Heat Transfer," 576 pp. New York, McGraw-Hill Book Co., Inc., 1958.

34. Faires, V. M., "Thermodynamics," 4th ed., 680 pp. New York, The Macmillan Co., 1962.

35. Bartlett, Edward P., "The Concentration of Water Vapor in Compressed Hydrogen, Nitrogen and a Mixture of These Gases in the Presence of Condensed Water," *J. Am. Chem. Soc.*, **49**, 65 (1927).

36. Pollitzer, F., and Strebel, E., "Über den Einfluss indifferenter Gase auf die Sättigungs-Dampfkonzentration von Flüssigkeiten," *Z. Physik. Chem.*, **110**, 768 (1924).

37. Saddington, A. W., and Krase, N. W., "Vapor-Liquid Equilibria in the System Nitrogen-Water," *J. Am. Chem. Soc.*, **56**, 353 (February 1934).

38. Smith, F. A., and Eiseman, J. H., "Saturation of Gases by Laboratory Wet Test Meters," National Bureau of Standards Research Paper RP1238, *J. Res. Natl. Bur. Std.*, **23**, 345 (September 1939).

39. Wexler, A., and Brombacher, W. G., "Methods of Measuring Humidity and Testing Hygrometers," National Bureau of Standards Circular 512, published by U.S. Government Printing Office, Washington D.C., September 28, 1951.

40. Wexler, A., "Divided Flow, Low-Temperature Humidity Test Apparatus," National Bureau of Standards Research Paper RP1894, *J. Res. Natl. Bur. Std.*, **40**, 479 (June 1948).

41. McHaffie, I. R., "The Effect of the Presence of an Indifferent Gas on the Concentration and Activity of a Vapour in Equilibrium with a Condensed Phase or System of Condensed Phases. (Part II.)," *Phil. Mag.*, 7th Ser., **3**, 497 (1927).

42. Wexler, A., "Recirculating Apparatus for Testing Hygrometers," National Bureau of Standards Research Paper 2145, *J. Res. Natl. Bur. Std.*, **45**, 357 (November 1950).

43. Wexler, Arnold, and Daniels, Raymond D., Jr., "Pressure-Humidity Apparatus," *J. Res. Natl. Bur. Std.*, **48**, Research Paper 2312, 269 (April 1952).

44. Webster, T. J., "The Effect on Water Vapour Pressure of Superimposed Air Pressure," *J. Soc. Chem. Ind.*, **69**, 343 (November 1950).

45. Washburn, Edward W., and Heuse, Edward O., "The Measurement of Vapor Pressure Lowering by the Air Saturation Method," *J. Am. Chem. Soc.*, **37**, 309 (Jan.–June 1915).

46. Goff, John A., and Bates, A. C., "The Interaction Constant for Moist Air," *Trans. Am. Soc. Heat. Vent. Engrs.*, **47**, 373 (1941).

47. Wentzel, J. D., "An Instrument for the Measurement of the Humidity of Air," *Trans. ASHRAE*, **68**, 204 (1962).

48. Carman, P. C., "Flow of Gases through Porous Media," 182 pp. London, Butterworths Scientific Publications, 1956.

49. Monteith, J. L., and Owen, P. C., "A Thermocouple Method for Measuring Relative Humidity in the Range 95–100%," *J. Sci. Instr.*, **35**, 443 (December 1958).

4. Wet-and-dry-plate Dew-point Hygrometer

KAMEKICHI SHIBA

Faculty of Engineering, Toyo University, Saitama, Japan

AND

TATSUMI TOZAWA

Utsunomiya Technical College, Tochigi, Japan

ABSTRACT

The wet-and-dry-plate dew-point hygrometer is composed of a wet-and-dry-plate hygrometer and a cooling apparatus.

A thin, long, rectangular mica plate with a thermopile attached to it to measure the temperature difference between the two ends of the plate is placed in a pipe with a reflective inside surface. The end of the mica plate covered by a wet gauze is the wet-bulb part; the other end is the dry-bulb part.

Appropriately cooled air flows through the pipe from the dry part to the wet part of the plate. The air temperature is measured by a thermistor thermometer.

The dew point of a gas is not changed when the gas temperature is varied at constant pressure, and the relation between the temperature difference $t - t_w$ and air temperature t is linear, for the region of small values of $t - t_w$, as is expected theoretically. The intersecting point of the straight line representing the relation and the axis gives the dew point t_D. The temperature scale may be modified to read dew point directly if the air temperature is automatically controlled to maintain a constant small wet-bulb depression.

INTRODUCTION

The ordinary dew-point hygrometer is, with a few exceptions, an instrument designed to measure the temperature of a cooled surface of a solid body, on which dew or frost is observed. For this kind of dew-point hygrometer, the surface temperature of the solid body should be kept exactly at the dew point. However, it is difficult to maintain this exact temperature.

With the wet-and-dry-plate dew-point hygrometer here reported, we can obtain the dew point without condensation of vapor into dew or frost. The instrument consists of a wet-and-dry-plate hygrometer[1] and a cooling apparatus. The former has a thermopile to measure the temperature difference between both ends of the plate and a thermistor to measure the air temperature (dry-bulb temperature); the latter is used to cool suitably the air flowing in the hygrometer.

The air is cooled to temperatures somewhat higher than the dew point, and the dew point is determined by extrapolation using data of the relation between air temperature and temperature difference.

THE THEORETICAL FOUNDATION

The temperature difference of two bulbs of a psychrometer is affected by the nature of the gas, its temperature, pressure, relative humidity, flow velocity, the condition of the gauze, the form of the thermometers, and the surroundings.

If all of these factors which determine the

64

temperature difference between the bulbs are kept constant, except the temperature and the relative humidity, the relative humidity varies with the temperature. When the relative humidity is 100 per cent, that is, when the temperature of the gas is the dew point, the temperature difference is zero, and vice versa.

Let the temperature of the gas (that is, temperature of the dry bulb) be t, the temperature of the wet bulb be t_w, and the dew point of gas be t_D. The relative humidity can be determined from the temperature of the gas and its dew point, and therefore, the temperature difference $t - t_w$ of both bulbs may be regarded as a function of t and t_D, that is,

$$t - t_w = f(t, t_D) \qquad (1)$$

The dew point t_D is not changed when the gas temperature is varied at constant pressure; therefore, for a variation of the temperature of gas t within a small range near t_D at constant pressure, we have

$$t - t_w = f(t_D, t_D) + \left(\frac{\partial f}{\partial t}\right) t_D \cdot (t - t_D) \quad (2)$$

From Eq. (1), we have, when $t = t_D$, $t - t_w$ must be zero, and therefore,

$$f(t_D, t_D) = 0 \qquad (3)$$

Thus Eq. (2) can be written in the form:

$$t - t_w = \left(\frac{\partial f}{\partial t}\right) t_D \cdot (t - t_D) \qquad (4)$$

This equation shows that, when the dew point is kept constant, the temperature difference $t - t_w$ between the bulbs varies proportionally to the difference $t - t_D$, or to the temperature t, near the dew point.

The temperature difference between the bulbs $t - t_w$ can be written in the form:

$$t - t_w = t - t_D - (t_w - t_D) \qquad (5)$$

that is,

$$t - t_w = \frac{1}{a}(t - t_w) - (t_w - t_D) \qquad (6)$$

where $a = (\partial f / \partial t) t_D$. Rewriting this equation we have:

$$t_w - t_D = \left(\frac{1}{a} - 1\right)(t - t_w) \qquad (7)$$

Equation (7) shows that the temperature difference $t - t_w$ is proportional to the difference between the wet bulb temperature t_w and the dew point t_D, within a small range near the dew point.

When the gas is cooled at constant pressure, the dew point is kept constant as long as the gas is not below the dew point, and so the plotted point of the measured values of the temperature difference $t - t_w$ between the bulbs for several temperatures t on a graph must be on a straight line within the small range of the gas temperature near the dew point.

The intersecting point of the straight line and t axis gives the dew point t_D.

When the gas is supercooled and its temperature t is lowered below the dew point t_D, a part of the water vapor contained in the gas is condensed and taken off; consequently the dew point of the gas is lowered, but the temperature difference between both bulbs is still zero.

As regards the air flow velocity, it is known that there exists a certain critical air flow velocity, such that when the air flow velocity is greater than the critical velocity, the temperature difference between the bulbs is unchanged, regardless of the variation of the air flow velocity. The critical air flow velocity is dependent on the structure of the psychrometer. For the above-mentioned dew-point measurement, it is considered that the smaller the critical air flow velocity the better. It is theoretically known that the less the heat exchange between the thermometers and surroundings (due to radiation and conduction), the less is the influence of air flow velocity on the temperature difference.

This wet-and-dry-plate dew-point hygrometer provides a primary method of measurement of the dew point, since no psychrometric formula need be assumed; therefore, it offers a standard method of measuring humidity.

For the moment, if we assume the well-known Sprung's psychrometric formula, which is recognized experimentally to be approximately applicable, the linear range of the relation between the temperature difference and the air temperature extends at least from 0 to 4 degrees of the temperature difference $t - t_w$.

STRUCTURE OF WET-AND-DRY-PLATE DEW-POINT HYGROMETER

To determine the dew point by the above-mentioned method, it would be convenient to measure the temperature difference $t - t_w$ between wet and dry bulbs and the dry-bulb temperature t (or wet-bulb temperature t_w), instead of measuring the temperatures of both bulbs as in the case of an ordinary psychrometer.

In our experiments, a newly designed wet-and-dry-plate hygrometer is used. The wet-and-dry plate is made of a thin, long, rectangular mica plate with a thermopile of fine wire attached near both ends of the plate. A sheet of gauze is wrapped near one end of the plate and is moistened with water to serve as a wet end (to take the place of the wet bulb); the other is the dry-end.

The temperature difference of both ends is measured by the thermopile, and the dry- or wet-end temperature is measured by a thermistor thermometer. The wet-and-dry plate and thermistor thermometer are inserted in a pipe with a reflective inside surface, and radiation shields are placed parallel to the thin mica plate. The air flows from the dry-end of the plate to the wet-end.

The wet-and-dry plate is shown in Fig. 1. The thermopile consists of 10 pairs of Cu-constantan wires of 0.16-mm diameter; it is fixed on a mica plate of $84 \times 12 \times 0.22$ mm

with vinyl chloride paints, the thermocouple junctions being set near both ends of the plate. The wet end, B, is covered with a sheet of gauze, and water is supplied to it from a water bottle. A small sensitive element of the thermistor thermometer is placed near the dry end, A.

This wet-and-dry plate is placed in a bakelite pipe of 22-mm i.d., 28-mm o.d., and 300-mm length whose inner surface is coated with a reflective aluminum foil to lessen the heat transfer by radiation. Moreover, two thin aluminum plates of $45 \times 8 \times 0.085$ mm are placed near both sides of the wet-and-dry plate and parallel to it as the radiation shield.

The air flow from the dry end, A, to the wet end, B, is caused by a suction fan.

The critical air flow velocity of this hygrometer is 0.6 m/sec; this value is remarkably smaller than that of Assmann's psychrometer, of which the critical air velocity is more than 3 m/sec.

The wet-and-dry-plate dew-point hygrometer is composed of the hygrometer described above and a cooling apparatus capable of cooling the gas. A schematic drawing of it is shown in Fig. 2.

EXPERIMENTAL RESULTS

Theoretically, the air may be cooled close to the dew point; however, when the air is

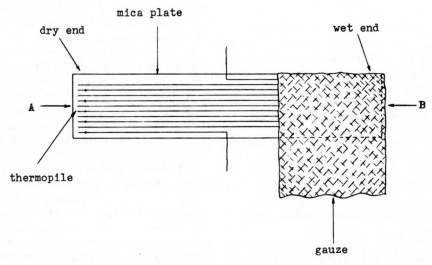

Fig. 1. Wet-and-dry-plate element.

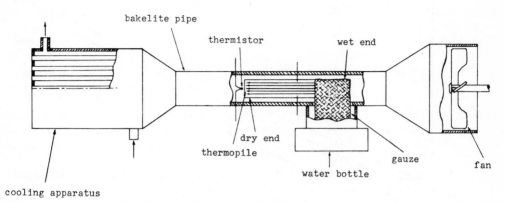

F$_{\text{IG}}$. 2. Schematic drawing of wet-and-dry-plate dew-point hygrometer.

cooled to a temperature lower than the dew point even locally, a part of the water vapor contained in the air is condensed and taken off, which lowers the dew point of the air. Therefore, in our experiments, cooling of the air is limited to a temperature somewhat higher than the dew point.

The fan placed in a wind-tunnel is driven constantly, and the air is drawn through the cooling apparatus. The temperature of the air is measured by a thermistor thermometer which is placed near the dry end, and the temperature difference between the two ends is measured by the thermopile.

Measurements are made for various cooling temperatures and for air of different dew points.

When the dew point of air differs notably from the air temperature, considerable cooling is necessary which causes local supercooling. In our experiments, such a supercooling is observed when the temperature difference $t - t_w$ is smaller than 2 degrees. Therefore, in our experiments, we obtain the relation between $t - t_w$ and t, by heating the air with high relative humidity, instead of cooling the air with low relative humidity.

In Figs. 3 and 4 are shown typical data on the temperature difference between the two ends *vs* the air temperature (dry temperature) obtained in such a manner. The dew point is determined as the intersecting point of the straight line and the t axis.

DISCUSSION

These examples show that the dew point can be determined with fair accuracy by the above method, as expected theoretically.

If the relation between the temperature difference $t - t_w$ and air temperature t is known for an extended range of air temperature, the dew point is obtained by the measured air temperature t, under the condition that the temperature difference $t - t_w$ is kept at an appointed constant value, for example $t - t_w = 2$ degrees. In such a case, if we graduate a dew-point scale instead of the air temperature scale of the thermistor thermometer, the dew point can be read directly.

Thus, this instrument can be made to automatically record and control the dew point.

To avoid local supercooling, it seems to be necessary that the appointed temperature difference be 2 to 3 degrees.

For the wet-and-dry-plate dew-point hygrometer, the Peltier cooling apparatus might be suitable, for it would serve as both cooler and heater.

CONCLUSION

A newly designed wet-and-dry-plate dew-point hygrometer, as reported here, is considered to have the following advantages:

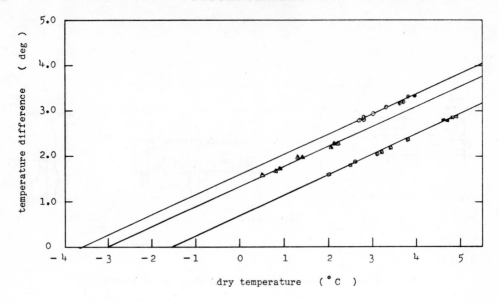

FIG. 3(a). Relation between the temperature difference and the dry temperature.

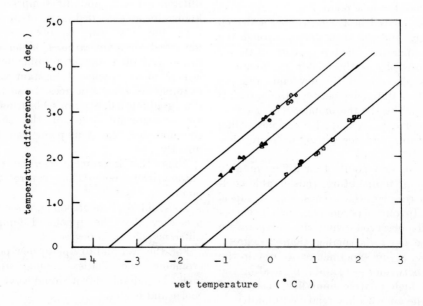

FIG. 3(b). Relation between the temperature difference and the wet temperature.

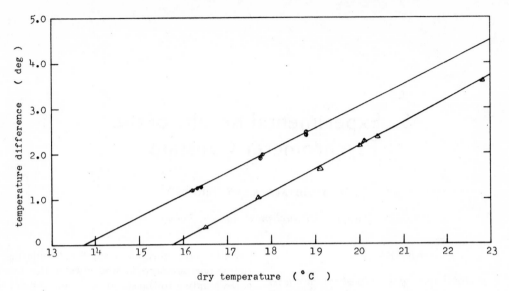

FIG. 4(a). Relation between the temperature difference and the dry temperature.

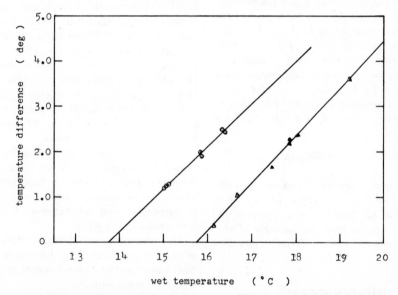

FIG. 4(b). Relation between the temperature difference and the wet temperature.

(1) Dew-point measurement with the wet-and-dry-plate dew-point hygrometer is carried out at a temperature higher than the dew point and is independent of any psychrometric formula.

(2) The wet-and-dry-plate dew-point hygrometer can be used for gases other than air.

(3) The wet-and-dry-plate hygrometer needs less cooling than ordinary dew-point hygrometers.

(4) If the temperature difference $t - t_w$ is kept constant, the dew point can be read directly when the relation between the temperature difference $t - t_w$ and the air temperature t is known.

(5) A wet-and-dry-plate dew-point hygrometer with Peltier cooling apparatus is now under consideration.

Reference

1. Tozawa, T., "Wet-and-dry-plate Hygrometer," *J. Soc. Inst. Contr. Eng.*, **2**, No. 3, 182 (1963).

5. Experimental Results of the Psychrometer Constant

M. Yoshitake and I. Shimizu

Japan Meteorological Agency, Tokyo

ABSTRACT

A modified type of ventilated psychrometer was constructed and is being used at meteorological stations in Japan. The psychrometer constant was established for this instrument. The vapor pressure was determined by the gravimetric method, and the dry- and wet-bulb temperatures were read by an observer. A total of 65 measurements were made in a temperature range of 5 to 34°C and a humidity range of 45 to 79 per cent over a period of 8 months. The psychrometric formula obtained for the modified psychrometer is

$$e = e_w - 0.70(1 - 0.0056t_w)(t - t_w)\frac{p}{1000}$$

where e, e_w, and p are expressed in the same units, and t and t_w are given in °C. It is noticeable that the psychrometer constant obtained here decreases with the increase of wet-bulb temperature, while Ferrel's constant increases.

INTRODUCTION

The Assmann psychrometer is the best available psychrometer for humidity measurement both in research work and in routine practice. It is often used as a secondary standard for calibration of other types of hygrometers. However, accurate measurements are not always expected by means of a commercial Assmann for the following reasons. (1) The ventilation speed to be measured varies with different instruments in the range between 2.5 and 5 m/sec, while the psychrometric formula used for calculating the vapor pressure is not always the one corresponding to the speed in the instrument. (2) The space between the inner metal duct and the thermometer bulb is very narrow and close, and it is difficult to set the duct and the bulb coaxially. Without their coaxial setting, uniform ventilation of the bulb is not expected. (3) As the bulb is not visible through the duct, great care must be taken in wetting the bulb. (4) Assmann psychrometers on the market are not suitable for permanent installation in a screen with wooden louvers because they have no stand.

For the purpose of removing these operational inconveniences associated with the Assmann psychrometer, a modified type of ventilated psychrometer was constructed and is currently used in stations of the Japan Meteorological Agency.

The present paper describes the measurement of the modified psychrometer constant, which is expected to be different from that of the ordinary Assmann.

MODIFIED TYPE OF VENTILATED PSYCHROMETER

A photograph of the modified type of ventilated psychrometer is shown in Fig. 1. Two mercury-in-glass thermometers with a spherical bulb are mounted on a rigid stand. The thermometer is of a sheathed type with the scale engraved on a milk glass plate attached to the thermometer tube inside the

70

sheath, and is of a larger size than that of the Assmann. It has a total length of 360 mm and a bulb diameter of 10 mm. The scale is graduated every 0.2°C, and the length of a centimeter corresponds to about 4°C.

Separate transparent glass ducts with an internal diameter of 16 mm are provided for the two thermometers instead of the double-walled metal ducts of the Assmann. The duct makes it quite easy to wet the bulb. As the modified psychrometer is to be used in a screen, the radiation effect may be negligible.

The bulb is mounted at the center of a glass duct and is ventilated at a constant speed of 4 m/sec by means of a fan driven by a micro-motor in the stand. The ventilation speed is measured with an inclined tube manometer connected through a rubber tube to a small static pressure hole in the wall of a measuring duct made of brass, of the same size and shape as the glass one, which is replaced by the brass one at the time of measuring the ventilation speed, as shown in Fig. 2.

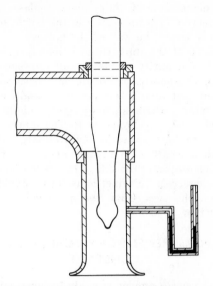

FIG. 2. Apparatus for measuring ventilation speed.

APPARATUS FOR MEASURING PSYCHROMETER CONSTANT

The psychrometric formula for the modified psychrometer may be written in the following form:

$$e = e_w - A(t - t_w) \frac{p}{1000} \qquad (1)$$

where t is the air temperature, t_w the wet-bulb temperature, p the air pressure, e the vapor pressure, e_w the saturation vapor pressure at the temperature t_w, and A the psychrometer constant.

Equation (1) can be rewritten as

$$A = \frac{(e_w - e)}{(t - t_w)} \frac{1000}{p} \qquad (2)$$

A can be found from Eq. (2), provided e is known at the time of reading t, t_w, and p.

In this experiment, e is determined by the gravimetric method, which is considered to be the most accurate at the present time.

Figure 3 shows a schematic diagram of the apparatus used for measuring the psychrometer constant. It consists mainly of a glass bottle B and three drying tubes A_1, A_2, and A_3 in series, and is set in a room with an area of 36 m², in which the diurnal temperature change is quite small.

The bottle is equipped with three cocks C_1, C_2, and C_3, a Geissler's tube G, and an open

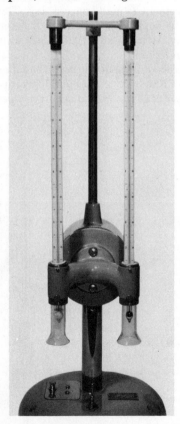

FIG. 1. Modified type of ventilated psychrometer.

oil manometer M. A mercury-in-glass thermometer T_b is suspended in the bottle so as not to touch the wall of the bottle.

Each of the three tubes is loosely packed with a quantity of glass wool impregnated with phosphorus pentoxide as a desiccating agent. The tube D is a dust filter, and I is an air intake, which is placed by the side of the duct of the psychrometer P. The intake and the two ducts are connected to a larger duct with a length of 3 meters, another end of which is open at the side of the room opposite the observer. This duct is useful for avoiding any influences from the presence of the observer.

MEASUREMENT OF PSYCHROMETER CONSTANT

The measurement is made by drawing air into the glass bottle through the three drying tubes and by reading the dry- and wet-bulb temperatures of the psychrometer. First, the bottle is evacuated through the cock C_3 with a rotary vacuum pump, the cocks C_1 and C_2 being closed. The vacuum is checked with Geissler's tube, and the cock C_3 is closed. After more than two hours, the psychrometer is set to work, and the three tubes and the cock C_1 are opened enough to complete the

air drawing in three minutes. The completion of air drawing is checked with the open manometer by opening the cock C_2. After reading the thermometer T_b, the cock C_1 and the three tubes are closed.

Each of the three tubes is weighed separately to tenths of a milligram before and after the run. An increase in the weight of the third tube A_3 is less than 0.5 per cent of the total increase m, and the vapor drawn into the bottle may be negligible.

Now, the vapor pressure e is determined by the following equation:

$$e = \frac{mRT}{V_0 T/T_b + mRT/p} \qquad (3)$$

where T is the absolute temperature of the air, T_b the absolute temperature of the thermometer T_b, R the gas constant of vapor, and V_0 the volume of the bottle, i.e., 11.08 liters.

As the room is not air-conditioned, the day suitable for measurement is selected. The measurement is made once a day. The room has to be kept under lock and key before each drawing. It takes about 2.5 hours to make a measurement.

A series of measurements in a temperature range of 5 to 34°C and a humidity range of 45 to 79 per cent has been made over a period of

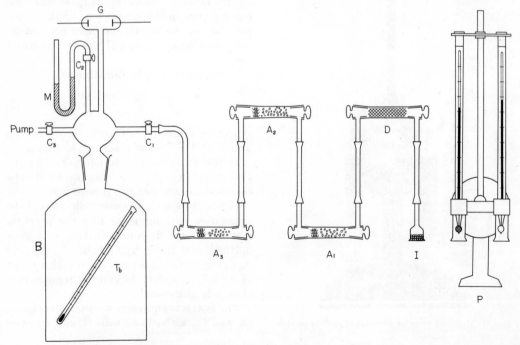

FIG. 3. Schematic diagram of the apparatus for measuring psychrometer constant.

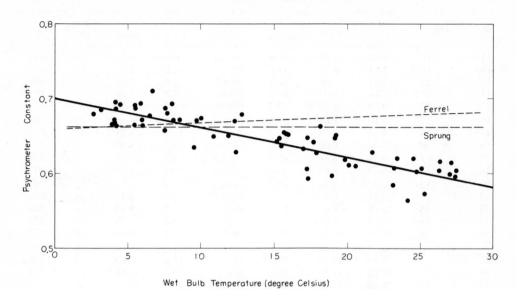

Wet Bulb Temperature (degree Celsius)

FIG. 4. Results of psychrometer constant measurement.

TABLE 1. FREQUENCY DISTRIBUTIONS OF TEMPERATURE AND HUMIDITY OF AIR AT THE TIME OF MEASURING THE PSYCHROMETER CONSTANT

Temperature (°C)	Relative Humidity (per cent)							Total
	45–49	50–54	55–59	60–64	65–69	70–74	75–79	
30–34					5	2	3	10
25–29					4	1		5
20–24		1	4	6	4	2	2	19
15–19			3	2				5
10–14	1	3	5	2				11
5–9	1	1	9	4				15
Total	2	5	21	14	13	5	5	65

TABLE 2. MEASUREMENT OF THE PSYCHROMETER CONSTANT

No.	Date	t (°C)	t_w (°C)	m (mg)	p (mb)	T_b (°C)	e (mb)	RH (%)	A
1	Dec. 21	11.58	7.54	65.3	1021.3	11.8	7.68	56	.657
2	25	11.96	7.73	64.1	1025.9	12.3	7.57	54	.680
3	26	11.99	8.56	75.0	999.1	12.1	8.84	63	.671
4	Jan. 25	9.30	5.50	54.9	998.1	9.4	6.42	54	.688
5	30	9.46	5.88	57.7	1015.5	9.7	6.75	57	.693
6	31	10.79	6.70	58.8	1023.9	11.1	6.90	53	.710
7	Feb. 2	7.85	4.47	51.8	1014.2	8.1	6.03	57	.692
8	6	8.91	4.18	45.0	1023.0	8.9	5.26	46	.695
9	11	7.53	4.22	·51.1	1014.9	7.8	5.94	57	.687
10	13	8.86	5.48	57.0	1010.9	8.9	6.66	59	.690

TABLE 2—*continued*

No.	Date		t (°C)	t_w (°C)	m (mg)	p (mb)	T_b (°C)	e (mb)	RH (%)	A
11		16	6.96	4.18	54.8	1011.5	6.9	6.36	64	.664
12		19	5.84	3.15	50.1	1011.3	6.1	5.79	63	.684
13		20	5.44	2.65	47.3	1019.5	5.6	5.46	61	.679
14		21	7.16	3.96	51.2	1019.9	7.3	5.94	59	.665
15		26	6.99	4.10	53.7	1010.1	7.0	6.23	62	.671
16		27	7.10	4.03	52.2	1019.0	7.3	6.06	59	.668
17	Mar.	5	9.90	6.03	57.5	1023.4	10.1	6.74	55	.664
18		6	9.59	6.00	59.0	1022.9	9.5	6.90	58	.671
19		7	8.94	5.46	56.9	1026.3	9.1	6.64	58	.664
20		13	10.23	6.56	61.1	1025.4	10.3	7.16	57	.677
21		14	10.94	7.61	69.3	1005.5	11.1	8.14	62	.687
22		20	13.94	9.59	77.4	1005.5	13.9	9.17	58	.634
23		25	12.61	8.07	64.5	1004.3	12.7	7.62	52	.693
24		26	13.14	8.15	62.8	1015.9	13.3	7.43	49	.671
25		28	14.36	9.76	76.2	1012.1	14.3	9.04	56	.671
26	Apr.	5	14.17	10.09	80.5	1014.7	14.3	9.55	59	.674
27		7	17.23	12.79	97.8	1018.7	17.3	11.69	59	.678
28		15	16.03	11.87	93.5	1018.7	16.1	11.14	61	.651
29		17	16.59	12.31	95.5	1017.9	16.7	11.39	60	.670
30		24	17.55	12.43	92.9	1024.3	17.8	11.13	56	.628
31		25	15.37	10.92	85.0	1016.3	15.5	10.11	58	.649
32	May	6	20.29	15.19	115.2	1019.3	20.6	13.91	59	.642
33		8	20.66	15.36	115.6	1013.3	21.0	13.97	57	.647
34		12	20.54	15.64	120.4	1005.9	20.8	14.53	60	.655
35		15	22.06	15.81	113.8	1010.5	22.3	13.82	52	.654
36		22	23.46	18.15	141.9	1012.5	23.7	17.25	59	.663
37		28	21.00	15.95	122.6	1003.3	21.0	14.80	59	.653
38		30	21.79	17.27	141.0	1000.3	21.9	17.02	65	.593
39	June	2	21.53	16.98	136.2	1004.1	21.6	16.45	64	.633
40		3	21.82	17.71	145.6	1011.7	22.0	17.58	67	.642
41		4	21.57	17.27	139.6	1018.5	21.8	16.86	66	.648
42		6	20.12	15.46	120.8	1012.2	20.4	14.56	62	.636
43		9	20.89	17.25	145.0	1002.1	21.0	17.46	71	.606
44		11	22.16	17.87	146.9	1005.0	22.4	17.76	67	.627
45		13	24.66	19.22	153.5	1008.3	24.9	18.70	60	.651
46		17	25.40	20.58	174.4	1013.3	25.6	21.25	66	.610
47		30	22.51	19.15	165.5	1006.5	22.6	19.98	73	.648
48	July	1	23.14	20.10	179.3	1007.1	23.3	21.65	76	.611
49		7	24.79	21.74	198.6	1007.3	25.0	24.08	77	.628
50		14	24.80	19.86	165.0	1012.9	25.0	20.08	64	.618
51		15	24.29	18.96	153.7	1008.7	24.5	18.70	62	.597
52		25	30.41	24.51	219.8	1021.1	30.6	27.06	62	.620
53		28	30.43	24.75	225.4	1008.9	30.7	27.75	64	.602
54		29	30.39	25.08	232.3	1009.7	30.7	28.57	66	.606
55	Aug.	1	27.77	23.14	209.9	999.3	27.8	25.63	69	.583
56		6	27.26	23.22	212.9	1010.2	27.4	25.98	72	.607
57		7	31.16	25.32	234.8	1005.0	31.3	28.92	64	.572
58		8	28.06	23.42	211.9	1002.7	28.2	25.92	68	.620
59		10	30.94	26.28	255.4	1008.5	31.0	31.33	70	.604
60		15	29.51	24.18	220.9	1011.0	29.7	27.11	66	.564
61		19	32.73	27.42	270.8	1003.4	32.7	33.35	67	.596
62		20	31.73	27.16	270.1	1006.6	31.7	33.16	71	.615
63		21	32.62	27.04	262.7	1007.1	32.5	32.37	66	.598
64		22	33.82	27.50	265.6	1007.7	33.8	32.86	62	.604
65		27	32.62	26.35	246.0	1013.4	32.8	30.39	62	.617

8 months. The frequency distributions of temperature and humidity are shown in Table 1. The data of 65 measurements are shown in Table 2.

Each psychrometer constant obtained is plotted in Fig. 4; the abscissa is wet-bulb temperature. These 65 points are situated near to a straight line. The line that best fits them is expressed by

$$A = 0.70(1 - 0.0056\, t_w) \qquad (4)$$

which is shown in a full line in Fig. 4. The dotted line in the Figure corresponds to Ferrel's result,[1]

$$A = 0.66(1 + 0.0015 t_w)$$

and the broken line to Sprung's result,[2]

$$A = 0.662$$

CONCLUSION

From the experiments, the psychrometric formula for the modified type of ventilated psychrometer is

$$e = e_w - 0.70(1 - 0.0056t_w)(t - t_w)\,\frac{p}{1000} \qquad (5)$$

where p, e, and e_w are in the same units, and t and t_w are in °C.

There may be a little uncertainty in the results due to errors included in the readings of temperature, but it is noticeable that the psychrometer constant obtained here decreases with the increase of wet-bulb temperature, while Ferrel's constant increases.

References

1. List, R. J., "Smithsonian Meteorological Tables," Washington, D.C., p. 365, 1958.
2. Bongards, H., "Feuchtigkeitsmessung," "Munich and Berlin, R. Oldenburg," p. 166, 1926.

6. The Response of a Psychrometer to Fluctuations in Vapor Pressure

R. J. TAYLOR

C.S.I.R.O. Division of Meteorological Physics, Aspendale, Victoria, Australia

ABSTRACT

Consideration is given to the rate of heat transfer to fine-wire resistance thermometers, and use is made of published data to express this rate in terms of the temperature difference between wire and air and the Reynolds Number based on wire diameter. This work is then extended to include wet wires (as used for wet-bulb temperature measurement), and a transfer coefficient is derived for latent heat in terms of Reynolds Number. The rates of heat transfer are related to rate of change of wire temperature, and time constants τ (sec) are derived for dry-bulb and wet-bulb thermometers. These are:

(1) for platinum dry bulb wires

$$\tau = 5.67 \times 10^3 r^{1.653} u^{-.347}$$

(2) for nickel dry bulb wires

$$\tau = 7.86 \times 10^3 r^{1.653} u^{-.347}$$

(3) for wet-bulb wires

$$\tau = \frac{8.20 \times 10^3}{1.52s + 1} r^{1.653} u^{-.347}$$

where $r(cm)$ is the radius of the wire, $u(cm\ sec^{-1})$ is the wind speed, and $s(mb\ °C^{-1})$ is the slope of the curve of the saturated vapor pressure of water against temperature.

The response of a psychrometer having wet and dry bulb thermometers to time constants τ_1 and τ_2, respectively, is examined, and isopleths of amplitude response and phase angle are presented in terms of $\omega\tau_1$ and $\omega\tau_2$ where ω is 2π times the frequency of a Fourier component of the fluctuating vapor pressure. The outstanding feature of these results is that very

large phase lags (approaching 270 degrees) may occur over certain ranges of $\omega\tau_1$ and $\omega\tau_2$.

The optimum design of a psychrometer, in applications where phase lag is unimportant, requires a value of τ_2/τ_1 ranging from one to about two, depending on the frequency range. When the covariance between vapor pressure and another variable is to be measured, values of this ratio generally in the same range are suitable, but consideration must also be given to the characteristics of the other measuring system.

INTRODUCTION

An important problem in the meteorology of the lowest layers of the atmosphere is the measurement of the vertical turbulent flux of water vapor which under certain (reasonably realistic) conditions is equal to the rate of evaporation from the underlying surface. The most direct method of assessing this flux is in terms of the covariance between specific humidity and vertical velocity component.[8] In practice, fluctuations of total air pressure are not important, and vapor pressure can serve as a measure of specific humidity. A demand therefore arises for an hygrometer which is very rapid in response yet sufficiently robust and reliable for field use. The requirements for accuracy are not exacting; in view of the inherent variability of the atmosphere, it is sufficient to measure vapor pressure fluctuations to within a few per cent.

The only instrument yet used which is suitable is the wet-and-dry-bulb psychrometer. McIlroy[4] has described a type of wire suitable for wet-bulb resistance thermometry. It consists of 0.001-in. diameter platinum wire wound in an open helix around a thin strand of cotton wicking; and McIlroy has found that, if properly cared for, it indicates true wet-bulb temperature with sufficient accuracy. There is, of course, no technical problem in constructing fine-wire dry-bulb resistance thermometers. In the application of a psychrometer, it is of interest to examine its response in terms of the characteristics of the resistance thermometers of which it is composed.

HEAT TRANSFER TO WIRES

Roberts[6] and Fishenden and Saunders[1] present data on the steady-state convection of heat to dry cylinders held transverse to a stream of fluid. (In what follows, transverse air flow will be assumed.) The former of these two references gives the information in the form of a graph from which it is clear that the assumption of forced convection holds good down to a Reynolds Number of 0.1, whereas in the present application, the relevant range of Reynolds Number is approximately 0.5 to 50. Within this range, information has been extracted from the sources quoted and is shown in Fig. 1. There are slight discrepancies between the two sources, and a more complex relationship than a simple power law is not justified. The calculated regression line is shown in Fig. 1 and represents the equation

$$\frac{H}{\varDelta T} = 6.50 \times 10^{-4} Re^{.347} \qquad (1)$$

where H is the rate of heat transport to the wire per unit length (watt cm^{-1}), $\varDelta T$ is the temperature difference (°C) from wire to air and Re is the Reynolds Number based on wire diameter.

To apply this steady-state relationship to the case of fluctuating temperatures, where the thermal boundary layer is continually adjusting itself, requires justification. At these Reynolds Numbers, the thickness of the velocity boundary layer[7] is of the same order of magnitude as the radius r of the wire and, to a sufficient approximation, the same will be true of the thickness of the thermal boundary layer. The time taken for the boundary layer to re-establish itself after a

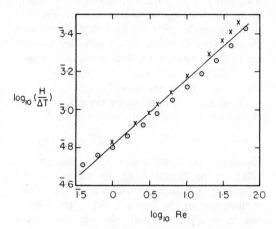

FIG. 1. Heat transfer rate (watt cm^{-1}°C^{-1}) as a function of Reynolds Number: x Fishenden and Saunders;[1] o Roberts.[6]

sudden change in air temperature will thus be of the order r^2/k where k is the thermal diffusivity of the air. For a wire of .001-in. diameter, this time is of the order 10^{-5} second, and the adjustment of the boundary layer is thus very much more rapid than any turbulent fluctuations in temperature which have yet been investigated in the lower atmosphere. The use of Eq. (1) when the air temperature is fluctuating is therefore permissible.

The analysis of heat transfer can now be extended to include wet wires. We take T_D(°C), T_W(°C) and T(°C) respectively as the dry-bulb temperature of the air, wet-bulb temperature of the air and temperature of the wire. When the wire is in equilibrium with the air, $T = T_W$ and the rate at which sensible heat is convected from air to wire due to the temperature difference between them is equal to the rate at which latent heat is extracted by evaporation. Thus, from Eq. (1),

$$\frac{LE}{T_D - T_W} = 6.50 \times 10^{-4} Re^{.347} \qquad (2)$$

where L is the latent heat of evaporation of water (joule g^{-1}) and E is the rate of evaporation per unit length (g $cm^{-1}sec^{-1}$).

The psychrometric equation[5] is experimentally well attested and states:

$$e = e_s(T_W) - \gamma(T_D - T_W) \qquad (3)$$

where e is the vapor pressure (mb); $e_s(T_W)$ the saturated vapor pressure (mb) at temperature

T_W; and $\gamma = p\,c_p/.622L$, p being the pressure of the air (mb), c_p its specific heat at constant pressure (joule g^{-1} °C^{-1}), and .622 the ratio of the densities of water vapor and air. According to the Smithsonian Meteorological Tables, $\gamma = 0.660$ mb °C^{-1} when $p = 1000$ mb, and this value will be accepted here.

From Eqs. (2) and (3) we then have, when the wire is in equilibrium with the air,

$$LE = 6.50 \times 10^{-4} Re^{.347}[e_s(T_W) - e]/\gamma \quad (4)$$

Equation (4) determines the transfer coefficient for latent heat in terms of the difference in vapor pressures at the wire surface and in the free air. When the wire is not in equilibrium with the air, the vapor pressure at its surface will be the saturated vapor pressure at wire temperature and we have

$$LE = 6.50 \times 10^{-4} Re^{.347}[e_s(T) - e]/\gamma \quad (5)$$

It may be noted that Eq. (5) could be deduced from Eq. (1) on the assumption of equality of transfer coefficients for heat and water vapor. The rate at which sensible heat is convected to the wire from the air is

$$H = 6.50 \times 10^{-4} Re^{.347}(T_D - T) \quad (6)$$

and, from Eqs. (3), (5) and (6), the net rate of heat loss by the wire is

$$LE - H = 6.50 \times 10^{-4} Re^{.347}$$
$$\{[e_s(T) - e_s(T_W)]/\gamma + (T - T_W)\} \quad (7)$$

In the atmosphere, we are usually concerned with the response of a wet-bulb thermometer to small fluctuations, of the order one or two degrees, about a mean wet-bulb temperature, $\bar{T}_W$. In this case, we can write

$$e_s(T) - e_s(T_W) = s(T - T_W)$$
where
$$s = (de_s/dT_W)_{\bar{T}_W}$$
and then
$$LE - H = 6.50 \times 10^{-4} Re^{.347}(T - T_W)$$
$$(s + \gamma)/\gamma \quad (8)$$

For convenience, values of s* are given in Table 1.

* Calculated from saturated vapor pressures published by the International Meteorological Organization, Publication No. 62, Lausanne 1949. Aerological Commission.

TABLE 1. VALUES OF $s = (de_s/dT_W)_{\bar{T}_W}$

$\bar{T}_W$(°C)	s(mb °C^{-1})
0	0.45
5	0.61
10	0.82
15	1.09
20	1.45
25	1.89

THERMAL TIME CONSTANTS OF WIRES

Equations (1) and (8) can both be put in the general form

$$H_1 = K\Delta T$$

where H_1 is a net heat transfer rate, equal to H for dry-bulb wires and $LE - H$ for wet-bulb, and ΔT is the appropriate difference in temperature. We also have that

$$H_1 = c\rho dT/dt \quad (10)$$

where c is the specific heat (joule g^{-1} °C^{-1}) of the wire, ρ is its mass per unit length (g cm^{-1}), and t is time. It follows that the response of the wire to a simple step function in ΔT, $\Delta T = \Delta T_0$ at $t = 0$, is given by

$$\Delta T = \Delta T_0 e^{-t/\tau} \quad (11)$$
where
$$\tau = c\rho/K \text{ (sec)} \quad (12)$$

In what follows, τ will be referred to as the "time constant" of the wire.

For dry-bulb wires, the values of c and ρ are readily obtainable from tables of physical constants. For wet-bulb wires, the situation is not so clear, and some measurements were made on a sample of the wire described by McIlroy.[4] The diameter was estimated at 0.010 in. (with an accuracy of about 10 per cent) by comparing it visually, while wet, with measured wires under a binocular microscope. The masses of (cotton + platinum) and water per centimeter were measured as 2.46×10^{-4} and 4.41×10^{-4} gram respectively, and it was estimated that the platinum contributed about 1.7×10^{-4} gram to the former. The mass of a cylinder of water of 0.010-in. diameter is 4.71×10^{-4} g cm^{-1}. In view of the uncertainties in the degree of wetness of the wicking and in the measurement of wire diameter, it is sufficient to consider the wet-bulb wire as composed entirely of water as far as its thermal properties are concerned and to adopt the corresponding value, $4.18 \, \pi r^2$ joule °C^{-1} cm^{-1}, for ρc.

From Eq. (12) we then have

(1) dry-bulb platinum wires

$$\tau = 5.67 \times 10^3 r^{1.653} u^{-.347} \qquad (13a)$$

(2) dry-bulb nickel wires

$$\tau = 7.86 \times 10^3 r^{1.653} u^{-.347} \qquad (13b)$$

(3) wet-bulb wires as described

$$\tau = \frac{8.20 \times 10^3}{1.52s + 1} r^{1.653} u^{-.347} \qquad (13c)$$

Values of τ have been calculated from Eqs. 13a), (13b) and (13c) for a range of diameters) and a wind speed of 100 cm sec^{-1}. These values are shown in Fig. 2. For other wind speeds, $\tau \propto u^{-.347}$.

McIlroy[3] reports some measurements made of the time required for a 90 per cent response

to a step function ($=2.3\tau$) made on wet bulbs of estimated diameter 0.008 in. These have been normalized to $u = 100$ cm sec^{-1} according to Eq. (13c), and the mean resulting τ is shown in Fig. 2. No record of mean wet-bulb temperature was kept during these measurements, which were not all made on the same thermometer nor on the same day. The agreement is as good as can be expected.

THE RESPONSE OF A PSYCHROMETER

If an input $a \cos \omega t$ is applied to a system having a time constant τ, the output is $a \cos (\omega t + \phi)/(1 + \omega^2\tau^2)^{1/2}$ where $\tan \phi = -\omega\tau$.[2] Here $\omega = 2\pi f$ where f is the frequency in cps. In the absence of experimental data on the spectra and cospectra of wet- and dry-bulb temperature fluctuations in the lower atmosphere, some assumption as to their probable nature is necessary before the above

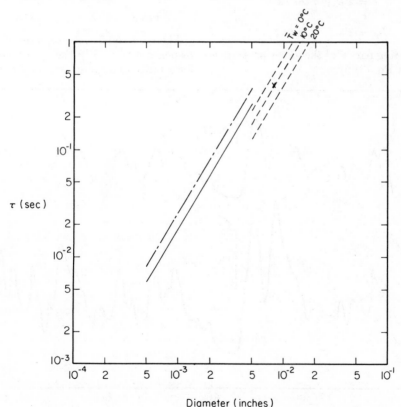

FIG. 2. Time constants of wires at $u = 100$ cm sec^{-1} (for other wind speeds $\tau \propto u^{-.347}$: ——— platinum dry bulb; — · — nickel dry bulb; — — — wet bulb; x Data from McIlroy.[4]

expression for output can be applied to vapor pressure fluctuations.

It is frequently noticed, when using the Assmann psychrometer, that the two temperatures tend to fluctuate together and by roughly equal amounts. There is a tendency for this to happen on a faster time scale, also. Figure 3 shows part of a record of wet- and dry-bulb temperature fluctuations made by McIlroy.[4] The recording galvanometers for both thermometers were of natural period 2.3 seconds and dominated the response so that the effective time constants for the two records may be considered equal. Although this is a selected example, such behavior is not uncommon, and it may not be too unrealistic to consider fluctuations made up of Fourier components which, for a given frequency, have the same amplitude and phase for both temperatures.

Taking, as a typical component

$$T_D = \bar{T}_D + a \cos \omega t$$

and

$$T_W = \bar{T}_W + a \cos \omega t$$

the fluctuating part e' of the vapor pressure is given from Eq. (3) by

$$e' = sa \cos \omega t \qquad (14)$$

and the fluctuating part e'_0 of the psychrometer output is given from Eq. (3) and the formula quoted on p. 79 by

$$e'_0 = \frac{a(s + \gamma)}{(1 + \omega^2 \tau_1^2)^{1/2}} \cos (\omega t + \phi_1) -$$

$$\frac{a\gamma}{(1 + \omega^2 \tau_2^2)^{1/2}} \cos (\omega t + \phi_2) \quad (15)$$

where τ_1 and τ_2 are the time constants of the wet- and dry-bulb thermometers respectively and $\tan \phi_1 = -\omega \tau_1$, $\tan \phi_2 = -\omega \tau_2$. Equation (15) can be put in the form

$$e'_0 = (X^2 + Y^2)^{1/2} \cos (\omega t + \theta) \qquad (16)$$

where

$$X = \frac{a(s + \gamma)}{1 + \omega^2 \tau_1^2} - \frac{a\gamma}{1 + \omega^2 \tau_2^2}$$

$$Y = \frac{a\gamma\omega\tau_2}{1 + \omega^2 \tau_2^2} - \frac{a(s + \gamma)\omega\tau_1}{1 + \omega^2 \tau_1^2}$$

$$\tan \theta = Y/X$$

Figures 4 and 5 show isopleths of amplitude response, $(X^2 + Y^2)^{1/2}/sa$, and phase angle ϕ for a range of $\omega\tau_1$ and $\omega\tau_2$. In the calculation

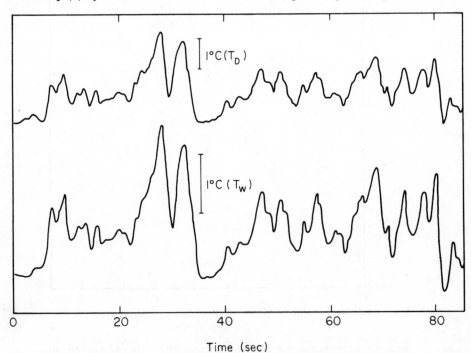

FIG. 3. Record of wet- and dry-bulb temperature fluctuations (8 Mar 55 Run 4).

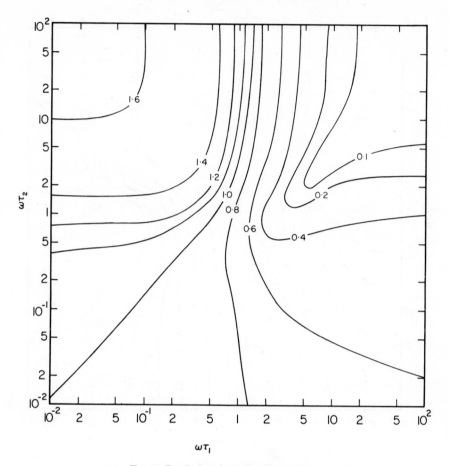

FIG. 4. Isopleths of amplitude response.

of these isopleths, s has been put equal to 1.09 mb °C^{-1}, corresponding to a $\bar{T}_W$ of 15°C. The most noticeable feature is the very large phase lags which may occur at some frequencies when τ_1 and τ_2 are suitably related. This is to be contrasted with the behavior of a psychrometer having wet- and dry-bulb thermometers of the same time constant, in which case the maximum possible phase lag (as $\omega \to \infty$) is 90 degrees.

CONCLUSION

The optimum design of a psychrometer, as far as the response times of its thermometers are concerned, must be considered in relation to the use to which the instrument is to be put. In the investigation of spectral and frequency distributions of vapor pressure fluctuations, phase shifts are not important

and the design criterion to be applied is that the amplitude response should be close to unity. Figure 4 makes it clear that no constant ratio of τ_2 to τ_1 (which would be represented by a line of unit slope in the Figure) can achieve this for all frequencies. However, as $\omega\tau_1$ and $\omega\tau_2$ are reduced, amplitude response of unity is approached by keeping τ_2/τ_1 equal to one. For larger $\omega\tau_1$ and $\omega\tau_2$, a rather larger value of the ratio τ_2/τ_1, ranging up to about two is to be preferred. It is also desirable that $\omega\tau_1$ should not be permitted to exceed about one.

When an evaluation of the covariance of vapor pressure with another variable is desired, it is necessary to ensure that the difference between the phase lags of the outputs of the two measuring systems does not exceed 90 degrees, otherwise the measured fraction of the covariance will be of the wrong

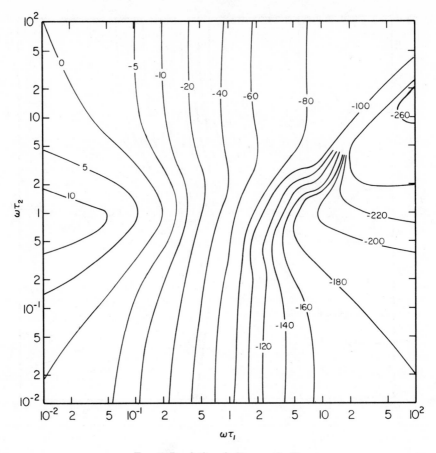

Fɪɢ. 5. Isopleths of phase angle (°).

sign. Values of τ_2/τ_1 between 1 and 2, as proposed in the previous paragraph, avoid this because a psychrometer so designed cannot itself have a lag exceeding 90 degrees (see Fig. 5). The choice of τ_2/τ_1 must be made in consideration of the response characteristics of the other measuring system so as to obtain that combination of amplitude response and relative phase which gives the best approximation to the true covariance.

References

1. Fishenden, M., and Saunders, O. A., "An Introduction to Heat Transfer," Oxford, Clarendon Press, 1950.

2. James, H. N., Nichols, N. B., and Phillips, R. S., "Theory of Servomechanisms", New York, McGraw-Hill Book Co., Inc., 1947.

3. McIlroy, I. C., C.S.I.R.O. Div. Met. Phys., Tech. Pap. No. 3, 1955.

4. McIlroy, I. C., C.S.I.R.O. Div. Met. Phys., Tech. Pap. No. 11, 1961.

5. Middleton, W. E. K., "Meteorological Instruments," Toronto, Toronto University Press, 1943.

6. Roberts, J. K., "Heat and Thermodynamics," London and Glasgow, Blackie & Son Ltd., 1940.

7. Schlichting, H., "Boundary Layer Theory," New York, McGraw-Hill Book Co., Inc., 1955.

8. Swinbank, W. C., C.S.I.R.O. Div. Met. Phys., Tech. Pap. No. 2, 1955.

7. An Integrating Temperature and Humidity Gradient Recorder

B. G. COLLINS

C.S.I.R.O. Division of Meteorological Physics, Aspendale, Victoria, Australia

ABSTRACT

The transportable equipment described in this paper measures, records and integrates vertical atmospheric temperature and humidity gradients over four height intervals between 1 and 16 meters. Miniature aspirated platinum resistance thermometers are used as the wet and dry thermometric elements in DC differential bridge circuits. Temperature differences up to $\pm 2.5°C$ can be recorded with an accuracy for half hour means of better than .05°C.

INTRODUCTION

Studies of the transport of heat and water vapor in the lower layers of the atmosphere which have been in progress in the Division of Meteorological Physics of C.S.I.R.O. have required the measurement of the vertical gradients of temperature and humidity. At the beginning, these gradients were determined using Assmann psychrometers, but a remote recording instrument was necessary, not only on the grounds of convenience but because under field conditions the presence of the observer reading the Assmann could cause sufficient disturbance of the atmospheric conditions to result in errors. The equipment presently described has been developed from earlier systems designed to meet this need.

These earlier systems all used platinum resistance thermometers for dry-bulb gradient measurements and similar thermometers with a moistened cotton sheath for wet-bulb gradients. These were arranged in DC differential bridges, the out of balance signals

from which were amplified by DC amplifiers and fed to a pen recorder. This technique has proved generally satisfactory and, with the replacement of the DC amplifiers and pen recorder by a multipoint potentiometric recorder and some other modifications in the light of experience, it has been retained in the present instrument. Integration and other facilities have, of course, been added.

DESCRIPTION OF THE EQUIPMENT

General

The present equipment was designed to measure, record and integrate, with respect to time, the atmospheric temperature and humidity differences over height intervals of 1 to 2, 2 to 4, 4 to 8 and 8 to 16 meters. Two ranges of temperature difference are provided, 0 to $\pm 1.25°C$ and 0 to $\pm 2.50°C$ (a negative reading indicates lapse and a positive reading, inversion). Reference temperature and humidity, with ranges of 0 to 40 and -20 to $+60°C$ dry and wet bulb, are also measured.

High and low level masts are used with suitable aspiration and water supply, and the whole equipment is transportable, operating from 230-V stabilized mains supply. An immediate photographic record of the integrator readings is obtained from a Polaroid camera.

Masts

It is mainly a matter of convenience that separate masts are used for the low- and high-level measurements. If low-level gradients

FIG. 1. Low-level mast.

steel sections and is raised into position by a winch and gin pole (Fig. 2).

Thermometer Elements and Housings

In earlier equipment it had been found that particularly with large wet-bulb depressions the humidity gradients obtained led to inconsistent results. The discrepancies could be attributed to shortcomings in the design of the wet-bulb element or its housing or to partial failure to maintain the wetness of the sheath. Both these points received attention during the design of the present instrument. In particular, capillary water feed by a cotton wick was given up in favor of a positive pressure supply.

only are required, the smaller mast can be erected manually in a few minutes, but the high-level mast requires considerably longer, since it uses fixed base and guy rope anchors and a winch for raising.

In each case the mast itself, which is of tubular construction, is used as the aspiration duct, and a standard domestic vacuum cleaner withdraws the air. These cleaners have a capacity which is more than adequate to ensure an airflow of 4.0 m/sec in each aspiration housing. In the high-level mast, the vacuum cleaner is placed in a box near the base of the mast but to eliminate interference to the natural airflow around the element housings on the low level mast a flexible aspiration duct allows a vacuum cleaner to be housed in the recorder trolley some 25 yards from the mast.

The low level mast shown in Fig. 1 consists of two duralumin sections and is lifted into position against three pairs of pre-located spring loaded guys. Cross arms which carry the element housings are two meters long and are located and fixed in position by quick acting clamps. The high-level mast has three

FIG. 2. High-level mast.

It is essential, for accuracy, that all the heat required for evaporation of the moisture must come from the air passing over the wet sheath. The extraneous sources of heat which will cause the wet bulb reading to be too high are:

(1) Radiation exchange with the aspiration housing if this is heated by insolation.

(2) Conduction of heat along the thermometer mountings and electrical connections.

(3) The water being fed to the sheath around the wet-bulb element at higher than wet-bulb temperature.

In conditions of large wet-bulb depression the heat carried to the wet bulbs in this way can result in errors in determination of specific humidity of the same order as the differences being obtained.

The aspiration housing finally used was designed to accommodate Degussa "Hart-glas" resistance thermometers 25 mm long and 2 mm diameter. These have a nominal resistance of 100 Ω at 0°C and a fundamental interval of 38.5 Ω (see Fig. 3). The housing is cylindrical, 25 mm in diameter with two resistance thermometers mounted axially on a removable slide, the dry bulb being in front of the wet bulb. Tests, both in the laboratory with a high-intensity light source and in the field in strong sunshine showed that if these housings were rhodium plated and fitted with a white painted external sunshade to prevent radiation falling on any part of them, no difference could be detected between the temperature in the housing and that in the free air using a shaded 46 SWG thermocouple as detector. An inner radiation shield was thus found to be unnecessary. Figure 4 shows the aspiration housing and sunshade.

Heat flow along the mountings is minimized by making them of a material of low thermal conductivity and of small cross section. The water supply to the wet-bulb sheath is carried by a piece of stainless steel hypodermic tubing so arranged that for the major part of its length, it is under an extension of the wet-bulb sheath. Hence, the water is precooled to wet-bulb temperature before it reaches the actual thermometric element. Since, therefore, no extraneous heat is being carried to the wet bulb with the water, no errors will be introduced by oversupply to ensure complete wetness under any conditions of evaporation. The electrical connecting leads are similarly carried under the extension of the wet-bulb sheath to eliminate heat transfer along them. The most satisfactory material for the sheath itself was found to be "Kleenex" paper handkerchief tissue. This gives a very rapid and even distribution of water and, when wet, will cling into position round the element without tying. Even under adverse conditions it does not need renewing more than once daily. The slide and housing are shown in Fig. 5(a), and the slide without the sheath on the wet bulb, in Fig. 5(b).

Two prototype elements developed along these lines were constructed and tested in the laboratory under controlled conditions against a pair of extended scale Assmann psychrometers and against each other. These tests, at wet-bulb depressions up to 12°C, showed that they gave readings which differed from the

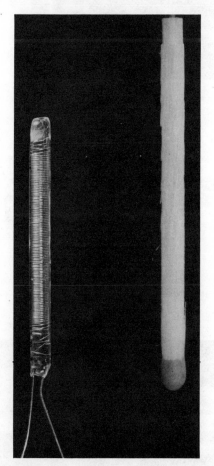

FIG. 3. Degussa "Hartglas" Resistance Thermometer compared in size with a match.

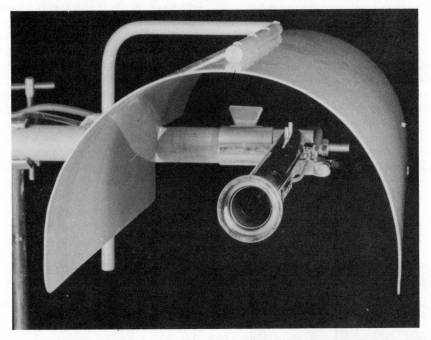

FIG. 4. Aspiration housing and sunshade.

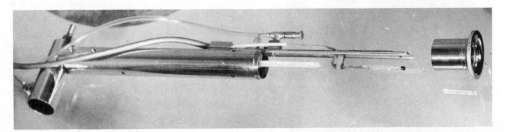

FIG. 5(a). Slide and aspiration housing.

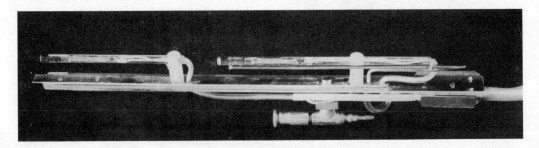

FIG. 5(b). Slide showing waterfeed but without sheath on the wet bulb.

mean Assmann readings only by the same order as the difference between the two Assmanns, i.e., ±0.03°C. Also, the over-supply of water to the stage when the sheath was dripping freely had no effect on the recorded wet-bulb temperatures.

The distilled water supply to the wet-bulb elements is from small "Perspex" header tanks mounted on each mast three feet above the level of the respective element housings and controlled in flow rate by needle valves. These tanks are replenished as necessary by a pneumatically operated water feed up each mast via small-bore copper tubes using containers at ground level which are pressurized by a car tire pump. The header tanks are clamped to the mast on 3-ft arms which can be turned through 90 degrees, such that when the mast is lowered the normal head of water

can still be applied to the wet-bulb elements and the needle valves controlling the flow rate can be adjusted as necessary.

Aspiration is at the rate of 4.0 m/sec. This may be checked by an orifice plate built in to each housing with pressure tappings connected with plastic tubing to a U-tube manometer. Each housing had a throttle valve for adjusting the rate of aspiration so that all housings could be set to have equal aspiration irrespective of their positions on the mast.

Arrangement of Bridges

Three conventional DC Wheatstone bridges are used, for low-level (1 to 4 meters) wet- and dry-bulb gradients, high-level (4 to 16 meters) wet- and dry-bulb gradients, and reference wet- and dry-bulb temperatures. The current supply for them is from large

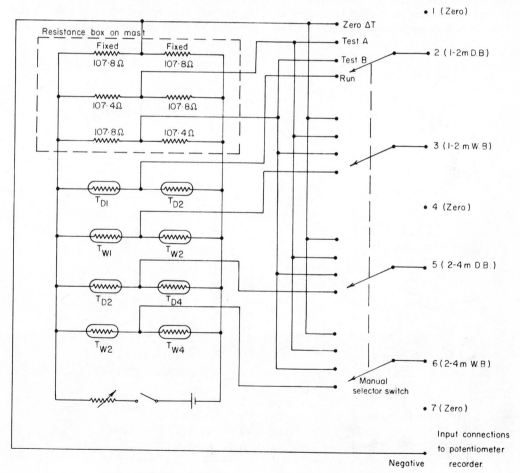

Fig. 6. Low-level temperature gradient bridge circuit diagram.

$1\frac{1}{2}$ V dry cells. The two ratio arms for each
bridge are equal to the resistance of the
Degussa "Hartglas" thermometers at 20°C.
Each bridge also has two other sets of fixed
arms to give a standard deflection in each
direction for test purposes. A four-position
manual switch giving positions "Zero," "Test
A," "Test B," and "Run" is interposed between the bridges and the recorder enabling
the whole system to be checked for correct
operation. A bridge current control is fitted to
compensate for any variation in battery
voltage. (For the circuit of a typical bridge,
see Fig. 6.)

The fixed bridge resistors, which are wound
of minalpha wire and hence have a low
temperature coefficient of resistance as well
as a low thermal EMF against copper, are
sealed into metal boxes with a suitable potting
compound. These boxes are clamped on the
respective masts and connected by multicore
cables to the element housings and to the
recorder mounted on a wheeled trolley which
may be placed up to 25 yards away.

Recorder and Integrator

A 16-channel DC recording potentiometer
with a span of ±0.5 mV and a five-second
printing interval is used. An alternative plug-
in range unit is available giving a span of
±1.0 mV. The integrator has a wheel with
alternate conducting and insulating peripheral
segments, from which pulses are delivered to
suitable high speed electro-magnetic counters
by means of a wiping contact driven by the
recorder slide wire servo motor. The counters
give 100 and 50 counts per millivolt deflection,
respectively, in the two ranges. A suppression
voltage provides a deflection to the extreme
left-hand edge of the chart and is connected to
channels 1, 4, 7, 10, 13, 16 from or to which the
deflections on the remaining ten channels are
integrated. This arrangement automatically
prevents any ambiguity between lapse and

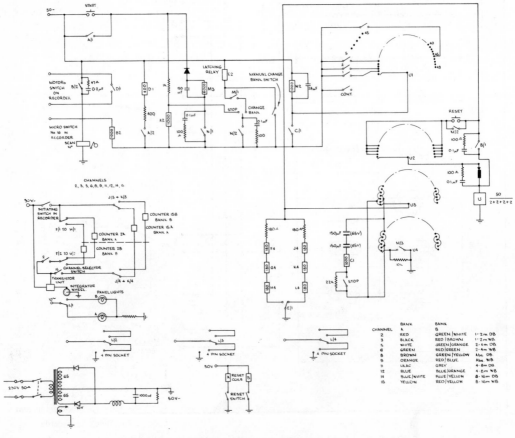

Fig. 7. Circuit diagram of control unit.

inversion integrations. The ten channels available for temperature and humidity gradients are allocated as follows:

Channel 2—1 to 2m dry bulb
3—1 to 2m wet bulb
5—2 to 4m dry bulb
6—2 to 4m wet bulb
8—reference dry bulb
9—reference wet bulb
11—4 to 8m dry bulb
12—4 to 8m wet bulb
14—8 to 16m dry bulb
15—8 to 16m wet bulb

A presetting control unit is provided so that after the recorder has been started it will run for a desired number of complete "scans," a scan being defined as the printing of the full sixteen recording points. At the completion of the pre-selected number of scans the control unit will, according to the position of a switch, either shut the recorder off or allow it to continue recording, the integrated values then being presented on a second bank of counters. Thus the equipment will operate continuously with runs of any desired length from 1 to 45 scans (80 seconds to 1 hour), integrating on the two banks of counters alternately. The readings for any run will then

be preserved until the end of the next run. The control unit circuit diagram is given in Fig. 7.

A Polaroid camera is mounted in front of the integrator unit so that a permanent record of the counter readings may be taken at the end of each run. Time, date and run number are also recorded on the same photograph. Floodlights illuminate the counters for photography at night. Figure 8 is a photograph of the recorder and integrator with the camera in place.

CALIBRATION

Initially a number of Degussa resistance thermometers were carefully calibrated over a range of 0 to 30°C against a substandard mercury-in-glass thermometer. They were then matched in pairs in terms of equality of fundamental interval. The pairs thus selected were used as upper and lower dry or wet thermometers in one height interval. It was found that within a group of eighteen thermometers, the absolute resistances at 15°C varied by less than $\pm 0.1\ \Omega$, and over the range 0 to 30°C, the slope of the calibrations

Fig. 8. Recorder trolley.

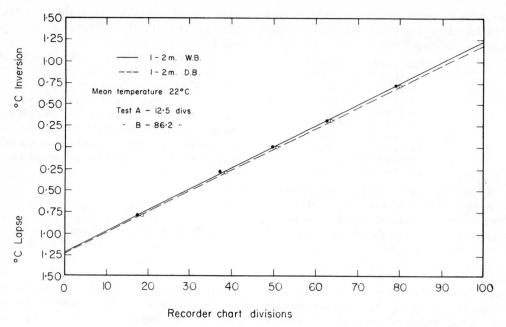

FIG. 9. Calibration graph for 1 to 2 meter interval.

(which were linear) varied within the limits ±1.2 per cent.

The selected pairs of thermometers were then connected to the bridge circuits mounted in their chosen slides and put in a stirred water bath at about 25°C. Small series resistors of "Minalpha" were inserted as trimmers to bring the recorder reading to zero for each pair. Two Dewar flasks were then used as calibrating baths to calibrate each pair against a Beckmann thermometer scaled to 0.01°C for temperature difference. It was convenient to interchange the elements between the two baths to give lapse and inversion readings. A small low-voltage immersion heater was used to alter the bath temperatures as required. The calibrations, of which there were two for each interval at mean temperatures of 20 and 40°C, respectively, were in terms of chart divisions on the recorder, the relationship between chart reading and counts on the integrator being already known. In the case of a small difference between the calibrations at 20 and 40°C, it was sufficient to interpolate for mean temperatures lying between these values. The calibrations obtained were checked at frequent intervals when operating in the field. Typical calibration graphs are shown in Fig.

9. Using the alternative 2-mV range unit in the recorder had the effect of doubling the temperature difference for any given recorder reading, and recalibration was unnecessary, since a temperature difference of ±2.5°F was not sufficient to drive the bridge into the nonlinear region.

The reference dry- and wet-bulb resistance thermometers were calibrated against a mercury-in-glass thermometer in the ordinary way, as no extreme precision was required from these.

Before and after each calibration run the equipment was operated for a short period with the selector switch in the "Test A" and "Test B" positions. The values of these test deflections are then associated with the particular calibration, and on any future check the bridge current control is, if necessary, adjusted to bring Test A and Test B back to these initial readings, thus correcting for any variation in bridge battery voltage.

ACCURACY

The Beckmann thermometer against which the temperature gradient was calibrated is accurate to at least ±0.01°C. The basic accuracy of the potentiometric recorder employed is ± 0.5 per cent of full scale deflection corresponding to $\pm 0.0125°C$ on the more sensitive gradient range. The limit of discrimination of the integrator, however, is twice this (1 count per scan = $0.025°C$). On multiple scan runs, the accuracies of the integrated values read off the high-speed counters will improve with the increasing number of scans.

The precision of measurement of atmospheric quantities which normally vary continuously can only be expressed statistically. For this purpose individual recordings in half-hour scans have been used to calculate the standard error of the mean temperature differences. In unstable conditions for the 4 to

8 meter interval, the standard error of the dry bulb was $0.02°C$ and for the 8 to 16 meter interval, $0.03°C$.

OPERATION

This equipment has been mainly used in field expeditions studying the turbulent transfer of heat and water vapor in the atmosphere near the ground. These expeditions have taken place during the (southern) summer in the northwest of Victoria where high day temperatures and low humidities are common. Under these conditions, the main difficulty in the determination of temperature and humidity gradients has hitherto been in

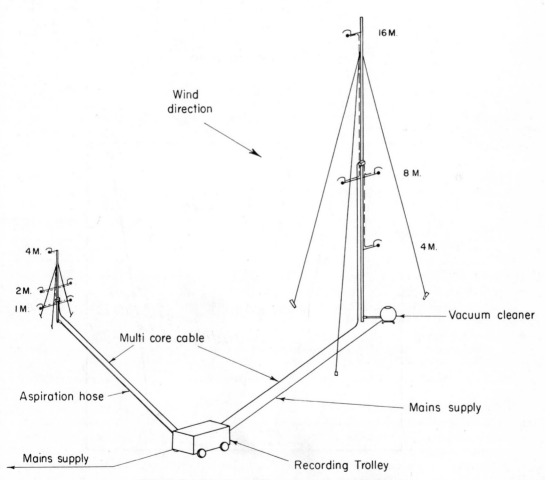

FIG. 10. Temperature gradient measurement: site layout.

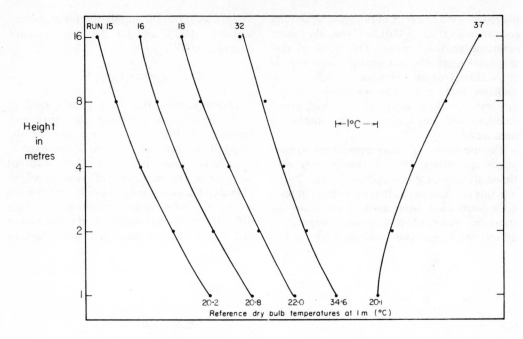

FIG. 11.(a) Typical dry-bulb profiles.

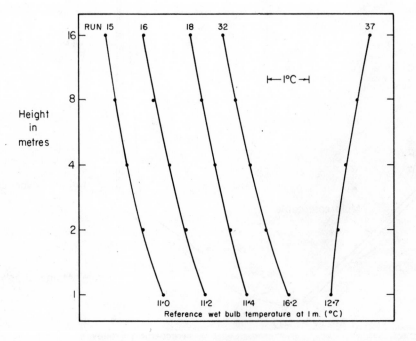

FIG. 11. (b) Typical wet-bulb temperature profile.

keeping the wet-bulb sheaths supplied with water at exactly the same rate as that at which it is evaporating, bearing in mind that this rate will alter from hour to hour through the day. In the instrument described in this paper, the difficulty has been overcome by cooling the water before it reaches the thermometric element since under these conditions oversupply of water will not introduce errors in readings. The rate of supply is therefore adjusted before the high-level mast is erected so as to be slightly in excess of the anticipated highest rate of evaporation for the day. With the low-level mast, of course, the water flow can be adjusted from time to time through the day with no difficulty.

It is essential to prevent direct solar radiation from reaching any part of the aspiration housing. When the sun is low, this is difficult if the wind direction makes it desirable to point the housings towards the sun. In these circumstances, more is to be gained by turning the mast so that all parts of the aspiration housings are shaded than by turning into the wind. Figure 10 shows typical relative positions of the two masts and the recording trolley.

The normal sequence of operations after the erection of the masts, etc., is to run the recorder on the zero position for a few scans to ensure that the electronic amplifier has reached stability and then to switch successively to Test A and Test B to check that these deflections are the same as they were when originally calibrated. This establishes that the calibration is still valid, and the equipment may then be run normally. In the investigations so far carried out, runs of 20 scans have been found most useful, and these take just under 27 minutes to complete.

RESULTS

In the present application the dry- and wet-bulb temperature differences which are obtained at logarithmically spaced heights have been used to build up the temperature and humidity profiles over the interval 1 to 16 meters. Examples of the results obtained are given in Table 1 for 5 runs from the series of about fifty which were taken during the summer of 1962–3 at a selected site at Kerang in northwestern Victoria. Of these, one (No.

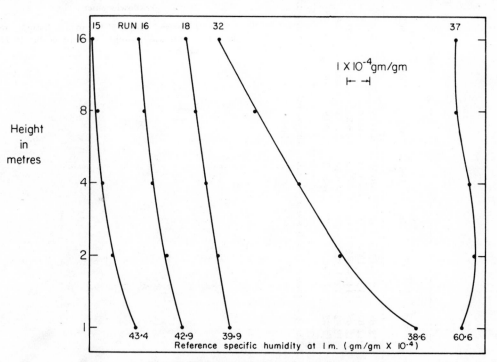

Fig. 12. Typical specific humidity profiles.

TABLE 1*

Date	Time	Run No.	1—2m		2—4m		4—8m		8—16m		Reference		Net RAD (mW cm⁻²)	Wind Speed (m/sec)
			DB	WB	DB	WB	DB	WB	DB	WB	DB	WB		
12/12/62	1210–1240	15	−0.89	−0.47	−0.75	−0.36	−0.59	−0.29	−0.47	−0.23	20.2	11.0	—	3.6
12/12/62	1245–1315	16	−0.93	−0.44	−0.72	−0.38	−0.58	−0.29	−0.43	−0.21	20.8	11.2	55.2	3.5
12/12/62	1408–1438	18	−0.85	−0.39	−0.71	−0.36	−0.65	−0.32	−0.45	−0.24	22.0	11.4	45.6	3.8
16/12/62	1203–1233	32	−0.70	−0.53	−0.54	−0.37	−0.45	−0.35	−0.60	−0.30	34.6	16.2	55.0	5.0
16/12/62	2135–2205	37	+0.32	+0.18	+0.50	+0.18	+0.80	+0.26	+0.82	+0.32	20.1	12.7	—	1.4

* Negative gradients indicate lapse; and positive, inversion; all temperatures are in °C.

37) was taken at night during a temperature inversion, and the remainder were taken in the daytime in lapse conditions. Net radiation and wind speed were also recorded during these runs.

The dry- and wet-bulb profiles are shown in Figs. 11(a) and (b), and the profiles of specific humidity derived from these measured dry- and wet-bulb gradients are given in Fig. 12.

CONCLUSIONS

The transportable field instrument which has been described provides satisfactory records of temperature and humidity gradients from 1 to 16 meters under conditions of high wet-bulb depression and high insolation. While requiring two men for the initial setting up of the two masts and the recording equipment, the subsequent running needs only one operator, and that largely in a supervisory capacity since the operation is semiautomatic, apart from the operation of the Polaroid camera to record the integrator readings.

Acknowledgment

The mechanical design of the masts, fittings, and aspiration and water supply systems is due to Mr. C. J. Sumner.

8. A Proposed Technique for Measuring Relative Humidity at Below Freezing Temperature

C. Ivan Branton

University of Alaska, Alaska Agricultural Experiment Station, Palmer, Alaska

ABSTRACT

The theory and procedure for making dew-point determinations from wet- and dry-bulb readings taken at an elevated temperature are discussed. By passing air through a device consisting of electrical heaters and a fan, air is heated without any change of moisture content. The dew-point is determined from wet- and dry-bulb temperature readings taken at the higher temperature. Relative humidity is calculated from the ratio of vapor pressure corresponding to the dew-point temperature divided by the vapor pressure corresponding to saturated air at the ambient dry-bulb temperature.

Wet-bulb temperature measurements of air near or below the freezing point can be facilitated by making them at an elevated temperature level. Heat added to an air stream raises both the dry-bulb and the wet-bulb readings but does not affect the dew point. The idea of using elevated temperatures to determine the dew point evolved from attempts to obtain wet- and dry-bulb readings with sling and motor aspirated psychrometers when the temperatures were from 32 to −30°F. Many problems were encountered in using the conventional equipment. After wetting the wick of the wet-bulb thermometer, a considerable period of time was required for it to attain equilibrium. When the wet-bulb readings were near 32°F, it was difficult to determine when equilibrium had been reached. At low temperatures, relative humidity changes are large in proportion to the difference between the wet- and dry-bulb readings. In most agricultural research with which the author has been associated, it has been quite satisfactory to know air temperatures to a precision of ±1°F. To make relative humidity determinations of air at temperatures of 32 to −40°F, thermometers need to be read to 0.1°F. Such thermometers are quite expensive and usually have a limited useful range. Some typical wet-bulb depressions to the nearest 0.1°F for the range of −50 to +5°F are included in Table 1. At −40°F and at 30.0-in. barometric pressure, a wet-bulb depression of 0.1°F indicates a relative humidity of 73 per cent, while a depression of 0.2°F indicates a relative humidity of 46 per cent. Actual moisture content in this case is only 0.6 grain per pound of dry air at 73 per cent humidity and 0.4 grain at 46 per cent.

TABLE 1

Dry-bulb Temperature (°F)	Relative Humidity (%)				
	90	70	50	30	10
−50	—	—	0.1	—	—
−45	—	0.1	—	0.2	—
−40	—	0.1	0.2	—	—
−35	—	0.1	0.2	0.3	—
−30	—	0.2	0.3	0.4	—
−25	0.1	0.2	0.4	0.6	0.7
−20	0.1	0.3	0.6	0.8	1.0
−15	0.2	0.4	0.7	1.0	1.3
−10	0.2	0.6	0.9	1.3	1.7
−5	0.2	0.7	1.2	1.6	2.2
0	0.2	0.9	1.5	2.1	2.7
+5	0.4	1.1	1.8	2.6	3.4

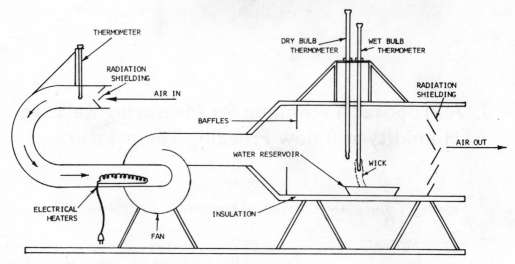

Fig. 1. Schematic arrangement for an elevated temperature motor psychrometer.

Figure 1 is a schematic diagram illustrating an arrangement of components to provide for an elevated temperature wet- and dry-bulb determination. It includes a fan, a source of heat and three thermometers, one of which serves as a wet bulb. Air entering the device passes a thermometer to ascertain the ambient dry-bulb temperature. It is then heated, passing into a fan from which it is blown into an insulated mixing chamber where the elevated wet- and dry-bulb temperatures are read. Thermometers must be shielded from hot or cold radiating surfaces so that they cannot "see" objects at temperatures radically different from that at which the measurement is desired. The air system must be tight to prevent picking up additional moisture. To obtain as uniform an air temperature as possible and minimize stratification, the heating unit is located on the suction side of the fan. This arrangement and the use of baffles facilitate thorough mixing. The size of the air chamber is such that a theoretical velocity of at least 1000 fpm past the thermometers is obtained. The water reservoir is enclosed to eliminate the possibility of adding moisture to the air system.

The heavy line drawn on the psychrometric chart in Fig. 2 illustrates the change which the air undergoes during the heating process. With a dry-bulb temperature at B of +10°F, heat is added and a reading of +52°F dry bulb and 36°F wet bulb is obtained. This is indi-cated as point A. Corresponding dew point is −2°F with a vapor pressure of 0.0344 in. of mercury. Comparing this vapor pressure to that for saturation at +10°F, 0.0631, a resulting relative humidity of 55 per cent is obtained.

Figure 3 shows graphically the difference in wet-bulb depression obtained with a 20°F increase in temperature from that of a direct reading psychrometer. In this situation air is being heated from 32 to 52°F for measurements of wet bulb. The top curve for the elevated temperature condition intersects the 100 per cent humidity line at a wet-bulb depression of 9 degrees, compared to zero depression with the direct reading psychrometer. Advantages of the elevated temperature procedure is to reduce the length of time required for a reading at the relative humidities near the saturation point and to obtain a more readable difference.

Figure 4 is a photograph of the first apparatus constructed to provide an elevated temperature measuring device. The blower unit is a commercial laboratory suction and blower. Two 350-watt heating elements, were placed in the circular brass chamber on the suction side of the fan. An insulated air mixing chamber was placed on the discharge side of the fan. When using this unit, the wet-bulb thermometer was removed to apply water to the wick. The two thermometers for reading the elevated temperatures are gradu-ated from 0 to 130°F in half-degrees. The

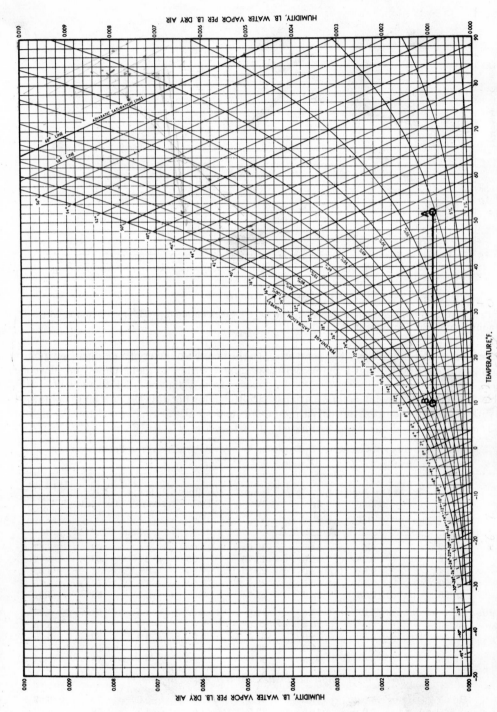

FIG. 2. Heating air at constant moisture—psychrometric chart for 29.92 in. Hg from Zimmerman and Lavine "Industrial Research Services Psychrometric Tables and Charts," 1945.

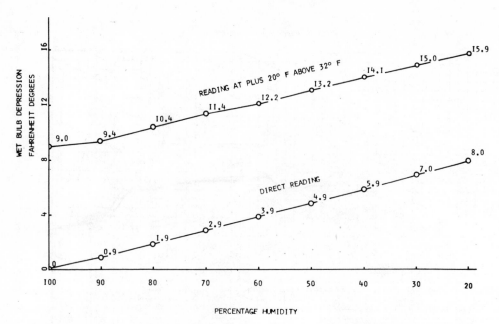

FIG. 3. Wet-bulb depressions for 32°F and 30 in. Hg—conventional psychrometer compared to readings with a 20°F increase in dry bulb.

thermometer used for ambient temperature is graduated from −50 to +50°F in one half-degrees.

Table 2 includes dew-point determinations made with the elevated temperature psychrometer. Temperature readings were estimated to the nearest quarter of a degree. Dew points obtained within an hour period on March 9 varied from a high of +6°F to a low of −2°F. On the following day, the dew points obtained during a similar period varied from a high of 0°F to a low of −4.5°F.

TABLE 2. DEW-POINT MEASUREMENTS USING AN ELEVATED TEMPERATURE PSYCHROMETER (PALMER, ALASKA)*

Date	Time	Dry Bulb Temp. (F°)	Elevated Dry (F°)	Temp. Wet (F°)	Readings Diff. (F°)	Dew Point (F°)	RH Per cent	Humidity (grains per pound dry air)
Mar. 9	09:39	9.5	45.0	32.0	13.0	−1	59	6.23
	09:42	9.25	31.0	23.75	7.25	+2	69	7.17
	10:04	9.5	33.0	25.5	7.50	+6	83	8.62
	10:20	9.25	32.5	25.0	7.50	+4.5	79	8.05
	10:35	9.25	33.0	24.5	8.5	−2	56	5.94
Mar. 10	10:40	4.0	23.5	17.0	6.5	−4.5	64	5.27
	10:43	4.5	26.5	20.0	6.5	−3.5	66	5.53
	10:48	4.5	28.0	21.5	6.5	±0.0	80	6.53
	10:52	5.0	41.0	29.5	11.5	−2.0	70	5.94
	10:55	5.0	41.5	30.0	11.5	±0.0	78	6.53
Effect of 0.5°F Difference in Reading Wet Bulb Temperature								
	10:55	5.0	41.5	30.0	11.5	±0.0	78	6.53
	0.5° (less)	5.0	41.5	29.5	12.0	−5.5	58	5.02
	0.5° (greater)	5.0	41.5	30.5	11.0	+4.0	95	7.86

* Barometric pressures: Mar. 9 = 29.67; Mar. 10 = 29.63.

Fig. 4. Elevated temperature psychrometer.

Fig. 5. A supplemental heater used to extend the range of a thermister psychrometer.

The precision of this method is limited by the closeness to which temperatures can be read. This is also true when using conventional psychrometers. The last three lines of Table 2 show the difference in dew points and absolute moisture contents which result from a half-degree reading error above or below the elevated wet-bulb temperature. Assuming the wet-bulb reading of 30.0°F at 10:55 to be correct, a half-degree reading error changes the dew point by 5.5 degrees and 4.0 degrees when it is, respectively, less than and greater than the indicated value. The moisture content in grains per pound of dry air changes by 1.51 and 1.33 grains with a wet-bulb reading error of 0.5°F less and greater. At lower temperatures the effect is larger. If temperatures can be read to 0.1°F, the elevated temperature psychrometer can be used with reasonable results for dew-point determinations when the outside temperature is −30°F.

Figure 5 is a photograph of a low wattage supplementary heater used to extend the range of a thermister psychrometer. The "control chamber" is partially filled with a saturated salt solution. Over the solution, samples of grain are exposed to obtain equilibrium moisture relationships. By using the heater it was possible to measure humidity at 0°F, although the lowest scale of the instrument was a +10°F. In this instrument the psychrometer has a small built-in fan. The temperature within the chamber was measured with a separate thermocouple which is not shown.

Procedure in using an elevated temperature measuring device is as follows:

(1) Ascertain that the wet bulb is properly saturated.
(2) Start fan and appropriate heater and operate until the three temperatures have attained stability.
(3) Read and record temperatures.
(4) Refer to psychrometric tables and determine the dew-point from the two elevated temperature readings. From tables determine the vapor pressures corresponding to the dew-point and the dry-bulb temperature at saturation. Using a ratio of these vapor pressures determine the relative humidity.

It is hoped that this technique can be useful to those who may be making humidity determinations of air where the wet-bulb temperatures are at 32°F or below.

General References

Marvin, C. F. "Psychrometric Tables," U.S. Weather Bureau, Department of Commerce, No. 235, p. 57, 1941.

Zimmerman, O. T., and Lavine, Irvin, "Industrial Research Service's Psychrometric Tables and Charts," p. 137, 1945.

9. A Thermocouple Recording Psychrometer for Measurement of Relative Humidity in Hot Arid Atmosphere

LEE RICHARDSON

U.S. Army Electronic Research and Development Agency, Fort Huachuca, Arizona

ABSTRACT

A method of obtaining accurate yet automatically recorded psychrometric data in a hot arid atmosphere is described. The technique utilizes dry- and wet-bulb thermocouple sensors with each output recorded on a potentiometer recorder. A unique feature of the system provides for pre-cooling of the water in the wet-bulb wick reservoir to eliminate the error of heat conduction from the reservoir, through the wick, to the wet bulb.

Cooling is accomplished by passing the aspirator air stream flow over the surface of the water in a shallow reservoir. Evaporation from the surface automatically cools the reservoir water to a temperature approaching the wet-bulb temperature. Average cooling of the reservoir water is approximately 70 per cent of the wet-bulb depression.

The level of the water in the reservoir is maintained constant by atmospheric pressure. A one-gallon glass jug "tank" continually supplies the wick reservoir and permits continuous unattended operation for as much as three days under the hottest and driest atmospheric conditions.

Observations were taken with the system at several levels on a 200-ft tower at Gila Bend, Arizona under 110°F ambient temperatures and less than 10 per cent RH. Wet-bulb readings of this system were lower and more nearly correct than those obtained by any other techniques.

Precise measurement of relative humidity in the atmosphere under conditions of high temperatures and low moisture contents such as occur in desert regions in summer is very difficult. This is particularly true if automatic operation and continuous recording of data are desired.

The Meteorology Department of the Electronics Research and Development Activity, Fort Huachuca, Arizona, encountered this problem when a requirement was received to provide humidity and temperature data at Gila Bend, Arizona, in support of field tests in connection with radio wave propagation studies. The temperature and humidity data were to be used in the computation of atmospheric index of refraction, and maximum precision was desired.

After study of the problem and consideration of availability of equipment and the location of the operation site, it was decided to use the measurement of dry- and wet-bulb temperatures for the determination of relative humidity. Copper constantan thermocouples were selected for the temperature sensors with the output recorded on recording potentiometers. One end of the wick on the wet-bulb sensor was immersed in a bottle of distilled water, and the sensor was mounted such that it could be suitably aspirated by means of an electrically driven blower which drew air over the sensor. This system had been described by Bellaire and Anderson[1] and others.[2, 3]

It was soon discovered by comparison of the performance of this system with that of a precision psychrometer that although the dry-bulb temperatures were in agreement, the wet-bulb temperatures recorded by the thermocouple system were always several degrees higher than the wet-bulb temperature indicated by the sling psychrometer. No amount of adjustment of the wick, position of the sensor, or aspiration rate would significantly improve the situation.

Analysis of this performance revealed that heat conducted to the wet-bulb sensor from the water reservoir through the wick was partially counteracting the evaporative cooling of the sensor. The water was essentially at ambient air temperature which might be as high as 110°F, whereas at low humidities the wet-bulb depression might be as much as 40°F. Because one end of the wick was continuously immersed in "hot" water, it was impossible to obtain as low a wet-bulb temperature as that obtained when the wick was wetted and then withdrawn from the water reservoir while the water on the wick evaporated.

One solution to this dilemma was to supply cold water to the wick of the wet-bulb sensor. However, the water could not be colder than the wet-bulb temperature. A temperature control was needed to automatically follow the change in wet-bulb temperature as the moisture content of the air changed and provision had to be made to heat or cool the reservoir water as needed. Further, operational conditions had to be considered; for example, the data were being collected from several positions up to 200 ft above the earth's surface using a tower to support the sensors, so that simplicity of operation was very important. Electromechanical refrigeration with thermostat control appeared to be much too complicated.

To solve this problem the water bottle was replaced by a small shallow water reservoir with a large surface area. The reservoir was temperature insulated around its sides and bottom and was placed in the aspirated air stream so that the flow of the air was directed over the surface of the water. The plastic insulation formed an inner reservoir which was free from the outside shell except at points of support. The air can move around it and past the muslin wicks which extend from the water and over the sides of the inner reservoir. It was found that with this arrangement the reservoir water could be cooled, due to the evaporation from its

Fig. 1. The psychrometer installed for operation.

Fig. 2. Shield and reservoir of the psychrometer.

surface, by about 70 per cent of the wet-bulb depression, even when the wet-bulb temperature was 40°F below the ambient temperature. The wick, therefore, was then supplied with relatively cool water. Since the water was cooled by evaporation, it could not be cooled below the wet-bulb temperature; therefore, the reservoir water temperature automatically followed any fluctuation in wet-bulb temperature without any additional control. The necessary heating and cooling of the water was automatically provided by the air itself.

Figure 1 shows the system installed for operation. The supporting arm is a 6-ft long rectangular tubing approximately $1\frac{1}{2} \times 2$ in. in cross section. A blower is mounted on one end with its intake port connected to the tube. The sensors are mounted on the opposite end in a solar radiation shield. The wick reservoir is mounted just under the shield and is supplied from the one-gallon water jug supported near the tower. A small tube connects the wick reservoir to the water jug. Atmospheric pressure maintains the level of water in the wick reservoir at a constant level as long as the supporting tube is maintained in a horizontal position.

Figure 2 shows the details of the sensor end of the system. The aspiration duct is open between the middle radiation shield plates. The dry-thermocouple temperature sensor is mounted just ahead of this opening. The wet-bulb sensor is mounted just inside the opening. The bottom of the aspiration ducting is

cut away above the wick reservoir so that the water surface is exposed to the air flow.

Figure 3 shows the radiation shield removed. Insulation of the wick reservoir is accomplished by lining the reservoir with $\frac{1}{16}$-in. thick polystyrene.

Tests of this design were made by comparison with wet- and dry-bulb readings from ASTM precision mercury-in-glass thermometers with the wet bulb wetted and aspirated and read at the lowest point with a simultaneous reading taken on the dry bulb, and also with readings taken from a standard sling psychrometer. Comparative readings were made twice a day over a twelve-day period to observe the accuracy and stability of the system with the following results:

	Precision Thermometers	Sling Psychrometer	Thermo couples
Av dry-bulb reading, °F	63.4	64.2	63.4
Av wet-bulb reading, °F	44.7	45.9	44.9
Av RH, %	21.8	24.0	22.4

The largest variance of the thermocouple from the precision measurements at any observation was 3 per cent RH which occurred on days of practically calm wind and rapidly changing humidities (the standard deviation was 1.5 per cent RH). The range of humidity measured was from 13 to 36 per cent in a temperature range of 46 to 75°F. Observations made at higher tempera-

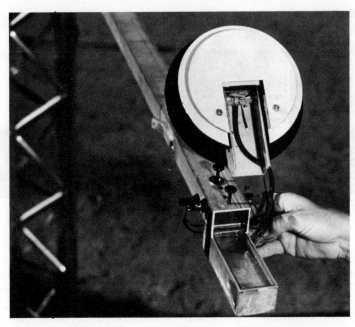

FIG. 3. Shield removed for servicing wick and reservoir.

tures and lower humidity conditions at the radio-meteorology test site following the above observations showed that the carefully aspirated precision thermometers and the thermocouples produced values as closely comparable as the above. The readings from a sling psychrometer were always higher showing that it is impossible to completely shield thermometers from outside radiation while reading the thermometers.

The equipment performed quite satisfactorily and was considered to be a very reliable relative humidity measuring system for summertime desert area use. Continuous unattended operation was obtained for as long as five days without apparent degradation of performance.

References

1. Bellaire, F. R., and Anderson, L. J., "Thermocouple Psychrometer for Field Measurements," *Bull. Am. Meteorol. Soc.*, **32**, No. 6, 217–220 (1951).
2. Holland, J., "A Meteorological Survey of the Oak Ridge Area," AEC Report ORO-99, 1953.
3. Thornthwaite, C. W., and Beenhouwer, Owen, "The Measurement of Humidity Profiles," in "Johns Hopkins University Publications in Climatology," Vol. 7, No. 2, Chap. 3, 1954.

10. Psychrometric Determination of Relative Humidities in Air with Dry-bulb Temperatures Exceeding 212°F

Honeywell Industrial Products Group, Philadelphia, Pennsylvania

ABSTRACT

Since water at a pressure of one atmosphere boils at 212°F, humidity determination at dry-bulb temperatures over this is usually ignored. However, RH can be ascertained through the use of wet-bulb vs dry-bulb comparisons provided wet-bulb temperature does not exceed 212°F and other limiting conditions are kept in mind. Percentage RH is defined by the following equation:

$$\% \ RH = \frac{\textit{partial pressure of moisture in air}}{\textit{saturation vapor pressure of water at same dry-bulb temperature}} \times 100$$

The saturation vapor pressure of water above the boiling point exceeds atmospheric pressure, but since it is used purely as a reference pressure in the above equation, it may be obtained from saturated steam table values for the air dry-bulb temperature. This poses no theoretical or practical difficulty in performing the experiments or interpreting the information obtained. However, in free air the partial pressure of the moisture in the air sample cannot exceed atmospheric pressure, which fixes the upper limit of the RH which is possible at each dry-bulb temperature.

We have performed experiments in our laboratories indicating the feasibility of this measurement to 325°F dry bulb and we have reports on operation to 400°F. The results show that a wet-and-dry-bulb psychrometer is a practical and inexpensive method for determining RH under conditions which render many commercially available elements useless.

It is imperative that all normal conditions for the proper operation of the wet-bulb assembly be observed. Particularly important is the need for a continuous, regulated supply of distilled water being made available to the tube. An air flow of 900 fpm over the wet bulb is preferred.

Many devices now exist for sensing humidity below 140 to 160°F ambient. Psychrometers are used for single and continuous measurements where moderate precision is needed and wet-bulb readings are acceptable. Electric hygrometers of the Dunmore type can be made to read RH directly and are capable of greater precision. However, a problem still exists in the measurement of humidities where the dry-bulb temperatures exceed 212°F. Measurement of atmospheric moisture in environmental chambers, furnace atmospheres, brick kilns and the like is generally neglected because most available equipment is unsuited for the extremes of temperature encountered. Self-heating dew-point sensors can be used for dew points to 160°F and are suitable up to perhaps 250°F ambient without the need for special equipment to cool the atmosphere. This has raised the maximum temperature somewhat, but is still limiting for many applications.

Since water at a pressure of one atmosphere boils at 212°F, humidity determination by the psychrometric method is usually not considered at dry-bulb temperature near or above this value. In actuality, the psychrometer is one of the best-suited devices for measurement in this region. If properly used, the equipment is virtually unaffected by the temperature extremes, and can safely read up to condensation humidity conditions without injury.*

The purposes of this paper are to show that psychrometric measurements are theoretically and practically feasible, to list the limiting conditions, and to present results of laboratory tests on commercial equipment.

Relative humidity in percentage RH is defined by the following equation:

$$\% \text{ RH} = \frac{\text{Partial pressure of moisture in air}}{\text{Saturation vapor pressure of water at same dry-bulb temperature}} \times 100$$

At water temperatures below 212°F, the vapor pressure of water is synonymous with the saturation pressure of water vapor. The saturation vapor pressure of water above 212°F exceeds normal ambient barometric pressure, and saturation pressures or saturation humidities cannot be achieved without providing an increased ambient pressure. In the present case, saturation vapor pressure of water above the boiling point is used as a reference only. We can obtain this value from Saturated Steam Tables covering the air dry-bulb temperatures.

Psychrometric charts are available from various sources for humidities at elevated temperatures. Good examples of these are Industrial Research Service's charts by Zimmerman & Lavine, or those by Carrier Corp., and Midland-Ross. Other companies such as Proctor & Schwartz have developed tables for their own use. Charts based on wet-bulb measurements, such as those based

on Ferrel's work, should be used, rather than charts of adiabatic saturation temperature. As mentioned earlier, psychrometric determination of relative humidity is possible using the tables referenced only at conditions where the total system pressure does not exceed 14.696 psia.*

Calculation of relative humidity using such charts is possible only when the partial pressure of water is less than the ambient pressure, normally. Because water at one atmosphere boils at 212°F, the wet bulb is obviously limited to temperatures below 212°F. This fact poses no theoretical or practical difficulty in performing experiments or interpreting information obtained. However, the boiling point of water fixes the upper limit of the relative humidity which is possible at each dry-bulb temperature. Table 1 illustrates the theoretical maximum RH at various dry-bulb temperatures up to 500°F.

TABLE 1

Dry-bulb Temp. (°F)	Vapor Pressure of Water (psia)	Max. RH that can be Measured at 14.7 psia (%)
212	14.7	100
220	17.2	85.5
230	20.8	70.7
240	25.0	58.8
250	29.8	49.3
260	35.4	41.5
270	41.9	35.1
280	49.2	29.9
290	57.5	25.6
300	67.0	21.9
320	89.6	16.4
340	118.0	12.5
360	153.	9.61
380	196.	7.50
400	247.	5.95
420	308.8	4.76
440	381.6	3.85
460	467.0	3.15
480	566.2	2.60
500	680.8	2.15

We have performed experiments in our laboratories verifying the feasibility of this method to 325°F dry bulb. From the Table, one can see that it is theoretically possible to

* Control of environment chambers near saturation is another good application of the psychrometer. If a dry-bulb-wet-bulb differential controller is set up to maintain a fixed difference, the dry-bulb temperature can be programmed according to various military specification tests, and the relative humidity will remain within narrow limits. The psychrometer is not affected by the high temperatures or by the near-saturation moisture levels. Since conditions near saturation are desired, the dry bulb cannot be programmed much above 200°F.

* Wet-bulb depression is due to a dynamic balance of heat and water diffusion rates. A change in pressure will affect both. Therefore, it is necessary to use conversion tables calculated for ambient pressure when this pressure deviates from standard.

exceed this dry-bulb temperature. The maximum of 325°F was dictated by the capabilities of the chamber which was used rather than by an arbitrary decision on our part. The results obtained verify computations performed. While the accuracies obtainable using this method of measurement in the field may be somewhat less than under optimum lab conditions, it is a practical and inexpensive method for determining RH conditions which render many commercially available elements useless.

In the field, several of our customers have reported worthwhile results at temperatures to 400°F using standard wet- and dry-bulb measuring instruments such as those illustrated in Fig. 1.

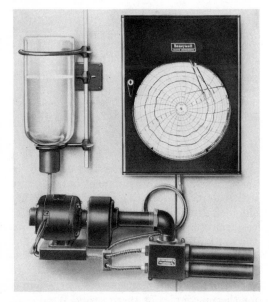

Fig. 1. Industrial dry- and wet-bulb recording psychrometer.

A ceramic tube psychrometer assembly is recommended. No other special equipment is required. All normal conditions for the proper operation of a wet-bulb assembly *must* be observed. Particularly important is the need for a continuous, regulated supply of distilled water to the tube. An air flow of 900 fpm over the wet bulb is preferred.

If the ceramic tube becomes too dry, steam may form within the tube or assembly. Since a pressure greater than the head of the supply water cannot be generated, there is little chance of internal rupture, but the results will be worthless. Good results are possible if the velocity of the air is at, or above, 900 fpm and if the ceramic tube has the capacity to keep a continuous film of water at the surface of the bulb.

Keeping the wet bulb saturated has been the paramount problem in all high-temperature humidity measurements of this sort. An alternate method to the ceramic tube psychrometer assembly is the use of an atomizer spray over the bulb. In this approach, a smooth tube surrounds the bulb in a vertical position and the spray is introduced at the top of this tube. Air flows through the tube to complete the system.

Other conditions significantly affecting the wet-bulb readings are:

(1) Temperature of the water supplied to the wet bulb should be preferably at, or slightly above, wet bulb. Higher water temperatures extend the time required to lower wet-bulb temperatures, so that equilibrium may not be reached. Lower water temperatures cause wet-bulb thermometer temperatures to climb during ventilation, resulting in instability or reducing the observed temperature.

(2) Contamination of the tube assembly, by water hardness salts or by hygroscopic salts in the atmosphere, dust, or other impurities can change the saturation pressure of the water or otherwise reduce the efficacy of the psychrometer assembly.

(3) Radiant heat raises wet-bulb temperatures so that a true depression is not obtained. Stem conduction of heat has a similar effect.

It is of course obvious that the accuracy, sensitivity and relative positions of the two thermometers are important. So also is the experience of personnel taking the readings to read the true wet-bulb temperature correctly, and to recognize when the operating limits are exceeded or the water supply is impaired.

Errors in relative humidity due to uncorrected errors in thermometers have been explored by Wexler and Brombacher in NBS Circular 512. Table 2 illustrates these errors and underlines the importance of good practice in attempting to measure relative humidity by the wet-bulb *vs* dry-bulb method for temperatures below 212°F dry bulb.

TABLE 2. ERROR IN RELATIVE HUMIDITY DUE TO UNCORRECTED ERRORS IN THE THERMOMETERS

(a) *Dry-bulb thermometer reads correctly; wet-bulb thermometer reads 1 deg F low*

Dry-bulb Temperature (°F)	Error in RH (%) at a Wet-bulb Depression of		
	0.1 deg F	1.0 deg F	10 deg F
150	2.6	2.6	2.1
100	3.6	3.5	2.9
75	4.6	4.5	3.7
50	6.7	6.6	5.6
32	10.5	10.3	—

(b) *Dry-bulb thermometer reads 1 deg F high; wet-bulb thermometer correctly*

Dry-bulb Temperature (°F)	Error in RH (%) at a Wet-bulb Depression of		
	0.1 deg F	1.0 deg F	10 deg F
150	2.6	2.5	2.0
100	3.5	3.4	2.6
75	4.5	4.4	3.1
50	6.6	6.4	4.3
32	9.8	9.4	—

(c) *Dry-bulb thermometer reads 1 deg F low; wet-bulb thermometer reads 1 deg F low*

Dry-bulb Temperature (°F)	Error in RH (%) at a Wet-bulb Depression of		
	0.1 deg F	1.0 deg F	10 deg F
150	0.00	0.02	0.11
100	.00	.03	.32
75	.00	.05	.51
50	.00	.11	1.24
32	.02	.26	—

(d) *Dry-bulb thermometer reads 1 deg F high; wet-bulb thermometer reads 1 deg F low*

Dry-bulb Temperature (°F)	Error in RH (%) at a Wet-bulb Depression of		
	0.1 deg F	1.0 deg F	10 deg F
150	5.1	5.0	4.1
100	7.0	6.8	5.4
75	8.9	8.7	6.7
50	13.0	12.7	9.8
32	19.8	19.3	—

In comparison, errors at high temperatures are computed on these levels with dry-bulb temperature 300°F and wet-bulb depression of 100°F in Table 3 as follows. With the dry bulb correct and the wet bulb 1°F high, the error is .36 per cent RH. With the wet bulb 10°F high the error increases to only 3.88 per cent RH. Errors usually appear in this direction as a result of interruption of the water supply to the wet bulb or like interferences. An additional uncertainty of ±2°F in the dry bulb temperature adds only ±.53 per cent RH error when the wet bulb is 1°F high.

TABLE 3. CALCULATION OF ERRORS POSSIBLE IF TRUE READING OF DRY BULB IS 300°F AND TRUE READING OF WET BULB IS 200°F

Dry-bulb Temp. (°F)	Wet-bulb Temp. (°F)	% RH Calculated	% RH Error
300 true reading	200 true reading	17.20 true RH	—
300	201	17.56	+0.36
300	210	21.08	+3.88
302	201	17.04	−0.16
298	201	18.09	+0.89

One of the problems in this system is that the wet bulb will add water to the space. In those cases where measurement is taken in a rather large space, the wet bulb will not significantly add to the moisture content of the atmosphere it is measuring. In other cases the wet bulb can be located in an exhaust line and the problem can be overcome in this manner. A third possible solution is to use very small psychrometer assemblies, such as for thermocouples or thermistors. We do not recommend a wet-bulb system for use in a small confined area.

The accuracy of a psychrometric system under *optimum* conditions including sensors and recorder conditions should approach ±1½ to 2 per cent RH. A partial tabulation of results of the test performed in our laboratories is included to support this contention. (See Table 4.)

It is felt that the determination of relative humidities by the psychrometric method above 212°F is a practical and economical method of approaching a problem area. Possible areas of use are in large environ-

TABLE 4. EXPERIMENTAL DETERMINATION OF EQUILIBRIUM CONDITIONS FOR RELATIVE HUMIDITIES AT TEMPERATURES TO 325°F

Dry-bulb Temp. (F)	D.B. Vapor Pressure (psi)	Wet-bulb Temp. (F)	W.B. Vapor Pressure (psi)	% RH Calculated	% RH Theoretical	% RH Error
200	11.526	172	6.2733	54.42	—	—
275	45.410	172	6.2733	13.81	14	0
300	67.002	172	6.2733	9.36	9.5	−0.14
325	96.167	166	5.4621	5.68	6.8	−1.12

mental chambers or those in which air can be exhausted past the wet bulb. Additional possibilities are in brick kilns, lumber drying kilns, lacquer drying applications and the like. Within the limitations cited above, the psychrometric method of humidity determination for process applications will continue to be useful.

CONCLUSIONS

The psychrometric method can be used for measurement above 212°F provided that the following conditions are observed:

(1) The conditions should not exceed the limits shown in Table 1.

(2) Adequate distilled water at the proper temperature should be supplied to a ceramic tube psychrometer tube assembly.

(3) The wet bulb should be located down-stream from the dry bulb, should be radiation shielded, and stem conduction should be minimized.

(4) Thermometer calibration should be sufficiently accurate for the desired RH accuracy.

(5) Suitable high-temperature psychrometric charts should be used to convert the readings to RH.

General References

1. Zimmerman & Lavine Industrial Research Services, "Psychrometric Tables and Charts," 1945.
2. Wexler, A., and Brombacher, W. G., NBS Circular 512, "Methods of Measuring Humidity and Testing Hygrometers," 1951.
3. Evans, R. C., "High Temperature Evaluation of Wet and Dry Bulb Ceramic Tube Psychrometric Assembly," 1958.
4. Gregory and Rourke, "Hygrometry," 1958.
5. Amdur, E. J., personal communication.

11. Design and Calibration of a Thermocouple Psychrometer which uses the Peltier Effect*

J. E. Box, Jr.

Soil and Water Conservation Research Division,
U.S. Department of Agriculture, Big Spring, Texas

ABSTRACT

A thermocouple psychrometer which utilizes Peltier effect cooling to condense water onto the wet-bulb thermocouple junction has been designed to measure the relative activity of water in the range 1.000 to 0.984 (corresponding to relative humidities of 100 to 98.4 per cent). Repeatability of approximately ± 0.00035 relative activity units for the entire calibrating range was obtained.

Three thermocouple junctions were calibrated over aqueous sulfuric acid solutions of known concentrations at 10, 24.8, and 50°C.

THERMOCOUPLE PSYCHROMETER

There has been concentrated effort by a few researchers to develop a highly accurate method for measuring relative humidities between 100 and 98.5 per cent. Soil physicists have been particularly active in this research because this is the range of availability of soil moisture to plants. Relative humidities of 100 to 98.5 per cent correspond roughly to soil moisture suctions of 0 to 20 bars, and exactly to relative activities of water, a_w, of 1.000 to 0.985. Most agricultural plants permanently wilt and die when soil moisture suctions in the root zone reach values between 15 and 18 bars.

---

* Contribution from Soil and Water Conservation Research Division, Agricultural Research Service, USDA, in cooperation with the Texas Agricultural Experiment Station.

Whereas engineers in the heating and air-conditioning fields use the term relative humidity, soil physicists commonly use the terms relative activity of water and soil moisture suction, expressed in bars. A multiple expression for a soil water system is shown in Eq. (1), which relates the several methods of expressing soil water potential at constant temperature.[8] The influence of gravity or other macroscopic external field is omitted from the equation. The expression is

$$\mu_w - \mu_w^0 = RT \ln p_w/p_w^0 = RT \ln a_w$$
$$= V_w(P - P^0) \quad (1)$$

where $\mu_w - \mu_w^0$ is the soil water potential relative to that of pure free water (j kg^{-1} water), R is the universal gas constant (j kg^{-1} deg^{-1}), T is the absolute temperature (°K), p_w and p_w^0 the water vapor pressure (d cm^{-2}) over the soil and over pure free water, respectively, a_w the relative activity of soil water, V_w is the partial specific volume of water in the soil, and $(P - P^0)$ is the absolute pressure difference (d cm^{-2}) that might exist across a membrane or at different depths in the soil. P is the system's absolute air pressure at which p_w exists and P^0 is the absolute air pressure that must exist in the system to increase its water vapor pressure to p_w^0 or that of pure free water. In this paper P is always less than P^0. In soil moisture studies the last term of Eq. (1) is generally negative and can be thought of as the suction that would have to be placed on pure free water to reduce its absolute activity to that of soil moisture at the same location and temperature. This last term of Eq. (1) is also referred to as soil moisture suction. This is generally analogous to osmotic pressure effects.

Relative humidity is the ratio of the partial pressure of water vapor in the atmosphere to saturation partial pressure at the ambient temperature. The ratio p_w/p_w^0, or a_w, in Eq. (1) multiplied by 100 is the relative humidity expressed as a per cent. Henceforth, in this paper the relative vapor pressure of water will be referred to as the relative activity of water, a_w, or its equivalent in bars of suction pressure (soil moisture suction).

In studying the energy relations of water extraction by plants and water retention by soil, it is desirable to measure the relative activity or soil moisture suction accurately to at least 0.1 bar, and more desirably to 0.01-bar suction. Precision should be sufficient to require only one or two measurements of the same sample. Presently, the most meaningful method of measuring soil moisture suctions accurately over the entire range of soil water availability to plants is the thermocouple psychrometer.[4, 5, 6, 7]

Spanner,[7] Richards and Ogata,[6] Korven and Taylor,[4] and Monteith and Owen[5] have designed and used a thermocouple psychrometer. Thermocouple psychrometer design has taken two basic approaches. Richards and Ogata placed a drop of water on the thermocouple psychrometer "wet" junction and allowed it to equilibrate with the surroundings, while the thermocouple reference junctions remained at ambient temperature. Spanner, Korven and Taylor, and Monteith and Owen utilized the Peltier effect for the condensation of moisture onto the "wet" junction from the ambient atmosphere.

A number of different thermal electromotive force (EMF) effects occur in metals. This research is principally concerned with the Seebeck and Peltier thermal EMF effects and their utilization in a thermocouple psychrometer. In 1821, Seebeck discovered that in a circuit consisting of two dissimilar metals formed into two junctions, a current flow is induced by a temperature difference between the junctions. Current flow is in such a direction as to equalize the temperature discrepancy. The hot junction tends to cool and absorb heat energy from its environment, and

the cold junction tends to warm and liberate heat energy to its environment. In 1834, Peltier discovered that when current flow is induced by a battery in a circuit having two dissimilar metals formed into two junctions, one junction cools and the other junction heats.

The Peltier effect is used in the thermocouple psychrometer of the research being reported to cool one junction (referred to as the Peltier or "wet" junction) below dew-point temperature for the purpose of condensing water out of the ambient atmosphere and onto the Peltier or "wet" junction. (The "wet" junction is dry until after Peltier cooling lowers the "wet" junction temperature below the ambient dew-point temperature.) Immediately after terminating current flow from the battery, the condensate starts evaporating and maintains the "wet" junction at the psychrometric wet-bulb temperature, causing the resultant Seebeck thermal EMF. The Peltier and Seebeck thermal EMF effects are used in the thermocouple psychrometers described by Spanner, Korven and Taylor, and Monteith and Owen.

All of these researchers have experienced difficulty in obtaining sufficient precision with the instrument to permit its use as a dependable laboratory or field device for measuring soil moisture suction over the range of 0 to 20 bars, corresponding to the relative activity range of approximately 1.000 to 0.985. No researcher has attempted to calibrate the Peltier thermocouple psychrometer over the temperature range 10 to 50°C, the range of most intense interest in plant-soil-water relationships.

The objective of this research was to develop a thermocouple psychrometer with sufficient accuracy, precision, and sensitivity, over the temperature range 10 to 50°C to be of use in laboratory studies of plant-soil-water relationships.

EXPERIMENTAL APPARATUS AND PROCEDURE

The experimental apparatus consists of an electrical curcuit for the thermocouple psychrometer and a controlled temperature bath for the bimetallic junction environment tem-

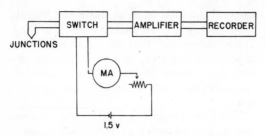

FIG. 1. Block diagram of circuit used with the Peltier junction.

perature control. Figure 1 is a block diagram of the circuit used with the thermocouple psychrometer. Reading from left to right of Fig. 1, there are shown the thermocouple psychrometer junctions, a double-pole double-throw switch, a DC amplifier and a recorder. A side circuit from the switch includes a milliammeter, variable resistor, and 1.5-V battery. The double-pole double-throw switch is used to switch the thermocouple psychrometer junctions from the circuit with the milliammeter to the circuit with the DC amplifier and recorder. (There are three bimetallic junctions in a thermocouple psychrometer: copper-constantan, copper-chromel P, constantan-chromel P, the latter is the Peltier or "wet" junction.) The "wet" junction is cooled below its environment dew-point temperature by switching the thermocouple psychrometer to the milliammeter, the variable resistor, the 1.5-V dry cell battery circuit, and allowing current flow. Current is flowed through the "wet" junction at a predetermined rate, for a predetermined duration, and proper direction to produce Peltier cooling of the "wet" junction. The thermocouple psychrometer is then switched from the current supply to the DC amplifier and recorder portion of the circuit. Evaporation of condensed water from the "wet" junction maintains it at ambient wet-bulb temperature and produces a thermal EMF. The thermal EMF is amplified through the DC amplifier and recorded by the chart recorder.

The DC amplifier is a Model 14 Beckman DC Breaker Amplifier.* Daily drift and noise

* Trade names and company names are included for the benefit of the reader and do not infer any endorsement or preferential treatment of the product listed by the U.S. Department of Agriculture.

in the amplifier is quoted by the manufacturer to be less than 0.005 μV. The double-pole double-throw switch is similar to the one described by Teele and Schuhmann.[10] The milliammeter has a range of 0 to 50 mA.

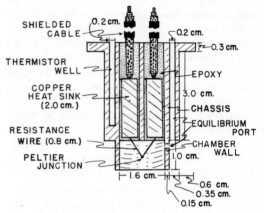

FIG. 2. Apparatus for measuring the relative activity of water, showing the "wet" (Peltier) junction assembly mounted in the chassis.

Figure 2 shows the thermocouple psychrometer designed for measuring relative activity of water or soil moisture suction. The psychrometer consists of a thermocouple junction assembly and chassis. The thermocouple junction assembly and the chassis were constructed separately, then united with an epoxy cement to form the thermocouple psychrometer. The thermocouple junction assembly is composed of the Peltier or "wet" junction (which consists of number 40 B & S gauge chromel P and constantan resistance wires), copper-chromel P and copper-constantan reference junctions, two copper heat sinks, and two shielded "low noise" electrical conductors. The chassis was machined from 5-cm diameter aluminum stock. The chassis has a 0.3-cm thick flange at the top below which a 2.6-cm diameter body extends downward 3 cm. At the chassis base is a chamber with a 1.6-cm i.d. and 0.15-cm wall thickness which houses the Peltier or "wet" junction. Holes were drilled in the chassis to accommodate the two heat sinks, equilibrium air ports, and a thermistor well. Heat sink holes are 0.75 cm in diameter. The equilibrium ports and thermistor well are 0.2 cm in diameter.

The thermocouple junction assembly was constructed by silver soldering a "low noise" electrical conductor into the upper end of each copper heat sink. Low thermal solder was used to solder the chromel P resistance wire into the lower end of one copper heat sink and constantan wire into the lower end of the other copper heat sink. These two resistance wires were then silver soldered together to form the Peltier or "wet" junction so that a 0.8-cm length of wire remained from either copper heat sink to the silver-soldered junction. The "wet" junction was examined under a binocular microscope for soldering flux. Remaining flux was removed by "teasing" it with a needle and boiling the "wet" junction in distilled water. The thermocouple junction assembly was then insulated with clear epoxy resin; the resin was allowed to dry, and the assembly was positioned in the chassis as shown in Fig. 2. Shieldings on the "low noise" wire leads were grounded to the chassis, and the cavities around the heat sinks were filled with clear epoxy resin. After assembling the thermocouple psychrometer, connecting its electrical conductors to the double-pole double-throw switch (the switch to the DC amplifier's shielded conductor) and washing the "wet" junction again, the apparatus was ready for use. Low thermal solder was used to connect the thermocouple psychrometer's electrical conductors and DC amplifier electrical conductors to the double-pole double-throw switch.

TABLE 1. THE RELATIVE ACTIVITY OF WATER IN SULFURIC ACID SOLUTIONS*

$m(H_2SO_4)$	0°C	25°C	40°C	60°C
0.0005	0.99998	0.99998	0.99998	0.99998
0.01	0.99959	0.99960	0.99961	0.99962
0.05	0.99809	0.99819	0.99822	0.99823
0.1	0.99620	0.9964	0.9964	0.9964
0.5	0.9817	0.9821	0.9822	0.9823

* Harned, H. S., and Owen, B. B., "The Physical Chemistry of Electrolytic Solutions," 2nd ed., pp. 435–438, New York, Reinhold Publishing Co., 1950.

Aqueous sulfuric acid solutions were used to calibrate the thermocouple psychrometer. Table 1, taken from Harned and Owen,[3] gives the relative activity of water in sulfuric acid solutions at 0, 25, 40, and 60°C for sulfuric acid concentrations of 0.0005, 0.01, 0.05, 0.1, and 0.5 molal. Calibrating solutions were titrated with sodium carbonate, as described by the Association of Official Agricultural Chemists.[1]

The apparatus was calibrated by inserting the body and chamber of the thermocouple psychrometer into a stainless steel vial containing the calibrating solution. The inside of the chassis chamber was lined with filter paper to hasten equilibrium of water vapor pressure in the chassis chamber. The filter paper extended down into the calibrating solution. The stainless steel vial with the thermocouple psychrometer was then inserted into the aluminum heat flux modulator shown in Fig. 3. The modulator was machined from 5-cm diameter aluminum stock. A large well 4.8 cm in diameter and 5 cm deep was bored in the upper end of the heat flux modulator. At the bottom of the large well, a well 2.5 cm in diameter and approximately 10 cm deep was bored. The stainless steel vial fitted snugly in this well.

The aluminum heat flux modulator with the thermocouple psychrometer and stainless steel vial containing the calibrating solution was mounted in a controlled temperature

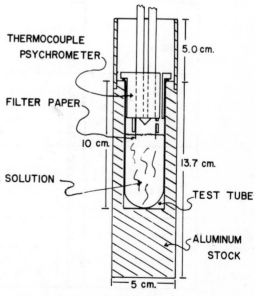

FIG. 3. Aluminum heat flux modulator containing chassis assembly and vial for calibrating solution.

bath. The bath controlled the temperature to
±0.0005°C.

The thermocouple psychrometer was ready
for calibration when it and the solution
reached a stable temperature equilibrium
condition with the bath, usually after 4 to 5
hours.

Before the thermocouple psychrometer
could be calibrated, the influence of current
flow rate, current flow duration, and environment temperature effects on thermocouple EMF output characteristics had to be
ascertained. The thermal EMF output characteristics of the thermocouple psychrometer
were evaluated for cooling currents of 5, 10,
15, and 20 mA; current flow durations of 15,
30, 60, and 120 seconds; environment temperatures of 10, 24.8, and 50°C; and relative
activities of water corresponding to approximately 0 to 21 bars suction. These results
were analyzed, and an optimum current flow
rate and flow duration were selected for use in
calibrating the apparatus over the temperature range 10 to 50°C, and relative activities
of water range 1.000 to 0.984, or approximately 0 to 21 bars suction at 25°C. Once the
optimum current flow rate and duration were
selected, the thermocouple psychrometer was
calibrated.

EXPERIMENTAL RESULTS

The results demonstrate the influence of
cooling current flow rate and current flow
duration, temperature, and relative activity
of water between 1.000 and 0.984 on thermal
EMF output of the thermocouple psychrometer (Figs. 4, 5, and 6). Figure 4 shows the
influence of cooling current flow rate on
thermocouple psychrometer EMF characteristics at 24.8°C and approximately 20 bars
suction. Neither 5 nor 10 mA flowing through
the "wet" junction for 60 seconds produces a
curve which is sufficiently flat at its maximum
equilibrium amplitude to be easily readable.
Under the same conditions, 15 mA for 60
seconds and 20 mA for 60 seconds produce a
curve which is flat for a sufficient time to be
readable. On comparing the 20 mA curve with
the 15 mA curve, one notes, however, that
the increase in the current flow rate from 15
to 20 mA caused a reduction in the equilibrium amplitude of the 20-mA curve. These
data indicate that the 15-mA flow rate is near
optimum for these conditions.

Figure 5 depicts the influence of duration
of cooling current flow on thermocouple
psychrometer EMF characteristics at 24.8°C,
approximately 20 bars suction, and 15 mA of

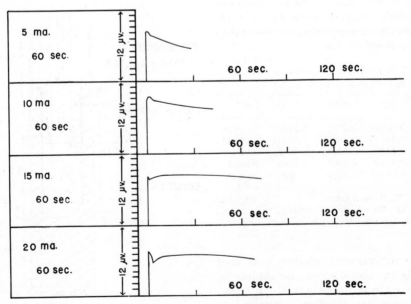

Fig. 4. The influence of current flow rate on thermocouple psychrometer EMF
characteristics at 24.8°C and 20 bars suction.

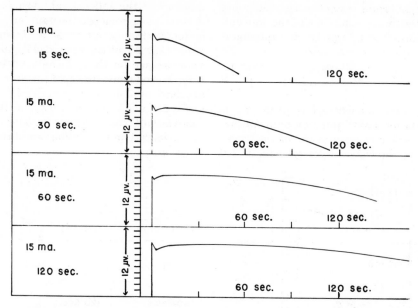

Fig. 5. The influence of duration of current flow on thermocouple psychrometer EMF characteristics at 24.8°C and 20 bars suction.

current. Durations of current flow tested were 15, 30, 60, and 120 seconds. Figure 5 indicates that 15 or 30 seconds of current flow at 15 mA did not produce a sufficiently flat curve of maximum amplitude to be useful in the calibration of the thermocouple psychrometer. Sixty- and 120-second current flow durations both produced equally desirable curves. From the standpoint of mechanics of time involved, a flow of 15 mA for 60 seconds through the "wet" junction was selected as the best for the Peltier cooling current flow rate duration combination for thermocouple psychrometer calibration.

Figure 6 depicts the temperature influence on thermocouple psychrometer EMF characteristics for a solution of approximately 18 bars suction. A 15 mA flow for 60 seconds was used at 10, 24.8, and 50°C. In general, increasing temperature increased the amplitude of the curves and decreased the sharp peak observed in the curve during the first few seconds of electrical output from the thermocouple psychrometer.

Figures 7, 8, and 9 show calibration curves for three thermocouple psychrometers at three temperatures, 10, 24.8, and 50°C. Thermal EMF's in microvolts, μV, for each thermocouple psychrometer are shown as a function of calibrating solution suctions. As the temperature of the system descreased, the microvolt output for any particular calibrating solution decreased.

Temperature depression (ΔT) to the dew-point temperature for condensation on the "wet" junction as a function of bars suction and ambient temperature has been calculated from chemical thermodynamic theory and is shown in Fig. 10. Theoretical calculations are based on the Clausius-Clapeyron equation and the latent heat of vaporization of water at 10, 25, and 50°C. Values for the relative vapor pressure or relative activity of water corresponding to 1, 5, 10, 15, and 20 bars suction were used.[9] The Clausius-Clapeyron equation is

$$\ln p_w/p_w^0 = -\frac{\Delta H_v}{R}\left[\frac{1}{T_2} - \frac{1}{T_1}\right] \qquad (2)$$

where p_w is the equilibrium vapor pressure of water at 1, 5, 10, 15, or 20 bars suction, p_w^0 the vapor pressure of pure free water, ΔH_v the latent heat of vaporization of water, R the universal gas constant, T_1 and T_2 are the ambient temperature of the system and the dew-point temperature of the "wet" junction, respectively, in degrees Kelvin.

The equilibrium temperature difference between the "wet" junction and the ambient, ΔT_{wj}, as described by the Arnold equation is

$$T_1 - T_{wj} = \frac{p_{wj} - p_w}{AP} \qquad (3)$$

where T_1 is the ambient temperature, T_{wj} is the equilibrium "wet" junction temperature, p_{wj} is the water vapor pressure of the "wet" junction, p_w the water vapor pressure of soil moisture or the aqueous calibrating solution, A is the psychrometric constant, and P is the system's absolute air pressure. It should be noted that ΔT of Eq. (2) and ΔT_{wj} of Eq. (3) are not equal for the same ambient temperature, T_1, soil moisture vapor pressure, p_w, and absolute system pressure, P. ΔT will be about 2 times larger than ΔT_{wj} at 10°C, 1½ times at 25°C, and 1¼ times at 50°C, depending somewhat on ventilation rate of the "wet" junction.

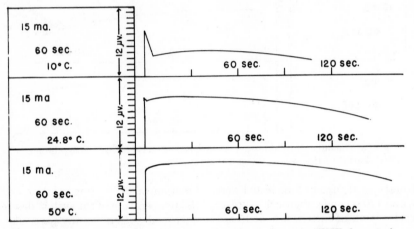

FIG. 6. Temperature influence on thermocouple psychrometer EMF characteristics for a solution of 18 bars suction.

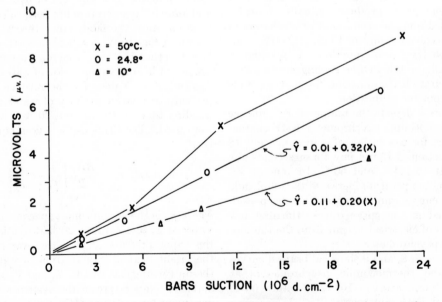

FIG. 7. Calibration curves for the "wet" (Peltier) junction, showing microvolt output as a function of bars suction at three temperatures, Unit 1.

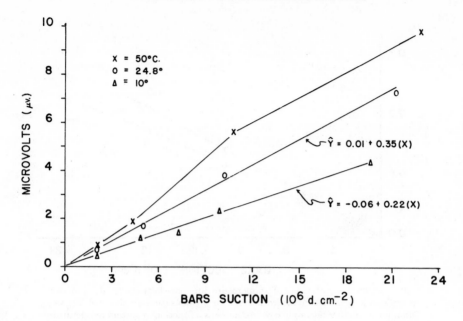

FIG. 8. Calibration curves for the "wet" (Peltier) junction, showing microvolt output as a function of bars suction at three temperatures, Unit 2.

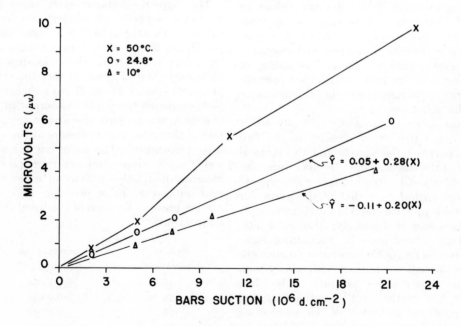

FIG. 9. Calibration curves for the "wet" (Peltier) junction, showing microvolt output as a function of bars suction at three temperatures, Unit. 3

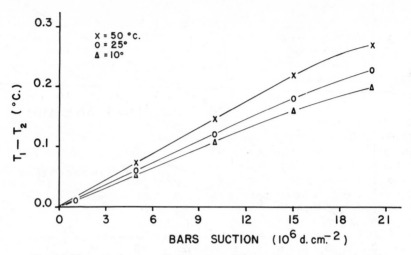

FIG. 10. Theoretical curves of temperature difference between the dry junction and the dew point temperature needed for condensation on the (Peltier) wet junction of the thermocouple psychrometer as a function of system temperature and bars suction.

Discussion of Results

Success with the thermocouple psychrometer depends upon an adequate system of temperature control, instrumentation with sufficient accuracy and precision for measuring thermocouple EMF, a clean Peltier or "wet" junction, elimination of spurious thermal EMF's from the electrical circuit, adequate electrical insulation and shielding, and good technique. An understanding of apparatus design and water vapor pressure theory is advantageous in thermocouple psychrometer use.

Temperature fluctuations critically affect both the water vapor pressure in the free atmosphere of the sample and the thermal EMF of the thermocouple. Temperature control of the water vapor in the free atmosphere is more critical than that of the particular bimetallic junctions used in the thermocouple psychrometer of this study. Also, good temperature control must be maintained sufficiently long for the thermocouple junctions to reach thermal equilibrium with the system, for the water vapor pressure in the free atmosphere of the "wet" junction chamber to equilibrate with that of the solution or sample, and for the measurement to be made.

The constantan and chromel P bimetallic junction used in the thermocouple psychro-

meter in this study has an EMF output of approximately 64 μV °C^{-1} at 25°C. Therefore, to calibrate this particular bimetallic junction to 0.1 μV the temperature must be controlled within $\pm$0.0009°C.

The thermal effects on water vapor pressure in a saturated atmosphere can be calculated. Calculations have been made for 10, 20, 25, 30, 40, and 50°C. This has been done by taking data from the "Handbook of Chemistry and Physics"[2] for the vapor pressure of water at the above temperatures and comparing the vapor pressure with that of a temperature one degree higher, to get the rate of change of vapor pressure at the specified temperature. The following gives the water vapor temperature control required to measure the relative activity of water vapor near saturation to a precision of 0.1-bar suction pressure for each of the listed system temperatures:

System Temperature (°C)	Temperature Control Required (°C)
10	$\pm$0.00054
20	$\pm$0.00059
25	$\pm$0.00061
30	$\pm$0.00064
40	$\pm$0.00070
50	$\pm$0.00074

From the above, it can be seen that temperature fluctuations must be controlled to within $\pm 0.0005°C$ to measure the suction pressure of an aqueous sulfuric acid solution approaching saturation water vapor pressure to 0.1 bar at 10°C and to $\pm .0007°C$ at 50°C.

No sufficiently precise reference was available to determine the absolute bath temperature. However, the bath was returned to within $\pm 0.005°C$ of the same temperature for each calibration temperature by use of a thermistor and wheatstone bridge circuit. It can be seen in Table 1 that for a 0.005 molal solution change in temperature from 0 to 60°C, did not alter the relative activity of water: while, for the 0.5 molal solution changing temperature from 0 to 60°C altered the relative activity by 0.0006 activity units. Therefore, at the highest concentration, a change in 1°C altered the relative activity by 0.00001 relative activity units. Return to the same absolute temperature within $\pm 0.005°C$ was satisfactory for the calibration done in this study as long as fluctuations in the temperature of the sample air relative to the calibrating solution did not exceed $\pm 0.0005°C$.

There were two objectives in the particular design of the apparatus shown in Fig. 2. The first objective was to design a unit that would permit the thermocouple junctions to reach rapid thermal equilibrium with the constant temperature bath. The second objective was to provide an isolated chamber for measuring the relative activity of water vapor. The first objective was accomplished by building an aluminum chassis for the apparatus. Thermal equilibration of the thermocouple junctions was facilitated by soldering one end of each thermocouple resistance wires into large copper heat sinks. The purpose of these large copper heat sinks is to dissipate the heat energy liberated at the copper-constantan and copper-chromel P junctions when current is flowed through them and the Peltier or "wet" junction. The heat energy liberated at these two reference junctions is first dissipated into the copper heat sinks and then secondarily dissipated into the aluminum chassis. It is also necessary to dissipate any heat flux being conducted to or from the surroundings through the "low noise" shielded cable. This heat energy is also dissipated by the copper heat sinks installed in the aluminum chassis.

By this design, it was possible to prevent spurious thermal EMF's at the junctions between the "low noise" shielded cable and the copper heat sinks, and the junctions between the copper heat sinks and the constantan or chromel P resistance wires.

The vapor pressure chamber served as an equilibrium chamber for the water vapor pressure and also as an electrical and thermal shielding from the surrounding environment. This chamber was lined with a plastic that was not attacked by sulfuric acid. In turn, the plastic lined chamber was fitted with a strip of filter paper that extended down into the aqueous sulfuric acid solution. The filter paper facilitated equilibrium between the chamber atmosphere and the aqueous sulfuric acid solution. It should be noted that the air port in the chamber wall must be open and a hole must be punched through the filter paper so that the atmospheric pressure in the chamber is constant and equal to that of the surrounding environment. Failure to have equilibrium atmospheric pressure conditions at all times results in erroneous relative water activity measurements.

The purpose of the "low noise" wire, low thermal solder, all copper and shielded circuit was to eliminate spurious thermal EMF's. For this particular apparatus and conditions of measurement, spurious thermal EMF's were reduced effectively to less than $\pm .015 \mu V$.

The EMF output of the thermocouple psychrometer is a function of the temperature difference between the equilibrium ambient temperature of the system and the wet-bulb temperature of the Peltier or "wet" junction, ΔT_{wj}, and of the EMF output characteristics of the particular materials from which the bimetallic junction is constructed. Thermodynamic theory predicts that as suction pressure increases (relative water activity decreases), the difference between the ambient and wet-bulb temperature increases. Experimental results and theory are in general agreement. It is also noted that as the ambient or system temperature increases, the temperature difference, ΔT_{wj}, also increases because the evaporation rate increases, transferring greater latent heat of water vaporization. It is concluded that the thermocouple psychrometer must be calibrated over the temperature ranges for which it is to be used.

Statistical analyses have been made for each of the three units for the 10 and 24.8°C curves. The nature of the 50°C curves are not understood at this time; therefore, no analyses were made for the 50°C curves. Regression equations are shown adjacent to the 10 and 24.8°C curves in Figs. 7, 8, and 9. Deviations from regression for the 10°C curves in Figs. 7, 8, and 9 are 0.08, 0.14, and 0.13, respectively. Deviations from regression for the 24.8°C curves in Figs. 7, 8, and 9 are 0.21, 0.23, and 0.20 respectively. All individual data points shown in Figs. 7, 8, and 9 reproduced in duplicate to less than ± 0.015 μV or less than 0.1 bar suction.

The discrepancy between precision obtained for individual solutions and that obtained for the regression lines of Figs. 7, 8, and 9 is possibly due to a lack of accuracy in the calibrating solutions. It is not presently known what exact effect the partial pressure of the sulfuric acid in the ambient "wet" junction atmosphere had on calibration of the thermocouple psychrometer. The "wet" junctions were thoroughly washed with distilled water each day they were used. It is presently felt that this is not a serious problem since a water film remains on the "wet" junction for a relatively short period of time, generally less than four minutes. As the molality of the sulfuric acid solution decreased, the length of time the water film stayed on the junction increased. Solutions used in this study were approximately 0.4 molal and less. However, further studies are necessary to compare the use of sulfuric acid solutions with other solutions for calibrating purposes. Absorption of carbon dioxide from the atmosphere by the calibrating solution is another possible source of calibration error.

Comparing the thermocouple psychrometer reported in this research with those of Spanner,[7] Richards and Ogata,[6] Korven and Taylor,[4] and Monteith and Owen,[5] it was found that the instrument reported here has a shorter equilibrium time, is calibrated over a wider temperature range, is more sturdily constructed, is potentially more versatile, and that heat generated from current flow through the reference junctions was more quickly dissipated. Specifically, the thermocouple psychrometer reported here has better accuracy and precision than reported by Spanner,[7] Korven and Taylor,[4] and Monteith and Owen.[5] It takes approximately two minutes to make a measurement instead of ten to thirty minutes and does not require a water drop of critical size on the "wet" junction, as does the Richard's instrument. This instrument has the potential of being used in circumstances not permitting the replenishment of the water drop, or where the drop would be dislodged from the "wet" junction by being jarred or shaken. However, it does not presently have the overall accuracy reported for the Richard's instrument.

SUMMARY AND CONCLUSIONS

A thermocouple psychrometer has been developed which employs the Peltier effect for cooling the psychrometer "wet" junction to the dew-point temperature. The apparatus has proved satisfactory for measuring the relative activity of water between 1.000 and 0.984 with a repeatability of ± 0.00035 relative activity units for the entire range.

The apparatus was calibrated using aqueous sulfuric acid solutions of known concentrations. It was found that as the system temperature increased from 10 to 50°C the calibration characteristics of the apparatus changed. Therefore, it is necessary to calibrate the apparatus for the temperature and relative water activity range over which it is to be used. The experimental results and theory for calibration curve characteristics for the relative water activity and temperature range studied were found to be in general agreement. The apparatus is presently a laboratory instrument.

References

1. Association of Official Agricultural Chemists, "Official Methods of Analysis," 7th ed., pp. 863–864, Washington, D.C., 1940.
2. "Handbook of Chemistry and Physics," 10th ed., pp., 1458–1461, New York, McGraw-Hill Book Co., Inc., 1961.
3. Harned, H. S., and Owen, B. B., "The Physical Chemistry of Electrolytic Solutions," 2nd ed., pp., 435–438, New York, Reinhold Publishing Co., 1950.

4. Korven, H. C., and Taylor, S. A., "The Peltier Effect and Its Use for Determining Relative Activity of Soil Water," *Can. J. Soil Sci.*, **39**, 76–85 (1959).

5. Monteith, J. L., and Owen, P. C., "A Thermocouple Method for Measuring Relative Humidity in the Range of 95–100%," *J. Sci. Instr.*, **34**, 443–446 (1958).

6. Richards, L. A., and Ogata, Gen, "A Thermocouple for Vapor Pressure Measurement in Biological and Soil Systems at High Humidity," *Science*, **128**, 1089–1090 (1958).

7. Spanner, D. C., "The Peltier Effect and Its Use in the Measurement of Suction Pressure," *J. Exp. Botany*, **2**, 145–168 (1951).

8. Taylor, S. A., Evans, D. D., and Kemper, W. D., "Evaluating Soil Water," *Utah Agr. Exp. Sta. Bull.*, **426**, 12–15 (1961).

9. Taylor, S. A., "The Activity of Water in Soils," *Soil Sci.*, **86**, 83–90 (1958).

10. Teele, R. P., and Schuhmann, S., "A Potentiometer for Measuring Voltages of 10 Microvolts to an Accuracy of 0.01 Microvolts," *J. Res. Natl. Bur. Std.*, **22**, 431–439 (1939).

SECTION II

DEW-POINT HYGROMETRY

12. The Basic Process of the Dew-point Hygrometer

R. G. WYLIE, D. K. DAVIES* AND W. A. CAW

National Standards Laboratory, C.S.I.R.O., Sydney, Australia

ABSTRACT

The growth and evaporation of a dew deposit are considered theoretically, and some experimental observations relating to deposit structure and the law of growth are reported. It has been found that for small rates of growth, practically no new droplets are nucleated on bare areas which exist between established droplets.

It is shown that under good conditions a dew deposit is detected visually at a surface density of the order of 3 $\mu g/cm^2$. The time required for the formation of a deposit of this density is calculated for various conditions.

Experiments show that at the threshold of visual detection the condensation process and the apparent dew point are extremely sensitive to airborne contamination. Photoelectrically, the onset of condensation can easily be detected 1°C above the true dew point, even on an unusually clean surface. Very exceptional cleanliness can lead to difficulties through the Kelvin effect.

It is concluded that results known to be accurate to much better than 0.2°C can probably be obtained only with automatic temperature control, photoelectric detection and heavy deposits. On the basis of the phenomena described, a specific procedure is proposed for testing the dependence of the apparent dew point on the surface density of the deposit. This has been found convenient in practice.

* Present address: Electrical Research Association, Leatherhead, Surrey.

INTRODUCTION

The essentials of the dew-point hygrometer were already embodied in a technique described by Le Roy[1] more than two centuries ago, but only recently has it been realized that the concept of a sharply defined temperature, at which condensation begins abruptly, represents only an approximation to the truth.

In 1948, Suomi[2] reported that a sensitive automatic dew-point hygrometer could detect incipient condensation at temperatures well above the true dew point, and the same phenomenon can be seen in the earlier results of Hixson and White.[3] Recent work by Davies[4] confirms that this effect is due to the presence of extremely small amounts of water-soluble matter on the condensing surface, which lowers the vapor pressure of the condensate (Raoult effect). A surface on which such matter is completely absent in normal circumstances is not achievable, nor is it desirable.

It has occasionally been considered (e.g., by Penman[5]) that the Kelvin effect, i.e., the elevation of the vapor pressure of small droplets due to the internal pressure arising from surface tension forces, could possibly have significant consequences. The consequences are probably more significant than has been realized. It is not surprising to discover that when little soluble matter is present on the surface, the Kelvin effect can lead to a considerable nucleation barrier to droplet growth. However, the effect appears to be important also in the growth of deposits in which coalescence is occurring.

In dew-point hygrometry, the usual simple concept of condensation is inadequate when the accuracy sought is higher than about 0.2°C. Unfortunately, to provide a basic hygrometric standard the method must be at least several times more accurate than this. Conventionally, estimates of the accuracy of dew-point determinations are based either on the difference between the temperatures of appearance and disappearance of dew or, especially for automatic instruments, on the repeatability of the results. Neither of these criteria bears much relationship to the absolute accuracy.

The results obtained in very careful work with a manually operated visual dew-point hygrometer are exemplified in the work of Wexler and Hasegawa.[6] Those authors found that, whereas the mean of five determinations of the dew point, made by a single observer, was reproducible to about 0.01°C, the mean difference of the temperatures of appearance and disappearance of the dew was 0.5°C. The absolute accuracy was thought to be about 0.1°C. Automatic dew-point hygrometers have sometimes been claimed to give results reproducible to 0.01°C, but the absolute accuracy is certainly much lower than this.

In the present paper, the basic process of the dew-point hygrometer is examined with the object of identifying the factors which limit the accuracy. Firstly, the structure of the dew deposit is considered theoretically and with reference to some experiments. An unexpected phenomenon, which is important for dew-point hygrometry, is described. The surface density of a dew deposit which is barely visible under good conditions is then shown in various ways to be of the order of 3 μg/cm^2. The time required for the formation of a deposit of this surface density is calculated for various conditions and found to be inconveniently long.

The experimental work of Davies, as well as some earlier work, which shows the great importance of the traces of water-soluble matter inevitably present, is outlined. Some new experiments, in which visual and photo-electric measurements of the amount of light scattered by the dew deposit have been made simultaneously, are then described.

In the conclusions, a method of determining the dew point with an assured high accuracy is proposed. This involves making observations with dew deposits of two or more substantially different surface densities. It will be assumed throughout that the dew deposit is detected by the light that it scatters.

SOME GENERAL CONSIDERATIONS

Consider first the properties of a dew deposit of lenticular droplets on a plane surface, assuming, for this purpose, that the Raoult and Kelvin effects are negligible except for their roles in droplet nucleation.

The Structure of a Growing Dew Deposit

The nucleation of droplets of a non-wetting liquid on a well washed solid surface at low supersaturation can occur only at specific surface features,[7] but such features are usually numerous. The formation of droplets repeatedly at the same sites on metal surfaces has been reported by Tammann and Boehme.[8] As a dew deposit grows it reaches a stage at which the droplets begin to coalesce. A deposit in which the droplets are still separated by distances comparable to or greater than their size, and which therefore grows without coalescence, will be termed an *open deposit*. As growth continues, a regime of repeated coalescence sets in. Each individual coalescence results in a reduction of the area covered, and new droplets may be nucleated on the surface thus freshly exposed. A deposit growing in this regime will be termed a *closed deposit*.

The angle of contact θ, which the liquid makes with the surface, usually has different values for advancing and receding edges. Under nominally clean conditions this hysteresis may be small, although observable, but under some conditions it is large and the receding angle may even become zero. Because of hysteresis, coalescence can produce a droplet which is not circular in basal shape.

Between coalescence events the radius of curvature of a droplet grows according to

$$dr = \frac{(1 + \cos \theta)}{(2 + \cos \theta)(1 - \cos \theta)} q'dt = q\, dt \quad (1)$$

where q' is the volume rate of condensation per unit area of the substrate. By considering the growth of two hypothetical closed deposits of the same detailed geometry but different scale, and noticing that the droplet size distribution must follow the same course in geometrically different closed deposits growing in the same conditions (e.g., two portions of the deposit on a surface), it is found that the droplet size distribution is expected to be of the form

$$dn = q^{-3}t^{-3}\phi(r/qt)dr \quad (2)$$

where dn is the number of droplets per unit area in the size range r to $r + dr$, and ϕ is an undetermined function of r/qt. Observation shows that the surface is covered predominantly by droplets in a relatively small size range. Thus the area-weighted distribution,

$$d\alpha = \pi \sin^2 \theta\, r^2 q^{-3}t^{-3}\phi(r/qt)dr \quad (3)$$

where $d\alpha$ is the fraction of the area of the surface covered by droplets in the size range r to $r + dr$, must have a maximum at a radius which may be designated r_m. This radius is expected to grow linearly with time. The linear growth of r_m with time has been confirmed experimentally for water on gold with θ approximately 70 degrees, using values of r_m of the order of 0.1 mm. To the extent that the distribution of Eq. (3) is symmetrical about the radius r_m, the constant of proportionality approximates $3q$, i.e.,

$$r_m = 3qt \quad (4)$$

This relationship probably holds reasonably well in practice, even though it has been found experimentally that the area-weighted distribution is not fully symmetrical. In fact, at least for slow rates of growth, it has been found that the actual distribution is bimodal. In addition to a large maximum occurring at a radius r_m, not much less than that of the biggest droplet present, a smaller maximum occurs at roughly one third of this radius. This secondary maximum is associated with the groups of drops which form in the areas denuded by coalescences of droplets of radius approximating r_m.

The description represented by Eq. (2) is in accordance with the observation that a rapidly growing closed deposit of discernible droplets, seen through a microscope, gives the illusion that it is steadily approaching; only the scale of the structure seems to change. For slow rates of growth, however, it has been found from measurements on a coarse dew deposit ($r_m \sim 0.1$ mm) that the relative size of the two maxima in the area-weighted distribution function changes with growth, so that Eq. (2) is only approximate in this case. The effect appears to be related to the phenomenon described towards the end of the section on the Kelvin and Raoult effects.

As the basal radius $\rho_m = r_m \sin \theta$ increases beyond λ, the wavelength of light, the light-scattering power of a growing closed deposit becomes very insensitive to the amount of water on the surface, practically tending to a limit. In a dew-point hygrometer with good viewing conditions, the limiting scattering is conspicuously visible, so that a closed deposit would be expected to become visible before ρ_m reached a value of about $\lambda/2$, provided θ were not too small. This criterion does not explicitly take account of the background scattering, against which the light scattered by the dew must be seen. However, it can be justified because of the extremely rapid rate with which the scattering changes with droplet radius when that radius is rather smaller than the wavelength of light.

Apart from optical interference effects, the light-scattering power of an open deposit increases progressively with growth.

The Structure of an Evaporating Dew Deposit

The evaporation of a closed deposit is entirely different from its growth, for, during evaporation, nothing analogous to the completely irreversible process of coalescence occurs. The contact angle takes the receding value everywhere, and, with the early evaporation of the smaller droplets, the larger droplets remain, separated by bare areas. The light-scattering power diminishes progressively, and generally the process differs little from the evaporation of an open deposit.

Particularly in automatic dew-point hygrometers, of which many have been described in recent years, the dew deposit may have a varied history of growth and partial evaporation. It is then possible to have, for example, a relatively small number of large droplets in what is otherwise a closed deposit of, small droplets. An important conclusion is that for a given light-scattering power, the amount of water on the surface and its distribution are *quite indeterminate*. To obtain determinacy, the deposit would have to be detected at an early stage, but this would be likely to lead to considerable systematic errors, as will be seen below.

The Kelvin and Raoult Effects

The equilibrium vapor pressure of a small droplet is affected by the internal pressure attributable to the surface tension of the curved surface (Kelvin effect) and by any dissolved matter present (Raoult effect). The elevation in vapor pressure Δp due to the first effect may be obtained from Kelvin's equation, namely

$$kT \log \frac{p+\Delta p}{p} = \frac{2\gamma}{r} v \qquad (3)$$

where p is the saturation vapor pressure of water at temperature T, r is the radius of curvature of the droplet surface, γ and v are respectively the surface tension and molecular volume of water, and k is Boltzmann's constant. The Raoult effect reduces the vapor pressure approximately by an amount xp, where x is the molecular concentration of the solute.

It is shown in the next section that dew is detected visually at a level of about 3 $\mu g/cm^2$. For such a deposit a layer of soluble matter only one molecule (or ion) thick will elevate the observed dew point by about 0.15°C at 0°C, while the Kelvin effect tends to lower it by an amount of about this magnitude. The importance of the Raoult and Kelvin effects for incipient condensation will be shown below by reference to experiments, but mention must be made here of some phenomena which they cause in relation to heavy dew deposits.

A very clean gold surface, as regards soluble matter, can be prepared by repeatedly blowing off the surface a heavy condensate formed from air which has been freed of condensation nuclei in a filter bed of fine car-

borundum. If a heavy deposit is formed on the clean surface from the gas and then evaporated, the droplet pattern is found to be invisibly imprinted on the surface in the form of minute traces of soluble matter. The pattern becomes visible if a barely visible dew deposit is formed. It seems that the soluble impurity is generated in the heavy dew deposit by chemical reactions sustained by gaseous impurities in the air, and insoluble impurities on the gold. Of course, in the presence of strong light, photochemical reactions may also contribute. If room air is drawn over the surface, the effect is accentuated to a marked degree, the soluble impurities being supplied by the condensation nuclei in the air.

An interesting phenomenon has been observed in the growth of a closed dew deposit on a "Drifilm"-treated glass plate ($\theta \sim 90$ degrees) and also on gold (with $\theta \sim 70$ degrees). For moderate or low rates of condensation, the nucleation of new droplets in a region freshly bared by coalescence is confined to a relatively small number of especially favored sites. Once these new droplets have been formed, no further droplets are nucleated on the bare areas between them, even though the condensation is occurring from unfiltered atmospheric air. Figure 1 shows a deposit growing in this way from room air. Clearly, an important factor is the continual sweeping of any water-soluble matter on the surface into the large droplets by the process of coalescence. Thus, the smaller droplets are relatively free of it, and when they are pulled away by coalescence, what little soluble matter they possess largely goes with them. Then the Kelvin effect ensures that nucleation on the freshly bared areas is difficult. It is not clear why nucleation in these areas is not promoted by the airborne condensation nuclei when room air is present. Possibly the nuclei are drawn to the water droplets by electrostatic forces.

This phenomenon has the important significance that, if a heavy deposit is formed and slightly evaporated, subsequent slight growth or evaporation can occur without any substantial changes in the number of droplets on the surface. The light-scattering power will follow the growth or evaporation, and it will be possible to tell when equilibrium prevails.

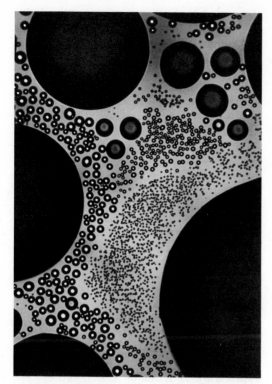

FIG. 1. Photograph of a dew deposit growing on a "Drifilm"-treated glass plate in room air (×35). Practically no new droplets are being nucleated in the bare areas.

The Surface Density of a Barely Visible Deposit

Visual observation is important not only for visual dew-point hygrometers but also for photoelectric instruments, to provide guidance for the operator. It is very desirable to know the order of magnitude of the surface density of a barely visible deposit. Of course, this density must depend on the optical conditions and, in particular, on the level of the background scattering from the dry surface.

For a well-polished surface an upper limit can be obtained using the criterion $\rho_m = \lambda/2$, implied above. Regarding the surface as half covered by droplets of uniform basal radius ρ_m, putting $\theta = 70$ degrees (a value which has been observed) and assuming $\lambda = 5000$ Å, the surface density is found to be 5 $\mu g/cm^2$, and the number of droplets on the surface to be 2.5×10^8 per cm². The result is not far from the value 3 $\mu g/cm^2$, derivable from the droplet radius 8×10^{-6} cm given earlier by one of the authors,[9] which was based on the

calculated light scattering of hemispheres on a reflecting plane surface. Davies' results for a mechanically highly polished surface, which are outlined below, when combined with other results given below for visual observation lead to threshold surface densities of 0.7 to 3 $\mu g/cm^2$ and droplet concentrations of 2 to 5×10^8 per cm². Further confirmation that the threshold surface density is of the order of 3 $\mu g/cm^2$ under good conditions can be obtained by comparing the calculated time for the formation of the deposit with the observed time; in the remainder of this paper, this value will be adopted.

In a well-known paper, Griffiths[10] described experiments in which the amount of dew on surfaces was measured in various ways. His lowest result, for a "slight deposit," was 36 $\mu g/cm^2$—roughly 10 times higher than the present adopted value. It appears that Griffiths was not referring to a deposit at the threshold of visual detection; in fact, a deposit of 3 $\mu g/cm^2$ would prove too fugitive for the experimental procedures which Griffiths used.

TABLE 1. CONVECTIVE HEAT- AND VAPOR-TRANSFER COEFFICIENTS, AND TIMES FOR THE FORMATION OF A DEW DEPOSIT OF SURFACE DENSITY 3 μg cm^{-1}, FOR A TEMPERATURE DEFICIT OF 0.1°C, GIVEN FOR THREE TEMPERATURES AND THREE VELOCITIES OF FLOW OF THE GAS PARALLEL TO A SURFACE OF 1 cm EXTENT

Gas Velocity (cm/sec)	Dew-Point Temperature		
	−20°C (dew, not frost)	0°C	+20°C
10	$h = 2.2 \times 10^{-4}$ cal.sec^{-1}cm^{-2} deg C^{-1} $f = 7.9 \times 10^{-7}$g sec^{-1}cm^{-2} (mm Hg)$^{-1}$		
	470 sec	110 sec	35 sec
100	$h = 7.1 \times 10^{-4}$ $f = 2.5 \times 10^{-6}$		
	150	35	11
1000	$h = 2.2 \times 10^{-3}$ $f = 7.9 \times 10^{-6}$		
	45	11	4

The Rate of Formation of the Deposit

Heat- and vapor-transfer coefficients are given in Table 1 for a range of conditions that could occur in a dew-point hygrometer.

The heat-transfer coefficients have been obtained from Pohlhausen's equations[11] but have been adjusted to allow for the absence of a leading edge in the assumed tangential flow and for the existence of some initial turbulence in the gas directed over the surface. The vapor-transfer coefficients have been computed from the heat-transfer coefficients using the psychrometer equation with the psychrometer constant not including radiation. The values relate to a surface 1 cm in extent in the direction of flow and to an air pressure of one atmosphere. They depend little on temperature.

In passing, it may be noted that even for a dew deposit 100 times thicker than the barely visible thickness (3×10^{-6} cm) and for the very high gas velocity of 1000 cm/sec, the temperature drop across the dew layer for an overall temperature difference of 30°C is only 0.015°C. Also, if the dew is formed under these conditions on a silver plate 1 mm thick, the temperature drop across the thickness of the plate is only 0.007°C. With proper instrument design these effects obviously are not serious.

Table 1 also shows the calculated time of formation of the barely visible deposit (*ab initio*) when the surface temperature is held 0.1°C below the dew point, the Raoult and Kelvin effects being neglected.

If, when dew is first detected in a manually operated instrument, the temperature is immediately made to rise at the rate at which it has been falling, the time which then elapses before the disappearance of the dew is the time required to grow the deposit from the threshold surface density to twice that density and then reduce it again to the threshold value. This interval is obviously about twice the time for the formation *ab initio* of the threshold deposit and so its measurement provides a value for the latter. According to Table 1, at 0°C the time of formation for a temperature deficit of 0.1°C is 11 seconds even at the very high gas velocity of 1000 cm/sec. Under more usual conditions, it is in the range of $\frac{1}{2}$ to 1 minute, which is a long time to have to hold the temperature within closer limits than ± 0.1°C by manual means. On Griffiths' minimum estimate of 36 μg/cm^2 for the dew-deposit surface density, the corresponding time range is 6 to 12 minutes, which, compared with experience, confirms that his estimate does not relate to the threshold of visual detection.

It is clear that in any procedure involving deposits of much greater surface density than the adopted threshold value, the time required for the deposit to grow or diminish appreciably is a major consideration. The situation is obviously much worse at low frost-point temperatures.

EXPERIMENTAL STUDIES

Hixson and White[3] published results which showed that the condensation process on their chromium-plated brass surface was of a

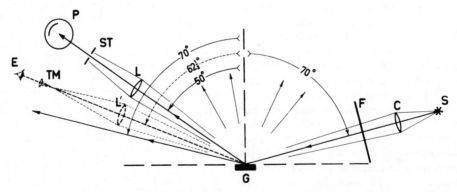

FIG. 2. Diagram showing the geometrical arrangement in Davies' experiments[4] (full lines) and in the experiments of Fig. 4 (whole diagram): C—collimating lens, E—eye, F—filter, G—gold surface, L—objective lens, L'—objective lens, P—photomultiplier tube, S—light source, ST—stop, TM—telemicroscope. Lenses L and L' are 6 cm from the gold surface and 1.5 and 0.9 cm in diameter, respectively.

complex nature, but their explanation of the observed phenomena, in terms of molecular aggregates in the gas adjacent to the surface, is untenable. Suomi[2] reported some careful observations with an automatic dew-point hygrometer incorporating a metal surface, probably plated with a noble metal. Although his results are for the frost-point range, it seems certain that the condensates which he detected even 8°C above the true "dew point" consisted of elements of liquid. Suomi says that probably there is a lowering of vapor pressure because of salt. He gives no detailed experimental results for the effect.

Incipient Condensation on Gold

Davies[4] has made an experimental investigation of the scattering of light from a gold surface at temperatures just above the dew point. The optical conditions are illustrated in Fig. 2. Using a condensing surface automatically held at any desired temperature to within 0.003°C, he recorded the steady scattering power of the condensate for each of a series of temperatures above the true dew point (0°C). Some of his results are plotted in Fig. 3. The horizontal broken line represents the background scattering of the surface; this was subtracted electrically from the response of the photomultiplier tube. I/I_0 is the amount of light scattered by the dew deposit on to the objective of the detector, divided by the amount that would be collected by that objective if it were directed into the specularly reflected beam and the reflectance were 100 per cent. Temperature is plotted on the abscissa, the true dew point being 0°C to within 0.003°C.

Curve A was obtained after preliminary washing of the surface for three hours by condensation from the nucleus-free gas. Curves B to D were obtained with the surface first washed in this way and then exposed to, respectively, 20 cc of room air from an air-conditioned room, four lots each of 50 cc of room air, and the continuous passage of room air through the apparatus at a rate of 8 cc/sec for 10 minutes. In the last case, most of the airborne impurities would have been carried right through the apparatus. The maximum in curve C and the minimum in curve D result from the use of nominally monochromatic light (of 4065 Å wavelength).

In cases C and D the entry of atmospheric contamination has increased the scattering power at a temperature of 0.1°C by no less than three decades. Davies has correlated these and other results using a theory which makes use of Kelvin's equation, Raoult's law and the known light scattering from complete spheres. He used the simple droplet model adopted above (p. 126), and his analysis shows that within the range of the experiments the dew was in the form of an open deposit, although closed-deposit conditions have almost been reached in the highest points on curve D.

Figure 3 gives values for N, the number of droplets per cm², and K, a quantity proportional to the average amount of soluble matter present in a single droplet. N is practically independent of the amount of soluble matter present.

Davies obtained correlations also for two different wavelengths, and for advancing and receding contact angles, in both cases without adjusting any parameters.

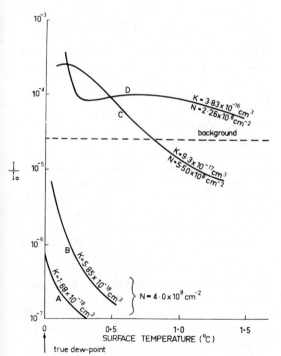

Fig. 3. Curves showing some of Davies' results[4] for the scattering of light by a gold surface as a function of the temperature of the surface, the true dew point being 0°C.

The Threshold of Visual Detection

In order to be able to derive approximate threshold deposit densities and some other information from Davies' results, measurements have been made of the threshold value of I/I_0 for visual detection. As shown by broken lines in Fig. 2, a telemicroscope was incorporated in the original apparatus so that visual and photoelectric observations could be made simultaneously. It is doubtful whether the difference between the corresponding angles of observation has affected the conclusions very much, as a direction closer to the direction of specular reflection results in a greater background as well as a greater intensity of light from the dew. For a rather similar reason there is probably little significance in the fact that blue light has been used rather than, say, yellow-green.

The results are given in Fig. 4. Curves A and B correspond to exposure to such quantities of room air as were necessary to bring the conditions within the desired range. Curves C to F represent successive additions of 2 cc of room air to the system. The experimental points are shown, and serve to mark the successive values at which the temperature was controlled, as well as to show the concordance of the results. Short horizontal bars on each curve correspond to experimental points between which a step in one direction produced the first visually observable increase in brightness and, equally, a step in the other direction produced the last observable decrease in brightness. Four observers obtained practically identical results; smaller temperature increments would have been necessary to obtain a scatter of results, as between observers. The threshold corresponds to a value of I/I_0 of about 6×10^{-5}. In conjunction with the analysis of the data of Fig. 3, this result leads to the range of threshold deposit densities already given above (see p. 129). The threshold value of I/I_0 is a little more than twice the background value for the bare surface. A change of a factor of two in the amount of scattered light is about the minimum which the eye would be expected to appreciate, unless the change occurred very rapidly or against a sharply differentiated reference area. In this context, it is worth noting that a surface is considered to be polished when no surface structure remains which produces obvious scattering, polishing being stopped when this criterion is satisfied.

Figure 4 shows that with a very limited exposure to relatively clean room air, and using visual detection under good conditions, the dew point could be overestimated by 0.2 or 0.3°C. With the surface in the condition corresponding to curve D of Fig. 3, the overestimate would be more than 1°C.

A striking feature in Fig. 4 is the intersection of the ordinate axis by curve A at a definite angle. The same effect is apparent in curve B Fig. 4, and in curve A of Fig. 3. It represents the existence of a nucleation barrier to droplet formation, and the possibility of growing a deposit consisting of large, discrete drops separated by bare areas.

CONCLUSIONS

With good viewing conditions, a dew

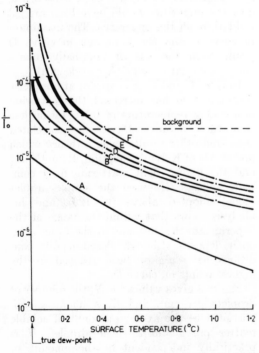

FIG. 4. Curves showing the threshold of visual detection of dew on a gold surface, in relation to the photoelectrically determined light scattering. Dew was detected visually in the region shown by the thickening of the curve, between short horizontal bars.

deposit forming on the metal surface of a typical dew-point hygrometer can be detected visually at a surface density of the order of 3 $\mu g/cm^2$. The dew can be detected photoelectrically at a much lower level, certainly at 1 per cent of this surface density. Even with visual detection, accurate dew-point hygrometry with unfiltered atmospheric air is out of the question except at unusually clean sites. If a very clean surface is achieved and the incoming gas is filtered, phenomena due to the Kelvin effect will be encountered if an accuracy much better than 0.2°C is sought. In most circumstances, even with efficient filters, an initially very clean surface will deteriorate slowly by accumulating a soluble contaminant. With practically all surfaces it would be possible to detect a dew deposit photoelectrically at temperatures well above the true dew point.

The conclusion is inescapable that in accurate work, whether with visual or photoelectric dew detection, there is an onus on the observer to prove that his criterion for the observation of the dew point leads to correct results with his instrument. Short of checking the instrument with gas of known humidity, he appears to have only one course—to show that the apparent dew point is practically the same for different surface densities of the deposit.

The surface density which when doubled leaves the observed equilibrium temperature unchanged within, say, 0.03°C is likely to be several times the barely visible density and could easily be considerably greater. In considering how slowly even the barely visible deposit forms and how poor a photometric instrument the eye is, one can see that it is impracticable to apply the criterion of the preceding paragraph to this accuracy when using a visual dew-point hygrometer involving manual temperature control.

A big advance can be achieved by using semiautomatic operation with a combination of visual and photoelectric detection. The control of the temperature as such allows the operator to explore the behavior at each of a series of temperatures in the neighborhood of the dew point. Any temperature can be held indefinitely while the deposit is observed visually, and the photoelectric system shows even small changes in the amount of light scattered. The criterion given above can then be implemented by the following procedure, which is based on the phenomena which have been described:

After the chemically inert surface has been cleaned by blowing off a liberal condensate, and allowed to dry at a temperature well above the dew point, the temperature is lowered and a deposit consisting of droplets which can be resolved with a low-power microscope is developed. It is assumed that the deposit is then of the closed form, as will be the case except under very unusual conditions. (The growth of a closed deposit of resolvable droplets is characterized by scintillations due to the coalescences which are occurring.) A small proportion of the deposit is then evaporated by a short excursion to a higher temperature, to ensure that coalescence events do not subsequently occur due to the creep of droplet edges which is encountered when the contact angle exhibits hysteresis. The deposit is now in a state such that small deviations of the temperature from the equilibrium value will cause more or less reversible drifts in the light scattering. More specifically, when the temperature is above that value the scattering will decrease, and when it is below, the scattering will increase.

When the equilibrium temperature has been observed, the deposit is grown to, say, twice the surface density, as judged by the visually observed separation of the droplets, and another equilibrium temperature is obtained by the same procedure. If the Kelvin effect is negligible (on account of the relatively large size of the droplets), the difference between the two temperatures is attributable to the Raoult effect and is approximately equal to the difference of the second temperature from the true dew point (apart from instrumental errors).

It should be noted that the validity of this procedure depends on the observation, recorded above in the section on General Considerations, that with small changes in temperature about the dew point, the number of droplets present remains practically unchanged.

Experimentally, it has been found that the procedure is convenient, and in experiments with gas of dew point 0°C, dew deposits with surface densities in a ratio of approximately 2:1 have had equilibrium temperatures differing by approximately 0.05°C. The droplet sizes involved were in the range 0.006- to 0.06-mm diameter.

It should be pointed out that if a number of dew-point determinations had to be made in sequence on the same stream of gas, it would not be necessary to make observations at two deposit densities for every determination.

References

1. Symons, G. J., "A Contribution to the History of Hygrometers," *Quart. J. Met. Soc.*, **7**, 161 (1881).
2. Suomi, V. E., "Moisture Measurement with an Electronic Dew-point Indicator," *Instruments*, **21**, 178 (1948).
3. Hixson, A. W., and White, G. E., "Accurate Determination of Dew-point," *Ind. Eng. Chem.*, *Analyt. Ed.*, **10**, 235 (1938).
4. Davies, D. K. "The Incipient Condensation of Water Vapour on a Gold Surface," *Brit. J. Appl. Phys.*, **14**, 567 (1963).
5. Penman, H. L., "Humidity," London, The Institute of Physics, 1955.
6. Wexler, A., and Hasegawa, S., "Relative Humidity-Temperature Relationships of some Saturated Salt Solutions in the Temperature Range 0° to 50°C," *J. Res. Natl. Bur. Std.*, **53**, 19 (1954).
7. Wylie, R. G., "The Condensation of a Vapour at a Crystalline Surface," *Australian J. Phys.*, **5**, 628 (1952).
8. Tammann, G., and Boehme, W., "Die Zahl der Wassertröpfchen bie der Kondensation auf verschiedenen festen Stoffen," *Ann. der Physik*, **22**, 77 (1935).
9. Wylie, R. G., "A New Absolute Method of Hygrometry. I," *Australian J. Phys.*, **10**, 351 (1957).
10. Griffiths, E., "Some Modified Forms of Hygrometers," *Proc. Phys. Soc.*, **34**, viii (1921-2).
11. Pohlhausen, E., "Heat Interchange Between Solid Bodies and Fluids of Small Viscosity and Heat Conductivity," *Z. Angew. Math. Mech.*, **1**, 115 (1921).

13. The Dew- or Frost-point Hygrometer

A. W. BREWER

University of Toronto, Toronto, Canada

ABSTRACT

Water vapor occurs in gaseous atmospheres in a very wide range of concentrations, and for different purposes, different ranges are important. In the atmosphere, for example, natural vapor pressures occur over a range of almost 10^5 to 1 which may be found in a single ascent through a depth in the atmosphere of little more than 10 km.

Relative concentrations less than about 2×10^6 are difficult to produce and are very difficult to maintain, while saturation sets an upper limit. All these concentrations can be measured as dew points or frost points with a single instrument. The scale is approximately logarithmic and the percentage accuracy of vapor pressure measurement changes remarkably little over the whole range. The only calibration required is a temperature calibration, and the measurement is then absolute. Since the thermometry can easily be made satisfactory, the instrument is stable. Especially for the low vapor pressure, careful instrument design and operation are necessary and these problems will be discussed.

INTRODUCTION

The water vapor concentrations found in gaseous atmospheres vary over a very wide range, and for different purposes, different ranges are important. Sometimes very wide ranges occur and must be measured continuously. Examples are perhaps unnecessary but a common circumstance in which high water contents are important is in the avoidance of condensation in a chimney; however, for air which is being prepared for liquifaction, extreme dryness is usually necessary. In the atmosphere, the problem presented by a wide range is very acute. The water vapor content of the tropospheric air varies very greatly from layer to layer as well as with place and time. For example, if we consider the variations to be found at Washington D.C., the surface vapor pressure in summer is quite commonly greater than 15 mb. In the troposphere above Washington any relative humidity between about 10 and 100 per cent is equally common, and the writer would expect that relative humidities of less than 1 per cent are fairly common, but judging from European experience, the lower stratosphere is very dry and the vapor pressure at 16 km probably varies very little from 2 or 3×10^{-4} mb, about 100,000 times lower than the highest water vapor pressure found at the surface.

In the measurement of these water contents, the main problems are to deal adequately with the very wide range involved, and to attain and maintain suitable accuracy. The dew- or frost-point hygrometer meets these needs; it has an approximately logarithmic scale, and accuracy is ensured if accurate thermometry of the deposition surface can be provided. It is however a relatively complicated instrument. It requires skilled operation, and a source of cold is necessary. These difficulties have greatly restricted its use. It may be made automatic but usually at considerable cost in terms of complexity and reliability, a point which will be discussed later. Peltier cooling offers considerable possibilities by providing a simple source of "cold."

DEFINITION OF DEW OR FROST POINT

The thermodynamic dew point and frost point temperatures are defined as the temperature T_d or T_f at which moist air at a temperature T and pressure p of mixing ratio r must be cooled in order that it shall be saturated, with respect to water in the case of T_d, the dew point, or ice for T_f, the frost point.

FUNDAMENTAL METHOD OF OPERATION

The dew- or frost-point temperatures are obtained in the dew- or frost-point hygrometer by cooling a surface, ventilated with or exposed to the air under test, to such a temperature that a deposit of liquid water or of ice is in equilibrium and is neither growing nor evaporating. The temperature of the surface gives the dew or frost point.

The deposit is usually detected optically. Alternative means of detecting a dew deposit include optical polarization phenomena and the absorpsion of alpha or other radiations. The electrical conductivity of the surface of an ionic crystal is used in what is a basically similar instrument which measures not the dew point but the condition of vapor saturation over a saturated solution of the salt. This is an excellent method of detection, but it has a restricted temperature range and it is not absolute; so that calibration is required. The advantage of optical detection lies in the increasing relative sensitivity which automatically occurs at low temperatures as the crystals of the deposit reduce in size. This advantage disappears near $-90°C$ when the deposit crystallizes too slowly, and other methods may then be superior. The deposits at these temperatures are very small, of the order of 10^{-8} gm/cm^2, and a very sensitive detector is necessary.

BASIC INTERPRETATION OF THE MEASUREMENT

When this equilibrium temperature has been obtained, it is then usually sufficiently accurate to assume that the partial water vapor pressure is equal to the saturation vapor pressure of water at the dew or frost point. This may be obtained with reference to standard tables or may be computed by suitable formulas such as those provided by Goff and Gratch. Use of this value assumes that the saturation vapor pressure of water is unaffected by the presence of the diluting atmosphere and that in the cooling process the water vapor and the "atmosphere" act as perfect gases. In the natural atmosphere the error caused will usually be less than 0.5 per cent, but in other conditions it is advisable to watch for the possibility of significant error, particularly if some component of the "atmosphere" has high solubility in water and is present in significant concentrations. The solution of this component may then affect the equilibrium vapor pressures.

With these limitations we then have

$$e_w(T_d) = \frac{r}{0.622 + r} p \qquad (1a)$$

or

$$e_i(T_f) = \frac{r}{0.622 + r} p \qquad (1b)$$

where $e_w(T_d)$ and $e_i(T_f)$ are the saturated vapor pressures of water and ice at the dew point T_d or the frost point T_f, p is the total pressure and r is the mixing ratio.

If the vapor pressure is less than 6.1 mb (the vapor pressure at 0°C), the deposit may be either of supercooled water or of ice, and for the same value of r, the dew point T_d or the frost point T_f may be measured. If the vapor pressure is less than about 0.5 mb, the deposit will usually be of ice (T_f lower than say $-27°C$). Where any ambiguity exists it is important to note the nature of the deposit and use Eq. (1a) or (1b) according to whether it is water or ice. A mixed deposit can hardly occur except very close to 0°C. It is unstable and quickly becomes ice.

GENERAL POINTS OF DEW-POINT HYGROMETRY TECHNIQUE

The Range of Dew- or Frost-point Hygrometers

The wide range has been commented upon. At vapor pressures which are still fairly high, though below room temperature saturation vapor pressure, the dew-point hygrometer works very easily, but at low water vapor contents corresponding to low frost points, the deposits obtainable become finer and their changes slower so that the instrument becomes increasingly difficult to operate. When the frost point falls below $-65°C$ additional difficulties arise owing to the reduction in the rate of crystallization at the very low temperatures because of the reduced mobility of the water molecules on the surface. In order to form visible crystals it is necessary for water molecules to move from the points where they are condensed, to vacant places at the growing point of the crystals; low mobility of the water molecules impedes this. This trouble is not serious in visual hygrometers until the frost point falls below about $-75°C$, but it increases rapidly at lower temperatures and entirely prevents any operation at about $-90°C$. At this and lower temperatures, the deposit is in the form of an invisible glass which crystallizes very slowly. Thus frost points lower than $-87°C$ can hardly be measured directly, and difficulty is experienced when measuring frost points between -80 and $-87°C$.

If a surface is cooled below $-90°C$ with air of frost point $-90°C$ over it, an invisible glassy deposit accumulates. If it is then heated to, say, $-80°C$ it will usually crystallize faster than it will evaporate. To an observer (or a photocell detector) the deposit will appear to grow, owing to the crystallization, before it later evaporates. This effect can cause confusion and should be guarded against. With extreme care and skill it might perhaps be used to extend the range of a hygrometer, but the author is glad that he has never encountered a frost point lower than about $-86°C$! As discussed below, the lower limit of operation can sometimes be extended by compressing the air.

Piping and Ducting the Air or Gases under Test

For dew-point hygrometry it is permissable and usually convenient to carry the air under test into the instrument by a pipe or duct. Occasionally the air is conveyed into an enclosure and isolated while its dew or frost point is measured. It is of course essential that the partial vapor pressure should not be changed, unless the change is due to changes in the total pressure which will be taken into account in using Eqs. (1a) or (1b). In this

case the mixing ratio must not be changed. Remember the risk that water may be removed by condensation in cold spots and then later added by evaporation if conditions change and that at low water contents desorption of water from the walls is very troublesome even though condensation has never occured on the surfaces.

Where extremes of water content or relative humidity are encountered, no precautions are too pedantic. Desorption of vapor is particularly troublesome if the low water contents are to be associated with low total pressures as occurs in the atmosphere. The low total pressures facilitate and speed the desorption as every vacuum physicist knows. Clean metal pipes, preferably stainless steel, and glass only are permissible. Rubber particularly must be avoided, and all plastics must be very strongly suspect except perhaps polytetrafluoroethylene.

Static systems are uncertain if the vapor pressure is below 6 mb, and when the vapor pressure is below 1.0 mb, all pipes should be large and substantial volumes of air should be passed through them. These limits may be lowered somewhat if the general temperatures are low and the relative humidity of the air in the pipes is about 50 per cent. Care of course should be taken to avoid leaks of any kind, particularly inward.

The Deposition Surface

In the instrument, the dew or hoarfrost is formed on a "deposition surface" which must meet a number of functional requirements. It must receive the deposit and facilitate its detection, and the temperature of the surface must be easily controllable and accurately measurable.

To receive the deposit, the surface must be inert and hydrophobic, but otherwise there is no evidence that its nature has any significant effect. It must be clean, and a reasonable deposit should be used. This is to ensure that the deposit is actually pure water and not hygroscopic dust particles which have grown by condensation or water deposited in scratches. This last point applies to visually controlled hygrometers. As will be discussed later, in automatic hygrometers it is usually necessary to use dust and scratches to ensure stability.

The surface must be at least mildly hydrophobic. If the surface is wetted by pure water, the dew deposit takes the form of a thin film and cannot be seen. Practical surfaces readily acquire sufficient grease to render them sufficiently hydrophobic. A surface like mica (which actually has little to recommend it) would be quite unsuitable on account of its persistently hydrophillic nature.

If frost points are to be measured in the region between 0°C and say −20°C the occasional appearance of dew deposits can be a nuisance. Visually they can be distinguished without trouble, but the reduction of the results must have regard to the nature of the deposit and if they change, the time taken for the transition to the stable ice delays the reading. Usually only new surfaces give trouble and the writer has found polishing with a suitable tissue moistened with saliva an effective and easy cure (a little spit and polish!).

Detection of the Deposit

For a visual hygrometer the best conditions for viewing the deposit are obtained with oblique, dark ground, illumination and low power ($\times 5$ to $\times 10$) optical magnification of good quality. The surface may be a bright specular reflector, which will appear relatively dark because of the oblique illumination; black anodized aluminum has been used successfully by the author. The presence of the oxide coat does perhaps cause some slight error in the temperature measurements at low relative humidity, but the surface is very durable and much more scratch resistant than most metals capable of receiving a high polish. The optical system should be free from flare. Even though the eye may not see the source of illumination, some of the light may fall on the lenses. This should not then reach the eye by reflection in one or more glass surfaces. If low frost points are to be measured, a very effective system is needed. A surface which looks clean and scratch-free when "looked at" under ordinary illumination will often seem very dirty and rough when examined by the hygrometer illumination and optics. A new and higher order of cleanliness and perfection may be found to be necessary for the surface.

The appearance of the deposit changes markedly with temperature. The heavy ice deposits obtained at temperatures between 0 and −10°C are easiest to see. Dew deposits though easy to see do not have the glittering brilliance of the ice. As the temperatures lower, the deposits become lighter until at −85°C a milky blue veiling only of the surface is obtained. The deposits at these low temperatures probably consist of only about 10^{-8} g/cm^2. This corresponds to less than a single molecular layer, and *prima facie* might seem undetectable. However, if it consists of 10^4 crystals, each 1 micron cube, per sq cm, these would be visible, and this seems to be the case.

Measurement of the Surface Temperature

It is of course necessary to measure the temperature of the deposition surface to the required accuracy. The deposition surface and the cooling arrangements must be designed with this in view. For this reason, materials which are poor conductors of heat may not be used for the deposition surface, nor may that surface take the form of a thin sheet of metal unless the special problems which this form presents are recognized and solved in the thermometry. Experience suggests that a thin film of lacquer or varnish can be tolerated, or an anodic surface on aluminum, except perhaps when high accuracy is required at low relative humidities.

Any convenient form of thermometer may be used. A thermocouple placed just beneath the surface is probably ideal, but for many applications the thermocouple may produce inconveniently small amounts of power to operate an indicator. In a visual hygrometer it is usually necessary to have the deposition surface part of a relatively large mass of metal of high thermal conductivity and possessing such thermal inertia that temperature changes do not take place too rapidly. In this case, by isolating the mass it is possible to ensure that the temperature of the mass is the same as the temperature of the surface. The temperature of the mass may be measured by any convenient method.

Ventilation of the Surface

The changes in the deposit of dew or hoarfrost are accelerated and the instrument is made more sensitive if the surface is properly ventilated. The ventilation produced by 2 to

10 cm of water pressure through an adequate jet is usually sufficient. Very heavy ventilation, particularly if the air under test has a low relative humidity, usually causes trouble through the excessive heating which it causes.

For visual hygrometers there is some advantage in ventilating part of the surface as fully as possible and part only slightly. The differences in the rates of deposition and evaporation on the different parts of the surface which are thereby obtained, are useful to assist the observer to determine whether the dew is increasing or evaporating.

Actual Manual Hygrometer Design

We may consider these points in relation to the design of a specific hygrometer. The hygrometer illustrated in Fig. 1 was designed for use in pressure cabin aircraft. It has been used extensively up to 50,000 ft in many parts of the world.

The whole instrument is enclosed in a cylindrical metal enclosure which is designed to be airtight. Outside air, which is the air to be tested, is brought to the instrument in great volumes, about 20 l/sec, via ½-in. inlet pipes. This air flushes the whole system, and most of it leaves again. A small amount, probably about 300 cc/min, is diverted. It passes through very short drilled holes through the jet and is directed across the thimble. The thimble is of black anodized aluminum manufactured to produce as perfect an upper surface as possible. Its temperature is measured by the resistance thermometer on the skirt. This is platinum wire wound on the anodized surface. Oblique, diffuse illumination of the surface is provided by the glass ellipse, ¼-in. thick, which is silvered on its edge so that light from the lamp which is at one focus is reflected to the thimble which is at the other focus. The hole in which the lamp is housed is ground for diffusion, and the hole over the thimble is conical to refract light down onto the thimble surface. Viewing is by the double, fixed focus ×6 magnifying lens, carefully designed to give high-quality magnification regardless of the position of the eye. The lower lens is quite thick, partly to reduce thermal conduction through the lens so that condensation does not occur on its upper surface and partly to prevent direct light from the lamp or ellipse from illuminating this surface and causing optical flare.

The temperature of the thimble is controlled by balancing natural heating against cooling which is provided by carefully regulated pumping of a suitable coolant into the hollow base of the thimble. The coolant may be liquid oxygen or nitrogen, or by suitable pump design, solid CO_2 and acetone mixtures may be used but very low temperature cannot then be obtained.

METHOD OF OPERATION OF A VISUAL HYGROMETER

The correct method of operation *which must be used* is as follows:

(a) Cool the surface until a small visible deposit is obtained.

(b) Hold the temperature steady at some chosen value and inspect the deposit at suitable intervals. In this way find a temperature at which the deposit is just growing.

(c) In a similar way find a temperature at which the deposit is just evaporating.

The dew (or frost) point is the average of the temperatures (b) and (c).

It is *most important* to remember that the procedure to determine these temperatures is to select a temperature for trial and to control the surface temperature at that value, inspecting the deposit from time to time to see whether it has changed.

The time taken for an observation varies greatly with the skill of the observer, the design of the instrument, and the frost point to be observed. Table 1 shows the sort of time required to determine whether a deposit is changing or not and the difference between the temperatures (b) and (c) which can be

TABLE 1

T_d or T_f	Time	Temp. (a) −Temp. (b)*
Above 0°C	5 sec	.1°C
−10°C dew deposit	10 sec	.2°C
−10°C ice	20 sec	.2°C
−50°C	½ min.	.5°C
−80°C	3 min.	1.0°C

* These figures greatly depend on circumstances and these represent favorable values.

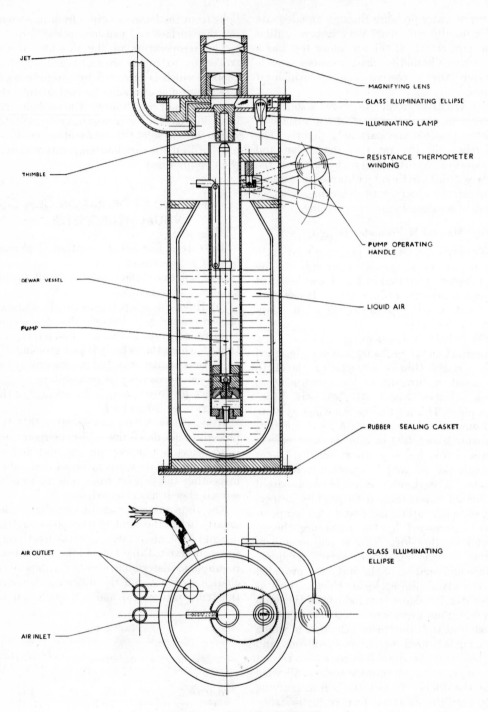

Plan View—Cover Plate Removed.

Fig. 1. Frost-point hygrometer for pressure cabin aircraft, diagrammatic illustration.

obtained. These represent favorable figures but sometimes the work can be speeded up if a larger separation between the temperatures (b) and (c) is accepted.

USE OF PHOTOELECTRIC DETECTION OF THE DEPOSIT AND ITS CHANGES

Photoelectric detectors may be used to replace the eye to detect the dew or hoarfrost and its changes. This may be done by (a) using the photocell to detect light scattered by the deposit or (b) using the photocell to detect variation of the specularly reflected light. The latter is normally more sensitive. In either case a second photocell is used to monitor changes in the illuminating intensity. Changes in the deposit are then indicated by the movement of a pointer controlled by the photocells. With such a device it is possible to find a temperature at which the deposit is not changing and thus measure the dew point directly rather than as the mean of two temperatures as described above. In the presence of dirt on the surface, a temperature about 1°C too high can easily be obtained if the dew detector is too sensitive. This is discussed below.

The advantages of this method (halfway to automation) are small, and it is not very common.

AUTOMATIC DEW- OR FROST-POINT HYGROMETRY

Manual operation requires so much skill if it is to be done accurately and speedily that many workers have been attracted to the possibilities of automation. One method of operation involves the continuous cooling of the deposition surface. In the absence of a deposit the temperature of the surface lowers until a deposit is formed. This is detected, say, photoelectrically, and then by means of a suitable servo amplifier, heat is supplied to the surface to control the deposit at a constant amount. Alternatively, if no dew is present the amplifier may produce cooling in Peltier elements, this cooling is switched off or controlled when the deposit reaches the required value. In this case Peltier cooling balances natural heating. The essential feature is that

the surface will thus be held at the dew point which may then be read off directly.

The following advantages are obtained or desired:

(1) A special observer is not required.
(2) The speed of observation can be increased, sometimes tenfold or more (at temperatures above 0°C, response times less than 0.1 sec can be obtained).
(3) Continuous indications can be obtained provided that the changes are not so rapid as to result in temporary loss of control.

There also are considerable problems, though these are by no means insuperable. The automatic dew-point hygrometer, like most mechanical servos, is inherently oscillatory. In the mechanical servo, stability is provided either by friction (deliberate or unavoidable) or by "phase advance" networks. Phase advance networks can be and are used in automatic dew-point hygrometers but they have limited power. More effective stabilization is provided, in a way which is not too easy to explain, by suitable distribution of the heating or cooling elements and some thermal inertia. The procedure is to locate the controlled (and therefore variable) heating or cooling directly at the deposition surface, or as close as possible to it, and back it up with a block of metal. This provides a thermal inertia which comes into effect after the surface has been subject to a change in heat supply. Many detailed arrangements are possible. The writer has successfully used a continuously cooled block and a heating element made from a slice of germanium with the heating current passing transversely through it. The dew was deposited on the surface of the germanium which was protected by a coat of lacquer.

Peltier elements seem to be eminently adapted to suitable construction. The cooling is naturally produced very close to the surface, and the mass of bismuth telluride of the Peltier elements provides a stabilizing thermal reservoir.

If a construction which obtains stability in this way is adopted (and it is usually necessary), this means that the deposition surface is the site of very strong heat fluxes, particularly if the depression of the dew point is considerable and a lot of heat is being brought by the necessary stream of air which is under test. These circumstances are not conducive to easy thermometry, and even though the surface may be accurately at the dew point, its temperature is difficult to measure precisely.

The nature of dew (or frost) deposits also presents special problems. If we plot apparent deposit against a continuously maintained surface temperature for a clean, scratch-free surface, the curve (a) as shown in Fig. 2 is obtained. It is a step function going from zero to infinity at the dew point. To sit on this edge for long is indeed an exercise in

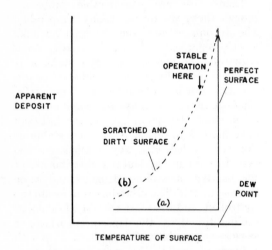

FIG. 2. A clean and perfect surface (a) gives a discontinuous change of the equilibrium deposit as the surface temperature passes through the dew point. A dirty surface (b) gives a smooth curve due to hygroscopic growth as the surface approaches the dew point. (Stable, if false, operation is thereby facilitated.)

brinkmanship! The surface inevitably has some temperature differences, and soon the slightly warmer parts become clear and the colder parts too thickly covered. With dew, this may result in a small pool of water which does not scatter light, and with frost it may result in the formation of a few large crystals. Both confuse the servo system with startling and misleading results. Frequent clearing of the deposit is the answer.

The system may also be confused by thermal precipitation of dust on the surface. It is well known that dirt deposits on cold surfaces, and the hygrometer surface meets this requirement exactly. Unless very clean

air is under test, the surface will require frequent cleaning.

It is, however, possible to use this dust advantageously if it is slightly deliquescent and it usually is. When it is present, the growth of these particles before the dew point is reached produces the stable curve (b) of Fig. 2. Now the servo can be adjusted to monitor the heating to set the operating point before true dew or hoarfrost is formed. Any slight difference of temperature across the surface ceases to be disastrous, and a stable, nonoscillatory servo operation is more easily achieved. Dust is liable to change, but dew or frost also forms in scratches before the dew point is reached owing to the reduction of the vapor pressure by the curvature of the surface in the scratches. A nicely scratched surface can usually be readily provided and it does not deteriorate with use. Unfortunately, when these artifices are used the surface temperature is no longer the dew or frost point but a value slightly higher.

Further difficulties arise when the frost point falls below about $-70°C$. It then becomes necessary to work with very small deposits which can easily be equalled or exceeded by deposited dust, and the small deposits are very difficult to detect. Also the servo loop can be confused by the combined effects of deposition of ice (which increases with lowering temperature) and its formation into visible crystals (which increases with rising temperature), as has already been discussed.

EXTENSION OF THE RANGE OF DEW-POINT HYGROMETERS

Experience shows that in the stratosphere the frost point is liable to become uncomfortably close to the lower limit of operation of a visual hygrometer, namely $-85°C$. Some extension of the range would be very valuable.

From Eq. (1b),

$$e_w(T_f) = \frac{r}{0.622 + r} p$$

it is readily seen that without changing r, the mixing ratio, we can raise $e_w(T_d)$ (and, hence, the dew or frost point) by compressing the air and raising p the total pressure.

The risk of adding water at the low water contents concerned is great, but experience shows that the air can be drawn through large pipes at a high flow rate from the compressors of a gas turbine engine with a $\times 8$ or $\times 10$ compression. The compressors handle air on such a large scale that no detectable change in the mixing ratio occurs. In this way, the range of visual hygrometers can be extended to at least $-90°C$ and automatic hygrometers can have their operation improved. The pressure at which the frost point is measured must of course be determined, and use must be made of Eq. (1b) to correct to the original pressure. It should be mentioned that the compression heats the air and this speeds desorption from pipes. It is repeated, therefore, that it is essential to convey the air through large pipes with large flow rates.

General References

1. Brewer, A. W., Cwilong, B., and Dobson, G. M. B., "Measurement of Absolute Humidity in Extremely Dry Air," *Proc. Phys. Soc. London*, **62**, 52–70 (1948).
2. Dobson, G. M. B., Brewer, A. W., and Cwilong, B., "Meteorology of the Lower Stratosphere," *Proc. Roy. Soc. London Ser. A*, **185**, 144–175 (1946).
3. Dobson, G. M. B., and Brewer, A. W., "Meteorology and High Altitude Aviation," *J. Roy. Aeron. Soc.* **50**, 787 (1946).
4. Goldsmith, P., "A Method of Increasing the Range of the Dobson-Brewer Frost-point Hygrometer in Jet Aircraft," *Quart. J. Roy. Meteorol. Soc.*, **81**, 607 (1956).

14. A Frost-point Hygrometer for Use at Low Frost Points

STANLEY MARTIN

British Scientific Instrument Research Association, "Sira," South Hill, Chislehurst, Kent, England

ABSTRACT

A frost-point hygrometer first described by Brewer and Dobson for investigations in the upper atmosphere has been redesigned for laboratory and industrial use, measuring dew points down to −80°C. A specially designed hand-operated pump directs a jet of liquid nitrogen on to the underside of a mirror mounted on an aluminum thimble. The thimble carries a platinum resistance thermometer winding, with which is associated a compact Wheatstone bridge calibrated to indicate directly in degrees C.

A stream of air from the atmosphere to be measured is directed across the mirror surface by a fine orifice, and the rate of cooling of the mirror is adjusted by operation of the pump until a frost pattern of characteristic shape forms. The mirror is illuminated by a small lamp and elliptical mirror, and it is observed through a magnifying eyepiece. This instrument may be made intrinsically safe.

INTRODUCTION

This paper describes a commercial version of a frost-point hygrometer somewhat similar to the aircraft instrument described by Brewer, Cwilong, and Dobson,[1] but suitable for laboratory and commercial use at much lower air flow rates.

The main requirement is to measure frost points down to the limit at which visual observation is possible. In practice this is about −90°C; below this temperature the frost deposits itself in the form of a glassy layer which is impossible to see. The upper dew-point limit is a few degrees below ambient temperature. A modification of the optical system described by Brewer is used to facilitate visual observation of the minute traces of frost which are deposited at the lower temperatures.

The cooling medium is liquid nitrogen, and a simple, manually operated piston pump was designed to direct a jet on to the underside of a mirror. By using an electrical heater, other systems (not employing a pump) could be devised to give somewhat smoother control of the mirror temperature. However, for commercial reasons, this instrument had to be intrinsically safe, and a heater was therefore undesirable. The temperature is measured by a platinum resistance thermometer.

THE PRINCIPLE OF THE METHOD

A metal mirror is cooled until dew or frost forms on the surface, and the temperature is adjusted until the deposit remains steady in amount. The temperature at which this occurs is taken to be the dew point.

APPARATUS

The Test Chamber and General Assembly

The test chamber is shown in Fig. 1. It consists of a circular brass base, 13.5 cm in diameter, and a cylindrical flanged brass cover which fits over it. The cylindrical chamber so formed is about 8.5 cm in diameter and about 6 cm deep.

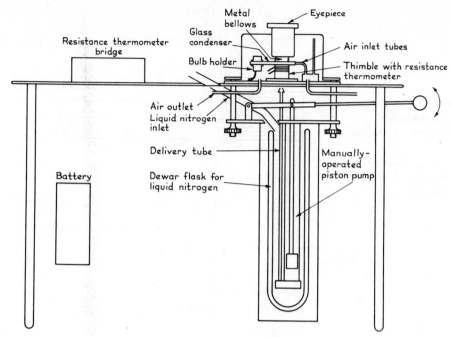

FIG. 1. Simplified sketch of general assembly.

On the base of the test chamber are fixed:

(1) The dew-point mirror. This is in the form of an aluminum "thimble" with a plate of silver/copper alloy attached. It fits over a hole in the base plate as illustrated in Fig. 3 and described below.

(2) The air inlet tubes shown in Fig. 1 and described on p. 147.

(3) A glass/metal seal through which the electrical leads are passed to the illuminating lamp and the resistance thermometer.

(4) Spring clips and rods which support an elliptical glass condenser and illuminating lamp. The rods and clips are not shown, but the condenser is further described in the section dealing with the optical system.

The cylindrical cover accommodates an eyepiece which is used to view the mirror surface. A magnification of about 7 is used and the design is that of Brewer.[1]

Although brass was used for this prototype instrument, stainless steel would be a better material, as it does not adsorb water vapor to the same extent.

The Mirror and Thermometer

The dew-point mirror is shown in Fig. 2. It consists of a cylindrical aluminum "thimble"

about 3.5 cm long and 1.5 cm in diameter with plate of 20 per cent copper/silver alloy soldered to the top. This alloy is used for the mirror in preference to pure silver as it is substantially harder[2] and therefore less easily scratched during cleaning. Its thermal diffusivity is about 80 per cent of that of pure silver. The top of the thimble is carefully polished and then rhodium plated. A thread of about 72 tpi is cut round the body of the thimble which is then anodized. A platinum resistance thermometer consisting of nine turns of 0.0008-inch diameter wire is then wound in the thread. The thimble is supported over a hole in the center of the base plate so that a jet of liquid nitrogen from a container underneath can be directed into the interior of the thimble, thus cooling the mirror.

The mounting has to satisfy the following conditions:

(1) It should not be thermally conducting so that temperature gradients in the thimble are minimized.

(2) It should not adsorb appreciable amounts of water vapor as this could lead to errors in the humidity measurement.

(3) It should withstand rapid cooling without cracking.

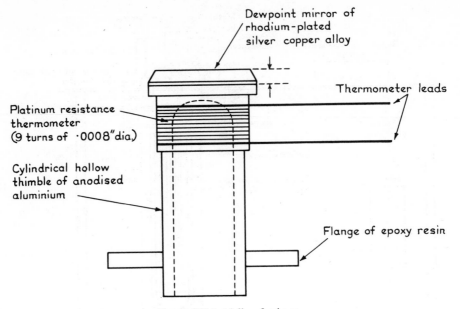

FIG. 2. "Thimble" and mirror.

(4) It must be hermetically sealed.

A reasonable compromise was found to be a mounting made as follows:

A flange of epoxy resin was cast on to the base of the aluminum thimble and then trimmed on a lathe. An O-ring seal was made on the base plate, the flanged thimble being attached by a ring as shown in Fig. 3. A slight clearance, d, exaggerated in the sketch, allows the resin flange to contract and expand without breaking.

The Optical System for Illuminating the Frost

In order to measure the lowest frost points effectively, it is very important to have an efficient system of illumination so that the growth and disappearance of minute traces of frost can be observed. Brewer described an elliptical glass condenser for this purpose, and a modification of this is used here. The arrangement is shown in Fig. 4. Two holes

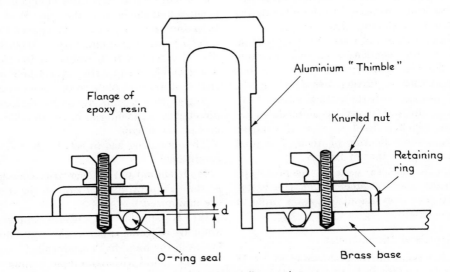

FIG. 3. The "thimble" mounting.

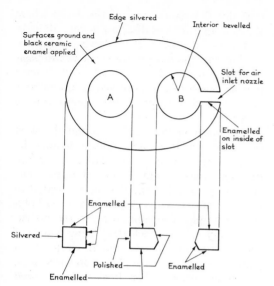

FIG. 4. Elliptical condenser.

are cut such that the centers of the holes are at the foci of the ellipse. A metal lamp holder, attached to the ellipse contains a 3.6-V, 0.5-A lamp. The filament is located at the center of the hole *A*. The center of the frost-point mirror is located at the other focus. The hole *B* is beveled (following Brewer)— this causes the light to be refracted on to the surface of the mirror. The upper and lower surfaces are ground and blackened by a ceramic enameling process, which prevents unwanted internal reflections. The periphery of the ellipse is silvered, and the interiors of the holes *A* and *B* are partly polished and partly blackened as shown in Fig. 4. The slot in the ellipse is to permit the entry of the air inlet nozzle.

A metal bellows is inserted between the hole *B* of the ellipse and the lower lens of the eyepiece. An inner chamber is thus formed, the walls being the lower surface of the lens, the bellows, the hole in the ellipse and the mirror surface. This is, of course, not a hermetically sealed enclosure, but this construction ensures a certain amount of turbulence at the surface of the mirror and increases the speed of frost formation and disappearance.

In order to make the instrument intrinsically safe, all the electrical connections inside the chamber are soldered and the power is derived from a miner's cap lamp battery which is housed in a steel case containing a current-limiting resistor.

The Pump and Liquid Nitrogen Container

Liquid nitrogen is contained in a Dewar flask under the baseplate of the hygrometer chamber. A simple manually-operated piston pump is immersed in it and directs a stream of liquid nitrogen into the thimble. Fig. 1 shows the location of the pump but not the details of the design which is fairly conventional. The barrel is made of brass but this is extended by a plastic tube to reduce conduction of heat into the liquid nitrogen. The piston rod and delivery tube are of thin-walled stainless steel. At the end of the delivery tube is a screwed connection and nozzles of various sizes can be attached, the smaller ones being more suitable for operation at higher temperatures. To avoid the pump seizing up due to contraction, there is considerable clearance between the barrel and piston and no piston rings or gaskets are necessary. Two simple phosphor-bronze ball valves are used. After impinging on the underside of the thimble, the excess liquid nitrogen is caught in a tube (not shown in the diagram) and is directed back into the Dewar flask. It is essential to keep the pump covered with liquid nitrogen during operation as frost will condense on it in the presence of air. A tube is therefore provided so that liquid nitrogen can be poured in with the Dewar flask in position. Alternative designs in which the flask was removed for refilling, and then replaced, were not satisfactory. Very occasionally the nozzle gets clogged up with frost, and when this happens the Dewar flask and pump are removed together by removing the knurled nuts (Fig. 1). The nozzle can then be cleaned without exposing the cold pump body to the atmosphere.

The Air Inlet System

The air inlet assembly consists of two tubes in parallel and a brass block which is screwed to the base plate. The block is recessed so that a filter can be accommodated if desired. One of the tubes terminates in a nozzle and directs air in the form of a fine jet over the surface of the mirror. In order to facilitate purging, the other tube directs air to the top of the outer chamber. The total flow is about 2 l/min. and about one fifth of this flows through the nozzle. The outlet is through a tube in the base, and a union is fitted so that a suction pump can be placed on the end if the test atmosphere is not at a sufficient pressure to flow through the instrument.

The Temperature Measuring Equipment

The leads from the platinum resistance thermometer are connected to glass/metal seals in the baseplate. Connections on the outside are made to a Wheatstone bridge of conventional design. The supply voltage is 4 V DC and on the variable arm is a dial calibrated directly in degrees C.

OPERATION OF THE INSTRUMENT

The test sample is passed through the chamber at about 2 l/min., and liquid nitrogen is poured into the Dewar flask after ensuring that the pump is completely dry. The illuminating lamp and bridge power supply are switched on. After the chamber has been completely purged, the pump is operated and the temperature falls. The temperature is followed on the bridge and as it falls the mirror is observed intermittently. A temperature is found at which there is a small amount of dew or frost in the center of the mirror which neither increases nor decreases in amount. In practice some experience is necessary to obtain good results. The mirror is usually cooled below the dew/frost point before dew/frost forms, and it is very easy to obtain a deposit which is too large for satisfactory observation.

The sensitivity of the instrument depends upon the particular dew point, being about 0.25 deg C near the top of the range where the dew appears and disappears very quickly and several degrees near the lower limit where the buildup and disappearance of the deposit is very slow. From 0 to about −40°C, both dew and frost can be observed on the mirror, and either dew point or frost point can be measured.

The thermometer winding round the skirt of the thimble does not accurately acquire the mirror surface temperature. The temperature difference may amount to several degrees, but the bridge can, nevertheless, be calibrated to read the mirror temperature with the aid of a thermocouple. The calibration of the instrument may also be checked by using liquids of known freezing point. Small droplets of suitable compounds are placed, in succession, on the mirror, and their freezing is observed through the magnifying eyepiece. Some users would find this more convenient than setting up a thermocouple.

As with all dew-point instruments, the mirror must be kept clean for good results. Traces of dirt or grease may cause incorrect results due to physical adsorption.

Acknowledgment. The author is grateful to Messrs. C. F. Casella & Co. Ltd., London, England, for permission to describe this instrument.

References

1. Brewer, Cwilong and Dobson, "Measurement of Absolute Humidity in Extremely Dry Air," *Proc. Phys. Soc.*, **60**, 52 (1948).
2. Martin, S., "A Laboratory Standard Manually Operated Dewpoint Hygrometer using Thermoelectric Cooling," Humidity and Moisture, Vol, 1, Reinhold Publishing Corp., New York, N.Y., 1964,

15. A Laboratory Standard Manually Operated Dew-point Hygrometer using Thermoelectric Cooling

Stanley Martin

British Scientific Instrument Research Association, "Sira,"
South Hill, Chislehurst, Kent, England

ABSTRACT

This instrument is a photoelectric version of the dew-point hygrometer designed for accuracy and simplicity of operation. It is intended to be used for checking the humidity of the atmosphere in a calibration chamber for thermo-hygrographs.

The mirror is cooled by a thermoelectric (Peltier effect) element, but the final adjustment of temperature to the dew point is made by a counteracting electric heater. The formation of dew is detected by means of a barrier-layer photocell connected to a galvanometer, and the temperature of the mirror is measured with a thermocouple. The heat sink and radiator for the thermoelectric cooler is a copper block in contact with a finned aluminum plate which forms the base for the instrument. The single-stage cooler gives dew points down to −15°C, or to −20°C with water cooling for the heat sink.

INTRODUCTION

In connection with the construction of a humidity cabinet for testing hair hygrometers, a dew-point hygrometer was required for use as a laboratory standard.

The range was to be from ambient temperature down to the lowest temperature which could be conveniently reached using a single stage of thermoelectric cooling. With this particular design it proved to be −15°C using air cooling without forced ventilation. Photoelectric detection of dew was specified, since previous experience had shown this to be very sensitive.

Manual operation was decided upon so as to achieve an accurate measurement with an inexpensive instrument.

THE PRINCIPLE OF THE METHOD

The dew-point principle is well known. Air whose dew point is required is passed over a clean mirror which can be cooled and whose temperature can be measured. The dew point is taken to be the temperature at which a small trace of dew remains on the mirror without increasing or decreasing in amount. It will be seen later that for accurate measurements, the mirror must be very clean and the trace of dew, although small, must not be too small.

THE APPARATUS

The complete apparatus is shown in Fig. 1, whereas Figs. 2 and 3 give more detailed pictures of the components of the dew-point chamber. The various components will now be described in detail.

The Chamber

This is a cylindrical box consisting of a circular metal base and a flanged cylindrical upper part which rests on the base and is sealed to it with a gasket. The chamber thus formed is about 12.5 cm in diameter and 4.5 cm deep.

The upper part contains the lamp housing, the lenses and slit to direct a beam of light on to the mirror, the photocell and an inspection window to facilitate the focusing of the light beam and the adjustment of the photocell.

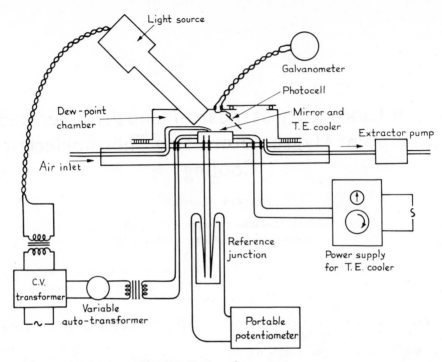

Fig. 1. The complete system.

The lower lens is hermetically sealed, and focusing is effected by moving the upper lens and slit, access to which is obtained by means of a slot cut in the side of the lens tube.

The leads from the photocell are connected to glass/metal seals in the top of the chamber.

The lower part is a brass base with an insert of copper in the center to provide a conducting path to the cooling fins which are fixed to the outside of the chamber.

The thermoelectric cooler and mirror are assembled at the center of the base plate, and the leads are taken out through glass/metal seals which are soldered into the base.

The air inlet is a copper tube sealed into the base. The tube is bent so as to direct the air stream on to the mirror. A tube is also sealed into the base of the chamber to serve as an air outlet. A small air pump attached to the outlet serves to draw air from the test atmosphere into the dew-point chamber. A speed of 1 or 2 l/min. is suitable.

The Cooling Assembly

The cooling unit used is a four-junction model, type BT4 made by Salford Electrical Instruments, Salford, Lancashire, England.

The cooling power is about 2.5 watts for 20 deg C temperature difference between the faces. A heater is also incorporated because, although the temperature can be controlled by the cooling current, a more satisfactory control can be effected by having a heater in close proximity to the mirror. The heater is made from a foil of 40 per cent silver-palladium of specific resistance 42 $\mu\Omega$ cm. A strip of foil $2'' \times 0.5'' \times 0.0005''$ is used, and the resistance at the ends where the current leads are attached is reduced by doubling the thickness and soldering the foil together.

The mirror consists of a block of 20 per cent copper-80 per cent silver alloy, $\frac{1}{2}'' \times \frac{1}{2}'' \times \frac{3}{32}''$, rhodium-plated on one of the $\frac{1}{2}'' \times \frac{1}{2}''$ faces and ground and lapped on the other. The choice of alloy was dictated by the following considerations.

To enable the temperature of the mirror to respond rapidly to changes in heater current it is necessary that the thermal diffusivity be high. This is $K/\rho\sigma$ where

K = thermal conductivity

ρ = density

σ = specific heat.

For some common metals, which might be considered as possible mirrors, $K/\rho\sigma$ is as follows:

Copper	1.13
Silver	1.65
Gold	1.11
Aluminum	0.87
Platinum	0.25

From these considerations, it is clear that silver is the preferred metal. A pure silver mirror however proves to be rather soft and easily damaged by repeated cleaning. The hard layer of rhodium and the necessary under-layers are too thin to prevent scratches appearing in the body of the material. An alloy of 80 per cent silver and 20 per cent copper is much more satisfactory; it is substantially harder and the thermal diffusivity is about 80 per cent of the value for pure silver.

Through the center of the mirror is a hole of about 0.020-in. diameter which accommodates a thermocouple as shown in Fig. 2.

The heater power is supplied by a constant voltage transformer feeding a 0- to 260-V variable autotransformer followed by a step-down transformer. The final usable output is approximately 0 to 1 V, 8 A.

The power supply to the thermoelectric cooler is a standard unit type DC/BTCV supplied by G.E.C. (England). This provides a manually variable output of 0 to 4 V DC, 0 to 15 A. The maximum ripple is 2 per cent.

The Optical System

The method of dew detection is to illuminate the mirror at an angle by a beam of light and locate a photocell so that no specular reflection is received. When dew forms on the mirror, scattered light is detected by the cell. The optical system is shown in Fig. 3. The lamp is fed from a stabilized supply, and a lens is used to focus an image of the filament onto a slit. An image of the slit is formed by the second lens approximately in the plane of the photocell. The photocell is a selenium barrier layer cell, 1-in. in diameter; it has a rectangular hole in the center 0.2 in. × 0.05 in. so that the specular beam passes through and is lost. The photocell output is connected to a portable light-spot galvanometer of variable sensitivity. There is also a control by which the zero can be adjusted mechanically over a wide range.

When dew forms on the mirror, scattered light falls on the photocell and deflects the

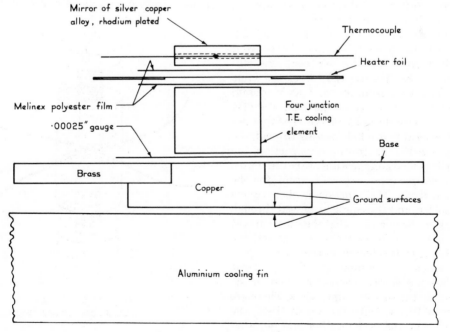

FIG. 2. The cooling assembly.

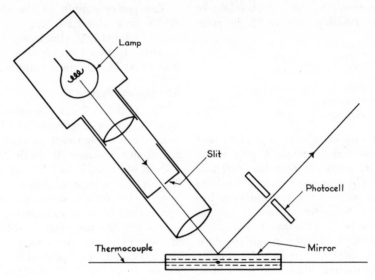

Lamp

Slit

Photocell

Thermocouple

Mirror

FIG. 3. The optical system.

galvanometer. There is also a certain amount of stray light which is "backed off" mechanically by adjusting the zero of the galvanometer.

The Temperature Measurement

The temperature is measured by a calibrated "Pallador" thermocouple and a potentiometer. "Pallador" is produced by Johnson Matthey & Co., London, England, and is the name given to a couple of 40 per cent palladium/gold and 10 per cent iridium/platinum. The thermal EMF is of the same order as iron-constantan, and at moderate temperatures it possesses the high stability associated with the noble metals. The thermocouple is located in a hole passing through the mirror (see Fig. 2). During construction, the couple is welded and the wires are covered with a high-temperature varnish, except for the junction itself. The junction is then tinned with solder, and the couple is passed through the hole in the mirror so that the junction is at the center. The assembly is heated, and the junction is thus soldered to the mirror.

In order to eliminate possible parasitic EMF's some special connectors were made for joining the thermocouple wires. These are shown in Fig. 4. With the aid of these, the two wires are pressed together and no other metal appears between them.

The reference junction is held at 0°C by an ice/water mixture, and the complete thermocouple circuit is shown in Fig. 1.

The potentiometer is a portable model, reading to an accuracy of 5 μV, with the built-in galvanometer replaced by an external box galvanometer with an optical magnifier giving an effective scale distance of 1.5 m.

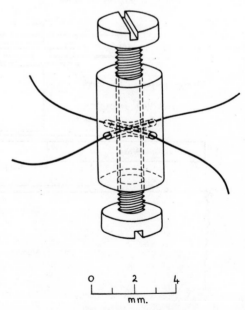

0   2   4
m m.

FIG. 4. Thermocouple connectors.

This allows the use of a suspension of 1-second period, of resistance low enough to be approximately critically damped by the thermocouple (30 Ω) and slide wire (max. 20 Ω), and the galvanometer is, at the same time, adequately sensitive. The resulting sensitivity is about 0.25 to 0.40 deg C per cm deflection, and the spot follows closely the movement of the heater control so that the operator can very quickly establish the required temperature and hold it steady.

OPERATION OF THE INSTRUMENT

To operate the instrument, the air pump is started and an air sample is drawn through the apparatus at a rate of about 1.5 l/min. After allowing a few minutes for the chamber to be purged, the thermoelectric cooler, heater and illuminating lamp are switched on. There is a certain amount of stray light inside the chamber, and this causes the photocell galvanometer to deflect. This deflection is backed off mechanically with the zero adjustment of the galvanometer. Temperature control is achieved by adjusting the heater current while observing the potentiometer galvanometer closely. The cooling current is held at a fixed value. The optimum cooling current depends upon the desired control temperature, and this is easily found by trial. The potentiometer galvanometer responds very quickly to changes in the heater control, and after a little practice any desired temperature within the range can be achieved very quickly and held to within a few hundredths of a degree. A temperature change of, say, one degree C can be achieved and stabilized in three or four seconds.

The temperature is reduced gradually until dew forms on the mirror. The photocell galvanometer then deflects. The sensitivity of the galvanometer is then adjusted so that the current for full scale deflection is about one third of the current produced by a heavy deposit of dew. (This operation necessitates adjusting the zero as well.) Once made, this adjustment need not be altered unless the lamp voltage varies or some adjustment is made which modifies the stray light. The temperature of the mirror is then changed until a galvanometer deflection of about $\frac{3}{4}$-full scale is maintained. When the meter

has been fairly steady for a few seconds, the temperature is read on the potentiometer. This is the dew-point temperature at the pressure obtaining in the chamber. It may be necessary to apply a correction if an appreciable pressure difference exists between the test atmosphere and the dew-point chamber.

ADSORPTION OF THE MIRROR

During experiments with earlier photoelectric dew-point hygrometers, it became obvious that the photocell galvanometer began to deflect when the temperature of the mirror was somewhat above the dew point, and the effect became more and more pronounced as the mirror deteriorated in quality or became dirty. It was thought that this was due to water vapor becoming physically adsorbed on the mirror, the effect being enhanced by the presence of traces of grease. Other workers have also concluded from resistance measurements on glass[1] that an adsorbed layer is formed above the dew point. With the present sensitive instrument, the effect is quite apparent, and Fig. 5 shows some curves of photocurrent plotted against mirror temperature. An air stream of steady humidity was passed through the apparatus, and the mirror was cooled gradually. When a slight photocurrent was observed, the temperature was held steady by the heater control, and temperature and photocurrent readings were taken. This was repeated at lower temperatures and heavier deposits. The measurements were stopped at medium deposits since heavy deposits result in erratic readings. Curve (a) of Fig. 5 shows the adsorption effect when the mirror had been exposed to the atmosphere for several days and traces of grease were present on the surface. When the mirror was cleaned, the adsorption above the dew-point temperature was much reduced as can be seen from curve (b). Curve (c) was obtained when the mirror was very thoroughly cleaned using solvents, followed by polishing with a lens cleaning fabric. This shows very slight adsorption above the dew point and represents the best result which could be obtained with this particular mirror. (This curve was obtained with air at a slightly different humidity and is consequently displaced).

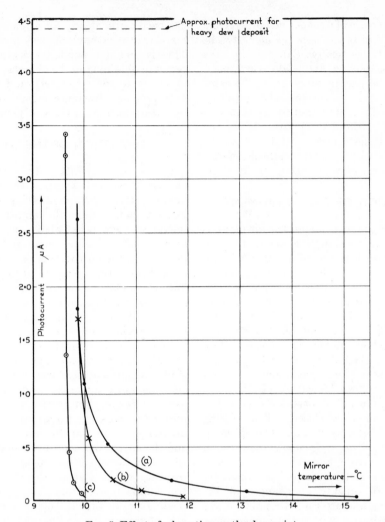

FIG. 5. Effect of adsorption on the dew point.

REPRODUCIBILITY AND ACCURACY

The instrument has been so designed that a reasonably experienced operator can obtain readings reproducible to a few hundredths of a degree C, provided of course the test atmosphere stays sufficiently constant. Mirror temperature measurements corresponding to various levels of dew can be conveniently made, thus providing a check on the cleanliness of the mirror. Such measurements are also used to ensure that a suitable operating point is used. A high level of dew is unsatisfactory as more sensitive operation is achieved with a small deposit. However, it should not be so small that the operating point lies on the curved portion of the photocurrent-temperature curve. If, after careful cleaning, the current-temperature curve approximates curve (a) of Fig. 5, this means the mirror has deteriorated and should be replaced.

The accuracy of the instrument depends upon the accuracy of calibration of the thermocouple, the quality of the potentiometer and the stability of the standard cell.

Acknowledgment. The author is grateful to Messrs. C. F. Casella & Co. Ltd., London, England for permission to describe this instrument.

Reference

1. Smail, G. G., Brooksbank, R. J., and Thornton, W. M., "The Electrical Resistance of Moisture Films on Glazed Surfaces," *J. Inst. Elec. Engrs.*, **69**, 427 (1931).

16. Design Features of the NYU Automatic Frost-point Hygrometer

ALAN M. NATHAN

New York University, New York, N.Y.

ABSTRACT

A description is given of a lightweight, automatic frost-point hygrometer developed for high-altitude balloon use. The hygrometer uses photoelectric balancing to control rf induction heating of the mirror, dry ice cooling, and a thermistor dew-point or frost-point temperature sensor. Instrumental accuracy and special design features are discussed. Models of this instrument have been carried into the stratosphere on many balloon flights conducted by several investigators.

INTRODUCTION

This paper presents a brief description of a lightweight, automatic, photoelectric frost-point hygrometer developed for stratospheric balloon soundings. The key design features of the instrument are described, and its accuracy and performance are discussed. The instrument was developed and tested by the Special Projects Group of the Research Division of New York University during the period 1952 through 1957, under the sponsorship of the Bureau of Aeronautics, Department of the Navy.

Prototype models were test flown at various times during that period, and in 1957 the final design was turned over to the Naval Research Laboratory. Since that date, flights have been conducted by NRL,[1, 2] BRL,[3] and the University of Denver,[4] all using basically the same model hygrometer. NRL[5] has greatly improved the accuracy of the high-altitude data collected with the instrument, by eliminating most if not all of the sources of potential moisture contamination in the flight package, and also by arranging to take data during the descent as well as ascent of the balloon. Much of the data collected with this hygrometer has been compiled by Gutnick[6] in a mean moisture profile for the stratosphere at mid-latitudes (Fig. 1).

The hygrometer employs a small circular rhodium-plated silver mirror, which is cooled by conduction downward from beneath the mirror center to a cold sink, and heated by rf induction heating of a thin iron sleeve plated around its periphery. The geometry of the mirror is such as to produce a very slight radial temperature gradient across its face, with the center cooler than the periphery. For this reason, the condensate grows outward from the mirror center as the mirror cools below the frost point. The radial size of the dew or frost spot is detected photoelectrically by means of a flashlight lamp and a pair of 922 vacuum phototubes connected in a balanced bridge circuit. One phototube views the specularly reflected light from the mirror, and the other views the light diffusely scattered by the condensate plus a portion of the direct source light. The unbalance signal from the phototube bridge, indicative of condensate spot size change, is amplified in a one-stage DC amplifier and used to control continuously the level of rf induction heating current so as to maintain spot radius constant.

A small bead thermistor is embedded in the mirror at the outer edge of the condensate spot so as to register true dew- or frost-point temperature. The resistance of the thermistor is thus a direct measure of frost point and is

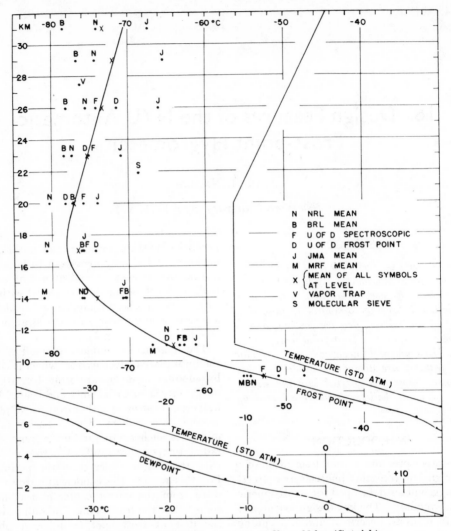

Fig. 1. Mean mid-latitude moisture profile to 31 km (Gutnick).

used to modulate the repetition rate of a radiosonde blocking oscillator in a standard manner. The design details and performance characteristics of the hygrometer are discussed at greater length below.

HYGROMETER GENEALOGY

Photoelectric detection of condensate formation on manually controlled dew-point hygrometers has been employed since the early 1930's, and in 1940, Thornthwaite and Owen[7] developed a servo-controlled version. Their instrument used a mirror cooled continuously by conduction to a cold sink and heated by a resistance heater just below the mirror surface. Diffusion of the specularly reflected light beam by condensate caused a drop in phototube current, which was used to actuate a relay which turned the heater on fully. Heat was thus supplied at a fixed rate greater than the cooling rate produced by the refrigerant, and the condensate was evaporated. When the amount of condensate was reduced sufficiently to increase the reflected light intensity to a threshold value, the heat was turned off. Mirror temperature was measured by a thermocouple junction on the mirror surface. Because of the on-off mode of operation of the servo system, the mirror temperature oscillated above and below the actual dew point.

A group at the University of Chicago next undertook the development of an improved hygrometer for high-altitude balloon soundings. They incorporated proportional control of heating rate so as to achieve a stable, continuous dew-point reading. They used rf induction heating, with the heating coil surrounding the mirror below its exposed surface. The mirror was a steel cap fitted onto a copper cold rod whose lower end was cooled by immersion in a dry ice-alcohol or freon bath. Mirror surface temperature was measured by means of a thermocouple.

The University of Chicago hygrometer was described by Brissman,[8] Suomi,[9] and Barrett and Herndon,[10] and balloon-borne versions weighing approximately 45 pounds were flown and described by Barrett, Herndon and Carter,[11] and Suomi and Barrett.[12]

More elaborate industrial versions of this type of hygrometer were developed at about the same time by Wallace and Tiernan, Inc., General Electric, and others. The Wallace and Tiernan instrument employed three separate servo loops: a fast loop to control the mirror heating, a slow-acting loop to adjust the operating point of the rf induction heater, and a loop to readjust optical balance with a motor-driven shutter after clearing the mirror with a manual overheat switch. The instrument used a thermocouple for mirror temperature measurement and required nine vacuum tubes. Photographs of the instrument are shown in Figs. 2 and 3.

NYU FROST-POINT HYGROMETER

The primary goals of the NYU hygrometer development program were to achieve an accurate, reliable and lightweight unit suitable for stratospheric balloon flights. The design goal was set at a maximum of 12 pounds, including batteries and telemetering transmitter.

Mirror and Cold Rod

To achieve this flight-package weight, a key element of the hygrometer, the mirror and cold rod, was completely redesigned. After much development, a silver and iron umbrella-shaped configuration was evolved (Fig. 4), which has proven quite successful. Unlike most prior arrangements, where heat input was substantially below the mirror surface, i.e., between mirror and cold sink, this configuration absorbs the rf heating power in an iron sleeve electroplated onto the periphery of the silver mirror surface. Cooling is effected by conduction down the central cold rod from the bottom center of the mirror. The top surface of the mirror is rhodium plated for durability and high reflectivity. For rapid cooling, it was found important to machine the mirror-cold rod from one solid rod of pure silver after having the iron heat-absorbing sleeve electroplated onto the top portion of the rod. Any soldered, brazed, or shrink-fitted junctions were found to degrade the cooling rate.

The particular configuration of mirror-cold rod shown in Fig. 4 has important advantages over earlier types. Because the heat flux originates in the concentric iron sleeve at the periphery of the mirror, heat flow is directed radially inward to the center of the mirror, and thence axially down the cold rod to the refrigerant. The surface of the mirror thus has a temperature gradient directed radially inward, and this causes condensate to begin to deposit from the center outward. At equilibrium, (i.e., constant frost point and stable system operation) the radius of the condensate spot will reach out to the vicinity of the thermistor which is mounted below the mirror surface part of the way out towards the mirror edge.

The temperature gradient across the mirror surface is very slight at equilibrium, because of the mirror-cold rod geometry. Furthermore, there is practically zero temperature gradient from the top to the underside of the mirror at the radius of the thermistor. Thus, the thermistor not only senses true frost point because of its location at the condensate spot edge, but also is relatively unaffected by changes in spot radius from the balance condition. An error in spot size results in only minor errors in frost-point reading, because of the small gradient across the mirror.

To verify this prediction, the mirror-surface temperature was explored by means of a fine constantan needle, whose tip created a thermoelectric junction with the silver mirror when it was used to probe the mirror surface.

Fig. 2. Wallace and Tiernan airplane dew-point hygrometer chassis.

Fig. 3. Wallace and Tiernan airplane dew-point hygrometer exterior.

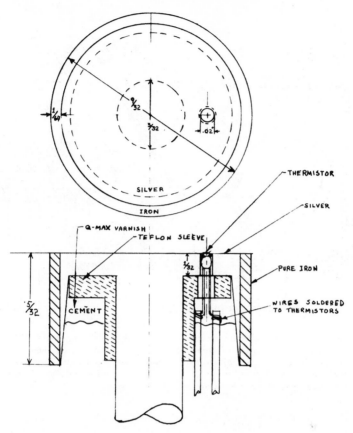

FIG. 4. Frost-point mirror and cooling rod.

The difference between the temperatures at the center and outer edge of the mirror was generally found to be considerably less than 1°C. Another test of this point was conducted by deliberately varying condensate spot size during stable operation at various frost points. When the spot was varied from complete mirror coverage to practically zero coverage (by changing the phototube-bridge balance with sample air at a constant frost point), the corresponding changes in the observed frost points as measured by the thermistor were as follows: $\Delta T_D = 0.2$ deg C at $-40°C$ frost point; $\Delta T_D = 0.5$ deg C at $-10°C$ frost point; $\Delta T_D = 0.8$ deg C at $+10°C$ dew point.

The mirror design offers two further advantages tending to increase the hygrometer's sensitivity. Because of the small temperature gradient at the border of the condensate spot, a small change in ambient frost point results in a large change in spot radius. Furthermore, since it is spot radius which changes rather than spot thickness, the photoelectric sensing system is much more sensitive to frost-point errors than earlier hygrometers.

A large temperature gradient exists down the cooling rod from beneath the center of the mirror to the refrigerant. The mirror cooling rate is accordingly quite high, and the transient response of the system to negative step-function changes in frost point is correspondingly rapid. The heating rate at the mirror is also high because the rf induction heater coil, closely surrounding the mirror, generates heat within the mirror's periphery directly and has only a small thermal mass to heat.

The cooling rod is thermally connected to the refrigerant by tight clamping in a hole reamed into a flange on the wall of the small aluminum pot containing the refrigerant.

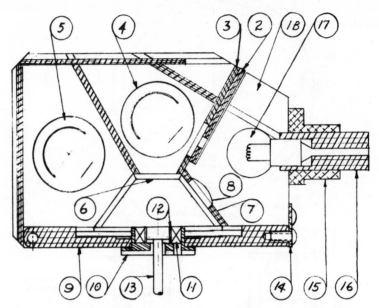

FIG. 5. Optical head and mirror assembly: (2, 3) variable aperture shutter,
(4, 5) type 922 vacuum phototubes, (6) polystyrene windows and sample air
duct, (7) "Bakelite" light shields, (8) collimating lens, (9) hinged floor plate—
"Bakelite," (10) "Teflon" collar, (11) rf induction heating coil, (12) "Teflon"
sleeve, (13) silver mirror—cooling rod, (17) 6-V lamp.

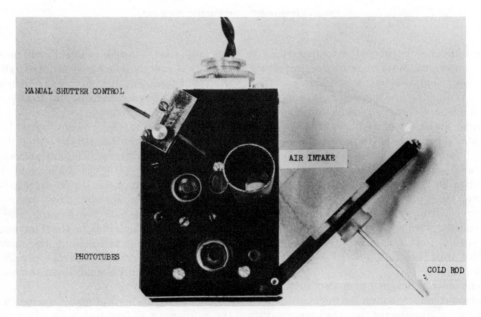

FIG. 6. Optical head with floor plate containing mirror open for inspection.

In order to reduce the average heat flux from heater to cold sink, the mirror and cold rod dimensions were scaled down as far as was feasible. Transient response was improved by this size reduction, and at the same time the amounts of heater power and refrigerant required were greatly reduced. The overall saving in weight was considerable, being approximately proportional to the square of the size reduction factor.

The thermistors used to measure frost-point temperatures were glass-coated beads of about 0.015-inch diameter, with two platinum leads emerging from one end. Various types have been used to get a desired resistance-*vs*-temperature curve. Mounting these beads in the mirror is best done with epoxy cements, a steady hand, and much patience. Tests have shown that the temperature of the thermistor is not at all affected by the rf induction field. Because of its location within the silver mirror, it is well shielded electromagnetically from the induction heating coil.

Optics

Type 922 vacuum phototubes were employed in a balanced bridge circuit as the photoelectric sensors. A schematic drawing of the optical head is shown in Fig. 5. One of the 922's views the light from the lamp after specular reflection at the frost-point mirror;

the other views a portion of the light diffusely scattered by the frost spot, and a portion of the direct source light. A manually adjustable shutter regulates the amount of direct light to the diffuse phototube so as to permit balancing of the phototube bridge circuit. Figure 6 is a photograph of a model of the optical head slightly different from that drawn in Fig. 5, the latter being the more recent version.

Electronics

Figure 7 is a schematic diagram of the control circuitry of the hygrometer. The output of the phototube bridge appears as a DC voltage across the grid of the pentode amplifier tube, a 6U8 pentode-triode. At balance, the phototubes generate equal current, and the voltage across the grid resistor is therefore zero. With an excessively large frost spot, the current through the specular phototube is decreased, that through the diffuse phototube is increased, and the amplifier grid is driven negative. A potentiometer and bias battery are connected in series with the amplifier grid resistor, to prevent the amplifier grid from drawing grid current and to permit control of condensate spot size.

The pentode DC amplifier drives a triode cathode-follower, whose cathode directly supplies the screen voltage to the 6L6 rf induction heating oscillator. The 6L6 screen

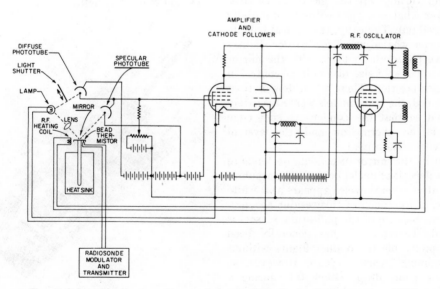

Fig. 7. Schematic diagram of control circuit of the frost-point hygrometer (NRL report 5551).

voltage is thus made to follow the plate of the pentode DC amplifier. Variation of the oscillator's screen voltage modulates the power output of the oscillator in the proper direction so as to regulate the induction heating. An increase in condensate spot size causes an increase in rf heating, thus shrinking the spot. The system is therefore one employing 100 per cent negative feedback.

Because of the 100 per cent negative feedback and the high gain of the optical-electronic-thermal amplifier, changes in the gain of any component, DC drift, or supply voltage changes have relatively little effect on the operation of the system.

The screen of the rf oscillator can be switched from the cathode-follower to the plate supply voltage, when it is desired to overheat the mirror to clear it. This procedure drives the rf oscillator at maximum power output and rapidly clears the condensate off the mirror. The oscillator supplies heat to the mirror at any level from 0 to about 10 watts, with efficiencies ranging up to about 60 per cent. The average heat drain is about 5 watts, depending on frost point.

HYGROMETER OPERATION

Normal operation of the instrument is achieved by filling the reservoir with refrigerant and turning on the electrical circuits. However, a balancing procedure must initially be carried out. Typically, the optical balancing shutter was adjusted for zero or slightly negative phototube output, with the mirror clear and the spot size bias voltage control in its center position. Then, when dew or frost had formed, the two controls were alternately adjusted so that the condensate spot edge was at the thermistor and the system sensitivity was optimal.

Clearing the mirror of condensate tends to leave a deposit of nuclei behind. The accumulation after several cycles appears as a white residue. If too much of this residue accumulates, the balance of the phototube sensors is affected. Therefore, it has generally been found preferable to conduct flights without programming clearing cycles. However, as the dew point drops below 0°C during a balloon ascent, a possibility of supercooling exists. The hygrometer may be reading vapor

pressure over water, rather than over ice, even at temperatures well below freezing. Two expedients are available to avoid this problem. First, the mirror should not be too clean. Experience has shown that accumulated nuclei and/or surface scratches on the mirror help promote freezing at temperatures close to 0°C. Second, by clearing the mirror once, shortly after the frost point has dropped below 0°C, supercooling of liquid droplets can be avoided and ice will be formed upon recooling.

Actually, confusion between ice and water has not been an important problem, since the difference between dew point and frost point does not exceed 2 deg C down to −20°C. With a normally dirty mirror, water tends to go over into ice at temperatures close to 0°C.

FLIGHT PACKAGING

The hygrometer has been packaged and powered in a variety of ways by different investigators. The basic hygrometer plus standard radiosonde and baroswitch weighed less than five pounds in the NYU version. Weight with batteries and rigging was under twelve pounds. Figure 8 shows the circuit board, baroswitch, and optical assembly. Figure 9 is a photograph of the hygrometer packaged by the Ballistics Research Laboratory and ready for flight.

Fig. 8. Layout of hygrometer circuit board, optics, and baroswitch.

FIG. 9. Hygrometer flight package (BRL).

PERFORMANCE AND ACCURACY

The accuracy and repeatability of NYU hygrometer measurements have been tested on several occasions in the pressure-humidity apparatus at the National Bureau of Standards, over a dew-point range from above 0°C to −53°C. The average reproducibility of the hygrometer reading at any nominal dew point between 0.4° and −39.1°C was within 0.4 deg C. The largest spread in readings for any nominal dew point was 0.8 deg C. The average reproducibility of the hygrometer reading after clearing the mirror was 0.3 deg C, and the largest spread under this condition was 0.6 deg C. The absolute errors, in terms of dew points, ranged from +1.7 deg C to −1.3 deg C, with an average error of ±0.7 deg C.

On another occasion, with a second instrument, average absolute accuracy of measurement was better than ±0.5°C. It should be pointed out that in these tests, the hygrometer thermistor resistance had been calibrated against temperature only. No dewpoint calibration of the hygrometer had to be carried out.

Heating the intake air line with a bunsen burner had no effect on frost-point readings, proving that the hygrometer is insensitive to ambient air temperature.

Transient response of the hygrometer to rapid changes in frost point was studied with a divided flow apparatus. Frost points from room temperature down to −53°C could be produced with this apparatus. At very low frost points, the hygrometer's cooling time constant (63 per cent of total change) was about five seconds. In the range from room temperature to −25°C, cooling time constants were on the order of one second. It should be noted that response time is a function of the temperature gradient between mirror and cold sink. At sea-level pressure and a frost point of −50°C, the gradient is only 28°C (dry ice = −78.5°C). In an actual balloon ascent, the drop in the sublimation temperature of CO_2 as atmospheric pressure drops with altitude, results in a larger temperature gradient and a correspondingly shorter cooling time constant. Heating time constant in all cases was on the order of one second.

CONCLUSIONS

Much of the developmental history of the NYU hygrometer has been described in project reports.[13,14,15] The instrument has proved to be useful. Much of the acceptable data on upper-atmospheric moisture content has been obtained with versions of this instrument. While the hygrometer was designed primarily for stratospheric soundings, some of its design features should be useful in hygrometers intended for other applications.

Acknowledgments. The author gratefully acknowledges the continuous personal interest and encouragement of Mr. E. F. Corwin of the Bureau of Naval Weapons (formerly Bureau of Aeronautics), whose support, as representative of the sponsoring agency, was largely responsible for the development of the NYU hygrometer.

Since 1957, the further refinement of the instrument and its utilization in flight programs have been the responsibility of the Naval Research Laboratory.

The author has appreciated the friendly and informative discussions he has had with Dr. J. E. Dinger and Messrs. H. J. Mastenbrook, R. E. Ruskin, and W. W. Werner, of NRL, and has profited from the papers published by this group.

The author wishes to express his particular gratitude for the conscientious and invaluable participation of Mr. Charles Lettre in the development and testing of this instrument. Dr. William D. Murray, under whose direction the program was initiated, and Mr. D. Slater, also contributed to the project.

References

1. Mastenbrook, H. J., and Dinger, J. E., "The Measurement of Water-vapor Distribution in the Stratosphere," U.S. Naval Research Lab., Report 5551, November 1960.
2. Mastenbrook, H. J., and Dinger, J. E., "Distribution of Water Vapor in the Stratosphere," *J. Geophys. Res.*, **66**, 1437–1444 (1961).
3. Marks, S. T., ed., "Summary Report on BRL-IGY Activities," BRL Report 1104, 1960.
4. Murcray, D. G., Murcray, F. H., and Williams, W. J., "Distribution of Water Vapor in the Stratosphere as Determined from Infrared Absorption Measurements," Univ. of Denver Scientific Report No. 1, 1961, Contract AF 19 (604)-7429.
5. Mastenbrook, H. J., "The Vertical Distribution of Water Vapor over Hyderbad, India, and Comparison with Mid-latitude Distribution, U.S. Naval Research Lab. Report 5817, August 1962.
6. Gutnick, M., "Mean Annual Mid-latitude Moisture Profiles to 31 Km," Air Force Surveys in Geophysics, No. 147, July 1962.
7. Thornthwaite, C. W., and Owen, J. C., "A Dew-point Recorder for Measuring Atmospheric Moisture," *Monthly Weather Rev.*, **68**, 315–318 (1940).
8. Brissman, D. N., "Preliminary Report on a Dew-point Hygrometer," Dept. of Meteorology, University of Chicago, 1945.
9. Suomi, V. E., "Moisture Measurement with an Electronic Dew-point Hygrometer," *Instruments,* **21**, 178.
10. Barrett, E. W. and Herndon, L. R., Jr., "An improved Electronic Dew-point Hygrometer," *J. Meteorol.*, **8**, 40–51 (1951).
11. Barrett, E. W., Herndon, L. R., Jr., and Carter, H. J., "Some Measurements of the Distribution of Water Vapor in the Stratosphere," *Tellus.*, **2**, 302–311 (1950).
12. Suomi, V. E., and Barrett, E. W., "An Experimental Radiosonde for the Investigation of the Distribution of Water Vapor in the Stratosphere," *Rev. Sci. Instr.*, **23**, 272–292 (1952).
13. Nathan, A. M., "Dew-point Hygrometer Development," New York University, Coll. of Eng., Tech. Rept. 272.03, December 1954.
14. Nathan, A. M., "Hygrometer Laboratory Tests," New York University, Coll. of Eng., Tech. Rept. 360.01, June 1955.
15. Lettre, C., and Slater, D., "Hygrometer Field Tests," New York University, Coll. of Eng., Tech. Rept. 381.04, July 1956.

17. An Automatic Dew-point Hygrometer with Thermoelectric Cooling*

Charles C. Francisco and David J. Beaubien

Cambridge Systems, Inc., Newton, Mass.

ABSTRACT

An instrument of the automatic dew-point hygrometer type with the feature of thermoelectric cooling is described. Particular emphasis is given to the selection of the thermoelectric module in terms of maximum cooling criteria, physical size, cost, and power requirements. A means for sensing and controlling the formation of dew or frost on the mirror surface is described, and performance data for the instrument is included.

An optical dew-sensing system compares a directly reflected light beam to the scattered light level. High sensitivity in the dew detection system permits low sampling rates in the order of 1 to 10 cc/sec and thereby minimizes the accumulation of mirror contaminants. The optical sensing system is shown to be insensitive to changes in ambient temperature over the range of −40 to +140°F as a result of the complimentary temperature coefficients of the photoresistors when used in a bridge configuration. By similar argument, the system is also insensitive to excitation light level changes.

A solid-state, high-gain proportional control system for electronic servo control of the mirror at the dew-point temperature is utilized. Silicon-controlled rectifiers are employed to regulate the direct current to the thermoelectric module. The proportional control circuit is shown to main-tain stable control of the system over ambient temperature between −40 and +140°F.

Attention is given to materials of construction in the dew-point sensor and to the rhodium-plated mirror assembly. The requirements for the mirror temperature readout system are also discussed. A miniature platinum-resistance thermometer is recommended although other temperature sensors may be used.

The performance of the thermoelectric dew-point hygrometer is included, and the results of a one-year field-test program are presented. The short-term and long-term accuracies of the instrument are discussed on the basis of available test data.

* This paper is an extension of the work reported by the authors at the 4th Conference on Applied Meteorology, at Hampton, Virginia, September, 1962 (Ref. 7). Revised descriptions of the production models for the modified AN/TMQ-11 Temperature-Humidity Set are included, together with updated field test data.

INTRODUCTION

The measurement of atmospheric moisture content can be classified as one of the most difficult of physical measurements which the meteorologist must make. During the past decade, several new approaches have been taken to improve the measurement of atmospheric moisture content in the field on a continuous basis. Most notable among these have been the infrared hygrometer originally described by Wood, Foskett and Foster in 1954,[1] and the microwave hygrometer described by Sargent.[2] Considerable attention has also been given to modernization of conventional hygrometers, particularly, studies of mirror-type hygrometers reported by Kobayashi.[3] This paper deals with the latter group and presents the design and evaluation of an electronic, thermoelectrically cooled, mirror-type dew-point hygrometer.

The mirror-type dew-point hygrometer has long been respected as one of the most accurate and wide-range instruments for measuring atmospheric moisture. The advent of reasonably efficient thermoelectric cooling modules has permitted a simple and convenient method for obtaining mirror cooling, thus eliminating the need for chemical or mechanical refrigeration.

The use of the thermoelectric cooler, coupled with a reliable solid-state proportional control circuit, tends to make the dew-point hygrometer compatible with the requirements for field equipment. This development was supported by Air Force Cambridge Research Laboratories under Contract AF 19(628)-410.

MEASUREMENT SYSTEM CONCEPT

The basic concept of the Peltier-cooled dew-point hygrometer is shown in Fig. 1. The sensing mirror is thermally bonded to, but electrically insulated from, a thermoelectric cooling module. The module, when excited with direct current of the proper polarity, causes heat to be pumped from the mirror and thus lowers the mirror temperature. As the mirror temperature reaches the dew point, condensate forms on the mirror surface. The condensate causes the visible light reflection characteristic of the mirror to change. This change is detected by the photoresistors in the optical sensing bridge and converted to an electrical signal, which drives an amplifier/power supply, the output of which is a direct current proportional to the input signal. Using this current to excite the thermoelectric cooler in a negative sense, i.e., causing the mirror to become cooler when a decrease in condensate occurs, it is seen that the system will stabilize on and control about a particular dew layer thickness. A measurement of the mirror temperature under stabilized conditions is taken to be a measurement of dew point.

THE THERMOELECTRIC COOLING MODULE

The thermoelectric couple consists of two rods of bismuth telluride, one doped P-type and the other N-type, bonded by a flat copper bar to provide a heat transfer surface as well as electrical conducting medium. The couples are arranged physically in parallel to provide

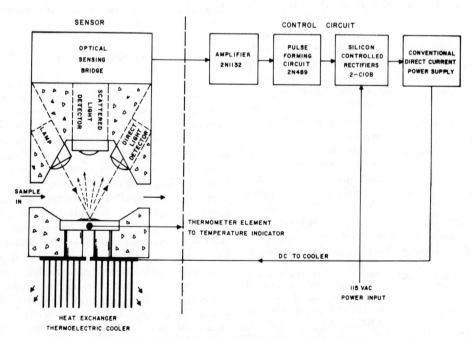

FIG. 1. Thermoelectric dew-point indicator, block diagram.

increased heat-pumping capability, and are connected electrically in series to increase the overall impedance level. A number of couples interconnected in this fashion are called a thermoelectric module. Such a device, when excited with direct current, causes heat to be pumped by Peltier action from one surface of the module to the other. A physical discussion of the action is not within the scope of this paper, but is given by Ioffe.[4] If a suitable heat exchanger is provided at the hot side of the module, so that the hot side can be maintained at or near the ambient temperature, the cold side can be reduced to a temperature more than 100 deg F below ambient for low heat-pumping rates. The performance characteristic of a typical thermoelectric module for a 77°F ambient temperature is shown in Fig. 2. The lower curve is taken with an ambient air heat load on the module. The upper curve is representative of the module characteristic with the additional loading of the dew sensor mirror, the thermometer element leads, and the vapor seal. The maximum temperature difference attainable with the sensor loads is 118 deg F with the ambient temperature at 77°F.

The maximum attainable temperature differential is also proportional to the absolute ambient temperature as shown in Fig. 3. The

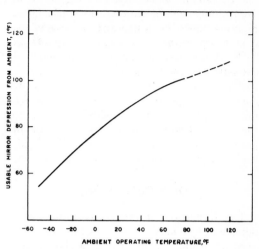

Fig. 3. Performance of thermoelectric module with sensor heat loads.

deterioration in heat-pumping capability at the lower ambient temperatures is due to changes in the physical properties of the semiconductor materials used in the module construction. The curve in Fig. 3 serves to define the lowest measurable dew or frost point at any ambient temperature within the −40 to +120°F operating temperature range.

The heat-pumping capacity of the thermo-

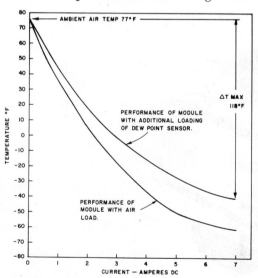

FIG. 2. Performance characteristic of a typical thermoelectric module for a 77°F ambient temperature.

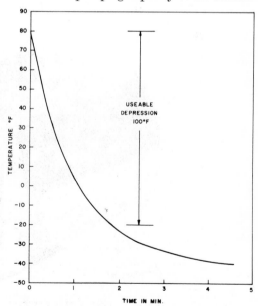

FIG. 4. Downward response of thermoelectric module.

electric module is also the limiting factor in determining the instrument response time. Figure 4 shows the downward response of the module operating in a dry atmosphere at 80°F. If the desired instrument response of one-half degree Fahrenheit per second or better is to be maintained over the entire operating range, it is necessary to define a usable depression limit which corresponds to the limit of desired response. For the ambient temperature situation presented in Fig. 4, the usable depression is seen to be 100 deg F.

DEW DETECTION

The formation of dew on the mirror is detected by means of a photoresistive, optical-sensing bridge, which is shown diagrammatically in Fig. 1 and physically in Fig. 5. The optics are arranged in such a way that a beam of light illuminates the mirror surface, and separate cadmium sulfide photoresistors compare the directly reflected light to the scattered light when dew forms. The photoresistors are chosen for detectors in the sensing bridge because of their small physical size and their low impedance suitable for driving other solid-state circuits. Like the majority of solid-state devices, cadmium sulfide photoresistors exhibit a pronounced temperature dependency. When the devices are required to operate over wide ambient temperatures, the temperature-induced resistance change can exceed the resistance increment imparted by the light level change. To effectively eliminate the temperature effects, two criteria must be met. First, the level of illumination supplied to the photoresistor must be high, since the temperature coefficient of the devices is inversely proportional to the light level, being lowest at full illumination. Second, the photoresistors must be used in a bridge configuration, so that the temperature-induced resistance changes tend to cancel each other. These conditions have been met, so that the unbalance of the optical system experienced over ambient temperatures between −40 and +120°F does not result in any measurable shift in the control point. The unbalance signal (caused by the dew formation) from the AC-excited bridge circuit is first amplified and then converted to pulses for operating silicon-controlled rectifiers, which in turn regulate the cooling

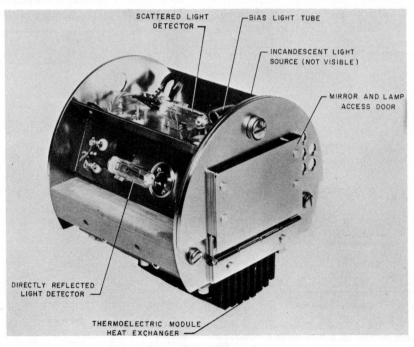

FIG. 5. Thermoelectric dew-point sensor.

FIG. 6. Field control package and dew-point sensor.

current delivered to the thermoelectric module.

The mirror can be instrumented with either a thermocouple, thermistor or resistance thermometer, depending on the requirements. In the sensor shown in Fig. 5, a platinum resistance thermometer element, physically integrated with the mirror structure, was used to provide linear temperature readout. In addition, an electrically insulated resistance-wire heating element (not shown for clarity) is wound within the mirror structure to permit removal of the dew by evaporation.

PRINCIPLE OF OPERATION

A sample of air is drawn across the plane of the mirror at a velocity of approximately .2 to 2 cm/sec, which corresponds to a flow rate of approximately 1 to 10 cc/sec. The measurement does not appear to be affected by changes in flow rate over this range. A second stream of air is circulated past the fins on the hot side of the thermoelectric module to permit removal of the rejected heat. The control system for the electronic dew-point indicator is shown diagrammatically in Fig. 1, and physically in Fig. 6. To set the automatic dew-point system into operation, it is necessary to unbalance the optical bridge so that cooling commences whenever dew is absent from the mirror. This is done by shifting, with a variable resistor, the electrical balance point of the bridge. The output from the unbalanced optical bridge is amplified and operates a unijunction relaxation oscillator, which in turn controls the conduction angle of the silicon-controlled rectifiers. The primary of a conventional DC power supply forms the load for the silicon-controlled rectifiers. The DC output of the power supply then supplies the thermoelectric module with cooling current. As the mirror cools to the dew point as a result of the unbalanced situation, the formation of dew on the mirror causes attenuation of the directly reflected light beam and an increase in the light received by the scattered photoresistor. This forces the bridge towards the balance point, proportionally decreasing the current supplied to the cooler until a stable current is attained, whereby a thin film of dew is maintained on

Fig. 7. Servo-balanced Wheatstone bridge indicator.

the mirror surface. With the mirror stabilized at the "dew point," the temperature of the mirror then represents the dew-point temperature. The instrument tracks the changes in dew point by increasing or decreasing the DC cooler current about the stable point in proportion to the thickness of the dew deposit on the mirror. Increasing the cooler current causes heat to be pumped from the mirror, thus lowering its temperature. Decreasing the current permits heat from the hot side of the cooler to leak into the mirror, thus raising its temperature. Operation in this fashion permits the use of a simple unidirectional control circuit.

The mirror temperature is sensed by a three-wire platinum resistance element. The temperature readout utilizes the standard AN/TMQ-11 servo-balanced Wheatstone bridge indicator and is capable of remote operation from the sensor up to 5000 ft. The readout indicator is shown in Fig. 7.

The overall instrument response from equipment turn-on for a particular set of meteorological conditions is shown in Fig. 8.

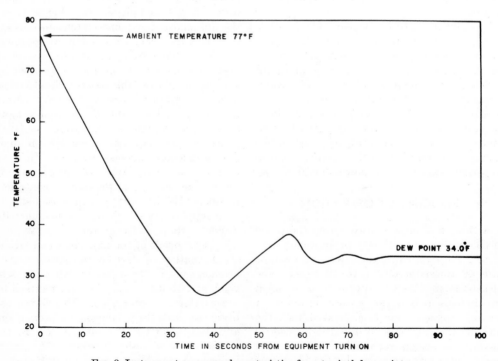

Fig. 8. Instrument response characteristics for a typical dew point.

The tracking response to changes in dew point, at the operating point shown, is determined to be 1.2 deg F/sec.

The operation of the overall system can be checked at any time by heating the mirror with the internal resistance element provided and observing that control is reestablished at the same temperature, assuming, of course, that the dew point has not changed.

TEST PROGRAMS, PERFORMANCE AND ACCURACY

The thermoelectrically cooled dew-point hygrometer, which was designed for use with the AN/TMQ-11 (Air Force) Temperature-Humidity Measuring Set and similar systems, has been field-tested for 3 months in a heavily industrialized area of Boston and further tested for 6 months at a runway site at L. G. Hanscom Field, Bedford, Massachusetts, during 1961 and 1962. The objective of the field tests was to determine the ability of the apparatus to measure dew points on a continuous basis without operator attendance and/or mirror maintenance. In lieu of a means of cross checking the sensor with another primary hygrometer, short-term repeatability data was obtained, rather than comparative accuracies. When meteorological conditions permitted, sling psychrometer readings were taken, but only as second-order data. Readings were also compared with a standard AN/TMQ-11.

The maintenance of the sensor centered around means of minimizing the rate of accumulation of particulate matter and evaporation films on the mirror. With the sensor mounted so that the mirror was in the horizontal plane, the major contaminant appeared to be soot particles, and these covered approximately 1 per cent of the mirror surface after a 2,000-hour operating period with a sample flow rate of 1 to 10 cc/sec. Mounting the sensor so that the mirror is in the vertical plane has significantly reduced the accumulation of heavy particulate matter. The effect of small quantities of this type of mirror contamination on the optical system is to reduce the amount of directly reflected light, but not in sufficient amounts to render the system insensitive to dew formation. Particulate matter does, how-

ever, affect condensate formation, since the individual particles can act as nuclei in frost-point situations. The more difficult class of contaminants are the thin, white, "evaporation films" which form gradually and are apparently depositions of the various aerosols normally found in the atmosphere. If the control point for the hygrometer is established on a perfectly clean mirror, formation of this film in sufficient quantity is interpreted as a dew (or frost) formation, and the cooling current ceases, rendering the instrument inoperable. It has been found, however, that after the initial film has formed on the surface, deposition of additional film has only a slight effect on the control point. If the control point is readjusted after the film has formed, which usually takes four to five hours, the system may be expected to operate for long periods of time without readjustment.

The instrument was operated continuously for a period in excess of 9 months, over natural dew points ranging from -20 to $+70°F$, with repeatabilities consistently better than ±0.5 deg F.

Over the 9-month test program, the failures experienced were limited to a lamp burnout and two lightning discharges. It has since been ascertained that the lamp burnout was attributed to inadequate ventilation of the bulb, since burnout occurred after 400 hours of operation, whereas the lamp is rated at 10,000 hours. Lightning protection has been added to the test installation, and this problem has been eliminated.

In September of 1962, a prototype thermoelectric dew-point hygrometer was furnished to the Air Force Cambridge Research Laboratory, Aerospace Instrumentation Laboratory (formerly the Meteorological Development Laboratory) for calibration testing. The results of these tests are not within the scope of this paper but are available to qualified Government Agencies from AFCRL. The calibration testing confirmed that the errors in the hygrometer were within the limits of ±1 deg F, for dew points between $+78$ and $-8°F$.

In January of 1963, a modified AN/TMQ-11 with the thermoelectric dew-point sensor was installed at the Joint Arctic Weather Station (JAWS), Alert, Ellesmere Island, NWT, Canada, through the joint cooperation of the

U.S. Weather Bureau, Polar Operations Office, and the Air Force Cambridge Research Laboratory, Aerospace Instrumentation Laboratory. For the months of January, February, and March of 1963, the system failed on one occasion due to a sensor lamp burnout. Large variations in the local line voltage coupled with marginal fusing accounted for an additional failure. Both of these problems were corrected by increasing the fuse ratings to accommodate the large line variations. Dew points measured during these months ranged from −48 to +27°F. Unfortunately, there are no other suitable dew-point or related apparatus at this site to permit an accurate comparison.

ADVANTAGES AND DISADVANTAGES

The major advantage of the electronic dew-point indicator is increased accuracy over a wide range. The sensor can measure dew points between −100 and +120°F. At dew points above −20°F, the resolution of the sensor appears to be in the order of ±0.50 deg. F, deteriorating at low frost points to ±2.0 deg F. The sensor is of the primary type and is readily checked for operability by clearing the mirror with the external heater and noting that the instrument repeats itself. The sensor is very flexible in terms of readout, since the mirror temperature can be obtained by any physically small electric thermometer. The sensor itself is physically small and operates automatically on a continuous and unattended basis. The extended performance offered by the sensor is summarized in Fig. 9.

The disadvantage of the sensor is that it is relatively complex when compared to other operational sensors such as hygroscopic resistance elements. Present-day thermo-electric coolers require relatively high direct currents at low voltages which dictate that the control circuit and power supply be located at the sensor site. This places a further requirement on the control equipment in that it must be capable of operating in the same environment as the sensor. Improvements in

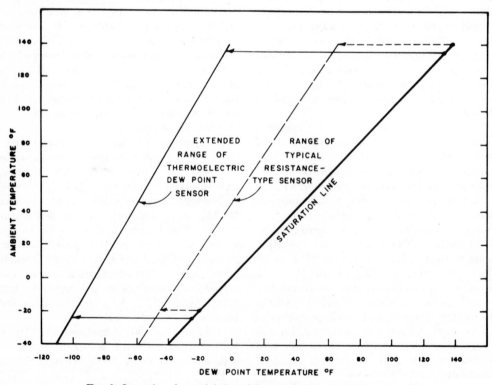

Fig. 9. Operating characteristics of thermoelectric dew-point sensor.

thermoelectric materials promise lower excitation currents. The problem of mirror contamination, although greatly minimized, must be considered disadvantageous. The data obtained on the system indicates that the mirror should be cleaned at approximately 3-month intervals, although greater intervals may be feasible at less-industrialized sites.

Acknowledgments. The authors wish to acknowledge the many useful suggestions on the materials of construction and the optical configuration offered by Dr. Jacob E. Dinger and Robert E. Ruskin of the Naval Research Laboratory. We would also like to thank the staff of Aerospace Instrumentation Laboratory, AFCRL, for their numerous suggestions in integrating the sensor with the AN/TMQ-11 Temperature-Humidity Measuring Set and the liaison furnished in the various test programs.

Thanks are also due to the Polar Operations Office, USWB, for their cooperation in the installation and collection of data at Alert, JAWS.

The development of the dew-point hygrometer was supported by the Air Force Cambridge Research Laboratories, Aerospace Instrumentation Laboratory, under contract AF19(628)-410.

References

1. Wood, R. C., Foskett, L. W., and Foster, N. B., "The Infrared Absorption Hygrometer—A Progress Report," Paper presented at the First International Congress and Exposition of the ISA, Philadelphia, Pa., 1954.
2. Sargent, J., "Recording Microwave Hygrometer," *Rev. Sci. Instr.*, **30**, 348–355 (May 1959).
3. Kobayashi, J., "Investigations on Hygrometry," *Papers Meteorol. Geophys. Tokyo*, Meteorological Research Institute, **11**, Nos. 2–4 (1960).
4. Ioffe, A. F., "Semiconductor Thermoelements and Thermoelectric Cooling," London, Infosearch Limited, 1957.
5. Mastenbrook, H. J., and Dinger, J. E., "The Measurement of Water-Vapor Distribution in the Stratosphere, U.S. Naval Research Laboratory, NRL Report 5551, Washington, D.C., 1960.
6. Kolomeots, N. V., *et al.*, "Measurement of Air Humidity Using Semiconductor Thermoelements," *Journal of Technical Physics*, USSR, **47** (1956).
7. Beaubien, D. J., and Francisco, C. C., "An Electronic Dew Point Indicator for Operational Use," Paper presented at the 4th Conference on Applied Meteorology, at Hampton, Virginia, USA., September 12, 1962.

18. Design and Applications of High-performance Dew-point Hygrometers

Louis C. Paine and H. R. Farrah

The Bendix Corporation, Research Laboratories Division, Southfield, Michigan

ABSTRACT

The paper presents a basic design for high-performance dew-point hygrometers starting with the application of a well-documented physical phenomenon. Design considerations, performance characteristics, and various instrument applications are described.

To achieve high performance, the rate-of-change of the dew or frost deposit should be zero at a constant dew point. This requirement is met by a basic system composed of (1) a metallic mirror, (2) a simple light source and photocell reflectivity detector, (3) a compensated control amplifier, and (4) a controllable heat source and sink combination. Continuous dew-point readings are obtained from the mirror's temperature sensors—a thermocouple and a thermistor.

The validity of the basic design has been proven by agreement between that calibration inferred from the mirror temperature calibration and an actual calibration using known dew-point samples. This suggests the use of this type of instrument as a calibration standard.

The basic design has evolved from the development of a number of specific dew-point hygrometers designed to fulfill various performance and environmental specifications. Meteorological models have been developed and field-tested for use in aircraft, balloonsondes, rocketsondes, and dropsondes. Other tested designs range from ground support instruments to laboratory instruments.

INTRODUCTION

Over a period of many years of meteorological sensor development, there has evolved, at the Bendix Research Laboratories Divi-

sion, a basic design for high-performance dew-point hygrometers suitable to aircraft, sonde, field, and laboratory environments. The development effort started with a survey of moisture measuring devices and techniques. This survey was conducted in an effort to select the most feasible approach to achieving high performance in an instrument for measuring atmospheric water vapor. The technique utilized in the dew-point hygrometer was selected. At the time of the survey, the performance capability inherent in this technique apparently had not been achieved after numerous independent attempts over a period of many years. However, the dew-point hygrometer's combination of fundamental simplicity with a well-documented physical relationship appeared to have greater potential for meeting the performance objectives than the more exotic or less-direct techniques reviewed. A progression of various designs for specific applications followed until finally a general-purpose basic design was evolved. This design combines high accuracy, fast response, and wide range with the ability to provide continuous readings, automatically, over a wide range of environmental conditions.

This paper discusses general considerations involved in each design area and describes a number of instruments for specific applications, including comments on their general performance. Since the intent of this paper is to present general design considerations rather than detailed derivations, none of the mathematical analyses or the theoretical studies are included.

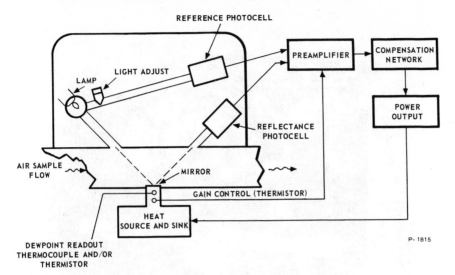

FIG. 1. Functional block diagram for basic hygrometer.

PRINCIPLE OF OPERATION

Briefly, the dew-point hygrometer operates on the principle that if a deposit of dew or frost on a non-sorptive, inactive surface is maintained at a temperature such that the deposit is neither increasing nor decreasing in thickness, then the saturated vapor pressure at the deposit temperature is equal to the partial pressure of water vapor in the air sample passing over the deposit. Thus, the temperature of the constant-thickness deposit is the dew (or frost) point of the air sample.

If the deposit is either increasing or decreasing in thickness, then the deposit temperature must be below or above the actual dew point. Although various averaging techniques can be used to obtain a dew-point reading from an oscillating deposit, the highest accuracy is obtained when a condition of equilibrium is maintained. This is especially true at very low dew points where the rate of frost growth is much slower than the rate of sublimation for a given difference between deposit temperature and actual dew point.

Incorporating this principle of operation into a practical instrument requires a suitable surface for the dew or frost deposit, a method for detecting changes in the deposit thickness, a device for controlling the surface temperature, and a temperature sensor. If the funda-

mental concept of deposit temperature being equal to the dew point is to be retained, it is imperative that the condition of deposit thickness equilibrium, stated previously, be unaffected by either the surface material or the deposit detection method. A rhodium-plated metallic mirror and a simple photoelectric reflectance detector satisfy this requirement.

A functional block diagram of the basic dew-point hygrometer is shown in Fig. 1. The photoelectric system, transistorized servo amplifier, heat source, and heat sink are used for controlling the mirror temperature to provide a constant reflectance or film thickness. An ultrasmall bead thermistor mounted directly below the mirror surface converts the mirror temperature (dew point) to a resistance analog output signal. A thermocouple is also mounted in the mirror rod; it can be used either as an output or to calibrate the thermistor.

PHOTODETECTOR

The photoelectric reflectance detector used in the basic hygrometer design is comprised of a standard long-life incandescent light source and a pair of cadmium sulfide photoresistive photocells. The photocells are physically arranged so that one photocell receives the reflected light from the hygrometer

FIG. 2. Photodetection test assembly.

mirror while the other photocell receives light directly from the light source. A simple wedge is used in the direct light path in order to balance the outputs of the two photocells. The light source is of sufficient intensity to provide high sensitivity to changes in the mirror reflectance and to permit operation of the photocells in the region of low temperature coefficient.

The two photocells are connected in an electrical bridge circuit. In addition to high sensitivity, this arrangement provides first-order compensation for variations in the light source. Variations in photocell resistance, caused by operation over the wide ambient temperature range experienced in atmospheric sounding, are compensated for by using photocells which have matched temperature coefficients.

Except for the mirror maintenance inspection port, no other lens is used in the basic photodetector. The light path is confined by use of small diameter passages molded in the detector housing. One of the passages is used to restrict the reflectance photocell field of view to the mirror surface. The angle of incidence, as determined by the light passages, is approximately 35 degrees. All components are potted in place, and a glass cover seals the light passages from the air sample.

A number of photodetector techniques and configurations have been experimentally evaluated in the laboratory using the test setup shown in Fig. 2. These experiments included studies of incidence angle effects on sensitivity and noise, evaluation of scattered light signals, and studies of methods to differentiate between dew and frost on the mirror. The photodetector studies demonstrated that very little performance improvement could be expected from configurations more complicated than the simple reflected light sensing arrangement previously described. In general the small improvements were greatly outweighed by the associated increase in complexity and reduction in reliability.

MIRROR

In addition to providing a non-sorptive, inactive, reflective surface on which the dew or frost deposit is maintained, the mirror must have negligible temperature gradients radially across the surface and axially through the region of the temperature sensor to achieve maximum accuracy. The mirror must also have a minimum thermal time constant if the dew-point hygrometer is to be stable and have a fast response. For a given mirror size, the ratio of thermal conductivity to volumetric specific heat provides a thermal response figure of merit for selecting materials.

Silver was selected as the base material for the mirror. This material rated highest on the combination of thermal conductivity for minimum temperature gradient and figure of merit for fast thermal response. In addition, silver rods or wires of high purity are readily available, the material is easily plated, and the thermocouple temperature sensor can easily be soldered in the base of the mirror. Rhodium plating was selected for the mirror surface because of its high reflectivity and excellent resistance to corrosion. The absence of mirror surface temperature gradients has been shown by the very uniform deposit consistently obtained on a clean mirror.

The general guide for determining the size of the mirror is to keep the size as small as possible to achieve fast response but retain sufficient area and volume to avoid complications in photodetector alignment and temperature sensor mounting. A 0.060-in. diameter mirror has been found to be a good compromise. The constant temperature region where the temperature sensors are mounted extends from the mirror surface to a distance of from 0.090 to 0.150 in. down the rod,

Fig. 3. Mirror subassembly.

depending on the type of heat source and sink being used. Figure 3 shows a typical mirror subassembly of the heater and evaporative heat sink type. The fiber disc directly below the mirror supports the temperature sensor leads during the final assembly.

With a small mirror surface, a thin dew or frost deposit, and a high-gain amplifier, the actual variation in the total mirror deposit mass is quite small over the normal instrument range of $+30$ to $-80°C$ dew point. This small change is especially important in retaining fast response at low dew points where the partial pressure of water is extremely low. The small mirror also permits operation at very low sample flow velocities without increasing the response time.

Other advantages of the small mirror include fast turn-on time over the full dew-point range and small volumetric sample requirements. The air sample duct through the sensor head normally has a cross-section area of about 0.06 sq. in. The small volumetric and velocity flow requirements are important in many micrometeorological dew-point measurements.

TEMPERATURE SENSOR

The considerations in selection of a mirror temperature sensor included accuracy, stability, sensitivity, and compatibility with the small mirror. Thermocouples made from calibrated copper and constantan thermocouple wire were extensively tested in the laboratory temperature calibration facility. Tests were conducted over the temperature range of $+50$ to $-65°C$, the limits of the test facility, with junctions formed by plating and by soldering using 0.005-in. diameter wire. Junctions formed by either method were found to be accurate to better than ±0.01 deg C over the entire temperature range. Junctions made from the same wire source a year later showed no change in calibration.

The temperature of the 0.060-in. diameter mirror can be measured quite accurately by a copper-constantan thermocouple if the small, 5-mil, wire is used and if special care is taken in fabrication. The insulation is stripped back approximately 0.020 in. from the end of the wire. Then the wires are tinned and inserted from opposite sides into a hole drilled radially through the mirror rod directly below the mirror surface. The entire assembly is then heated, and the wires are soldered in the hole. When this operation is performed correctly, the thermocouple junction is formed entirely within the mirror rod and no electrical contact is made to wire surfaces extending outside the mounting hole. The wires are then wrapped around the silver rod about ½ turn and bonded to the rod to reduce temperature gradients in the area of the thermocouple junction.

The advantages of the thermocouple are high accuracy, long-term stability, and conformance with a standard calibration curve. The limitations are primarily related to the need for a reference junction and a standard voltage source.

The subminiature bead thermistor has also been used extensively as a mirror temperature sensor. A 0.014-in. diameter bead with 0.002-in. diameter leads is quite compatible with the small mirror, and the mounting is similar to that of the thermocouple except for the use of epoxy to bond the bead in the hole. The advantages of the thermistor are high sensitivity and a resistance analog output. Long-term calibration drift and nonstandard calibration curves are the primary disadvantages. The exponential temperature characteristic can be either an advantage or a disadvantage depending on the application. This characteristic is desirable for many telemetry systems, especially those in current meteorological sounding packages. For other applications, the calibration curve can be modified by using appropriately selected series and parallel resistances.

Resistance wire temperature sensors were also reviewed. Although these sensors, especially platinum, have many highly desirable characteristics, no suitable form was found for mounting them in the small mirror rod. The problems associated with obtaining a usable resistance value, providing electrical insulation, eliminating temperature gradients, and avoiding mechanical stresses in the wire, were believed to outweigh the advantages of the resistance wire thermometer. Resistance wire or film temperature sensors could be used advantageously with large mirrors; however, the fast response and other advantages of the small mirror were

considered more important to the overall performance of the hygrometer than the advantages offered by this form of temperature sensor.

The mirror temperature measurement technique used in the basic dew-point hygrometer involves both the copper-constantan thermocouple and the bead thermistor. The thermistor output is used in applications where the thermocouple is unsatisfactory, and the thermocouple is used for periodic calibration of the thermistor.

Environmental tests have demonstrated the success of this temperature-sensing technique. One of these tests consisted of operating a hygrometer with a constant −65°C dew-point sample while the sample temperature was elevated to +65°C. To a measurement accuracy of better than ±0.1 deg C, no variation in indicated dew point was shown by either of the mirror temperature sensors.

MIRROR DEPOSIT

One of the fundamental characteristics of the mirror-type dew-point hygrometer is the fact that the dew-point calibration is independent of deposit thickness, within a limited thickness range. To achieve high accuracy, the hygrometer must be designed to operate within this thickness range over the full dew-point scale.

The output of the photodetector in the dew-point hygrometer is a direct analog of the mirror reflectance and a function of the absolute dew- or frost-deposit thickness. For convenience in the following discussion, a linear scale of zero to 100 per cent will be assigned to the photodetector output. On this scale, 100 per cent represents a condition where the mirror deposit is so thick that the presence of a reflective surface below the deposit is indiscernible and an increase in deposit thickness does not produce a change in the photodetector output. The zero value represents a clear mirror with no dew or frost deposit.

The basic dew-point hygrometer is designed to operate within a deposit thickness range of approximately 40 per cent to 5 per cent where the thickest deposit (40 per cent) occurs at the highest dew point and the thinnest deposit

(5 per cent) occurs at the lowest dew point. The normal dew-point range of the instrument is +30 to −80°C.

Degradation in instrument performance and accuracy can occur if the deposit is either too thick or too thin. With a thick dew deposit, the droplets may rapidly coalesce to form a few very large drops on the mirror and cause the hygrometer to operate erratically. Thick deposits can also cause errors due to temperature gradients and increase the effective response time of the hygrometer. At the other extreme, the very thin deposit (below approximately 5 per cent) has been experimentally observed to cause errors of greater than 1 deg C in the indicated dew point. The indicated dew point is higher than the actual dew point, and the error increases with decreasing deposit thickness. Within the operating range of 40 per cent to 5 per cent no variations in reading as a function of thickness have been observed with readouts sensitive to better than ±0.05 deg C.

Several experimental studies concerning supercooled dew were conducted. During these studies, thin (5 per cent) deposits of supercooled dew were maintained at temperatures as low as −28°C and were found to be quite stable. The dew did not freeze even when subjected to sudden mirror temperature transients, mechanical vibration, or turbulence in the air stream. When the deposit thickness was increased to approximately 20 per cent the condition of supercooled dew rarely occurred below −18°C.

Most of the experiments with supercooled dew were conducted by using two dew-point hygrometers connected in parallel to a common air supply of variable dew point. The dew point was lowered to approximately −50°C and then raised to the region of study. The mirror of one hygrometer was heated and cleared by means of an electrical control in the amplifier. On return to normal operation, a fresh deposit was formed on the mirror. The output readings of the two instruments were then compared to determine the presence of frost or supercooled dew. In the case of supercooled dew the difference in readings was found to agree with the tabulated saturated water vapor pressures over water and over ice.

No extensive studies of supercooled dew

prevention were conducted; however, one method of determining the presence of a supercooled deposit was found to work adequately. This technique employed a mirror constructed with a wire placed concentrically in the mirror and electrically insulated. The electrical resistance between the bare end of the wire and the mirror was then used to determine the presence of supercooled dew. The resistance ranged from 10^6 to 10^7 ohms for dew and greater than 10^9 ohms for frost.

AMPLIFIER DESIGN

The requirements for rapid transient response, stable operation, and high accuracy jointly dictate the design of the sensing element and the associated electronics. The fast transient response requirement originally stemmed from meteorological applications. However, it has been found that even for general purposes, a fast response is desirable since it greatly extends the applications of the instrument.

There are three major factors that influence the transient response of the instrument. These are the rate at which frost increases or decreases on the mirror surface, the thermal response of the mirror, and the electronic compensation network employed in the amplifier. Unfortunately, the frost growth rate is not constant but depends on various factors, the most important of which is the dew point. In general, the rate of frost growth is fast at high dew points and very slow at low dew points; the change in growth rate can vary as much as 500 to 1 in the range from +25 to −80°C dew point. At dew points above −20°C, the rate at which frost grows is rapid enough so that the thermal response of the mirror is predominant in affecting the transient response of the instrument. At temperatures below −50°C, the frost growth rate is the predominant factor.

The rate of frost growth and the mirror thermal response are physical factors which affect the overall transient response. It remains to optimize the electronics and to provide for a suitable compensation scheme to take full advantage of the physical parameters. Referring to Fig. 1, the bridge arrangement of the two photocells provides an output which is a function of frost thickness. The output of the bridge drives a preamplifier, a compensation network, and a power output stage which in turn controls the heat sink and heat source of the mirror surface.

Frost thickness, to a first approximation, is an integral relationship of the dew point and the mirror temperature and thus involves a 90-degree phase lag. The second major lag in the system is the thermal lag of the mirror. Even though this is basically a second-order system, instability can occur under closed loop conditions if suitable compensation networks are not used. The additional phase shift past 180 degrees which can cause oscillation, is produced by an aggregate of small phase lags caused by the electronics and the imperfect heat transfer in the heat sink and mirror system.

The compensation scheme employed is relatively straightforward. It consists of two lead networks with a total lead gain of about 50. Optimization is based on obtaining a step response with a 20 to 30 per cent overshoot with as high a band width as possible.

Within the scope of the compensation scheme the ultimate response is also determined by the forward gain of the servo loop. If the gain is too high the system becomes unstable; if the gain is too low the system becomes sluggish. The optimum gain setting is related to the criterion of obtaining a 20 to 30 per cent overshoot in the step response. Unfortunately, the rate of frost growth, which appears as a gain factor in the forward servo loop, is a nonlinear function of dew point, changing almost logarithmically by a factor of 500 to 1 over the dew-point range of interest. The obvious difficulty is that it is impossible to obtain an optimum gain setting over the complete dew-point range. If the gain is set for a fast response at low dew points, then the instrument has a tendency to oscillate at high dew points. Conversely, if the gain is set for optimum response at high dew points, then the system will be unduly sluggish at low dew points. What is required is some sort of adaptive gain control system that automatically compensates for this change in gain. This is accomplished in the present instruments by embedding a thermistor in the silver rod near the mirror surface so

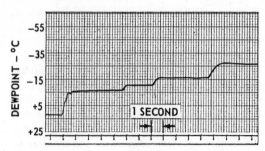

FIG. 4. Transient response to step changes in dew point.

that its resistance will decrease with increasing dew point. This thermistor is placed in the feedback loop of the preamplifier, and with suitable thermistor padding, the preamplifier can be made to have a gain which is roughly inversely proportional to the rate of frost growth over the dew-point range of interest. This unique adaptive gain control system optimizes system response over a wide range. However, at dew points in the −65°C range and below, it is not possible to com-

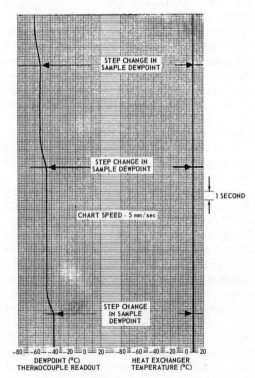

FIG. 5. Transient response at low dew points for a two-stage thermoelectric hygrometer.

pletely optimize the response due to noise in the system, and the system response is slightly overdamped. Above these dew points, however, the system maintains an optimum response characteristic.

Figure 4 illustrates the transient response of the dew-point sensor to rapid changes in dew point. For this test, the dew point was decreased in small steps. Note that at $-25°C$ the response time for 90 per cent of the step change is still less than 1 second. Figure 5 shows a typical instrument response at low dew points. At $-40°C$ the response time is a little less than 2 seconds, and at $-60°C$ the response time is about $3\frac{1}{2}$ seconds.

HEAT SOURCE AND HEAT SINK DESIGN

Basically, these hygrometers employ one of two techniques for controlling the temperature of the mirror.

The first of these is diagrammed in Fig. 6. Low temperatures are obtained by immersing the silver rod in a fluid that has a low boiling point. A resistance wire heater, wound on the silver rod approximately 0.09 in. from the mirror surface, is used to control the mirror temperature by supplying heat to the silver rod. Also shown in this diagram is the relative placement of the temperature sensors used to detect the mirror surface temperature. This configuration restricts the region of high heat flow to the lower portion of the silver rod and

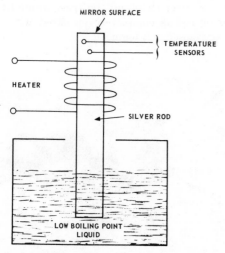

Fig. 6. Resistance heater and evaporative heat sink diagram.

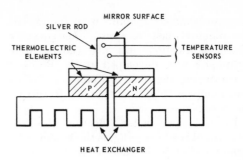

Fig. 7. Thermoelectric temperature control diagram.

does not contribute to temperature gradients in the sensitive region of the mirror and temperature sensor. The overall time constant of this assembly is about 2 seconds; it is determined by the dimensions of the silver rod and the placement of the heater. This response is typical for these units. The low-boiling-temperature liquids which have been used successfully are oxygen, nitrogen, and nitrous oxide.

Although the use of a liquid heat sink and a heater to control the temperature of the mirror surface is adequate and provides for excellent sensor performance, the logistics problems associated with supplying cryogenic fluids for the instrument resulted in the development of a second technique, the thermoelectric dew-point hygrometer. This technique uses a thermoelectric heat pump to cool the mirror surface. Figure 7 shows a representation of this method. Again, a silver rod is used, and the same temperature sensors are placed below the mirror surface; however, in place of a heater and cryogenic liquid, a thermoelectric junction, constructed of P- and N-type bismuth telluride elements, is used. This junction is placed in about the same place as the heater in the previous example. A heat exchanger is employed to dissipate the heat liberated at the hot junction. The thermal time constant of this mirror assembly is determined primarily by the thermoelectric elements rather than the silver rod.

In order to make the thermoelectric dew-point hygrometers competitive in performance with the evaporant heat sink types, the thermal response of the mirror assembly must be on the order of 2 seconds. This places a burden on the thermoelectric heat pump, since no commercial units were found with the required fast response. Consequently, special fabrication and material handling techniques were developed at the Research Laboratories Division for producing small heat pumps with all the desirable features of the larger units.

The principal factor effecting the time constant of the heat pump is the length of the bismuth telluride thermoelectric elements. In order to realize a 2-second time response, the elements had to be made 90 mils long; then to minimize heat losses a circular heat pump was used. Each of the thermoelectric elements consists of a semicircular wafer 90 mils long by 200 mils in diameter. Figure 8 shows the resultant thermoelectric elements prior to mounting on the heat exchanger and silver rod.

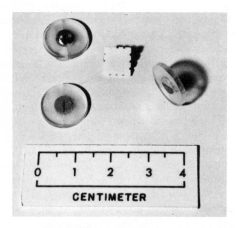

FIG. 8. Thermoelectric elements.

Unlike the cryogenic-liquid types, the minimum dew-point temperature that can be measured using the thermoelectric-type instrument is a function of the cooling efficiency of the heat pump and the hot junction temperature. Using a single-stage thermoelectric cooler, dew points can be measured 50 deg C below a $+25°C$ ambient (hot junction) temperature. Thus, if the ambient temperature is $+25°C$, dew points down to $-25°C$ can be measured. This performance has repeatedly been demonstrated with an air sample flow of 10 ft/sec at a temperature of $+25°C$. The maximum temperature difference attainable with a single-stage thermoelectric cooler decreases with hot

junction temperature. At an ambient temperature of $-60°C$, the temperature difference is about 20 deg C with a single-stage cooler.

For some commercial applications, a single-stage cooler is not sufficient to read the low dew points required. In this case, a two- or even a three-stage cooler can be used. From room temperature a typical three-stage unit is capable of reading dew points down to $-70°C$. It is apparent that except for very unusual situations, the thermoelectric dew-point hygrometer can replace the older evaporant heat sink types. Although general overall performance is not improved, the simplifications achieved in logistics and handling more than make up the difference.

SAMPLE HANDLING

The gas or air sample handling system is of primary importance in the overall assembly of a dew-point hygrometer. To obtain a true dew-point measurement, the air sample must be ducted from the source through the mirror chamber without distortion of the partial pressure of water vapor. Sampling provisions include the exclusive use of non-hydrophilic materials such as "Teflon," "Kel-F," and passivated stainless steel.

A typical sensor head or mirror chamber assembly is shown in Fig. 9. The internal duct is "Kel-F", and the tubing fittings are stainless steel. To avoid contamination of the air sample, the photocell assembly is sealed with a glass cover slide and the space around the mirror rod is completely insulated with an epoxy closed-cell foam.

FIG. 9. Complete thermoelectric mirror assembly.

Variations in air sample temperature do not alter the dew point provided no change in pressure occurs and the lowest temperature is above the sample dew point. In some applications, such as aircraft hygrometers, heated sample ducts are necessary to prevent condensation during descent.

Sample pressure changes are unavoidable in many hygrometer applications. Instruments for these uses can either control or measure the sample pressure in the mirror chamber to provide data for correction of the indicated dew point. In these cases, the control devices and pressure transducers must be located downstream from the mirror chamber to prevent contamination of the sample.

The avoidance of particles on the mirror surface is a problem in some applications involving dusty or dirty samples. Thin woven screens are effective in stopping the particles, but the collected particles then act as hygroscopic surfaces and produce long time lags during transients in the air sample dew point. A method used quite successfully on a number of hygrometers utilizes a straight-through sample duct with a small bypass for the mirror chamber. In this arrangement, the heavier particles do not enter the mirror chamber.

APPLICATIONS

This basic design for a high-performance dew-point hygrometer has evolved from a number of programs to design, fabricate, and test dew-point sensors for several different applications. Brief descriptions and comments are presented in chronological order.

1957—Aircraft Unit

In 1956 and 1957, a dew-point hygrometer was developed for use in high-performance jet aircraft (see Fig. 10). The functional block diagram for this unit is shown in Fig. 11. This sensor was designed to automatically provide continuous dew-point readings in digital form, corrected to static pressure. To accomplish this the instrument included an air sample pressure ratio control, a mirror-type dew-point hygrometer, and a dew-point computer and digitizer.

The air sample pressure controls system maintained the mirror chamber pressure at a fixed ratio above the static pressure over the normal flight profile of the aircraft. Since the partial pressure of water vapor was changed by the same ratio, the mechanization required to compute static pressure dew point was reduced to a simple nonlinear feedback potentiometer in the mirror temperature readout system.

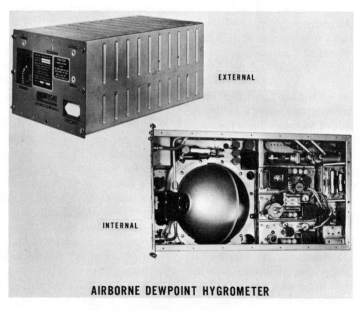

EXTERNAL

INTERNAL

AIRBORNE DEWPOINT HYGROMETER

FIG. 10. The 1957 aircraft hygrometer.

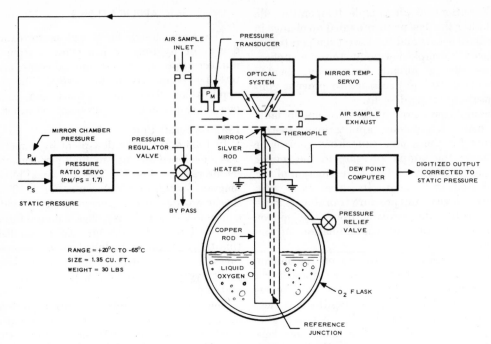

RANGE = +20°C TO -65°C
SIZE = 1.35 CU. FT.
WEIGHT = 30 LBS

FIG. 11. Functional block diagram for 1957 unit.

The dew-point sensor was composed of a photodetector, a vacuum tube and magnetic amplifier temperature control, a 2½-liter liquid-oxygen heat sink, and a small mirror with a resistance heater. One filling of the heat sink was sufficient for approximately 11 hours of operation. The mirror temperature was measured by a three-couple, copper-constantan thermopile. Reference junction temperature was provided by the boiling liquid oxygen.

The dew-point computer consisted of a self-balancing potentiometer using a feedback potentiometer padded to compensate for both the thermopile nonlinearities and the air sample pressure ratio. The shaft position was a linear function of static pressure dew point and was directly encoded by a mechanical digitizer.

The unit included an automatic mirror clearing and photocell balancing cycle which occurred every 15 minutes and lasted for approximately 15 seconds. A number of special circuits were also included, such as mirror heater protection and pressure limiters, to protect the instrument against unusual operating conditions.

This instrument operated over the range of +20 to −65°C and exhibited good repeatability. Although the unit could be calibrated, direct agreement between independent temperature calibration and direct dew-point calibration was not demonstrated. Temperature gradients through the thermopile were believed to be responsible for the discrepancy. Since this unit did not employ the variable-gain mirror temperature control, the operation at low dew points was somewhat sluggish by comparison to later designs.

1959—Aircraft Unit

As part of the AMQ-15 Air Weather Reconnaissance Program, a completely transistorized aircraft hygrometer of improved design was developed and flight tested. This unit is shown in Fig. 12. A 2½-liter liquid nitrogen heat sink and a resistance wire heater were used in this model. Through the use of the variable or adaptive gain control and improved amplifier compensation networks, this unit achieved very good response and stability performance over a dew-point range from +30 to −75°C.

Since this hygrometer was designed to

FIG. 12. The 1959 aircraft hygrometer.

operate as part of an air weather system employing a central computer, actual mirror temperature and mirror chamber pressure were supplied as outputs in resistance analog form. A bead thermistor was used as the mirror temperature sensor, and a copper-constantan thermocouple was included for calibration purposes. The unit also included the automatic periodic mirror clear and photocell balance cycle.

This instrument was flown on several test flights in the Seattle, Washington area. Figure 13 shows a portion of the data from one of these flights. On all flights the instrument performed very well. On one flight a test was conducted to determine the sensor recovery time after clearing the mirror. With a dew point of −65°C at an altitude of 40,000 feet, the frost reformed on the mirror within

10 seconds after the mirror had been completely cleared by heating to +70°C.

Tests conducted with the automatic photocell balancing system demonstrated that even after 5 hours of bench operation and 5 hours of flight test the balance setting remained the same as the initial setting. Therefore, it is doubtful that an automatic balancing system is needed.

Dew-point calibration tests were also conducted on this unit. The instrument demonstrated very good repeatability and could easily be calibrated. However, the independent mirror temperature calibration did not agree with the direct dew-point calibration over the full range. The thermocouple mounting was again suspect. The mounting technique described earlier in this paper had not been employed at this time.

1959—Dropsonde and Rocketsonde Units

The aircraft dropsonde and descent measurement rocketsonde dew-point sensors designed and tested on the AMQ-15 Program were complete with self-contained sealed heat sinks capable of extended storage periods. This design eliminated the problem of heat-sink filling in the field. The rocketsonde unit is shown in Fig. 14, and a disassembled dropsonde unit is shown in Fig. 15.

The prototype units used in the program flight tests were approximately 9 in. long by 4¾ in. diameter and weighed about 3 pounds. The rocketsonde sensor differed from the dropsonde unit in that it incorporated an

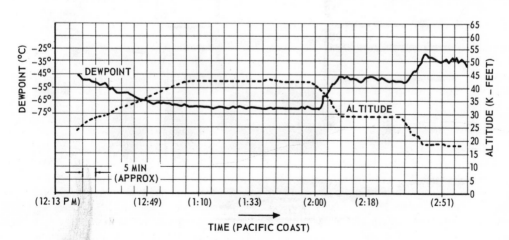

FIG. 13. Flight test August 18, 1959.

FIG. 14. Rocketsonde hygrometer. Bendix Research rocket-borne dew-point sensor.

automatic acceleration-actuated switch mechanism to initiate venting of the nitrous oxide heat sink. The dropsonde heat sink was manually actuated prior to ejection from the aircraft. The nitrous oxide heat sink operated for 20 to 30 minutes after actuation of the vent valve.

To obtain maximum speed of response, these sensors employed an on-off or "bang-bang" type of mirror heater control. While some advantage in response time was obtained, the reduction in accuracy at very low dew points resulted in a decision to return to the proportional type of control.

Prior to the flight test phase of the program a sonde dew-point sensor was subjected to environmental conditions simulating the rocket vehicle. During the acceleration test, the sensor and mounting fixture broke loose from the centrifuge and smashed part way through a $\frac{1}{4}$-in. thick steel safety wall. The sensor was immediately checked and found to operate normally. This performance gave ample verification of the ruggedness of the entire sensor, including the photodetector.

A modified version of this sonde dew-point sensor has been successfully flight tested in a small meteorological pod for external aircraft mounting.

1960—Portable Field Hygrometer

In 1960 a self-contained, portable dew-point hygrometer was developed for field use in measuring the moisture content of stored gases. The instrument, Model DHGM-2L, is shown in Fig. 16. This unit employs a resistance mirror heater and a $2\frac{1}{2}$-liter liquid nitrogen heat sink.

In field use this hygrometer can operate for 10 hours without external power or additional liquid nitrogen. The dew-point range of the sensor is -18 to $-72°C$. Gas samples can be supplied over the range of $2\frac{1}{2}$ to 6000 psig at temperatures up to $+65°C$. Output readings are obtained directly from the dial of a manually balanced bridge. A visual alarm is provided which is energized whenever the dew-point is above a set value.

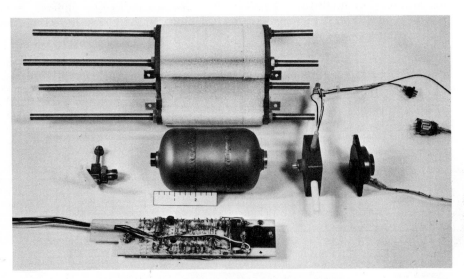

FIG. 15. Disassembled dropsonde hygrometer.

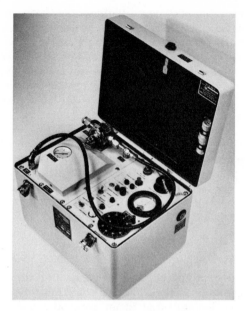

FIG. 16. Self-contained portable hygrometer.

This instrument represented a major advance in the hygrometer design in that direct agreement was shown between independent mirror temperature calibration and actual dew-point calibration. The accuracy of this instrument, including the entire readout system, was shown to be about ± 0.3 deg C. Over 85 per cent of the readings were ± 0.2

deg C or better. The mirror in this unit was constructed as described previously in this paper.

1961—Dropsonde Thermoelectric Hygrometer

In 1960 and 1961 a two-stage thermoelectric dew-point sensor was developed as part of the Vertical Sensor Techniques Program. This instrument was developed to prove the feasibility of using thermoelectric dew-point sensors in descent measurements of atmospheric dew point and to provide basic sensor technique design information. Figure 17 shows one of the units ready for installation in a balloon-borne dropsonde for dew-point measurement from 100,000 feet to sea level.

This unit was designed with an integrated mirror and controlled first-stage thermoelectric cooler. The second-stage cooler was operated directly from the battery pack. Since the second-stage cooler was operated continuously, the temperature control amplifier was designed to operate the first thermoelectric stage in either a cooling or a heating mode.

Extensive performance tests were conducted on this instrument to determine response and to evaluate operation under various environmental conditions. The response test was shown in Fig. 5. In the

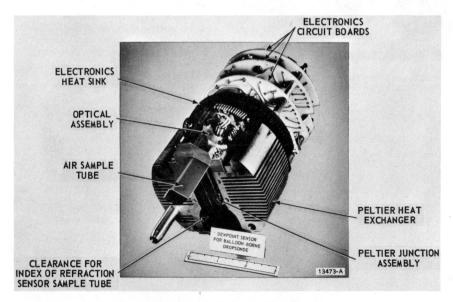

FIG. 17. Dropsonde thermoelectric hygrometer.

environmental tests, the sensor performed satisfactorily after being subjected to 75-g shock, 100-g acceleration, and ± 10 g over a frequency range of 20 to 2000 cps.

1963—General-purpose Thermoelectric Hygrometer

The latest dew-point hygrometer, designated the Model DHGF-1P, is shown in Fig. 18. The sensor head assembly for this unit was shown in Fig. 9. This instrument utilizes the integrated mirror and single-stage thermoelectric cooler. Due to the modular construction, additional thermoelectric stages can easily be added.

The basic instrument including the sensor

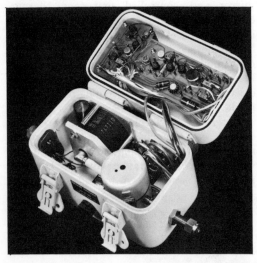

Fig. 18. General purpose thermoelectric hygrometer.

head, amplifier, and small exhaust blower to provide an air sample flow, is packaged in a weatherproof case measuring 4″ x 4½″ x 7″. The weight is 2 pounds. A power supply for operation from 115 vac, 60 cps, is packaged separately in a 8″ x 8″ x 8¾″ case and weighs 15 pounds. The power supply can be located up to 100 ft from the sensor.

Performance characteristics for this unit include a maximum dew-point depression of 50 deg C from an ambient air temperature of $+25°C$ and a response time as shown in Fig. 4. The basic readouts are a thermocouple and a thermistor, but 0 to 10 volt or 0 to 1 mA analog outputs are also provided.

SUMMARY

High accuracy, fast response and stable operation over a wide dew-point range have been demonstrated in an automatic mirror dew-point hygrometer. The basic design principles have been proven in a number of instruments. Environmental tests in the laboratory and in the field have demonstrated the ruggedness of the design including the ability to withstand rocket vehicle conditions.

Acknowledgment. The development of dew-point sensors at the Bendix Research Laboratories has been largely supported by the United States Air Force through meteorological sensor contracts and subcontracts. The most recent of these was a contract for dew-point, pressure (hypsometer), ozone, and index-of-refraction sensors awarded in 1960 by Aeronautical Systems Division with technical cognizance at Air Force Cambridge Research Laboratories.

19. An Automatic Frost-point Hygrometer using Radioactive Detection

JOHN G. BALLINGER

Honeywell, Military Products Group, Research Department, Minneapolis, Minn.

ABSTRACT

This paper describes a new type of automatic frost-point hygrometer for measurement of the stratospheric distribution of water vapor. The frost deposit is detected directly by energy attenuation of alpha radiation. An automatic control maintains a constant mass deposit of frost on a cooled surface by controlling the direction of current flow through a thermo-electric cooler. Advantages of this sensing technique over the usual optical method are indicated. Instruments suitable for balloon flights are described, and the results of several flights are discussed.

INTRODUCTION

Measurement of water-vapor content of the stratosphere is one of the most difficult problems in hygrometry. Frost-point hygrometers offer a logical approach to this problem because of their potential speed and accuracy. Previous automatic frost-point hygrometers used for these measurements employed changes in the light reflectivity of a cooled-mirror surface to indicate changes in the condensate on the surface. This paper describes an instrument which uses a more fundamental approach. Optical sensing is replaced by the direct technique of mass sensing by energy attenuation of alpha particles[1, 2, 3, 4] passing through the frost layer.

The surface upon which the frost (or dew) forms in this hygrometer is an alpha-particle emitter, cooled to the frost point by a miniature thermoelectric cooler. An electronic control system varies the temperature of this surface by alternate heating and cooling to maintain the frost-layer mass (or thickness) nearly constant, thus keeping the surface at the frost-point temperature. A solid-state alpha-particle detector converts changes in the alpha-particle energies (due to changes in the frost-layer thickness) into changes in amplitude of voltage pulses. A flip-flop with a fixed trigger level is used to compare the count rate from this detector with the count rate in a reference channel for error information.

This mass sensing technique is capable of providing extreme sensitivity; present instruments employing this technique respond to a 1 $\mu g/cm^2$ change in frost-layer thickness. Since the energy attenuation of alpha particles is the same for equal mass deposits of water or any of the crystalline forms of ice, the sensitivity of detection remains constant for any water state. This is a distinct advantage in automatic instruments. In addition, the average mass deposit about which the frost layer varies can be precisely set by means of a calibrated foil.

The concept of this instrument originated at Honeywell, where initial feasibility models were built; further development of the instrument has been and is currently supported under Contract AF 19(604)-8418 with the Meteorological Development Laboratory of Air Force Cambridge Research Laboratories. Further detail on the work presented in subsequent sections of this paper may be found in reports issued under this contract.

In the following discussion, the theory of operation and results of balloon flight experience are described.

189

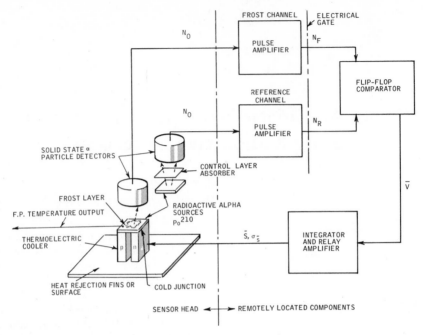

FIG. 1. Alpha-radiation hygrometer block diagram.

THEORY OF OPERATION

In the block diagram of Fig. 1, two sources of alpha radiation (Po^{210}), one on the cooled surface and one on a reference plate, emit particles of energy 5.3 MEV. The particles from one source pass through the frost layer, and those from the other source pass through the control layer absorber. All alpha particles pass through the absorbing media with a resultant attenuation in energy. Changes in thickness of the frost layer do not generally result in changes in the pulse rate N_0 passing through the preamplifiers; however, changes in the distribution of pulse energies do occur. An electrical threshold level is set at the flip-flop so that only the higher energy pulses can pass; a change in frost-layer thickness causes a change in frost-channel pulse rate, N_F, which occurs beyond this electrical gate. The same electrical threshold is applied to a reference channel. The pulse rate, N_R, occuring past this gate, determines the frost-layer thickness control point about which the instrument cycles. The use of the reference channel, which has no frost layer, provides an automatic correction for changes in density of the air gap between source and detector, which is important for stratospheric flights.

Figure 2 shows the two random trains of input pulses to the flip-flop and the resultant output waveform. The reduction in pulse height as a result of absorption in the frost and control layer absorber is shown together with a typical electrical gate setting. A pulse from one channel trips the flip-flop to one state where it remains until a pulse from the other channel drives it to the opposite state. Since the input pulse trains are random, the flip-flop switching is also random. However, the output pulses are now stretched by the delay between pulses from opposite channels.

The long-term average output voltage from the flip-flop as it swings between states is related to the ratio of time spent in each state, and this is in turn related to the pulse rates N_F and N_R. The average value of this output voltage is

$$\overline{V} = \left[\frac{N_F - N_R}{N_F + N_R}\right] V \qquad (1)$$

where

N_F = frost channel long-term counting rate average

N_R = reference channel long-term counting rate average

V = flip-flop state voltage.

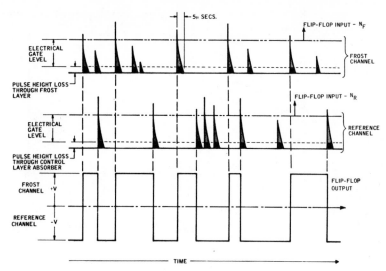

FIG. 2. Flip-flop input and output waveforms.

This voltage, when integrated and amplified, becomes the mean error signal $\bar{S} = K\bar{V}$ which drives the thermoelectric cooler to the balance condition, $N_F = N_R$.

The frost-channel configuration is shown in Fig. 3. The alpha particles (trajectories denoted by arrows) can pass into the detector at all angles between those shown, and attenuation of energy occurs in all layers between the point of emission within the source and the sensitive region of the detector. In the figure, the line spectrum of a collimated polonium source with no absorption is shown. The geometry and absorption effects shift and smear the spectrum toward lower energies. With an increase in the frost-layer thickness

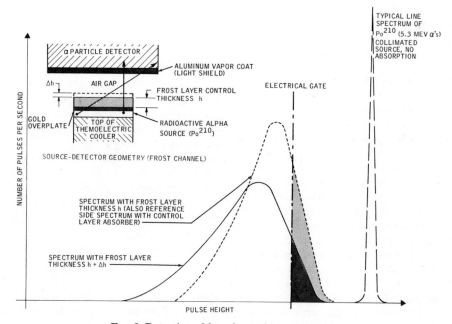

FIG. 3. Detection of frost-layer thickness changes.

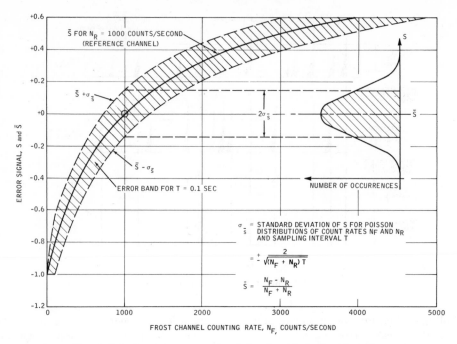

FIG. 4. Counting rate *vs* error signal showing effect of randomness.

from h to $h + \Delta h$, further displacement and smearing occur.

Both spectra are for the same total number of pulses per second, N_0. The number of pulses per second passing the gate in the first spectrum is N_F, and in the second spectrum it is $N_F - \Delta N_F$. At balance $N_F = N_R$, and it can be seen that for the typical spectrum shown, the ratio of $\Delta N_F/N_R$, which is a measure of the sensitivity, will increase as the gate is moved to higher energy levels for any change in thickness Δh. We also notice that raising the gate to higher energies reduces the number of pulses per second triggering the flip-flop.

In order to evaluate the overall capability of the sensing technique, we must now consider the fact that the signals in the two channels are random pulses since they are caused by radioactive emissions. The magnitude of a change in the signal which can be seen above its randomness must be known; this is referred to as resolution. To evaluate the resolution, the mean and variance of the error signal must be known as a function of a change in thickness Δh. For purposes of discussion, the entire circuit between the flip-flop

output and thermoelectric cooler input will be considered as a sample data system. The pulse rates N_F and N_R have a Poisson distribution, and we may obtain from probability theory the variance of the error signal. For a reasonable sample size, the variance will be

$$\sigma_{\bar{S}} = KV\left[\frac{2}{\sqrt{(N_F + N_R)T}}\right] \qquad (2)$$

where T is the sampling time. Figure 4 shows the error signal and its variance for typical operating conditions. (Note that KV has been normalized to unity.)

We may say that at the normal operating point ($N_F = N_R$ and $\bar{S} = 0$) the signal must vary from $+\sigma_{\bar{S}}$ to $-\sigma_{\bar{S}}$ if it is to be resolved. To detect a thickness change Δh, the error signal must change by the amount

$$2\sigma_{\bar{S}} = \frac{2\sqrt{2}}{\sqrt{N_R T}} \qquad (3)$$

where it is assumed that this change is sufficiently small for $\bar{S}$ to be considered a linear function of h.

The resolution requirement may then be expressed as

$$\frac{\Delta N_F}{N_R} = \frac{4\sqrt{2}}{\sqrt{N_R T}} \qquad (4)$$

Thus, the resolution provides a limit on the increase in sensitivity by setting the gate to higher energies. Since a higher gate setting increases $\Delta N_F/N_R$ at the expense of decreasing N_R, it can be seen that an optimum gate setting will exist such that the resolution constraint will be satisfied for minimum Δh. For the sample data system discussed, the best gate setting can be calculated from a measurement of the pulse-height distribution of signals in the frost channel. Current instruments are more complex in that the frost and reference channels are continuously compared. The optimum gate setting for either the sample or continuous system, however, is readily determined by observing the response of the unit to an increment Δh which is brought about by introducing a thin film into the sensor.

The best sensitivity which satisfies the resolution requirement is determined by factors in addition to the trigger-level setting. An increase in the total count rate N_0 relaxes the resolution requirement, while the sensitivity is improved by a more peaked energy spectrum of the radiation. More monoenergetic radiation is achieved with tighter geometry (a smaller solid angle of detector acceptance) and by the use of a thinner source. The count rate N_0, however, is increased by the opposite measures. Thus the sensitivity-resolution compromise is seen to be quite generally in evidence.

FROST-LAYER DYNAMICS

Effective instrumentation of an automatic frost-point hygrometer and a confident interpretation of the data it provides require paying considerable attention to the basic principles of such an instrument. A knowledge of frost-layer dynamics is essential to the design of an adequate servo-control system. By frost-layer dynamics, we mean the rate of change of the thickness of the frost for a given condition of operation (ambient pressure, temperature, and humidity and the nature of any ventilation used). The physical form of the frost must also be known in order to optimize the design of sensor elements. Both the dynamics and the physical form of the frost must be understood in order to relate the surface temperature data obtained to the actual frost point of the ambient atmosphere.

One of our early studies of frost-layer dynamics was to investigate with a kinetic theory treatment the maximum rate of frost formation and sublimation for very low water vapor concentrations. This would define minimal requirements for the servo system of a continuously monitoring hygrometer at high altitude.

The rate of mass impingement upon the surface is

$$\frac{d\sigma_A}{dt} = 1/4\rho \overline{V} \qquad (5)$$

where

$\sigma_A =$ mass per unit area striking the surface

$\rho =$ mass density of water vapor

$\overline{V} =$ mean velocity for a Maxwellian distribution.

This mean velocity is

$$\overline{V} = 2\left(\frac{2RT}{M\pi}\right)^{1/2} \qquad (6)$$

where

$R =$ gas constant per mole

$M =$ molecular weight

$T =$ temperature in degrees Kelvin.

Since

$$\rho = \frac{MP}{C_v RT} \qquad (7)$$

where P is the partial pressure of the water vapor, and since $C_v \cong 1$, we have

$$\frac{d\sigma_A}{dt} = \left(\frac{M}{2\pi R}\right)^{1/2} \frac{P_A}{\sqrt{T_A}} \qquad (8)$$

Assuming a small saturated layer of vapor above the frost, which remains in equilibrium with the frost and at its temperature T_E, we have for the rate of mass evaporation

$$\frac{d\sigma_E}{dt} = \left(\frac{M}{2\pi R}\right)^{1/2} \frac{P_E}{\sqrt{T_E}} \qquad (9)$$

The vapor-pressure relation $P_E(T_E)$ was approximated by the first term in an expansion about $T_E = T_0$, T_0 taken as the equilibrium temperature for which thickness of the frost layer remains constant. Since it is known that $\log P_E(T_E)$ is a slowly varying function of T_E,

$$P_E(T_E) \cong P(T_0)e^{C(T_E - T_0)} \qquad (10)$$

where $C = \dfrac{d \log P_E}{dT_E}\bigg|_{T_0}$.

The net thickness change in time t is

$$\Delta\sigma(t) = \left| \int_0^t \left(\frac{d\sigma_A}{dt} - \frac{d\sigma_E}{dt} \right) dt \right| \qquad (11)$$

For equilibrium (a constant frost-layer thickness) at time $t = 0$, and taking constant ambient conditions and linear heating and cooling rates,

$$T_E = T_0 \pm \xi t$$

we have for cooling

$$\Delta\sigma(t) \cong \sqrt{\frac{M}{2\pi R}}$$

$$\left[\frac{P_A}{\sqrt{T_A}}\, t - P(T_0) \int_0^t \frac{e^{-C\xi\tau}}{(T_0 - \xi\tau)^{1/2}}\, d\tau \right] \qquad (12)$$

and for heating

$$\Delta\sigma(t) \cong \sqrt{\frac{M}{2\pi R}}$$

$$\left[P(T_0) \int_0^t \frac{e^{C\xi\tau}}{(T_0 + \xi\tau)^{1/2}}\, d\tau - \frac{P_A}{\sqrt{T_A}}\, t \right] \qquad (13)$$

The integrals were evaluated with a digital computer. For saturated ambient conditions with a frost point of $-70°C$, the time required to deposit or sublime 1 $\mu g/cm^2$ varies from 0.4 to 2.4 seconds for heating or cooling rates from 4 deg C/sec to 0.1 deg C/sec.

Although this rate of thickness change is encouragingly high, the kinetic theory treatment used can be expected to yield only an upper limit for the actual rate of mass transfer. An analysis of frost-layer dynamics valid for all stratospheric water vapor measurements involves an application of heat and mass transfer and boundary-layer theory. Such a study has been initiated; however, it is evident that a considerable amount of research in previously unexplored areas remains to be done.

In an attempt to provide preliminary information suitable from the standpoint of instrumentation, a less ambitious approach has necessarily been taken. The simplest approximation one can take for the frost-layer dynamics is clearly

$$\frac{d\sigma}{dt} = -K(T - T_0) \qquad (14)$$

where σ is the thickness of frost and K is a positive quantity depending upon ambient conditions and ventilation. This approach then involves an experimental evaluation of K for typical conditions of operation.

To accomplish this, the sensor can be placed in an environmental chamber which reproduces flight conditions. The unit is operated both in a closed-loop fashion and with arbitrary surface temperature inputs, and energy distributions of the alpha radiation are taken in fast sequence to provide an accurate measurement of thickness dynamics.

In addition to exploring the problem of thickness dynamics, these experiments which are now under way include continuous observation of the frost layer. Much information should then be obtained about the physical form of the frost and its effect on the frost-point measurement. The Raoult and Kelvin effects[5] and ambiguities between frost points and dew points can be studied. An additional biasing effect due to thermal diffusion can also be examined.

Based upon the approximate form of frost-layer dynamics given in Eq. (14), an analog computer simulation of the control system has been studied. Both relay and proportional control were examined using values of K estimated with the kinetic theory analysis. Transfer functions of the various components were based upon experimental data from the instrument, and the effect of hysteresis due to a "dead zone" in the sensor was included. This hysteresis is present since there exists a minimum detectable difference between signals from the sensor and reference channels which will not switch the control from heating to cooling, or vice versa. This study, however, did not include the random pulse nature of the instrument in that the frost-layer thickness was represented by an analog signal which was continuously compared with a DC level representing the reference channel.

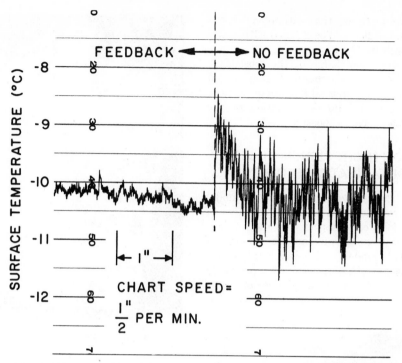

Fig. 5. Rate of change of frost-layer thickness simulated from thermoelectric cooler current.

The two main results of this investigation are as follows:

(1) Any small amount of hysteresis is very destructive, leading to large oscillations of the surface temperature T about the equilibrium temperature T_0. Proportional control is seemingly better than relay control in the absence of hysteresis, but worse when an amount corresponding to only 1 μg/cm^2 of minimum detectable thickness change is present (the present instrument uses relay control, and the amount of hysteresis present is of order of 1 μg/cm^2).

(2) A rate feedback introducing the rate of change of the frost thickness, $d\sigma/dt$, into the reference signal leads to a much improved system for either relay or proportional control. The feedback damps out the oscillations of T about T_0 and reduces the effect of hysteresis. Minimum detectable thickness changes of up to 30 μg/cm^2 had little effect on relay control with feedback present, but amounts of 15 μg/cm^2 still caused instability with proportional control.

The desired feedback is $d\sigma/dt$, but this is not easily obtained in the actual instrument without increasing the time constant of the device. However, if the approximate form of the frost-layer dynamics is adequate, a measure of $d\sigma/dt$ is available from the surface temperature T, which is continuously monitored. Moreover, since the transfer function for the thermoelectric cooler in the hygrometer is known, $d\sigma/dt$ can be extracted from the thermoelectric driving current.

A feedback signal based on the thermoelectric current was used in an actual instrument. Figure 5 shows the hygrometer tracking the frost points with and without feedback. Without feedback the frost point varies $\pm\frac{3}{4}$ deg C about the mean due to surface temperature "swing" and random switching. Introduction of feedback reduces oscillations in the surface temperature by a factor of about ten.

A further computer study was made in which the statistical nature of the radiation signals was simulated by a noise source. It showed that randomness acts as a dither signal and is useful in stabilizing the instrument. It can be shown that without noise, the system (essentially a type-2 servo with static and Coulomb friction) is unstable.

With better knowledge of the frost-layer dynamics from the experimental program and a more general theoretical treatment, a more thorough analysis and optimization of the control system will be possible.

BALLOON FLIGHT RESULTS AND THE CONTAMINATION PROBLEM

Figure 6 shows an early experimental model of the hygrometer used on a large number of flights made in conjunction with the infrared spectrometry work of the University of Denver. This model, which weighs about six pounds less batteries, has been used primarily for circuit development and studies of venti-

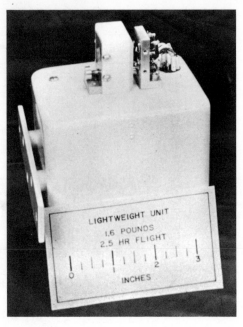

FIG. 7. Lightweight radiosonde hygrometer.

lation using blowers and balloon ascent ram pressure. From two to four of these hygrometers were carried on every flight, with relatively good correspondence.

Figure 7 shows a lightweight version for radiosonde use, weighing 1.6 pounds complete with a 2½-hour battery supply. An additional battery pack of 0.9 pound permits a flight duration of over eight hours. In this unit, the complete servo loop contains only nine transistors.

Although the primary purpose of the balloon flights was to test the instruments under actual atmospheric conditions, some creditable stratospheric moisture measurements resulted, as well as an insight into problems associated with the measurement beyond those of the instrument. In particular, moisture carried by the instruments and balloon system from the wet layers of the troposphere can be released in the stratosphere under the influence of solar radiation. Questions have thus arisen as to the validity of frost-point data so obtained.

Figure 8 shows the instrument package used on the 17 January 1963 flight. The main gondola, which carried the infrared solar spectrometer of the University of Denver, contained large quantities of "Styrofoam"

FIG. 6. Early experimental hygrometer.

FIG. 8. Instrument package for 17 January 1963 flight.

and cardboard with extensive surface areas directly exposed to the atmosphere. The hygrometers were located on booms extending approximately five feet from the main package, placing them outside the aerodynamic boundary layer of the package during the ascent. Large amounts of "Styrofoam" were again present on the 5 April 1962 package. In this case the hygrometers were mounted one-half foot to the side of the package. Figures 9 and 10 show the frost-point profiles obtained on the two flights. In view of the contamination argument, one should note in the April profile a steadily decreasing frost point to −87°C at 63 mb and an increasing frost point above this level after sunrise. It would be unwise at this time, however, to discount the possibility that this "sunrise" phenomenon may be a real effect. The January flight showed a considerably wetter stratosphere than the April flight, but it should be noted that the stratosphere was also much warmer.

It can be seen on both flights that the frost point increased in time during the constant-altitude float and eventually reached a nearly saturated value. In an attempt to show quantitatively that the desorbing wall of the package could have contaminated the measurements, the problem was treated as a one-dimensional diffusion case.

The one-dimensional diffusion equation for one gas (water vapor) diffusing into another gas (air) is

$$D_{12} \frac{\partial^2 n(z,t)}{\partial z^2} = \frac{\partial n(z,t)}{\partial t} \tag{15}$$

where

$n(z,t) =$ excess concentration (particles/ unit volume) of water vapor

$z =$ distance from the wall (one dimension)

$D_{12} =$ mutual diffusion coefficient.

This case may be regarded geometrically as that of an extended wall in the x-y plane at $z = 0$ from which particles diffuse in the z-direction. The boundary condition that is

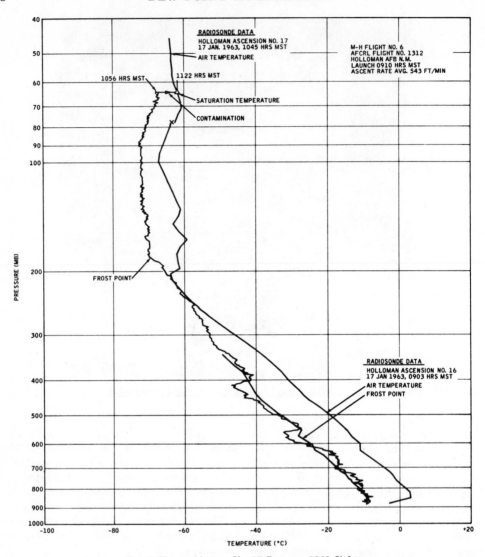

FIG. 9. Frost-point profile, 17 January 1963 flight.

assumed is that the sample is saturated at all times along this extended surface, i.e.,

$$n(0,t) = N = \text{saturation concentration}$$

$$n(\infty,t) < \infty$$

$$n(z,0) = 0, \; z > 0$$

A solution meeting these boundary conditions is

$$n(z,t) = N\left[1 - 2\Phi\left(\frac{z}{\sqrt{2D_{12}t}}\right)\right] \quad (16)$$

where

$$\Phi(w) = \frac{1}{\sqrt{2\pi}} \int_0^w \exp\left(\frac{-\xi^2}{2}\right) d\xi \quad (17)$$

Comparison of flight data and theory is presented in Figs. 11 and 12. Considering the simplicity of the analysis, the agreement between theory and experimental data is excellent. The predicted increase in time-lag for more distant locations of the hygrometers, i.e., the time before the effects of contamination first appear, is seen to agree well with the flight data.

Let us now estimate the total efflux of water vapor from the package that would be needed to produce such effects. Use of the above solution and Fick's diffusion law provides an estimate of M_T, the total efflux of

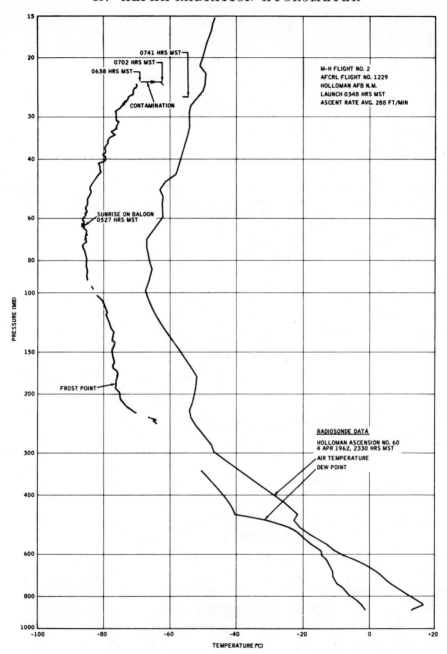

Fig. 10. Frost-point profile, 5 April 1962 flight.

particles per unit area from the wall in time T,

$$M_T = 2N\sqrt{\frac{D_{12}T}{\pi}} \qquad (18)$$

For the 5 April 1962 flight, we find for $T = 1$ hour, that M_T corresponds to a layer of water approximately 4×10^{-7} cm thick (less than twenty molecules). This is a minute amount and it is entirely reasonable to expect that such a quantity could be readily sorbed by almost any material. It should also be noted that the conclusion that contamination is a serious problem would be only slightly modified even if the results were in error by as

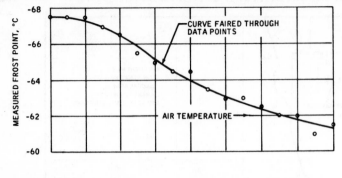

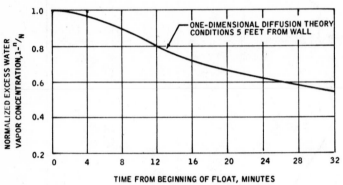

M-H FLIGHT NO. 6, AFCRL. FLIGHT NO. 1312

HOLLOMAN AFB N.M.

FLOAT ALTITUDE 67 MB (61,000 FT.)

HYGROMETER LOCATED 5 FEET FROM SIDE OF "WET" GONDOLA

FIG. 11. Contamination of air sample by instrument package, 17 January 1963 flight.

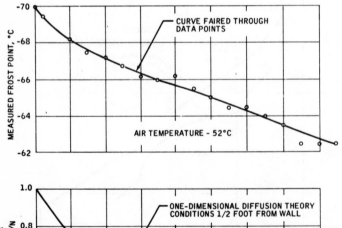

M-H FLIGHT NO. 2, AFCRL. FLIGHT NO. 1229

HOLLOMAN AFB N.M.

FLOAT ALTITUDE 24 MB (83,000 FT.)

HYGROMETER LOCATED 1/2 FOOT FROM SIDE OF "WET" GONDOLA

FIG. 12. Contamination of air sample by instrument package, 5 April 1962 flight.

much as an order of magnitude. Due to the serious contamination that can result from very thin layers of water, the expedient of placing the hygrometers outside the aerodynamic boundary layer of the package does not insure the validity of data taken on ascent, since the balloon material might desorb a significant amount of moisture into the balloon wake.

CONCLUSION AND SUMMARY OF WORK IN PROGRESS

It is felt that the feasibility and advantages of the Alpha Radiation Hygrometer have been adequately demonstrated by extensive laboratory tests and flight data, and that the extreme sensitivity of this instrument gives it unequaled potential among today's automatic frost-point hygrometers. It is felt in addition that the stratospheric measurements which have been made, while not entirely free from difficulties and uncertainties, are nonetheless of considerable interest. Much effort will be required, however, to eliminate the sources of difficulty which have been experienced and which have given rise to doubts about the reliability of virtually all balloon flight water-vapor data existing today.

Efforts are at present being made along the three following lines in an attempt to improve the quality of measurements:

(1) Theoretical and experimental work is in progress on the complicated question of the dynamics and physical form of the frost layer. The rates of formation and sublimation, types of condensate encountered, surface effects, interpretation of frost-point measurements, etc., are being investigated.

(2) Efforts to improve the instrumentation are under way. Although current instruments have proved to be satisfactory for present applications, anticipated applications involve more demanding conditions of operation. The simple expedients of increasing the source activity and trigger level will both improve the sensitivity and simultaneously reduce the effect of randomness, since the present instrument is far from the thick-source limitation

described previously. An increase in the information rate of more than a factor of ten is well within the band-pass capability of the amplifiers presently used. The incorporation of rate feedback based on the surface temperature or thermoelectric driving current could reduce temperature oscillations considerably. Since the question of whether a servo mechanism is operating properly is crucial to the validity of data, efforts will be made on future flights to monitor the frost-layer thickness continuously by means of an auxiliary circuit. This procedure should be advocated for all frost-point hygrometers, since temperature data recorded during periods when the frost layer is far from an equilibrium state (if even present) can hardly be considered meaningful data. In addition, it is desirable to make corroborative measurements simultaneously by use of as many independent units as possible.

(3) The problem of contamination is under investigation. It is believed that this problem will prove to be the most difficult, but that it must be solved if any reliable data are to be taken.

Acknowledgments. The author wishes to acknowledge the contributions of Messrs. L. Kirvida, M. P. Fricke, and R. D. Murphy to the development of this instrument, and to thank Dr. W. T. Sackett for many helpful suggestions. I would also like to thank Dr. P. R. Gast of AFCRL and Mr. D. G. Murcray of the University of Denver for their encouragement and help during the balloon flight program.

References

1. Gardner, R. P., and Ross, H. H., "Alpha Gauge for the Measurement of Small Density Thickness," *Rev. Sci. Instr.*, **33**, 1227 (1962).
2. Anderson, Herbert L., "Alpha Particle Thickness Using a Solid State Detector," *Nucl. Instr. Methods*, **12**, 111 (1961).
3. Ramavataram, K. and Porat, D. I., "Measurement of Surface Density of Thin Foils," *Nucl. Instr. Methods*, **4**, 239 (1959).
4. Becker, L. C., Tandon, G. K., Jobes, F. C., McIntyre, J. A., and Watts, T. L., "Notes on the Uniformity of Commercial Foils," *Nucl. Instr. Methods*, **21**, 298 (1963).
5. Wylie, R. G., and Davies, D. K., "The Basic Process of the Dew-Point Hygrometer," Humidity and Moisture, Vol. 1, Reinhold Publishing Co., New York, NY., 1964.

20. The Direct Measurement of Dew-point Temperature with Semiconducting Thermoelements

Victor Armstrong

Texas Instruments Incorporated, Dallas, Texas

ABSTRACT

Recent advances in semiconductor technology have produced materials which operate as efficient thermoelectric (Peltier) coolers.

Utilization of these materials has led to the development of a small, accurate device for measuring directly the dew-point temperature of the air or gas. The device described uses "N" and "P" doped bismuth telluride as the semiconducting thermoelements.

In block form, the device consists of (1) a power supply, (2) a light source, (3) a photodiode, (4) a transistorized amplifier, and (5) a mirrored surface cooled by the thermoelements.

The system is a closed loop servo with feedback control to stabilize the measurements.

In operation, the light is reflected from the mirrored surface into the photodiode. This photodiode drives the transistorized amplifier to develop high current densities in the thermoelements. As a result of the Peltier effect, the mirror temperature decreases until atmospheric moisture begins to condense on its surface. When the condensation forms, the light is diffused and less light impinges upon the photodiode. The amplifier, operating as a proportional control, reduces the current to the thermoelements, and the mirror temperature tends to rise. As the temperature rises, the condensate disappears and more light impinges upon the photodiode. Again the amplifier drives the thermoelements to a lower temperature until condensation forms. The dew-point temperature, or the temperature at which moisture begins to condense from the atmosphere, may now be measured by means of a copper-constantan thermocouple or a bead thermistor embedded in the surface of the mirror. The equipment is stabilized and ready to measure the dew-point temperature to an accuracy of $\pm.1$ deg C within two minutes after power is applied. The power consumption of the device is low, and it may be carried into the field for measurements in remote areas not serviced by powerlines. In previous dew-point measuring systems, contamination and clouding of mirrors by dust motes and aerosols has been a major problem. A great amount of research has been directed at this problem, and as a result, a practical mirror has been developed for the system.

A modification of the device may be used in a space probe to measure captive moisture content of the lunar surface or other extraterrestrial bodies.

The stringent requirements of science and technology warrant the use of a new family of measuring and monitoring instruments in meteorology and related fields, and in industry and commerce more accurate methods of humidity detection and control are required. The Energy Conversion Department of Texas Instruments set out a program to improve these measurements by utilizing new techniques in semiconductor technology. Actually the accurate measurement of humidity goes hand in hand with the atmospheric tolerances of semiconductor manufacture.

Without precise control, it is impossible to develop reliable transistors and diodes.

Many types and variations of hygrometers have been developed or described in the technical journals. Of these, the most promising is the type using a chilled mirror for detection of dew-point temperature. Commonly, the mirror is cooled with an ice bath or a low-temperature gas such as carbon dioxide or "Freon". Some types have used mechanical refrigeration methods. These instruments require either a source of gas from a bulky container or ice which may not be available in remote areas. The utilization of semiconducting thermoelements exhibiting the Peltier effect is a logical answer for overcoming the inconvenience of the usual dew-point hygrometer. The techniques employed are relatively simple yet extremely accurate. Thermoelectric coolers based upon the Peltier effect have been impractical until recent years. With the refining equipment now available, it is possible to produce efficient metallic alloys that exhibit this effect.

Peltier, in 1834, discovered that if an electric current is passed through the junction of two dissimilar metals, one junction will absorb heat while the other junction will liberate heat. This effect is related to the Seebeck effect that was discovered a few years earlier.

Peltier coolers have been designed which will approach a temperature of $-100°C$. This is the device which may be considered the heart of the instrument.

First, a multiple voltage power supply was designed which would provide power for a light source, the transistorized amplifier, and the Peltier cooler. The light source is a No. 47 bulb mounted rigidly in a bracket above the mirror. The transistor amplifier requires 12 V at a current of from 10 to 25 mA. The Peltier cooler requires 100 to 500 mV at currents of from 200 to 6000 mA. Attached to the cooler is a mirror whose surface temperature is monitored by a miniature thermocouple. The thermocouple is attached to a chart recorder and a running record of dew-point temperature is provided. The detector senses light from the source reflected by the mirror. The detector eye is a 1N2175 silicon photoduodiode. The photodiode forms one leg of a balanced differential amplifier which uses two transistors. Reflected light causes an unbalance in the amplifier, and this unbalance is amplified by a succeeding silicon transistor voltage amplifier. Enough voltage is now developed in order to drive a medium-power germanium transistor. This medium-power unit is used as a proportional control amplifier which controls the current flow through the final transistor. The final transistor is a germanium high-power device whose emitter lead is connected in series with the "N" and "P" doped bismuth telluride legs of the Peltier cooler and the power supply. As current flows through the power transistor, it also flows through the Peltier cooler.

Immediately upon application of primary power, light is reflected, detected and amplified causing the cooler temperature to drop rapidly. As the mirror reaches the dew-point temperature, moisture begins to condense on the surface and less light is reflected. The more diffused the light is, the less current flow occurs in the cooler. As the cooler current is reduced nearly to zero, the temperature of the mirror begins to rise toward atmospheric. There is, however, a thermal or more appropriately, a cryogenic inertia which results in temperature overshoot. This overshoot takes the form graphically of a critically damped wave which is typical of closed loop servo systems, i.e., a finite time is required for stabilization. In this system an average time is two minutes. At this point, the detector will follow minor fluctuations of dew point and will also follow rapid gross or minute changes in humidity.

Operational tests performed in an environmental chamber indicated an ability to detect moisture levels of less than 1 ppm (parts per million). The readings were monitored and compared with a Consolidated Electrodynamics Corporation type 26-303 MB moisture monitor. The range of this instrument is from 1 to 100 ppm of moisture. Since our standards would not respond to the lower percentages, we were unable to determine the absolute minimum our hygrometer would detect.

One instrument undergoing tests on our rooftop laboratory some 40 feet above ground level was able to detect the turn-on turn-off variations in the atmosphere caused by a lawn sprinkler at a building over two blocks away. This, perhaps, does not seem unusual, but the prevailing winds were from the south-east, and the lawn sprinkler was to the north-west of the instrument. The dew-point detector was also able to detect the cyclic variations of the atmosphere coincident with the operation of the air-conditioning cooling tower on our own building. Again, this tower is downwind from the instrument shelter.

Another curiosity exhibited by this instrument was its ability to detect the passage overhead of jet aircraft at altitudes from 500 to 1500 ft. The chart recorder would print a small spike 2 to 3 seconds after the plane had passed. At first it was thought that an aerosol of oil from the jet exhaust had formed, but microscopic examination of the mirror surface showed no such formation. The possibility of acoustical noise was considered and steps were taken to eliminate this. The detector was placed in a solid box and foam rubber and fibre-glass sheets were packed around it. The detector continued to function as it had previously, plotting exactly the passage of each jet airplane as it occurred.

Initial experiments on this type of dew-point detector disclosed a need for a mirrored surface that would withstand atmospheric conditions which would be encountered anywhere in the world.

Gold-plated copper mirrors appeared to have the most desirable qualities because of the nontarnishing surface. The gold did not withstand weathering as anticipated, nor did it withstand the wear of periodic cleaning. Finally, a rhodium over nickel-plated mirror was selected because of the high reflectivity and wearability displayed in environmental tests. This type of mirror was used in a dew-point hygrometer on board the antarctic research vessel U.S.N.S. Eltanin.

With additional contacts, the recorder from the hygrometer may control air-conditioning or dehumidifying equipment for tight control of environmental conditions in white rooms or dry boxes. Another variation of this unit might be used in a space probe to measure the captive moisture content of the lunar surface or other extraterrestrial bodies.

The models that have been built are by no means the ultimate in humidity detection devices, but the present accuracy of ± 0.1 deg C and the fact that battery powered models have been tested and have performed quite well in remote areas, are suggestive of units which may be made in the future.

21. Dew-point Apparatus of High Accuracy

J. L. Hartley, J. L. Chamberlin* and W. D. Huff

Sandia Laboratory, Albuquerque, New Mexico

ABSTRACT

A dew-point hygrometer was constructed in which dew was formed on a polished steel surface and was viewed by means of a 20-power stereomicroscope. The temperature range of the hygrometer was —30 to +30°C. When dew points measured by the hygrometer were compared with calculated values from a two-pressure generator operating at 80°F, the maximum difference was 0.093 deg C, and the arithmetic mean of the differences was 0.028 deg C. When compared with a 0°C dew-point generator, the maximum difference was 0.105 deg C and the arithmetic mean of the differences was 0.002 deg C.

INTRODUCTION

Three major requirements must be met in measuring the dew point of a moist gas using the Regnault type of dew-point hygrometer. These requirements are:

(1) A relatively clean polished surface must be provided for collecting dew;

(2) A means must be provided for detecting the dew as it forms on the surface, and

(3) An accurate and stable method must be used to measure the surface temperature.

A dew-point hygrometer has been constructed that meets each of these requirements to a considerable degree.

DESCRIPTION

To provide the required polished surface, a stainless-steel disk $\frac{1}{16}$-in. thick was brazed to a section of $\frac{1}{2}$-in. diameter copper rod (see

* Present address National Bureau of Standards, Washington, D.C.

Fig. 1). The extent of the bond between the disk and rod was checked by X-rays. Greater than 90 per cent bonding was obtained by repeated brazing. This insured that, in use, the temperature gradients across the polished disk would be small. After a satisfactory bond had been made, a $\frac{3}{16}$-in. hole was drilled in the copper rod at an angle as shown in Fig. 1. The hole was extended into the back side of the steel disk to within 0.015 in. of the front surface. The front surface of the steel disk was then ground and lapped to one-half fringe of optical flatness.

A small-mass thermocouple was used to measure the mirror surface temperature. The measuring junction was made of AWG No. 40 chromel-constantan wire which was looped over a slotted copper plug. As shown in the enlarged view of Fig. 1, the measuring junction was located at a corner of the plug, and the plug was pressed into the $\frac{3}{16}$-in. hole drilled in the copper rod. Pressing the copper plug to the bottom of this hole brought the measuring junction to within 0.020 in. of the polished front surface. Locating the thermocouple as near the surface as possible minimized the error in temperature measurements.

Another method of locating the temperature measuring junction near the polished surface was tried before the method described above. The two thermocouple wires were imbedded in the polished surface from the front. After crossing the face of the mirror, the extending wires were placed alongside the $\frac{1}{2}$-in. rod. In crossing the face of the mirror, the extension wires were exposed to the temperature of the moist air. Thus, heat flow from the wires into the surface caused dew to form elsewhere on the polished

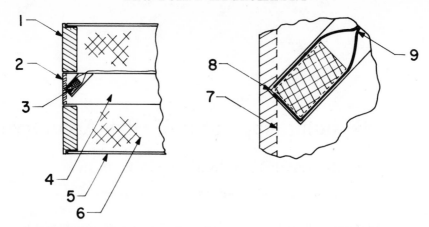

Fig. 1. Dew-point hygrometer mirror and thermocouple location. (1) "Teflon" plug, (2) stainless-steel mirror, (3) copper plug, (4) copper rod, (5) 2-in. brass tube, (6) insulation. (7) copper-to-steel solder line, (8) couple junction, (9) couple extension wire.

surface before forming at the junction of the wires and the surface. Because dew formed uniformly over the mirror surface with the thermocouple imbedded behind the mirror, it was concluded that this method introduced the least error in dew-point temperature measurements.

AWG No. 24 thermocouple wire was spliced to the No. 40 wire a few inches from the measuring junction, to minimize the electrical resistance of the thermocouple circuit. Reducing the electrical resistance provided greater sensitivity when using a moving coil galvanometer as a potentiometer null indicator. The reference junction was placed in a 7-mm glass tube closed at one end and filled with wax for protection. The reference junction was kept at a constant temperature by placing the glass tube in a triple-point-of-water cell.

After the measuring junction was placed in position behind the mirror, the thermocouple was tested to establish its EMF-temperature relationship. An NBS-certified platinum resistance thermometer was used as a standard for measuring the temperature at 16 test points ranging from +100 to −80°C. Fifth-order, sixth-order, and seventh-order polynomials of the type $E = a + bt + ct^2 + \ldots$ were fitted to these points by method of least squares. Using the three empirical equations, three tables were prepared with EMF listings at intervals of 1 deg C. No significant difference in the three tables was noted. It was later learned from extensive testing that a third-order polynomial is adequate and possibly preferred.

It was considered important to be able to retest the thermocouple used in the hygrometer at a later date. Because of the hygrometer design, this presented a problem. After the thermocouple was positioned in the copper rod and after the copper rod was insulated, the thermocouple could not be removed and retested. A completely adequate solution to the problem was not found. However, at the time the hygrometer thermocouple was calibrated, a second thermocouple identical to the one used in the hygrometer was calibrated at the same test temperatures. One year later the second thermocouple was retested at different temperatures. Using the earlier calibration values, the second thermocouple was found to agree with an NBS-certified platinum resistance thermometer to better than 0.06 deg C. Thus, by inference it was concluded that the temperature-EMF relationship of the thermocouple placed in the hygrometer changed very little, if at all, from the time of initial calibration. No attempt was made to improve the stability of either thermocouple by annealing before the initial calibration.

The complete assembly of the dew-point hygrometer is shown in Fig. 2. The short copper rod containing the thermocouple and mirror assembly was attached to a 12-in. section of rod placed inside a 2-in. brass tube

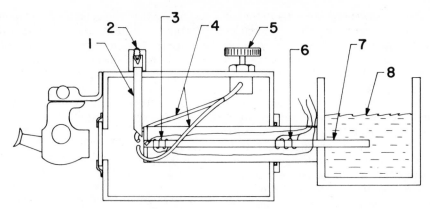

Fɪɢ. 2. Dew-point hygrometer inside airtight box. (1) "Lucite" lighting rod, (2) prefocused lamp, (3) Heater B, (4) dual air lines, (5) air control valve, (6) Heater A, (7) copper rod, (8) dry ice and alcohol.

and thermally insulated. A container of dry ice and alcohol or ice and water was used for cooling. A length of resistance wire was wrapped around the copper rod near the ice container to form Heater A, Fig. 2. Heater B was wrapped about ¼ in. from the mirror end of the rod.

OPERATION

To measure dew-point temperature the hygrometer was placed inside an airtight box (Fig. 2). An O-ring provided an air seal around the brass tube extending through the box wall. Two diametrically opposing air lines were located in front of the mirror. Moist air from a two-pressure humidity generator was discharged across the mirror surface from the two air lines. The rate of air flow was adjusted by a valve to range from 0.5 to 6 cfh. Light from a prefocused GE 222 lamp was "piped" down a lucite rod. The end of the rod near the mirror was cut at an angle to cause the light to strike the polished surface at an angle of approximately 70 degrees from the surface normal. This semitangential lighting caused the mirror to appear as a dark background before the dew formed. As dew droplets formed, they became visible against the initial dark background. Observations were made with the aid of a stereomicroscope.

Dew was made to form and disappear by adjusting Heater A, Fig. 2, to a constant power level and making small adjustments in the power supplied by Heater B. The power

supplied by Heater A ranged from 0 to 30 watts, and for Heater B from 0 to 5 watts.

By setting the microscope at a magnification of 20, it was possible to detect dew forming and disappearing within a temperature spread of 0.05 deg C for dew-point temperatures above 0°C. For dew-point temperature ranging from 0 down to −30°C, the temperature spread increased to 0.4 deg C. The use of this type of dew-point hygrometer became increasingly more difficult for dew-point temperature measurements below −15°C. This difficulty resulted primarily from crystallized ice formations on the surface along with a background of what was assumed to be vitreous ice or supercooled water.

However, because a distinctive change in the surface appearance occurred when supercooled water or vitreous ice formed, this formation was taken as the dew-point indication. Dew-point temperature measurements below −30°C are deemed impractical unless crystallized ice is taken as the dew-point indication.

EXPERIMENTAL RESULTS

The dew-point hygrometer was compared with two moist-air generators (see Table 1). First, moist air from a two-pressure humidity generator was used to provide dew-point temperatures ranging from −30 to +20°C. With the exception of values listed at 20 per cent RH, each hygrometer dew-point temperature listed in Table 1 represents a mean of one to four observations, the larger number being taken wherever greater differences occurred. A single observation is being defined as the average of three to five readings taken in succession without any change in test conditions. For 20 per cent RH, five observations were made with the generator operating at 80°F and seven with it operating at 40°F. The larger number of observations at 20 per cent RH is the result of additional tests performed to measure the changes in dew-point temperature as the moist-air flow rate was changed from 0.5 to 5.0 cfh. No measurable difference due to flow rate changes was noted. A two-pressure generator determination was made each time a dew-point observation was made. The generator dew-point temperature was computed from generator gauges accurate to 0.2 per cent. The measurements were used in the equation

$$\frac{e}{e_s} = \frac{P_c\,(1 - 0.00019\,P_c)}{P_s\,(1 - 0.00019\,P_s)}$$

where P_c is the pressure inside the dew-point box, and P_s is the saturator pressure. The value e_s is the vapor pressure of water at the temperature of the saturator, and e is the vapor pressure of water inside the dew-point box. Thus, the saturation temperature corresponding to e is the dew-point temperature determined from the two-pressure generator. All observations are referenced to saturation vapor pressure over a plane surface of water.[1]

Over a dew-point temperature range of −15°C to 20°C, the maximum difference between the hygrometer observations and the two-pressure generator was found to be −0.093 deg C. The arithmetic mean of the differences was −0.028 deg C. A maximum difference of −1.656 deg C was found when the dew-point range was extended down to −30°C; the arithmetic mean of the differences was −0.529 deg C.

A second comparison was obtained by using a 0°C dew-point generator. Dry air was passed over the surface of melting ice, saturating it with a water vapor pressure of 6.1078 mb (vapor pressure of water at 0°C). The moist air was discharged across the hygrometer mirror surface. Table 2 lists dew-point temperatures indicated by the hygrometer. Each listed temperature is an observation, the mean of three to five readings.

Assuming that the generated dew-point temperature was 0°C, the greatest difference indicated by the hygrometer was 0.105 deg C; the arithmetic mean of all measured differences was 0.002 deg C.

TABLE 1. HYGROMETER COMPARED WITH TWO-PRESSURE HUMIDITY GENERATOR

RH at Generator Temperature (%)	Dew-point Temperature (deg C)		
	Hygrometer	Generator	Difference
Two-pressure Generator Operated at 80°F			
5	−15.483	−15.411	−0.072
10	− 6.739	− 6.786	+0.047
20	1.398	1.306	+0.092
30	6.830	6.873	−0.043
40	11.063	11.138	−0.075
50	14.410	14.440	−0.030
60	17.316	17.409	−0.093
70	19.777	19.824	−0.047
Two-pressure Generator Operated at 40°F			
5	−30.281	−32.437	−1.656
10	−25.237	−25.045	−0.192
20	−17.466	−17.125	−0.341
40	− 8.927	− 8.474	−0.453
60	− 3.705	− 3.266	−0.439
80	+ 0.326	+ 0.531	−0.205
95	+ 2.628	+ 3.043	−0.415

TABLE 2. HYGROMETER COMPARED WITH ZERO °C DEW-POINT GENERATOR

Date	Dew-point Hygrometer Indication (°C)	Date	Dew-point Hygrometer Indication (°C)
1-22-63	−0.027	1-25-63	+0.008
1-22-63	−0.027	1-25-63	−0.013
1-23-63	−0.089	1-25-63	+0.021
1-23-63	−0.006	1-25-63	+0.027
1-23-63	+0.012	1-25-63	+0.029
1-23-63	−0.105	1-25-63	−0.019
1-23-63	+0.015	1-25-63	−0.011
1-23-63	+0.046	1-25-63	+0.026
1-24-63	−0.071	1-25-63	+0.043
1-24-63	+0.033	1-25-63	+0.011
1-24-63	−0.032	1-28-63	+0.004
1-24-63	−0.035	1-28-63	+0.024
1-24-63	−0.021	1-28-63	+0.014
1-24-63	+0.014	1-28-63	−0.010

Reference

1. List, Robert J., "Smithsonian Meteorological Tables," Sixth Revised Edition, Table 94, Smithsonian Institute, 1958.

22. A Recording Dew-point Hygrometer

Einar Brendeng

Institutt for kjøleteknikk, Norges tekniske høgskole, Norway

ABSTRACT

An instrument for the measurement and recording of water vapor pressure in air at cold storage temperatures has been developed at Institutt for kjøleteknikk, Norges tekniske høgskole (Refrigeration Department, Norwegian Institute of Technology). The instrument is based on the measuring principle suggested by H. Glaser.

Air from the cold room is compressed in a small two-stage membrane compressor plant and led over the dew-point mirror, which is enclosed in a pressure chamber. The temperature of the mirror is kept constant at 0°C, by means of a thermocouple, a servo amplifier energizing a servo motor, and a motor-operated valve regulating a flow of cold alcohol to the underside of the dew-point mirror. The deposit of dew on the surface of the mirror is observed by a photoresistor, connected in a bridge, and the output from this bridge is fed to a second servo amplifier with servo motor and motor-operated air pressure valve. The air pressure is recorded by means of a strain gauge pressure transducer and a strip chart recorder.

When the water vapor pressure on the surface of the mirror is in equilibrium with the water vapor pressure in the air, the thickness and reflectivity of the dew deposit is constant, and the air pressure over the mirror is also kept constant. Thus, the water vapor in the air under test is easily calculated from the water vapor pressure corresponding to the temperature on the surface of the mirror, and the pressure ratio between the pressure over the mirror and the atmospheric pressure.

The accuracy of the instrument, when the pressure is read from the pressure gauge, is about ±0.5 per cent at water vapor pressures of about 0.3 Torr. Used as a recorder, the accuracy is also dependent on the accuracy of the pressure transducer and the recording instrument.

INTRODUCTION

In research in the refrigeration field it is often desired to measure the humidity in the air at low temperatures with a high degree of accuracy. In an investigation carried out on the desiccation of cold stored goods, for instance, it would be necessary to measure the water vapor pressure in the air with an accuracy of 1 per cent, in order to achieve an accuracy of about 10 per cent in the difference in water vapor pressure between the surface of the goods and the air, when the relative humidity is 90 per cent.

Apart from being highly accurate, the ideal instrument should not require calibration, or the initial calibration should not shift. Further, it should be possible to connect it to a recorder. Moisture should not be added or extracted from the air under test during the measurement. An easily portable instrument would be of advantage in most circumstances, but in laboratory use, this is not of prime importance.

Some years ago, at the Refrigeration Department at the Technical University of Norway, we were in need of a hygrometer satisfying these demands. No suitable instrument seemed to be commercially available, however, and we therefore built an instrument based on the measuring principle suggested by H. Glaser,[1] and investigated by L. Prins.[2]

209

MEASURING PRINCIPLE

The air under test is compressed and led over the cold surface of the dew-point mirror. Since the pressure of the water vapor is increased in the same ratio as the total pressure, the initial water vapor pressure P_a in the air can be calculated from the simple formula:

$$P_a = \frac{P_m}{P/P_0}$$

where

P_m = water vapor pressure at the mirror

P = total pressure over the mirror

P_0 = initial total pressure

Since the necessary pressure ratio quickly increases with decreasing dew point in the air, it is essential to keep the temperature of the dew-point mirror as low as practical. If uncertainty in the character of the deposit is to be avoided, 0°C is the lowest temperature to be permitted. Figure 1 gives the relation between pressure ratio and dew point, with a mirror temperature of 0°C.

At low dew points in the air under test, a lower temperature of the mirror may be employed in order to avoid undue high pressures. At a mirror temperature of −8°C, for instance, the necessary pressure ratio is reduced 50 per cent.

When the deposit on the mirror is permanent, as is the case when the instrument is in equilibrium, the forming of undercooled water is unlikely to occur. Thus no error should arise from the use of a lower mirror surface temperature.

Due to the influence of the pressurized air on the vapor pressure, a small deviation occurs from the simple formula given for the calculation of the vapor pressure. Pollitzer and Strebel[3] suggest a method for calculation of this deviation.

$$\frac{\Delta P}{P_m} = \frac{v(P - P_m)}{RT}$$

where

ΔP = increase in water vapor pressure at mirror, in relation to P_m

P_m = saturated water vapor pressure, under absence of air

R = gas constant

T = absolute temperature

v = mole volume of liquid water

The equation of Pollitzer and Strebel gives the increase of the water vapor pressure at the dew-point mirror, in relation to the theoretical pressure. The deviation is about 1 per cent at a pressure of 13 atm (kg/cm² absolute), as shown in Fig. 2.

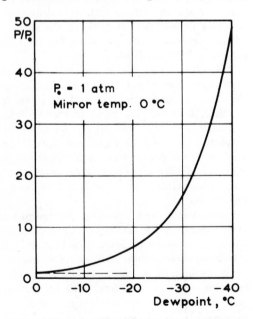

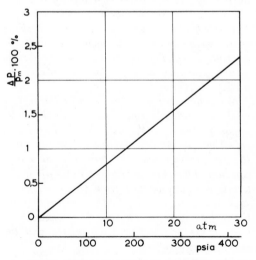

FIG. 1. Pressure ratio in relation to dew point at a mirror temperature of 0°C.

FIG. 2. Deviation from theoretical dew point due to presence of air in relation to air pressure.

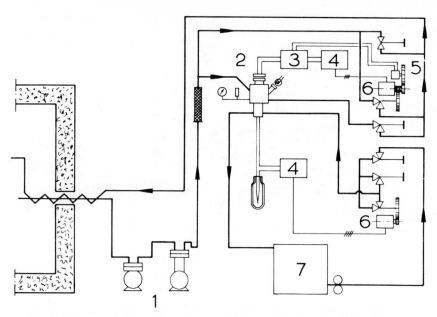

FIG. 3. Diagram of the instrument: (1) low- and high-stage membrane compressors, (2) pressure chamber with pressure gauge and pressure transducer, (3) bridge, (4) DC amplifiers, (5) potentiometer driven by servomotor, (6) servo motors, (7) sealed refrigerating unit for cooling of alcohol.

DESCRIPTION OF THE INSTRUMENT

Figure 3 shows a diagram of the instrument. The air under test is compressed in a two-stage plant. Both stages are of the membrane type to avoid difficulties with deposits of oil on the mirror. Rubber is used in the low stage, while the high stage is a steel membrane compressor manufactured by Corblin, Paris.

A heat exchanger is fitted in the suction line, serving the double purpose of reducing the temperature of the air returning from the instrument, and heating the suction line so that no ice crystals can accumulate in the suction tube. Air is returned to the cold room from the hygrometer in order to avoid influence of the measurement on the humidity condition in the room.

Figure 4 shows a cross section of the metering unit with the mirror. The mirror is inserted in the pressure chamber, Fig. 5, and the coolant is alcohol, cooled by a small domestic sealed refrigerating unit.

The surface of the mirror consists of a thin disc of constantan, 0.1 mm thick, into which is soldered a thin constantan wire. The copper wire for the thermocouple is soldered into the

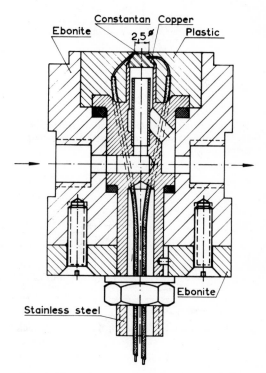

FIG. 4. Metering unit with thermocouple. Diameter of mirror = 2.5 mm.

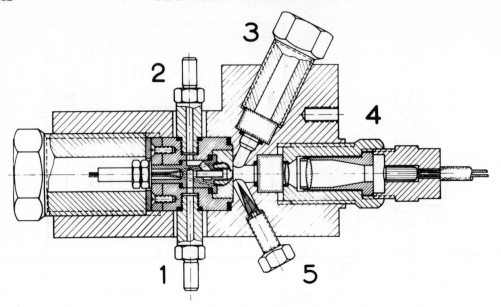

FIG. 5. Pressure chamber with metering unit: (1, 2) coolant inlet and outlet, (3) window for illumination, (4) optical system with photoresistor, (5) Trap for reflected light.

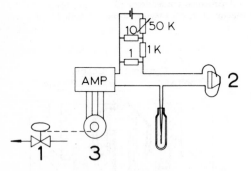

FIG. 6. Automatic control of the mirror temperature: (1) servo valve, (2) mirror with thermocouple, (3) servo motor.

copper body of the mirror. The temperature of the mirror is maintained constant by means of this thermocouple and a Honeywell DC amplifier. The amplifier energizes a servo motor which adjusts a valve, regulating the flow of cold alcohol to the mirror (Fig. 6).

Since the mechanical chopper of the amplifier might give a small stable unbalance of a few μV, a series resistance connected by a voltage divider, is incorporated in the thermocouple circuit.

An 8-V, 50-watt projector lamp, operated at a reduced, stabilized voltage, is used as the

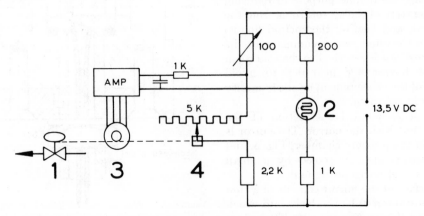

FIG. 7. Automatic control of the pressure: (1) servo valve, (2) photoresistor, (3) servo motor, (4) potentiometer with friction drive.

light source. The reflected light passes through lenses to the photoresistor, Clairex CL604L. This photoresistor is connected in a bridge, and the output from the bridge is fed into a second Honeywell amplifier, energizing a servo motor adjusting a valve that regulates the air pressure in the chamber (Fig. 7).

Since the dew will continue to fall out on the mirror even with decreasing pressure, as long as the pressure is higher than the pressure corresponding to the actual dew point, a stabilizing factor is necessary in the circuit (Fig. 8). Therefore the servo motor also drives a potentiometer, forming part of one branch in the bridge. Thus, the resistance in this

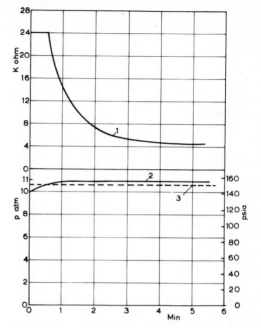

FIG. 9. Development of resistance of photoresistor: (1) resistance of photoresistor, (2) air pressure over mirror, (3) pressure corresponding to actual dew point.

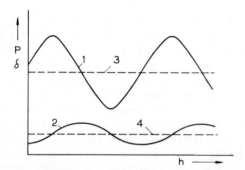

FIG. 8. The development of pressure and thickness of dew layer: (1) pressure, (2) thickness of dew layer, (3) pressure corresponding to actual dew point, (4) mean thickness of dew layer.

branch is increasing with increasing pressure and oscillation of the pressure is avoided. The potentiometer is protected by a friction drive.

The flow of air through the chamber is regulated with manual valves, and the flow of coolant is also partly regulated with manual valves, to avoid hunting.

The pressure in the chamber is connected to an ordinary pressure gauge, as well as a strain gauge pressure transducer. A strip chart recorder is used for recording the pressure variations.

CHARACTERISTICS OF THE INSTRUMENT

The best results are obtained when the working point of the instrument, i.e., the actual resistance of the photoresistor, is about midway on the useful range. Figure 9 shows

the development of the resistance when the pressure over the mirror is higher than the value corresponding to the actual dew point. With increasing thickness of the dew layer, the resistance reaches a minimum value, and if the pressure is not reduced, bigger droplets of water start forming on the surface of the mirror. The reflectivity of these droplets is small, and the resistance of the photoresistor increases. Thus, the dew layer must not become too thick. A useful working range is about 18,000 to 5,000 ohms, and the resistances in the bridge must be chosen according to this.

The instrument, used as a recorder, can not follow very rapidly changing vapor pressures, due to the capacity of the pressure vessels in the air system. These vessels are necessary in order to avoid heavy fluctuations in the air pressure due to the reciprocating compressors.

Figure 10 shows the development of the pressure, as redrawn from the chart of the recorder, when the water vapor pressure was changed instantaneously by means of a three-way valve in the suction line.

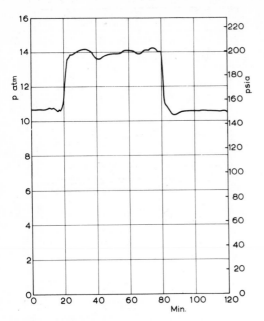

FIG. 10. The development of pressure at a sudden change of water vapor pressure.

SOURCES OF ERRORS

An error in the measurement of the mirror temperature gives approximately the same degree of error in the dew point of the air under test. The actual temperature of the thermocouple junction depends mainly on the accuracy of the balance point of the DC amplifier. This balance point was checked with the input to the amplifier short-circuited, and the error in the temperature is negligible.

Due to the design of the metering unit, the thermocouple junction is separated from the surface of the mirror by a constantan disc with a thickness of 0.1 mm. The maximum possible error in the dew point due to this design feature is less than 0.05 deg C.

The error in the water vapor pressure is proportional to the error in the measurement of the pressure ratio, i.e., at a pressure ratio of 10, an error of 0.1 kg/cm^2 in the pressure gives an error of 1 per cent in the water vapor pressure.

ACCURACY

In order to control the accuracy of the instrument, a simple calibrating vessel, filled with ice, was used (Fig. 11). Since the air under test is continuously passing through the ice, the relative humidity should be 100 per cent. The temperature of the ice was measured with a thermopile frozen into a piece of ice. Table 1 gives some results of the calibrations.

The instrument was run automatically during the tests, but the values for the pressure were read from the pressure gauge and not from the chart of the recorder. The accuracy as read from the recorder depends naturally also on the accuracy of the pressure transducer and the recorder.

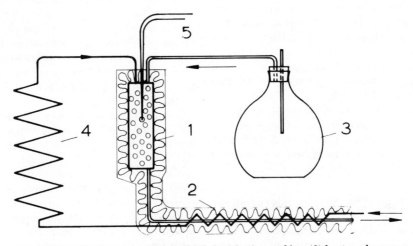

FIG. 11. Calibrating unit: (1) vessel filled with pieces of ice, (2) heat exchanger, (3) large vessel, fitted into the system in order to avoid influence of room air, (4) coil for the cooling of returning air, (5) thermocouple.

TABLE 1*

Ice Temp. (°C)	Vapor Pressure (mm Hg)	Pressure Ratio	Mirror Temp. (°C)	Vapor Pressure at Mirror† (mm Hg)	Measured Vapor Pressure (mm Hg)	Measured RH (%)
−28.31	0.3405	13.58	0	4.63	0.341	100.2
−28.29	0.3410	13.62	0	4.63	0.3395	99.5
−28.29	0.3410	13.58	0	4.63	0.341	100.0
−28.29	0.3410	13.58	0	4.63	0.341	100.0
−25.46	0.455	10.2	0	4.615	0.453	99.5
−25.41	0.457	10.2	0	4.615	0.453	99.1
−25.41	0.457	10.1	0	4.615	0.457	100.0
−25.41	0.457	10.17	0	4.615	0.454	99.4
−25.41	0.457	10.17	0	4.615	0.454	99.4
−25.41	0.457	10.1	0	4.615	0.457	100.0
−24.79	0.4865	9.50	0	4.612	0.4860	99.9
−24.79	0.4865	9.48	0	4.612	0.4865	100.0

* The measurements in each series were made with intervals of 10 minutes.

† The values are corrected for the influence of the air pressure.

FUTURE DEVELOPMENT

The possible use of a lower mirror temperature, with the advantage of a simpler air compressor equipment, should be investigated. If the refrigerating system for the cooling of the mirror could be abandoned in favor of a Peltier element, the size of the instrument could be reduced.

The system for the regulation of the pressure might be changed. The method shown was chosen more because of the equipment availability than because of a really thorough examination.

Acknowledgment. Thanks are due to Professor G. Lorentzen for his great interest in the development of the instrument. Mr. Inge Mohus, Institutt for Reguleringsteknikk (Division of Automatic Control), N.T.H., has given valuable advice on the design of the pressure regulation system. Figures were drawn by Mr. Kåre Aflekt.

References

1. Glaser, H., "Feuchtigkeitmessung mit Hilfe des Taupunktsspiegels," *Kältetechnik*, **5**, 126 (1950).
2. Prins, L., "Investigation of a New Dew-Point Hygrometer," Proceedings of the VIII International Congress of Refrigeration, p. 295, London, 1951.
3. Plank, R., "Handbuch der Kältetechnik," **2**, 272, (1953).
4. Brendeng, E., "On the Development of a Recording Hygrometer," Annexe 1961–3 au Bulletin de l'Institut International du Froid, p. 191.

SECTION III

ELECTRIC HYGROMETRY

23. Review of the Lithium Chloride Radiosonde Hygrometer

Donald A. Mathews

U.S. Weather Bureau, Washington, D.C.

ABSTRACT

Little information has been published on the flat-strip lithium chloride radiosonde hygrometer since its introduction in 1942. An attempt is therefore undertaken to review the entire history of the hygrometer, to bring it up to date, and to assess the state of the art of its performance.

Dunmore at the National Bureau of Standards developed the first lithium chloride radiosonde hygrometer in 1938. A low-cost version, the flat-strip design, was introduced in 1942 by Onderdonk, at Friez Instrument Division, The Bendix Corporation. Examination of the procurement specifications discloses that the state of the art of its performance changed little, 1944 to 1962, but there were improvements in manufacturing the element and small improvements in the element itself.

It is shown that economic factors, a lack of information about the element, a fixed calibration chart, and the carbon element, have all contributed to the lithium chloride radiosonde hygrometer's failure to improve very much.

INTRODUCTION

Dunmore published his lithium chloride radiosonde hygrometer developments in 1938,[1] 1939,[2] and 1940,[3] but the later work by Onderdonk was not published. Wexler at the National Bureau of Standards, published brief descriptions of Onderdonk's design in 1949,[4] and 1957.[5] Kobayashi at the Meteorological Research Institute, Tokyo, Japan, in 1960 published a report of his investigations of both the U.S. and his own lithium chloride element designs which has not been well circulated in this country.[6]

DEVELOPMENTS BY DUNMORE 1938-1940

Dunmore described in 1938 his first electric hygrometer[1] designed to replace the slow-responding hair hygrometer of the National Bureau of Standards audio modulated radiosonde.[7] He wound two fine tinned copper wires spirally on a thin-walled etched glass tube to form twenty bifilar turns/in. After the glass tube was wound, it was coated with a dilute solution of lithium chloride in water. Only the more hygroscopic salts were tried. Lithium chloride was chosen for its high degree of activity; it is a dry powder and a nonconductor below about 12 per cent relative humidity (value depends on temperature), but at higher humidities it takes up moisture from the air to become a conducting film. The resistance of this conducting film varies with humidity and temperature and is read between the bifilar-wound electrodes.

Dunmore found this design had undesired effects, the most serious being water trapped in the glass etchings upon which the bifilar coils were wound. After many different water-resistant coatings had been tried on the glass, a polystyrene coating was found to overcome the effect. The coating was applied by dipping the thin glass tube in a solution of dissolved polystyrene.

The next year, 1939, Dunmore published a

description of a new design in which partially hydrolyzed polyvinyl acetate was added to the lithium chloride solution. This bound the lithium chloride to the base and aided in the formation of an even film. Dunmore also noted a reduction of the polarization, or counterelectromotive force, set up by the direct current flowing through the hygrometer when it was connected to the radiosonde.

Dunmore did not fully understand the reduction of polarization by addition of partially hydrolyzed polyvinyl acetate to the solution. Much later the writer observed that partially hydrolyzed polyvinyl acetate (polyvinyl alcohol)* exhibited weak detergent activity. Detergents as a class have the property of releasing from electrodes the charged gas bubbles that cause polarization, although some ionic detergents may introduce polarization.

In the 1939 design, Dunmore replaced his previous thin-wall glass tube with a thin-wall aluminum tube coated with a thin insulating layer of polystyrene. He thus obtained the better thermal conductivity and small mass for his base material which he believed was necessary for most accurate humidity measurement in changing temperatures. He found that his previously used tinned-copper wires corroded or aged at the surface and that platinum and palladium wires were the only kinds that eliminated this aging effect. He used palladium because it was cheaper than platinum. "Twenty bifilar turns per inch of 38 AWG gave the best results. A reduction in the number of turns per inch increases the current density at the surface of the wire, which tends to increase the polarization effect in DC circuits. Fewer turns, however, make a unit which covers a greater range of humidity for a given resistance change."

Dunmore was saying here that moving electrodes closer together steepens the resistance-relative humidity characteristic and moving them apart flattens the characteristic. By spacing electrodes closely, Dunmore effectively lengthened them; having more electrodes in a given space lessened the current density problem, reducing polarization. But closely spaced electrodes have

troubles inherent in a too-steep resistance-relative humidity characteristic. The low relative humidities have excessively high resistances, and bringing these in to a measurable range by adding lithium chloride results in jamming the higher relative humidities together so that there is not enough resistance difference between 75 per cent RH and 95 per cent RH. The radiosonde resistance range that Dunmore was trying to match was the same then as it is now, a few thousand ohms for 100 per cent RH to approximately 6 MΩ for about 15 per cent RH.

Dunmore obtained an optimum resistance-relative humidity characteristic with three coils coated respectively with 3 per cent, 2 per cent and 1 per cent lithium chloride solutions,* with partially hydrolyzed polyvinyl acetate binder, connected in parallel with resistances in series with the 2 and 3 per cent units. The three-coil hygrometer was used with U.S. Navy radiosondes, 1938–43. Since then, various combinations of bifilar-wound-coil designs have been used in hygrometers for surface use. In the radiosonde, the disadvantages were cost and difficulty with calibration accuracy.

Dunmore's lithium chloride element developments required a long series of tedious experiments involving different solutions and calibrations. One of his assistants was heard to remark, "The lithium chloride hygrometer is the wettest and driest subject on earth."

DEVELOPMENTS BY ONDERDONK, 1942

The hygrometer that was to achieve widespread use in the radiosonde appeared quietly in 1942 without publication and with little explanation. Its design, as shown in Fig. 1 was a flat sheet of smooth polystyrene, 4 in. $\times$ $11/16$ in. $\times$ $1/32$ in., with tin electrodes affixed to the long edges by spraying hot tin on blanks having the center areas masked with tape that did not leave a residue on the surface of the strip. After spraying the tin on the edges, the tape was pulled off leaving clear areas of polystyrene on the two flat, smooth sides the width of the tape, $7/16$ in.,

---

* Polyvinyl alcohol is made by the partial or complete hydrolysis of polyvinyl acetate.[8]

* Hereafter where percentage of coating is given, it refers to the percentage by volume of a saturated solution and water.

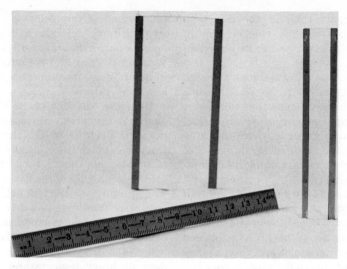

Fig. 1. The wide and the standard (narrow) lithium chloride radiosonde hygrometer elements.

between the two tin electrodes. The blanks
were then sensitized by immersion endwise in
a solution of about 4 per cent lithium chloride
and 3 per cent partially hydrolyzed polyvinyl
acetate. The amount of lithium chloride film
acquired by the element was a function of the
speed of withdrawal of the element from the
dipping solution, plus other factors given in
detail in another paper.[8] Quantities of
elements could be suspended on racks and
dipped simultaneously using a motor-driven
arrangement.

The flat-strip element was a modification
of Dunmore's lithium chloride designs developed by John Onderdonk at the Friez
Instrument Division of The Bendix Corporation. The method of packaging Onderdonk's
version of the lithium chloride element was
new. At relative humidities above about 12
per cent, the lithium chloride element absorbs
moisture, with prolonged exposure resulting
in excess lithium chloride solution that may
run along the element and ruin its calibration.
Onderdonk's element was kept dry (it thus
remained chemically inert) by sealing it in a
small glass vial with enough dry silica gel to
desiccate the element. A cobaltous chloride
color change indicator was enclosed to reveal
vial leakage. The element was kept in the
desiccated vial until immediately before use
when the seal was broken and the element was
removed and placed in the radiosonde.

Dunmore had filed patents on his lithium
chloride hygrometer designs in 1938 and
1940.[9, 10] A patent for Onderdonk's modification was not considered possible, instead,
proprietary secrecy was maintained on the
making of the element. In 1952, during the
course of some basic research on the lithium
chloride element, the author determined all
one needed to know in designing the flat-strip
lithium chloride hygrometer:

(1) Moving the electrodes much farther
apart than they had been in Dunmore's coil-
type designs flattened the resistance-relative
humidity relationship similar to that obtained
by Dunmore through use of three or more
coils.

(2) The slopes of these resistance-relative
humidity relationships varied with the metal
used in the electrodes. It was difficult to find
a metal better than tin for the fine range of
relative humidity it gave within the resistance
range of the radiosonde.

(3) Tin polarized less than many metals,
including gold, with lithium chloride solutions. Palladium and platinum were not tried
by the author. While Onderdonk's tin-edged
element polarized, this was not considered
excessive in view of the fact that it partly recovered while resting between readings and
its anticipated use in flights was less than an
hour.

(4) Shortening the electrodes and moving

them farther apart than in the coil type hygrometer meant that a thicker film of lithium chloride solution had to be placed on the element.

The compact size of Onderdonk's design allowed the hygrometer to be placed inside an air duct in the radiosonde that shielded it from direct impingement of precipitation. Even so, there were instances where unusually heavy precipitation resulted in an excess of moisture on the element, ruining its calibration. This damage, called "washing out," became less serious in later years as improved grades of partially hydrolyzed polyvinyl acetate (polyvinyl alcohol) became available, particularly after about 1947.[8] As explained in this reference, a grade of polyvinyl alcohol was selected that resisted "washing out."

Dunmore determined in 1938 that there was no tendency for a lithium chloride coating to evaporate at low atmospheric pressures. He placed a 3 per cent lithium chloride element at 150 mb of pressure for one hour. He found no change in resistance of the element after this test.

A qualitative test in 1949 at the U.S. Weather Bureau confirmed Dunmore's result. The technique used was to place the elements in a pressure chamber with pressure controlled by continuous pumping and allowing an adjustable leak into the chamber from the room. The true relative humidity at low pressure was computed by multiplying the room relative humidity by the ratio of the two pressures. The temperature difference of the chamber was monitored and was found not to exceed 0.2 deg C from room temperature. The pressure was cycled from 1009 to 504 mb three times with relative humidity readings taken at each pressure. No errors in the readings of two lithium chloride elements were found at low pressure that could be ascribed to the pressure.

EVALUATION OF THE STATE OF THE ART

1943–1944

In 1942, the state of the art of the radiosonde hygrometer was that of the hair hygrometer, ± 10 per cent calibration accuracy and 30 seconds or less time lag for 63 per cent change in relative humidity at temperatures above freezing. The hair hygrometer did not function effectively below 0°C. The new flat-strip lithium chloride hygrometer became operational in February 1943 with the U.S. Weather Bureau, and the next year was spent in determining its properties, particularly at low temperatures.

Dunmore had, in 1939, made a calibration chart for his three-coil element covering the range $+40$ to -60°C. These curves contracted so much below -50°C that they were of questionable use. It was found that the calibration curves of the flat-strip hygrometer were unduly contracted below -40°C and they were terminated at that point.

In 1940, Dunmore experienced difficulty in controlling and measuring relative humidities below about -15°C. To obtain calibration data at lower temperatures, he placed his hygrometer in an enclosure in which saturation was maintained as the temperature was lowered by dry ice. This gave him points for the 100 per cent lines of his calibration chart at different low temperatures. The method was used as late as 1944. All the known calibration data were entered on a large graph of the logarithm of resistance *vs* temperature and lines of constant relative humidity were drawn. The 100 per cent RH line was constructed from $+30$ to -40°C. The lower values of constant relative humidity were then drawn as extrapolations from the known data to -40°C nearly parallel to the 100 per cent RH line. These smoothed data were then transferred to a large chart of the logarithm of resistance *vs* relative humidity where lines of constant temperature were drawn and smoothed. This gave smooth data for constructing the calibration chart, where the ordinates were recorder divisions (resistance) *vs* temperature with the data plotted as lines of constant relative humidity. These charts were found to be remarkably good later when more detailed low-temperature calibrations become available.

Evaluation of the state of the art of the flat-strip lithium chloride radiosonde hygrometer at low temperature was made by each of the agencies concerned. The finding was that it did not meet the stringent meteorological requirements that existed due to its slow speed of response at low temperatures. The finding was a stimulus for a faster-responding hygrometer development being investigated by the U.S. Army Signal Corps. This was the carbon element radiosonde hygrometer, to be the subject of a large research effort for the next dozen years.

1944–1962

As perishable resistors, lithium chloride elements are subjected to 100 per cent testing only in the selection test, where each element is required to fall within ± 3 per cent of a reference relative humidity or it is rejected. In other tests, samples are taken to represent lots of elements, usually 100. The fiscal year 1962–1963 procurement specifications require that calibration tests be performed on 4 out of each 100 elements: "If more than one of the 4 elements fail, the entire lot of 100 shall be rejected. However, if only one element fails, eight more shall be taken from the lot and tested. If all the second group pass, the lot shall be accepted. If one of the second group fails, however, the entire lot shall be rejected."

For polarization: One element out of each 100 shall be tested; if it fails, two other elements shall be tested. Should one of these fail, the lot shall be rejected.

Elements are not used again after tests. They are discarded or are cleaned in water for redipping. The specifications for testing the elements offer a method of following improvements from year to year as each year's specifications represent the state of the art of the previous year.

The state of the art disclosed by the procurement specifications does not reveal the improvements in manufacturing control that have been obtained since 1944. Then, controls were so poor (by today's standards) that it was difficult for manufacturers to produce uniform elements. Doubts existed that it would ever be easy to make the element. On a factory visit in 1945, while viewing cartons of rejected elements, the author little anticipated he would visit a factory in 1962 and overhear, ". . . over 50,000 consecutive elements without a failure. *Something must be wrong.*" But 8 of these 1962 elements were added to a special calibration of carbon elements made soon afterward at the National Bureau of Standards, and in a calibration test much more demanding than those listed in the procurement specifications (calibrations at 25 points at $\pm 20°C$ and at $+0.5°C$ in a test lasting 7 hours), the maximum deviation was 3 per cent RH, with departures predominantly 0 per cent and 1 per cent RH. Another paper[8] describes how to make elements of this quality.

The numerical evaluation of the low-temperature state of the art had to await construction of humidity-test apparatus that could go reliably to low temperatures. Finally, in 1947, Wexler calibrated elements at -1, -10, -20, -30 and $-40°C$, using the divided-flow, low-temperature humidity apparatus, and found an average deviation of

STATE OF THE ART

Test*	1944	1945	1962
Selection	$\pm 3\%$ of a reference RH	Same as 1944	Same as 1944
Calibration	2 out of each 100 tested between 20% and 90% ascending and descending RH at 8 points. Errors not to exceed $\pm 5\%$	Same as 1944 except 4 out of each 100 tested and an error of $\pm 7\%$ allowed on one test point	Same as 1945 except test limits 20% to 95%
Polarization	No test	1 out of each 100 tested, P.I.† not to exceed 6%	Same as 1945
Time lag	$\frac{1}{10}$ of 1% of units tested between 40% and 90%; lag not to exceed 25 seconds for 63% of the change, wind speed 200 m/min.	Same as 1944, except not over 15 seconds for 90% of the change, wind speed 250 m/min.	Same as 1945 except direction, 90% to 40%

* Tests performed at room temperature.

† P.I. (Polarization Index) is the drift of an element when switched 15 seconds "on" and 30 seconds "off" for 30 minutes at a constant relative humidity.

±2.4 per cent RH from the mean calibration of all the elements tested. The maximum deviation did not exceed 10.5 per cent.[4] These figures were encouraging since they could be improved by redrawing the calibration chart and by improving manufacturing controls.

Wexler's low-temperature time lags gave, at wind speed of 525 feet per minute for −20°C a 63 per cent response time of 50 to 150 seconds; at −40°C, 200 to 400 seconds. These figures showed that the earlier decision to discontinue the calibration chart at −40°C had been wise, and they verified the fact that the element was too slow in response at low temperature to meet stringent meteorological needs.

In 1960, Jones and Wexler at the National Bureau of Standards published low-temperature time lags for the lithium chloride element at wind speed of 525 fpm.[11] At −20°C, 63 per cent lag times of 51 to 74 seconds were obtained; at −40°C, 120 to 480 seconds. These figures showed that little change in response time had occurred since 1947.

FREEZING OF DESIGNS, 1946–1948, AND THE WIDE ELEMENT

In 1945, 1946, and 1947, improved low-temperature calibrations were becoming available, and several new calibration charts were issued during each of these years. In 1948, U.S. Weather Bureau Chart No. 800B, Fig. 2, was issued and has been in use since then. Effectively, this froze the design of the lithium chloride radiosonde hygrometer. Since 1948 it has not been possible to change the making of the element significantly without departing from Chart 800B.

The new chart incorporated design changes in the element made by Dember at Friez Instrument Division in 1946.[12] Without changing the dimensions of the flat-strip hygrometer base, Dember effectively increased the electrode-film interface by not removing a metal ridge formed during the metallizing process. This followed Dunmore's principle of decreasing polarization by lessening current density at a point on the electrodes. The improvement did not result in a change in the state of the art as viewed through the procurement specifications, but it was one of the things that helped manufacturers to operate better within the requirements; the addition of nonionic detergent to the dipping solution, after 1951, was another.[13]

Chart 800B had more sensitivity at subfreezing temperatures (greater distance between lines of constant relative humidity) than its predecessor, U.S. Weather Bureau Chart No. 730B issued the previous year. Chart 800B reflected an international agreement made at the August, 1947, meeting of the World Meteorological Organization in Toronto, Canada, to compute relative humidities at subfreezing temperatures with respect to liquid water. Chart 730B had been drawn with relative humidities computed with respect to ice at subfreezing temperatures.

In 1947, the U.S. Army Signal Corps developed a radiosonde with approximately triple the measuring-circuit resistance of previous radiosondes. Craig, U.S. Army Signal Corps Laboratory, investigated the design of a lithium chloride element with three times the resistance of previous elements.

(1) The humidity-sensitive film on the standard lithium chloride element was thinned to give approximately 3 times the previous resistance.

(2) The element was shortened to about one-third its previous length.

(3) The element was widened to about three times its previous width.

Both thinning the film and shortening the element gave excessive polarization. However, widening the element improved polarization, Craig found, although it gave up to 50 per cent slower speed of response (for 63 per cent of the change). The wide-element design, Fig. 1, was adopted by the U.S. Army Signal Corps. Craig recently explained to the writer that while the humidity-active film of the wide element was of the same thickness as that of the narrow element, its speed of response was slower because it needed to pick up, or release, about three times as much moisture during relative humidity changes. From this principle, it can be argued that hygrometer elements will be speeded up in response not only by making the films thinner, but also by decreasing the size of the film area. Craig's experience has been, ". . . a small hygrometer should give optimum speed of response, provided making the design small does not make the film thick."

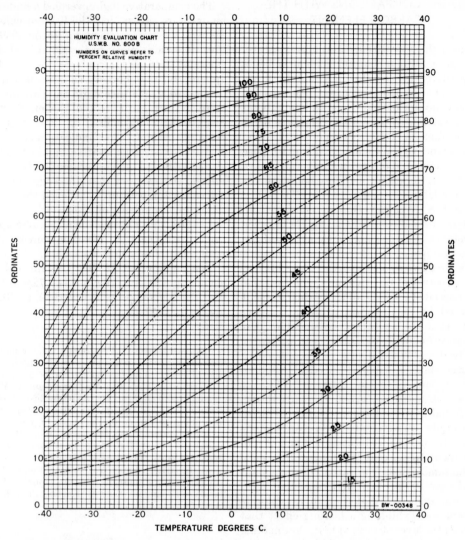

Fig. 2. Chart 800B, used since 1948 in evaluating readings of the lithium chloride radiosonde hygrometer element. Ordinates are recorder divisions (resistance).

The wide element was included in an investigation of lithium chloride hygrometers by Morris and Sobel in 1954.[14] They found it to be influenced in speed of response by its orientation in the air stream.

The narrow and wide elements were not interchangeable, and each has been used only in the radiosonde for which it was designed. The importance of good packaging for these delicate-to-moisture devices cannot be overemphasized. The seals of the glass vials originally used with the narrow element had long-period leakage problems, due to the strain of daily atmospheric pressure and temperature change. The wide element was first packaged with silica gel desiccant and cobaltous chloride leakage indicator in a specially designed flat tin can; later it was placed inside the standard round tin can used by the food industry. As air shipments became common a more pressure-resistant seal was needed for packaging the narrow element, and it, too, was placed inside a round tin can of suitable size.

FLIGHT COMPARISONS WITH THE CARBON ELEMENT

During the first fifteen years of its existence, the narrow lithium chloride element lacked a competitive element that it could be flown with and compared against. The carbon element did not emerge from its long laboratory development until 1957. The first flight comparisons in 1957, between the lithium chloride and carbon elements, in which all the agencies joined, did not turn out well due to defective calibrations of the carbon elements then available.

The U.S. Weather Bureau continued to make occasional comparative flights between the narrow lithium chloride element and the carbon element.

The first finding was that there was little to choose between the two in flight and the faster speed of response of the carbon element observed in the laboratory did not assert itself. This was an early assessment of performance on predominantly clear or partly cloudy days. When flights were confined to overcast days, a superior speed of response began to emerge below about −15°C as a characteristic of the carbon element. It was also found that the lithium chloride element, so carefully calibrated at steady-state factory temperatures, was exhibiting a tendency to read about 10 per cent RH too low in clouds. In the same clouds, the carbon element indicated near 100 per cent RH consistently.

It was suspected that the lithium chloride element was exhibiting a heating effect that warmed the layer of air next to it, thus making the relative humidity lower. The element then read this lower relative humidity correctly, according to this analysis. However, many of the carbon elements in these flights were made on the same tin-edged polystyrene blanks used by the lithium chloride elements, and if the heating effect was caused by the thermal lag of the base material, it should equally affect both elements. Joule heating of the lithium chloride element by measuring circuit current also did not explain the effect as the heating was small and both elements were subjected to it. A remaining explanation was that the exothermic liberation of heat in the lithium chloride film as it absorbed moisture from the clouds was sufficient to create the effect.

The comparative flights verified a finding of many years earlier that the lithium chloride element was an excellent indicator of cloud tops. It became moist in the cloud, and upon emerging into dry air above the cloud, it apparently was shocked, as seen in a quick downward displacement of one-half inch or more on the recorder record, the length of the displacement depending on how wet the element became. The indication then decreased toward true relative humidity as the element dried. At the lower temperatures, this process became very slow and suggested that the colder temperatures hardened the binder, inhibiting the release of moisture.

In 1963, the carbon element became operational with the U.S. Weather Bureau along with the lithium chloride element.

The unit price of the lithium chloride element in 1944 was 76¢; in 1945, 72¢; in 1963, 62¢. The highest price was in 1949, $1.10; the lowest, in 1952, 60¢.

Acknowledgments. For review of preliminary versions of this paper and providing backgrounds on the following subjects, the author is indebted to C. Harmantas, U.S. Weather Bureau and L. Wood, Bendix Radio Division for the entire history of the radiosonde and of the lithium chloride element and for calling attention to the work of Onderdonk; L. Craig, Aerological Research, Inc., the wide element; J. Ford, U.S. Weather Bureau, specifications and costs. For review and constructive comment the writer thanks W. Windsor, Bendix Radio Division; M. Friedman and A. Jones, Molded Insulation Company; and P. Rogers, Friez Instrument Division.

References

1. Dunmore, F. W., "An Electric Hygrometer and its Application to Radio Meteorography," *J. Res. Natl. Bur. Std.*, **20**, 723 (1938).
2. Dunmore, F. W., "An Improved Electric Hygrometer," *J. Res. Natl. Bur. Std.*, **23**, 701 (1939).
3. Diamond, H., Hinman, W. S., Jr., Dunmore, F. W., and Lapham, E. G., "An Improved Radio Sonde and its Performance," *J. Res. Natl. Bur. Std.*, **25**, 327 (1940).
4. Wexler, A., "Low-temperature Performance of Radiosonde Electric Hygrometer Elements," *J. Res. Natl. Bur. Std.*, **43**, 49 (1949) (circulated within the government in 1947).
5. Wexler, A., "Electric Hygrometers," *NBS Circ.*, **586** (1957).
6. Kobayashi, J., "Investigations on Hygrometry," Meteorological Research Institute, Tokyo, 213, 1960.

7. Diamond, H., Hinman, W. S., Jr., and Dunmore, F. W., "A Method for the Investigation of Upper-air Phenomena and its Application to Radio Meteorography," *J. Res. Natl. Bur. Std.*, **20**, 369 (1938).

8. Mathews, D., "Some Research on the Lithium Chloride Radiosonde Hygrometer and a Guide for Making it," Humidity and Moisture, Vol. 1, New York, Reinhold Publishing Corp., 1964.

9. Dunmore, F. W., Humidity Measuring, U.S. Patent 2,295,570 (Dec. 22, 1938).

10. Dunmore, F. W., Humidity Variable Resistance, U.S. Patent 2,285,421 (June 8, 1940).

11. Jones, F. E., and Wexler, A., "A Barium Fluoride Film Hygrometer Element," *J. Geophys. Res.*, **65**, 7, 2087 (1960).

12. Dember, A. B., Humidity Responsive Resistor, U.S. Patent 2,481,728 (Oct. 24, 1945).

13. Harmantas, C., and Mathews, D., Sensing Element for the Electric Hygrometer, U.S. Patent 2,710,324 (Feb. 4, 1953).

14. Morris, V. B., Jr., and Sobel, F., "Some Experiments on the Speed of Response of the Electrolytic Hygrometer," *Bull. Am. Meteorol. Soc.*, **35**, 5, 226 (1954).

24. Some Research on the Lithium Chloride Radiosonde Hygrometer and a Guide for Making It

Donald A. Mathews

U.S. Weather Bureau, Washington, D.C.

ABSTRACT

Little information has been published on the flat-strip lithium chloride radiosonde hygrometer since its introduction in 1942. An attempt is, therefore, undertaken to bring about a better understanding of the hygrometer and to disclose how to make it, by reviewing, principally, research performed at the U.S. Weather Bureau since 1943.

Procedures for obtaining consistent time-lag data are presented. It is shown that the speed of response of the element becomes slower with decrease of air speed or air ventilation. An error due to thermal lag was disclosed when the temperature was changed and the relative humidity was held nearly constant. It was found that addition of a nonionic wetting agent to lithium chloride solutions decreased polarization and that addition of aluminum chloride increased speed of response.

Thinning a lithium chloride solution produced faster-responding elements. AC measuring circuits do not polarize the element, and a simple, low-cost AC circuit was built using a Shockley diode. The research that developed an independent method of making the elements is disclosed. A complete guide supplies details for producing today's lithium chloride radiosonde hygrometer overseas.

INTRODUCTION

The lithium chloride radiosonde hygrometer is a polystyrene blank with conducting tin edges that is dipped in a formula of lithium chloride, polyvinyl alcohol, water and a nonionic surface-active agent. Its resistance varies with relative humidity and temperature and is read by the radiosonde measuring circuit.

From the vantage point of the U.S. Weather Bureau, the history of the lithium chloride radiosonde hygrometer may be considered to have begun when placed in operational use in February, 1943. Its history still continues. The period 1943 to 1963 is preserved in research performed during individual years. An attempt has been made to select research material of the most lasting interest.

HOW TIME LAGS WERE MADE

The flat-strip lithium chloride hygrometer has been associated with the radiosonde since 1942 and is still in use. The radiosonde is attached to a helium-filled balloon and is released to rise about 1000 fpm until the balloon bursts. As it rises, the radiosonde senses relative humidity, temperature and pressure, and it simultaneously transmits these measurements to a ground station via radio. With one variation of the radiosonde, the rawinsonde, height and the vertical and horizontal angles of the flight are converted to winds-aloft data. With the dropsonde, the sonde is dropped from an aircraft, and measurements are taken as the instrument floats to earth via parachute. Finally, with the rocketsonde, a rocket replaces the aircraft.

In sonde service the lithium chloride hygrometer is used in severely differing climates and may rise through dry air or clouds that are several miles thick. It rises through air that becomes less dense and generally colder, and at −40°C the element is too sluggish in response to be evaluated at lower temperatures. The importance of speed of response in this service is suggested by the fact that the lithium chloride hygrometer replaced its predecessor (the hair element) hygrometer in the radiosonde in 1943, because of its superior speed of response, particularly at low temperatures. Speed of response at low temperatures continues to be stressed today—the lithium chloride element is being replaced by a faster-responding radiosonde hygrometer, the carbon element.

The speed of response of a hygrometer may be measured in the laboratory by exposing it at one relative humidity, then quickly shifting it to another and measuring the time required by the hygrometer to acquire the new relative humidity condition. The hygrometer "lags" behind the change, thus the term "time lag" is used meaning "time of response." Without observing the following techniques for handling the lithium chloride element, consistent time-lag data were found to be difficult to obtain.* In all the time-lag data presented here, a set of standard conditions were used (unless otherwise individually noted):

Temperature: room (about 27°C)
Air speed: approximately 800 fpm
Orientation of element: edgewise to air stream
Direction of change: decreasing RH
Magnitude of RH change: about 45%
Initial RH: about 80%
Exposure time at initial RH: uniform lengths of time; after 1948 two minutes

Long wind tunnels approximately 2 ft × 3 ft in cross section, made of plastic or of plywood with a large air blower mounted in one end, were used. Both ends of the tunnel were open into the room, necessitating use of room relative humidity and temperature.

The air speed was that of the specifications,

* Wexler at the National Bureau of Standards has noted, "Actually, the speed of response is an involved function of temperature, magnitude and direction of the relative humidity change, initial relative humidity, orientation of the elements, and air velocity."[1] Windsor, at Bendix Radio Division, The Bendix Corporation, when reviewing this paper suggested adding to the list, ". . . turbulence of the air stream."

250 m/min., since 1945. Orientation was edgewise, with the air stream flowing over the two flat sides. This orientation gave a faster time lag than when the air was directed against only one side of the element. It was also observed that insertion of psychrometer or thermometer stands in the tunnel upwind from the element lent turbulence to the air stream that slightly decreased the time lag of the element.

For research purposes, control of the value of initial relative humidity and the time exposed to it were found to possess the most significance. An example is found in the following test of December 16, 1949, with a room relative humidity of 20 per cent.

Initial RH (%)	90% Time Lag (sec)
68 to 75	4.9 (average of 7 lags)
76 to 80	5.5 (average of 4 lags)
81 to 85	6.3 (average of 4 lags)
86 to 90	7.5 (average of 2 lags)

These values were plotted on a semilogarithmic scale, Fig. 1, and the slope of a straight line drawn through the mean of the points indicated the effect of the initial relative humidity on the time lag. Such lines are useful in comparing lags made with different initial humidities when times of exposure to the initial humidity are similar.

The lithium chloride element gave time lags that did not follow known mathematical rules or allow use of the exponential decay law as does the radiosonde thermistor. The 90 per cent time-lag value was preferred by the writer over the 63 per cent time-lag value as more fully representing the actual behavior of the element during the lag, and it was used by the author after 1944. Changes in resistance of the element during the time lag were measured through a radiosonde that transmitted signals to a nearby set of radiosonde ground equipment. The paper-feed gears on the strip-chart recorder were interchanged to feed paper at the rate of one inch per 7.5 seconds. This speed expanded the trace recorded of the time lag so that each second of the change could be examined.

A time-lag test was started by adjusting low reference of the radiosonde to 95.0 divisions on the strip-chart recorder. The element, after exposure to the initial relative humidity, was inserted in the radiosonde measuring circuit, and the value representing the initial relative

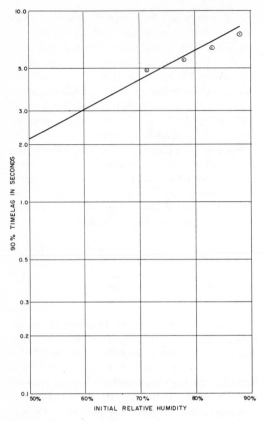

FIG. 1. A relationship between initial relative humidity and time lag for the lithium chloride radiosonde hygrometer element to reach 20 per cent RH.

humidity was traced on the recorder for a few seconds. The element was then quickly shifted into the wind tunnel. The lag curve of the change of the element from the initial humidity to the lower humidity of the wind tunnel was traced on the strip-chart. Air speed of the wind tunnel was noted. After about fifteen seconds of tracing the lag curve, the element was rested intermittently by short circuiting it. The short circuit depolarized the element and represented low reference to the radiosonde. Depolarizing the element intermittently allowed it to read the final equilibrium relative humidity of the wind tunnel more accurately. For the definition and a discussion of polarization see p. 237.

Different methods were used to transfer the element from the initial relative humidity chamber to the wind tunnel. When the element was transferred quickly, the evaluation of the recorded lag curve was simply a determination

of the time taken to reach 90 per cent of the difference between the initial relative humidity and the final, equilibrium relative humidity. Experience suggested that a simple method of transferring the lithium chloride element into the wind tunnel was satisfactory; a small humidity test box to provide the initial relative humidity (near 80 per cent) was placed next to the wind tunnel. The element was snapped into two electrical clips mounted on a rubber cork that fitted identical openings in both the top of the humidity test box and the side of the wind tunnel. When these openings were not in use they were plugged with rubber corks. The arrangement allowed stabilizing the humidity test box near 80 per cent RH, plugging the element into it for two minutes, then transferring the element into the wind tunnel. The transfer was made by hand quickly when the two openings were arranged a few inches apart.

Relative humidity corrections to the element were made from psychrometers in both the humidity test box and the wind tunnel for evaluating the time-lag trace. Corrections were often found to be unnecessary.

Time-lag tests were made at low temperatures in a refrigerated room. Two humidity test boxes were placed side by side in the cold room and allowed to cool to a low temperature. Time lags were performed by entering the cold room and plugging elements back and forth between the humidity test boxes. Wires lead out of the cold room for measuring and recording the lag tests. The method is best suited to low-temperature comparisons; it is difficult to obtain accurate readings of air speed inside a small, closed humidity test box.

Fast-responding recording devices are needed in taking time lags. The strip-chart recorders used had full-scale response times of the order of 0.6 second; this was not considered when evaluating 90 per cent lags of the standard lithium chloride element.

EFFECT OF AIR VENTILATION ON TIME LAG

Close agreement between individual time lags remained elusive when the air speed was decreased. This brought about the practice of taking groups of readings and obtaining an average for each group. The principle is illustrated by the following time lags made in 1946.

Temperature (°C)	From RH (%)	To RH (%)	Air Speed (fpm)	Time for 90% of Change (sec)	Average Time for 90% of Change (sec)
30.4	89	29	890	5.0	
30.7	75	29	890	5.1	5
31.0	75	29	600	7.2	
30.9	81	29	590	8.6	8
31.1	76	30	320	16.4	
31.2	80	30	330	17.3	
31.2	75	31	320	19.3	18
30.9	78	29	900	5.1	
30.9	73	29	880	5.1	5

The tabulation discloses the dependence of the time lag of the element on the air speed.

In flight, the radiosonde ascent rate was about 1000 fpm.

However, the density of air decreases with altitude. When the radiosonde reaches a point in the atmosphere where the air density is half that near the surface, only half as much air is flowing past the hygrometer. Effectively, the air ventilation has been halved. It is only because evaluation of the lithium chloride element has been discontinued at −40°C that the effect of decreased ventilation with decrease in air density has not assumed a more important place in the history of the lithium chloride element.*

To reproduce the average effective air ventilation which the lithium chloride element is exposed to during the part of the flight it is evaluated, air speeds of 500 to 800 fpm were most often used in time-lag tests.

THERMAL LAG OF THE ELEMENT

The laboratory calibration tests of the lithium chloride element have been made at steady-state conditions of relative humidity and temperature. The deficiencies of such

steady-state calibrations when applied to the dynamic changes encountered in flight have been recognized,* but procedures and facilities for dynamic testing of elements have not been established to date.

In steady-state calibrations at room temperature, the element is allowed a number of minutes to reach equilibrium with the ambient temperature and relative humidity. In flight, however, the element may not reach equilibrium with either temperature or relative humidity before rising into different temperatures and relative humidities. That the element responds to the changes in relative humidity in the atmosphere as a function of its speed of response at the ambient temperature, has been well recognized. The effect of the element's thermal lag has not been as clear-cut. But it is clear that a hygrometer, not at the same temperature as the air surrounding it, will exchange temperature with that air and in so doing will change the relative humidity of the surrounding air.† When the element warms the air next to it, the relative humidity will be made too low; when the element cools the air next to it, the relative humidity will be made too high. Obviously, these effects are not confined to the lithium chloride hygrometer, although they may be larger due to exothermic heating as the salt gains moisture and endothermic absorption of heat as the salt loses moisture.

Dunmore, in his early work in developing the first lithium chloride radiosonde hygrometers at the National Bureau of Standards, paid much attention to the thermal conductivity of his hygrometer bases.[5] He developed hygrometers on thin aluminum tubing bases with a thin coating of polystyrene for electrical insulation. Wire electrodes were wound over the polystyrene and the unit was dipped in a lithium chloride solution; this design was flown in U.S. Navy radiosondes 1938–1943. The aluminum base of this design

---

* Kobayashi, at the Meteorological Research Institute, Tokyo, Japan, found the reciprocal of the time lag to be approximately proportional to $(\rho V)^{0.46}$, where V is air speed and ρ is the density of air. He found this relation to be in close agreement with that of the bimetal thermometer, for 63 per cent time lag.[2]

* Marchgraber at the U.S. Army Signal Corps Laboratories has discussed the need for dynamic testing of humidity elements in general.[3]

† Bunker at the Woods Hole Oceanographic Institution noted in 1953: "It may be reasoned that if a (lithium chloride) humidity strip is warmer than the surrounding air, by virtue of its large thermal lag, it will heat the air immediately in contact with it, thereby changing its relative humidity."[4]

was second in thermal conductivity only to copper, of the common metals. The design was considered expensive for radiosondes and in 1942 John Onderdonk at Friez Instrument Division of The Bendix Corporation developed a modification of the Dunmore design with a unit cost of about 75 cents. Onderdonk's design was a flat sheet of smooth polystyrene, 4 in. × $^{11}/_{16}$ in. × $^{1}/_{32}$ in., with tin electrodes affixed to the long edges by spraying hot tin on blanks having the center areas masked with a tape that did not leave a residue on the two surfaces of the strip, Fig. 2. After spraying the melted tin on the edges, the tape was pulled off leaving clear areas of polystyrene on both flat smooth sides the width of the tape, $^{7}/_{16}$ in., between the two electrodes. The blanks were then sensitized by immersion endwise in a solution of about 4 per cent lithium chloride and 3 per cent partially hydrolyzed polyvinyl acetate.* The amount of lithium chloride film acquired by the element was a function of the speed of withdrawal of the element from the dipping solution, plus other factors, listed in a later section. Quantities of elements could be suspended on racks and dipped simultaneously using a motor-driven arrangement.[6]

Onderdonk's design of the lithium chloride radiosonde hygrometer became operational

* Hereafter, when a percentage of coating is given, it refers to the percentage by volume of a saturated solution and water.

with the U.S. Weather Bureau in February, 1943, and a thermal effect was observed soon thereafter with use of the element during cold weather at northernmost radiosonde stations. The radiosonde, prepared for flight, when taken from a warm office into the cold outdoors might not correctly report the outdoor relative humidity for periods longer than twenty minutes. Instructions were issued to expose the radiosondes outdoors for specific lengths of time at different temperatures before releasing them.

The same thermal effect was investigated by the author on a subfreezing day in 1950. It was reasoned that if a radiosonde operating with the lithium chloride element was transferred back and forth between indoors and outdoors, both at the same relative humidity, all effects observed should be thermally caused.

When the radiosonde was moved from indoors (25°C) to outdoors (−1 to −2°C) at approximately the same relative humidity, readings of the lithium chloride element undershot the true relative humidity, reading lower than true by −20 to −25 per cent RH. During the next 2 to 5 minutes, depending on the ventilation, these negative departures became smaller until equilibrium at true relative humidity was reached.

When the element was changed from outdoors to indoors, readings were immediately about 8 per cent RH higher than true relative

Fig. 2. The wide and the standard (narrow) lithium chloride radiosonde hygrometer elements.

humidity, with the departures positive for 3 or 4 minutes when equilibrium at true relative humidity occurred.

The investigation was not ideal as the ventilation was uncontrolled, but it was important in showing the direction and magnitude of the relative humidity errors when the element was either warmer or colder than the ambient air.*

A small thermocouple junction was melted into the polystyrene base of an element from which the lithium chloride solution had been removed. The thermal time lag was taken by heating this element about 10°C above ambient temperature and plunging it into the wind tunnel. At an air speed of 800 fpm, a time lag of about 24 seconds for 90 per cent of the thermal change was obtained, the value varying with the depth that the thermocouple was melted into the polystyrene.

Interest in decreasing the thermal lag of the lithium chloride element led to designs of hygrometer bases with less mass. One of these is shown in a patent filed in 1953.[7] Saran monofilament, .005 in. in diameter, carrying the lithium chloride solution, was wound around a coil of parallel aluminum electrodes. The thermal conductivity of saran is poor, as are plastics generally, but the design minimized the mass of the material in contact with the humidity-active film.

In a less costly design, mass was minimized by clamping thin plastic film between two flat metal washers. The plastic film needed only sufficient strength to support itself and a small electrode piercing its center. The change in resistance with change in relative humidity was measured between the inner electrode and the outer washers.

In 1954 a number of round and square elements were made. One electrode ringed the outer edges. Second electrodes of various sizes were inserted in the center of the plastic. Some were made with saran film .001 in. thick. (Today, "Mylar" could be used.) Others were made with thicker plastics. Aluminum electrodes were used. These elements demonstrated

that electrodes need not be of the same length with direct current, although the polarity of the measuring current needed to be observed with some solutions. With formula 145 (described on p. 236), the polarity gave a barely detectable difference in resistance below 40 per cent RH with no differences observed above 40 per cent RH. Formula 145 on a round element gave a time lag of 1 second. The room temperature resistances of these elements varied with relative humidity between 5,000 and 250,000 Ω. A round aluminum element coated with a 6 per cent lithium bromide solution, with the center electrode connected to negative polarity of the measuring circuit, calibrated at room temperature -4 to $+6$ per cent RH departures from Chart 800B, Fig. 3.

The round design remains attractive because it allows connecting together individual elements like beads on a string, slightly separated and suitably supported, to obtain a large total film area to use with the thin humidity-active films needed for fast speed of response, at the same time reducing the thermal effect.*

INVESTIGATIONS IN MAKING ELEMENTS

Water solutions of salts do not spread evenly on smooth plastic surfaces unless a surface-active (wetting) agent is used in the solution. In 1951 investigations were made of a wetting agent said to have been used in making lithium chloride elements—"aerosol." It was spread on used lithium chloride element bases from which the lithium chloride solution had been removed. By spreading the aerosol thickly the resultant hygroscopic device covered nearly the resistance range of the radiosonde. But the polarization was excessive.

It was reasoned that the wetting agent should not contribute to polarization in the lithium chloride element. A search for a wetting agent that gave minimum polarization when spread on a blank element led to "Triton" X-100, a nonionic surface-active

---

* Kobayashi exposed an element at 0°C and 75 per cent RH, then changed it quickly to 16°C and 52 per cent RH and obtained similar departures. A thermocouple embedded on the surface of the polystyrol base of his element took over 7 minutes to reach temperature equilibrium in calm air, 3 minutes with ventilation of 3 m/sec.[2]

* To minimize the thermal effect, Kobayashi made an element on a thin copper plate coated with polystyrol resin. He reported that he did not consider the resistance of this element good because of its surface roughness.[2]

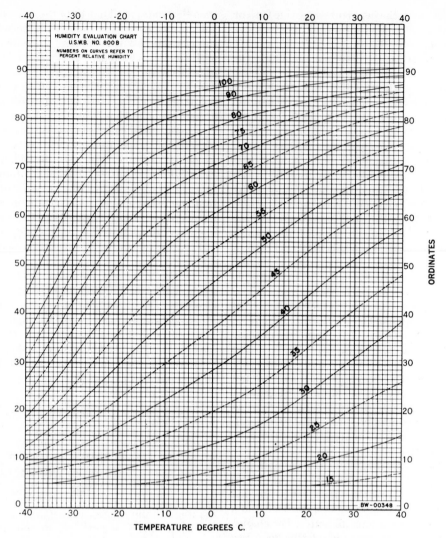

FIG. 3. Chart 800B used since 1948 in evaluating readings of the lithium chloride radio-sonde hygrometer element. Ordinates are recorder divisions (resistance).

agent of a series described as alkyl aryl polyether alcohols.*

At concentrations down to 0.01 per cent, "Triton" X-100 wetted used blanks well, and uniform films were obtained by hand dipping.

* "The water solubility and surface activity of these nonionic surface-active agents depend on the hydrophilic nature of the ether linkages in the polyoxyethylene chain, rather than on the presence of a hydrophilic ion as in the case of anionic and cationic surface-active agents. . . . Most dissolved salts have a greater affinity for water than do the ether linkages of the nonionics and essentially dehydrate the nonionics."[8]

The blanks were immersed in a small beaker containing the solution, wetted, and withdrawn to form films on their surfaces as a function of surface tension as the excess solution ran off. A tendency for detergent solutions to foam when mixed was eliminated by the use of minute amounts of Dow Corning "Antifoam A," a chemically inert silicone, in solutions.

When spread on the standard tin-electrode blanks, "Triton" X-100 polarized in the radio-sonde circuit, but not as much as other wetting agents did. A solution of lithium iodide and

"Triton" X-100 polarized with tin electrodes. Polarization was less marked with carbon electrodes. Addition of lithium chloride to the solution also gave polarization with tin electrodes.

Polarization increased when powdered carbon was added to a solution of lithium chloride and "Triton" X-100 with tin electrodes; polarization increased when stannic chloride was added to the solution.

Identical polystyrene blanks were made with aluminum electrodes. "Triton" X-100 spread alone on these blanks did not polarize. Here was a good combination for a radiosonde electric hygrometer if it were not for slow speed of response. The electrical resistance of "Triton" X-100 was high. So much needed to be spread on the blank to bring the resistance to the range of the radiosonde that it was sluggish in response.

The thickness of a sensitive film with a given resistance can be lowered by lengthening the electrodes. A large aluminum gridwork in the form of interlocking combs was made on polystyrene, with 20 electrodes in each comb. "Triton" X-100 was coated on this gridwork to bring the resistance within the range of the radiosonde. Time lags, in the direction of increasing relative humidity were made, giving 20 to 30 seconds.

"Triton" X-100 was tried later on other designs of electrodes, with the finding that its resistance was always too high. To investigate the effect of "Triton" X-100 on the speed of response of a salt solution, 6 per cent lithium chloride solutions were mixed with different concentrations of "Triton" X-100. It was found that as much as 15 per cent concentration of "Triton" X-100 had negligible effect on speed of response. At concentrations of 20 per cent and above, the presence of "Triton" X-100 slowed the speed of response.

An ionic detergent, "Triton" 770 Concentrate, gave fast speed of response when poured on a blank directly from its container. "Triton" 770 is sodium alkyl aryl polyether sulfate and is supplied as 30 per cent active ingredient in isopropanol and water.[9] It was found to possess an unusual property for a "salt"—it could be placed on a blank element and suspended at 100 per cent RH overnight with no indication of wetting or running. It gave elements too high in resistance when

coated on the standard blanks, although its resistance was much lower than that of "Triton" X-100. It did not polarize when used alone as the sensor, with tin electrodes, but it did polarize when lithium chloride was added. A dilute solution of "Triton" 770 was painted on the saran coil, previously described, and its speed of response was a fraction of one second.

After exposure at low relative humidity, elements made of "Triton" 770 did not recover their speed of response until conditioned by exposure to high relative humidity. Apparently a hard crust formed on its surface at low relative humidity that inhibited passage of water vapor. It was reasoned that a small percentage of a binder sensitive to low relative humidity would make openings in the hard crust of the "Triton" 770 to allow passage of moisture into the film interior. It was found that the addition of about 10 per cent of either gelatin or hydroxyethylcellulose to "Triton" 770 eliminated the sluggishness after exposure to low relative humidity. This appeared to be related to a similar effect observed when acetone was added to lithium chloride experimental elements. It was believed that the acetone in drying tunneled its way out of films; later, water vapor found these tunnels a fast route for entering and leaving the film interior.

In 1952 while examining the properties of chlorides, bromides, and iodides, it was observed that when aluminum chloride was added to a lithium chloride solution, the speed of response was improved and polarization was negligible with aluminum electrodes.

An investigation was made to pinpoint the optimum mixture of the two salts for fastest speed of response. It was also desired to determine the effect of leaving binders out of elements, and to determine if there were beneficial results from baking elements after they were made.

Thirty-two solutions were made in which the ratios of aluminum chloride to lithium chloride were varied in steps designed to pinpoint the best ratio. Additional solutions were made up to examine the other questions, bringing the total to over 50 solutions.

Comparative speeds of response of these elements were taken as 90 per cent of their linear change in time-lag tests; the fastest solutions were:

Solution No.	Formula
35	7.5% LiCl, 1.87% TX-100
15	7.5% LiCl, 7.5% TX-100
115	7.5% LiCl, 7.5% TX-100, 0.24% AlCl$_3$
45	7.5% LiCl, 0.9% TX-100
145	7.5% LiCl, 0.9% TX-100, 1.87% AlCl$_3$
25	7.5% LiCl, 3.75% TX-100
156	15% LiCl, 0.47% TX-100, 1.87% AlCl$_3$

All of the formulas were made on both tin and aluminum electrodes, and some were made on blanks with zinc electrodes. The electrode metal did not affect the speed of response, but did affect the slopes of the calibration curves and polarization.

The time lags of formula 145 were the fastest. This was verified by making fresh mixtures of the fastest solutions and performing time lags with elements made from the new solutions. Formula 145 was a ratio of four parts lithium chloride to one part aluminum chloride. It did not polarize with aluminum electrodes. A calibration chart was made for formula 145 elements, and time lags of 1 second were obtained. This chart was later extended to −40°C by extrapolation of low temperature calibrations and was used to evaluate two comparative flights made with lithium chloride elements at Silver Hill, Maryland, in 1954. In flight, formula 145 elements were faster responding at low temperature to relative humidity changes than the standard lithium chloride element.

Elements made from the more than 50 solutions were stored over dry silica gel and studied after aging for many months. Some flaking off of the films was observed. The conclusion was that a binder was needed to obtain good storage properties.

No effect was determined from baking some of the elements of this group after being dipped. However, as will be shown later, when elements are made using the binder of the standard lithium chloride element, polyvinyl alcohol, there are effects when newly dipped elements are baked.

The linear method used for evaluating lags of elements without calibrations is useful for comparisons. It assumes that the departure from calibration linearity is similar for the same family of solutions.

The variable amount of the "Triton" X-100 in the seven fastest solutions verified the earlier finding that its presence in concentra-tions less than about 20 per cent did not impede speed of response. In other tests it was found that while 0.01 per cent "Triton" X-100 was enough to provide suitable wetting, an extra amount (apparently to saturate the electrodes) decreased polarization. To provide enough "extra," 1.0 per cent "Triton" X-100 was recommended, and has been used, in making the standard lithium chloride element.

It was found that formula 145 solution decreased in resistance with age. This was a good effect if controlled, as it allowed a thinner, faster film for the same resistance. It was found that the aging effect could be reproduced by boiling the solution.

Greater familiarity with formula 145 revealed that its resistance also decreased with use on aluminum electrodes. Small amounts of hydroxyethylcellulose were added to formula 145 as a binder, and a lowering of resistance at the higher relative humidities with use was traced to the aluminum electrodes. A conclusion was reached that an AC measuring circuit was needed in order that formula 145 could be used on tin electrodes without polarization.

Making Fast-responding Elements

In 1954, polystyrene blanks 2 in. × 4 in. were masked by tape so that when molten tin was sprayed on clear areas between pieces of tape, an interlocking comb of grids $\frac{1}{10}$ in. wide separated $\frac{1}{6}$ in. were formed on one side of each blank. A solution of 2 per cent lithium chloride and 2 per cent "Triton" X-100 was poured on one of these blanks (in lieu of dipping the blank in the solution), and the excess solution was allowed to run off. The resultant element agreed within 1 per cent RH of Chart 800B at intermediate relative humidities and had a maximum deviation of 5 per cent RH at 82 per cent RH.

The solution was diluted to 1.4 per cent lithium chloride and 1.4 per cent "Triton" X-100, and coated on two of the blanks, giving calibrations 5 to 7 per cent RH above Chart 800B. When diluted to 0.33 per cent lithium chloride and 0.33 per cent "Triton" X-100 and coated on two of the blanks, the elements were low on Chart 800B. When diluted to 0.15 per cent lithium chloride and 0.15 per cent "Triton" X-100 and coated on four of the blanks, the calibration was nearer Chart 800B. Time lags were made with the elements at the

1.4, 0.7, 0.33, and 0.15 per cent concentrations and were evaluated by the linear method previously described. The results are shown in Fig. 4.

These results are conservative since the time lag of the recorder was not considered, and the linear evaluation gave time lags estimated to be slow by a factor of two. The four elements were the equivalent of one element 8 in. × 8 in. coated on one side or an element 4 in. × 8 in. sensitized on both sides. To fit in a radiosonde, the design can be folded or spiralled to decrease the size. The design has remained of interest as a means of increasing the speed of response of film elements.*

Polarization

Dunmore, in 1939, defined polarization as the counterelectromotive force set up by the direct current of the radiosonde measuring circuit. He recommended, "For use other than in the radiosonde, the (lithium chloride) hygrometer should be used in an alternating-current circuit, as polarization is thereby eliminated."[5]

Dunmore noted that polarization for the radiosonde was not a serious factor as it did not alter the operation of the hygrometer "sufficiently to change the calibration during the period of time (1 hour maximum) in which the unit is used." Polarization was also lessened in the radiosonde by transmitting relative humidity and temperature alternately. By transmitting temperature over twice as long an interval as relative humidity, the hygrometer was in use only one-third of the time and was resting, and "depolarizing," two-thirds of the time. Dunmore found that adding partially hydrolyzed polyvinyl acetate to the lithium chloride solution reduced polarization. Dember at Friez Instrument Division in 1946

* In 1952, Windsor, Sobel, Morris and Wood, at Friez Instrument Division, investigated lithium chloride elements for the U.S. Navy. They found, using cellulose gum (sodium carboxymethylcellulose) as the binder, that they were able to make thinner lithium chloride films. It was believed that the ionic nature of the cellulose gum required less lithium chloride for equivalent sensitivity. Exposure at high relative humidity was necessary to reduce hysteresis to a minimum. With cellulose gum and lithium chloride on standard blanks, they obtained time lags for 80 per cent of the change 3 to 4 times as fast as the standard lithium chloride element.

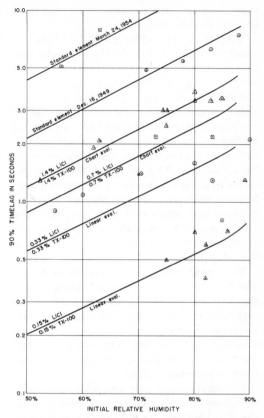

FIG. 4. Time lags of some fast-responding, experimental lithium chloride radiosonde hygrometer elements. Final RH was 35 per cent for all curves.

effectively increased the electrode-film interface by not removing a metal ridge formed during the metallizing process.[10] This followed Dunmore's principle of decreasing polarization by lessening current density at a point on the electrodes. Polarization was also improved by introducing nonionic detergent into the dipping solution after 1951.

A review of the procurement specifications for lithium chloride elements reveals, however, that the polarization test limits remained unchanged from 1946 through 1962. This was a result of polarization being a headache for manufacturers. Quantities of lithium chloride elements have been manufactured successively with little polarization-test trouble. Then polarization-test failures have suddenly cropped up and have threatened to shut down production lines. The trouble was usually traced to something very simple, such as a slight impurity in a procurement of tin used to make the electrodes.

Interest in providing an AC radiosonde measuring circuit for the lithium chloride element, to eliminate polarization, has existed since the element became operational in 1943. But AC circuits using vacuum tubes were too elaborate and expensive for the radiosonde. In 1945, the writer investigated the scheme of placing a capacitor, about 1 μF (microfarad), in series with the lithium chloride element in the radiosonde. This arrangement placed AC on the hygrometer element. Such circuits were found to work partially, but they possessed an inherent instability that was unsuitable for the radiosonde. In 1959 a simple series-capacitor circuit, Fig. 5, was built using the Shockley diode.*

The circuit has good temperature stability. The Shockley diode switches "closed" when the voltage on the capacitor rises to its switching voltage—this function has little temperature dependence. When closed, the Shockley diode discharges the capacitor until the total current through it falls to a value where it switches "open."[11]

It was reasoned that changing the above circuit to its multivibrator equivalent, using two Shockley diodes would allow operation on voltage only, giving minimum sensitivity to temperature. A model was built, and it was found that dry ice could be placed on either of the Shockley diodes with little effect. However, Clevite Transistor warned against accepting this finding until many different Shockley diodes were tried in the circuit.

Absolute stability is not required in the radiosonde measuring circuit. The present vacuum tube measuring circuit drifts slowly during flight as a result of changes in pressure, temperature and battery voltages. The radiosonde transmits reference signals showing how much it has drifted which allow the recording equipment at the ground to be adjusted to compensate for the drift.

Making Elements to Match a Standard Curve

The author knew little more about making the standard lithium chloride radiosonde hygrometer in mid-1953 than was available in

* "Shockley diode" is a name for the 4-layer diode used by its manufacturer, Clevite Transistor.

Dunmore's publications of 1938, 1939 and 1940. In beginning this investigation, it was not at first understood that in order to make elements matching calibration Chart 800B exactly, it was necessary to use materials that duplicated those used in making the elements that were used for the calibrations from which Chart 800B was drawn originally in 1948.

Silicones can be applied to hygrometers in very thin films that are transparent to water vapor, yet are repellent to liquid water. Thin films were obtained by diluting a small amount of silicone in a large quantity of solvent. Solvents such as "Varsol" (kerosene) and ethyl alcohol craze polystyrene, but petroleum ether does not. A 2 per cent silicone solids solution of Dow Corning 1107 (today 1109 could be used) in petroleum ether was applied quickly to the standard lithium chloride element, allowed to dry, then moderately heated to harden (polymerize) the silicone film. Standard lithium chloride elements were also vapor-treated with Dow Corning methyl-diethoxysilane (no longer available; an effective substitute is Dow Corning 1208).

Investigations of the silicone-treated elements revealed that while the areas of the electrodes had obtained an invisible film of silicone with good water repellency, the humidity-active films were a difficult problem. Detergents caused siliconed surfaces to become non-water-repellent until the detergent was washed off. Freed of detergent, the siliconed surfaces regained water repellency.

This investigation led to an understanding that the element needed a flexible, continuous, water-vapor-transparent "raincoat" around it that would confine the detergent in the film to the inner surface of the silicone. In 1958, Dow Corning Corporation investigated treating elements to give this result. However, in Dow Corning's treatment, carbon elements were substituted for lithium chloride elements because the carbon elements were, at that time, subject to an ionic leakage effect at high relative humidities known as "the hump." (Since then, improved formulations have minimized or eliminated "the hump.") Dow Corning Corporation successfully applied XR-6-2000, a silicone combining the properties of a rubber and a resin, to the carbon elements. The successful application was of interest because more detergent is used in the

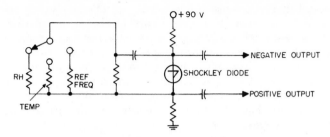

SAWTOOTH OSCILLATOR

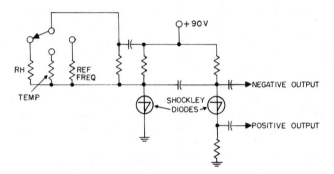

FREE- RUNNING MULTIVIBRATOR

Fig. 5. AC measuring circuits. The output voltage pulses are of magnitudes large enough to modulate radiosonde transmitters without amplification. Frequency of oscillation is controlled by resistances of RH (relative humidity element), TEMP (temperature resistor), and REF FREQ (reference frequency resistor).

carbon element than in the lithium chloride element.

The treatment resulted in films of silicone on the carbon elements that were too thick; speeds of response were slowed to about one-third of the untreated speed of response. This was considered promising because it appeared that future developments should allow improvements in the thinner silicone films and better water vapor transmission. Aging of the silicone film caused the resistance of the carbon elements to shift for reasons not well understood. The water repellency of these treated elements was excellent. The silicone films extended entirely around the carbon elements, allowing them to be immersed in beakers of distilled water up to clips contacting the electrodes, without apparent leakage effects.

Dunmore in 1939[5] specified as binder: "Use of partially hydrolyzed polyvinyl acetate . . .

(36 per cent saponifiable.)" Polyvinyl alcohol is made by the partial or complete hydrolysis of polyvinyl acetate and has been hydrolyzed in grades that range from water-insoluble to soluble.[12] Between these two extremes of solubility are grades that are suitable compromises between water permeability and water resistance. "Washing out," an effect of the film becoming too wet at saturation relative humidity, running, and even dropping off the element (ruining the calibration), is resisted by a grade of polyvinyl alcohol having slow water solubility. This type of polyvinyl alcohol apparently became widely available about 1947 because after this date reports of "washing out" became isolated.

Selected for this investigation was duPont grade 52-22 polyvinyl alcohol (86 to 89 per cent hydrolyzed), whose resistance to dissolving in water may be demonstrated by the fact that it can take two or three days for 65 grams to dissolve well in 1000 grams of distilled water. The first attempts to match Chart 800B with 1 per cent grade 52-22 polyvinyl alcohol in the lithium chloride solution were nearly successful—for example, the elements might match the chart at low humidity and not be more than 5 or 6 per cent away from the chart at high humidity. Individual variations between elements were not at first understood and were partly attributed to the hand dipping. However, elements made from a solution and dried in the room might exhibit altogether different calibration characteristics on different days. The only variable was that the humidity in the room had changed. Oven-dried elements also displayed different characteristics when the oven temperatures were changed, and some of those baked exhibited hysteresis.

No good theory on the form assumed by the film of the lithium chloride element was available. However, it seemed logical to the writer that the polyvinyl alcohol should start "drying" at relative humidities less than saturation, while the lithium chloride should dry at about 12 per cent RH; the value depends on the temperature.[13] Moreover, polyvinyl alcohol resins are swollen by moisture, and the lithium chloride solution is swollen by increased relative humidity. Therefore, having visualized the combination of the two drying as a polyvinyl alcohol sponge having cells filled with liquid lithium chloride solution, it followed that both the size of the sponge and the size of the cells in the sponge should be determined by the relative humidity at which the unit dried.

This concept may or may not have been correct. No microscope studies were made. Instead, the concept was tried out, and it allowed a rapid zeroing-in on Chart 800B. To do so required relinquishing the misconception that the element could be speeded up by using a minimum amount of polyvinyl alcohol binder and still match Chart 800B. Tests showed that the calibration of the lithium chloride element was a balance between an electrical insulator, polyvinyl alcohol and an electrical conductor, lithium chloride. Elements could be raised or lowered overall and at the high-humidity end of Chart 800B by adding lithium chloride to the solution, but the high resistance end (low relative humidity)

was controlled mainly by the amount of polyvinyl alcohol in the solution.

A chamber was arranged in order that air might be gently stirred past a tray of salt to establish a constant relative humidity, then past the newly dipped elements. Drying the elements at 30 per cent RH in this box gave elements within 10 per cent of Chart 800B using a solution of 4.2 per cent lithium chloride, 3.0 per cent polyvinyl alcohol and 1.0 per cent "Triton" X-100. When elements made from this solution were dried at 42 per cent RH, they were 3 per cent above Chart 800B at low humidity and 7 per cent above at high humidity. Drying the elements at 52 per cent RH gave zero departure at 30 per cent, and 3 per cent RH too high at 52 and 80 per cent RH. These results were entered on a graph that revealed a technique for zeroing-in on Chart 800B: decrease solution to 4.10 or 4.15 per cent lithium chloride to lower the element relative to Chart 800B, or lower the element by drying it at about 58 per cent RH. No salt was available for 58 per cent RH, but sodium dichromate gave 52 per cent RH. The amount of lithium chloride in the solution was reduced slightly, and the resultant elements zeroed in when dried at 52 per cent RH.

In the next section, this method of making the lithium chloride element is brought up-to-date using a dipping machine with the controls needed for uniform production.

Radiosonde flight data traditionally have been evaluated by human computers. Evaluation by automatic processing or by electronic computer is desirable. To evaluate the readings of the lithium chloride element, the electronic computer must be supplied with the calibration of the lithium chloride element in some form.

Early attempts to derive an equation for Chart 800B were not successful. In 1960, two equations were derived: one for above 0°C, the other for below 0°C. The two equations* are accurate to ± 4 per cent RH within the temperature range specified:

0°C and above

$$T_{DP} = 177.2 + .001761T^2 - 0.035T \log R$$

* "An equation of the form:
$$T_{DP} = a + bT^2 + c(\log R)^2 + dT \log R$$
would approximate the characteristics of the element more closely." (N. Wallach, 1963).

0°C and below

$$T_{DP} = 162.5 + 0.001827T^2 - 0.02647T \log R$$

where

T_{DP} = dew-point temperature, °C + 273
T = temperature, °C + 273
R = resistance of element, Ω.

The experience in making elements to match Chart 800B suggests that given an equation that approximates the characteristics of the element, an element can be made to match this equation.

GUIDE FOR MAKING TODAY'S LITHIUM CHLORIDE RADIOSONDE HYGROMETER

Today's lithium chloride radiosonde hygrometer is made to match Chart 800B. This requires manufacture of electrodes of uniform length and spacing on a flat strip of polystyrene, 4 in. $\times$ $^{11}\!/_{16}$ in. $\times$ $^1\!/_{32}$ in., with high-purity tin electrodes on the long edges separated $^7\!/_{16}$ in., Fig. 2. A method used to obtain these dimensions is shown by Dember.[10] Tape, $^7\!/_{16}$ in. wide, that does not leave a residue is wound around the middle of the blank plastic strip, lengthwise, and molten tin is sprayed on the exposed plastic edges. The tape is then pulled off the strip to form a clear area, $^7\!/_{16}$ in. wide, between the electrodes on the edges. Another method has been to spray conducting silver paint on the edges of the polystyrene strip, masking the center part with plastic, then electroplating tin over the silver paint.

The blank strips are dipped in the lithium chloride solution endwise, coating both sides simultaneously. Before dipping, new blanks are washed in water containing a small amount of nonionic detergent. Used or rejected elements are soaked in water to soften the old coating, then brushed with a soft sponge, and washed with water containing nonionic detergent. Ultrasonic methods also have been used successfully in cleaning relative humidity element blanks.

Matching Chart 800B for extended periods of time requires controlled conditions of temperature, relative humidity, and withdrawal rate.

(1) The solubility of lithium chloride in water, near 20°C, changes about $^3\!/_4$ per cent/deg C.[14] The formula for the lithium chloride dipping solution was worked out for mixing with the lithium chloride saturated solution at 80°F (26.8°C).

(2) A controlled room temperature of 75°F (23.9°C) and a controlled room relative humidity of 40 $\pm$ 2 per cent with the dipping machine enclosed in a cabinet controlled at 80°F have been used with the following formula. With the dipping machine enclosed in a cabinet that was temperature-controlled at 80°F, a withdrawal rate of $1\frac{1}{2}$ minutes for the entire length of the element was found to be optimum. In another room controlled at 35 $\pm$ 2 per cent RH, a withdrawal rate of $2\frac{1}{2}$ to 3 minutes was found to be optimum.

(3) The resistance characteristics of the element are tilted relative to Chart 800B by the relative humidity at which it dries.* For the process given here a relative humidity of 54 per cent is used for drying the freshly dipped elements. Fifty-four per cent RH is obtained with a saturated solution of sodium dichromate enclosed in a drying box that is temperature-controlled at or near 25°C.[13]

The relative humidity of a room or chamber is brought to the controlled value by cooling the incoming air to a fixed dew-point temperature, then warming the air to a fixed temperature before bringing it into the room or chamber. The ratio of these two temperatures determines the relative humidity, which is calculated by aqueous vapor pressure relationships of the two temperatures.

The controlled room may have double doors to prevent the operators from upsetting the controlled conditions when passing in or out.

Enclosing the dipping machine retards evaporation of the dipping solution. Drying of the elements during dipping is retarded by the higher ambient relative humidity created by evaporation of the dipping solution inside the dipping cabinet.

The lithium chloride-polyvinyl alcohol ratio controls the slopes of the resistance curves of the elements relative to Chart 800B. Separation of the lithium chloride element formula shown above into Part A and Part B allows adjustment of the ratio of lithium chloride to polyvinyl alcohol. Nominally, Part A and

* Kobayashi has made a similar observation: ". . . the change in drying process remarkably affects the characteristics of the element."[2]

LITHIUM CHLORIDE HYGROMETER FORMULA AT 80°F
(26.8°C) FOR 2500 ELEMENTS

	1953 Experimental Hand Dipping	1963 Machine Dipping	
Part A	67.6 g	67 to 71 g	Polyvinyl alcohol (duPont Grade 52-22 or equivalent.)
	21.8 cc	20 cc	Nonionic wetting agent (Rohm & Haas "Triton" X-100, or equivalent)
	1000 cc	1000 cc	Distilled water
Part B	89.4 cc	90.5 to 95.9 cc	Lithium chloride saturated solution
	1000 cc	1000 cc	Distilled water
	(1.32)	(1.35)	Lithium chloride (cc) polyvinyl alcohol (g) ratio

Part B are mixed in equal amounts, and the resulting elements are calibrated to determine the change in the ratio of Part A to Part B needed, if any, for subsequent batches.

(1) If the elements read too low at low relative humidity, they may be raised relative to Chart 800B by adding small additional amounts of Part B.

(2) If the elements read too high at low relative humidity, they may be lowered relative to Chart 800B by adding small additional amounts of Part A.

(3) Small adjustments to the low relative humidity end of Chart 800B will have negligible effect on the high relative humidity end.

The elements may be adjusted to Chart 800B, at the high-relative-humidity end, by changing the amounts of lithium chloride or distilled water in the formula:

(4) If the elements read too low at high relative humidity, they may be raised relative to Chart 800B by adding small amounts of saturated lithium chloride solution to the solution. Steps 1 and 2 above are then performed to match the elements to Chart 800B at low relative humidity.

(5) If the elements read too high at high relative humidity, they may be lowered relative to Chart 800B by adding small additional amounts of distilled water to the solution. Steps 1 and 2 above are then performed to match the elements to Chart 800B at low relative humidity.

The dipping tank should be of material which will not react with the ionic lithium chloride. Relative humidity element makers operating on long work shifts, have stored the dipping solution overnight in the dipping tank, but they found that the next morning it was necessary to add fixed amounts of distilled water to replace that which evaporated overnight. Measurements of the electrical conductivity and viscosity of the solution are made to keep the solution continuously the same.

The 1953 formula was derived from elements that were immersed in the solution by hand and were then quickly withdrawn and allowed to drain, with uniform films forming as a function of surface tension. Hand dipping is fine for experimental work, but there is no substitute for a dipping machine in actual production.

The dipping machine may be simply constructed by using a variable-speed motor driving a geared shaft, on one side of the dipping tank, to raise two metal arms that extend out over the dipping solution. The rack holding the elements to be dipped is placed on the two arms with the blank elements hanging between and below the two arms. The blank elements may be lowered into the dipping solution manually; the motor then takes over and lifts the elements out of the dipping solution at the prescribed rate.

After dipping, any surplus of solution that has collected on the bottom edges of the blanks is removed with a sponge. The elements are then moved without delay into the drying chamber to prevent them from drying at a humidity other than 54 per cent. A drying time of four hours has been used.

The drying chamber size should be compatible with the number of elements made. Air in the drying chamber is stirred lightly past the saturated solution of sodium dichromate and over the drying strips. The sodium dichromate will continue to absorb moisture until it is not a saturated solution and no longer will maintain 54 per cent RH. It can be recharged by adding dry sodium dichromate or by heating to drive out the moisture it has absorbed. To "charge" the silica gel used with the relative humidity elements, it is baked for a long period of time at a temperature which does not scorch it, to drive out the moisture the silica gel has adsorbed.

After drying, each element is given a selection test at two different values of relative humidity. The good ones are selected for use and the others are rejected, to be cleaned and redipped later. This procedure allows selecting lithium chloride elements to any limit of accuracy. However, as the selection accuracy is tightened, the production yield goes down correspondingly, so some compromise between selection and yield must be made.

In practice, a selection accuracy twice that of the specification requirement is often used. Thus, with a specification of ± 5 per cent accuracy, a selection limit of about one-half, or ± 3 per cent, is used, and all elements exceeding ± 3 per cent departure from the selection values are rejected. Test points near 35 per cent and 80 per cent relative humidity are most often used in selection tests. However, at time of production troubles, other points and other selection accuracies may be used, if by so doing elements that meet specifications are "selected."

The testing of each element at two selection points may be performed quickly. A rack of elements is brought to the test point relative humidity, and elements are individually switched into the measuring circuit. A quick reading may be taken to determine if the element is within the limits selected. These limits may be offset suitably toward higher relative humidity to allow for the polarization that would occur in a full 15-second reading. After this rather quick test, the rack of elements is removed from the relative humidity test box and those elements not within limits are rejected.

Automatic selection of elements is being made. An operator inserts the elements on special clips attached to a traveling belt that carries them to a controlled humidity chamber. The resistance of the element is balanced electronically so that "out of limits" creates an unbalance that is amplified to trip a solenoid that ejects the element from the clips into the reject tray.

Those elements that pass at both selection test points are placed at low-relative-humidity storage of less than 10 per cent RH where they may remain indefinitely. At this low relative humidity, the lithium chloride dries and the element assumes a frosty appearance. Absence of water in a salt means that it is no longer ionized; it is chemically inert. After elements have been subjected to several years of low-humidity storage, however, it is considered good practice to run tests to determine if they are still good. Possibly some of the dry lithium chloride not entirely bound up by the polyvinyl alcohol may sift away from the element during long storage. Also, the color-change indicator enclosed with the elements can mislead over a period of time; for example, a leaking container shows no leakage after storage in a dry place. However, lithium chloride elements three to five years old have given calibrations well within the original specification requirements, suggesting that handling, shipping, and storage conditions may be factors affecting the quality of aged elements.

Elements may be placed in low-relative-humidity storage by sealing the element in desiccated vials or cans. The containers are desiccated with small units of silica gel. A color-change indicator made of cobaltous chloride is added, blue indicating desiccation and pink indicating moisture leakage.

For many years lithium chloride elements were packaged in glass vials with various types of seals. As air shipments became more common, the need for a seal that would better withstand air pressure differences brought the round tin can into use. The element is sealed inside the can by methods like those used in the food industry. The importance of good packaging for these delicate-to-moisture devices cannot be over-emphasized.

Publications are available for testing hygrometers in general.[15] Mass-production testing of radiosonde relative-humidity elements has evolved some specialized techniques. The testing required is prescribed by specifications. Four elements out of each "lot" of 100 are calibrated, and one out of each 100 is tested for polarization at room temperature. At the start of each new production year, representative samples are tested for speed of response, usually at room temperature but also at low temperatures, and for low temperature calibration. These tests may be repeated during the year if necessary.

Room-temperature calibrations of relative humidity elements require metal or plastic boxes, or boxes lined with such material (wood is hygroscopic); a good size is about $1\frac{1}{2} \times 1\frac{1}{2} \times 1\frac{1}{2}$ ft (see Figs. 6 and 7). An electrically driven blower is used to circulate the air over the tray of salt, around the elements, and past the psychrometer. The psychrometer is mounted in the top side of the box for convenience in reading. The wet-bulb thermometer is mounted on a removable rubber stopper so it may be taken out of the box for wetting of the cloth wick. It is good practice to moisten the wet-bulb wick several minutes before each reading. The blower and motor are mounted for optimum ventilation of the psychrometer. These motors become warm when operated, and although they may be insulated from the blower by means of a plastic rod, some heat may leak to the blower housing. As a result, it has become standard practice to pull rather than push the air past the psychrometer. The motor should be mounted outside the box.

Large producers of elements have found it expedient to calibrate them in four test boxes each separated in relative humidity by about 20 per cent. The temperature of the room will dictate the value of relative humidity given by most salts. At 25°C suggested values are

Potassium acetate	25% RH
Sodium dichromate	54% RH
A mixture of sodium chloride and sodium nitrate	68% RH
Zinc sulfate	88% RH

Saturated solutions of these and other salts are made by placing dry salt in a tray and then adding enough water to wet all the salt but not enough to dissolve more than one-third to one-half of it, leaving a generous amount of un-dissolved salt.* If all of the salt becomes dissolved, the desired relative humidity point may no longer be obtainable (it may no longer be a saturated solution). The solution may be recharged by adding dry salt or by drying, as previously described in recharging the sodium dichromate used in drying strips. Some salts may need agitation, usually provided by

* Wexler and Hasegawa at the National Bureau of Standards have described such a saturated salt solution as a "slushy mixture."[13]

FIG. 6. Front view of humidity test box (1963 design) for carbon and lithium chloride radiosonde hygrometers. Measurements are made with wet-and-dry-bulb thermometers.

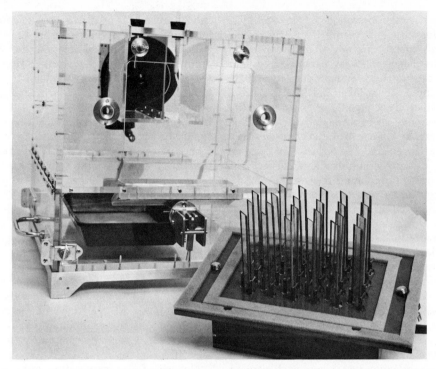

FIG. 7. Side view of humidity test box (1963 design). This utilizes saturated salt solutions to establish equilibrium relative humidities. Provision is made in the box to close off the salt-tray partition during the change of saturated salt solutions.

vibration of the blower or the motor, to break up a film of unsaturated solution that may form on the surface.

A shallow tray is placed at the bottom of the test box. Many salts have a tendency to creep, in time, up the sides of the tray. This may be retarded with a coating of silicone such as Dow Corning DC-4.

Other salts useful in testing are, at 25°C[13]

Magnesium chloride	33% RH
Sodium chloride	76% RH

Water is sometimes useful in obtaining humidities higher than 90 per cent although it may not stabilize well at any one value for a long period of time. One-half to one teaspoonful of sodium chloride in the tray of water has been used to increase the stability.

A useful salt is sodium carbonate, 87 per cent RH at 24.5°C.[16] Ref. 16 lists nearly two pages of constant relative humidities of salts at various temperatures. It has been found advisable to remove alcohol vapors and ammonium salts from the vicinity of the tests.

The four boxes are stabilized at the four test humidities chosen by operating the blowers for a period of time, sometimes overnight. A shield on the front of each box may be removed for insertion of the hygristors to be tested, by clamping the rack of hygristors on the front of the box in a leakproof arrangement. The box blower motor is turned off during this operation to minimize loss of constant-relative-humidity conditions due to entry of room relative humidity into the box. After clamping the rack of elements tightly onto the front of the box, the blower motor is turned on, and the time required to reach relative humidity equilibrium then depends on how much room relative humidity has leaked into the box and how far removed room relative humidity is from box relative humidity.

The psychrometer wet bulb is wetted and monitored. When relative humidity conditions are stable at that relative humidity test point, the individual elements are calibrated. A radiosonde measuring circuit, with radio-frequency section disconnected, is used. The measuring circuit is coupled directly to the frequency meter through a small capacitor. Some frequency meters, particularly older types, may not have enough gain to operate at this input signal level and may require a preamplifier. The impedance that the radiosonde circuit sees through this coupling capacitor may change its audio characteristic; the impedance should be adjusted or selected so that the audio is standard "on curve." The entire unit, radiosonde measuring circuit, frequency meter and recorder, is calibrated beforehand and thereafter as required. Adjustment of this equipment to linearity is desirable, otherwise the calibration deviations must be applied to readings as corrections.

In all tests, the power supply to the radiosonde measuring circuit should be as stable as possible to avoid drifts in reference frequency. The measuring circuit current, called "grid current," is set to not exceed 300 μA.

As perishable resistors, lithium chloride elements are subjected to 100 per cent testing only in the selection test, where each element is required to fall within ± 3 per cent of a reference relative humidity or it is rejected. In other tests, samples are taken to represent lots of elements, usually 100. The fiscal year 1962–1963 procurement specifications require that calibration tests be performed on four out of each 100 elements at 8 points between 20 and 95 per cent RH, errors not to exceed ± 5 per cent RH, except on one test point an error of ± 7 per cent RH will be allowed.

"If more than one of the four elements fail, the entire lot of 100 shall be rejected. However, if only one element fails, eight more shall be taken from the lot and tested. If all the second group pass, the lot shall be accepted. If one of the second group fails, however, the entire lot shall be rejected."

One element out of each 100 is tested for polarization; if it fails, two other elements are tested. Should one of these fail, the lot is rejected. In the polarization test, each element is switched into the measuring circuit for 15 seconds and then switched out for 30 seconds. Thus only three elements can be accommodated in a polarization test at a time. Polarization tests are best performed by motor-driven switches. The relative humidity is held constant in this test for a 30-minute interval, and the polarization occurring during the 30 minutes is used to accept or reject the lot of 100 elements represents by the element tested. Acceptable polarization for the 30-minute period is 6 per cent RH or less. Polarization tests are made at relative humidities where most polarization trouble occurs, usually between 80 and 90 per cent. Generally, temperatures much above 27°C should be avoided for polarization tests since higher temperatures may increase polarization and, at the same time, do not well represent the temperatures to which the element will be exposed in flight.

Time-lag tests, as outlined in the first part of this paper, are performed upon $\frac{1}{10}$ of 1 per cent of the elements. A speed of response of 15 seconds for 90 per cent of the relative humidity change is required.

Chart 800B was drawn for vapor pressure over water at all temperatures. In tests at subfreezing temperatures, it should be verified that the relative humidity-psychrometric tables used are for vapor pressures over water at subfreezing temperatures.[17]

One set of low-temperature tests per year (more often if production changes or new ingredients call for them) may not justify the cost of low-temperature relative humidity testing equipment. It may be feasible to consider arranging with an organization possessing low-temperature relative humidity testing equipment to do the testing, for a fee.

The container of an element from a lot that has passed all the tests is given a label or is rubber-stamped to indicate that a humidity element is enclosed. Date of manufacture and the lot number stamped on the container may be of interest later.

A final check on the accuracy of the element is performed immediately before use. After the radiosonde has been prepared for flight, the element is removed from its sealed container and is placed in the radiosonde. The radiosonde is placed in a humidity test box at a constant relative humidity between 60 and 90 per cent. After reaching equilibrium with the relative humidity inside the test box, the radiosonde is switched between references, temperature and relative humidity. In this baseline test, the difference between the psychrometer- and the radiosonde-relative humidity values must not be more than 10 per cent or the humidity element is rejected. Ten per cent error is allowed because this figure may include errors of the psychrometer, the recorder, and particularly the radiosonde relative humidity measuring circuit. The baseline test relative humidity error is applied to subsequent flight readings when it exceeds 3 per cent RH.

Acknowledgments. The writer expresses his appreciation to G. Miller, U.S. Weather Bureau, for details of making today's lithium chloride element; to C. Harmantas, U.S. Weather Bureau; W. Windsor, Bendix Radio Division; P. Rogers, Friez Instrument Division; M. Friedman and A. Jones, Molded Insulation Company, for review and constructive comments; to T. Rowland, Rohm and Haas Company, for information on detergents; to P. Weygandt, Clevite Transistor, for information about the Shockley diode; and to R. Bright, Dow Corning Corporation, for data on silicones.

References

1. Wexler, A., "Low-temperature Performance of Radiosonde Electric Hygrometer Elements," *J. Res. Natl. Bur. Std.*, **43**, 49 (1949).
2. Kobayashi, J., "Investigations on Hygrometry," Meteorological Research Institute, Tokyo, (2, 11) 213, 1960.
3. Marchgraber, R. M., "Carbon-type Humidity Element, Resistance ML-476(2, 11)/AMT," USASRDL Tech. Report 2052, 128, 1959.
4. Bunker, A. F., "On the Determination of Moisture Gradients from Radiosonde Records," *Bull. Am. Meteorol. Soc.*, **34**, 9, 406 (1953).
5. Dunmore, F. W., "An Electric Hygrometer and its Application to Radio Meteorography," *J Res. Natl. Bur. Std.*, **20**, 723 (1938); "An Improved Electric Hygrometer," *J. Res. Natl.*

Bur. Std., **23**, 701 (1939); Diamond, H. W. S., Hinman, Jr., Dunmore, F. W., and Lapham, E. G., "An Improved Radio Sonde and its Performance," *J. Res. Natl. Bur. Std.*, **25**, 327 (1940).
6. Mathews, D., "Review of the Lithium Chloride Radiosonde Hygrometer," Humidity and Moisture, Vol. 1, New York, Reinhold Publishing Corp., 1964.
7. Harmantas, C., and Mathews, D., "Sensing Element for the Electric Hygrometer," U.S. Patent 2,710,324 (Feb. 4, 1953).
8. Triton Surfactants, Rohm & Haas Co., Philadelphia, 1960.
9. Rohm and Haas Sanitary Chemicals, Rohm & Haas Co., Philadelphia, 1963.
10. Dember, A. B., Humidity Responsive Resistor, U.S. Patent 2,481,728 (Oct. 24, 1945).
11. Shockley, W., and Gibbons, J. F., "Introduction to the Four-layer Diode," *Semicond. Prod.*, **1**, 1, 9 (1958).
12. *Modern Plastics Encyclopedia*, **1A**, 303 (1963).
13. Wexler, A., and Hasegawa, S., "Relative Humidity-Temperature Relationships of Some Saturated Salt Solutions in the Temperature Range 0° to 50°C," *J. Res. Natl. Bur. Std.*, **53**, 1, 19 (1954).
14. "International Critical Tables," Vol. 4, pp. 233, New York, McGraw-Hill Book Co., Inc., 1928.
15. Wexler, A., and Brombacher, W. G., "Methods of Measuring Humidity and Testing Hygrometers," *Natl. Bur. Std. Circ.*, **512** (1951); "Methods of Calibration and Testing of Hygrometers," *Natl. Bur. Std., Letter Circ.*, **LC1026** (1957).
16. "Handbook of Chemistry and Physics," 42nd ed., p. 2499, Cleveland, The Chemical Rubber Publ. Co., 1960.
17. "Relative Humidity-Psychrometric Tables," Washington, USWB, 1953.

25. The Aging Effect of An Electrolytic Hygrometer

J. Kobayashi and Y. Toyama

Meteorological Research Institute, Mabashi, Suginami, Tokyo, Japan

ABSTRACT

The results of an investigation on the method of protecting an electrolytic hygrometer from the aging effect are presented.

The physical and chemical changes in the electrodes and the moisture sensitive film may be given as the main causes of the aging effect. Particularly, the aggregation of absorbent embedded in the film and the breaking of the film near the electrodes seem to occur gradually and discretely under conditions above 95 per cent RH.

In the fabrication of improved humidity elements, a small amount of gelatin was added to the LiCl-polyvinyl alcohol solution used in general. In order to investigate the aging effect, the element was mounted horizontally on a frame in a test chamber. The humidity of the air in the chamber was always maintained at about 100 per cent RH. In the course of the experiment, the humidity of the surroundings was occasionally cycled from about 100 per cent RH to about 40 per cent RH. Several experimental results show that the shift in indication of the improved element exposed in circumstances above 95 per cent RH is apt to increase gradually with time, and its amount ranges within 5 per cent RH after a lapse of 30 days. Therefore, it may be concluded that the improved element has a higher value in comparison with the old type.

INTRODUCTION

At present, the Dunmore electric hygrometer is familiar to us as one of the representative hygrometers. This type was the first that answered the requirements of humidity measurement at temperatures below 0°C. The appearance of the electric hygrometer shed a fresh light on the need to make the sensing element respond more quickly to changes in humidity likely to be encountered in the upper atmosphere. At that time, however, the stability in indication of the sensing element was contrary to expectation. One of the greatest defects inherent in the electrolytic hygrometer is the change in humidity characteristics of the sensitive film coating the electrical insulator, which always appears at higher humidities. The other is the relatively slow response to changes in humidity, especially at low temperatures. The latter presents a question in the use of radiosondes for the measurement of humidity in the atmosphere. However, it is especially hoped that some devices to counteract the aging effect will be developed, because this type of hygrometer has merits which make it suitable for remote recording and capable of easily measuring humidity in a small confined space under ordinary conditions. Furthermore, such advantages as simple fabrication, low cost, and adaptability for mass production, compared with other hygrometers, cannot be ignored.

In our work, a more or less morphological approach has been taken to the problem of developing a more stable electric hygrometer. An attempt was made to protect the sensor from the aging effect. It is the purpose of this paper to show the behavior of the sensitive film at temperatures of 15 to 25°C and humidities above 95 per cent RH.

A SURVEY OF METHODS OF PROTECTING SENSORS FROM THE AGING EFFECT

The aging effect may be classified into two kinds, long-period and short-period. The origin of the former could be explained as follows:

(1) Some parts of an electrode in contact with the sensitive film may be damaged by chemical reaction between them. This will lead to changes in surface electrical resistivity of the film.

(2) Permanent changes in chemical composition in the film will be caused by both the excessive current passing through the film between two electrodes and the transitional deformation of the film to a more stable state.

(3) The corrosion of the electrodes in use and the attachment of sediments floating in the air on the surface of the film may affect the resistance-humidity characteristics of the sensor.

On the other hand, the short-period aging effect can often be observed, particularly when the sensor is exposed in air of humidities above 95 per cent RH. The effect is apt to appear when the element is left inclined or is shaken up and down in a highly humidified environment. When the relative humidity of the air is high, a large amount of water has to condense on the film to dilute the solution enough to balance the ambient vapor pressure. Infinite dilution is necessary for 100 per cent RH. The water film actually tends to turn to one side or to break in order to form many semispherical drops. Consequently, the origin of the short-period aging effect may be classified into two sources:

(a) The amount of absorbed water in the sensitive film is too much.

(b) Affinity among the constructing materials of the element becomes weak in the highly humidified air.

The effects listed in (1), (2) and (3) will be reduced to some extent if the element is handled with care. Therefore, it becomes a very important point to concentrate on the factors shown in (a) and (b).

It is first necessary to determine how to minimize the amount of absorbed water on the sensitive film and to check the aggregation among clusters of absorbing solvent without injuring the performance of the element, even

if the concentration of the solvent is diluted considerably in the high humidity environment.

Several attempts have been made to satisfy these requirements since the Dunmore-type element was developed.[1] The main objectives could be summarized as follows:

(1) To devise an element on which the electrical resistivity of the film would change reversibly with the physical adsorption and desorption of water vapor.

(2) To develop some devices to keep the initial homogeneous distribution of absorbent in the film for a greater length of time.

Physical adsorption is characterized by the small amount of absorbed water. Therefore, such an approach could conceivably lead to the development of a stable humidity sensor, if only the affinity between adsorbing materials and a base plate is not injured. Some attempts[2, 3] have already been made to realize this goal. These devices are characterized by a fast-responding rate, so, they will answer our expectations in the near future. It is to be regretted, however, that they are little suited for mass production and possess a slight hysteresis effect. In these respects, the Dunmore type is superior to them.

If a large amount of absorbed water on the Dunmore-type element is considered as an inevitable detriment, the method shown in the latter item will be explored. In this case, the aging effect of the film itself can be reduced to some extent by baking the element in an oven at about 60°C.[4] The movement of absorbent embedded in the sensitive film can often be checked by using such porous materials as porcelain clay, paper, bark and so on as a base plate. However, it is often observed in air of humidities above 90 per cent RH that clusters of absorbent tend to move to a more stable state according to the surface property of the base plate on which the absorbent is coated. Once this happens, the leakage resistance of the sensor changes abruptly and becomes entirely different from the original value. This problem is not settled conclusively, even if the performance of the sensor does not change under conditions of ordinary temperatures and humidities. Consequently, it becomes important to search for the suitable materials for use as binders, taking the affinity among the materials used into consideration, and to find some devices to keep the uniformity of absorbent as initially distributed on the film in all cases.

In our case, consideration was particularly given to such properties as the vapor pressure of the constituents of the sensitive film, adhesion to an insulating substrate, stability of the deposited film and the resistance-humidity characteristics of the element. On the basis of these considerations, some experiments were performed.

ELEMENT DESIGN

The element consists of the humidity-sensitive film, an insulating substrate on which the film is coated, and electrodes between which the electrical resistance can be measured by means of an electrical circuit.

The substrate used in most work is a strip of methacrylic resin, 50 mm × 10 mm × 1 mm. For comparison with this strip, substrates were provisionally used which were made of either "Styrol" or surface-treated "Teflon." These were cleaned by rinses in distilled water and ethyl alcohol. The substrate was again cleaned after electrodes were formed.

The electrodes, whose gap distance was about 3 mm, were parallel strips of gold foil of $5\text{-}\mu$ thickness. They were glued on to one side of the substrate so that the paste might not be pressed out. The construction of the element is shown in Fig. 1.

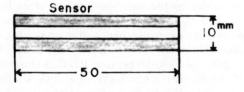

Sensor

FIG. 1. Example of a sensor.

Thin sensitive films were produced by dipping the substrate vertically into a mixture and then raising it at the rate of 1 mm/sec. As soon as the substrate was covered with the film, all edges and the other side of the substrate were wiped by a sheet of blotting paper, and then the element was mounted horizontally on a support in a desiccator and stored.

The main constituents of the mixture were polyvinyl alcohol, water, LiCl and a nonionic lyophilic dispersing agent. A large amount of a colloidal graphite solution was occasionally added to the mixture in order to get a linear relationship between relative humidity and electrical resistance and to improve the polarizabilities of the constituents. In the same manner, either gelatin or carboxymethylcellulose (CMC) was added to the mixture in order to check the movement of clusters of absorbent embedded in the film.

The proportion of components of the mixture is given in Table 1.

TABLE 1. COMPOSITION OF SOLUTION

Solution		Per Cent
Solvent	Water or colloidal graphite solution diluted with water	94–96
Absorbent	LiCl (40%)	1–2
Dispersing agent	Nonionic surface-active agent (Nonion)	0.03
Binder	Gelatin (Ge)	3–4
	Carboxymethyl-cellulose (CMC)	
	Polyvinyl alcohol (PVA) or PVA-Ge mixture (1:1)	

Kinds of Colloidal Graphite Solutions

Name	Kinds of Binders
Ga 29	Inorganic binder
Ga 79	PVA and polyvinyl acetate (PVAc)
Ga 94	Vinyl resin

Kinds of Base Plates

Surface-treated "Teflon" (T)
Methacrylic resin (M)
"Styrol"

TEST METHODS AND APPARATUS

The element was calibrated at ordinary temperatures (15 to 25°C) in a sealed bottle in which the relative humidity was known. Several bottles were used for the calibration; a small amount of solution, 100 cc in volume, was put in each bottle. As a chemical, sulfuric acid is generally employed. (The equilibrium values of relative humidity over sulfuric acid solutions are well known as a function of temperature and concentration.) The temperature of the calibrating space in the bottle was measured by a small mercury thermometer. In order to obtain a homogeneous distribution of the moisture in the bottle, the bottle itself was rotated slowly with respect to its horizontal central axis. In this case, the air in the bottle was always surrounded with a film of the sulfuric acid-water mixture on the inner wall of the bottle. The attainment of the equilibrium was remarkably accelerated, while the elements were left without being shaken. Figure 2 shows a cross-sectional diagram of the sealed bottle. A set of sealed bottles, in which water replaced the sulfuric acid, was used for studies on the effect of prolonged exposure to a high relative humidity (above 95 per cent) on the performance of the element.

Prior to the calibration, the element was not cycled between a high and a low relative humidity. Most of the elements were calibrated at one temperature. In the calibration, the element was exposed to a cycle of relative humidity, first of decreasing values and then of increasing values. After the calibration, the element was put into the sealed bottle containing water. A calibration was occasionally performed during the prolonged exposure of the element to the highest humidity in order to confirm whether or not there was any drift or shift in indication over the humidity range.

The resistance of the element was measured by an amplifier with a meter. The amplifier consists in principle of an AC-type Wheatstone bridge. The applied voltage to the bridge circuit was 6 V at 200 cps. The measuring accuracy mainly depends on that of the

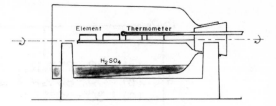

FIG. 2. Calibrating apparatus.

variable resistor which makes up one arm of the bridge circuit and is below 0.3 per cent. In practice, the calibration of the meter was made by substituting a known resistance each time the measurement was done. The effect of the magnitude of the applied power on the performance of the element was considered to be negligible as has already been shown in the literature.[4] Figure 3 shows the circuit diagram of the amplifier with a meter.

The indicated resistance of the element obtained during the long-period storage was corrected, taking the temperature coefficient of the element into consideration, because the temperature in the sealed bottle was often different from that of the surroundings where the element was calibrated initially. Five elements were calibrated at temperatures of 25, 20, 15 and 10°C to get data on the temperature coefficient of the same kind of elements. The same relationship as shown in reference 4 was obtained.

The response time of the element to abrupt changes in relative humidity was not studied here, because we could not observe any enormous difference between the Dunmore

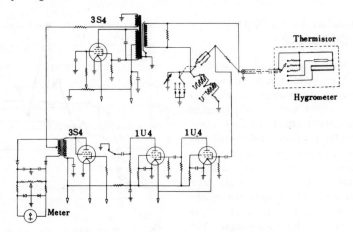

FIG. 3. Circuit diagram of a resistance meter.

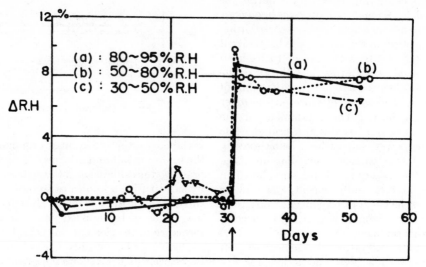

FIG. 4. Abrupt changes in indication often observed during long-run tests. The ordinate shows the deviation in terms of per cent relative humidity from the initial value.

type and the improved type at ordinary temperatures. However, it is necessary to examine whether or not any difference in response time exists between them.

Polarization tests also were not made here, because we considered that the magnitude of the polarization was of the same order shown in our previous work.[4]

Studies were made of the effect of continuous a.c. excitation, prolonged exposure to the highest relative humidity and heat treatment on the performance of various kinds of elements.

95 to 30 per cent RH each time the calibration was made, and was then stored in a desiccator. Each zigzag line shown in the figure gives the mean values of the shifts in indication of the element over a restricted humidity range. Abrupt changes in indication as shown in this Figure occurred immediately after the element had been inserted in a sealed bottle, in which the relative humidity was kept near 100 per cent. Before and after that day, a discrete shift was not observed. So, it may be concluded that the large amount of absorbed water on the film

EXPERIMENTAL RESULTS AND DISCUSSION

It was shown in the paper of reference 4 that the addition of colloidal graphite to the sensitive film seemed to protect the element from the running effect and, in addition, to reduce the polarization effect. In fact, some experimental results obtained under ordinary conditions showed that there existed only a slight shift in indication, though the element was cycled several times between a high and a low relative humidity. The magnitude of the shift was within the measuring error of ± 2 per cent RH (Fig. 4). In this experiment, the element was exposed to a humidity cycle from

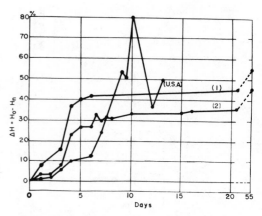

FIG. 5. Short-period aging effect of sensors at a humidity above 95 per cent RH.

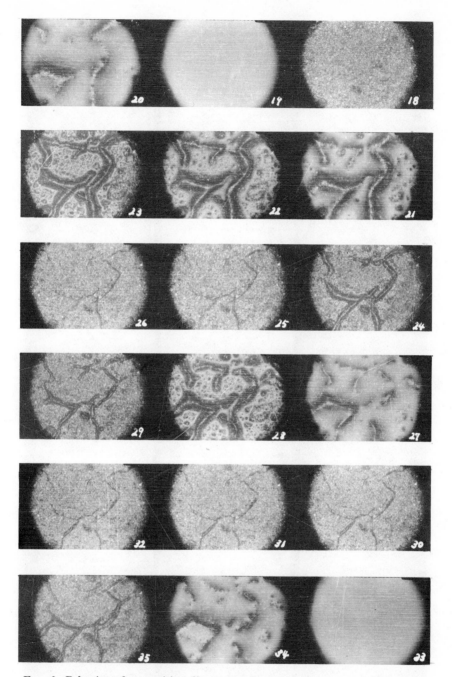

Fig. 6. Behavior of a sensitive film containing a quantity of graphite particles ("Nikkaloid" MR-2, Hitachi Mfg. Co.) on a methacrylic resin plate, which is exposed to a cycle between a moistened and a dried state. The element is subjected to a water spray in an air stream on the cycling course.

	Initial State	Moistened	Middle	Recovered
1st trial	No. 18	No. 19	No. 24	No. 26
2nd trial	26	27	29	32
3rd trial	32	33	35	

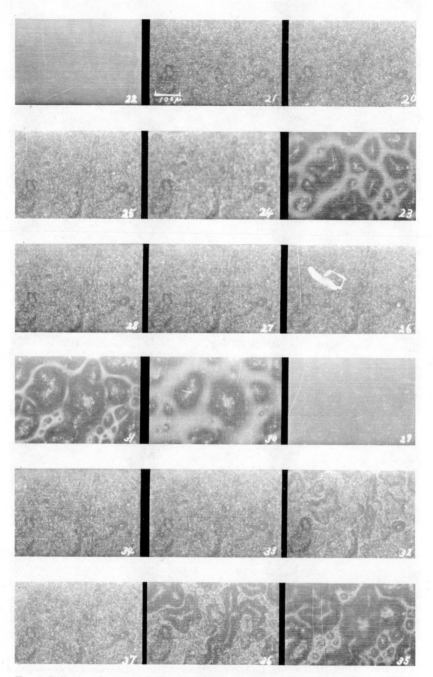

Fig. 7. Behavior of a sensitive film containing a quantity of graphite particles (MR-2) on a surface-treated "Teflon" plate along the same course as shown in Fig. 6.

	Initial State	Moistened	Middle	Recovered
1st trial	No. 21	No. 22	No. 24	No. 28
2nd trial	28	29	32	34
3rd trial	34		36	

seems to be one of the factors responsible for damaging the performance of the element. We must take every precaution in handling the element, particularly when we want to use it in highly humidified air. Adding a colloidal graphite solution to the film was not sufficient to protect the element from this running effect.

In order to confirm the behavior of the element, studies on the resistivity of the element were undertaken together with microscopic studies. The element now used in the U.S. and the above-mentioned elements were employed as test specimens. In this test, all the elements were left in an environment of about 100 per cent RH, except when the calibration was made. The base plates of our elements were made of methacrylic resin and surface-treated "Teflon," respectively. Both of the sensitive films were composed of the PVA-water-LiCl mixture with a large amount of colloidal graphite solution and a small amount of dispersing agent. The effects of prolonged exposure of the elements to an environment of the highest humidity are shown in Fig. 5. As to the U.S. element, its resistivity at the humidity does not show any remarkable change at the start, but it begins to increase gradually with time. Once this tendency

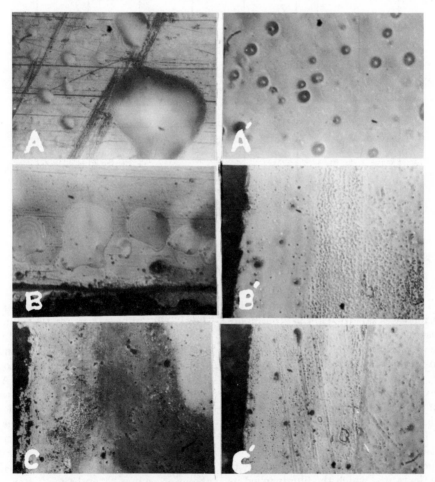

FIG. 8. Behavior of a sensitive film of the U.S. element (A, B and C) and that of a gelatin-PVA sensitive film (A', B' and C') along the same course as shown in Figs. 6 and 7.

A and A': moistened state near the center of the film
B and B': moistened state near the electrode
C and C': recovered state near the electrode

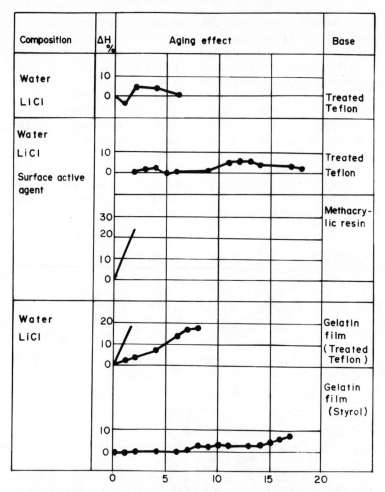

FIG. 9. Short-period aging effect of sensors at a humidity above 95 per cent RH.

becomes conspicuous, the resistance of the element increases rapidly. On the other hand, the resistance of our element is inclined to increase remarkably from the beginning in order to reach its own stable state as fast as possible. It may be concluded, therefore, that there exist some fundamental differences between them. Microscopic studies were made of the behavior of the sensitive film at the highest humidity and when subjected to a humidity cycle.

For further progress, it became necessary to increase the rate at which the film reached its final state. The element was subjected to a water spray in an air stream without washing out the absorbent embedded in the film, and then dried in a dry air. Photographs were taken before and after the spray treatment. Figure 6 shows the appearance of the film on a methacrylic resin plate; Fig. 7 that of the film on a surface-treated "Teflon" plate, and Fig. 8 that of the USA element. Both photographs, Figs. 6 and 7, show a similar pattern. A sort of stripe pattern is formed at the end of the trial, though it is not entirely observed at the initial stage. Probably, it may be due to the aggregation of colloidal graphite particles in the film. This stripe pattern remains unchanged, although the film is subjected to the above procedure several times after the first trial.

On the other hand the U.S. element exposed to the same circumstances shows an entirely different pattern. At the initial stage, the distribution of salt embedded in the film was uniform, but clusters of salt were formed after several trials, which are seen in Fig. 8. In particular, the breaking of the film near the electrodes and the aggregation of salt are clearly observed.

As one method of protecting the element from the above-mentioned unfavorable effects, gelatin was considered to be suitable for a binding material and a small amount of it was added to the mixture already used. The effective use of gelatin was examined, using several kinds of base plates and comparing the results with those obtained using carboxy-methylcellulose as a binder. The proportion of these chemicals in the solution is shown in Table 1. Experiments on the resistivity were made with the same procedure as described above; the results are shown in Figs. 9, 11, 13 and 14.

In Figs. 9 and 10, the use of a water-LiCl solution with no binder is shown, where "Teflon" and methacrylic resin are employed as base plates. The examples shown here give a clear answer to the question of whether or not any difference exists between a lyophobic and a lyophilic plate. The wettability of the surface-treated "Teflon" is better than that of the others employed here. Judging from these results, such an element will probably become available, if only the surface of the element such as a "Teflon" plate can be treated and coated with the solution uniformly. In practice, the surface property of the surface-treated "Teflon" plate used is not always uniform. Therefore, results shown in Fig. 9 may not be obtained frequently. It is noticeable, however, that no tendency to gather clusters of salt can be observed. This is also verified by the fact that the element in the lowest row in Fig. 9 shows a good performance

during prolonged exposure. In this case, styrol is used as a base plate and the surface of the plate is coated with a thin gelatin film. This result suggests that gelatin acts as a good binder in using a lyophobic base plate. The two curves shown in this row tell us that gelatin is an "ampholytoid."

Figure 11 shows comparative results on the effect of various binders on base plates used. The binders employed were gelatin, carboxy-methylcellulose, gelatin-PVA mixture and gelatin-CMC respectively. In this figure, T, G-T and M respectively show abridgements of base plates used, which are a surface-treated "Teflon," a surface-treated "Teflon" plate coated with a gelatin film and a methacrylic resin plate. On the whole, it can be perceived that gelatin serves to supress the tendency of the resistance to increase during prolonged exposure, and there exist some distinct differences in intersurface properties among base plates used. When the water-LiCl solution with no binder was used, the element, whose base plate was a surface-treated "Teflon" plate covered with a gelatin film, had no adaptability as shown in Fig. 9, but this tendency was not observed in the solution which contained gelatin as a binder. From this fact, it can be assumed that the intersurface property of the base plate plays a very important role on stabilizing the performance of such an element as mentioned here. In fact, no condition favorable to such a lyophobic material as methacrylic resin was found until a gelatin-PVA mixture or a gelatin-CMC was employed as a binder. Particularly, the element, No. 19, shows a very slight shift in indication during the test, whose result is shown in the lowest row of Fig. 11. Figure 12 shows the surface pattern of the element made during the exposure from ordinary humidities to the

FIG. 10. Behavior of a sensitive film made of a water-LiCl solution on a methacrylic resin plate in the same course as shown in Figs. 6 and 7.

b-1: normal state
b-2: moistened state
b-4: recovered state

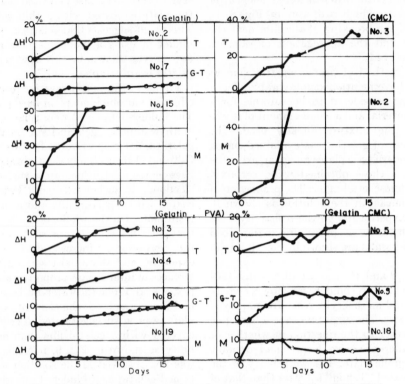

FIG. 11. Short-period aging effect of sensors, where gelatin, CMC, PVA-gelatine and PVA-CMC are used as binders respectively.

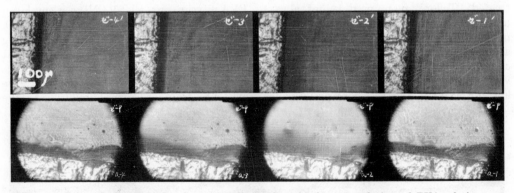

FIG. 12. Behavior of two kinds of sensitive films, whose binders are gelatin and PVA-gelatin, on a methacrylic resin plate in the same course as shown in Figs. 6 and 7.

Upper photograph: gelatin
Lower photograph: gelatin and PVA
1′ and a-1: normal state
2′ and a-2: moistened state
4′ and a-4: recovered state

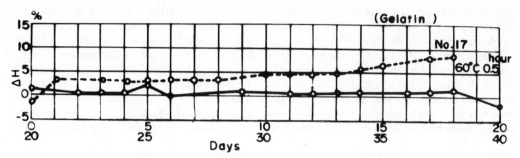

FIG. 13. Effect of heat treatment (60°C, 0.5 hour) on a short-period aging effect. Gelatin is added to the PVA solution as a binder.

highest. No change in surface pattern is observed.

Next, four elements fabricated in the same manner were heated to 60 to 70°C in an electric furnace in order to examine the effect of heat treatment on the performance of these elements. They were exposed to the atmosphere for 0.5, 1.0 and 3.5 hours respectively. Then, the furnace was turned off and the elements were cooled to room temperature. The heat treatment resulted in the increase in resistance. One of the results is shown in Fig. 13. The other elements showed a shift of 5 per cent RH after 20 days. The aging effect of the heat-treated element seems to be larger than that of the ordinary element as shown in the curve, No. 19, in Fig. 11. The shift of the ordinary element which was concurrently compared with element No. 17, shown in Fig. 13, was below 4 per cent RH after 38 days. The resistance of the element made of the PVA solution is generally unchangeable under ordinary humidities, but tends to increase abruptly under higher humidities above 95 per cent RH. In this case, heat treatment results in a significant increase in resistance. This treatment does not serve to improve storage stability remarkably. Therefore, it is noticeable that the addition of a small amount of gelatin to the ordinary solution considerably serves to reduce the magnitude of the shift in indication of the sensor and to secure storage stability.

Figure 14 shows a series of experimental results obtained by the use of elements whose sensitive films contain a quantity of graphite particles of about 2μ in diameter. In this case, all calibrations were made immediately after the formation of a sensitive film on the base

plate. Dashed lines shown in this Figure show that the film is very thick. Ordinarily, the sensitive film is produced by dipping the substrate in the solution and raising it at the rate of 1 mm/sec. PVA and gelatin (Ge) are added to the solution as binding chemicals. The significant difference in intersurface property of materials used as base plates is perceived again (see the results obtained by use of colloidal graphite solutions, Ga 79 and Ga 94, with no binder such as PVA and Ge). On the whole, it is perceived that the addition of gelatin is effective. The binding chemicals in the solution, Ga 79, are PVA and PVAc. The stability of a thin film made of the Ga 79 solution on a methacrylic resin plate is very good. On the other hand, the stability of the element containing gelatin as a binder is worse. This might be due to the handling of the element: it was calibrated without being dried in a desiccator after it was made. As to the Ga 94 group, the resistance and the sensitivity of these elements are higher than those of the above-mentioned elements. Consequently, they are not intended for practical use.

The resistance-humidity characteristic of an element made by using the colloidal graphite solution of Ga 79 with a small amount of gelatin is shown in Fig. 15. The increase in the ratio of the graphite solution to water results in the linear relationship between the resistance of the element and the relative humidity of its environment. This suggests that a resistor might be inserted in parallel with the sensitive element, particularly in the region of lower humidities. The surface pattern is shown in Fig. 16.

In Table 2 a summary of these experimental results is shown. The results of elements with thin films are shown in the left-hand side of columns 2 and 3, and those of elements with thick films, in the right-hand side.

The letters A, B, C and D shown in this Table correspond to curves shown in Fig. 17. Curve A refers to the element whose shift in indication does not vary by more than ±5 per cent RH from the value obtained at the same conditions in the initial calibration, when it is kept at humidities above 95 per cent RH. Curve B refers to the element whose resistances show gradual increase with time during the long exposure to air of humidities above 95 per cent RH. Curve C indicates the element whose resistance changes largely and rapidly within a few days at the beginning of the exposure and then approaches to its own stable value. Curve D is often seen using the U.S.

TABLE 2. CLASSIFICATION OF EXPERIMENTAL RESULTS

Composition (Base)					Treated Teflon (1)	Methacrylic resin (2)	Gelatin Film (1)	Gelatin Film (2)	Styrol
W	S				A			C	B
"	"	N			A	C			
"	"	"	CMC		C	D			
"	"	"	Ge		C	C	C		
"	"	"	Ge	PVA	B	C A	B		
"	"	"	Ge	CMC	C	C	C		
"	"	"	Ga29			B C	C		
"	"	"	"	PVA	C	B			
"	"	"	"	Ge		B C	C		
"	"	"	Ga79			C A			
"	"	"	"	PVA		C			
"	"	"	"	Ge	A	A A			
"	"	"	Ga94			B B			
"	"	"	"	PVA	D	B			
"	"	"	"	Ge	B	A			

W = water
S = LiCl
N = surface active agent ("Nonion" 210)
CMC = carboxylmethylcellulose
Ge = gelatin
PVA = polyvinyl alcohol
Ga = colloidal graphite ("Hitasol" 29, 79 and 94)

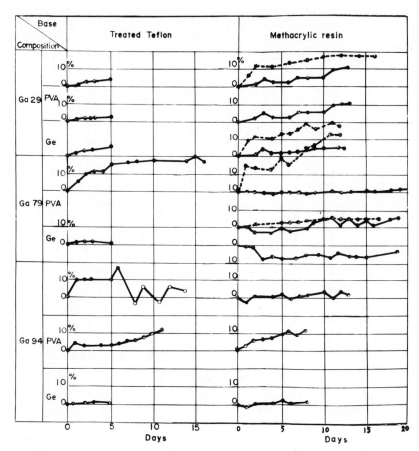

FIG. 14. Short-period aging effect of sensors, where colloidal solutions, Ga 29, Ga 79, and Ga 94, are added to the water-LiCl solution, and PVA and Ge (gelatin) to the above mixture.

element employed in radiosonde observation. In this case, the resistance of the element does not remarkably change during the first few days at the beginning of the exposure, but after that time it changes rapidly and does not settle down to a stable value.

From Table 2, it can easily be seen that the addition of a small amount of gelatin to the normal solution is effective for the prevention of the aging effect, and that the intersurface property of materials used as the base plate plays an important role. That is to say, the short-period aging effect observed in the high humidity region above 95 per cent RH may be due to both the aggregation of salt embedded in a sensitive film and the breaking of the film. Both of them will be caused by the large amount of absorbed water and the lowering of

adhesive power between the film and the base plate. Judging from the fact that the addition of gelatin to the normal solution serves to reduce the magnitude of the shift in indication, it can be concluded that some properties which an "ampholytoid" such as gelatin possesses generally play an important role. In fact, it might be said that this was verified by employing extraneous materials as base plates.

SUMMARY AND CONCLUSIONS

The aging effect raises a question in the use of an electrolytic hygrometer for the measurement of humidity in the air. This effect may be classified in two ways: long-period and short-period. In a laboratory study of the

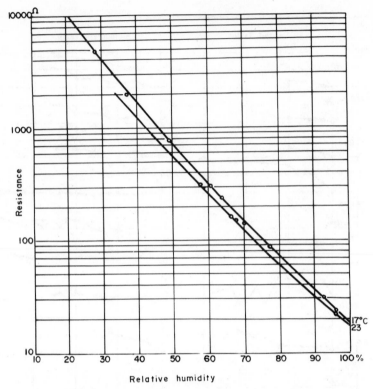

Fig. 15. Resistance-humidity characteristic of an improved sensor at temperatures of 17 and 23°C.

short-period aging effect, the improved element showed a slight shift in indication during long storage at high humidity. The sensitive film of this element was made of a gelatin-PVA mixture and fabricated on a methacrylic resin base plate.

In the ordinary element, the lowering of the adhesion of the sensitive film to the base plate at high humidities is its Achilles' heel. This unfavorable behavior causes the aggregation

of absorbent embedded in the film, and the electrical resistance of the element changes abruptly and becomes larger and larger. A laboratory study was performed in order to find a method to reduce this effect. Before searching for the physical processes of this phenomenon, it was necessary to obtain some information on the behavior of the element under conditions of ordinary temperature and high humidities. The behavior was

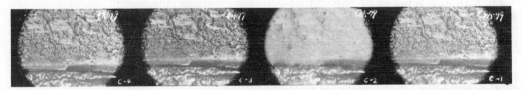

Fig. 16. Behavior of a sensitive film made of a solution consisting of water, LiCl and colloidal graphite solution ("Hitasol" Ga-79, Hitachi Mfg. Co.) on a methacrylic resin plate in the same course as shown in Figs. 6 and 7.

c-1: normal state
c-2: moistened state
c-4: recovered state

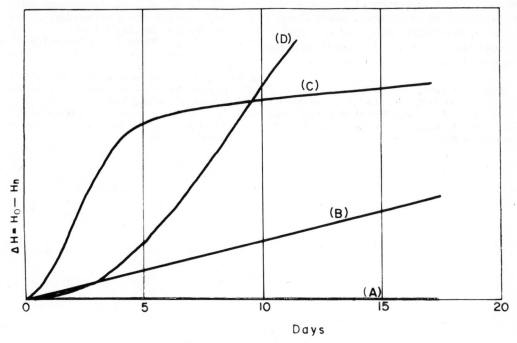

Fig. 17. Classification of the short-period aging effect.

phenomenologically investigated through microscopic observation and the measurement of the electrical resistivity of the surface of the element.

Our results can be summarized as follows:

(1) If only the surface of the base plate is lyophilic and it is covered uniformly with active centers absorbing moisture, the element will be of practical use, because no aggregation will be found. In this case, it should be determined whether the so-called hysteresis effect appears or not.

(2) It is important to consider the affinity between the solution and the materials used as base plates and to select a suitable chemical binding them. For example, PVA and PVA-PVAc mixtures are suitable as binders in using methacrylic resin as a base plate. In our experiments, the addition of a small amount of gelatin to the normal solution as a binder succeeded to some extent in protecting the element from aging at the higher humidities.

(3) Heat treatment results in an increase in electrical resistance. This treatment does not remarkably prevent the aging effect.

(4) The addition of a colloidal graphite solution to the normal solution, for example Ga 79, serves to improve the resistance-humidity characteristic of the element. In this case the addition of gelatin does not spoil the performance of the element.

On the whole, our laboratory study led to the conclusion that the short-period aging effect of the element can be reduced to some extent by using the PVA-gelatin mixture as a binder and a methacrylic resin plate as a base. In particular, gelatin acts effectively when the element is left alone in the environment at higher humidities for a long time. Probably, this may be due to the "ampholytoid" nature of gelatin.

In order to increase our information on the method of preventing the aging effect, it is necessary to examine the ζ potential of gelatin in the mixture and the surface potential of the sensitive film, taking physical and chemical variables into consideration, e.g., the magnitude of absorbed water, the pH of the wet film, the intersurface tension of materials employed, etc.

Furthermore, it would be desirable to examine other properties of the improved element such as resistance-humidity characteristics, polarization effect and response at temperatures below 0°C, because these areas were not stressed in these experiments.

Acknowledgments. We wish to express our appreciation to Mr. C. Ishii, chief of our division, for his encouragement extended in executing this work and to Mr. H. Ikegami for his earnest assistance in drawing the figures.

References

1. Dunmore, F. W., "An Electric Hygrometer and its Application to Radio Meteorography," *J. Res. Natl. Bur. Std.*, **20**, 723–744 (1938).
2. Jones, F. E., and Wexler, A., "A Barium Fluoride Film Hygrometer Element," *J. Geophys. Res.*, **65**, 2087–2095 (1960).
3. Jones, F. E., "A Review of Evaporated Thin Film Humidity Transducers," presented at the ISA 16th annual meeting, Sept. 11–15, 1961.
4. Kobayashi, J., "Investigations on Hygrometry," *Papers Meteorol. Geophys.*, *Tokyo*, **11**, 213–338 (1960).

26. A Study of the Accuracy of Dunmore Type Humidity Sensors*

G. O. HANDEGORD AND C. P. HEDLIN

Prairie Regional Station, Division of Building Research, National Research Council, Saskatoon, Saskatchewan

AND

F. N. TROFIMENKOFF

Department of Electrical Engineering, University of Saskatchewan, Saskatoon, Saskatchewan

ABSTRACT

This paper describes an investigation of some of the characteristics of commercially available Dunmore-type humidity sensors in the temperature range from 0 to 70° F, with particular reference to their application in research work where accuracies greater than those guaranteed by the manufacturer are required. A two-temperature recirculating-type atmosphere producer was used as a calibration standard in these studies.

Results indicate that such sensors have a potential accuracy ranging from ±0.1 per cent RH for low-range elements to ±0.5 per cent RH for high-range elements under short-term exposure to conditions within their prescribed measuring range. When exposed to a high relative humidity for 24 hours, a decrease in cell resistance was observed. Storage over desiccant for periods from four months to four years resulted in a shift in calibration at a rate less than one per cent per year for almost all sensors. Measurements on sensors that have been stored in the laboratory and used occasionally for up to fifteen years indicated substantial changes in calibration with time. Exposure of sensors to a limited number of atmospheric contaminants indicated that ammonia and sulfur dioxide could produce changes in calibration and that vapors of mercury, isooctane, iodine and calcium bromide solution had little detrimental effect on low range units.

It is concluded that with careful selection and careful recalibration, commercial sensors may be used for relative humidity measurements to accuracies substantially better than ±1.5 per cent RH, provided reasonable care is taken in their use. For precise measurements, calibration before and after use is necessary.

INTRODUCTION

The Dunmore-type of electric hygrometer has a number of distinct advantages as a humidity measuring device in research applications. It is of small size, does not substantially add to or remove moisture from the air, and is extremely sensitive to changes in relative humidity at normal temperatures. These factors have led to its increasing use in control and measurement applications in research studies of the Division of Building Research, National Research Council.

The sensitivity of commercially available sensors is much greater than that indicated by the accuracy tolerance guaranteed by the manufacturer. This suggests that under cer-

* This paper is a contribution from the Division of Building Research, National Research Council, and is published with the approval of the Director of the Division.

tain circumstances, commercial sensors might be used for more precise measurement of humidity after calibration to a closer tolerance than the ±1.5 per cent normally specified. With this possibility in view, investigation of the characteristics of commercial Dunmore sensors was initiated in 1958 upon completion of a precise calibration facility at the Prairie Regional Station of the Division of Building Research. Preliminary calibration work was carried out by the third author as part of his M.Sc. thesis program at the University of Saskatchewan in 1959, and it formed the basis for a continuing program of investigation. This paper summarizes the results of this work up to the present time.

FIG. 1. Two-temperature recirculating-type atmosphere producer.

CALIBRATION APPARATUS

The two-temperature recirculating type atmosphere producer used as a calibration standard in this study has been described in detail in the literature.[1] A photograph of the unit is shown in Fig. 1 and a schematic diagram illustrating the various components, in Fig. 2. The present form of the apparatus differs slightly from the original in that the calibration chamber and heat exchanger are both immersed in a constant temperature bath in the same way as the saturator section. This provides for some improvement in temperature control and distribution in the high temperature side over that provided by the original apparatus.

The basic principle of operation of the unit involves the recirculation of moist air in a closed system over a flat water surface in a saturator at one temperature, and heating of the airstream to the higher temperature of a calibration chamber. By recirculation and cooling to the temperature of the water

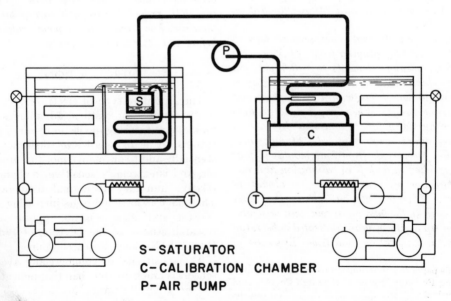

S – SATURATOR
C – CALIBRATION CHAMBER
P – AIR PUMP

FIG. 2. Schematic diagram of two-temperature recirculating-type atmosphere producer.

surface, the moist air is brought to an equilibrium condition with this surface, and its saturated condition is determined by the temperature and total pressure conditions in the saturator. Reheating of the airstream is then used to bring its relative humidity to the desired value; measurement of the temperature and total pressure in the calibration chamber enables calculation of the resultant moist air conditions.

In practice, it is not desirable to operate the unit as a completely closed system because of pressure changes resulting from adjustments in temperature. A small connection to the ambient atmosphere is therefore incorporated at the outlet of the diaphragm pump. The error introduced through this arrangement, combined with those resulting from errors in temperature variation and measurement, have been discussed in a previous paper.[1] The calculated maximum errors as presented in this paper are reproduced in Table 1.

TABLE 1. MAXIMUM UNCERTAINTY IN RELATIVE HUMIDITY EXPRESSED IN PER CENT RH

Temperature (°F)	RH (%)				
	10	25	50	75	100
90	0.03	0.06	0.14	—	—
70	0.03	0.06	0.14	0.20	0.29
50	0.04	0.08	0.14	0.21	0.29
30	0.06	0.11	0.18	0.25	0.33
10	—	0.17	0.24	0.34	0.40

The sensors to be calibrated are placed in the calibration chamber on a mounting strip cantilevered from the chamber cover. The mounting strip extends down the length of the chamber and can accommodate as many as twenty sensors. The standard procedure for calibrating the sensors is to record their resistance with a recording microammeter as the saturator temperature is increased and then decreased in small steps. The use of a recording instrument enables the observer to determine more easily when sensor equilibrium is established. In most calibrations, the sensors are preconditioned in the calibration chamber for up to 24 hours, with the actual calibration period involving an additional 8 to 16 hours.

PRELIMINARY INVESTIGATION

A number of commercial Dunmore sensors had been in use for control and measurement applications at the laboratory for many years before the atmosphere producer became available. These sensors had been stored in unsealed containers in a laboratory environment with air conditions ranging from 70°F and 5 per cent RH to 80°F and 50 per cent RH, with no particular precautions taken to avoid exposure to contaminants. It was conceivable that some of them had been exposed to high humidity or condensation in use.

Calibration of a total of forty-one sensors, four to eleven years in age and having initial humidity ranges from 7 to 90 per cent RH, indicated that substantial shifts from the manufacturer's calibration had occurred for some of the sensors. The midrange relative humidity (that corresponding to a sensor resistance of 1.0 MΩ) was determined for each sensor. The difference between this value and the initial value provided by the manufacturer was used to determine the yearly shift in midrange relative humidity. The relationship between these values and the original midrange relative humidity of the sensors is shown in Fig. 3.

It may be noted that the largest shift in calibration generally was experienced by sensors having a low initial humidity range. It is also significant that only nine of the forty-one sensors exhibited a shift of over 1.5 per cent per year, and that almost all of these were the oldest and most likely to have experienced contamination or damage.

SHORT-TERM ACCURACY

Most of the sensors involved in this initial work, including some that had undergone a large shift in range, exhibited a reproducibility of better than ±0.5 per cent RH during calibration. Thirty-four of these sensors, together with seventy-seven new ones, were calibrated in the atmosphere producer in 1960. The operating range of each sensor was traversed by increasing the humidity in steps and observing the equilibrium sensor resistance after each change until the top of the range was reached. A similar procedure was then followed for conditions of decreasing humidity,

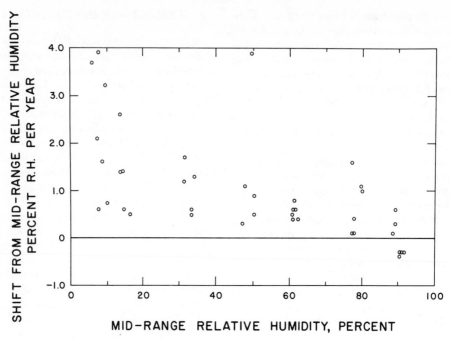

FIG. 3. Shift in midrange relative humidity of sensors stored under general laboratory conditions.

each calibration loop consisting of about ten observations. From one to four sets of observations were obtained for each group of sensors. These calibration runs involved test periods of a minimum of three and a maximum of seven days, during which the sensors remained in a clean environment at a humidity within their operating range. On the basis of these data, the mean midrange relative humidity was determined for each sensor and the maximum deviation from this value for any individual calibration was determined. These maximum deviations are plotted for all one hundred and eleven sensors against average midrange relative humidity in Fig. 4. Sensors that had previously shifted to higher ranges are indicated by the solid circles.

The average maximum deviations for each of four humidity ranges are shown in Table 2, together with the total number of sensors and the number showing deviations greater than the average. It would appear that with careful selection, most commercial sensors could be used for measurements to accuracies better than ± 0.5 per cent, perhaps to ± 0.1 per cent in the case of low-humidity sensors.

A study of saturated salt solutions,[2] in which sensors of all ranges were recalibrated after exposure in their operating range for periods up to two weeks, confirmed that a reproducibility of ± 0.5 per cent could be expected under such conditions.

TABLE 2. DEVIATION IN MIDRANGE RELATIVE HUMIDITY OF SENSORS UNDER SHORT-TERM EXPOSURE TO NORMAL OPERATING CONDITIONS

Humidity range, %	0–25	25–50	50–75	75–100
Mean maximum deviation, %	± 0.1	± 0.2	± 0.4	± 0.4
Total number of sensors	38	22	21	30
Sensors showing deviation greater than mean	8	5	7	4

STORAGE OF SENSORS OVER DESICCANT

It is reasonable to assume that the most ideal storage conditions would be those in which the sensor is held in an atmosphere having a relative humidity consistent with its measuring range. This presents many difficulties in practice, however, and one of the simplest methods of assuring constancy of conditions is by storage over mineral desiccants such as silica gel. This practice is followed by at least one manufacturer and was adopted at the Prairie Regional Station, National Research Council, for the storage of Dunmore sensors in 1959.

An indication of the drift in the calibration of sensors stored over silica gel was obtained from tests on a group of sensors obtained in 1959. These sensors were calibrated in the atmosphere producer when received and recalibrated after two years of storage and occasional use. The results indicated a shift that exceeded 1 per cent RH for approximately one-half of the sensors. Subsequent recalibration of these and other sensors involving storage over silica gel for periods ranging from four months to four years have provided the results shown in Fig. 5. In this Figure the relationship between the shift in midrange value per year and the final midrange relative humidity for a total of seventy-nine sensors is shown. Although some scatter of points is apparent, only three of the sensors exhibited a shift in midrange humidity of more than 1 per cent per year. The pattern of experimental points further suggests that shifts tend to be positive for low-range elements and negative for those of high humidity range, the crossover occurring at approximately 60 per cent RH.

EXPOSURE TO HIGH HUMIDITY AND CONDENSATION

The application of Dunmore sensors to the measurement of humidity may involve the risk of short-term exposure to high humidity or condensation under certain circumstances. In order to evaluate the possible effects of high humidity exposure, three calibrated sensors in each of six humidity ranges from 9 to 60 per cent RH were exposed in the calibration chamber of the atmosphere producer to a relative humidity of 98.5 per cent at 70°F for 24 hours. The sensors were then removed, stored in containers over silica gel for approximately two weeks, and recalibrated. The initial and final midrange relative humidity for each of the sensors is listed in Table 3, with the shift in midrange humidity tabulated in

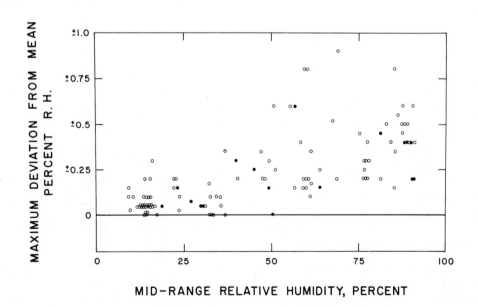

Fig. 4. Maximum deviation of midrange relative humidity from mean value for short-term exposure in normal humidity range.

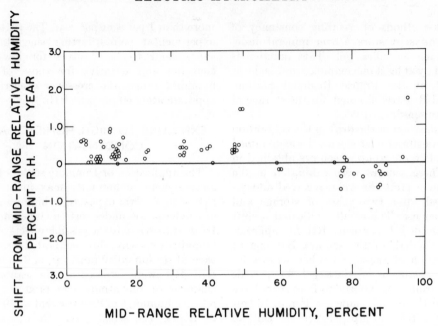

Fig. 5. Shift in midrange relative humidity of sensors stored over desiccant.

TABLE 3. EFFECT OF EXPOSURE TO HIGH HUMIDITY ON DUNMORE SENSORS AT 70°F

| Sensor | Midrange Relative Humidity | | Shift (% RH) |
	Before Exposure	After Exposure	
1	9.0	7.2	−1.8
2	9.2	5.3	−3.9
3	9.1	6.4	−2.7
4	14.6	11.5	−3.1
5	14.5	13.0	−1.5
6	14.8	13.0	−1.8
7	22.5	22.5	0
8	22.4	13.1	−9.3
9	22.9	17.0	−5.9
10	33.2	19.0	−14.2
11	32.0	12.0	−20.0
12	32.5	15.6	−16.9
13	54.4	50.5	−3.9
14	52.6	45.5	−7.1
15	52.0	43.4	−8.6
16	60.0	56.3	−3.7
17	60.3	57.3	−3.0
18	59.5	58.5	−1.0

the last column. In all cases but one a negative shift representing a reduction in sensor resistance was observed, the largest change occurring in sensors of the 30 per cent RH range.

Some information as to the effect of condensation on another group of sensors in the 65 to 80 per cent range was obtained inadvertently during their recalibration. A malfunction of the calibration chamber temperature control system resulted in a drop in temperature to a level below the dew point for a short period of time. When control was reestablished the sensors were calibrated once more and the shift in midrange relative humidity was determined. The results are presented in Table 4 in a similar way to Table 3. All the sensors except sensor No. 24 showed a shift in midrange relative humidity similar

TABLE 4. EFFECT OF CONDENSATION ON DUNMORE SENSORS

| Sensor | Midrange Relative Humidity | | Shift (% RH) |
	Before Exposure	After Exposure	
19	64.0	61.8	−2.2
20	64.0	61.2	−2.8
21	65.3	61.7	−3.6
22	65.3	59.0	−6.3
23	65.7	61.8	−3.9
24	69.2	69.7	+0.5
25	74.7	69.8	−4.9
26	77.5	73.5	−4.0
27	78.8	73.8	−5.0
28	77.5	72.0	−5.5
29	77.5	73.5	−4.0

in magnitude and sign to that of comparable sensors exposed to high humidity. Sensor No. 24 may not have experienced as severe condensation as the others, and its change in midrange humidity may have resulted from other causes.

EXPOSURE TO CONTAMINANTS

A number of air contaminants are listed by sensor manufacturers as affecting their calibration. No exhaustive tests were undertaken to evaluate the effect of contaminants, but some information was obtained for a few substances to which sensors might be exposed when used at Saskatoon. The sensors used were those having a nominal midrange relative humidity of 15, 25 and 60 per cent. They were calibrated, placed for a period of time in a sealed vessel containing the contaminant, and subsequently recalibrated. In all cases except those involving a salt solution as a contaminant, moist silica gel or a saturated solution of calcium bromide was used in the sealed vessel to maintain the relative humidity within the 15 to 25 per cent range. A number of sensors were also stored in sealed containers over silica gel and calcium bromide solution without

TABLE 5. EFFECT OF SOME CONTAMINANTS ON DUNMORE SENSORS

Contaminant	Concentration (% by vol)	Temperature (°F)	Cell No.	Nominal Midrange RH (%)	Exposure Time (days)	Shift in Midrange RH at 70°F (%)
Sulfur dioxide	2	70–75	38	15	20	4.1
	2	70–75	39	15	10	2.5
	2	70–75	40	15	5	1.6
	0.1	70–75	32†	15	30	1.7
	0.1*	70–75	35†	15	81	4.7
	0.1	70–75	41	60	30	−1.4
	0.1*	70–75	42	60	81	−1.1
Ammonia	4.5	70–75	43	15	14	5.6
	4.5	70–75	44	15	9	3.8
	4.5	70–75	45	15	5	2.1
	0.5	70–75	37†	15	30	5.1
	0.5	70–75	34†	15	81	3.0
	0.5	70–75	46	60	81	2.3
	0.5	70–75	47	60	30	1.9
Mercury	Equilibrium	70–75	30	15	96	0.3
		70–75	31	15	61	0.1
		70–75	32	15	30	−0.2
Isooctane	Equilibrium	70–75	33	15	96	0.1
		70–75	34	15	61	−0.2
		70–75	35	15	30	−0.1
Iodine	Equilibrium	70–75	36	15	96	−0.1
		70–75	37	15	30	+0.1
Calcium bromide	Saturated	70–75	48	15	67	0.0
	solution of	70–75	49	15	96	0.0
	the salt	70–75	4	15	34	0.0
Silica gel	17% RH	70–75	50	15	67	0.0
		70–75	51	15	96	0.3
		70–75	52	15	34	0.2
	Dry	70–75	53	15	200	−0.1
Antimony trichloride	Saturated solution	85	54	25	0.7	2.5
		85	55	25	0.7	5.5
		85	56	25	0.7	6
Calcium chloride	Saturated solution	85	57	15	5	0.8
		85	58	25	0.7	0.3

* SO_2 leaked out of the container and none remained at the end of the 81-day period.
† Cells were used earlier in investigations with mercury, isooctane or iodine.

any contaminants in order to provide a control. The results of those tests and those with contaminants are presented in Table 5, listing the concentration of contaminants, temperature, humidity, duration of test, and resultant shift in midrange relative humidity.

Exposure to sulfur dioxide resulted in an upward shift in calibration for sensors of the 15 per cent RH range and a downward shift for those of the 60 per cent range. Significant upward shifts were measured for sensors of both ranges exposed to ammonia, and for sensors of the 25 per cent RH range exposed to a saturated solution of antimony trichloride. Observation of the resistance of sensors over antimony trichloride and calcium chloride during exposure indicated a decreasing sensor resistance with time (negative shift in midrange value), but on subsequent recalibration the opposite shift in midrange relative humidity was observed (Table 5). For those sensors exposed to antimony trichloride, the response time had increased to the extent that several hours' exposure to constant humidity at room temperature was not sufficient for them to reach equilibrium.

Relatively small shifts in midrange relative humidity were observed for those cells exposed to iodine and isooctane. No independent measurement of contaminant concentration was made, the concentrations listed were those corresponding to the vapor pressure at the temperature used. Calcium bromide solution was used, however, to maintain the relative humidity in the vessel, and it may have lowered the concentration of the contaminants.

CONCLUSIONS

The results presented in this paper indicate that commercial sensors of the Dunmore type have a potential accuracy substantially better than the normally specified tolerance of ± 1.5 per cent RH. The accuracy to which they may be used is dependent on the precision of the calibration facilities available to the user and on the nature and duration of the conditions to which the sensors are exposed.

It is demonstrated that accuracies in relative humidity from ± 0.1 to ± 0.4 per cent may be realized during short-term exposure of sensors to atmospheres within their operating range. Under longer periods of similar exposure, accuracies of ± 0.5 per cent are possible.

Storage of sensors in a dry atmosphere appears to result in a shift in calibration of less than 1 per cent per year, the change being toward a higher humidity range for low-range sensors and to a lower range for high-range sensors. The simplicity of this method of storage and the slow rate of shift that occurs suggest a means for maintaining an inventory of individually calibrated sensors for precise measurement. With calibration facilities of suitable accuracy available and a program of periodic recalibration, it is practical for sensors to be made available for laboratory measurement with an accuracy of ± 0.5 per cent. Attainment of this precision in measurement would require assurances that the sensor would be handled carefully and not exposed to contaminants, high humidity, or condensation. In special cases, accuracies in measurement to ± 0.1 per cent RH might be realized through calibration before and after use.

References

1. Till, C. E., and Handegord, G. O., "Proposed Humidity Standard," *Trans. ASHRAE*, **66**, 288–308 (1960).
2. Hedlin, C. P., and Trofimenkoff, F. N., "Relative Humidities over Saturated Solutions of Nine Salts in the Temperature Range from 0 to 90°F," Humidity and Moisture, Vol 3, New York, Reinhold Publishing Corp., 1964.

27. A Resistance-humidity Relationship for Sensors of the Dunmore Type*

C. P. Hedlin

Prairie Regional Station, Division of Building Research, National Research Council, Saskatoon, Canada

ABSTRACT

Conventional methods of graphical presentation of resistance-humidity characteristics for commercial sensors of the Dunmore type have some shortcomings in regard to the interpolation of experimental observations. This paper suggests a method by which calibration data can be represented by a linear relationship which is believed to simplify greatly both the construction of calibration curves and the application of these data in practice.

From experiments with commercially available sensors it was found that if sensor conductance is plotted against relative humidity on logarithmic coordinates, the resulting isotherm is nearly linear. With this system, linear interpolation between established isotherms, along lines of fixed conductance, yields accurate temperature corrections over the temperature range from 0 to 70° F where most of the studies were conducted. It permits a substantial reduction in the number of points required for accurate calibration of an individual sensor.

From a relationship similar to that mentioned above an equation is developed that describes the electrical conductance of this type of sensor in terms of relative humidity and temperature using four empirical cell constants.

* This paper is a contribution from the Division of Building Research, National Research Council, and is published with the approval of the Director of the Division.

INTRODUCTION

The Dunmore-type humidity sensor consists basically of a substrate supporting a thin film of hygroscopic material and a pair of electrodes. The electrical resistance of the hygroscopic film varies greatly in response to changes in temperature and humidity. In general, therefore, it is necessary to find the relationship that exists between these variables by calibrating such a sensor before it can be used.

Calibration data (for these sensors) are usually presented as isotherms plotted on graphs that have resistance-relative humidity or current-relative humidity coordinates. The manufacturer supplies the same graph for all sensors of a given humidity range, with a correction value for each calibrated sensor. These graphs are suitable for normal use when the precision specified by the manufacturer (usually not better than ± 1.5 per cent RH) is adequate. It has been found, however, that better precision is attainable with these sensors if special care is taken in their calibration and use. A single calibration point cannot completely define the resistance-temperature-humidity relationship, and when good precision is required, it is necessary to calibrate the sensors individually to account for the small deviations from the average, which some of them exhibit. To make precise calibration practical, it is important to keep the number

273

of observations as small as possible and to present the results in a convenient form.

In this paper, a graphical method of presenting the data is discussed and equations showing the relationship between resistance, temperature, and humidity are presented.

GRAPHICAL REPRESENTATION

If the isotherms are plotted on logarithmic coordinates using the sensor conductance (or resistance) and the relative humidity as parameters, the resulting relationship is nearly linear in most cases over a resistance range of about 2 decades. Within this range, low- and high-range sensors display some curvature; as the range is extended, the departure from a straight line will increase significantly. A desirable characteristic of this method of plotting is that a fairly accurate isotherm can be found with only two points.

In order to aid the plotting of the data special graph paper has been used. Two scales are provided on the ordinate: a logarithmic scale covers a little more than two decades of conductance, and a current scale is matched to it. (The latter corresponds to the micro-ampere scale used on many measuring instru-

ments, and the current-conductance relationship will vary somewhat between instruments.) A logarithmic scale is provided on the abscissa and the relative humidity is plotted on it.

A number of sensors have been calibrated in a two-temperature recirculating atmosphere producer[1] at the Prairie Regional Station. Some 70°F isotherms plotted on these coordinates are shown in Fig. 1; the abscissa covers a 10 to 1 range. Since the isotherms in the high humidity range are too steep when plotted on this paper, a 2 to 1 range is more suitable for sensors in the region above 40 per cent RH (Fig. 4).

When the observed temperature is different from the established isotherms, it is necessary to interpolate. With both conventional plots and the one described here, it is convenient to do this by linear proportion along the appropriate line of fixed conductance. If the corresponding relationship between temperature and humidity is not linear, an error will occur whose size depends on the separation of the isotherms and the degree of nonlinearity. The dependability of this procedure for conventional and logarithmic plots is illustrated in Fig. 2, where data have been plotted for

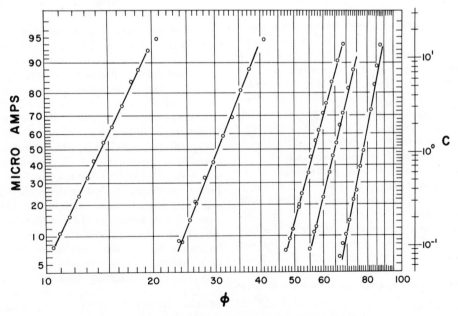

FIG. 1. Plot of 70°F isotherms on logarithmic coordinates.

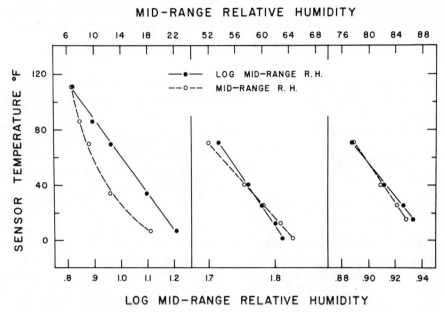

Fɪɢ. 2. Plots of midrange relative humidity, on linear and logarithmic coordinates, *vs* sensor temperature.

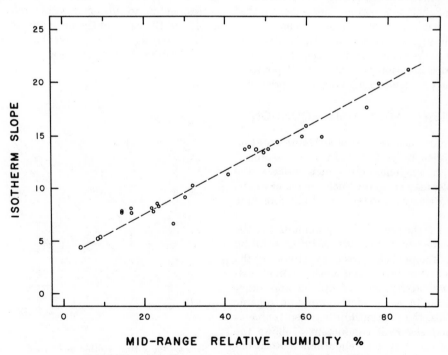

Fɪɢ. 3. Plot of isotherm slopes *vs* midrange relative humidity.

several sensors. These graphs suggest that for limited ranges of temperature, the linear proportion interpolation is suitable for both methods of plotting. In this and all other cases in this paper the relative humidity for temperatures below 32°F is based on the vapor pressure over subcooled water rather than ice.[2]

This method of plotting data provides a basis for the systematic comparison of sensors. For example, cell-to-cell variation is illustrated in Fig. 3, where the slopes

$$\left(\frac{\partial \log C}{\partial \log \phi}\right)_T \qquad (1)$$

of a number of 70°F isotherms have been plotted against their midrange (1.0 μ mho) relative humidities. Generally, the slopes of sensors in the same humidity range are nearly equal and the variation with midrange relative humidity follows a definite pattern. In some cases, sensors have shifted out of their original ranges. Some of these have followed the trend line and, as far as the slope is concerned, can legitimately be identified with the sensors in the region to which they have moved. Others have moved out of their original ranges and conform neither to their original slopes nor to those of their new region. This suggests that although it is probable that sensor characteristics will agree closely with standard calibration curves, there is no guarantee that this will be so, and calibration at a number of points is necessary to ensure a high degree of precision.

REPRESENTATION WITH EQUATIONS

For most purposes, graphical representation is likely to be preferred. In some instances, however, an equation which relates the variables may be useful. Such equations can be formulated by an extension of the foregoing analysis.

Because the present discussion falls into the same category, it may be useful to mention some of the published results of studies of the effect of temperature and moisture on electrical conductivity, in hydrophilic and other materials. In much of the work on organic materials, the relationship between temperature and electrical conductance follows the form of the Arrhenius equation.[3-5] Relationships between moisture content and electrical conductivity have been proposed for hygroscopic, fibrous materials[6] and for several inorganic materials including glass and porcelain.[7] As a result of the investigation reported in Ref. 7

$$\log (i/i_0) = \alpha m \qquad (2)$$

was found to relate the current flow i and moisture content m. Work of this type has been done with chromium films[8] and anodized aluminum.[9] One of the most extensively investigated organic materials is wood, much work having been done to determine the relationship between moisture content and electrical conductivity.[10]

When isotherms are plotted on logarithmic coordinates, it is apparent that they are not parallel and, if extrapolated, will intersect one another (Fig. 4). It is not suggested that the extrapolated isotherms constitute a valid representation of the conductance-humidity relationships in the conductance region above 10 micromhos. The extrapolation is done only for purposes of the analysis. Although it is not possible to locate the intersection points very precisely, it seems practical to assume that all the isotherms for a given sensor intersect at the same point. The value of the abscissa corresponding to this point will be referred to as A, and the value of the ordinate, as C_0.

The analysis is more conveniently carried out if the difference, $\log A - \log \phi$ or $\log (A/\phi)$,

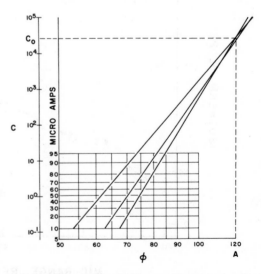

FIG. 4. Plot of three isotherms of a sensor showing the region at which they intersect one another.

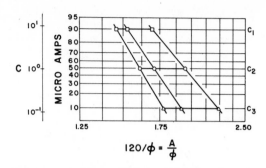

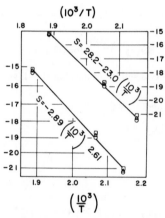

Fig. 5. (a). Plot of the same isotherms shown in Fig. 4, using $120/\phi$ instead of ϕ. Coordinates are logarithmic.

(b) Plot of isotherm slopes *vs* $10^3/T$ using logarithmic coordinates and linear coordinates.

is used as the coordinate instead of $\log \phi$ [Fig. 5(a)]. The isotherm equation is

$$\log C = \log C_0 + S \log (A/\phi)$$

or

$$\log \frac{C}{C_0} = S \log (A/\phi) \qquad (3)$$

and

$$S = \frac{\log (C/C_0)}{\log (A/\phi)} \qquad (4)$$

The isotherm slope S is a function of the temperature. In Fig. 5(b) the slope is plotted against the reciprocal of the absolute temperature, using two different coordinate systems. In one case logarithmic coordinates are used, in the other, linear coordinates.

In the first instance, the slope-intercept equation is

$$\log S = \log K + a \log (1/T) \qquad (5)$$

or

$$S = K(1/T)^a \qquad (6)$$

The final equation is

$$\log C/C_0 = K(1/T)^a \log (A/\phi) \qquad (7)$$

In the second case the slope intercept equation is

$$S = D + (b/T) \qquad (8)$$

The final equation is

$$\log (C/C_0) = (D + (b/T)) \log (A/\phi) \qquad (9)$$

These equations each contain four unknown constants. Consequently, at least four experimental points are required for complete calibration of a sensor, unless it can be shown that the constants are not all independent of one another, or that one or more can be evaluated from fundamental considerations.

In Figs. 6 and 7 the experimental values corresponding to Eqs. (5) and (6) are plotted for two of the sensors. Values of A and a are found by graphical means, and the abscissa values are calculated. The values of A are found to vary from just over 100 for high-range sensors to values exceeding 1000 for low-range sensors.

CONCLUSION

In developing the plotting technique and the equations, it was assumed that linear isotherms result from a logarithmic plot of sensor conductance and relative humidity. For sensors operating in the region below 80 per cent RH, this is generally correct to better than 0.5 per cent RH over a range of about two decades of conductance. For sensors in a higher humidity range, a significant amount of curvature exists, with the result that the calibration data may depart by as much as 1.5 per cent RH from the straight line of best fit. Part of this deviation will be caused by scatter of points due to hysteresis. Similarly, in applying temperature corrections, an error will result if the relationship used is not linear. Three different functions of temperature have been used in this paper. All appear to fit the data with a degree of precision that is consistent with the precision of the calibration data. The apparent linearity of all the relation-

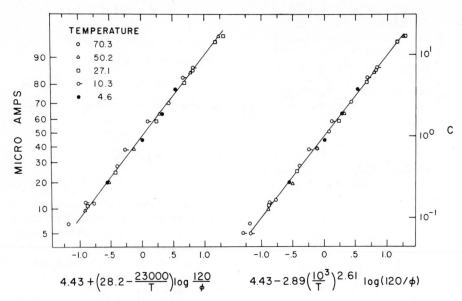

$$4.43 + \left(28.2 - \frac{23000}{T}\right)\log\frac{120}{\phi} \qquad 4.43 - 2.89\left(\frac{10^3}{T}\right)^{2.61}\log(120/\phi)$$

FIG. 6. Plots of the values of $\log C$ calculated using the two equations developed in Figs. 4 and 5. The equations are

$$\log C = 4.43 + (28.2 - 23000/T)\log(120/\phi)$$

and

$$\log C = 4.43 - 2.89(10^3/T)^{2.61}\log(120/\phi)$$

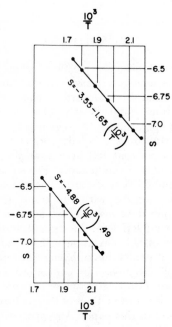

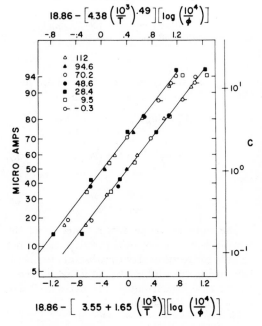

FIG. 7. (a) Plot of isotherm slopes vs $10^3/T$ on logarithmic and linear coordinates. The midrange relative humidity at 70°F for this sensor is 15 per cent.

(b) Plots of the two equations for this sensor.

ships is due in part to the fact that the range of temperatures covered is not large.

This method of plotting calibration data is useful when sensors are to be used for research and will therefore be recalibrated frequently. Because of their near linearity, a reliable isotherm can be established with two accurate calibration points. With two isotherms that differ by 30 or 40°F, linear interpolation between the isotherms and limited extrapolation beyond them can be expected to provide a good degree of precision in relating sensor conductance or resistance to relative humidity over the normal temperature range. With the information provided by two such isotherms, individual deviations of sensors from the average will be taken into account. In subsequent checks of the calibration, a single value will be sufficient to reestablish the conductance-humidity relationship unless a large shift has occurred, in which case a more complete recalibration will be required.

In developing an equation for a sensor, two well-spaced isotherms are required. The constants A and C can be found by locating their point of intersection. The slope equation can then be calculated to complete the sensor equation. If shifts in the calibration occur, a corresponding change must be made in the equation.

SYMBOLS

a = constant, dimensionless
A = constant, relative humidity
b = constant, °R
C = electrical conductance, micromhos
D = constant, dimensionless
K = constant, °R
p = vapor pressure at temperature t
p_s = vapor pressure at saturation at temperature t
T = temperature, °R (Rankine)
ϕ = relative humidity, p/p_s

References

1. Till, C. E., and Handegord, G. O., "Proposed Humidity Standard," *Trans. ASHRAE*, **66**, 288–308 (1960).
2. "International Critical Tables," Vol. 3, p. 211.
3. Reihl, N., "Relation between Electrical Conductivity and Energy Diffusion in Proteins," *Kolloid Z.*, **151**, 66–72 (1957); *C.A.*, **50**, 8292F.
4. Inokuchi, H., Kurada, H., and Akamatu, H., "The Electrical Conductivity of Organic Thin Films: Perylene, Coronene and Violanthene," *Bull. Chem. Soc. Japan*, **34**, 749–53 (1961); *C.A.*, **56**, 92i.
5. "Symposium on Electrical Conductivity in Organic Solids," New York, John Wiley & Sons, Inc., 1961.
6. Lehmann, J., "Dependence of Electric Conductivity of Hygroscopic Fibrous Materials on the Water Content," *Naturwissenschaften*, **45**, 35–36 (1958); *C.A.*, **52**, 9691b.
7. Kawasaki, K., "Variation of Surface Conduction Current of a Solid that Absorbs Water Vapor and the Phase Transition of the Adsorbed Layer," *Bull. Electrotech. Lab. Tokyo*, **19**, 825–32 (1955); *C.A.*, **50**, 11076h.
8. Seehof, J. M., and Trurnit, H. J., "Effect of Sorbed Water Vapor on the Electrical Conductivity of Condition Chromium Films," *J. Chem. Phys.*, **23**, 2459–60 (1951).
9. Jason, A. C., and Wood, J. L., "Electrical Effects of the Adsorption of Water Vapor by Anodized Aluminum," *Proc. Phys. Soc. London*, **68B**, 1105–16 (1955).
10. Wood Handbook No. 72, U.S.D.A., 1955.

28. An Application of the Dunmore Electric Hygrometer to Humidity Measurement at Low Temperatures*

G. O. HANDEGORD AND C. E. TILL

Prairie Regional Station, Division of Building Research, National Research Council, Saskatoon, Canada

ABSTRACT

The limited range of individual humidity sensors of the Dunmore type and their decreased speed of response at low temperatures tend to restrict their use as direct humidity measuring devices in some applications. Under certain circumstances a considerable increase in range and improvement in sensitivity may be possible with sensors of a lower humidity range by raising the temperature of the air being sampled. This paper discusses a method employing this principle that has specific application to the measurement of atmospheric humidity under low temperature winter conditions.

The particular device described uses a low-range sensor to control the heating of a continuously sampled airstream to maintain the resistance of the sensor at a constant value. The resultant temperature of the sensor provides an index of the humidity of the sample, the relationship between dew-point temperature and sensor temperature being almost linear. With a sensor having a nominal relative humidity range at $60°F$ of 3 to 8 per cent, dew-point temperatures from -25 to $+25°F$ may be measured with sensor temperatures between 40 and $140°F$. Substitution of a second higher-range sensor increases the maximum measurable dew point to above $50°F$ with a limiting sensor temperature of $140°F$.

The accuracy of the method is critically dependent on the sensitivity and stability of the Dunmore sensor; however, with precise calibration, measurements of subzero dew-point temperature to within $\pm1.5°F$ are possible.

INTRODUCTION

The limited range of individual sensors of the Dunmore type and their decreasing sensitivity with decreasing temperature tend to restrict their use as direct humidity measuring devices in some low temperature applications. In many such cases, however, the ambient relative humidity levels are high and the possibility of preheating a sampled airstream and employing a sensor of lower humidity range offers advantages. Increasing the ambient temperature at the sensor will improve its response in the first instance, because this characteristic is markedly influenced by sensor temperature.[1] Secondly, as the sensor resistance is primarily dependent on relative humidity, adjustment of the ambient temperature can be used as a means of extending its operating range.

The device described in this paper represents an application of these principles to the measurement of atmospheric humidity under the low-temperature conditions of the Canadian Prairies. Specifically, it involves the

* This paper is a contribution from the Division of Building Research, National Research Council, Canada and is published with the approval of the Director of the Division.

use of a Dunmore sensor to control the temperature of a sampled airstream so as to maintain a constant sensor resistance. Under these conditions the sensor temperature provides an index of the humidity of the airstream, the relationship depending on the characteristics of the sensor involved. This particular approach was followed primarily as a means of extending the operating range of a single sensor, but also to provide an output in terms of temperature, in keeping with the recording instrumentation available at the site.

The initial development of the apparatus was undertaken by the second author as his undergraduate thesis problem in Engineering Physics at the University of Saskatchewan in 1956. The subsequent availability of a precise humidity calibration facility at the National Research Council laboratory in Saskatoon made possible a more complete assessment of the accuracy of the device.

DEW-POINT TEMPERATURE–SENSOR TEMPERATURE RELATIONSHIP

The calibration information supplied by manufacturers of this type of sensor is usually presented as a series of isotherms showing the relationship between relative humidity and sensor resistance or intrument reading. On the basis of these curves, relative humidities for different sensor temperatures can be obtained for any given sensor resistance or scale reading. Using these relative humidity values, it is possible to compute the relationship between dew-point temperature and sensor temperature for a constant sensor resistance. This relationship, based on midrange resistance, is shown graphically in Fig. 1 for two commercial sensors of different nominal humidity range.

If it is assumed that the operating temperature range of the sensors is from 40 to 140°F, sensor A, with a nominal midrange relative humidity of 3 per cent at 60°F, can be used to measure dew-point temperatures from −25 to +19°F; and sensor B, with a nominal midrange relative humidity of 12 per cent at 60°F, covers the dew-point range of −2 to + 57°F. These two sensors can therefore span a range of relative humidities from 4 to 100 per cent at 40°F if operated between the prescribed

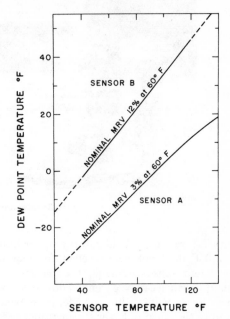

FIG. 1. Dew-point temperature–sensor temperature relationship for two commercial sensors at constant midrange resistance.

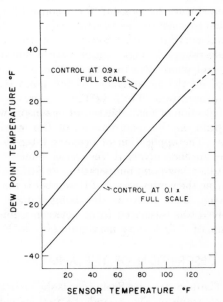

FIG. 2. Dew-point temperature–sensor temperature relationship for single commercial sensor at two levels of constant sensor resistance.

FIG. 3. Low-temperature hygrometer.

temperature limits. Although the upper limit of 140°F may not be exceeded for fear of permanent sensor damage, the measurable humidity range can be extended downward to much lower values, due consideration being given to the effect of lower sensor response.

An extension of range is also possible through adjustment of the control point to higher or lower values of sensor resistance. This is illustrated in Fig. 2 for sensor C which has a nominal humidity range between that of sensors A and B of Fig. 1. The upper curve represents the dew-point temperature–sensor temperature relationship for a control point equal to 0.9 of the instrument scale range, the lower curve that for a control equal to 0.1 of scale range. A single sensor with a suitable control point adjustment could therefore be used for the measurement of dew-point temperatures from 60 to −14°F, or lower.

Selection of a suitable sensor or sensors will depend on the requirements of the specific case. The application of primary interest to the authors involved the measurement of outdoor dew-point temperatures at Saskatoon during the winter period of December through March. The practical dew-point range involved was estimated to be between a minimum of −40°F and a maximum of +40°F.

DESCRIPTION OF THE APPARATUS

The device used in Saskatoon is shown in the photograph of Fig. 3, and the various components are illustrated diagrammatically in Fig. 4. The air sampling system consists of a 3-in. diameter plastic tube fitted with an elbow at the intake end and a small centrifugal blower at the other. The intake elbow incorporates a glass-fiber filter, a 400-watt bare wire heating element, and a 140°F limiting thermostat. The entire assembly is mounted on a platform extending through a window opening in a heated building, the outside air sample being drawn from below this platform at the heater location and discharged to outside at the blower outlet.

The sensor is located in the horizontal section of the pipe, immediately downstream of a rectangular orifice designed to increase the air velocity over the sensor to approximately 2500 fpm. The sensor is connected to a conventional two-position indicator-controller, which operates a $\frac{1}{160}$ rpm reversible motor. This motor positions a variable voltage transformer, which supplies power to the bare wire heater through the limit thermostat. A thermocouple at the sensor location is used to measure temperature.

GENERAL PERFORMANCE AND ACCURACY

The specific arrangement of components and the control system used resulted in a cyclical fluctuation in temperature at the sensor of less than ±1°F, corresponding to a dew-point temperature variation of approximately ±0.5°F. This fluctuation was considered to be due largely to the transient spatial variation in air temperature resulting from the bare wire heater and air turbulence

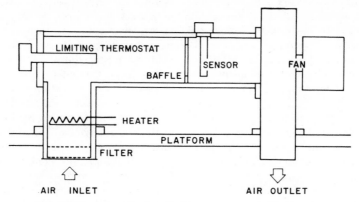

FIG. 4. Diagrammatic sketch of low-temperature hygrometer.

in the duct. Operation of the system during periods of constant outdoor temperature with a fixed voltage applied to the heater produced similar fluctuations that tended to confirm this possibility.

The response of the device to changes in atmospheric temperature and humidity during the winter proved to be satisfactory, but no rapid changes in sample inlet conditions were experienced. To provide a measure of its response under such conditions, the device was removed quickly from its normal outside air sampling position, exposed to room air conditions until equilibrium was established, and then returned to its original position. Outside air conditions were constant at 18°F with a dew-point temperature of 16°F, room air, at 72°F with a dew-point temperature of 22°F. The time required to reach equilibrium in each case was approximately 18 minutes.

The accuracy of the device is to a large extent dependent on the accuracy to which the sensor can be calibrated and on its stability under operating conditions. The sensor used for most of the measurements in Saskatoon was calibrated in a two-temperature recirculating atmosphere producer[2] capable of accuracies to better than 0.5 per cent RH. The resultant dew-point temperature–sensor temperature curve is illustrated in Fig. 5.

The potential accuracy of the device, based on a sensor calibration to within ±0.5 per cent RH, may be calculated as ±0.9°F at a dew-point temperature of −12.5°F. Assuming the potential error in temperature measurement

to be equal to the fluctuation observed, the corresponding error in dew-point temperature measurement would be ±0.5°F. The total error in dew-point measurement, considering calibration tolerance and temperature deviation, may therefore be estimated at ±1.4°F.

The potential error at a dew point of 29.5°F, corresponding to a sensor temperature of 110.5°F, would be considerably greater because of the psychrometric relationships involved. Using the same basis for calculation,

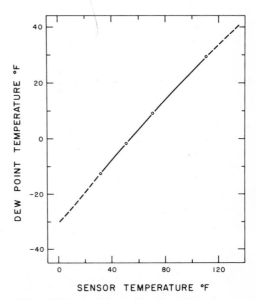

FIG. 5. Dew-point temperature–sensor temperature calibration of commercial sensor at constant midrange resistance.

it may be estimated at $\pm2.3°F$. Some improvement in accuracy at this dew-point temperature could be realized by utilizing a sensor of higher humidity range.

The sensor used was recalibrated after exposure in the device for a period of one month, having operated within a range of temperature from 40 to 100°F. This recalibration revealed an upward shift in the curve of Fig. 5, corresponding to a change of approximately 1.5°F in dew point. A second sensor, of the same humidity range but exposed to slightly higher temperatures and for a longer period in the device, exhibited an upward shift in calibration of some 3°F in dew point.

SUMMARY AND CONCLUSIONS

The technique described in this paper suggests a means of extending the range of a single Dunmore sensor by utilizing it to control the temperature of a sampled airstream. The accuracy of the device is critically dependent on the accuracy of calibration of the sensor used and on its stability under operating conditions. With precise initial calibration and periodic recalibration, accuracies of better than $\pm1.5°F$ are possible at below zero temperatures. It is of interest to note that the almost linear relationship between dew-point temperature and sensor temperature permits some simplification in calibration procedure.

The improvement in speed of response of the sensor with operation at higher temperatures is not reflected directly in the output of the device, but is important in the operation of the control system. When it is desirable to measure more rapid fluctuations in humidity at low temperatures, control of air temperature directly and observation of sensor resistance change may be an alternative technique. When outside dry-bulb temperatures remain constant for suitable lengths of time, manual adjustment of heat input offers a basis for a simple indicating instrument. For such applications, a heating arrangement providing a more uniform airstream temperature would be desirable.

References

1. Morris, V., and Sobel, F., "Some Experiments on Speed of Response of the Electrolytic Hygrometer," *Bull. Am. Meteorol. Soc.*, **35**, 226 (1954).
2. Till, C. E., and Handegord, G. O., "Proposed Humidity Standard," *Trans. ASHRAE*, **66**, 288–308 (1960).

29. A Method of Measuring the Moisture Content of Air directly in Grains Per Pound of Dry Air

E. E. Stanley and P. J. Cousins

The Heating and Ventilating Research Association, Bracknell, Berkshire, England

ABSTRACT

Three commercial makes of humidity sensing elements were tested at three constant temperatures of 80, 100 and 120° F. For two matched pairs, the electrical resistance values differed by negligible amounts. Results were obtained at both equilibrium conditions and for time response to wetting and drying changes.

At 120° F operation and for operating theater or similar environments, the electrical output could be calibrated directly in grains of moisture per pound of dry air. This method of use also eliminates the ambient temperature as a relevant variable when measuring moisture gains. The element is also protected from the deleterious effects of high humidity which may cause a secular change of characteristic. Such a change was recorded during the tests due to the action of an unknown gaseous pollutant.

The manufacturer's data for one element were examined to seek a method of combining two elements to give a continuous single output monitoring of moisture gain in an air stream. A method using the element to control the air around it to a constant relative humidity of about 17 per cent was discovered which would require a very close control of the resistance characteristic by the manufacturer.

INTRODUCTION

A research study of the air conditioning of hospital operating theaters required the moisture gain to be measured from a particular theater over a period of several weeks and with normal working activity. The plan was to measure the total moisture gain into the ventilation air passing through the theatre and to relate the result to the recorded number of persons in the theater at different times. In this way, the extra moisture in excess of normal physiological releases could be attributed to steam release from an adjacent sterilizing plant or to washing down procedures.

Initially, two thermohygrographs were used to measure the moisture gain. These instruments provided continuous seven-day records of both temperature and humidity. One instrument was placed on a stand in the theater adjacent to an outlet grill. The second instrument was housed in a special design of thermally insulated box which received a sample flow of air from the air supply duct immediately before the inlet grill to the theater.

Secular changes of the instrument calibrations (observed at weekly checks with a wet- and dry-bulb whirling hygrometer) led to errors, as did stiction effect and unequal slow response rates to a change in humidity. The man-hours required for the subsequent analysis of the chart data were also excessive.

Although with these instruments the measured mean values of moisture gain, taken over a period of several weeks, seemed to be of the expected order of magnitude, it was not possible to measure with reasonable accuracy the moisture gain at any particular instant of time.

It was thought that a great improvement

would result if two electrical resistance humidity sensing elements were used. Each could be made to respond to an appropriate sample stream of air heated at constant moisture to a fixed high temperature of 120°F. The air temperatures in the theater and the supply duct would no longer be relevant variables since direct calibration in terms of grains per pound of dry air is possible without their values being known. The humidity elements would be protected from the known deleterious effects of near-saturation conditions occurring in the theater during washing down. Hysteresis effects and secular changes of characteristics might therefore be reduced. The response rates would be more equal and possibly faster due to the effect of the high temperature on the rates of the physico-chemical reactions at the active surface of the element.

The most simple experimental data for a moisture balance would result if in some way a single differential output measure of moisture gain was available by linking the two elements into a common circuit.

A suitable velocity delay could be introduced in the sampling line from the air duct to allow a correction for the time taken for the air to travel through the theater.

There are obvious further applications of such an instrument to the control of drying processes or other processes and studies where moisture gain or loss to a stream of air has to be monitored accurately.

An indicating instrument is easily constructed to show gain (or loss) of moisture. Two adjacent current meters could be used, requiring a mental subtraction of the readings, or the movements could be housed in a single case with a calibration of the region where the pointers cross each other (Fig. 1).

It proved much more difficult to establish a method of combining the elements into a single circuit but a possible method of obtaining an output measure proportional to moisture gain was worked out from the manufacturers data for the type b element (Fig. 4). The detail of the method is discussed in a later section (p. 293). In the discussion of equilibrium calibration curves (p. 290), the experimental data obtained for the constant temperature operation of the elements is presented.

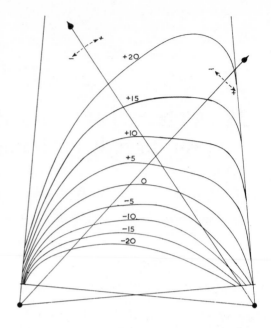

Gain— gr/lb dry air

Fig. 1. Possible calibration of a "moisture-gain in air" meter. Two type b elements (see Appendix) are considered. These are held at 120°F in suitable streams of air. The meter movements are considered as linear 100 μA, and the elements each receive a constant drive of 3.16 V (AC).

It must be emphasized that this work was carried out only as a feasibility study designed to examine the possibility of making use of the special properties of the electrical element for assessing moisture gains in room environments.

EQUIPMENT USED FOR THE TESTS

The humidity of the air contained in a cubic cabinet of 6-ft side length, constructed mainly in aluminum sheet and angle, could be varied by using either a drying or a wetting procedure. Drying was obtained by recirculating some of the air through ¼ cu ft of silica gel of size "on No. 6 mesh". The silica gel was supported in two drawers (Fig. 2) supported inside a sealed box mounted on the outside surface of the cabinet. After sufficient drying of the air, the unit was completely sealed off from the cabinet by screwing down two disc valves. One disc sealed a 4-in. wall-mounted circulation fan and the second sealed a 4-in. diameter port located in the wall and vertically above the fan (Fig. 3). The wetting procedure required the injection from the filling tube of a hypodermic syringe of a measured amount of water. The filling tube was first passed through a hole, normally sealed, in the wall of the cabinet, and the water was then ejected into the dished lid of a tin. Contained in the tin was a 600-watt electrical fire element. A desk fan was used to quickly mix the steam into the air during the subsequent boiling-off operation. The fan pulled the steam toward the center of the cabinet to avoid condensation onto the adjacent walls of the cabinet. Condensed water films were not easily reevaporated into the air. Condensation at the higher humidities due to cold drafts outside the cabinet was successfully avoided by installing a thermostatically controlled heater inside the cabinet.

A continuous sample of air was withdrawn from the cabinet through a plastic tube and glass wool filter at a rate of 500 cc/min. This

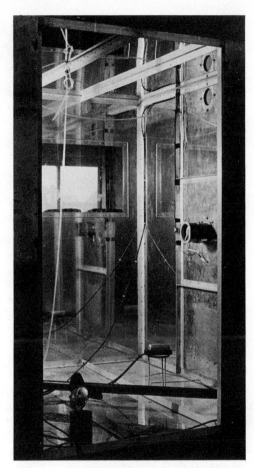

FIG. 3. View of the interior of the aluminum cabinet.

FIG. 2. View of the drying compartment. The drawers containing silica gel are shown partially withdrawn.

air, after passing through the sensing line, was returned to the cabinet. Two humidity elements for each of three different commercial types (Fig. 4 and Appendix) were tested simultaneously. They were mounted in brass capsules (Fig. 5) and joined in line so that the same air passed over each in turn (Fig. 6). The elements fitted into suitable base mountings formed from PTFE, Perspex, or ceramic sealed with Perspex cement. The base connections were joined with EHT cable to a high insulation selector switch. When necessary, a high resistance of 67 MΩ, maintained at constant temperature in a Dewar flask, was joined in parallel with the elements. This technique allowed a more useful resistance range to be used on the Wayne Kerr 2 per cent Component Bridge which was used to measure

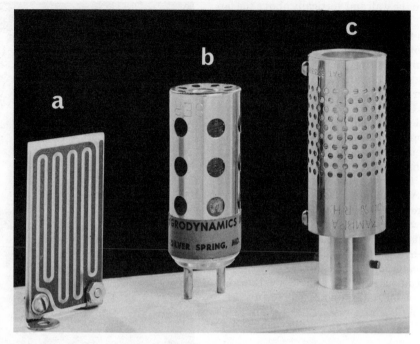

FIG. 4. The three types of element tested. (Further details are given in the Appendix.)

all the resistance values. The AC 50-cps loading of the elements was of a negligible order of magnitude, as were the changes in the self-capacity of the elements during all the testing.

A water-filled thermostatically controlled bath was used to hold the capsules at a chosen temperature, and a coiled copper heat exchange tube, also immersed in the thermostat, ensured that the air stream was adjusted to the same temperature before passing over the first element. Thermocouples in the air stream were used to check that the heat exchange tube was of sufficient length.

The first and last elements were a matched pair of type b (see Appendix for manufacturer). This arrangement, to some extent, allowed immediate indication and observation of any leakage of water into the measuring line. A more critical measure of the leakage was obtained by recirculating the air through a

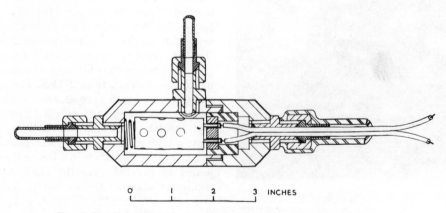

FIG. 5. Detail drawing of a capsule for containing one of the elements.

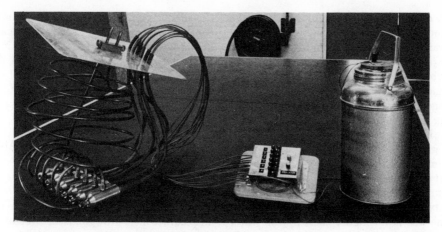

FIG. 6. Shows the capsules connected in line, the selector switch and the Dewar flask containing the high resistance.

bypass which isolated the large volume of air in the cabinet. The small leakage rate then gave a very much increased change in moisture content of the air in the sampling line. The leakage always had a negligible effect at the 500-cc/min. flow rate when the circuit included the large volume of air in the cabinet. It was possible to use oil in the thermostat, but there would then have been no check of any leakage occurring and the oil could be a nuisance if it spread onto the surface of the elements. An "in-line" dew-point meter was used to obtain an absolute check of the moisture content. The dew point could be consistently measured to one-tenth of a degree centigrade. The observation of the mist layer was made more

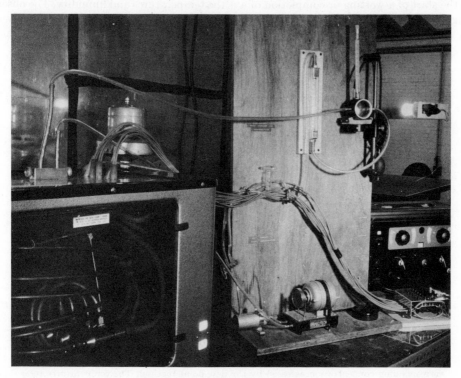

FIG. 7. General view of the apparatus.

easy by mounting a yellow light in front of the instrument. Faster response, an extended lower range and freedom from ice blockage of the air jet were improvements obtained when the air bubbled through the ether in the dew-point meter was first passed through a heat exchange tube immersed in an ice and salt freezing mixture.

The hermetically sealed air circulation pump was fitted with a bypass so that the 500-cc/min flow rate could be established without appreciably increasing the air pressure in that part of the flow line containing the elements. An oil manometer showed that the flow line was never higher than 1½ in. water gauge above the laboratory air pressure. It was not necessary to include a correction for the small changes of barometric pressure when obtaining the grains per pound of dry air from tables[1] giving this value for various dew points. The experimental set up is shown in Fig. 7.

At the 500-cc/min flow rate it was estimated that "plug" flow would clear the sensing line in less than one minute. The dew-point meter gave a constant reading from five minutes after the start of a wetting or completion of a drying operation. The dew point was in some cases a little above laboratory temperature,

the slight extension being possibly due to the control of the cabinet air temperature and the high temperature of the thermostatic bath. Extension of the calibrations above the highest recorded values would have required control of the laboratory air temperature to avoid condensation in the plastic flow tubes.

EXPERIMENTAL PROCEDURE AND RESULTS

Equilibrium Calibration Curves

As the study was strictly related to finding an accurate measure of moisture liberated into the air in a room, the opportunity was taken during these tests to observe how closely the water boiled off into the air in the cabinet could be measured by a change in the dew point of the air. To do this, the humidity of the air in the cabinet was reduced to a suitable low value, and this was followed with step increases in the moisture by the wetting procedure described. The pounds of dry air in the cabinet should have been between fifteen and sixteen depending on the precise conditions of the temperatures and humidity. The observed value calculated from the slopes of the lines in Fig. 8 varied between 11.3 and 17.5 pounds.

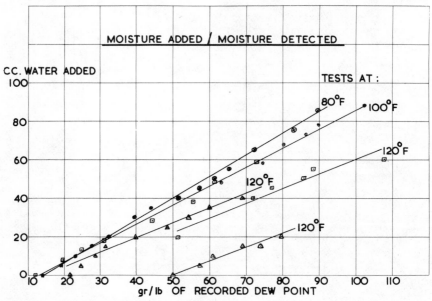

Fig. 8. Correlation of the volume of water added to the air in the cabinet with the corresponding concentration assessed by the dew-point method. The temperatures refer to the thermostat-controlled bath.

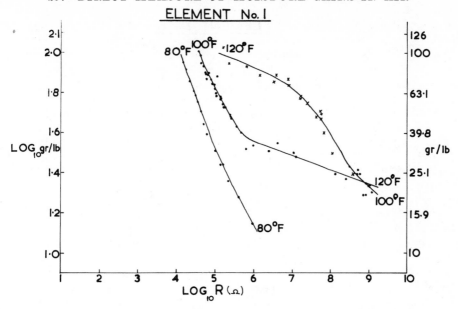

FIG. 9. Constant-temperature calibrations for a type c element (see Appendix). Note: The results were taken after equilibrium was established, and the curves include points for both wetting and drying changes.

In Figs. 9, 10, and 11, there are shown examples of the equilibrium curves obtained for the different elements. Suitable periods of time sometimes in excess of one hour were allowed for the resistance of the elements to become constant in value. The difference in response time between the elements is discussed later. Matched elements were used both for type b and type c. The results for the second element were in each case very similar and are not recorded. A second element of type a gave very peculiar results and was therefore

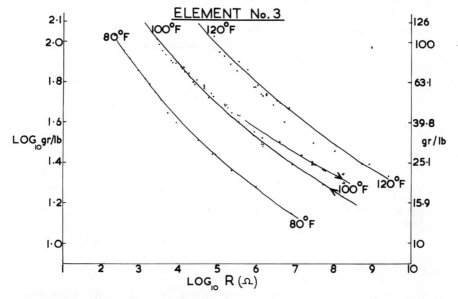

FIG. 10. Constant-temperature calibrations for a type b element. Refer to note of Fig. 9. The change of characteristic for the drying section of the 100°F curve was a result of some pollution of the element.

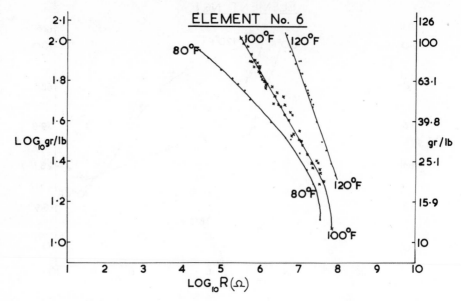

FIG. 11. Constant temperature calibrations for type a element. Refer to note of Fig. 9.

assumed to be damaged in some way. The calibration at each temperature includes both wetting and drying results along it. The strange response of the type b (Fig. 10) elements observed for the 100°F calibration was at first attributed to hysteresis. No similar splitting of the characteristic was observed for the other elements. Subsequent results indicated that all the elements moved finally to higher resistance lines. It is now thought that the elements were polluted by a gaseous contaminant contained in the silica gel sample. The gel had been dried in a domestic gas oven supplied with town gas.

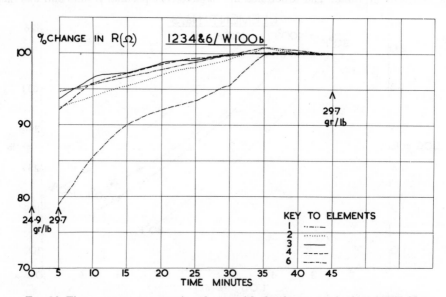

FIG. 12. Time response to a wetting change with the thermostat bath at 100°F. Note: The dew point was constant after five minutes. The elements are identified in the Appendix. Readings were taken at approximately two-minute intervals, i.e., the graphs must not be considered as continuous.

The type a and c elements were therefore less responsive to the pollutant than was type b.

There is no special advantage in the characteristic being a straight line although equal curvature, type b, may simplify the form of the ambient temperature correction when the element is used for measuring relative humidity values. Type c elements have a spiral of glass fiber wound onto four vertical thin rod terminals connected together in diagonal pairs. The surface of the fiber was sensitized with calcium chloride solution. Type b has a pair of spiral electrodes wound on to the surface of a plastic cylinder, and type a is probably very similar chemically to type b but is of thin plate form with interleaved electrodes bonded to the sensitized surface. For some parts of the characteristics, the equilibrium sensitivity was of the order of one grain per pound of moisture in the air. The slow response rate would not however allow a measuring accuracy for changing moisture equal to the sensitivity attainable at equilibrium conditions.

The approach to equilibrium was examined for a few cases of drying and wetting changes. The drying change was not a step change of moisture taking up to ten minutes to achieve. Constant dew point was however observed from five minutes after the drying was stopped.

A similar speed of dew-point response was obtained for the wetting process. Resistance values were measured at approximately two-minute intervals for each element. The results in Figs. 12, 13, 14 and 15 show that the response at a particular temperature to drying is generally slower than the response to wetting at the same temperature. Response to drying is slower at the higher temperature with the converse being true for wetting. An exception was the response of the two type c elements to drying at 120°F. Each gave 100 per cent response after five minutes.

It was not possible because of the change in characteristic caused by the pollution to convert these results into the more useful curves based on grains per pound rather than resistance.

Slow response rates would normally be interpreted as hysteresis effects during the observation of up and down cyclic changes of humidity.

A Single Output Measure of the Difference in Moisture Content

Manufacturers data for element b are re-plotted in Fig. 16 to illustrate the similarity that exists between the variation of resistance with temperature at constant humidity for the element and the well-known "thermistor"

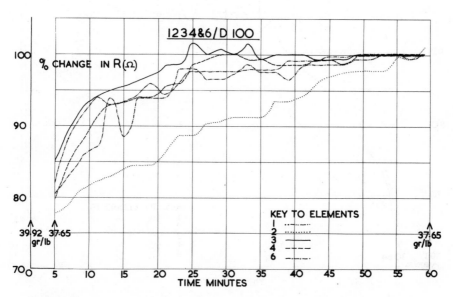

FIG. 13. Time response to a drying change with the thermostat at 100°F. Refer to note of Fig. 12.

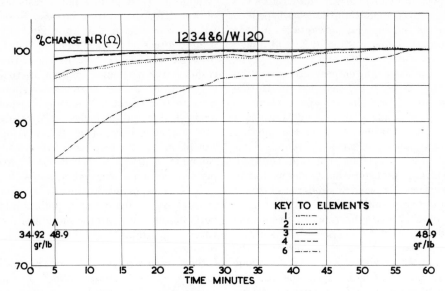

FIG. 14. Time response to a wetting change with the thermostat at 120°F. Refer to note of Fig. 12.

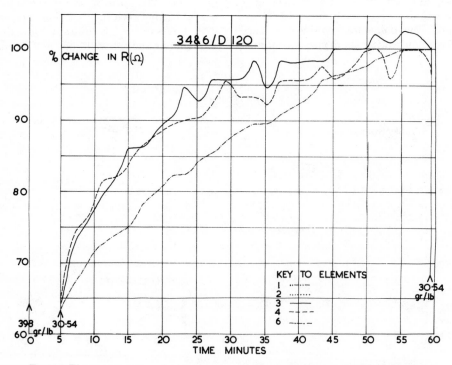

FIG. 15. Time response to a drying change with the thermostat at 120°F. Refer to note of Fig. 12.

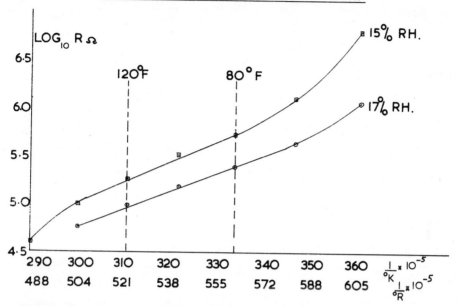

FIG. 16. Constant humidity characteristics for a type b element. The straight section (80 to 120°F) indicates that the resistance change with temperature is of a form which can be matched with a suitable thermistor.

characteristics. The linearity between the 80° and 120°F levels of temperature shows that it is possible to obtain a thermistor with the same resistance-temperature characteristics for this region of the curves. The thermistor can then be used as one arm of a Wheastone bridge circuit with the element as another arm. In this way, the temperature of a stream of air can be controlled automatically to ensure that the element is reading constant humidity (i.e., the air is heated until its humidity falls to a constant value, say 17 per cent).

In Fig. 17 it is seen that the moisture content of the air is proportional to the reciprocal of the resistance of the element when this is constrained to be at constant humidity.

If the bridge is fed from a constant voltage supply (V) the current will be equal to V/R and therefore proportional to the grains per pound moisture in the air passing over the element and thermistor. The difference in currents from two bridges provides a single output measure which is proportional to the difference in the grains per pound of moisture in the two samples of air.

The calibration of the type b elements indicated a departure from the published characteristics which, as shown schematically in Fig. 18, resulted in a critical change in slope of the constant humidity lines. The corresponding resistance changes at constant humidity could therefore not be matched with a suitable thermistor as the resistance was in fact now increasing with temperature.

CONCLUSION

Electrical resistance humidity elements may be used when maintained at a fixed high temperature to measure the moisture content of air. The calibration in grains per pound of dry air is independent of the room air temperature. The element is protected against any secular change that might result from exposure to occasional high humidities. Sensitivities of the order of one grain per pound are possible, provided the moisture content of the air is constant or changing very slowly. Gaseous pollutants must be absent from the air.

Visual indication of moisture gain (or loss)

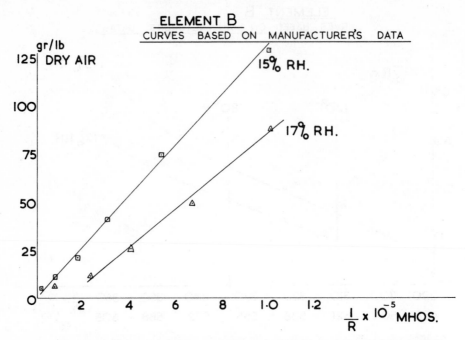

FIG. 17. These constant humidity response curves (type b element) show that the moisture content of the air stream is proportional to the reciprocal of the resistance. Therefore current flow through the element is also proportional to the moisture content provided a constant-voltage (AC) drive is used.

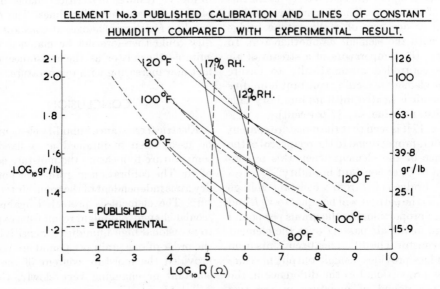

FIG. 18. These characteristics for a type b element show schematically how the constant humidity lines differed from the expected values.

between two points in an air stream is possible by using two elements.

A single output measure for recording moisture gains may be possible if two elements (type b) with suitable characteristics can be selected and used as described to maintain an air stream at constant low humidity. The ultimate success of the method would depend on the speed of response of the element to a changing temperature.

APPENDIX

Elements 1 and 2 (type c Fig. 4). Manufactured by Negretti and Zambra Ltd., Stocklake, Aylsbury, Bucks, England. These are usually called Gregory elements.

Elements 3 and 4 (type b Fig. 4). Manufactured by Hygrodynamics Inc., Silver Springs, Maryland, U.S.A. The elements were a matched pair of the Company's Red Range.

Elements 5 and 6 (Type a Fig. 4). These were supplied for testing by A. M. Lock and Co. Ltd., 79 Union Street, Oldham, Lancashire, England.

The American manufacturer is unknown to the writers, but the elements are built to British Patent Specification No. 822808 held by the Phys-Chemical Research Corporation of New York.

Reference

1. Institute of Heating and Ventilating Engineers, "Hygrometric Data," in "Guide to Current Practice," Section VIII, 1959.

30. Apparatus for the Assessment of Equilibrium Relative Humidity in the Temperature Range of 0 to −30°C

Lajos Szalai

Central Food Research Institute, Budapest, Hungary

There are many methods known for the measurement of equilibrium relative humidity. Most of them are not suitable for determinations below 0°C, or the relative error is great. However, since large stocks of valuable goods, mostly foods, are stored below freezing point, it is of great importance to find a solution to this problem. Therefore, it was our aim to construct an apparatus that would enable us to gain satisfactory results.

The crucial part of the apparatus is a ceramic tube with a thin wall impregnated with lithium chloride solution. This tube is put in the same closed container with the sample. At a given temperature, the electric resistance of the ceramic tube is a function of water vapor pressure. The resistance of the tube is determined with the aid of an AC source and a vacuum tube voltmeter instrument.

The equipment used for the calibration of the sensing cell is based on the following principle: when ice is stored in a closed container of temperature τ, a water vapor pressure p will develop. The same pressure will prevail in another container, connected to the first one, but thermally separated and of t temperature. By arbitrary adjustment of t and τ temperatures, the water vapor pressure may be fixed with satisfactory accuracy. When the air had been removed from the apparatus, the free path of the water vapor molecules increased and within two hours the diffusion equilibrium became stabilized.

This paper discusses the method of making the sensing cell and the results of calibration. Determinations may be reproduced with an accuracy of ±2 per cent.

Out of the innumerable problems related to the determination of relative humidity, we are concerned with the equilibrium relative humidity of foods. Since the majority of foodstuffs is of hygroscopic character, from the point of view of storage the relative humidity of the environment is of vital importance. If the relative humidity of the storage room is lower than the equilibrium relative humidity of the stored goods, these will lose moisture until their moisture content reaches the level determined by the relative humidity of the environment. The correlation between the moisture content and equilibrium relative humidity of various substances is described by their sorption isotherms. From the knowledge of these quantitative correlations conclusions may be drawn as to the extent of changes to be expected.

There are many methods known for measuring of equilibrium relative humidity. Most of them are based on the determination of dew point or vapor pressure. There is a special group of methods based on the assessment of equilibrium created by the moisture content of the substance and its environment mutually affecting each other.

The determination of the equilibrium relative humidity in the range below 0°C is a problem of its own. The difficulties met with in this range do not occur at higher temperature levels. The problems concerned with the technique of measurement are of greatest interest. For instance, in the temperature range below 0°C there is only a slight absolute difference between the vapor tension of pure ice, on one hand, and the water vapor tension in the atmosphere formed above moisture-containing substances, on the other. This small difference further decreases with decreasing temperatures. Thus, the lower the temperature at which the dew point or relative humidity tests are carried out, the more sensitive are the methods which have to be applied. For the same reason, since the difference between dew point and actual temperature is diminishing, severe problems of measuring technique and thermostability arise.

We do not know a multimember series of crystals with well-defined water vapor pressure belonging to the saturated solution of each member, in the range below 0°C. Since salt solutions of exactly standardized concentrations are not available, a calibration method had to be worked out, too, for the apparatus developed.

The methods generally used for the determination of relative humidity in the range below 0°C are not suitable for the assessment of relative humidity in a small closed chamber. The ice covering the sensing cell sublimates during the actual measurement into the atmosphere contained in the detector chamber and thereby falsifies the prevailing humidity conditions. It is evident that in a detector chamber of small dimensions, minute quantities of added vapor cause a large increase in the percentage of relative humidity.

Since valuable goods such as foodstuffs are stored below 0°C, it is of great importance to find a solution to this problem. The losses occurring during storage originate from the sublimation of ice formed in the goods or from the partial evaporation of the condensed cytoplasm.

Since the problem of assessing relative humidity below 0°C is of vital importance, we aimed at designing and constructing an apparatus for the exploration of this field.

In the preliminary investigations, a method based on the change of electric resistance of a porous ceramic tube impregnated with LiCl solution was applied with good results. A sensing cell of this type proved to be suitable for measurements in the temperature range below 0°C.

Our first aim was to increase the dependability and accuracy of the measurements. For the determination of the resistance of electro-lytes, in order to avoid polarization, alternating current is always used. With this principle in mind, we took one more step forward by limiting the voltage of the alternating current. Thus the decomposition voltage of the LiCl could not be reached by the detector voltage, even at its peak, and a satisfactory safety margin was left. For this reason the detector voltage was set at 500 mV.

The main parts of the apparatus are as follows:

(1) Stabilized AC source of 500 mV, independent of supply voltage variations;

(2) Detector switch;

(3) VT voltmeter for alternating current with high internal resistance;

(4) Sensing electrolyte cell;

(5) Sample container with temperature control.

The stabilization of the detector voltage proved necessary, because sudden variations in the supply voltage caused false readings. A bolometer bridge was used to stabilize voltage. Allowing for a ± 10 per cent variation in supply voltage, the deviation in the voltage of the circuit stabilized from the nominal voltage does not exceed 0.5 per cent, which in our case amounts to ± 2.5 mV. This accuracy is quite adequate for our purpose.

In the construction of the detector switch, no problem apart from that of shielding arose.

For the determination of the voltage across the sensing electrolyte cell, an 1315/D type Hungarian low-frequency VT voltmeter was used. This instrument, a highly sensitive multirange meter of great internal resistance and stability, is very suitable for the purpose.

The principal part of the apparatus is the electrolyte cell. The resistance of the cell is a function of the vapor pressure and the temperature. The cell is a ceramic tube of 4-mm diameter, 30-mm length and 0.2-mm wall thickness, made porous by chemical treatment. On each end of the tube, a silver ring of 2-mm width was formed by thermal process. The output leads were soldered to these silver rings. The ends of the tube are not closed by soldering and they allow for free circulation of the surrounding air. As a consequence, moisture could diffuse from the tube from both ends, thereby shortening the time of response as compared to the time needed with a closed tube.

To attain the desired degree of sensitivity, LiCl solutions of various concentrations were tested. Best results were obtained, in the temperature range applied, with a 1.6 per cent LiCl solution. Another condition of satisfactory cell operation is a possibly short period of time needed to follow changes in humidity.

To determine the time constant, the air was conducted through a bubbling vessel filled with glass beads. The vessel contained solid salt in a saturated solution. The air passing the bubbling vessel was conducted into a sensing cell built in a glass tube. To circulate the air, a pulsating pump of 1 l/hour capacity was used. The equilibrium relative humidity of the air, as determined by the salt solution, was reached within 30 minutes. When equilibrium was reached, the resistance of the cell was determined. Another sample of air of known relative humidity was conducted to the sensing cell. The new resistance value was obtained within one minute.

The production of sensing cells of identical resistance is facilitated by the parallel application of several sensing cells. Thus, sets of sensing elements, satisfying practical requirements, may be assembled.

The sensing element was built in the cover of a metal chamber of approximately 100-ml volume, by means of hermetically tight screws. An "Amphenol" connector was also built in in the cover. The inside insulator of the connector was made of "Teflon." "Teflon," besides being an excellent electric insulator, is at the same time hydrophobic. This is of importance because the apparatus is to be used for the determination of equilibrium relative humidity of foods of high moisture content. In these foodstuffs, the equilibrium relative humidity closely approximates 100 per cent.

The material to be tested is placed into the rubber-gasketed threaded metal chamber, and the desired temperature level is attained with the aid of an accurately set ultrathermostat.

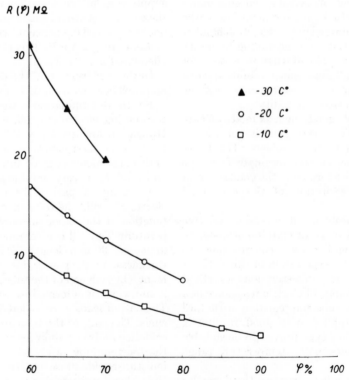

FIG. 1. The electric resistance of a ceramic sensing tube, sensitized by impregnation with lithium chloride, plotted against relative humidity at various temperature levels.

The analysis is accomplished when the equilibrium between humidity and sensing cell is reached.

First the supply voltage of the cell is set at exactly 500 mV, then the VT voltmeter is connected after the cell with the detector switch, and the voltage across the cell is established. With the knowledge of the latter value, the supply voltage, and the internal resistance of the VT voltmeter, the resistance of the sensing cell may be calculated.

The traditional methods were not suitable for the calibration of the apparatus. A new apparatus had to be used for the calibration of the ceramic sensing cells. Two containers that could be evacuated were connected by a large cock. The temperature of the containers could be accurately set even at low temperatures by a controlled heat jacket. The temperature of the container with the sensing cell to be calibrated was set at the test temperature, while the other container was set at the desired dew-point temperature. Temperatures were stabilized by means of ultrathermostats with a high degree of accuracy. The two containers were thermally divided by metal grids. The whole unit was evacuated to a pressure of 10^{-3} torr. During calibration, the voltage of the VT voltmeter, sufficiently amplified, was recorded. In this way, the establishment of the state of equilibrium could be better observed. The principle underlying this calibration method is that above water or ice contained in a closed chamber at dew-point temperature, the vapor pressure is determined by the temperature. The same pressure prevails in another chamber containing the sensing cell and connected to the first one, however thermally isolated. Since the temperature and dew-point values in the apparatus may arbitrarily be chosen, the humidity of the air can be adjusted with satisfactory accuracy at the given temperature. In order to reach the state of equilibrium in a short time, the chamber was evacuated and was filled only by vapor, thus the free path of the molecules became longer.

Figure 1 shows the results of calibration. On the vertical axis, the resistance of the electrolyte cell in megohms is plotted; on the horizontal axis, the relative humidity values are plotted. The reference basis for the calculation of relative humidity values is not the vapor tension of ice, but the tension of undercooled water at the test chamber temperature.

The line marked by triangles gives the results attained at $-30°C$, the line marked by circles gives those at $-20°C$, and the line marked by squares those at $-10°C$. The reproducibility of results is ± 2 per cent RH.

With the aid of this apparatus, the equilibrium relative humidity of a number of quick frozen goods was established so that the optimum storage and packaging conditions could be chosen for the items tested.

31. A Small Electrical Hygrometer for Microclimate Measurements*†

MARLIN N. ROGERS

University of Missouri, Columbia, Missouri

ABSTRACT

A small-sized modification of the Dunmore electrical hygrometer (2 × 12 mm) has been constructed and used to make direct relative humidity measurements as near the leaf surface as 0.75 mm. This remote reading instrument removed almost negligible quantities of moisture from the air during use and may be used in still air or in small enclosed spaces. It reaches equilibrium with its environment within one to three minutes, and with suitable indicating devices, it measures relative humidity reliably to an accuracy of one per cent or better.

The instrument can be used by plant physiologists to measure moisture gradients outward from the surface of a leaf in studies relating to transpiration and the mechanism of stomatal movement. It may also be used by plant pathologists in studies of the effects of moisture in the microclimate of the leaf upon infection by leaf-invading microorganisms, or it may be used by entomologists investigating the activities of leaf-inhabiting insects.

INTRODUCTION

The precision of relative humidity measurements has never remotely approached the exactness of temperature measurements. This probably has been due to two main reasons:

* This study was carried out in the Department of Plant Pathology at Cornell University between 1953 and 1956.
† This paper has been published previously in somewhat condensed form in *Plant Disease Reporter*, **41**, No. 10, 897–902 (1957).

(1) the lack of precise, readily obtainable working standards of known relative humidity values and (2) the inherent lack of sensitivity in nearly all types of measuring devices so far invented.

Middleton[14] says:

"We must note one important distinction between instruments used to measure relative humidity and those discussed in previous chapters. While barometers and thermometers can easily be made far more accurate than is necessary in meteorological practice, instruments for measuring humidity are seldom as precise or as accurate as desired. In consequence of this, the measurement of humidity is one of the least satisfactory of instrumental procedures in meteorology, and in this field there is still a great opportunity for research and invention."

The study in progress at the time the present instrument was devised was an investigation of the effects of relative humidity of air adjacent to the surface of the leaf upon infection and disease development by several humidity-sensitive plant pathogens. This, therefore, presented a measuring problem of more than ordinary difficulty.

REVIEW OF LITERATURE

McDougal[13] described a hygrometer depending upon the water uptake and curvature of a piece of photographic film that could be placed on the surface of a leaf to determine whether stomata were open or closed. Livingston[12] improved the precision of cobalt chloride paper by preparing stable color standards of Prussian blue that could be used as end points when measuring transpiration from plant surfaces. Buxton and Mellanby[2] reported use of a paper hygrometer that increased in weight in the presence of a moist atmosphere. An accuracy of ± 2 per cent was claimed when used for measuring the relative humidity at the surface of leaves.

Ramsey et al.[15] measured the relative humidity gradients above transpiring leaves with a very tiny hair hygrometer. An accuracy of ± 1 per cent was claimed for this instrument; however, comparative readings made with the hair hygrometer described and a very small evaporimeter were not completely comparable. Yarwood and Hazen[21] reported that measurements of the temperature depressions resulting from use of green leaves tightly clamped around thermometer bulbs (instead of moistened cotton wicks) could be used for calculation of the relative humidity at the surface of the leaf.

Delp[3] attempted to measure relative humidity by use of a wet thermocouple near the surface of the leaf, but stated:

"It was not considered that this method or any other method found in the literature was adequate for a precise measure of the humidity in the microclimate of a germinating spore on a transpiring leaf."

Still others had made attempts by indirect methods to determine the relative humidity at the surfaces of leaves. Using the data of Ramsey et al.,[15] Frampton and Longrée[8] were able to calculate theoretical relative humidity values at zero distance from the leaf, i.e., at the surface of the leaf. Shaw[16] and Thut[18] derived values for the relative humidity of intercellular spaces and for the stomatal openings, respectively.

All of the methods described above had at least one or more serious drawbacks for the present work. The ideal instrument was visualized as having the following general characteristics.

(1) It must not add or remove large quantities of water from the area. This eliminates most types of wet- and dry-bulb apparatus and any method involving absorption of large quantities of moisture.

(2) It should not affect the temperature of the immediate area or involve mass air movement, which would interfere with leaf temperature depressions by complication of the heat transfer conditions around the leaves. This

precludes use of most psychrometric methods and dew-point apparatus.

(3) The method should be remote-reading so that measurements can be made while leaves are subjected to experimental conditions. This would seem to make some electrical method necessary.

(4) The sensing element must be relatively small to prevent accumulation of transpirational moisture between the instrument and leaf surface.

(5) The method must be accurate, sensitive and reliable.

(6) It would be advantageous if the instrument were also easy to make and calibrate, simple to use, inexpensive, mechanically foolproof and adaptable to continuous recording.

At about this time we became familiar with the Dunmore electrical hygrometer, which was used originally in radiosonde weather instruments carried aloft by balloons to measure relative humidity conditions of the upper air. Reduced to bare essentials, this instrument consisted of two electrodes connected with a hygroscopic salt bridge. As the salt absorbs or loses moisture in equilibrium with the atmosphere to which it is exposed, the electrical resistance of the bridge changes. The resistance can then be measured with the appropriate measuring instruments.

In this original report, Dunmore[5] described his sensing element as being constructed by winding a bifilar winding (with wires about 1 mm apart) of tinned copper wire on an etched glass cylinder. The entire assembly was dipped in a water absorbent material such as silica gel or gelatin and then into a solution of some hygroscopic salt such as lithium chloride. The speed of response of such an instrument was from $2\frac{1}{2}$ to 10 times that of a hair hygrometer, but it was found to have a temperature error of about 1 per cent for each $2°C$ temperature change. Two serious defects were noted: (1) a long-term aging effect, which caused a gradual increase in resistance with the passage of time and (2) a serious hysteresis effect when passing from high to low humidity values.

The following year, Dunmore[6] reported improvements that corrected the major faults of the original device. The long-term aging was found to be due to gradual oxidation of the tinned copper winding, and the hysteresis resulted from water adsorption on the etched glass surface. By use of wires of a more inert material, e.g., platinum, palladium or gold, wound on water-resistant, polystyrene-coated, thin-walled aluminum tubing, both difficulties were overcome. In addition, use of the aluminum tubing instead of glass resulted in a more rapid temperature equilibrium between air and the sensing element, so that the temperature error of the new instruments was reduced to less than 2 per cent at $25 \pm 10°C$.

Improvement of the hygroscopic coating was achieved by addition of the lithium chloride to partially hydrolyzed polyvinyl acetate. This resulted in a tightly adhering, homogeneous film that permitted rapid passage of moisture.

Evans and Davenport[7] showed the temperature effect to be the result of interaction of two opposing tendencies, which tend to neutralize each other. Increasing temperatures decrease the resistance of the electrolytic solution but also increase the vapor pressure of the solution in the film. This latter effect causes water to pass from the film and increases the resistance.

The Institute of Paper Chemistry Staff[10] reported construction of a battery-powered, readily portable hygrometer based on the Dunmore principle. Since Dunmore had shown earlier[6] that continued use of direct current across the bridge resulted in polarization, these authors obtained alternating current by use of a vibrator such as that used to supply alternating current for automobile radios. The same group (Institute of Paper Chemistry Staff)[11] later prepared a smaller, flat-surfaced type of sensing element by sputtering a platinum film on a small block of polystyrene, then grooving out a narrow gap across the film with a shaper. The gap was bridged with the lithium chloride-polyvinyl acetate mixture previously reported. Later, Van den Akker[19] used small $\frac{1}{2}$-in.-square glass plates carrying evaporated platinum film electrodes, separated by a narrow gap.

Dobrin,[4] using this type of sensing element, determined that the amount of moisture absorbed by the hygroscopic coating at 75 per cent RH was of the order of 0.000116 to 0.000128 mg/mm^2 of absorbing surface. Thus the instrument will not add or remove appreciable quantities of moisture from the area being measured—a very desirable characteristic.

More recently, Brastad and Borchardt[1] have described the smallest hygrometer of this type so far noted; one constructed inside a 0.050-in. diameter hypodermic needle. They state that if a current density of more than 0.05 μA per linear inch of active coating is employed, the instruments will have a relatively short useful life. A carbon film electric hygrometer reported by Smith and Hoeflich[17] seems to have several advantages over the basic Dunmore instrument, for example, more rapid response, higher sensitivity, absence of polarization, and lack of temperature error between 0 and 40°C. Manufacture of the sensing elements is, however, a difficult task, which, up to the present, can be done only by highly skilled workers.

THE HYGROMETER

Preparation of the Sensing Elements

Thin picture glass, 0.04 in. thick, was plated on one side with a thin, evaporated rhodium film.* except for 0.03-in.-wide gaps left at intervals across the plate. These gaps were obtained by stretching pieces of flat-drawn wire tightly across the surface of the glass before plating. The "shadow" cast by the wire during the plating operation gave the desired width gap.

Rhodium was selected as the plating metal for two reasons: (1) it is almost as inert chemically as platinum or palladium, so that long-term aging of the hygrometers should not be a problem, and (2) it forms a hard surface that adheres very firmly to the glass. Ordinary polishing will not damage the film, and it is sufficiently adherent so that lead wires could be soldered directly to the film, using ordinary resin-core solder.

The plates were cut into pieces about 2×12 mm with the gap across the center as shown in Fig. 1. Then leads of 18-gauge insulated copper wire were soldered to the ends of the elements. Following this, the hygroscopic coating was applied, the soldered leads were insulated with a liquid polystyrene, nonconducting coating, and the sensing elements were aged for about 2 weeks before calibration.

A small, uniform-sized drop of the hygroscopic coating in 50 per cent alcoholic solution

* This was done by Evaporated Metal Films, Inc., 147 E. State St., Ithaca, N.Y.

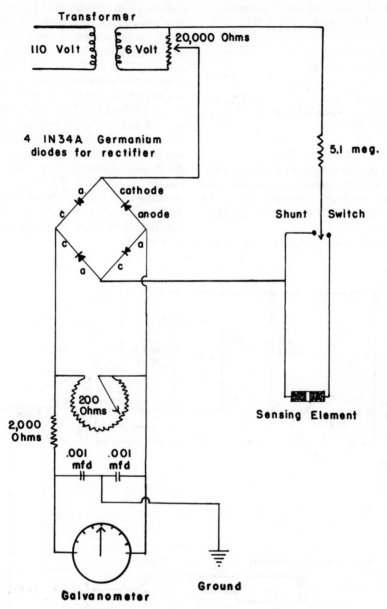

FIG. 1. Circuit diagram for the laboratory indicating instrument.

was applied to each element using a thinly drawn-out pipette. If the same sized drop is applied to different elements, their calibration curves will be very nearly the same. The composition of the coating solution is given in Table 1.

Since any given element covers only 15 to 20 per cent of the entire relative humidity range, a graded series of elements had to be prepared to cover the entire working range desired. Different ranges were covered by using different concentrations of lithium chloride in the coating mixtures—more lithium chloride for low humidity elements and less for those to be used at high relative humidity levels.

TABLE 1. COMPOSITION OF THE HYGROSCOPIC
COATING FOR SENSING ELEMENTS

Water, ml.	50
95% Ethyl alcohol, ml.	50
Polyvinyl acetate-alcohol,* g.	2
Lithium chloride, g.	0.02 to 1.5

* "Solvar" brand polyvinyl acetate, 36% hydrolyzed, secured from Shawinigan Products Corp., Shawinigan Falls, Quebec.

The Indicating Instruments Used

One of the instruments built to measure the current across the hygrometers was based on the original electrical circuits given by Dunmore.[5] The circuit diagram used is shown in Fig. 1.

Alternating current at 110 V from a voltage stabilizer was transformed to 6 V AC. It was then passed through a 20,000 Ω voltage divider which could be used to make the fine adjustments necessitated by slight changes in line voltages. The current then passed either through the hygrometer element or, by means of a switch, across a shunt to the rectifier and thence to the DC galvanometer. At the beginning of any group of readings, a maximum galvanometer scale deflection of 100 mm was established by passing the current across the shunt and adjusting the voltage divider previously mentioned. Then the hygrometer could be switched into the circuit in place of the shunt and a reading of less than 100 resulted, depending upon relative humidity conditions.

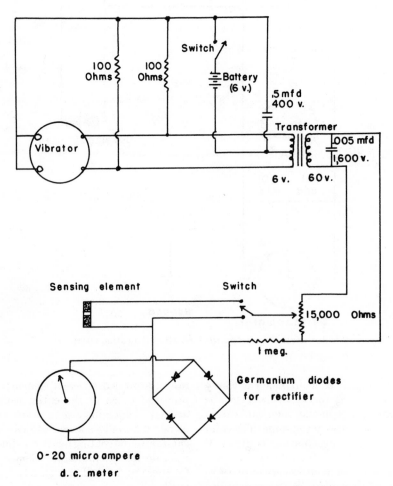

FIG. 2. Circuit diagram for the portable indicating instrument.

The rectifier used was composed of four germanium diodes (Sylvania 1N34A) connected as illustrated. A full-wave selenium instrument rectifier had been tried at first, but was found to leak too much current to be usable. The germanium diodes worked perfectly.

The galvanometer used was a Leeds and Northrup Type R, with separate lamp and scale, having a sensitivity of 0.003 μA/mm scale division and a critical external damping resistance of 2000 Ω. By limiting the maximum scale deflection to 100 mm, the maximum current that could ever flow across the hygrometer was 0.3 μA. Two 0.001-mfd capacitors were connected in parallel across the galvanometer contacts and grounded as shown in the diagram to reduce the deflections caused by extraneous electrical influences. Shielded lead wires to the hygrometers had been tried before installation of these capacitors, but they could not be used due to the severe reduction in sensitivity that they introduced.

A second indicating instrument was constructed which was portable and could be used for making relative humidity measurements in the greenhouse or in the field. This was powered with a 6-V dry battery. A Mallory 859 vibrator was used to give alternating current, which is necessary to prevent polarization of the hygrometer sensing elements. A 0 to 20-μA DC ammeter installed in the unit was used to indicate the flow of current. The wiring diagram is shown in Fig. 2 and was given by the Staff of the Institute of Paper Chemistry.[10]

The portable instrument was not as satisfactory as the laboratory instrument. One of the main reasons may have been that the larger currents required to deflect the less-sensitive meter caused an increase in resistance of the elements. A slight downward drift occurred in the readings if current was passed through the elements for more than a few seconds at a time. This fact made it necessary to standardize the time of reading to a uniform period, after current began passing through the elements, for critical work. Such a drift was not noted when using the laboratory instrument. With it, the currents flowing through the circuit were apparently so small that no change in resistance occurred even though the elements were used continuously for fairly long periods of time.

Calibration of the Elements

Calibration of the elements was found to be a very time-consuming job. Galvanometer readings were obtained when the hygrometers were exposed to controlled relative humidity atmospheres inside the desiccator-calibration chamber diagrammed in Fig. 3. These were plotted against relative humidity values computed from wet and dry thermocouple readings obtained simultaneously inside the same chamber. The small fan inside the chamber was necessary to secure correct wet-bulb thermocouple readings, but also served to cause rapid equilibrium between the sulfuric acid solutions placed in the base of the desiccator and the atmosphere contained therein. Different relative humidity conditions were obtained inside the chamber by using sulfuric acid solutions of varying concentrations.[9, 20] The desiccator had several holes in its sides so that 8 to 12 hygrometers mounted in rubber stoppers could be calibrated simultaneously. After changing solutions, about 2 hours was allowed, with the fan running, for equilibrium to occur. Since any one element covered only about 15 per cent of the entire relative humidity range, acid solutions were prepared at relative humidity intervals of about 3 per cent, in order to establish several points on the

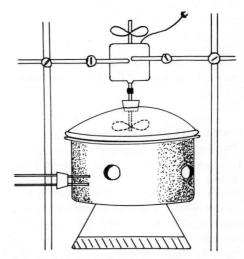

Fig. 3. Calibration chamber used. Readings from hygrometers inserted through holes in sides of desiccator calibrated against wet and dry thermocouple readings taken simultaneously. Relative humidity in chamber controlled by sulfuric acid solutions.

calibration curve of each hygrometer used.

If an easier and quicker method of calibration were available, the usefulness of the hygrometers would be increased greatly. Use of a divided flow apparatus, in which separate streams of moist and dry air could be mixed in different proportions, would seem to have considerable promise.

The Elements in Use

The elements were employed in several ways. They could be used simply to indicate ambient relative humidity of the atmosphere to which they were exposed. They were also utilized to make rapid measurements of relative humidity near the surfaces of leaves. A period of thirty seconds or less was required for equilibrium to be reached. The element could be clamped directly to the leaf with only 0.75 mm separating the moisture-absorbing surface of the hygrometer and the surface of the leaf.

In addition, moisture gradients were measured near leaves by mounting an hygrometer on the moving pin of a mechanic's micrometer, so that relative humidity determinations could be made at accurately measured distances (0.75 to 10 mm) from the leaf (Fig. 4). The micrometer setting could be adjusted by remote control so that the operator did not disturb the atmosphere near the plant. This was accomplished by connecting the micrometer holding the leaf and hygrometer to a second micrometer with a length of automobile speedometer cable. Adjustments then were made by turning the latter instrument.

CONCLUSIONS

Advantages of the Instrument

This instrument appears to have several advantages over many previously reported devices for making relative humidity measurements near the surfaces of leaves or in small enclosed spaces. The sensing element is small enough that there should be no trapping or accumulation of transpirational moisture between the instrument and the leaf surface during routine use. Being an electrical method, it is remote reading, so that measurements may be made while leaves are subjected to experimental conditions or in controlled-environment chambers. The hygroscopic coat-

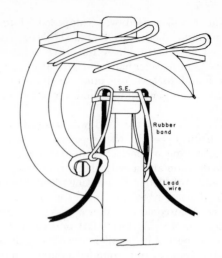

Fig. 4. Micrometer used to position sensing element at accurately controlled distances when measuring humidity gradients near the leaf.

ing removes negligible quantities of moisture from the atmosphere;[4] therefore, the relative humidity conditions are not appreciably affected.

The instrument may be used in completely still air or in small enclosed spaces. Mass air movement is not necessary for attainment of equilibrium (as is required with psychrometric methods). Equilibrium is reached quickly, usually within less than one minute. With proper indicating instruments for measurements of the current, a sensitivity of one-fourth of one per cent can be attained. It is doubtful, however, if the sensing elements could be calibrated to this degree of accuracy without very expensive equipment. An accuracy of ± 1 per cent should be readily attained, however.

Limitations

For certain types of measurement, the instrument has definite limitations. The sensing elements can not be used reliably at relative humidity values of 95 per cent or higher, or in locations where liquid water is likely to be deposited on them, because of the danger of removal of minute quantities of the hygroscopic coating, with consequent changes in the calibration of the elements. Because of this feature, the use of the instruments as permanently installed elements in the field would be precluded.

Each element covers only about 15 per cent of the total relative humidity range; therefore, if the conditions being measured varied more than that amount, a series of elements would be necessary to cover the range.

For best results, a very low current density across the salt bridge is necessary. This results in an increased useful life of the individual sensing element and freedom from drift during reading. In order to hold the current down, very sensitive galvanometers are needed for best results. Therefore, use of the instrument is best restricted to a laboratory or greenhouse where the delicate indicating devices may be properly supported and maintained. For the worker with a field problem, this feature would be a distinct disadvantage.

References

1. Brastad, W. A., and Borchardt, L. F., "Electric Hygrometer of Small Dimensions," *Rev. Sci. Instr.*, **24**, 1143–1144 (1953).
2. Buxton, P. A., and Mellanby, K., "The Measurement and Control of Humidity," *Bull. Entomol. Res. London*, **25**, 171–175 (1934).
3. Delp, Charles J., "Effect of Temperature and Humidity on the Grape Powdery Mildew Fungus," *Phytopathology*, **44**, 615–626 (1954).
4. Dobrin, Saxe, "The Moisture Transmission of Packaging Materials at Low Temperatures," Ph.D. Thesis (unpublished), Cornell University, pp. 39–63, 1949.
5. Dunmore, Francis W., "An Electric Hygrometer and its Application to Radio Meteorography," *J. Res. Natl. Bur. Std.*, **20**, 723–744 (1938).
6. Dunmore, Francis W., "An Improved Electrical Hygrometer," *J. Res. Natl. Bur. Std.*, **23**, 701–714 (1939).
7. Evans, R. N., and Davenport, J. E., "A Study of the Electric Hygrometer," *Ind. Eng. Chem. (Anal. Ed.)*, **14**, 507–510 (1942).
8. Frampton, Vernon L., and Longrée, Karla, "The Vapor Pressure Gradient above a Transpiring Leaf," *Phytopathology*, **31**, 1040–1042 (1941).
9. Hepburn, J. R. I., "The Vapor Pressure of Water over Sulfuric Acid-Water Mixtures at 25°C and its Measurement by an Improved dew-point Apparatus," *Proc. Phys. Soc. London*, **40**, 249–260 (1928).
10. Institute of Paper Chemistry Staff, "An Electric Sword Hygrometer for Measuring the Relative Humidity of Air Inside Packages and Other Enclosures," *Paper Tr. J.*, **116**, No. 24, 16–19 (1943); **117**, No. 1, 12–15 (1943).
11. Institute of Paper Chemistry Staff, "Progress Report on the Development of Two New Electric Methods for the Measurement of Water Vapor Permeability," *Paper Trade J.*, **122**, No. 1, 35–44 (1946).
12. Livingston, B. E., "Improvements in the Method for Determining the Transpiring Power of Plant Surfaces by Hygrometric Paper," *Plant World*, **19**, 287–309 (1916).
13. MacDougal, D. T., "A New Hygrometer Suitable for Testing Action of Stomata," *Torreya*, **1**, 18–20 (1901).
14. Middleton, W. E. K., "Meteorological Instruments," pp. 1–231, Toronto, University of Toronto Press, 1947.
15. Ramsey, J. A., Butler, C. G., and Sang, J. H., "The Humidity Gradient at the Surface of a Transpiring Leaf," *J. Exp. Biol.*, **15**, 255–265 (1938).
16. Shaw, Luther, "Intercellular Humidity in Relation to Fire-blight Susceptibility in Apple and Pear," *N.Y. State Agr. Exp. Sta. Memoir*, **181**, 1–40 (1935).
17. Smith, W. J., and Hoeflich, N. J., "The Carbon Film Electric Hygrometer Element," *Bull. Am. Meteorol. Soc.*, **35**, 60–62 (1954).
18. Thut, Hiram F., "The Relative Humidity Gradient of Stomatal Transpiration," *Am. J. Botany*, **26**, 315–319 (1939).
19. Van den Akker, J. A., "Application of the Electric Hygrometer to the Determination of Water Vapor Permeability at Low Temperature," *Paper Trade J.*, **124**, No. 24, 51–56 (1947).
20. Wilson, R. E., "Humidity Control by Means of Sulfuric Acid Solutions, with Critical Compilation of Vapor Pressure Data," *Ind. Eng. Chem.*, **13**, 326–331 (1921).
21. Yarwood, Cecil E., and Hazen, W. E., "The Relative Humidity at Leaf Surfaces," *Am. J. Botany*, **31**, 129–135 (1944).

32. The Measurement of Relative Humidity in Confined Spaces*

J. E. KENNEDY

Defence Research Medical Laboratories, Toronto, Ontario, Canada

ABSTRACT

Conventional psychrometric and gravimetric methods of hygrometry are not readily adaptable for use in confined spaces. Alternative approaches depend upon materials having some physical property sensitive to changes in relative humidity; these suffer in general from a slow response. In recent years, humidity sensing elements of an electrolytic resistance type, in which a change in resistance of an electrically conducting film occurs with a change of ambient relative humidity, have found wide acceptance for both measurement and control. These elements are reasonably stable, have a fast response, and may be used with a simple measuring circuit. Available elements of this type are too large, however, for some research applications, such as the exploration of the sub-clothing microenvironment on clothed human subjects.

The characteristics desired in elements suitable for microclimate studies are outlined. A number of presently available elements have been considered but were found unsatisfactory or unsuitable either in test performance in a controlled humidity cabinet or by reason of their structure and physical dimensions. A concentrated effort to produce dependable and versatile elements of miniature size is urgently required.

INTRODUCTION

The problem of the measurement of relative humidity in confined spaces is not new. It has become of greater importance in recent years

* DRML Technical Note 511, PCC D49-70-01-03.

as scientific investigation has been extended to fields in which microenvironmental conditions are of primary interest such as packaging and clothing. For some time, it has been apparent that measurement of aqueous vapor pressure within biological systems such as plants and animals, as well as in experimental apparatus in which vapor pressure gradients exist, would contribute to the understanding and potential control of the vapor and thermal transfer processes. While substantial strides have been made in the development of humidity sensing elements of greater reliability and convenience, the production of elements of truly miniature size has not been achieved on any scale suitable for application where spatial limitations are extreme.

A particular interest of our laboratories serves as a basis for this discussion. Nude man and his immediate environment comprise two complex systems between which heat and water vapor are exchanged. For the clothed man these exchanges are modified when resistance added by the clothing system is introduced. Depending on its design and the environmental conditions, clothing may either increase or relieve the thermal stress on the body. In evaluating clothing assemblies designed for protection against particular environments, the measurement of the microclimate within the clothing on the man offers a useful approach to the analysis of the problem.

Temperature and relative humidity in a clothing system must be measured while the clothing is being worn under the climatic conditions for which it was designed. Relative humidity has proved to be by far the more difficult quantity to measure adequately. Clothing is, in general, a porous flexible system of low thermal capacity through which air, heat and water vapor pass continually. The measurement of relative humidity within such a system must not disturb appreciably any of these gradients; i.e., the total thickness, heat conductance and porosity of the clothing at the points of measurement should remain unaffected. This requires either a very small humidity element or one of a particular geometry. A postage-stamp size element (2 cm × 2 cm) would fulfil these particular requirements provided it were less than 1 mm thick and as permeable to water vapor as a woven fabric.

The hands and feet generate considerable quantities of perspiration, and handwear and footwear made of leather offer considerably more resistance to water vapor escape than other components of the clothing system. Relative humidity has been measured with some success by the "patch" technique in heavy socks worn under cold weather footwear (Fig. 1). This approach depends on the moisture absorption properties of a textile fabric and on accurate determinations of the weight of a patch of fabric before and after use at the

point at which relative humidity is to be determined. The gain in weight of the patch can readily be interpreted in terms of the relative humidity prevailing there at the time of its removal. While some information can be gained in this manner, it is impossible to follow the dynamic changes in relative humidity taking place within the system. Patches of fabric can be and have been used at almost any point in the clothing system, but the number and accuracy of the measurements and the extent of the information obtainable are limited severely in this approach.

CHARACTERISTICS

The relative importance placed upon the characteristics desired in miniature humidity sensing elements may vary with the intended application. From the research point of view, some requirements are more stringent than others, and these can be listed as primary characteristics; additional desirable features are secondary considerations.

Primary Characteristics

Size and Adaptability. The primary requirement for any element is that it can be located accurately at the site of the measurement. While an element about the size of a pin head would suffice everywhere, in many situations the limitations of space are imposed in only one dimension; in these applications a thin disc-type element might serve. The maximum thickness permissible in the restricted dimension could be of the order of 1 mm, and flexibility in this plane might be essential. For all but pin-head sized elements, appreciable permeability to water vapor and air are required to minimize the effect of the measuring element upon the local vapor pressure and air movement.

Hysteresis. All moisture absorption systems exhibit hysteresis. For the measurement of vapor pressures where each observation may differ from the previous one, hysteresis increases the error of measurement. An important consideration, therefore, in assessing the suitability of a sensitive material for the element is the magnitude of the hysteresis.

Temperature and Time Dependence. The response of elements with which we have

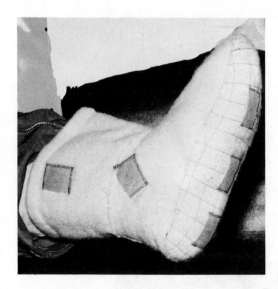

Fig. 1. Patches of wool fabric, inserted in pockets of fiberglass mesh provide a means of measuring relative humidity by the "patch" technique at a number of locations on the duffle sock, part of a cold weather footwear assembly.

gained experience is dependent upon temperature, and exhibits drift over extended intervals of time. To measure relative humidity at a point in a combined temperature and vapor pressure gradient, the temperature coefficient of the element should be as small as possible. Some lack of stability with time is tolerable, but necessitates calibration at more frequent intervals.

Speed of Response. For studies in which equilibrium or steady-state conditions prevail, speed of response or time constant may be disregarded. In clothing and in many other applications, relative humidity changes may occur rapidly and for either monitoring or control purposes these changes should be detected with the minimum delay.

Secondary Considerations

The durability of the elements and the complexity and cost of auxiliary measuring equipment are matters which must be viewed in relation to the intended research. In the total absence of means of measuring the relative humidity in confined spaces, the cost can be weighed only against the value of the research data sought. In most laboratories in which such measurements would be valuable, manpower is insufficient for the development of elements to meet specific local requirements; this situation has contributed to slow progress in this area.

OUR EXPERIENCE WITH SMALL ELEMENTS

Elements in which electrical resistance is a function of ambient relative humidity offer the greatest convenience in microenvironmental studies of clothing. Some of the available commercial elements of this type might be expected to satisfy or be adaptable to the requirements already outlined. To explore this possibility, a number of elements (Fig. 2 and Table 1) were compared with calibrated Class A Hygrodynamics elements in a controlled atmosphere. The measuring circuit comprised a stabilized 3-V 60-cps supply connected to

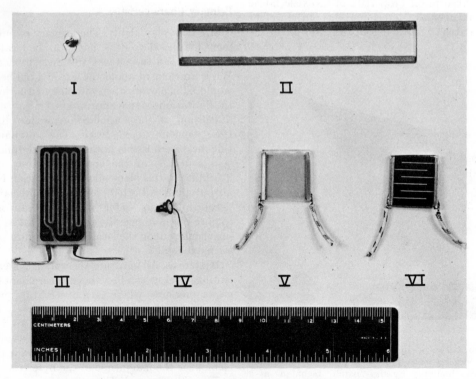

FIG. 2. A selection of small humidity sensing elements. All but type I are available from commercial sources. The dimensions of these elements appear in Table 1.

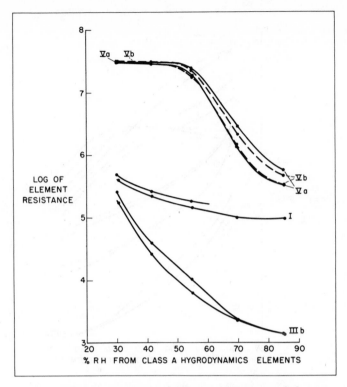

Fig. 3. Electrical resistance of three of the types of elements shown in Fig. 2, measured at selected relative humidities; corrections for lead capacitance have not been applied. Curves (a) and (b) refer to different specimens of the same type of element.

the humidity sensing element and an AC vacuum tube voltmeter in series. Values of 1.00 MΩ and 18.8 kΩ could be selected for the input impedance of the voltmeter, with full scale ranges of 3, 1 and 0.3 V.

TABLE 1

Element	Dimensions
I	6.5-mm diameter × 0.5-mm thickness
II (a) and (b)	100 × 17 × 1 mm
III (a) and (b)	40 × 21 × 1.3 mm
IV (a) and (b)	6-mm diameter × 7-mm height with mount
V (a) and (b)	21 × 21 × 3 mm
VI	21 × 21 × 3 mm

The elements under test were exposed to relative humidity cycles from 85 to 5 per cent and back again at a constant temperature of 85°F. The time of exposure at each constant relative humidity level was at least 18 hours. These results are summarized in Figs. 3 and 4.

Values shown are the resultant of the element resistance shunted by the wiring capacitance, which was about 40 pf. The effect of this shunting capacitance is illustrated by the calculated data of Table 2, showing the difference between the measured and true element resistance in the higher range under this condition of measurement. In normal usage of an element in clothing, wiring capacitance might well exceed this amount.

TABLE 2

Resultant impedance shown	30 MΩ	40 MΩ	50 MΩ
True element resistance	34 MΩ	51 MΩ	80 MΩ

The elements exhibiting the best combination of desirable properties on the basis of these results are II and III. Both are rather large and are impermeable to water vapor.

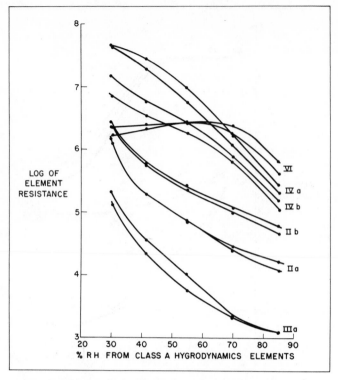

FIG. 4. Electrical resistance of four of the types of elements
shown in Fig. 2, measured at selected relative humidities; corrections for lead capacitance have not been applied. Curves (a) and
(b) refer to different specimens of the same type of element.

Element I, an anodized aluminum disc type,
exhibited erratic behavior, and valid readings
could not be obtained for the last two points
on the cycle. This particular element was
fragile, and had probably suffered from
previous handling. Nevertheless, it exhibited
less change of resistance than most during
test. It may be observed that only element III
returned to its initial resistance value.
Element V would be useful only above 50 per
cent RH; Element VI exhibited a maximum
in resistance between 55 and 60 per cent RH;
Elements IV, V and VI showed appreciable
drift in resistance.

REQUIREMENTS

In considering the need for miniature
elements, a clear distinction must be drawn
between routine applications for which only a
completely "foolproof" item will prove satisfactory, and research applications for which a
considerable sacrifice of robustness and general
convenience of operation may be tolerable.

There are at least ten, possibly more, independent approaches which have been
applied to the measurement of relative humidity. Attempts have been made in several of
these approaches to miniaturize humidity
elements, although difficulties of stability and
durability remain very considerable. Of these
ten, which then can be most readily adapted
for the measurement of relative humidity in
confined spaces?

Transistors, thermistors, and ferrite cores
are three examples of electronic components
whose size has been spectacularly reduced in
the past two decades. The ideal type of
humidity element for which we are searching
is one in which a reduction in size comparable
with the examples cited above can be realized
without the introduction of serious complications in the measurement. Electrical elements,
in which resistance is a function of the relative

humidity, offer the greatest potential in this respect, provided that the reduction in physical dimensions will not be accompanied by a major increase in resistance.

A significant advantage would result from a capability of the element and its associated circuitry for adaptation to short range telemetry in applications such as clothing research. Conventional measurements of temperature at several locations on a clothed subject require a corresponding number of lead wires to recording instruments. In ambient outdoor conditions, where a subject is exposed to climatic effects which cannot be duplicated in the environmental chamber and in which it is desirable to have his normal tasks carried out without restriction, recording of such measurements appears feasible only through telemetering systems.

All presently known means of measuring relative humidity should be reexamined, and an assessment should be made of the extent to which miniaturization of these devices appears practical. Without miniature elements of adequate precision, stability, and speed of response, research in a number of fields has been and will be severely limited. We do not believe that we in clothing research are alone in this dilemma.

Acknowledgment. The assistance of Dr. L. E. MacHattie in measuring the resistance of the humidity sensing elements and preparing this data for publication is gratefully acknowledged.

33. Carbon Humidity Elements — Manufacture, Performance and Theory

S. L. STINE

*U.S. Army Electronic Material Support Agency, Electronic Command,
Fort Monmouth, New Jersey*

ABSTRACT

A method of fabricating carbon humidity elements which produces a reasonable yield of uniform units is described. A procedure of testing the element performance for compliance with government specifications also is included. The response of the element to changes in humidity and temperature is presented, and anomalies in the performance are, where understood, related to the film structure. A simple theory of mechanism of response is proposed, with such data as are available to support the theory. Recommendations for design to improve element performance and reliability are offered for consideration.

INTRODUCTION

The theory and studies reviewed herein encompass the efforts of a great many persons over a period of twenty years. The basic concept of the carbon humidity element was suggested by Dr. E. K. Carver of the Eastman Kodak Research Laboratory to Dr. Charles W. Brasefield of the U.S. Army Signal Corps Research Laboratory, Fort Monmouth, N.J., in 1942. The Signal Corps and the Eastman Kodak Research Laboratory initiated studies in this area in 1942 under the direction of Dr. Brasefield. Additional studies were conducted later with the assistance of the following organizations:

(a) Eastman Kodak Research Laboratories
(b) Arthur D. Little Corporation
(c) General Electric Research Laboratories
(d) Minneapolis-Honeywell Regulator Company
(e) Bendix-Friez Division of Bendix Corporation
(f) Monmouth Electric Corporation.

In addition to these groups, the assistance of the Department of the Air Force, the Department of the Navy and the Department of Commerce is gratefully acknowledged.

Time and space will not permit the proper accrediting of each and every individual for his contribution to the development of this sensor; however, it is important to note that the sensor is the product of a great many persons schooled in widely diversified disciplines. We are deeply grateful to each and everyone who contributed their knowledge and efforts to make the sensor a practical reality. As a further note, the author of this paper did very little of the work discussed here; it has been his lot to collect and consolidate the technical facts regarding the sensor for the guidance of the research workers.

Considerable effort and time was expended exploring methods of mass producing the sensor. Two of these methods, the Arthur D. Little spray technique and the Monmouth Electric Corp. dipping procedure, proved especially fruitful with respect to the formulation of a theory of operation. Most of the results described herein are derived from elements manufactured by these processes.

The method of manufacture described below

316

is essentially the dipping procedure. Nearly half a million sensors have been produced by this basic technique or by minor modification of the procedure. The procedure described is primitive in design and requires an excessive care in preparation that makes the manufacture of the sensor more costly than is warranted. In the hands of careful, experienced laboratory technicians, however, the procedure described will provide elements of superior quality.

The performance of the sensors when manufactured for use in radiosondes is specified by Military Specification MIL-H-13186B (SigC). This document is currently in need of revision, both from the standpoint of element capability and from consideration of modern weather forcasting data requirements. The full performance capability of the sensor is not being utilized in the radiosonde, and as a result, much less information is obtained from radiosonde flights than would otherwise be possible.

While details of manufacture and performance will be discussed herein, the primary emphasis will be on the theory of operation. The theory expressed herein is, for the most part, unsubstantiated and is offered to stimulate thought and study in this field.

PHYSICAL DESCRIPTION OF THE ELEMENT

Radiosonde Element

The carbon humidity element, as produced for radiosonde usage is $2\frac{1}{2}$ in. long, $^{11}\!/_{16}$ in. wide and 0.040 in. thick. It consists of a flat acrylic plastic strip with the long edges metallized. The entire plastic strip is completely coated with a gelatinous cellulose coating that contains finely divided carbon particles in suspension.

Cylindrical Elements

The sensor has been produced in the form of a plastic rod having diameters ranging from $\frac{1}{8}$ to $\frac{3}{4}$ in. and lengths from $\frac{1}{4}$ to 4 in. In some of these elements, the ends of the rod have been metallized to serve as electrodes; in others a spiral set of metallized strips along the rod have been employed. In either case the plastic rod has been coated with a gelatinous cellulose film similar to the flat radiosonde element.

Experimental Sensors

Self-supporting Films. The cellulose film may be cast or extruded from dies entirely free of substrate support of any nature. Generally, electrical contact to such films is made by wires to which the film will adhere, if, prior to initial contact with the film, the wires have been wetted by dipping in the cellulose mix or deionized water.

Nylon Cloth Substrate. Sensors have been prepared by immersing nylon stocking fabric (undyed, grey base material) in the cellulose-carbon mixture. The sensor may be produced in two forms by this process; one in which the interstices of the substrate are filled and a second in which only the threads of the substrate are coated. The latter form is more flexible and shows faster response to changes in relative humidity. However, the manufacturing technique is quite involved. Electrical contact is made by metallizing the edge of the fabric or by clamping a v-shaped metal strip over the edge of the fabric.

Paper Substrate. Edge-metallized strips of paper have been substituted for the flat plastic strips. No appreciable improvement in performance has been attained with those units which responded to changes in humidity.

Welsbach-mantle Form. The sensor has been made (experimentally) in the form of a Welsbach-mantle with one electrode consisting of the metallized edge of the mantle base and the other electrode being a metal insert pressed into the fabric substrate at the apex of the mantle. The fabric substrate was a heavy-gauge nylon cloth, which was coated with the cellulose-carbon mixture in such manner that the interstices of the substrate were open.

Thread Form. The cellulose-carbon mixture has been extruded and partially polymerized in the form of a continuous filament. The filament was cut into various lengths and the ends metallized for electrical contact. They showed equal response in many respects to the flat elements and could be wound into many interesting shapes. The breaking strength of the filaments was low.

Stabilized Foamed Substrate. Thin slabs of metallized edge polystrene foam were coated by the dipping technique. No appreciable improvement in performance was noted over that of the flat element.

Foamed Cellulose-carbon Mixture. An attempt was made to form partially polymerized foamed sheets or thin slabs of the cellulose-carbon mix. The attempt was only partially successful, and the performance of the end product was questionable.

Bubble Films. The partially dried film from bubbles of the cellulose-carbon mixture was investigated. Large bubbles were difficult to form and their electrical resistance was high.

A METHOD OF MANUFACTURING CARBON HUMIDITY ELEMENTS

The procedure described herein evolved from the study of many different production procedures. Elements have been produced by this method in quantity with a yield rate as high as 80 per cent. Other procedures are used which are also capable of providing high yield in quantity production; for the most part, these procedures are less expensive in time and money. There is in development at least one manufacturing method which, theoretically, should reduce the production of these elements to a machine process.

SUBSTRATE PREPARATION

Materials

(a) Flat acrylic plastic strips, $3\frac{1}{4}$ in. long by $1\frac{1}{16}$ in. wide and 0.04 in. thick.

(b) duPont conductive silver paint No. 4916 or equivalent.

(c) Butyl acetate.

(d) "Alconox" cleaning detergent or equivalent.

(e) Deionized water.

(f) "Amberlite" or "Amberlite 200" deionizing material or equivalent.

(g) Polyethylene or "Teflon" chemware.

(h) Infrared drier.

(i) Clean room.

(j) Vacuum plating equipment (or chemical plating equipment, as alternative to painting electrodes).

(k) Gold.

Procedures

(a) Clean the strips of all grease, oil and dirt by use of ordinary methods. It is good practice to avoid touching the strips with the hands after cleaning.

(b) Coat the long edges of the strips with the conductive silver paint, being especially careful to avoid splattering the paint between the designated areas for the electrodes.

(c) Dry the paint under the infrared drier avoiding temperatures in excess of the softening temperature of the substrate.

Alternate, preferred technique: Vacuum deposit or chemically deposit gold on the long edges of the strip. Hot pressed gold leaf will function equally successfully if done with care.

(d) Check the dimensions of the electrodes. The electrodes should be $\frac{3}{32} \pm \frac{1}{64}$ in. wide. Inspect each strip for clarity of center section. Reject any strips having electrode material between the designated areas for the electrodes.

(e) Clean the strips by vigorous agitation in hot water to which a mild detergent and wetting agent such as "Alconox" has been added. This can be efficiently accomplished by loading the strips in a polyethylene or "Teflon" open weave basket and dousing the basket vigorously in the bath.

(f) Rinse and agitate the strips in their basket container in warm running water until no soap bubbles appear for at least 15 minutes of agitation.

(g) Rinse the strips thoroughly in baths of running (not recirculated) warm deionized water. At least three separate baths are recommended.

(h) Store the blank strips in deionized water so that they do not touch each other and there is free circulation of freshly deionized water about them.

COATING MIX PREPARATION

Materials

Equipment. (1) Clean room: dust free, temperature controlled to $25 \pm 2°C$, humidity controlled to 33 ± 2 per cent RH.

(2) Controlled ambient hood: dust free, preferably vapor and carbon dioxide free, temperature controlled to $25 \pm 1°C$; humidity controlled to 33 ± 1 per cent RH; ventilated.

(3) Stirrer: Waring Blender (or equivalent type) equipped with "Teflon" or polyethylene coated blades.

(4) Stirrer: laboratory type; equipped with "Teflon" or polyethylene coated blades.

(5) Chemical balance: minimum sensitivity 0.001 gram.

(6) Laboratory torsion balance: minimum sensitivity 0.1 gram.

(7) Chem-lab ware: preferably made of polyethylene or "Teflon."

(8) Desiccators.

(9) Source of clean, filtered dry air; 30 pounds of pressure.

(10) Vacuum pump.

(11) Buchner filter: vacuum, 4 in.

(12) 200-mesh stainless steel filter screen.

(13) Ball mill: kilo capacity, stone balls $\frac{1}{2}$ to $\frac{3}{4}$-in. diameter.

Chemicals. (1) Hydroxyethylcellulose (HEC): WP-3 as made by Union Carbide and Carbon Corporation.

(2) Deionized water: deionized by continuous passage over 3-ft beds of "Amberlite" or "Amberlite 200" as made by Rohm and Hass, Inc.

(3) Nonyl phenyl polyethylene glycol ether: nonionic, "Tergitol, Nonionic NPX, Anhydrous," as made by Union Carbide and Carbon Corporation.

(4) "Triton" wetting agent: WR-1339 as made by Rohm & Hass Co.

(5) Carbon dust: "Elf" 1 as made by Godfrey L. Cabot Inc.

(6) Carbon dust: "Elf" 2 as made by Godfrey L. Cabot Inc.

(7) Sorbitol: G-2240 as made by Atlas Power Co.

Procedure

General Notes. The preparation of the coating mix must be carried out most carefully. All weighing, mixing and other operations should be conducted in the controlled ambient of the hood described under equipment. Ten days should be allowed for the preparation of the mix.

Mixture 1. *Ingredients.* (a) 25 grams of hydroxyethylcellulose (HEC) WP-3. (The HEC should be kept under desiccants for at least 1 month before use. HEC which has been stored open to the atmosphere apparently agglomerates and will not perform properly).

(b) 470 cc of H_2O—must be deionized in "Amberlite" to 1.5×10^{-7} mho or lower in conductivity.

(c) 4 cc of "Tergitol," nonionic NPX, anhydrous.

Procedure. Mix the "Tergitol" drop by drop (28 drops "Tergitol" = 1 cc) with the water while hand-stirring the water. Continue stirring by hand for about 15 minutes or until the "Tergitol" appears to be in solution. Then stir with motor stirrer for 30 minutes at such speed that no bubbles are formed. Increase stirring rate to high speed and sift in HEC, preventing clumps of HEC in excess of $\frac{1}{16}$ in. from entering solution. The rejected (clumped) HEC must be weighed and this weight of usable HEC then added.

The solution must be stirred until all HEC is in solution—usually about 2 hours. The solution will be very bubbly and a foam will cap the liquid. Break down the foam with a fine jet of *filtered* air, cover and set aside for about two days to permit bubbles to disperse. During this period, the solution will gel to a greater or less extent. If a brown colored liquid separates from the gel, discard the solution and start over. If the brown liquid persists in forming in each successive solution, replace all ingredients with new, fresh materials.

If the gel is clear, break up the gel by hand stirring and pass it through a $\frac{1}{2}$ in. layer of "Amberlite" in a 4 in. Buchner filter, applying vacuum gently to the filter. The "Amberlite" is best supported on a 200-mesh stainless steel filter screen as made by Hansen, Munsell and Van Winkle. Continue filtering until conductivity is 0.2×10^{-7} mho or less. Store in burette (large with large opening).

Mixture 2. *Ingredients.* 10 cc "Triton" solution (See below) WR-1339 (Rohm and Hass Company, Philadelphia 5, Pa.); 5.75 grams carbon (70 per cent "Elf" 1, 30 per cent "Elf" 2; Godfrey L. Cabot, Inc); 20 cc H_2O deionized in "Amberlite" (Rohm & Hass Co).

Procedure. (1) Triton Solution: 10 cc "Triton," 100 cc H_2O (deionized).

Dissolve "Triton" in hot deionized water. When cool, add 50 grams "Amberlite" and shake. Decant into burette and cap.

(2) Carbon Mix: Pour "Triton" solution into the 20 cc of water and hand stir until well-mixed. Sift carbon into solution, eliminating clumps as before and hand stir.

Mixture 3. *Ingredients.* 80 cc HEC solution from mixture 1; 210 cc H_2O, deionized; 60

drops G2240 Sorbitol, Atlas Powder Co.

Procedure. Hand stir HEC solution while slowly adding H_2O from burette until mixture is uniform. Continue stirring and add G2240.

Mixture 4. (1) Slowly hand stir carbon mix from mixture 2 while adding solution from mixture 3. Blend at moderate speed in Waring Blender for 1 minute. Use jet of filtered air to eliminate bubbles. Ball mill for 2 hours.

Mixture 4 may be stored in "Teflon" or polyethylene containers for long periods, but it must be thoroughly stirred when re-used. Sedimentation of carbon during storage may be counteracted during element manufacture by slower rates of withdrawal during dipping. It is advisable for best results to tumble or ball mill the mix between uses rather than to store statically. The mix will show change with age.

ELEMENT DIPPING

Procedure

Mounting in Dipping Rack. The blank strips, if wet, should be dried with infrared radiation in a controlled ambient immediately before dipping in the coating solution. The end half-inch of 20 to 100 blanks are edge-mounted in the metal (preferable phosphor bronze, gold plated) contacts of the dipping rack. The dipping rack must be scrupulously clean and the mounting contacts should touch as little of the element blank as possible.

Dipping. The dipping rack is then mounted on a mechanism whose vertical range and rate of movement can be accurately controlled. The element blanks are lowered into the mix, held for 10 seconds and then carefully and uniformly withdrawn at a *constant rate*. The rate of withdrawal is very critical. For the mix to be described herein, the best rate of withdrawal was found to be $2\frac{1}{8}$ in. per 25 seconds.

Drying. When the dipping rack is removed from the mix, it should be immediately exposed to briskly moving air stream having a temperature of $23 \pm 3°C$ and a relative humidity of 33 ± 3 per cent. The elements will appear to be dry in about 5 minutes; however, they should be kept in this atmosphere for at least 24 hours before final adjustment. It is desirable to connect at least one element from the center of the array on each dipping rack to a Wheatstone bridge and make

frequent checks of its resistance. When the resistance has stabilized to within $\pm 100\ \Omega$ for a period of four hours, the elements are ready to be cut and adjusted.

Cutting. The end of the element which last left the dipping solution should be cut off for a distance of $\frac{1}{4}$ in. In addition, the uncoated portion of the element (where it was gripped by the metal electrodes of the dipping rack) should also be cut away for $\frac{1}{2}$ in., reducing the overall length from $3\frac{1}{4}$ to $2\frac{1}{2}$ in.

Adjustment. The element will normally be about 10 per cent low in resistance before adjustment. If it should be high, it can only be discarded. The element is exposed to an atmosphere controlled to a temperature of $23 \pm 3°C$ and 33 ± 3 per cent RH, and the resistance is measured on an indicating instrument—preferably a deviation bridge utilizing 60-cycle AC current. The film is abraded by scratching with a pin and dimpling with the fibers of a stiff brush, or by scraping a portion of the film away, until the resistance comes into tolerance. The element is then stored for 8 to 10 days in the same atmosphere while frequent checks are made of its resistance. The resistance should normally drop by about 3 to 4 per cent during this storage.

PERFORMANCE

Resistance-Humidity Response of 25°C

The electrical resistance of the sensor as a function of the ambient relative humidity at 25°C is shown in Fig. 1. As indicated, the resistance curve shows an open loop, commonly called the "hysteresis" curve of the sensor. Elements acceptable for radiosonde usage are calibrated for both increasing and decreasing humidities, and if the difference in indicated humidity exceeds ± 3 per cent from the 25°C adsorption isotherm, the element is rejected. The "hysteresis" loop of the element is one of the characteristics of the unit and, as will be shown later, is probably due to the physical form of the element.

As shown in Fig. 2, the resistance-humidity response curve tends to flatten at high humidities. This "flattening" or "hump effect" has been found to be due to ionic impurities in the mixture from which the cellulose film was made. Elements manufactured under "sterile" conditions have very little "hump" in their

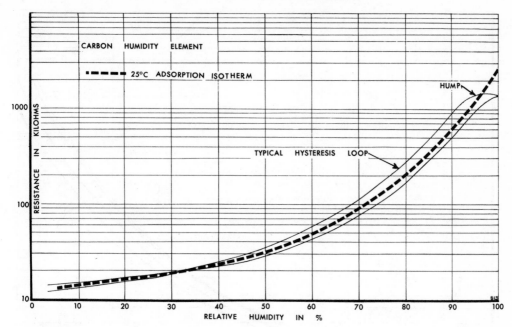

FIG. 1. Response of the carbon humidity element. The dotted line is the specified 25°C adsorption isotherm.

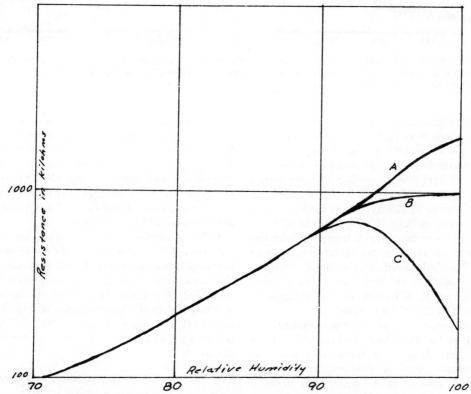

FIG. 2. "Hump" effect. Curve A shows a desirable average response. Curve B shows an average production lot response. Curve C shows the effect on the average curve of ionic pollution of the wet stage of manufacture.

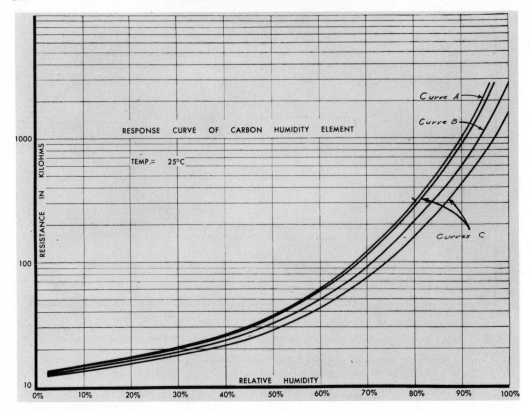

FIG. 3. Specified limitations on 25°C adsorption isotherm. Curve A: Upper limit of deviation of response from 25°C adsorption isotherm due to hysteresis. Curve B: Specified 25°C adsorption isotherm. Curve C: Tolerance on 25°C adsorption isotherm.

characteristic curve as compared with elements made from cellulose mixtures containing known amounts of ionic contamination. Sensors made from contaminated mixes will generally have a negative-slope characteristics curve above 90 per cent RH.

The curves of the hysteresis loop of Fig. 1 cross in the vicinity of 33⅓ per cent at 25°C. This crossover has never adequately been explained, although some theoretical reasons have been advanced. For a given cellulose-carbon mixture, the crossover point is fixed, and major modification of the formula is required to produce a change.

While several empirical mathematical expressions for the characteristic curve have been derived, none of them have been expressed in terms of the properties of the materials present in the sensor. Attempts to arrive at an equation for the characteristic curve from empirical data alone, usually are found to be dependent on the form or shape of

the element, and they fail to describe the response of a differently formed element made from the same coating mixture. For this reason, it is necessary to designate the dimensions and shape of the element very carefully. In this section of this report, only the performance of the flat, military, radiosonde sensor will be described.

It has been found that the statistical distribution of the response data about the mean curve for the loop in Fig. 1, will generally, if the sensors are carefully manufactured, be such that 80 per cent or more of the sensors will fall within the limits shown in Fig. 3 at +25°C. The uppermost curve in Fig. 3 shows the acceptable limitation for the "hysteresis" deviation.

Temperature Effect on Characteristic Curve

The resistance of the sensor at +25°C over the range of humidity for which it was designed is given in Table 1 in terms of the resistance

TABLE 1. NOMINAL RESISTANCE RATIOS AT +25°C

RH (%)	R/R_{33}	R
10	0.700	14,000
20	0.810	16,200
30	0.940	18,800
33 (R_{33})	1.000	20,000
40	1.175	23,500
50	1.580	31,600
60	2.500	50,000
70	4.600	92,000
80	10.60	212,000
90	30.00	600,000
100	145.0	2,900,000

ratios contained in MIL specification MIL-H-13186 (B) SigC. The resistance ratio at each temperature T is defined as

$$\frac{\text{Resistance at } x\% \text{ RH and } T°C}{\text{Resistance at } 33\frac{1}{3}\% \text{ RH and } T°C}$$

where the resistance at $33\frac{1}{3}$ per cent RH and 25°C is specified to be 20,000 Ω. Typical values at other temperatures are 21,600 Ω at 0°C, 24,500 Ω at −20°C, and 29,000 Ω at −30°C. The resistance ratios at various temperatures are shown in Fig. 4, each curve being resistance ratio referred to the value of 1 at $33\frac{1}{3}$ per cent RH, independent of changes of absolute resistance value at that point as temperature changes.

The resistance-humidity isotherms for the sensor are shown in Fig. 4. The data supporting these curves is far too sparse and too inaccurate to permit any general statements to be made. It was originally thought that the change in humidity indication with temperature at a given resistance would be a simple function such that for each successive decrease in temperature, the change in indicated humidity would be some constant fraction of the preceding humidity change. Examination

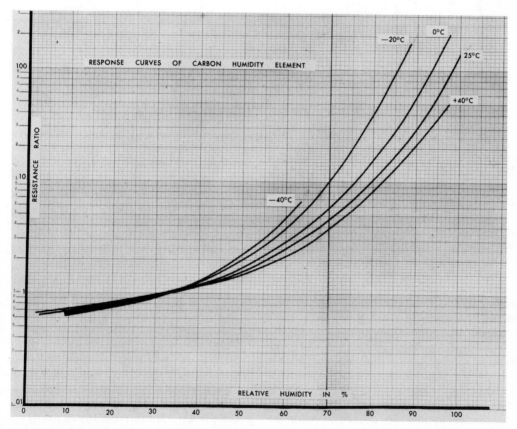

FIG. 4. Resistance ratio isotherms. The ratio of 1 at $33\frac{1}{3}$ per cent RH typically represents 20,000 Ω at 25°C, 21,600 Ω at 0°C, 24,500 Ω at −20°C, and 29,000 Ω at −30°C.

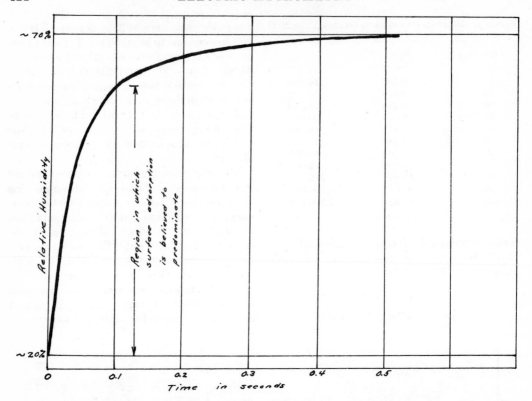

FIG. 5. Curve illustrative of the response with respect to time of the carbon element. For precise information on this factor, refer to Paper 12.

of the data in Fig. 4 will reveal that the above concept is not supported by the data; however, the inaccuracies of measurement and the variation among the sensors from which the data were derived were such as to preclude immediate rejection or acceptance of the idea. There are physical reasons to believe that such a simple empirical relationship will only hold between about +40 and −40°C, in that the materials of which the sensor film is composed change in their elastic properties in the vicinity of these temperatures.

A very serious deficiency in the status of our knowledge concerning these sensors is contained in the data of Fig. 4 which were taken from an early production run of elements. To date, no statistically conclusive and consistent evidence has been obtained regarding the low-temperature response of the element. Until such time as well-designed experiments are conducted to determine this data, we cannot expect to measure humidity with an accuracy better than 10 per cent at temperatures below freezing.

Time Constant of Sensor

The time response of the sensor is illustrated in Fig. 5. The response is not a simple exponential function and has prompted many conjectures as to the physical process involved in the adsorption of water vapor. The accuracy of the measurements from which Fig. 5 was derived was not better than ±3 per cent RH, but the deviations of the curve from the exponential shape exceed this figure, and it is believed that the sensor must possess a multiplicity of time constants. A physical mechanism which may account for such a phenomena is described in the section on theory (p. 330).

Polarization

No measurable effects similar to polarization have been reported for this sensor. There is some evidence that the capacitance of the sensor will affect the transmission of radiofrequency currents through the element, but the exact nature of this effect is not known. Calibration is usually done with 60-cycle AC current or direct current. No difference is observed that exceeds the probable error of measurement.

Aging

The sensor will shift, in resistance at $33\frac{1}{3}$ per cent RH and 25°C as shown in Fig. 6. The initial change after adjustment is usually to a lower value after which a very gradual increase in resistance can be measured over a period of months. The sensors will, on the average, remain within usable limits for periods of 2 to 4 years if stored properly (above freezing and at, preferably, 30 to 90 per cent RH).

Washout and Contamination

The sensor is not seriously affected by condensation or liquid water unless it is immersed for several hours. When liquid water is on the surface of the element, its indications are in error; however, the element will usually read within ±3 per cent RH after the liquid water is removed. Elements soaked in a water bath for 3 hours showed physical deterioration

and serious change in calibration, but they responded repeatedly within ±3 per cent RH to a new characteristic curve.

The element is relatively insensitive to contamination after initial aging. In an effort to induce the "hump" effect in elements that were initially free of this defect, six elements were soaked for 2 hours in a 10 per cent brine solution. The elements showed relatively slight deterioration and did not display the "hump" effect. It is interesting to note, however, that six elements whose substrates were deliberately handled with bare fingers before coating showed a severe "hump" effect. The element is very susceptible to ionic contamination during fabrication.

THEORY OF OPERATION

General Remarks

The original concept of the sensor was simple and clear-cut. It was proposed to suspend conductive particles in a matrix which would expand and contract with changes in the relative humidity of the

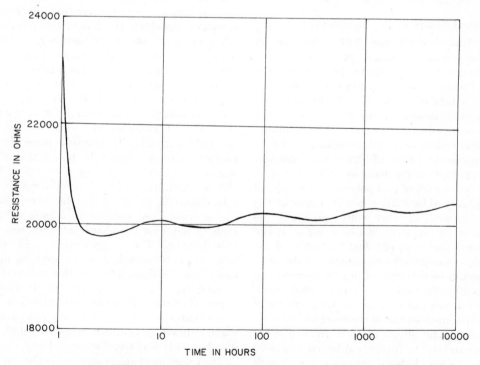

FIG. 6. Typical data showing the aging of the carbon humidity element. The wave-like character of this line is not to be taken too seriously. No two elements behave the same, but the general nature of their aging curves is similar to this.

ambient. It was expected that the conductivity of the matrix would vary as the conducting particles were moved about by the motion of the matrix.

Many materials were investigated to serve as the matrix, and this study still continues, for the response of the element is primarily a function of the hygroscopic properties of the matrix. The term "carbon humidity element" is really a misnomer, but it is probably too well established to warrant changing it at this late date. While the element does contain finely divided carbon, the carbon is comparatively inert to water vapor, and the reaction of the sensor to humidity can be attributed primarily to the cellulose ingredients in its recipe. It would perhaps be better to call this sensor the "cellulose electric hygrometer."

The ingredients of the sensor film are:

(1) Hydroxyethylcellulose (HEC)
(2) Sorbitol
(3) Carbon and wetting agent
(4) Gelling agent.

In addition to the above materials, of course, a substrate provided with the proper electrical contacts must be available.

Chemical Nature of the Ingredients

Hydroxyethylcellulose (HEC). The reaction of the sensor to changes in ambient water content is so closely linked to the nature of the HEC, that it is necessary to review briefly the basic nature of cellulose itself. By the term cellulose, is meant "chemical cellulose" or the pure material—not the material encountered in paper making or in cotton clothing. Cellulose is reported to consist of long-chain condensation products of β-glucose as shown in Fig. 7. The "products" of this polymerization are all chemically alike except in the length of the chain formed; in other words, except in the value of n in the formula shown in Fig. 7. The chemical and most physical properties of the cellulose molecule are reasonable similar in so far as can be determined until n decreases to approximately 500, at which point some chemical rates of reaction and the degree of cellulose involvement in the reaction changes. The last factor affects the performance of the sensor and will be further explained. Cellulose molecules tend to bond or cross-link with each other along their length. When the chain length is long, say $n = 3000$ or greater, the number of bonds or cross-links become very large, and the molecules form semi or partial "crystals" of cellulose along portions of their length. If the cross-linking assumes a regular pattern with respect to the molecule, truly crystalline structure can be detected. In general, however, the molecules in a solution or wet film of cellulose are randomly oriented with respect to each other, and the cross-linking can only take place at those points between the molecules where the major axes of the molecules come into close proximity. Since the molecules of cellulose tend to form loose helices, the cross-linking is enhanced by the spacial interweaving of the molecules. Molecules whose major axes are parallel and whose spiral convolutions are regularly intertwined have the greatest number of cross-links. Such materials show the strongest and best defined X-ray diffraction patterns and are probably the most nearly perfect "crystals" of cellulose that exist. Areas of cellulose films demonstrating this highly ordered pattern of molecules have the lowest expansion and contraction with changes in the relative humidity of the environment. It appears reasonable to assume that adherence of water molecules to the molecules of cellulose takes place at the same points along the cellulose molecule as the cross-linking, and that the bonding mechanism is similar.

The structural formula of hydroyethylcellulose is shown in Fig. 8. The basic cellulose chain structure is the same, but ethylene alcohols of various lengths have been substituted for the CH_2CH radicals in some of the glucose units. It should be noted that the degree of substitution is never known to be 100 per cent. The effect of introducing these side chains is to shield the basic cellulose chains from close proximity to each other, thereby reducing the chance of spontaneous cross-linking. The hygroscopicity of the molecule is increased, and the swelling and contraction of films made by this material is greater than that of pure cellulose. It would appear that the HEC molecule is more free to move than the pure cellulose molecule. HEC readily dissolves in water, whereas cellulose dissolves only slightly, if at all.

The exact mechanism governing the swelling action of cellulose is not completely understood, but it is believed that the adherence of

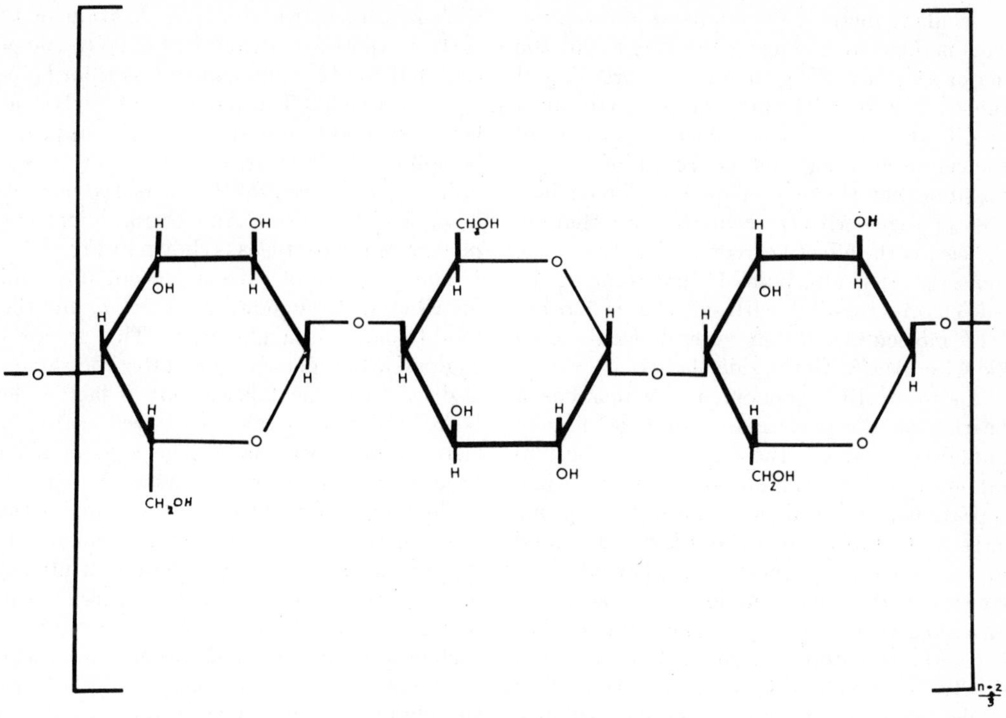

FIG. 7. Cellulose Structural Formula.

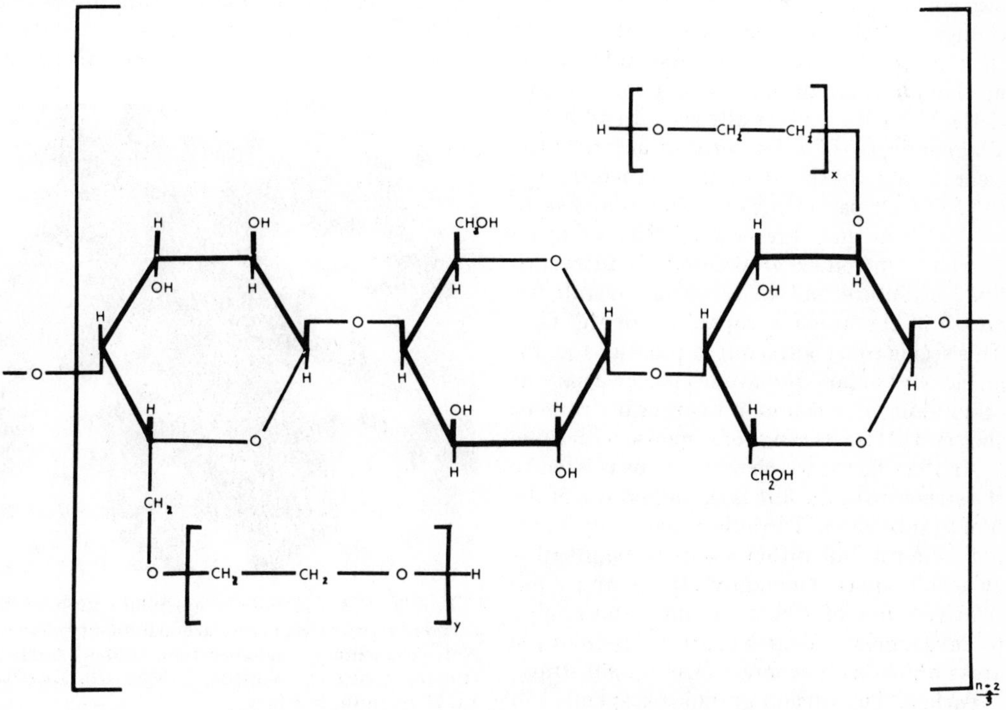

FIG. 8. Hydroxyethylcellulose Structural Formula.

water to the HEC molecule causes the molecule to increase the diameter of its spiral. This is done by a counter-twisting about the major axis, involving thereby a shortening of the overall spiral length, rather than by a modification of the basic form or spacing of the cellulose core structure. In addition, it is possible that the side chains are forced into greater angles with the cellulose core, thereby increasing the effective overall diameter of the molecule. It is also possible that some of the side chains cross-link with side chains of other HEC molecules and that water molecules may likewise bond with the side chains.

An interesting phenomenon which has a bearing on the performance of HEC film in humidity sensors is the tendency of the film material to assume an ordered structure when repeatedly stretched mechanically along one axis. A film (unsupported) of the mixture used in radiosonde sensors was supported in a controlled atmosphere under a microscope on an arrangement of pulleys in such manner that it could alternately be stretched and released slowly. After each of 50 stretches, the motion of the carbon granules was measured (photographically) as the ambient relative humidity was raised and lowered. It was found that the movement of the carbon granules for a given change in RH approached constant value as the number of stretches increased and that the motion of carbon granules near clear portions of the film fell to practically zero. In addition, a higher degree of order in the structure of the clear portions of the film was observed than in the less transparent regions. This would seem to indicate that exercise of this material tended to introduce an ordered "semicrystalline" structure and to cause an overall decrease in the swelling capability of the film. This seems to be borne out in practice too, for an element exposed to atmospheric variations of humidity in a common weather instrument shelter will lose its range of response with time.

Another factor which seems to be related to the structure of the film is the adherence of the film to substrates. The adherence of the film is not uniform, but rather seems to be greatest at small areas. Generally, these areas are relatively free of carbon granules and appear to have a greater degree of structure than the areas which easily separate from the substrate.

Carbon. The carbon granules suspended in the HEC matrix appear to be relatively inert with respect to water vapor. A gram of the carbon exposed to an ambient of 90 to 100 per cent RH for 12 hours gained less than $\frac{1}{2}$ per cent by weight. The particles of carbon are between 1 and 10 μ in diameter and appear to be spherical. The particle size is remarkably uniform, 99 per cent of the measured particles being 3 ± 1 μ in size. An electron microscope picture of the particles is shown in Fig. 9.

The particles of carbon are not uniformly distributed throughout the matrix, but they tend to clump or agglomerate. This process of agglomeration persists even after the element is dried following fabrication; in fact, it has been observed to take place years after an element has been made. The agglomeration process is apparently accelerated by exercise of the film. A film of the same mixture as that used on the dipped radiosonde element, but free of any substrate, was mounted under a microscope in a controlled ambient cell in such manner that the size of a single clump of carbon could be observed and measured while the humidity in the cell was cycled. The size of the clump increased from approximately 90 to over 700 μ in its long dimension after 150 cycles from 20 to 90 per cent RH and back. The matrix surrounding the clump was relatively clear of carbon particles at the end of the experiment. It is believed that this process

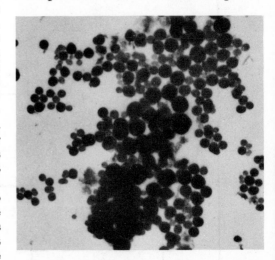

FIG. 9. Electron microscope photograph of the carbon particles used in the carbon humidity element. Note elementary agglomeration. About 4000 X. (Photographed by William F. Nye, USAELDRA, Ft. Monmouth, N.J.)

and the development of ordered matrix structure produce the very gradual increase in resistance of the element with time.

It has been observed that carbon clumps ranging in size from 100 to 300 μ tend to work their way out of the film. They appear, under the microscope, to be entirely free of any type of "wetting" by the matrix. Examination of the clumped particles that have worked out of a film reveals no definite structure.

The distribution of the carbon along the edge of the contact is shown in Fig. 10. It should be noted that areas relatively clear of carbon occur along the contact edge. The same feature is observed anywhere that the substrate shows a departure from a strictly flat plane. At the contact, a rise of .005 to .020 in. existed. Painted contacts demonstrate this effect more severely than plated or evaporated contacts.

Humectant (Sorbitol). It was found that the addition of a humectant to the mix enhanced the mechanical and electrical response of the film to changes in humidity. The exact process, on the molecular scale, from which this improved response is derived, has not been firmly established. The presence of the humectant in this case, sorbitol, seems to eliminate partially the development of ordered HEC structure. It is believed that the sorbitol molecules provide a "solution" in which the HEC molecules are semi-suspended but free

to expand and contract. The sorbitol molecules are considered to form a "cushion" barricade between HEC molecules that inhibits the cross-linking of the HEC.

Sorbitol absorbs water strongly. However, the change in physical dimensions with absorbtion is only about $\frac{1}{100}$ that of HEC. It is interesting to note that the HEC shows about 20 per cent more dimensional change if in a gel containing sorbitol. This increase is considered to be due to the increased number of positions for water to adhere to the HEC molecule because the sorbitol has prevented cross-linking.

It is also possible that the presence of sorbitol permits a more rapid diffusion of water molecules into the film, thus making available the underlying molecules of HEC for participation in the mechanized reaction. Certainly the time response of the film is measureably enhanced if sorbitol is present.

Wetting Agent (Triton). Improved performance has been observed if the carbon is mixed with a wetting agent initially in the preparation of the film. Without the wetting agent, the agglomeration of the carbon is more pronounced.

Gelling Agent (Tergitol). "Tergitol" imparts to the finished film a soft gel-like structure in which the HEC is relatively free to move. Depositions lacking "Tergitol" have a "wet" appearance and will stain anything that touches them. The response is not as uniform or repeatable.

Physical State of the Film

Structure. When dried, after dipping, the element has a uniform black plastic-like appearance. Detailed microscopic study of the surface reveals that the surface film is actually randomly mottled with clumps of carbon. The film is constantly in motion, rarely uniform over its entire surface. Thus one portion of the surface may be expanding while an adjacent portion is contracting. The motion is primarily in the thickness direction. The relative change is 5 to 30 times greater in thickness than length or width.

Electrical Response. The resistance change of the element is a smooth function of the relative humidity. No step function change in resistance is observed. Step-type response should not be observed, if the orientation of

FIG. 10. Microphotograph of carbon humidity element along contact. Solid portion of photo at top is the contact. Note clearer areas adjacent to contact.

the absorber is random. The response is not measureably altered by a change in frequency of the impressed voltage within the limits of 0 to 400 cps.

Time Response. The shape of the time response curve for the element is such as to indicate that more than one time constant is present. This effect may be explained in terms of the composition and mechanical motion of the film. The initial very quick response is thought to be due primarily to surface adsorption. About 85 per cent of the total resistance variation takes place during this initial change. The balance of the change takes place at about $\frac{1}{10}$ the rate of the initial change and is thought to be dependent on the diffusion of the water into the film. About 50 per cent of the expansion of the film takes place during this second phase of the changes. The expansion of the film and the twisting of the spirally shaped HEC molecules provide more positions for adsorption of water molecules. It is believed that the initial adsorption is primarily on the sorbitol, which induces the necessary mechanical motion of the HEC.

Hysteresis. The phenomenon of hysteresis is believed to be primarily a surface effect of the film. When the ambient humidity is decreased, the average number of water molecules per unit surface at any given instant almost immediately decreases. The surface then tends to bond together and contract, trapping water molecules that have been absorbed into the body of the film. In support of this view, it has been observed that the area between a rising humidity curve and a decreasing humidity curve for the element is a direct function of the thickness of the film (over the thickness tested). Extremely thin self-supported films, exposed to the ambient on all sides, have much less hysteresis and are much faster in response.

Humping. The tendency of these films to demonstrate a negative resistance-humidity slope at humidities in excess of 90 per cent has been traced to ionic "poisoning" of the wet element during fabrication. Elements manufactured under "sterile" conditions do not display a negative slope. Elements manufactured from deliberately polluted mixes do show a negative slope. The minimum resistance ratio at which the hump may occur at various relative humidities is shown in Table 2.

TABLE 2. MINIMUM ACCEPTABLE VALUES OF THE RESISTANCE RATIO FOR THE REGION WHERE "HUMP" MAY OCCUR

RH (%)	R/R_{33}
88	23.5
89	25.5
90	28.0
91	30.0
92	32.0
93	34.0
94	36.0
95	37.8
96	39.2
97	40.0
98	41.1

CONCLUSIONS

The theory and conjectures outlined above are reviewed to stimulate study of these films. It is felt that not only will a better humidity sensor result from a properly manned study of these phenomena, but a great deal may be learned of the nature of molecular bonding and adsorption. A thorough study of this film will benefit many disciplines of scientific effort.

34. The Dynamic Behavior of the Carbon Humidity Element ML-476

R. M. Marchgraber and H. H. Grote

*U.S. Army Electronic Research and Development Laboratory,
Fort Monmouth, New Jersey*

ABSTRACT

Measurements of the step-function response of the carbon humidity element ML-476 taken at different environmental temperatures and with humidity steps of different magnitude are presented. The measurements were performed on a two-pressure system of high precision with a test port modified to allow exposure of the elements under test to controlled humidity steps of negligible rise-time anywhere within the operating temperature range of the elements.

The response characteristics obtained show a fast initial response followed by a slower drift to equilibrium.

Mathematical models of second order and third order for the response of the carbon element are given in a form which yields to the restoration of the input time function from the measured output of the humidity sensor, using an analog technique. Though data restoration with this method is possible with a high degree of precision even with temperature varying coefficients in the modeling differential equation, the obtainable accuracy is limited by the quality of the chosen model, but especially by the "memory" feature of the carbon element, its hysteresis, and the consequent necessity for using a mean calibration curve in the evaluation of actual flight data.

INTRODUCTION

The carbon-type humidity sensor is gaining more and more attention as replacement for the lithium chloride element in radio-sounding of the atmosphere.

The reason may be found in its faster response, particularly at the lower regions of the temperature environment, its higher resistivity against washout effects, and its narrower hysteresis loop.

At this time, the evaluation of humidity data obtained in radiosonde flights makes use of mean calibration characteristics obtained in static testing and neglects altogether the dynamic behavior of the sensor which is responsible for an output which is increasingly distorted if the lag-time of the sensor increases with decreasing environmental temperatures and with increasing rate of change of the humidity atmosphere probed.

The humidity sensor behaves as a low-pass filter with a temperature-dependent cutoff, increasing input frequencies being transferred with increasing shift in phase and decreasing amplitudes, both functions of the temperature-dependent filter characteristic. Increasing lag-times thus degrade the value of measurements in many applications unless a detailed knowledge of the sensor's behavior allows the application of some corrective means.

To obtain a picture of the sensor's low-pass characteristic and to find, if possible, an analytic expression for it, the transient response of the carbon element was measured at different temperatures and varying changes in humidity.

To limit the scope of the study, which was to be of only an exploratory nature, a number of assumptions were introduced, the implications of which have to be considered.

To allow analytic treatment, the assumption of a linear behavior* at least for each single experiment was assumed with the implication that a step-function response of the sensor will sufficiently describe the dynamics of the sensor. Secondly, the attempt was made to eliminate the influence of calibration characteristics varying between samples and during experimentation (fabrication spread and memory). Thirdly, it was assumed that for eventual input restoration, an output of the sensor will be available as a continuous analog or that, at least, a constant sampling rate meets the requirements of the sampling theorem and thus insures no loss of intelligence if conversion back to analog, as needed for input restoration, is performed.

MEASURING TECHNIQUES

The transient tests were performed with a "two-pressure" humidity atmosphere producer built by the Minneapolis-Honeywell Research Center and with a modified test chamber insert.

In the two-pressure method developed by

* This does not exclude nonlinear calibration characteristics.

Weaver and Riley,[9] A. Wexler,[10] and E. Amdur,[1] air is saturated with water vapor at a pressure above ambient. Isothermically expanded to ambient pressure, the relative water vapor content is reduced very nearly* proportional to the ratio of the pressure in the test chamber to the pressure of saturation.

By keeping control over the temperature of saturation and test chamber areas, atmospheres of precisely known relative humidities can be established. Figure 1 shows an oversimplified schematic of the two-pressure system and the modified insert for the test chamber. The insert consists, following a proposal of E. Amdur, of a small chamber which may be closed or opened instantaneously by means of a piston operated by compressed air.

With the elements in place and the small lag chamber open, a certain humidity atmosphere is established, the elements under test are stabilized, and a measurement is taken.

Closing the lag chamber allows changing of the humidity atmosphere in the large chamber while the elements are still in the previous environment. Opening the lag chamber finally

* A correction for nonideal behavior of the water vapor is readily applied.

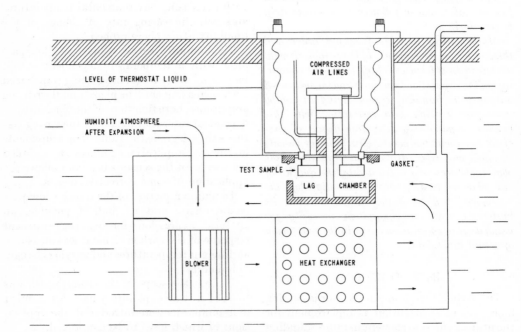

FIG. 1. Test chamber (schematic) with insert for lag measurement.

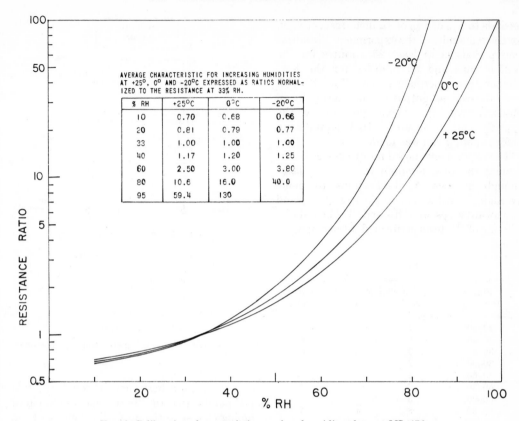

FIG. 2. Calibration characteristic—carbon humidity element ML-476.

exposes the test samples to the new humidity environment. A ventilation rate of approximately 600 fpm (to simulate balloon flight conditions), continuous exchange of the air within the test chamber, and the 1:50 volume ratio of small and large chambers insure nearly instantaneous mixing and exposure of the test samples to a step in relative humidity.

Experiments at 25°C, where present carbon-type humidity elements have rather quick response, show no indication of delayed mixing.

The carbon element, described elsewhere,[2, 4-6, 8] responds to changes in atmospheric humidity with a change of its electric resistivity, caused by a sequence of sorption and diffusion of water vapor, and dilation of the hygroscopic film, thus changing the conductive path by changing the average spacing of the carbon particles in the film.

A glance at the average calibration of the carbon element, Fig. 2, shows the rather large variation in resistance which is to be expected

in transient tests employing large steps in the humidity atmosphere, and which suggests the use of a non-linear resistance scale for the recording of the element resistance versus time.

A constant voltage source with adjustable resistor in series with the element under test, and a low impedance, fast-responding current instrument may be easily fitted to the varying conditions of the experiments. Figure 3, which is self-explanatory, shows the circuit used and the provisions for adjustment and calibration. The measuring voltage (AC to avoid eventual polarization of the elements) is so regulated that the current through the element does not exceed 50 μA, thus avoiding any possible loading effects on the samples under test.

The recording was made on a Visicorder with M 100-350 galvanometer inserts, flat in response within ± 5 per cent from 0 to 60 cps, and with a sensitivity of 6.3 μA/in. A speed of 1 in./sec was employed for the early phases of the transient and was changed after about 20 seconds to $\frac{1}{10}$ or $\frac{1}{20}$ of an inch, respectively, for the remainder of the experiment. Stabilization periods of at least 25 minutes for the $+25°C$ runs and 60 minutes for the low-temperature experiments were allowed. In all cases the element output was monitored by an observer over the whole duration of the experiments to insure actual equilibrium before another run was made.

The experiments posed no specific problems besides the time required to obtain a large enough number of observations to make averaging sensible. For this reason the up and downward steps were limited. Table 1 shows a listing of the tests performed. Step responses

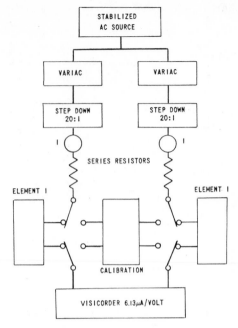

FIG. 3. Circuit for measuring step-function response.

TABLE 1

Step	Number of Measurements		
RH (%)	25°C	−5°C	−20°C
20–40	4	—	—
30–60	6	5	4
30–80	3	3	5
30–90	2	—	—
40–60	4	—	—
60–80	6	5	4
60–90	3	—	—
60–30	5	4	4
90–60	2	—	—
90–30	2	—	—
80–60	4	5	4
80–30	2	3	4
60–40	4	—	—
60–30	5	5	4
40–20	4	—	—

were measured over a total of 36 elements from one production lot.

The measurements yield resistance *vs* time characteristics for each applied step function input which have to be translated to the response characteristic of interest, i.e., the function of indicated humidity (in per cent RH) *vs* time. It is here that a serious problem arises; it is necessary, as mentioned before, to eliminate the influence of calibration uncertainties in order to obtain the true transient response of the sample. To accomplish this, a precalibration or an "average" calibration as supplied by the manufacturer cannot be used. Since for each step performed, the two boundary values were available from the precisely known test chamber settings, the translation of the recording was accomplished

by first fitting a best curve through the two end points (where "best" means a curve coming closest to the normalized curve of the manufacturer's specification and going through both the upper and lower end point). This curve is then used as translator from resistance *vs* time to relative humidity *vs* time. The response characteristics so obtained show the well-known increase in response time for decreasing temperature. For each specific temperature, little variation with the size of the steps applied is observed but a definite pattern of slower response, particularly evident during the earlier phases of the transient response, for desorption than for absorption steps and a slightly slower response for steps in both directions at higher humidity levels were noted. This is somewhat expected from the physics involved, considering the exothermic character of sorption, the work needed to overcome the surface tensions in micro pores, and the generally endothermic character of desorption. No attempt is made, however, pending further investigations, to explain the observed characteristics one way or another. The changes of response with varying humidity levels, though in agreement with the findings of Morris and Sobel[7] on electrolytic

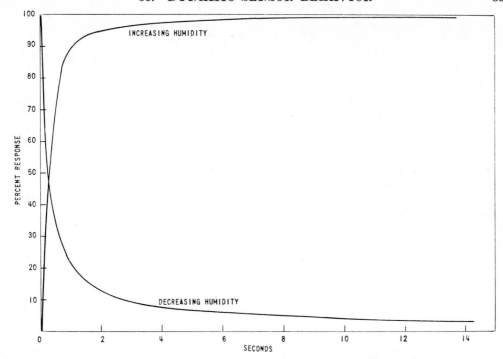

Fig. 4. Step response of ML-476 for increasing and decreasing humidities at 25°C and 600-fpm ventilation.

hygrometers, are so small that more experimentation is needed to establish their quantitative behavior. For this reason, the only differentiation made at this time is the separation of response to sorption and desorption steps and naturally to steps at different environmental temperatures. Figures 4, 5 and 6 show the results in normalized form, i.e., reduced to percentage change *vs* time. (Full response is indicated by reaching the 100 per cent line for steps of increasing humidity and the 0 per cent line for steps of decreasing humidity.) The response is shown in two time scales in Figs. 5 and 6 to show early phase and total of response more clearly.

SIMULATION

The character of the response observed suggests attempting mathematical description with time variable equations having coefficients which depend only upon the environmental temperature.

It will be shown later that a differential equation or a system of differential equations describing the sensor's performance will allow data restoration, i.e., obtaining the actual sensor input from its output as a function of time, with the only restriction that all inputs must cause an output significantly above the transducer noise.[3]

The first attempt at simulation with two independent first-order differential equations in a coarse, lumped, approximation of sorption and diffusion proved to be inadequate. The addition of a third first-order equation, was necessary.

The set of Eqs. (1) through (5) allows simulation which is better than the assumed precision of the experimentally established mean response characteristic.

$$\alpha i = o_1 + \tau_1 \frac{do_1}{dt} \qquad (1)$$

$$\beta i = o_2 + \tau_2 \frac{do_2}{dt} \qquad (2)$$

$$\gamma i = o_3 + \tau_3 \frac{do_3}{dt} \qquad (3)$$

$$\alpha + \beta + \gamma = 1 \qquad (4)$$

$$o_1 + o_2 + o_3 = o \qquad (5)$$

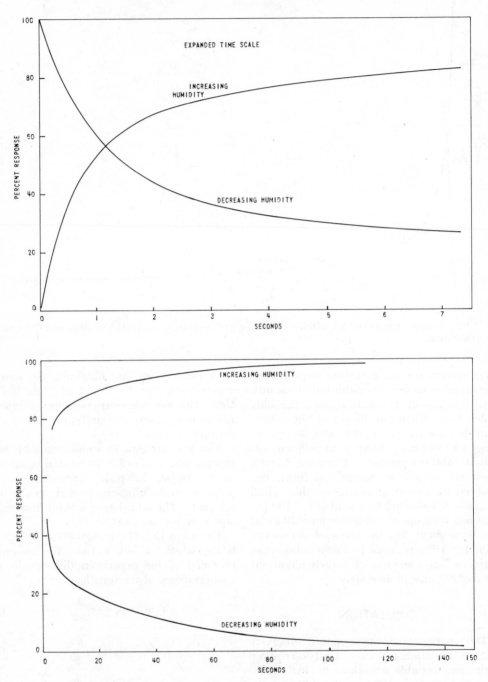

FIG. 5. Step response of ML-476 for increasing and decreasing humidities at −5°C and 600-fpm ventilation.

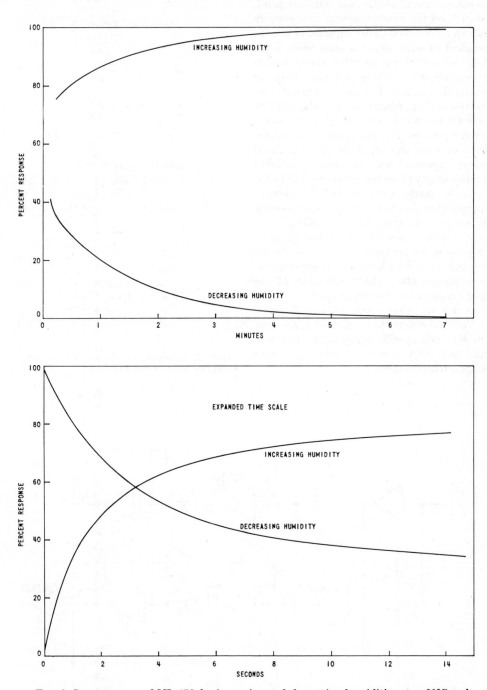

FIG. 6. Step response of ML-476 for increasing and decreasing humidities at −20°C and 600-fpm ventilation.

Figure 7 shows the numerical values of the time constants and coefficients, which depend, as stated, on the environmental temperature only. The three first-order equations are independent of each other in that there is no linkage between them other than the normalizing conditions that their summed outputs have to equal the simulated element's output, and a corresponding condition for the inputs, which determines the amount of contribution of each equation. Following usual nomenclature, i denotes the input to the simulated element expressed here in units of relative humidity at any given temperature. Under the previously made assumption of linearity (superposition theorem holds), i may assume any conceivable time function $RH(t)$. The sensor's output is described by o, and o_1, o_2 and o_3 represent its components. The units are again units of relative humidity, assuming that proper means allow the translation of the sensor's resistive or electric output.

The dimensionless coefficients α, β and γ and the time constants τ_1, τ_2, and τ_3 are constant for each specific temperature environment, but they vary as tabulated with changing temperatures.

EQUATIONS OF SIMULATION

$$\alpha i = o_1 + \tau_1 \frac{d o_1}{d t}$$

$$\beta i = o_2 + \tau_2 \frac{d o_2}{d t}$$

$$\gamma i = o_3 + \tau_3 \frac{d o_3}{d t}$$

$$\alpha + \beta + \gamma = 1 \qquad o_1 + o_2 + o_3 = 0$$

NUMERICAL VALUES OF COEFFICIENTS

COEFF.	STEP	-20°C	-5°C	+25°C
α	UP	0.270	0.541	0.871
	DOWN	0.020	0.372	0.591
β	UP	0.458	0.174	0.111
	DOWN	0.580	0.333	0.322
γ	UP	0.272	0.285	0.018
	DOWN	0.400	0.295	0.087
τ_1	UP	0.764	1.230	0.584
	DOWN	0.764	1.610	0.432
τ_2	UP	2.990	4.550	4.880
	DOWN	2.990	4.050	2.390
τ_3	UP	80.000	27.800	156.000
	DOWN	80.000	81.300	29.100

FIG. 7. Simulation of the response of the carbon humidity element ML-476.

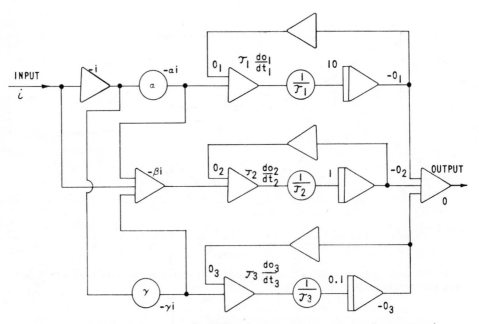

FIG. 8. Simulation of the response of the carbon humidity element ML-476 instrumentation.

It has to be stressed that the simulation of the response characteristics is primarily only a mathematical description, advantageous for analytic treatment and input restoration. But even if it is not denied that the selection of the type of equations used is influenced by considerations of physics, the equations finally found are not unique and their coefficients and time constants have to be found by "best fit" techniques. The necessity for introducing three time constants, however, leads to certain speculation about the mechanism of the element and may influence at a later time the design of humidity sensors.

The set of equations for simulation can be easily implemented on differential analyzers. Figure 8 shows the circuit used for simulation on the Electronics Associates Analogue Computer TR 10; Fig. 9, as an example, gives the simulated response characteristic with separated individual time functions, for the $-20°C$ response.

With the simulation accomplished, data restoration becomes possible.

DATA RESTORATION

With a set of differential and conditional equations known and the coefficients and time constants established for each temperature environment, the problem of reconstructing the input to the sensor from the recording of its input can be approached. With the exception of the previously mentioned single restriction of the signal-to-noise requirement, restoration is theoretically feasible for the present case. The technique, however, is less direct than simulation; there, the nature of the equations allowed solving for the output by independently solving the three differential equations and adding their solutions. Restoration requires solving the same set of equations for the input with the output known. Coefficients and time constants for the restoration are equally known, but the variable (the output o) does not appear directly in any one of the differential equations. This requires modifying the original set of equations to allow the determination of the components

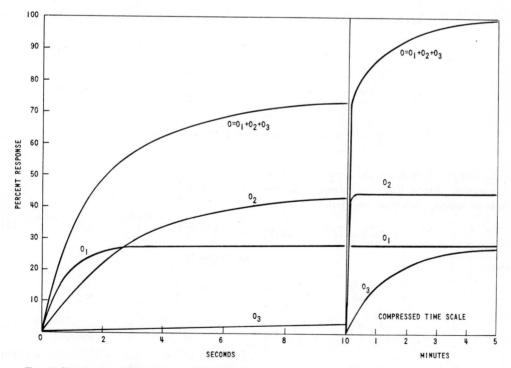

Fig. 9. Simulation of ML-476 at $-20°C$, 600-fpm ventilation for steps of increasing humidities.

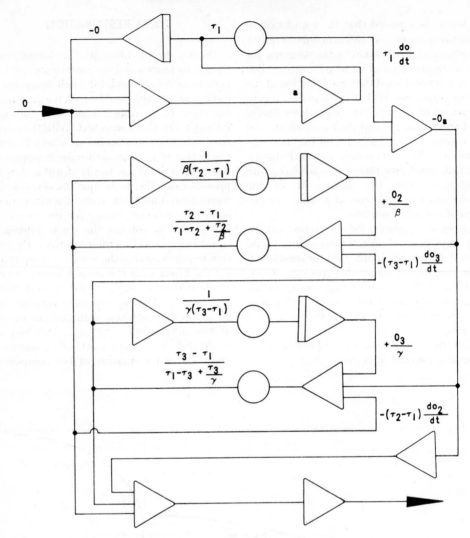

Fig. 10. Restoration circuit for optimum restoration.

o_1, o_2 and o_3 which form the output by their summation. From Eqs. (1) through (5) one finds by simple manipulation that

$$\frac{o_2}{\beta} + \frac{\tau_2}{\beta}\frac{do_2}{dt} = i = \frac{o_3}{\gamma} + \frac{\tau_3}{\gamma}\frac{do_3}{dt} \quad (6)\ (7)$$

and

$$i = o + \tau_1\frac{do_1}{dt} + \tau_2\frac{do_2}{dt} + \tau_3\frac{do_3}{dt} \quad (8)$$

$$i = o + \tau_1\frac{do}{dt} + (\tau_2 - \tau_1)\frac{do_2}{dt} + (\tau_3 - \tau_1)\frac{do_3}{dt} \quad (9)$$

and introducing a new variable o_a

$$o_a = o + \tau_1\frac{do}{dt} = \frac{o_2}{\beta} -$$

$$\left(\tau_2 - \tau_1 - \frac{\tau_2}{\beta}\right)\frac{do_2}{dt} - (\tau_3 - \tau_1)\frac{do_3}{dt} \quad (10)$$

and equally

$$o_a = o + \tau_1\frac{do}{dt} = \frac{o_3}{\gamma} -$$

$$(\tau_2 - \tau_1)\frac{do_2}{dt} - \left(\tau_3 - \tau_1 - \frac{\tau_3}{\gamma}\right)\frac{do_3}{dt} \quad (11)$$

This new set of equations yields the solution for the input (i). The instrumentation for these equations on an analog computer is shown in Fig. 10.

Using the described technique, it is possible to reconstruct any time-varying input function if only the output time function is known and no input signal components exist whose corresponding output is lost in noise, with the precision of the used analog instrumentation and within the representativeness of the simulation equations. With many types of transducers, restoration to almost any degree of reasonable accuracy is possible. A difficulty, however, exists in the very nature of the present-day humidity elements, especially of the type investigated, which has varying response characteristics from sample to sample, even within one production lot. Although this condition, at least for the present, eliminates the possibility of perfect input restoration in the routine use of these elements, results obtained with restoration equations based on mean element response characteristics show considerable improvement as compared to the untreated raw data.

Figure 11 shows an example of data restoration for a carbon-type humidity element used at −20°C temperature environment. This Figure also shows the degree of restoration of a step function input which can be expected by using a small analog computer (TR 10 of Electronic Associates). The initial curvature in the restoration of the step function is caused by limitation in the differentiating process inherent to analog computers. The variability of the response with temperature poses no problem. If the environmental temperature is known, it may be taken care of in instrumentation by automatically adjusting the translation unit (resistance-humidity values) and the constants in the restoration circuit.

The mentioned variability of the elements (probably explained by variation of film thickness, differences in film surface and pore structure, etc.) and the necessity to use, in practical applications, the same restoration circuit for increasing and decreasing humidities which makes true restoration impossible, suggests investigating simpler restoration solutions which may be expected to show an even greater invariance for element variability.

The simplest possible restoration which can be conceived, viz, restoration with a single

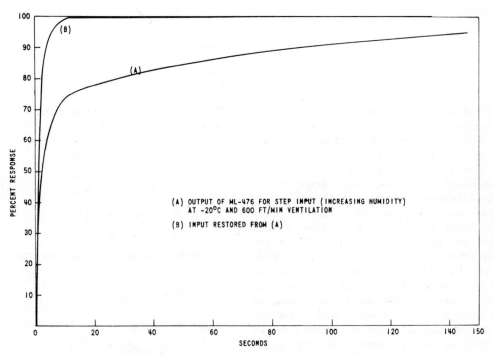

FIG. 11. Restoration of input for ML-476 humidity element.

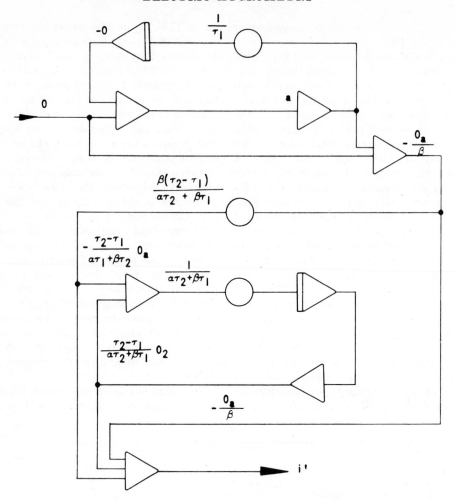

FIG. 12. Restoration circuit for 2-equation approximation.

first-order equation, was unsuccessful. Approximation, however, by a set of two first-order equations and two conditional equations proved highly successful.

The set of equations used shows close similarity to the simulation equations. It should be noted, however, that the similarity is only superficial; the time constants and coefficients have no relation whatsoever with the ones found for simulation. While the perfect simulation circuit was uniquely determined by the known simulation equations and the numerical values of their coefficients and time constants, any approximate solution requires a trial and error method for the determination of a set of coefficients and time constants, judged to be a "best" approximation with the set of equations chosen.

The choice of the set of equations Eq. (12) through (15),

$$\alpha i = o_1 + \tau_1 \frac{do_1}{dt} \qquad (12)$$

$$\beta i = o_2 + \tau_2 \frac{do_2}{dt} \qquad (13)$$

$$\alpha + \beta = 1 \qquad (14)$$

$$o_1 + o_2 = o \qquad (15)$$

yield similarly as in the rigorous case treated above:

$$i = o + \tau_1 \frac{do}{dt} + (\tau_2 - \tau_1) \frac{do_2}{dt} \qquad (16)$$

and introducing again a new variable o_a

$$o_a = \beta \left(o + \tau_1 \frac{do}{dt} \right) \qquad (17)$$

and

$$o_a = o_2 + (\alpha\tau_2 + \beta\tau_1)\frac{do_2}{dt} \qquad (18)$$

Equation (17) can be solved by synthesis on the analog computer, and with o_a known, Eq. (18) also presents no problem. Combining o_a and o_2 in accordance with Eq. (16) yields the

solution for the restored input [Eq. (19) for i'].

$$i' = \frac{o_a}{\beta}\left(1 + \beta\,\frac{\tau_2 - \tau_1}{\alpha\tau_2 + \beta\tau_1}\right) - o_2\frac{\tau_2 - \tau_1}{\alpha\tau_2 + \beta\tau_1} \quad (19)$$

The instrumentation is shown in Fig. 12. Figure 13 presents the results obtained by using the simplified restoration technique for

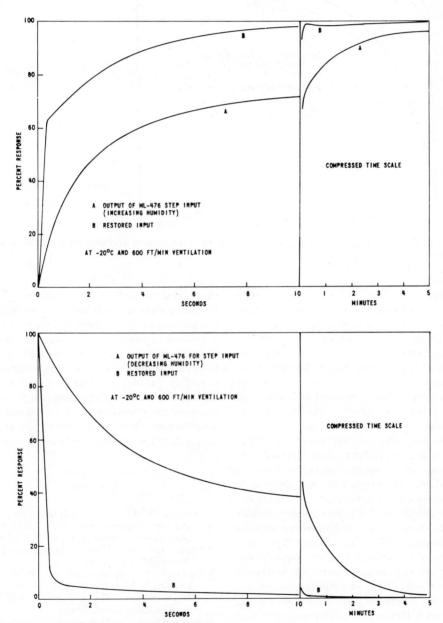

Fig. 13. Restoration of input for ML-467 humidity element using approximation by two first-order differential equations.

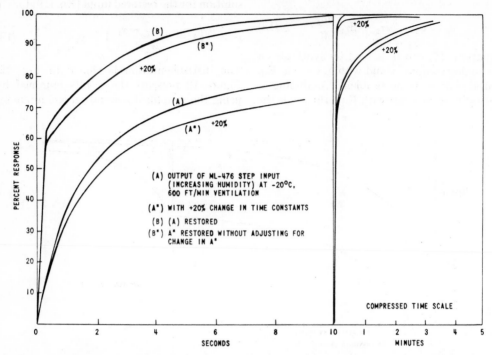

FIG. 14. Restoration of input for ML-476 humidity element using approximation by two first-order differential equations.

increasing and decreasing humidities with expanded scale for the earlier parts of the response. It can be noticed that the restoration yields, even with this simplified technique, significant improvement over the untreated outputs of the sensor. Figure 14 shows the effect on response and simplified restoration of variations in time constants which may be expected between different elements of the same type.

In summing up, the exploratory character of the studies presented is again stressed. The variations in element behavior between samples are, unfortunately, not limited to variations in the response characteristic alone; memory of the element to its exposure history and slope changes in the resistance *vs* humidity characteristic which determines the basic accuracy of a measurement are equally disturbing in the measurement of humidity profiles in the free atmosphere as in the laboratory, where they render investigations of element behavior more difficult.

It is hoped, however, that progress will be made in two areas by continuing the study of

the transient behavior of the carbon-type humidity element; a better understanding of the physics of the element should result in an improved element with a more uniform behavior not only in the transient phase of its response, and also in improving atmospheric humidity probing by eliminating the errors introduced by the very large lags at low-temperature environments with the technique described which is not limited to use with one particular type of humidity transducer.

References

1. Amdur, E. J., "The Research Center Two-Pressure Atmosphere Producer," Minneapolis-Honeywell Research Center GR 2998-R1 1956.
2. Craig, Leo S., "Electric Hygroscope," U.S. Patent 2,714,149 (1955).
3. Grote, H. H., "Restoration of Time Functions Distorted by Transducers Described by Differential Equations," TR 2337, USAELRDL, March 1963.
4. Kobayashi, J., "Investigations on Hygrometry," *Papers Meteorol. Geophys. Tokyo*, 11, 213–388 (1960).

5. Little, Arthur D., Inc., "Improvement of Hygrometer Elements for Meteorological Use," Contract W 36-039 SC-32054, Progress Reports 7-50 and Final Summary Report, July 1950.
6. Marchgraber, R. M., Technical Report No. 2052, USASRDL, July 1959.
7. Morris, Vernon B., and Sobel, Frederick, "Some Experiments on the Speed of Response of the Electrolytic Hygrometer," *American Meteorological Society Bulletin*, **35**, No. 5, 226–229 (1954).

8. Smith, Walter J., and Hofflich, Nancy J., "The Carbon Film Electric Hygrometer Element," *American Meteorological Society Bulletin*, **35**, No. 2, 60–62 (1954).
9. Weaver, E. R., and Riley, R., "Measurement of Water in Gases by Electrical Conduction in a Film of Hygroscopic Material and the Use of Pressure Changes in Calibration," *Natl. Bur. Std.*, **40**, 169–214 (1948).
10. Wexler, A., and Daniels, R., "Pressure Humidity Apparatus," *J. Res. Natl. Bur. Std.*, **48**, 269–274 (1952).

35. Polyelectrolyte Electrical Resistance Humidity Elements*

Robert C. Musa and George L. Schnable

Lansdale Division, Philco Corp., Lansdale, Pennsylvania

ABSTRACT

Variation in electrical resistance of the polyelectrolyte humidity element ("Humistor"**) with relative humidity is a result of the varying ionic conductivity of a hydrophilic film with properties similar to those of ion-exchange resins. This report outlines the design, fabrication, measurement and testing of experimental models of polyelectrolyte humidity sensing elements developed for radiosonde applications.

The sensing elements were prepared by spraying a suspension of cross-linked polystyrene sulfonic acid particles (H^+ form) onto a $4 \times 2 \times 0.04$ in. polystyrene cell having two interdigitated silver electrodes and a cell constant of about 10^{-3} cm^{-1}.

Typical resistance of completed elements at 25°C and 70 per cent RH was about $1 \times 10^3 \Omega$; at −40°C resistance was $5 \times 10^4 \Omega$ at 70 per cent RH. Useful response was obtained in the temperature range from −65 to +35°C. Isothermal plots of the logarithm of element resistance vs per cent relative humidity approximated straight lines with slopes corresponding to about 18 per cent RH per cycle, at temperatures from +25 to −40°C.

Extended measurements have indicated an upward drift in electrical resistance with time. While calibration immediately before use can minimize the error due to increased element resistance, additional work is required to correct the stability problem.

* This work was supported in part by the United States Air Force, Cambridge Research Laboratories, under U.S. Government Contract No. AF 33(600) 42522.

** Registered Trademark, Philco Corporation.

INTRODUCTION

The electrical conductivity through ion-exchange resins is dependent upon the moisture contained in the resin. This paper is a report on work aimed at developing a humidity sensor based on this phenomenon. The objectives of the program were to produce suitable humidity elements for radiosonde test evaluation and to make the necessary modifications to the circuitry of the AN/AMT-4 radiosonde so that side-by-side comparisons between the sensor under development and the carbon element could be obtained. The desired objectives for the elements encompassed a range of dew points from +35 to −80°C with an electrical resistance range consistent with the modulator capabilities of the radiosonde. Rapid response characteristics were required.

ELECTRONIC-CONDUCTANCE ELEMENTS

An electrical resistance element currently employed for humidity measurement in radiosondes and dropsondes is the carbon element, ML-476/AMT. This element is an example of the class of electronic-conductance humidity sensors in which change of resistance with relative humidity depends on the dimensional variability of a hydrophilic matrix containing conducting particles. The carbon element has been investigated and studied by several different groups.[1-5] The presently available units have the disadvantages of slow response at low temperatures, washout in high humidity conditions, and shunting caused by ionic conduction across the surface. Surface ionic conduction can produce a "hump" in the resistance *vs* relative humidity curve at relative humidities in the range of 85 to 100 per cent.

ELECTROLYTIC-CONDUCTANCE ELEMENTS

The class of electrical resistance humidity element reported on in this paper has been previously investigated[6] along with the electronic-type units for potential application to meteorological problems. This type of element depends upon the internal conduction of ions within a film to produce variation of electrical resistance with relative humidity. In this sense only it is similar to ionic elements, such as the Dunmore unit, that have previously been used and tested for meteorological purposes.[7] The units investigated do not depend on a soluble electrolyte, such as LiCl, supported in a binder. These elements are based on the properties of ion-exchange resins. Materials of this type have bound counter ions that become mobile as water concentration is increased within the system.

In the polyelectrolyte electrical resistance humidity element, variation of electrical resistance with relative humidity depends on the varying conduction of ions within a film. The polyelectrolyte consists of a high polymeric cross-linked structure with polar groups of negative charge. Associated with these polar groups are ions of opposite charge which are held by electrostatic forces to fixed polar groups. One feature of such a polyelectrolyte is that it is hydrophilic. In the presence of water vapor, water is absorbed and the electrostatically held ions become mobile. When a voltage is impressed across the resin, the mobile ions are capable of electrolytic conduction.

In general, ion exchange can be defined as a reversible exchange of ions between a solid (resin) and a liquid (water), without substantial change in the solid. An ion-exchange resin particle can be visualized as an elastic, three-dimensional hydrocarbon network to which is attached a large number of ionizable groups.

The nature of the hydrocarbon network affects the chemical behavior of the exchanger in degree but not in kind. A suitable hydrocarbon network is that formed by the copolymerization of styrene and divinylbenzene. This structure gives a maximum resistance to oxidation, reduction, mechanical wear and breakage, and it is insoluble in common solvents.

The ion-exchange resin used to develop the polyelectrolyte electrical resistance humidity element is a strongly acidic cationic type used in the H^+ form. The resin is formed first by the copolymerization of styrene and divinylbenzene. The polymer is next sulfonated to introduce an SO_3^- group on the nucleus of the C_6H_5 group of the styrene molecule. The SO_3^- group is *para*-oriented.

Figure 1 shows a typical structural diagram of the resin in the swollen state.[8]

The polyelectrolyte, or ion-exchange material, can be cast in insolubilized films or can be made insoluble by cross-linking the basic material. Extensive fundamental work has been reported in the measurement of the thermodynamic properties of similar ion-exchange materials.[8-12] In particular, the water vapor sorption properties of both linear polystyrene sulfonic acid,[10] and cross-linked polystyrene sulfonic acid resins,[11] have been thoroughly investigated. Methods have been devised for preparing interpolymer, ion-selective membranes containing polystyrene sulfonic acid and "Dynel".[12] The fundamental papers referenced herein have provided background information useful in the development of the polyelectrolyte electrical resistance humidity element.

DESIGN CONSIDERATIONS

For fast response time, the film of polyelectrolyte must be kept thin. This minimizes the time required for the film to come to equilibrium with the ambient, but it also produces a sheet whose resistance is very high at very low humidities. In order to minimize the measured resistance, the interdigitated electrode configuration shown in Fig. 2 was chosen. The electrodes are silver paste silk-screened onto polystyrene blanks. The polyelectrolyte film was sprayed over the electrode array. Two sizes of polystyrene blanks were employed, 4 in. × .688 in. × .04 in., and

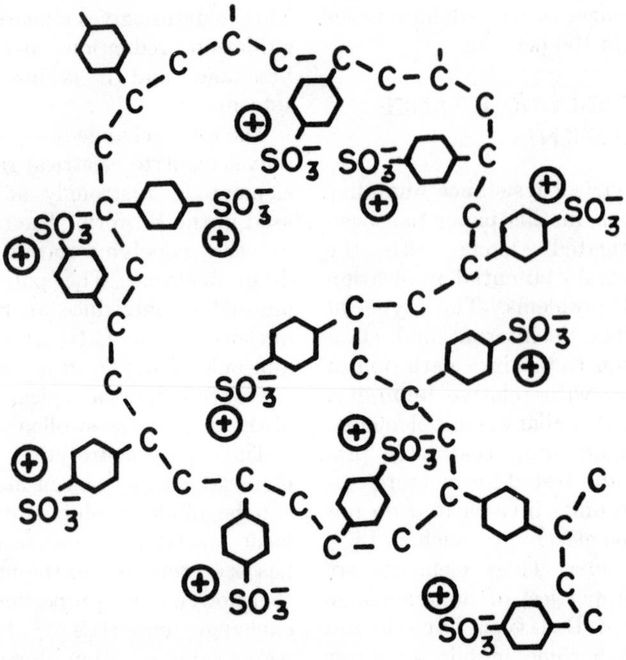

FIG. 1. Typical structural diagram of a sulfonated styrene-
divinylbenzene copolymer in the swollen state.

4 in. × 2 in. × .04 in. These two sizes are
typical of the humidity sensors used in dropsonde and radiosonde equipment.

The closer the electrode spacing, the lower
is the resistance measured for any humidity
condition. For minimum resistance at low
humidities, the electrode spacing should be as
small as possible. Spacings ranging from .015
to .0015 in. were investigated. The electrode
width was in all cases equal to the electrode
spacing, thereby assuring that the series
resistance along the electrode fingers was a
constant, negligibly small fraction of the
resistance through the film between the
fingers. For the silk-screen process the smallest
practical spacing was found to be .005 in.
Samples of silk-screened blanks with electrode
spacings of .0015 and .002 in. demonstrated
that fabrication difficulties would lead to
extremely high and impractical costs. Cells
with .015 and .005 in. electrode spacings (and
widths) were used.

"HUMISTOR" FABRICATION

Blanks

Polystyrene blanks with silver electrodes
were purchased and inspected for uniformity
and reproducibility. The inspection procedure
consisted of cleaning the blanks and testing
for shorts and opens. The capacitance of each
blank was measured at 1.0 Mc as a test of the
uniformity of the electrode configuration. The
capacitance variation was less than 3 per cent
within a batch. The cell constant for each
blank was determined. The method developed
consisted of measuring the conductivity between the electrodes on a blank immersed in
flowing deionized water. The cell conductance
was measured using a Serfass conductance
bridge with an Industrial Instruments Inc.
conductivity cell (0.01 cell constant) as a
monitor reference downstream in the deionized water. Lots having less than 10 per
cent variation in cell resistance were con-

sidered acceptable. Blank cell resistance converted to a cell constant gave values of the order of $10^{-3} cm^{-1}$.

Early lots of blanks as received from the vendor were found to have an order-of-magnitude variation in cell resistance. The source of this variation was traced to a silicone mold-release agent which was used in the molding of the polystyrene for the blanks. The silicone crept and insulated portions of the silver electrodes, thereby causing the wide range in cell resistances. Subsequent lots prepared without the release agent had acceptable ranges of resistance values.

Materials used for the spray solution were "Dowex" 50W ion-exchange resin with "Dynel" as a binder and dimethyl formamide and toluene as the solvent. "Dowex" 50W ion-exchange resin is a strongly acidic cation-exchange resin made by the nuclear sulfonation of polymeric styrene-divinylbenzene beads. The particular resins used were 4X and 8X resins; i.e., resins cross-linked with 4 and

8 per cent divinylbenzene (DVB), respectively. Cross-linkage adds a third dimension to the polymer network and makes it insoluble. The fraction of divinylbenzene in the bead determines the extent to which the ion-exchange resin is free to swell and shrink. As the amount of cross-linkage increases, the wet volume capacity increases, but the diffusion of ions becomes slower, causing a decrease in the response rate of the humidity element.

Resins containing more than 30 per cent divinylbenzene are so tightly cross-linked that it is difficult to prepare ion-exchange resins from them and they are somewhat brittle. On the other hand the low-cross-linked resins (<4 per cent) are highly swollen, soft and easily deformed. Thus, from the physical standpoint of the resin, the desired cross-linkage appears to be obtained with 4 to 10 per cent DVB.

"Dynel," a copolymer of vinyl chloride and acrylonitrile, was used as the binder to hold the resin to the "Humistor" element. It is

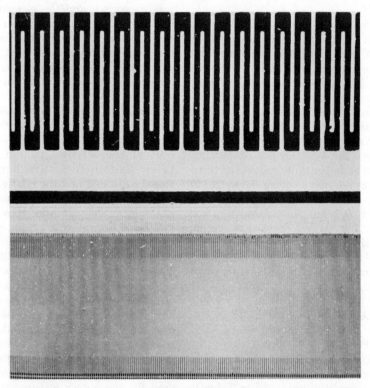

Fig. 2. At top, 4 in. × .688 in. × .04 in. polystyrene blank with 15-mil interdigitated silver electrodes and spacing; at bottom, polystyrene blank with 2-mil electrodes.

soluble in the dimethyl formamide-toluene mixture and, on evaporation of the solvent, leaves behind a film containing the resin. The concentration of "Dynel" was 5 or 10 per cent, based on the dry weight of the resin-"Dynel" mixture. Dimethyl formamide was used as the solvent for the "Dynel" and the dispersing agent for the resin. Toluene was added to improve the adherence of the film to the Humistor cell.

A typical electrolyte composition consisted of a mixture of 4.75 grams of "Dowex" 50W-X4 resin, 0.25 gram of "Dynel," 80 ml of dimethyl formamide and 20 ml of toluene. The mixture was milled in a grinding jar for not less than 65 hours to reduce the resin particle size. The "Dowex" resins, as purchased, are 200 to 400 mesh. After milling, 95 per cent by weight of the resin particles have a diameter of less than 4 μ as determined by sedimentation tests. The effect or 4X and 8X resin cross-linkage with 5 and 10 per cent "Dynel" concentrations was studied.

Film Spraying

The polyelectrolyte film was sprayed onto the blanks on a spray wheel. A glass slide was sprayed with each group. To insure uniform thickness, the film was built up in thin layers. Typically, eight passes before the spray nozzle on the spray wheel were employed. Partial drying between coats was accelerated by heaters completely enclosing the spray wheel except at the spray nozzle opening. Air was circulated through the heated portion. The weight of resin per unit area on the tared glass slides was inferred as being the weight of film per unit area on the elements. Approximately 0.025 to 0.030 mg/cm² of resin film was employed for the various batches of sensors employed in this program. This corresponds to an average film thickness of about .01 mil.

The elements were dried a minimum of 16 hours at 60°C.

EVALUATION OF ELEMENTS

Element Response

The average resistance values for a number of "Humistors" at two temperatures and at two relative humidities are listed in Table 1. Standard deviations both in resistivity reading and in indicated relative humidity are also

given. These measurements were taken in a Tenney environmental chamber using AC resistivity bridge techniques. Typical response curves for a batch of elements are given in Fig. 3. The sensitivity of the elements (resistance change per unit change in humidity) is so great that relatively large deviations in resistance from unit to unit correspond to relatively small changes in indicated humidity from unit to unit. The temperature sensitivity of the elements is evident in Fig. 3. It is presumed that both the mobility of the charge carriers, hydrogen ions, and the number of carriers (degree of dissociation of the hydrogen ions in the resin) are temperature sensitive. The temperature sensitivity of the device is thus expected, and the calibration and use of the sensors requires simultaneous knowledge of sensor resistance and temperature.

Response Time. Elements, with electrical connections, were put in a closed cylindrical container containing H_2O or P_2O_5, and the container was placed in the Tenney chamber. The element resistance in the closed cylinder was measured, and the element, which was attached to the lid of the cylindrical container, was then quickly lifted out of the container by means of a pulley arrangement. The element, when raised above the container, was in the air stream of the circulating fan in the Tenney chamber. The time required for the element resistance to change to a resistance corresponding (as indicated by the individual element response curve) to $1 - 1/e$ or 63 per cent of the relative humidity change between the initial relative humidity in the closed container and the relative humidity in the Tenney chamber, was measured. For example, an element inside the closed cylinder at a given time after insertion, showed, based on its resistance, that the relative humidity inside the closed cylinder was 20 per cent. The element was quickly withdrawn from the closed vessel and brought out into the Tenney chamber, where the humidity was 60 per cent. The time required for the resistance of the element to change to that indicated by the response curve for a relative humidity of 45 per cent [20 + 0.63 (60 − 20)] was measured with a stopwatch. A General Radio bridge was used for the longer response times. For the shorter response times, such as those at room temperature, the element was connected to a

TABLE 1. STANDARD DEVIATION OF THE RESISTANCE OF TWO POINTS (30 AND 70% RH) ON RESPONSE CURVES OF "HUMISTORS" AT 25 AND −40°C

Electrode Spacing (mils)	Batch No.	Temp. (°C)	RH (%)	Number of Samples	$\bar{r}$ (ohms)*	σ (ohms)**	V (%)†	σ RH‡
15	3	25	30	10	1.88×10^5	1.17×10^5	62	3
	4	25	30	15	1.68×10^5	4.7×10^4	28	1.5
	5	25	30	29	2.07×10^5	1.04×10^5	50	2.5
	3	25	70	10	8.11×10^2	5.20×10^2	64	7.5
	4	25	70	15	9.7×10^2	2.5×10^3	26	3
	5	25	70	29	11.6×10^2	5.3×10^2	46	6
	3	−40	30	10	11.78×10^6	6.56×10^6	56	3
	4	−40	30	15	7.51×10^6	2.08×10^6	28	2.5
	5	−40	30	29	8.8×10^6	4.2×10^6	48	4
	3	−40	70	10	8.36×10^3	9.5×10^3	114	—
	4	−40	70	15	4.7×10^4	1.3×10^4	28	2.5
	5	−40	70	29	7.7×10^4	5.2×10^4	68	7.5
5	4	25	30	16	4.08×10^4	2.05×10^4	50	3
	5	25	30	19	4.65×10^4	2.42×10^4	52	3
	4	25	70	16	2.77×10^2	1.21×10^2	44	6
	5	25	70	19	2.29×10^2	1.02×10^2	45	8.5
	4	−40	30	16	2.59×10^6	2.70×10^6	104	—
	5	−40	30	19	2.12×10^6	9.2×10^5	43	3.5
	4	−40	70	16	1.2×10^4	5.6×10^3	47	4
	5	−40	70	19	2.06×10^4	1.51×10^4	73	5
5 and 15 in series	4	25	30	5	9.08×10^4	2.09×10^4	23	1
	5	25	30	5	14.6×10^4	2.7×10^4	18	2.5
	4	25	70	5	12.4×10^2	4.29×10^2	35	3.5
	5	25	70	5	23.2×10^2	6.4×10^2	28	4
	4	−40	30	5	16.9×10^5	8.7×10^5	51	5
	5	−40	30	5	27.0×10^5	9.9×10^5	37	3
	4	−40	70	5	4.44×10^4	1.44×10^4	32	5.5
	5	−40	70	5	9.22×10^4	3.21×10^4	35	7

* Average resistance reading for batch.
** Standard deviation of resistance readings.
† Relative deviation, $V = 100 \, \sigma/\bar{r}$.
‡ Standard deviation of indicated relative humidity.

modified AN/AMT-4 radiosonde, and the output of the radiosonde was picked up on a receiver, the audio output of which was fed into an oscilloscope. The sweep frequency of the scope was set for the blocking oscillator frequency which would indicate the resistance corresponding to 63 per cent of the total relative humidity change, and the time required for the change was measured.

Observed response times are tabulated in Table 2 for regular 5-mil and 15-mil elements at several temperatures. Response times for elements with extra thick coatings (40 spray passes instead of 8) are listed for comparison. Air velocity in the test chamber was 250 fpm, i.e. about one-fourth the typical rise velocity of

a radiosonde, so that the response times are probably conservative.

It is apparent that the normal "Humistor" which was sprayed with a layer of about 0.03 mg/cm² has a more than adequate response time for radiosonde and dropsonde applications. It also appears that by using a thicker humidity-sensitive layer, a 15-mil element grid could be used to produce devices with cell resistances comparable to those obtained with 5-mil grids, without too much loss in response time.

Similarly, where response time is not critical, more sensitive elements could be made by the use of the thicker coatings. The 5-mil elements sprayed with 40 passes, for example,

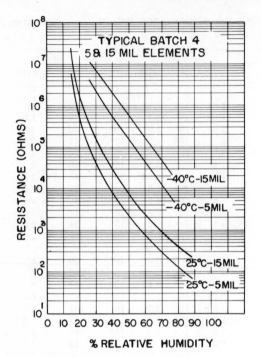

FIG. 3. Resistance *vs* relative humidity for typical "Humistors".

had useful response down to about 100 ppm at 25°C (less than 1 per cent RH). Resistance at 100 ppm at 25°C was about $8.7 \times 10^7 \, \Omega$.

Hysteresis. The following hysteresis data are based on comparison of response curves determined by decreasing the relative humi-

dity from 80 to 10 per cent stepwise in the Tenney chamber and then increasing it stepwise. The complete cycle required approximately one day at each temperature.

Twenty elements at 25°C and at 30 per cent RH had a mean per cent indicated relative humidity difference of 2.85 between increasing and decreasing humidity response curves with a standard deviation on the difference of 0.81 per cent; at 70 per cent RH, the mean per cent indicated RH difference was 2.55 with a standard deviation of 0.22 per cent. At 5°C and 30 per cent RH, the mean per cent indicated relative humidity difference was 4.3 with a standard deviation of 0.87 per cent; at 70 per cent RH the mean per cent indicated RH difference was 3.7 with a standard deviation of 0.5 per cent.

Element Stability

Resistance measurements were taken on 128 elements in a Craig chamber held at 60 per cent RH for approximately 1 month at room temperature, which ranged from 25 to 31°C. Then, elements from each group were cycled in the Tenney chamber and returned to the Craig chamber, and resistance measurements were taken again. Preliminary stability data after cycling indicated that elements sprayed with 10 per cent "Dynel," 8X resin, appeared to be superior. Resistance measurements were continued daily for 2 more weeks, and then all

TABLE 2. RESPONSE TIME MEASUREMENTS

	Temp. (°C)	No. of Elements Tested	From % RH	To % RH	Median Response Time (sec)
Batch-5 elements	25	3	100	52	2.6
(8 spray passes)	25	3	12	61	1.4
	5	3	100	63	6.0
	5	3	12	66	2.4
	−20	3	85	33	12
	−20	3	12	15	15
	−40	3	85	65	66
	−40	3	12	80	32
Batch-X elements	25	2	100	28	11
(40 spray passes)	25	1	12	60	1.4
	5	1	100	58	32
	5	1	12	64	4.4
	−20	1	85	33	30
	−20	1	12	57	10
	−40	1	85	72	78
	−40	1	12	80	20

elements were cycled. The elements continued to be read once a week for an additional month and a half. The ratios of initial resistance values to values after the three intervals described above are listed in Table 3.

TABLE 3. RESISTANCE RATIOS* OF STABILITY EXPERIMENT

Process**	After 1st Cycling (1 month)	After 2nd Cycling (1½ months)	After 3 Months
5% 4XC	6.0	7.1	8.8
5% 4XSB	3.3	3.8	7.6
5% 8XC	6.0	7.6	14.2
5% 8XSB	8.2	10.0	15.4
10% 4XC	3.7	5.2	13.8
10% 4XSB	3.6	5.1	11.6
10% 8XC	2.1	2.5	5.3
10% 8XSB	1.9	2.4	4.5

* Ratio of resistance at cited time interval to initial resistance.

** *Key for Sprayed Solutions and Cell Treatment*
5% 4XSB—5% "Dynel," 4X resin, sandblasted
5% 4XC—5% "Dynel," 4X resin, clear
5% 8XSB—5% "Dynel," 8X resin, sandblasted
5% 8XC—5% "Dynel," 8X resin, clear
10% 4XSB—10% "Dynel," 4X resin, sandblasted
10% 4XC—10% "Dynel," 4X resin, clear
10% 8XSB—10% "Dynel," 8X resin, sandblasted
10% 8XC—10% "Dynel," 8X resin, clear

It appears, based on the resistance ratios after 3 months, as indicated in Table 3, that the elements made using 10 per cent "Dynel" and the 8X resin undergo the least resistivity change with time, an increase by a factor of about 5. The calibration is shifting with time such that after 3 months the relative humidity indicated by the "Humistor," based on its initial calibration, would only be 75 to 80 per cent of the true relative humidity. This is a serious problem for which a ready solution is not obvious.

RADIOSONDE MODIFICATION

The "Humistor" conducts ionically so that a DC potential placed across its terminals will cause it to polarize. The resistance of the "Humistor" must, therefore, be determined using alternating current. Radiosonde telemetry is based upon modulating a transmitted carrier signal with the output of a blocking oscillator. The blocking oscillator

repetition rate is determined by an RC time constant in the grid circuit of the blocking oscillator. The resistance in this RC time constant is made up partially of the resistance of a temperature or humidity sensor depending upon whether temperature or humidity information is being transmitted. As the resistance of the sensor changes with changing ambient, the oscillator repetition rate varies concomitantly and the information is transmitted.

The resistance range of the "Humistor" (10^2 to $10^8 \Omega$) is too great to be used directly in this circuit. Furthermore, the waveform of the voltage which would be placed across the "Humistor" would be such as to polarize the cell. For these reasons, the circuitry of the AN/AMT-4 radiosondes had to be modified in order to flight test the "Humistors."

The initial scheme for modifying the radiosonde circuits was to provide a fixed-frequency audio oscillator to supply the AC voltage for the "Humistor" and convert the AC voltage appearing across the "Humistor" (proportional to its resistance) to DC, and to use this voltage, which varied with "Humistor" resistance, as a variable bias in the grid circuit of the blocking oscillator. This arrangement worked well for bench testing; however, the circuit proved completely unstable at low temperatures due to changes in the characteristics of the transistors at low temperatures. It had been presumed that the heat generated by the radiosonde batteries would keep the circuit in a stable operating temperature range. Such was not the case.

An all passive component circuit modification was finally employed. A portion of the modified circuit is shown in Fig. 4. This circuit provides a relay which switches the resistive portion of the RC blocking oscillator grid circuit out of the circuit and inserts a second RC network containing the "Humistor." The relay was actuated by modifying one of the normal switching functions of the aneroid contactor strip in the radiosonde. To minimize temperature sensitivity, passive components having low temperature coefficients were used for the modifications.

The blocking oscillator pulse repetition rate as a function of "Humistor" resistance for a typical modified radiosonde is given in Fig. 5.

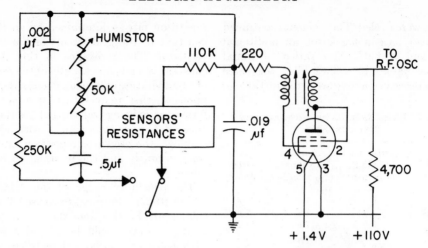

FIG. 4. Simplified schematic diagram of modified radiosonde modulator T-435/AMT-4B.

Combinations of "Humistor" Elements

"Humistor" elements made with 5-mil grid spacing have lower resistance, at a given relative humidity, than do "Humistors" with larger grid spacing, for example, 15-mils. Regardless of the grid spacing, the response curve of "Humistors" approximates a straight line when plotted as log of resistance *vs* relative humidity. The response curve of the modified radiosonde circuit, however, is S-shaped. Thus, as indicated in Fig. 5, circuit sensitivity is considerably higher at intermediate resistances (30 to 300 K) than at resistances below 1,000 Ω or above 1 MΩ.

Figure 6 shows typical response curves of 5- and 15-mil elements taken from Fig. 3 and, in addition, shows the resultant curves when these elements are put in series, with a 100-K resistor in parallel with the 15-mil element. The combination curves were calculated from 5- and 15-mil element response curves. The series combination was selected so as to have,

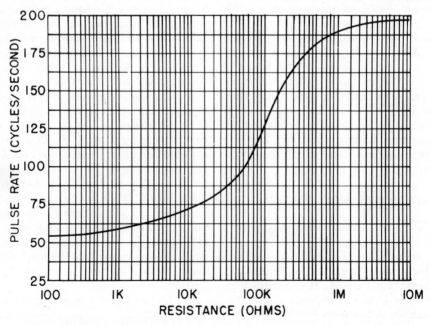

FIG. 5. Blocking oscillator frequency *vs* resistance for a typical modified radiosonde.

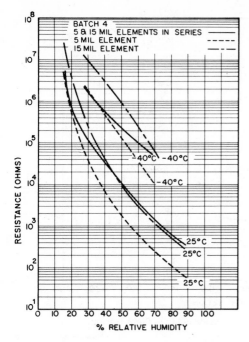

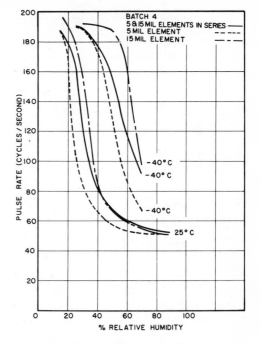

Fig. 6. Average response of elements with 5-mil and 15-mil electrodes.

Fig. 7. Radiosonde blocking oscillator frequency *vs* per cent relative humidity.

essentially, the response characteristics of the 15-mil element at high humidities and that of the 5-mil element at low humidities. The response curves, in terms of cycles per second (radiosonde blocking oscillator frequency) *vs* relative humidity are shown in Fig. 7. Again, the response combines the advantages of both the 5- and 15-mil "Humistors."

Other series combinations with fixed parallel resistances can be used to provide the best characteristics of two types of "Humistor" elements without requiring a switching circuit to connect each element at particular times.

FLIGHT TESTS

Atmosphere soundings were made using modified AN/AMT-4B radiosondes. Based on the soundings, it was concluded that the lithium chloride element and the "Humistor" had good overall agreement, with the "Humistor" showing greater response and more sensitivity. The carbon-type element agreed with the lithium chloride and "Humistor" elements down to −20°C, but its response fell off at lower temperatures. Figure 8 is a plot of the "Humistor" and carbon elements from a comparison flight test. Some-

what more detail is evident in the "Humistor" trace. Figure 9 is a plot of another "Humistor" sounding. Both the ascending and descending transmissions were received and are shown. Whether the unit was hunting or transmitting accurate information during the descending portion of the trace is open to question. The general agreement between the ascending and descending portions is good and indicates the rapid response of the "Humistor."

Baseline checks were made prior to flight tests. The flight test baseline calibration was a comparison of the wet-bulb and "Humistor" RH indications and is given in Table 4. Only four of the last eleven flights showed reasonable agreement between the two readings of relative humidity. The seven "Humistor" readings which showed poor agreement were low, with a 24 per cent average difference between the relative humidity values indicated by the "Humistor" and the values calculated from wet and dry bulb readings. This difference is believed to be due to the upward drift in resistance values of the "Humistor" elements cited earlier. Because of this calibration shift, the flight tests were of qualitative value only.

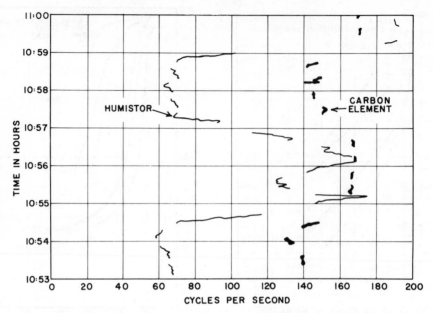

FIG. 8. Comparison of "Humistor" and carbon elements in flight testing.

TABLE 4. FLIGHT TEST BASELINE
CALIBRATION DATA

Flight Test No.	Dry-bulb Temp. (°C)	% RH as Indicated by Wet Bulb	% RH as Indicated by "Humistor"	Low Reference Frequency (cps)
1	25	75	52	181
2	28	66	46	177
3	23	76	79	185
4	23	84	62	178
5	24	84	>80	182
6	24	79	63	180
7	25	77	61	184
8	26	78	80	190
9	27	72	46	167
10	19	78	>80	184
11	20	78	32	177

CONCLUSIONS

The flight tests indicate qualitatively that satisfactory response curves can be obtained for approximate relative humidities from 10 to 80 per cent at 25°C, and from 20 to 80 per cent at −40°C, with the range limited principally by circuit sensitivity rather than "Humistor" sensitivity. The response time of the "Humistor" elements was such that small rapid changes in humidity with elevation could be easily detected. Unfortunately,

neither rain nor heavy cloud conditions occurred during the flight test period so that the washout characteristics were not observed. However, "Humistors" subjected to complete immersion in deionized water underwent no significant change in calibration.

Extended measurements have indicated an

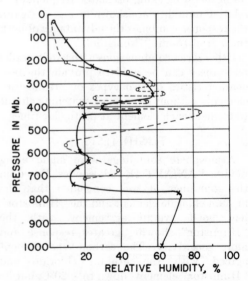

FIG. 9. Atmospheric sounding made using a "Humistor" in a modified AN/AMT-4B radiosonde. The ascending trace is shown by the solid line and the descending trace by the dotted line.

element stability problem, i.e., an upward drift in electrical resistance with time, for which the responsible mechanisms have not been verified. Calibration or baseline checks immediately before use can minimize the error; however, a more linear circuit response would be necessary to make such baseline adjustments meaningful.

Acknowledgment. The authors gratefully acknowledge the help and cooperation of the personnel of the Test Branch, Aerospace Instrumentation Laboratory, Air Force Cambridge Research Laboratories, L. G. Hanscom Field, Bedford, Massachusetts in the flight testing of these "Humistor" elements.

References

1. Smith, W. J. and Hoeflich, N. J., "The Carbon Film Electric Hygrometer Element," *Bull. Am. Meteorol. Soc.*, **35**, 60 (1954).
2. Final and Summary Report on Improvement of Electric Hygrometer Elements for Meteorological Use, C-57178, A. D. Little, Inc., July 31, 1950.
3. Final Report on Development and Manufacture of Electric Hygrometer Elements for Meteorological Use, C-58178, A. D. Little, Inc., March 31, 1952.
4. Final Engineering Report, Vortex Hygrometer, Minneapolis-Honeywell, Contract No. DA-36-039-SC-64715, Serial No. 8757, January 1956.
5. Hasegawa, S., Rinehuls, K., and Wexler, A., "Calibration of the Carbon Film Electric Hygrometer Element ML 476/AMT," *National Bureau of Standards Report* 6176, NBS Project 0602-20-3510, Report to Bureau of Aeronautics, Department of the Navy.
6. Final Engineering Reports, Phase I and Phase II, Philco Corporation: Study and Investigation of Electrical Resistance Humidity Elements, U.S.A.F. Contract No. AF 33(616)-5224, Task No. 60578, Project No. 6020, Wright Air Development Center (1958 and 1959).
7. Wexler, A., "Low Temperature Performance of Radiosonde Electric Hygrometer Elements," *J. Res. Natl. Bur. Std.*, **43**, 49 (1949).
8. Gregor, H. P. and Frederick, M., "Thermodynamic Properties of Ion-Exchange Resins: Free Energy of Swelling as Related to Ion Selectivities," *Ann. N.Y. Acad. Sci.*, **57**, 87 (1953).
9. Gregor, H. P., *et al.*, "Studies on Ion-Exchange Resins. V. Water Vapor Sorption," *J. Colloid Sci.*, **7**, 511 (1952).
10. Waxman, M. H., Sundheim, B. R., and Gregor, H. P., "Studies on Ion-Exchange Resins. VI. Water Vapor Sorption by Polystyrenesulfonic Acid," *J. Phys. Chem.*, **57**, 969 (1953).
11. Sundheim, B. R., Waxman, M. H., and Gregor, H. P., "Studies on Ion-Exchange Resins. VII. Water Vapor Sorption by Cross-Linked Polystyrenesulfonic Acid Resins," *J. Phys. Chem.*, **57**, 974 (1953).
12. Gregor, H. P., *et al.*, "Interpolymer Ion-Selective Membranes. I. Preparation and Characterization of Polystyrenesulfonic Acid-Dynel Membranes," *J. Phys. Chem.*, **61**, 141 (1957).

36. Humidity Meter using Cerium Titanate Elements

CLARK E. JOHNSON, JR.* AND STEPHEN R. DUGGAN**

Telostat Corporation, Hopkins, Minnesota

ABSTRACT

A humidity monitoring device has been developed using a cerium titanate type humidity transducer. The response of the element is approximately exponential with RH. The element is driven with AC to prevent polarization. By use of a special amplifier and attenuating system, nearly linear output is achieved. The response time of the meter in still air is approximately 30 seconds, and it is characterized by no saturation effects in high relative humidity. The effect of temperature on resistance at constant relative humidity is very small in the room temperature range, a characteristic of the cerium titanate material.

INTRODUCTION

Ceramic humidity sensing elements of cerium oxide-titania composition were developed in 1955 by Horizons, Inc., and subsequently patented under U.S. Patent No. 2,862,090. This material has not found widespread use, primarily due to its intrinsically very high impedance. The cerium titanate sensor has several advantages however. It is not affected by long exposure to very high RH, it has a very low temperature coefficient of resistance, and it may be fabricated in such a way that uniform humidity sensitive elements result. We have developed circuitry not only to handle these high impedance elements but also to compensate for the

* *Present address*: Minnetech Laboratories, Inc., Minneapolis, Minn.
** *Present address:* Minnesota Honeywell Company, Ordnance Division, Hopkins, Minn.

exponential dependance of resistance upon RH.

This paper will be divided into essentially three sections; the mechanics of fabricating the elements, the electrical characteristics of the elements, and the circuitry.

FABRICATION OF ELEMENTS

It seems that many titanates possess humidity sensitive characteristics with certain advantages. Of these, the titanates formed by cerium appear to possess the most useful combination of properties. To prepare the sensing elements, a blend is formed of powdered materials composed of cerium oxide (or a material pyrolytically reducible to cerium oxide) and titanium dioxide. The blend is then passed through a micro-pulverizer. After it has been reduced to an extremely fine powder, it is charged into crucible and calcined at 2100°F for one hour. The calcined product is then ground again in a crusher, after which it is ball-milled in a water slurry for several hours in order to reduce the particles to a fine powder. The fine powder is then dried at about 100°C; it can then be shaped or extruded in the desired configuration. The green elements are fired at approximately 2200°F for roughly 1 hour. After the firing process, electrodes can be attached by one of many suitable processes, such as electroplating, vacuum evaporation, silver painting (which is subsequently fired), etc.

It is important that the starting materials be of extremely high purity. For example, the titanium dioxide should be pigment grade, so that additional refining is not necessary. The cerium compound which is combined with the titanium dioxide can be cerium hydrate, such as $CeO_2 \cdot 2H_2O$, and should be AR grade. An example of a suitable starting charge is 11.5 parts by weight of cerium hydrate and 6.5 parts by weight of titanium dioxide. This gives a mole ratio of approximately 3 parts titanium dioxide to 2 parts cerium oxide.

The electrical characteristics of the finished product are particularly sensitive to finished element density. The final density is affected by the final firing and/or the amount of ball-milling. The speed of response and intrinsic impedance both decrease with increasing density.

PHYSICAL AND ELECTRICAL CHARACTERISTICS

The cerium titanate elements made by the above process can be fabricated into humidity sensors in a number of ways. For example, they can be extruded in long rods, fired, and then sawed up into wafers. The leads can be attached to these waters either on the flat parallel sides, on the opposite sides of the diameter, or in many other geometrical configurations. The disadvantage in using the flat parallel sides is that this material, being a titanate, has a fairly high dielectric constant (approximately 4), and the capacitance creates a shunt impedance when the element is used in AC circuits. Alternatively, the green calcined mix may be pressed into pills on a pellet press and then fired. The latter approach has the advantage of extremely uniform green density and, if the firing conditions can be maintained accurately, yields reproducible elements.

A typical response curve of such an element is shown in Fig. 1. The "dry" resistance is something in the neighborhood of 10^4 MΩ. This decreases approximately exponentially to about 5 MΩ at 100 per cent RH at room temperature. As may also be seen in Fig. 1, there is a very small change of characteristics as temperature is varied from 50 to 100°F. A typical run of material will show uniform characteristics within about ± 10 per cent in resistance at a given relative humidity. Since the humidity sensitive effect evidently takes place on the surface, some control over the characteristics are possible by varying the

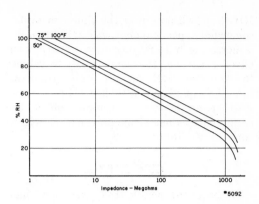

FIG. 1. Composite CT element impedance characteristics at 60 cycles.

geometry and electrode placement. A rather suitable geometry seems to be a pill, approximately $\frac{1}{4}$ in. in diameter and about .075 in. thick.

While cerium titanate elements are not particularly subject to polarization effects from DC, it seems impossible to prevent oxidation of the electrodes when the elements are operated with DC potential. The use of AC has one serious drawback, the effect of shunt capacity. This masks the humidity response at low RH. For example, at 60 cycles it is difficult to measure RH below about 20 per cent at room temperature.

The time responses of the cerium titanate elements follow typical absorption-desorption curves. Figure 2 shows the response of a typical element as the humidity is suddenly switched from 33 to 100 per cent RH. Curve B shows the downhill response as the humidity is shifted back again from 100 to 33 per cent

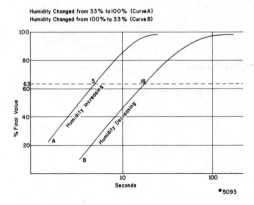

FIG. 2. Response time of CT element at 75°F.

RH. You will note that the time constant is somewhat dependent on whether the humidity is increasing or decreasing. Also, no saturation effects occur; i.e., the element may be subject to 100 per cent RH indefinitely and still maintain its rapid time response characteristic. Further, no detectable hysteresis effects are exhibited by these elements when allowed to come to equilibrium.

CIRCUITRY

In order to handle the extremely high impedances presented by the cerium titanate elements, a circuit whose block diagram is shown in Fig. 3, was developed. It is essentially a constant voltage source driving a low input impedance high gain amplifier in series with the humidity sensitive element. The current into the amplifier is E/R, where E is the supply voltage and R is the resistance of the element. The output current from the amplifier is the input current multiplied by the gain of the amplifier, β. In order to achieve a fairly linear scale, the amplifier is followed by a logarithmic attenuator network whose characteristics are approximately $I_0 = k \log I_{in}$. The response of the humidity sensitive element is approximately $R = R_0 e^{-\alpha(RH)}$. where α is a pro-

portionality constant. The output current, I_3 of the device is approximately linear in RH, and can be approximately represented by: $I_3 = k \log \beta E/R_0 + k\alpha(RH)$. This equation breaks down at low relative humidity where the indicating meter loads the circuit.

A voltage control allows compensation for variation in amplifier gain, "dry" resistance of the elements, etc. It should also be pointed out that temperature effects on the amplifier gain have only negligible effects on the output current, since changes in β only show up as a logarithmic variation in I_0. Certain precautions must be taken, of course, in fabrication of the amplifier. Since the element impedance is very high, shunt capacities to ground must be avoided. This means that the amplifier must be located in the neighborhood of the sensitive element. Further, any leakage paths to ground must be eliminated. In addition to this, certain parameters of the amplifier components must be specified to prevent erratic and nonreproducible effects.

CONCLUSION

The cerium titanate elements described herein have several unique properties not found in other electrical humidity transducers. These are: very low hysteresis; low temperature coefficient, unaffected by long exposure to 100 per cent RH; rapid time response; and reproducible elements made by standard manufacturing techniques. The primary shortcoming of these elements is their extremely high impedance.

Research now being carried out indicates that this impedance can be reduced by perhaps as much as a factor of 100 with very little effect on the other desirable parameters. This means that such an element could be used directly in a humidity monitor or switch without the need for complicated and expensive high gain amplification at high impedance.

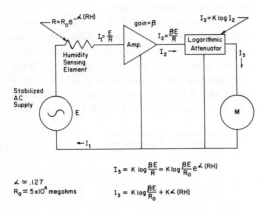

Fig. 3. Block diagram of circuit.

37. A Study of the Variation of the Surface Electrical Resistance of Lead Iodide Films with Relative Humidity at Room Temperature[*][†]

FRANK E. JONES

National Bureau of Standards, Washington, D.C.

ABSTRACT

The variation with relative humidity of the surface electrical resistance of lead iodide films at room temperature, 24°C, has been studied. Plots of the logarithm of surface resistance against the logarithm of relative humidity indicate that the relative humidity range can be divided into three regions characterized by the slopes of the straight line segments fitted to the data points. The first region lies below about 42 per cent RH, the second region lies between approximately 45 and 92 per cent RH, and the third region lies above 92 per cent RH. There is a possible discontinuity in the vicinity of 45 per cent RH.

The 45 to 92 per cent RH region was studied in some detail. The relationship between resistance, R, and relative humidity in this region is given by

$$R = R_c(RH)^{-7.0}$$

where R_c is a resistance characteristic of the individual film specimen.

The possible relationship between the surface resistance or conductance and the adsorption of water vapor on the films is discussed.

INTRODUCTION

As part of a program for the development of rapidly responding electric hygrometer elements, preliminary work has been done on the use of thin films of lead iodide as the humidity sensitive material. Lead iodide elements[1,2] have several important potential advantages over other film elements.[1-4] Among these are the promise of greater stability under storage and a significantly smaller temperature coefficient of electrical resistance, TCR. The application of electrodes over, rather than under, the lead iodide film has been found to further reduce the TCR to such an extent that preliminary laboratory tests have indicated that the effect of temperature on resistance might be negligible at temperatures as low as −30°C.

The present work was undertaken to provide information on the variation with relative humidity at room temperature of the surface electrical resistance of lead iodide films. At this writing, the exact chemical composition of the films is not known, and therefore the term "lead iodide" is used throughout with the understanding that a pure film of PbI_2 is not implied.

PREPARATION AND TREATMENT OF THE FILMS

The lead iodide films were deposited on glass substrates from a subliming source in vacuum. The substrates had been cleaned by washing in detergent and water, rinsing in "demineralized" water (water which had passed through an ion-exchange resin cartridge), rinsing in Spectro grade isopropyl alcohol, degreasing in a vapor degreaser employing Spectro grade isopropyl alcohol as

---

* Work sponsored by the Bureau of Naval Weapons of the Department of the Navy.

† Based on a thesis submitted in partial fulfillment of the requirements for the degree of Master of Science in Physics at the University of Maryland.

the solvent, and passing through the flame of a Fisher burner. The substrates were exposed to a DC glow discharge just prior to the deposition of the films. The lead iodide (Baker and Adamson reagent grade) was sublimed from a molybdenum resistance-heated "boat" in a helium-flushed vacuum chamber at a pressure of approximately 3×10^{-5} mm of Hg. The temperature (determined from the indication of a platinum, platinum-rhodium thermocouple embedded in the lead iodide in the "boat") was maintained at 350°C during the 2-minute interval in which the substrates were exposed to the subliming lead iodide. The thickness of the film, determined interferometrically, was 2200 Å with an estimate of standard deviation of 45 Å.

The films were sintered[5] by heating in water vapor saturated air (in a sealed chamber over "demineralized" water) maintained at 52°C for 24 hours. The sintering treatment was intended to stabilize the films. Gold film electrodes were vacuum deposited in an intermeshing-comb configuration on top of the sintered lead iodide films. The configuration was established by a magnetically retained mask.[6]

APPARATUS AND PROCEDURES

Four film specimens 21 mm wide by 8, 10, 23, and 63 mm long were placed in a specimen holder. The specimens were attached by spring clips to terminals in a Kovar seal in the holder. Strips of gold foil were pressed against the gold film electrodes by the clips. Additional clips were used to increase the gold-to-gold contact and to prevent loss of contact due to abrasion of the soft gold film. The specimen holder was designed to be sealed into chambers in which various values of relative humidity were maintained.

Control of Relative Humidity

The sealed chambers were maintained at a number of values of relative humidity by saturated aqueous solutions of various salts.[7, 8] The relative humidity values and the corresponding salts were: 12 per cent, LiCl; 33 per cent, $MgCl_2 \cdot 6H_2O$; 42 per cent, $Zn(NO_3)_2 \cdot 6H_2O$; 45 per cent, KNO_2; 54 per cent, $Mg(NO_3)_2 \cdot 6H_2O$; 66 per cent, $NaNO_2$; 76 per cent, NaCl; 80 per cent, $(NH_4)_2SO_4$; 92 per

cent, KNO_3; and 97 per cent, K_2SO_4. "Demineralized" water was used to maintain 100 per cent RH.

AC Ohmmeter Circuit

Measurements of the AC surface electrical resistance of the specimens were made using an ohmmeter circuit.[9] The block diagram of the circuit is shown in Fig. 1. The multivibrator provided 100-cps excitation to the film specimen which was protected from DC by a high quality "Mylar" capacitor. The film specimen was connected into the voltage divider employing four pairs of "front-to-back" silicon diodes, whose voltage-current characteristics made the divided voltage proportional to the logarithm of the specimen resistance. The divided voltage controlled the frequency of the voltage-controlled oscillator. The output of the oscillator was fed into a commercial counter-timer.

FIG. 1. Block diagram of the AC ohmmeter circuit.

The voltage-controlled oscillator frequency varied with both the resistance and the capacitance of the specimens from 218.5 to 356.0 cps over the resistance range 8.5×10^3 to 2×10^{10} Ω and the capacitance range 9 to 469 pf. The wide capacitance range is primarily due to the variation of specimen capacitance with relative humidity.[1]

Experimental Procedures

The specimens were humidity cycled before the electrical measurements were made. They were exposed to 10 cycles between the chamber in which 100 per cent RH was maintained and another chamber in which phosphorous pentoxide, P_2O_5, maintained an atmosphere approaching 0 per cent RH. The specimens remained in each chamber for approximately 10 minutes in each cycle. Such humidity cycling had been found in earlier work[1, 3] on other film materials to be effective in reducing hysteresis effects.

Following the humidity cycling the specimens remained in the 100 per cent RH chamber until the specimen resistances, monitored by the use of an impedance bridge, had apparently come to equilibrium. The parallel capacitance and the dissipation factor of each specimen were determined at equilibrium using the impedance bridge. Each specimen was then connected into the AC ohmmeter and the counter-timer was used to count the number of cycles generated by the voltage-controlled oscillator during a 10-second interval.

A partial calibration of the ohmmeter was made for each specimen at each RH point. Since the ohmmeter was sensitive to both resistance and capacitance, it was necessary to consider both the resistance and the capacitance of the specimens in the calibration of the ohmmeter. A capacitance corresponding to the parallel capacitance of the specimen was substituted in parallel with each of several precision resistors whose values bracketed the resistance of the specimen as determined from the capacitance and dissipation factor. The count indicated by the counter-timer was noted for each of the substitutions. Specimen resistances were subsequently determined from plots of the logarithm of substituted resistance against counter-timer count. These procedures were repeated for each of the relative humidities in the following order: 12, 97, 33, 92, 42, 80, 45, 76, 54, and 66 per cent. This order was chosen to provide additional humidity cycling of the specimens. The measurements were made at a room temperature of approximately 24°C.

RESULTS

Preliminary electrical measurements were made on the day the films were deposited and about two months later. The measurements of interest in the present paper were made almost five months after the films were deposited. The film specimens were stored in a sealed chamber over silica gel between the days in which measurements were made.

Figure 2 shows a typical plot of the logarithm of specimen resistance against the logarithm of relative humidity for specimen No. 4. The plots indicate that the RH range can be divided into three regions characterized by the slopes of the straight line segments fitted to the data points. The first region lies below about 42 per cent RH, the second region

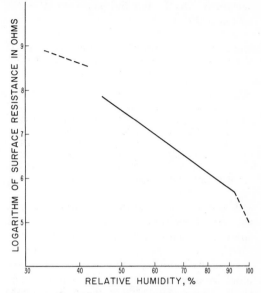

FIG. 2. Plot of the logarithm of surface resistance against relative humidity for specimen No. 4. The solid line is the least squares straight line for the 45 to 92 per cent RH region. The dashed lines are drawn through the points in the other two relative humidity regions.

lies between approximately 45 and 92 per cent RH, and the third region lies above 92 per cent RH. There is a possible discontinuity in the vicinity of 45 per cent RH.

Inasmuch as the high resistances in the 12 to 45 per cent RH region made measurement difficult and since there was variation with specimens of the slopes of the straight lines in the 92 to 100 per cent RH region, detailed study was limited to the 45 to 92 per cent region.

The method of least squares was used to fit straight lines to the data points for each specimen in the 45 to 92 per cent RH region using the equation

$$\log_{10} R = a + b \log_{10} RH \qquad (1)$$

where R is specimen resistance and a and b are constants. The results are presented in Table 1 and the least squares straight lines are plotted in Fig. 3. The standard error of estimate for relative humidity, defined as the estimate of the standard deviation of the data points about the least squares straight line, was 1.2 per cent RH for specimen No. 1, 1.6 per cent RH for specimen No. 2, 1.2 per cent RH for specimen No. 3, and 3.6 per cent RH for specimen No. 4.

TABLE 1. CONSTANTS CALCULATED FOR EQ. (1) RELATING LOGARITHM OF RESISTANCE TO LOGARITHM OF RELATIVE HUMIDITY

Specimen	a	S.D.*	b	S.D.*
1	19.33	0.63	−6.94	0.35
2	20.31	0.81	−7.30	0.44
3	19.98	0.54	−6.86	0.29
4	19.40	1.34	−6.98	0.73

* Estimate of standard deviation.

The statistical "t" test[10] was applied to test the hypothesis that the values of b for the 4 specimens are not different. The values of "t" for the various pairings of specimens range between 0.04 and 0.21. Since these values are much smaller than the critical values of "t" at the 1 per cent level, 3.707, 3.499, and 3.355, for the appropriate numbers of degrees of freedom, the "t" test provides no evidence for the existence of any differences between the slopes, b, among the specimens.

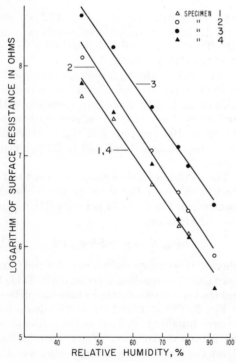

FIG. 3. Plots of the least squares straight lines for the 4 specimens in the 45 to 92 per cent RH region.

DISCUSSION

From Eq. (1) the relationship between R and RH in the 45 to 92 per cent RH region at 24°C is given by

$$R = 10^a(RH)^b \qquad (2)$$

Since it can be considered that no differences exist between the values of b for the 4 specimens the mean, −7.0, of the 4 determinations can be taken to be characteristic; a can be considered to be the $\log_{10}$ of a resistance, R_c, characteristic of the individual specimen and depending principally on the length of the specimen.

If both sides of Eq. (2) are inverted, we obtain

$$G = G_c(RH)^{7.0} \qquad (3)$$

where G is specimen conductance and G_c is a conductance characteristic of the individual specimen.

The dependence of film specimen surface resistance and, therefore, surface conductance on relative humidity is hypothesized to be due to water vapor physically adsorbed on the lead iodide film. The amount of water vapor adsorbed is a function of the relative pressure, p/p_s, the ratio of the ambient water vapor pressure to saturation water vapor pressure, and is, therefore, a function of relative humidity. In terms of relative pressure, Eq. (3) becomes

$$G = G_c'(p/p_s)^{7.0} \qquad (4)$$

where $G_c' = 10^{14} \times G_c$.

Physical adsorption studies for the films have not as yet been made and therefore the relationship between Eq. (4) and the physical adsorption isotherm for the films is not known. However, it is interesting to apply Birstein's[11] data for the 25°C adsorption isotherm for water vapor on bulk lead iodide with the understanding, of course, that the adsorption isotherm for the lead iodide films in the present work might not correspond to Birstein's isotherm. The method of least squares was used to fit a straight line to Birstein's data in the 53 to 92 per cent RH region using the equation

$$\log_{10}(v/v_m) = \alpha + \beta \log_{10}(p/p_s) \qquad (5)$$

where v/v_m is the number of monolayers of water adsorbed and α and β are constants.

The constant α was found to be equal to 2.12 and β was found to be equal to 6.18. The relationship between v/v_m and p/p_s becomes

$$v/v_m = 132 \, (p/p_s)^{6.18} \qquad (6)$$

The standard error of estimate for relative humidity for Birstein's data was 1.3 per cent RH. Combining Eqs. 4 and 6, we get

$$G = G_c'' \, (v/v_m)^{1.1} \qquad (7)$$

where G_c'' is a conductance characteristic of the individual specimen. The "t" test was applied to test the hypothesis that the exponent of v/v_m is acceptably close to 1, noting that the exponent is equal to the ratio of the negative of b to β. The value of "t" was found to be 0.30, which, since it is much smaller than the critical value at the 1 per cent level, 3.250, indicates that the exponent of v/v_m is acceptably close to 1. Therefore, if Birstein's adsorption data were applicable to the lead iodide films, the conductance of the film specimens in the 53 to 92 per cent RH region could be considered to be directly proportional to the number of monolayers of water vapor adsorbed. It should be emphasized that the adsorption isotherm for the lead iodide films in the present work might not correspond to the adsorption isotherm for bulk PbI_2. Also, there is controversy in the literature regarding Birstein's data.[12,13] For these reasons one should not attach too much significance to Eq. (7) and the tentative conclusion regarding the relationship between specimen conductance and the number of layers of water vapor adsorbed. It is interesting, however, to note that the results in the present work seem to confirm the ionic conductance mechanism discussed by Curtis,[14] Law,[15] Kawasaki,[16] and others. These results indicate the desirability of performing physical adsorption studies (i.e., the determination of the adsorption isotherm) on lead iodide film specimens simultaneously with resistance measurements in order that the conductance mechanism or mechanisms might be studied.

The resistance ranges for the specimens in the present work are not optimum. More favorable ranges for application to the development of thin film hygrometer elements have been obtained in other work on lead iodide films, and it is to be expected that resistance ranges perhaps as favorable as those for the barium fluoride element, for example, are obtainable.

References

1. Jones, F. E., "Evaporated-film Electric Hygrometer Elements," *J. Res. Natl. Bur. Std.*, **66C**, 209–216 (1962).
2. Jones, F. E., "Hygrometer Elements," U.S. Patent 3,058,079 (1962).
3. Jones, F. E. and Wexler, A., "A Barium Fluoride Film Hygrometer Element," *J. Geophys. Res.*, **65**, 2087-2095 (1960).
4. Jones, F. E., "Performance of the Barium Fluoride Film Hygrometer Element on Radiosonde Flights," *J. Geophys. Res.*, **68**, 2735–2751 (1963).
5. Papée, H. M., "On the Preparation and Sintering of Cloud Precipitating Agents. Lead Di-iodide Microcrystals," *Can. J. Chem.*, **36**, 1443–1448 (1958).
6. Jones, F. E. and Castle, A. B., Sr., "Magnetically Retained Evaporation Mask," *Rev. Sci. Instr.*, **34**, 1055 (1963).
7. Wexler, A. and Hasegawa, S., "Relative Humidity Temperature Relationships of Some Saturated Salt Solutions in the Temperature Range 0°C to 50°C," *J. Res. Natl. Bur. Std.*, **53**, 19–26 (1954).
8. "Handbook of Chemistry and Physics," 36th Ed., pp. 2309–2310, Cleveland, Ohio, Chemical Rubber Publishing Co., 1954.
9. Bowman, H. A. and Allison, L. M., "A Log-response 5-decade AC Ohmmeter," to be published as a *Natl. Bur. Std. Technical Note*.
10. Youden, W. J., "Statistical Methods for Chemists," p. 24 New York, John Wiley & Sons, Inc., 1951.
11. Birstein, S. J., "The Role of Adsorption in Heterogeneous Nucleation, I: Adsorption of Water Vapor on Silver Iodide and Lead Iodide," *J. Meterol.*, **12**, 324–331 (1955).
12. Papée, H. M. "Microcalorimetry of Adsorption of Water Vapor on Lead Di-iodide," *Can. J. Chem.*, **37**, 375–383 (1959).
13. Moskvitin, N. N., Dubinin, M. M., and Sarakhov, A. I., "Adsorption of Water Vapor on Crystalline Silver and Lead Iodide Dust Particles," *Acad. Sci. USSR. Phys. Chem. Sect.*, **122**, 725–728 (1958).
14. Curtis, H. L., "Insulating Properties of Solid Dielectrics," *Bull. Bur. Stands.*, **11**, 359–417 (1915).
15. Law, J. T., "A Mechanism for Water Induced Excess Reverse Dark Current on Grown Germanium n-p Junctions," *Proc. I. R. E.*, **42**, 1367–1370 (1954).
16. Kawasaki, K., "On the Variation of Ionic Conduction Current Along the Surface of Solid by the Adsorption of Water Vapor and the Phase Transition of Adsorbed Layer," *Ôyô Butsuri*, **27**, 216–219 (1958).

38. A Ceramic Relative Humidity Sensor

Elias J. Amdur and D. E. Nelson

Minneapolis-Honeywell Regulator Company, Minneapolis, Minnesota

AND

J. C. Foster

Minneapolis-Honeywell Regulator Company, Rio Piedras, Puerto Rico

ABSTRACT

The need for humidity sensors which may be operated at dry-bulb temperatures as high as 125°C led to consideration of hygroscopic inorganic systems as most likely to yield a satisfactory product. Sensors were developed which consisted of a specially compounded ceramic base impregnated with certain slightly soluble inorganic salts, generally lithium fluoride and carbonate.

The sensors obtained by the final procedure show many favorable properties.

Life tests conducted on these sensors indicated that they were reliably stable in clean atmospheres. Subsequent exposures to industrial atmospheres resulted in rapid changes in calibration due apparently to sorption of contaminants.

Protective systems which were developed were found to reduce the rate of calibration shift but did not eliminate it completely. As a result of this difficulty further work with ceramic humidity sensors was abandoned. Protected sensors of this type have been used in the humidity meter of the Project Mercury capsule and in other short-duration applications, but they have not been made available for general distribution.

INTRODUCTION

The purpose of this paper is to describe the properties of a device which almost fulfilled the design specification for a multipurpose relative humidity sensor. It illustrates the problems which limit progress in this field of instrumentation and at the same time indicates the possibility of a dead end in the described line of investigation.

The measurement of humidity at high temperatures is frequently required in industrial processes. Wet- and dry-bulb psychrometry remains the only method which can be used, but this method is not satisfactory for a number of reasons. Because of this, the development of a high-temperature humidity sensor has been a perennial objective in the Honeywell laboratory.

The most desirable sensor for this purpose would conform to the following specifications:

(1) It would be of the electrical resistance type, with resistance values between 1000 Ω and 10 MΩ in its range of usefulness.

(2) It would cover the full range of relative humidity and be capable of operation to 125°C.

(3) Temperature compensation should be easily accomplished if necessary.

(4) It should be easy to make to a standard calibration curve.

(5) It should be insensitive to a maximum number of contaminating or otherwise destructive influences and should not be subject to changes with time.

Because of the high operating temperatures specified, it was natural to consider inorganic systems, particularly those based on ceramic compositions. The electrical resistance of many ceramic materials varies with relative humidity, but generally in the multi-megohm range. Such sensors will be found to be surprisingly nonreproducible and unstable with time. Nevertheless, at the outset of this program it was felt that ceramic materials offered the best possibility for progress in this field.

We shall not detail the logic which led to the development of the particular sensor described below. After some period of experimentation it was found that soft fired kaolinic bodies treated with boiling dilute solutions of slightly soluble lithium salts gave sensors with interesting properties. Studies of variations in body mix, the degree of compression, the temperature and duration of firing were made. A method of applying a gold electrode grid was developed, and a treatment procedure evolved. Continuous property investigations were conducted in the Honeywell humidity standard and used to direct the course of each investigation. The final sensor is shown in Fig. 1.

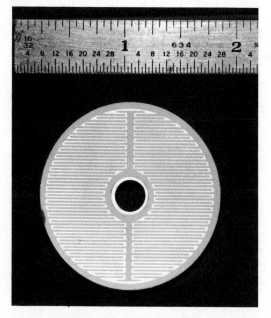

FIG. 1. Single ceramic sensor.

DESCRIPTION OF THE SENSOR

The sensor blank mix was fixed to contain principally kaolin with a small amount of nepheline syenite plus organic binders which burned out during firing. The blanks were hard pressed and fired to produce a porous material of 1.32 to 1.34 bulk density, having an apparent porosity of 75 to 76 per cent. The fired blank had dimensions of 1.615-in. o.d., .272-in. hole, and was .073 to .075 in. thick. After firing, a gold electrode grid was silk screened on the blank using Hanovia 23-carat gold paste, and the blank was again fired. This blank was then boiled in a saturated solution of lithium fluoride or lithium carbonate and finally boiled in several changes of distilled water.

UNIQUENESS OF SENSOR

During the course of development the properties of this sensor were compared with the properties of sensors based on porous alundum or porous glass bodies. It was found that these relatively inert bodies could not hold the ionic material against leaching, and the resulting sensors had quite different response curves of resistance *vs* relative humidity. Sensors based on alundum or porous glass bodies gave curves similar to those obtained when the pure salts were investigated between electrodes, while the sensor formed by reaction between the kaolinite base and lithium salts had quite another curve (Fig. 2).

As a consequence of these observations, a series of test procedures were performed to determine if the kaolinite body and lithium salts actually reacted in some manner to form a substance with unique properties. X-ray analysis failed to find evidence of lithium fluoride or carbonate in these sensors. Boiling in distilled water failed to remove more than a small amount of lithium salt in each cycle of washing, and the lithium could not be removed quantitatively by even a large number of washings. It was felt therefore that this sensor body was in a sense unique compared to previously used materials.

REPRODUCIBILITY OF SENSOR

In order to be of maximum usefulness, a relative humidity sensor must have a reproducible calibration curve so that if one sensor is destroyed or altered it can be replaced by another without recalibrating the instrumentation used with it. It was found that these ceramic sensors could be prepared in commercial quantities to lie within a ± 2 per

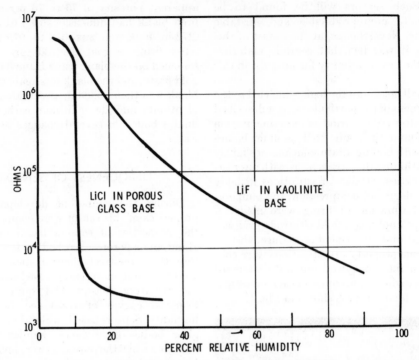

FIG. 2. Calibration comparison of base materials (25°C).

cent RH tolerance from a standard curve, with a yield of 90 per cent of all bases started through the process (Fig. 3).

VARIATION OF CALIBRATION CURVE WITH TEMPERATURE

Figure 4 shows isotherms of the ceramic humidity sensor, based on the vapor pressure of water below freezing. In the development of this sensor, an effort was made to position these isotherms in the resistance range indicated, in order to avoid instrumentation difficulties at higher and lower impedance levels. This sensor is most useful above −5°C, and temperature compensation is easily designed for the −5 to +70°C range. The impedance level at low temperatures is high enough to present design problems, particularly since the sensor must be operated with alternating current. A wide range of blank compositions, process variations and grid designs was studied in an effort to lower the impedance level of this sensor for low-temperature applications. It did not seem possible to do this by further combinations of these variables.

HYSTERESIS

This ceramic sensor has no hysteresis in the ordinary sense. If a sensor is calibrated starting at 10 per cent RH and successive points are taken at intervals until 95 per cent RH is reached, a curve is obtained which may be reproduced by calibrating at the same intervals in the direction of decreasing relative humidity. However, the porous ceramic body seems to be subject to slow secondary changes in resistance. For example, if a sensor is held at 10 per cent RH for several days, a shift of 2 per cent RH will occur. This is reversible by exposure to 90 per cent RH. The sensor thus has a multiple time constant effect rather than hysteresis.

TIME CONSTANT

The primary response time to 63 per cent of a step change is about 15 seconds at room temperature for the standard ceramic sensor described above.

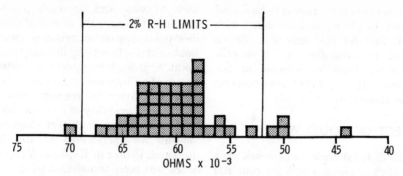

FIG. 3. Distribution of ceramic elements due to manufacturing uncertainty (45 per cent RH, 25°C).

CURRENT RATING

These sensors have a current limitation of 50 μA AC for continuous duty. The current may be greater than this at room temperature, but at elevated temperatures the sensor calibration may be shifted by long time exposure to excessive currents. For short periods (24 hours), a current of 350 to 500 μA does not seem to damage these devices.

EFFECT OF HIGH HUMIDITY AND CONDENSATION

Some hygrometric systems are adversely affected by exposure to relative humidity in excess of 90 per cent RH and to condensation. Resistance to the effects of moisture seems to be a useful property. The ceramic sensor was found to be quite stable to both high humidity and condensation. Mil-H-14410A, paragraph

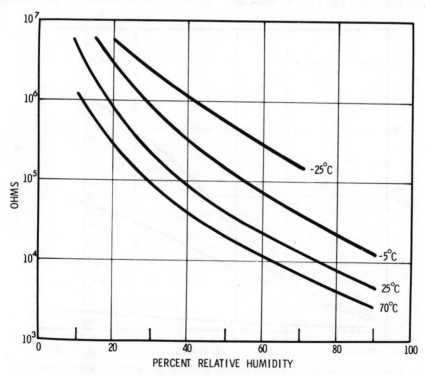

FIG. 4. Calibration isotherms for the ceramic humidity element.

4.1.5.2, specifies that the sensor is to be cooled to −20°C and then brought into contact with air at 75°F and 50 per cent RH. Seven repetitions of this procedure caused no calibration change. Actually, because of the porous nature of this sensor no condensation was noted in these tests.

EFFECT OF LIQUID WATER

Boiling in distilled water will result in a calibration shift of about 3 to 5 per cent RH per procedure. The sensor is not permanently injured by this procedure and may be re-used if recalibrated. While this method might be used to renovate contaminated sensors, it is presented here solely as an illustration of the resistance of the sensor to liquid water.

CONTAMINATION-INDUCED CALIBRATION SHIFTS

In spite of the many fine properties of the ceramic sensors described above, it was found that they were subject to unexplainable shifts in calibration. All humidity sensors are subject to contaminants in the air. For example, the

wick of wet- and dry-bulb psychrometers requires changing; the mirror of a cold mirror dew-point apparatus requires cleaning; the bobbin of a self-heating lithium chloride dew-point hygrometer requires retreatment; the optics of an infrared system must be cleaned. This sensitivity to contamination detracts from the desirability of a particular system.

Most of the original work done on ceramic sensors was performed at the Honeywell Research Center in Hopkins, Minnesota. This work was later transferred to the Honeywell Main Plant, where it became evident that these sensors were not as stable as previous work had indicated. Figure 5 shows the effect of exposing groups of ceramic sensors at two locations in the Main Plant, compared to controls kept in a sealed bottle except when calibrated at weekly intervals. Since obvious chemical contamination could be detected in this case, a series of field tests were run to determine whether other industrial locations were similarly contaminated. It was found that in almost every case, similar calibration shifts occurred. Surprisingly, sensors kept buried in grain to monitor the grain moisture condition were found to be virtually un-

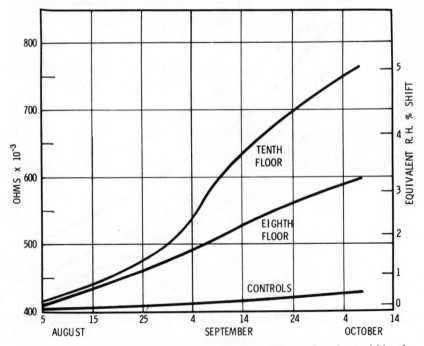

Fig. 5. Comparison of contamination effect at different locations within the Honeywell main plant (25 per cent RH, 25°C).

affected in spite of direct contact with the dust, soil and bran of the environment.

As the result of these experiences, a program of devising protective procedures for the sensors was begun. Treatment with protective coatings and covering with non-hygroscopic cloth helped somewhat, but the best results were obtained by means of a second (un-treated) sensor blank superimposed on the face of the sensor and sealed around the edges. The contamination-induced shift was considerably reduced, but the sensors were still affected at too rapid a rate for industrial purposes. This protected sensor is shown in Fig. 6. The time response of this sensor was lengthened about 10 times over that of the single-layer sensor.

FIG. 6. Double ceramic sensor.

MECHANISM OF DETERIORATION

Experimental work with these ceramic sensors, and with lithium zeolite sensors, in-dicated that these extremely porous materials absorb quantities of contaminants on their internal surfaces. These contaminants ap-parently interfere with the conductive mech-anism, as in all cases the deterioration was in the direction of an increase in the resistance *vs* relative humidity curve. While several mechanisms may be considered for this reduc-tion in conductivity, one observation is that in these materials, the humidity-actuated con-ductivity mechanism must be a very feeble one, using a very small fraction of the internal surface of the solid. The water molecules probably are sorbed only on certain polar positions within the structure, scattered over a very large area. The bulk of the internal area probably has little attraction for water, and the bond strength at the active sites must vary considerably. The contaminants compete with the water molecules for these positions. Since the contaminants are probably more strongly attracted at some of these positions, the positions which may be utilized by water molecules are reduced progressively as more contaminating molecules are ab-sorbed.

Because of the unfortunate lack of stability of this otherwise very useful sensor and because of the realization that all porous materials probably would show this defect, work on humidity sensors in this laboratory is now directed toward nonporous systems.

These nonporous materials operate by means of variations in body properties rather than surface properties. Contamination-induced calibration shifts are much less in these sensors.

39. Some Properties and Limitations of the Aluminum Oxide Hygrometer

A. C. JASON

Department of Scientific and Industrial Research, Torry Research Station, Aberdeen, Scotland

ABSTRACT

An account is given of the origins, construction, properties, theory and applications of the hygrometer based on the electrical properties of anodized aluminum.

The advantages, limitations and accuracy are critically examined and possible methods of overcoming the principal limitation, that of long-term aging, are discussed.

An apparently new effect, the generation of an EMF across the anodic layer and its dependence on humidity, is described, and an attempt is made to explain it. By analogy with the property of a thermocouple, this behavior has been termed the hygroelectric effect.

INTRODUCTION

The aluminum oxide hygrometer owes its origin in its present form to a chance discussion in 1952 between the author and F. Ansbacher on possible methods of measuring diffusion of water in fish muscle during drying. A nondestructive method was required for the continuous measurement of the concentration of water at a number of points in a series of planes perpendicular to the direction of mass flow. Ansbacher recalled that in earlier work[1, 2] on electron bombardment conductivity in aluminum oxide, the capacitance of the condenser formed between the base of an anodized aluminum plate and an aluminum electrode evaporated onto the exposed oxide surface fell substantially when the material was placed in a system that was then evacuated.

The change of capacitance was ascribed to the removal of water from the porous oxide layer.

A number of anodized aluminum moisture probes were constructed in the hope that if they were inserted into fish muscle the partition of moisture between the water in the muscle and that in the aluminum oxide would lead to capacitance changes in the probes. However, the method failed in its original purpose owing to the effects of contamination by electrolytes present in the muscle and to their insensitivity to changes of moisture at high levels of hydration of the muscle.

Nevertheless, it was by this time clear that both the capacitance and the resistance of an element were extremely sensitive to changes in atmospheric humidity[3, 4] and hygrometers based on either or both of these properties were known by the generic title of "capacitance-resistance hygrometers."[5]

Attempts were made to develop the instrument commercially, but success was thwarted principally because, in common with most other forms of electric hygrometer, long-term aging effects limited the period during which a calibration remained reasonably accurate. In addition, aging was accelerated by repeated large changes of relative humidity and temperature so that the elements were very vulnerable under field conditions. Aging was found to be progressive, unless an element was stored at low humidity, and eventually the variation of both capacitance and resistance with changes of relative humidity became so small (except at high relative humidities) as to make the instrument useless.

Prior to 1953[3] there appears to be no reference in the scientific literature to the effect of humidity on the electrical properties of anodized aluminum. However, some years after 1953 the attention of the author was drawn to a patent published in 1941 by Koller[6] describing a hygrometer based on the electrical impedance of a plate condenser formed by anodizing aluminum and depositing a metal electrode on the oxide surface.

Having outlined the origins of the instrument, the purpose of this paper is to give a brief review of a number of investigations which have led to the elucidation of the mechanisms giving rise to the observed effects and to give an account of recent, unpublished, work.

STRUCTURE AND FUNCTION OF ANODIC LAYER

The physical structure of the anodic layer is very dependent on the conditions of anodizing, the gross features of the various forms being well described in the copious literature on the subject. Depending on the temperature, composition and concentration of the electrolyte, the anodizing time, and either the formation voltage or the current density, a great variety of thicknesses and porosities may be produced. Broadly there are two classes of structure, the porous and the nonporous, their electrical properties being well typified by these two classes. Figures 1 and 2 show the influence of the type of electrolyte on the variation with relative humidity of capacitance and resistance respectively of layers of equal area. These clearly illustrate the remarkable effects of changes generally observed in porous layers formed in acid electrolytes, and the relative insensitivity of nonporous layers.

Calculations of the apparent dielectric constant of the porous oxide layers based on their thickness and area indicate values in excess of 1000 at high relative humidities, a magnitude considerably in excess of that attributable to adsorbed water and normally associated only with ferroelectric materials. However, it will be shown that a satisfactory explanation of the observed behavior can be given without invoking ferroelectric effects.

Workers who studied the formation and structure of porous oxide layers had proposed

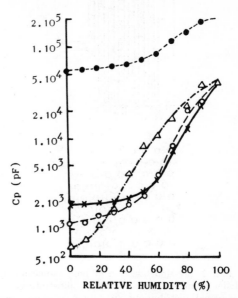

FIG. 1. The influence of the type of electrolyte on the variation of equivalent parallel capacitance C_p with relative humidity. Anodized area 1.96 cm². Measurements made at 1000 cps.

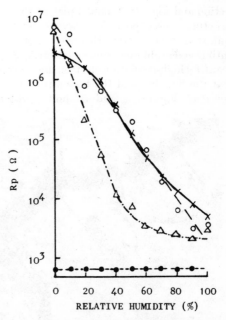

FIG. 2. The influence of the types of electrolyte on the variation of equivalent parallel resistance R_p with relative humidity. Anodized area, 1.96 cm². Measurements made at 1000 cps.

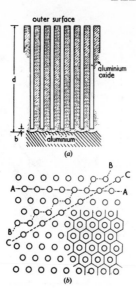

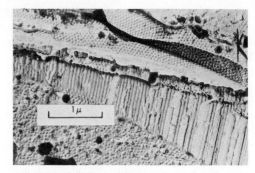

FIG. 5. Hexagonal pattern in a "crater" at the metal-oxide boundary (Booker[8]).

FIG. 3. (a) Model section of pore structure. (b) Model plan of pore structure illustrating: (i) hexagonal distribution; (ii) origin of pore base pattern; (iii) three possible cleavage lines obtainable in a cross section AA, BB, CC (Booker and Wood[7]).

an idealized model in which the solid oxide is permeated by parallel tubular pores hexagonally packed and perpendicular to the plane of the layer. Figure 3(a) shows a model section and Fig. 3(b) a model plan of the pore structure; three possible cleavage lines are indicated in the latter. However, it was not until Booker[8] obtained some most striking and beautiful high-resolution electron micrographs that the fine detail of the pore structure was revealed. Figures 4 and 5 show "craters"

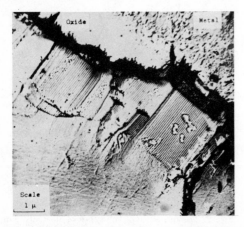

FIG. 4. Cross section through oxide near boundary with metal, showing "craters" containing pore structure (Booker[8]).

exposed where the oxide layer has broken away in minute "chips"; the former shows cleavage through a plane of weakness and the latter shows the close-packed hexagonal structure. Booker and Wood[7] confirmed that the pore structure extends throughout the entire thickness of the oxide to the pore base layer and that the pore diameter and spacing do not vary much through the oxide layer. These authors give the following dimensions, which may be regarded as typical of the pore structure of layers formed in sulfuric acid:

Thickness of oxide layer	30 to 127 μ*
Pore spacing	450 to 600 Å
Pore density	13×10^9 cm^{-2}
Pore base thickness	~500 Å or less
Pore diameter	190 to 300 Å*
Pore volume/volume of oxide layer	13%*
Pore surface area	0.2 m² cm^{-2} of superficial oxide area

* Depending on anodizing conditions.

It is evident that the porous nature of the layer presents an enormous area for the adsorption of gases and vapors and, furthermore, that the structure of the layer is very regular and offers the possibility of constructing "tailor-made" surfaces.

The manner in which the anodic layer functions as an electric hygrometer element is conditioned by its structure. At low humidities the measured capacitance of the element is almost entirely derived from the bulk mixed dielectric consisting of air, aluminum oxide and water. The dielectric properties of such a mixture have been investigated by Wood[9] who has shown that both the real and imaginary dielectric constants vary with frequency in a manner that is related to the amount of water added. The real component ϵ' varies between about 3 at frequencies in excess of about 1 Mc/sec and 10 at zero frequency. For a given frequency, ϵ' increases with the amount of added water.[10]

With increasing humidity, parallel conduction paths through the adsorbed water are formed down the pore surfaces, so that the electrical characteristics are largely determined by the magnitude of the combined resistance of these conduction paths and the capacitance between the pore base and the metal. The pore base thickness b is extremely small, as indicated above, so that the pore base capacitance is very large. As saturation is approached, the pore surface resistance becomes almost negligible so that the measured capacitance between the outer conducting layer and the metal base is virtually that between the pore base and the metal.

THEORY

The equivalent circuit, based on the structure of the anodic layer, is shown in Fig. 6 for a single pore. Since all the pores are identical and parallel, any given area of the layer may be represented by the same equivalent circuit with appropriate values for the parameters. The capacitance between the two outer conducting layers separated by the mixed dielectric of thickness d is C_o. The leakage resistance through the thickness d of the solid crystallite aluminum oxide is R_o. The remainder of the equivalent circuit is that corresponding to the specific effects of the pore, the region at the base of which provides almost the entire contribution to C_2, the pore base capacitance. R_1 is the resistance along the pore side between the porous conducting layer deposited on the outer oxide surface and the capacitance C_2. R_2 is the leakage resistance through the thickness b of the aluminum oxide at the pore base. The pore side resistance R_1 is strongly dependent on the quantity of water adsorbed on the pore surface and, except at low humidities, is the dominant parameter.

At a frequency f the parallel capacitance equivalent to the circuit in Fig. 6 is

$$C_p = \frac{C_2 R_2^2}{(R_1 + R_2)^2 + 4\pi^2 f^2 R_1^2 R_2^2 C_2^2} + C_o \quad (1)$$

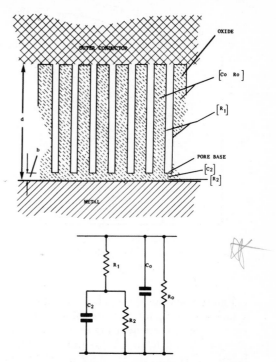

Fig. 6. Equivalent circuit of a single pore. C_o = capacitance of entire oxide layer; C_2 = pore-base capacitance; R_o = resistance of solid aluminum oxide; R_1 = pore-side resistance; R_2 = pore-base resistance.

and the equivalent parallel resistance is given by

$$\frac{1}{R_p} = \frac{R_1 + R_2 + 4\pi^2 f^2 R_1 R_2^2 C_2^2}{(R_1 + R_2)^2 + 4\pi^2 f^2 R_1^2 R_2^2 C_2^2} + \frac{1}{R_o} \quad (2)$$

Equations (1) and (2) may be combined to eliminate R_1 and to give

$$C_p - C_o = \frac{A}{8\pi^2 f^2} \pm$$

$$\frac{1}{2}\left[\left(\frac{A}{4\pi^2 f^2}\right)^2 - \frac{1}{\pi^2 f^2 R_p^2}\right]^{1/2} \quad (3)$$

where $A = 4\pi^2 f^2 C_2 + 1/R_2^2 C_2$

The curve TUVW in Fig. 7 represents Eq. (3), the parameter R_1 varying along this curve. The point U, where $R_1 = 0$, lies in the branch VT where $2\pi f C_2 R_2 > 1$, i.e. the positive sign of the root is taken. The portion UV of this branch represents the near-saturated condition. In all other cases, the negative sign condition holds so that in general R_p decreases as $C_p - C_o$ increases.

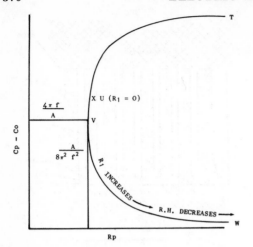

Fig. 7. Theoretical relationship between R_p and $C - C_o$.

Figure 8 shows values of $C_p - C_o$ plotted as a function of R_p for various thicknesses d of oxide layer. By substituting measured values of $C_p - C_o$ and R_p in Eq. (3) and obtaining a mean value for A, the theoretical curve for an element may be calculated. Figure 8 shows how close the agreement can be between the experimental and theoretical forms of the curve.

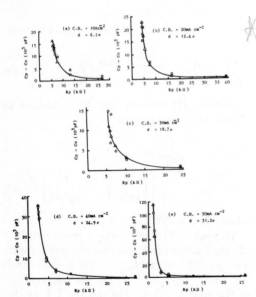

Fig. 8. Relationship between $C_p - C_o$ and R_p at 1 kc/sec for oxide layers of various thicknesses d anodized in sulfuric acid at various current densities C.D. Circles represent experimental values and triangles theoretical values.

Table 1 gives values of the parameters A, C_2 and R_2 for the examples shown in Fig. 8.

TABLE 1. PORE-BASE CAPACITANCE AND RESISTANCE FOR VARIOUS THICKNESSES OF OXIDE LAYER

Oxide Thickness, d (μ)	A	C_2 (pf)	R_2 (kΩ)
6.2	2.52	19,000	5.5
12.4	3.04	25,000	4.38
18.7	3.2	15,800	5.0
24.9	5.5	40,000	2.53
31.2	9.2	118,000	1.35

The variation of characteristics with frequency are qualitatively in accord with theoretical predictions.[5,10] In general, it is desirable for practical purposes to use low frequencies since the variations of C_p and R_p with relative humidity are more pronounced than at high frequencies.

CONSTRUCTION OF ELEMENTS

The shape of an element may correspond to any desired configuration, though it has been found most convenient to construct it in the form of a thin rod. It is not essential to use aluminum of high purity, normal commercial purity being adequate for the purpose.

By way of example the construction of two forms of hygrometer element* will be described. These may be conveniently made up in batches of 20 or 30.

Rod Elements

Aluminum welding rod, diameter 3 mm, is cut into suitable lengths and carefully degreased in an organic solvent. The rods are immersed to a known depth in 17.5 per cent v/v sulfuric acid at a controlled temperature of 30°C and anodized, usually for 30 minutes, at a constant current density. The choice of current density is to a certain extent arbitrary, but it should not exceed 50 mA cm^{-2} otherwise the oxide layer tends to flake off during anodizing. (For reasons that are apparent from the theory, the shape of the curves relating both C_p and R_p to relative humidity are dependent on the thickness d of the oxide

* Patent applied for.

layer since R_1 is proportional to d. Figures 9
and 10 very clearly illustrate the effect.) After
the rods are removed from the electrolyte they
are thoroughly washed in tap water and then
allowed to soak for about an hour in distilled
water. Figure 11(a) shows details of the construction of a rod element.

The first stage in the construction is to coat a
thin sleeve of "Araldite" onto the rod just above
and slightly overlapping the oxide layer. The
sleeve should be smoothly tapered onto the
layer. Two short lengths of rubber tubing of
suitable diameter are slipped over the rod, one
covering about 2 mm of the tip of the anodized
portion, the other fitting over about 3 mm of
the "Araldite" sleeve and a short length of the
untreated rod. The purpose of the rubber
tubing is to prevent aluminum from condensing on the tip and at the junction of the
insulating sleeve with the rod during the next
operation, which is the vacuum deposition of a
thin film of aluminum (or any suitable conducting coating). In order to produce a uniform film of metal, it is advisable to rotate the
rod in a jig during the evaporation process.
Copper wire, typically of 32 SWG, is tightly
coiled in an open helix and cemented in place
by means of an electrically conducting

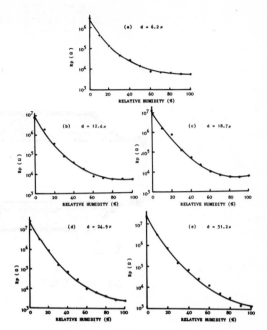

FIG. 10. Effect of thickness d of oxide layer on
resistance R_p.

adhesive cement (Messrs. Johnson Matthey
and Co. Ltd.: resin FSP 49R and hardener
FSP 49H). The conducting cement is trimmed
on a lathe, and the final stage is to coat the
untreated rod and most of the cement by
dipping in "capping solution" taking care that
none overlaps the sensitive area. The plastic
film formed when the capping solution dries
serves to insulate the untreated shank of the
rod. The shank is bared for about 1 cm at its
end, and this serves as one electrode of the
element, while the copper wire serves as a connection to the other.

Needle Element

In some cases it might be necessary to
measure humidity in extremely small locations
and it is possible to do this by suitably modifying the above form of construction.

A short length of $\frac{1}{2}$-mm diameter aluminum
wire is fixed to the end of a 3-mm diameter
aluminum rod by cementing it into a hole
about 1 cm deep drilled into the end of the rod,
using the conductive adhesive cement referred
to above. A thin sleeve of "Araldite" is coated
onto the rod and smoothly tapered onto the
surface of the wire as shown in Fig. 11(b). The

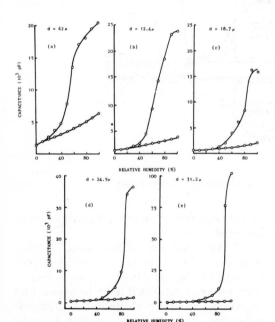

FIG. 9. Effect of thickness d of oxide layer on
capacitances C_p and C_o.

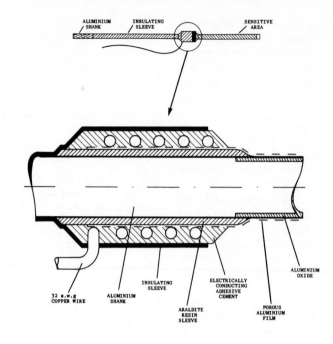

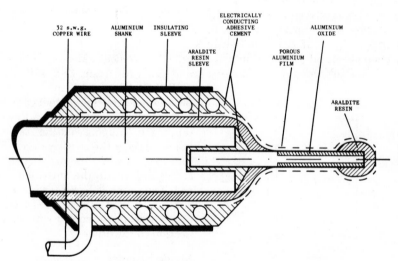

FIG. 11. Details of construction: (a) rod element (b) needle element.

exposed portion of the wire is anodized and, after washing and drying, the tip is coated with a small quantity of "Araldite" for mechanical protection. The element is coated with a conducting layer as described above for the rod element and the lead from the outer electrode is similarly attached to the base of the shank. A photograph of the needle hygrometer element is shown in Fig. 12.

Whatever the form of construction of the elements there are four general principles to be observed:

(1) The "transmission line effect" (arising from the linking together of individual pore systems by high resistances so as to form a sequence of π networks) must be avoided by depositing an outer electrode of negligible resistance. In practice this requires that the resistance of the evaporated layer should be less than about $10 \, \Omega$ per square.

FIG. 12. Photograph of needle element.

(2) Care must be taken to avoid covering any portion of the anodized surface with material other than that of the outer electrode since this can result in the trapping of moisture and the introduction of severe apparent hysteresis effects.

(3) Contact resistance between the lead and the outer electrode should be negligible.

(4) Sharp edges should not be coated with a conducting film as cracks in the oxide layer easily form in regions of high curvature and give rise to short-circuiting of the element when the outer electrode is deposited.

It is now clear that a major factor contributing to aging effects in all elements constructed as described in a previous paper[5] is the progressive increase of contact resistance between the outer electrode and its lead. Furthermore, if the outer electrode is composed of colloidal graphite, its resistance increases progressively with time and the "transmission line effect" gives rise to a

decreasing C_p and an increasing R_p at a given relative humidity, which accentuates aging effects due to other causes.

SOME PROPERTIES OF PRACTICAL IMPORTANCE

Reproducibility

In the commercial production of hygrometers that are not absolute instruments, it is clearly desirable to avoid the necessity of calibrating individual elements if possible. It is therefore of interest to examine the reproducibility within a batch of the calibration of aluminum oxide elements, since, if the structure can be "tailor-made," as previously suggested, the calibration will be uniform and it should then be necessary to calibrate only a few elements. In order to assess approximately the magnitude of error in estimating relative humidity from a mean calibration curve obtained in this way, 5 rod elements were anodized at a current density of 40 mA cm^{-2} for 30 minutes, constructed in the manner described above, and calibrated at a frequency of 1592 cps. The results are shown in Fig. 13 as relationships between log $(C_p - C_o)$ and relative humidity, and between log R_p and relative humidity. The calibration points were

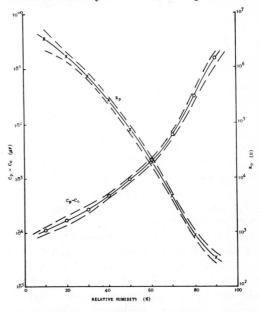

FIG. 13. Relationships between log $(C_p - C_o)$ and relative humidity and log R_p and relative humidity for 5 elements. Broken lines indicate 90 per cent confidence limits.

in each case so close together as to cause confusion if plotted individually and it is for this reason that three lines are shown for each relationship, the continuous lines being drawn through mean values and the broken lines indicating approximate 90 per cent confidence limits for estimating relative humidity. These may be derived from Fig. 13 for each relationship, and are shown in Table 2 expressed as deviations from the indicated relative humidity at various values using the mean curves. In general there is little to choose between each relationship, the accuracy being about 1 or 2 per cent RH except at the extremes of low and high humidities. The precision of an individual calibration is, of course, very much better than that indicated in Table 2. The confidence limits given above refer to the bias in relative humidity indicated by a particular element.

TABLE 2. 90% CONFIDENCE LIMITS FOR ESTIMATING RELATIVE HUMIDITY FROM MEAN CURVES OF LOG $(C_p - C_o)$ vs RELATIVE HUMIDITY AND LOG R_p vs RELATIVE HUMIDITY

| RH (%) | 95% Confidence Limits Expressed as Deviations from Indicated Value | |
	From log $(C_p - C_o)$ vs RH (% RH)	From log R_p vs RH (% RH)
10	+2.5 −4.5	—
20	±3.5	+2.5 −4.0
30	±2.0	+1.5 −2.0
40	±1.6	±1.5
50	±1.6	±1.0
60	±1.0	±1.1
70	±1.8	±1.3
80	±1.8	±1.7
90	±2.0	±2.5

Hysteresis

Figure 14 illustrates typical measurements of C_p and R_p at various relative humidities at 30°C. The points plotted for increasing relative humidity (ringed) and decreasing relative humidity (unringed), between 0 and 90 per cent RH, show that any effects due to hysteresis are sufficiently small as to be masked by the scatter of the points themselves. However, prolonged exposure to saturated conditions can give rise to apparent hysteresis effects, corrosion, and final breakdown of the element.

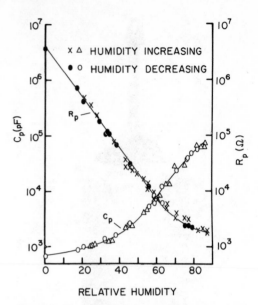

FIG. 14. Variation of C_p and R_p with relative humidity showing absence of pronounced hysteresis.

Influence of Temperature

Temperature has little influence on the calibration of an element in the range −15 to +80°C, though at the higher values the rate of aging is very rapid. Between −15 and −30°C, a change occurs in the magnitude of variation of C_p and R_p, presumably due to a change from an electrolytic to a solid-state conduction mechanism in the pore side. Figure 15 shows the variation of C_p with relative humidity at

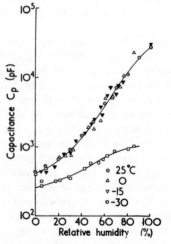

FIG. 15. Variation of C_p with relative humidity at various temperatures.

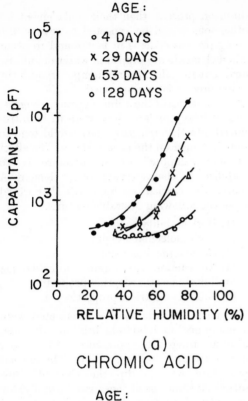

AGE:

○ 4 DAYS
× 29 DAYS
△ 53 DAYS
○ 128 DAYS

(a)
CHROMIC ACID

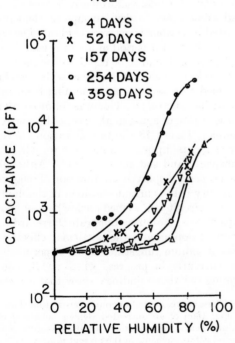

AGE:

● 4 DAYS
× 52 DAYS
▽ 157 DAYS
○ 254 DAYS
△ 359 DAYS

(b)
OXALIC ACID

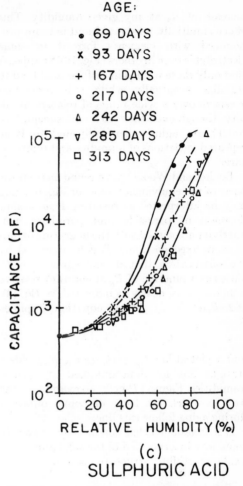

AGE:

● 69 DAYS
× 93 DAYS
+ 167 DAYS
○ 217 DAYS
△ 242 DAYS
▽ 285 DAYS
□ 313 DAYS

(c)
SULPHURIC ACID

Fɪɢ. 16. Effect of type of anodizing electrolyte on the aging of elements (a) chromic acid (b) oxalic acid (c) sulfuric acid. Area of elements 1.5 cm². Capacitance measured by repeated ballistic discharge at repetition rate of 100 sec⁻¹.

various temperatures in the range −30 to +25°C.

It is known that elements are sensitive to water vapor at −80°C and at temperatures just below the melting point of aluminum (658°C), but no calibrations have been attempted. It is to be expected, though it has not been confirmed, that the stability of elements increases with decreasing temperature.

Aging and Its Prevention

Immediately after anodizing the aluminum base and constructing an element, there is normally a reduction of C_p and a corresponding increase of R_p at any given humidity. This effect is initially very rapid and is more pronounced with elements formed in some electrolytes than in others (Fig. 16). It appears that only those formed in sulfuric acid tend to stabilize eventually while still remaining sensitive over a wide range of relative humidity, though even these elements succumb to progressive aging when subjected to large repeated variations of humidity and temperature.

Booker and Wood[10] have found that on the basis of the equivalent circuit of Fig. 6, aging may be interpreted as resulting from a slow decrease in pore-side and pore-base conductivity associated with the migrating of ions to more fixed positions. This is suggested by the observation that during aging $C_p - C_o$ varies as a function of R_p at constant relative humidity very nearly as indicated by Eq. (3). If $2\pi R_p(C_p - C_o) \ll 1$, the equation simplifies to

$$C_p - C_o = 1/A R_p^2 \qquad (4)$$

and a plot of log $(C_p - C_o)$ vs log R_p yields a straight line for data obtained at various humidities. Figure 17 shows an example of the way in which the locus of points obtained during aging follow this line.

If it is assumed that conduction ions are in some way incorporated in the solid aluminum oxide crystallite structure, say by a slow

diffusion process, then their replacement by other ions would be expected to reverse the aging process. This is in fact found to occur when elements are dipped in water or sulfuric acid, but the effect is only temporary and the aging process is soon resumed.

The kinetics of the diffusion process suggest that if heavy or large ions were to be introduced into the structure, they would tend to remain longer on the pore surfaces. The effect of such "doping" would therefore be to stabilize the characteristics of an element. A search was carried out for a salt that would have the following desirable features:

(1) High stability
(2) High molecular weight
(3) Large ionic dimensions
(4) No reaction with aluminum or its oxide
(5) Suitable water sorption properties
(6) Suitable electrical properties.

Among the salts that were selected were ammonium molybdate, lithium fluoride, lithium tungstate, potassium dihydrogen phosphate and thallium sulfate. The normal procedure was to dip the elements into saturated solutions of these salts (usually) for one or two seconds, shake off any free solution, and allow them to dry. Groups of elements treated in various ways were calibrated every few weeks over a period of about a year.

Aging was found to be rapid during the first few weeks in each case, an effect which can be ascribed to a loss of ions remaining from the anodizing electrolyte. This was followed by a reduced rate of aging in all except the control samples. Figure 18 shows calibration curves for elements dipped in potassium dihydrogen phosphate and sodium tungstate.* Although the property displayed as a function of relative humidity is the current obtained in the diode pump circuit (described below), and not capacitance, the curves illustrate the retarding effect of doping and the particular effectiveness of sodium tungstate. Aging experiments are currently in progress which, while confirming the above findings, show that a more

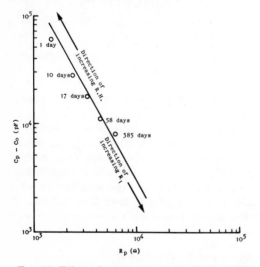

FIG. 17. Effect of aging compared with humidity dependence. Points refer to aging at 75 per cent relative humidity; all measurements at 1 kc/sec (Booker and Wood[10]).

* These curves are to be compared with that shown in Fig. 16(c) of an untreated element anodized in sulfuric acid. Unfortunately experiments were conducted before elements of the present improved construction were developed. High contact resistance between the outer electrode and its lead (~ 1 kΩ) limited the current at higher humidities.

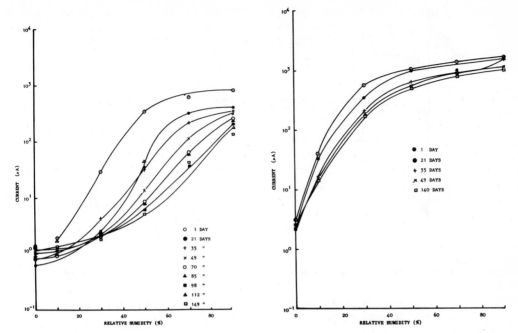

FIG. 18. Effect of doping on the aging of elements anodized at a current density of 40 mA/cm² dipped in saturated solutions of (a) potassium dihydrogen phosphate and (b) sodium tungstate.

suitable calibration curve can be obtained with elements of improved construction doped with sodium tungstate. Of the salts thus far investigated, none is as effective as sodium tungstate.

Transient Response

Analysis of the kinetics of surface adsorption[11] shows that water molecules would penetrate to the base of the pores in the oxide layer in less than a second. In addition it is to be expected that if water penetrates the crystallite structure, as evidenced by the slight dependence of C_2 on relative humidity and certain other electrical properties,[10] this initial rapid uptake will be followed by a slower diffusion phase. Data obtained by means of a vacuum microbalance[12] have been supplied by Day (1953, private communication) showing the variation with time of the weight of water adsorbed onto or desorbed from 1.5-mm diameter anodized aluminum wire (Fig. 19). The absorption curves reveal the existence of both types of penetration, and there is clear evidence for this, too, in the desorption curve, also shown in Fig. 19.

The two phases in the sorption behavior due to surface and bulk effects are reflected in the response curves of elements subjected to rapid changes of relative humidity. Figure 20 shows the variation with time of capacitance (displayed as mean ballistic current (applied voltage 9 V; repetition rate 100 sec⁻¹), discharged through a low resistance galvanometer) when an element of somewhat slow response is subjected to such changes. There is, in addition, evidence that the response to decreasing relative humidity is somewhat slower than to increasing relative humidity, a feature revealed in the desorption curve in Fig. 19. Reference to Fig. 13 shows that the *indicated* relative humidity accentuates this difference because the slope of the calibration curve increases with increasing relative humidity. Because of such considerations, response time varies with conditions, but, in general, for small changes of relative humidity (of the order of ± 10 per cent relative humidity), it is about 1 second with most elements.

Response to Other Vapors

The vapors of polar substances other than water influence both C_p and R_p. In general, the

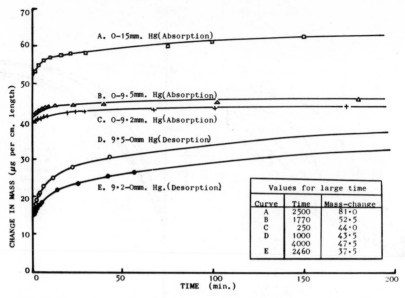

FIG. 19. Absorption and desorption curves at 21.6°C of water on 1.5-mm diameter anodized aluminum wire for various vapor pressure changes.

Values for large time		
Curve	Time	Mass–change
A	2500	81·0
B	1770	52·5
C	250	44·0
D	1000	43·5
	4000	47·5
E	2460	37·5

greater the polarization, the greater is the effect. For example, benzene (almost zero polarization) has a detectable but very small effect, while ammonia (very high polarization) has a greater influence even than water. The latter sensitivity is matched only by the response to methylamine, dimethylamine and trimethylamine vapors. Since each of these

substances is present in spoiling fish, there is an obvious application in the measurement of freshness, but the author has found the practical difficulties associated with this problem so great as to prevent the instrument being used quantitatively.

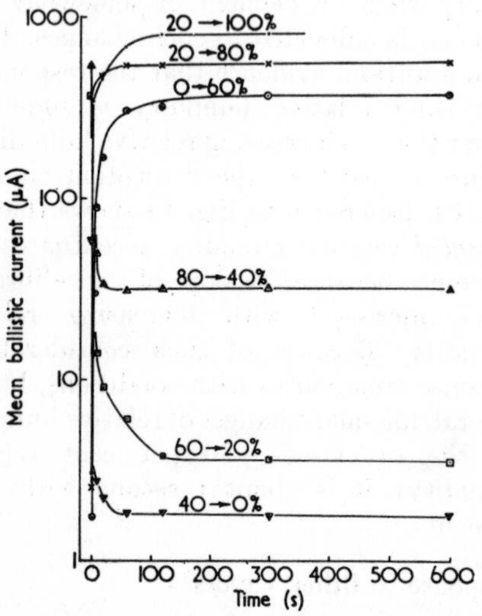

The problem of the effects of vapors in general on the electrical properties of anodized aluminum has not been studied systematically and would merit further investigation.

SOME PRACTICAL CIRCUIT ARRANGEMENTS

While the measurement of C_p and R_p presents no difficulties in the laboratory, quadrature balancing is not a desirable feature of an industrial instrument and some form of meter indication is to be preferred. Koller[6] proposed that the admittance of the element as displayed by a meter in series with the element and an AC source should be used to indicate relative humidity. However, AC meters of the sensitivity required are so delicate and so expensive as to exclude their use, except perhaps in the laboratory.

A very simple way in which capacitance can be displayed is by the method of repeated ballistic discharge, to which reference has

FIG. 20. Response characteristics of an element anodized in sulfuric acid.

already been made. The arrangement for doing this consists of a single pole electro-mechanical changeover switch (e.g., a vibrator or a high-speed relay driven from a low-frequency AC source) which alternately charges a capacitor from a DC source and discharges it through a low-resistance meter. If the process is repeated at the frequency with which the changeover contacts operate, then the mean current through the meter is approximately

$$I = 2fC_pE$$

where f is the frequency of the source driving the switch and E is the EMF of the DC source. However, owing to polarization and other effects associated with the aluminum oxide elements, this relationship is not strictly applicable. Nevertheless the method is reasonably satisfactory for the purpose of direct indication and recording of relative humidity. Its chief drawbacks are a tendency towards the development of contact bounce and the limited lifetime of the contacts.

A contactless method which performs a similar function, is made possible with modern high-efficiency semiconductor diodes. It consists of the "diode-pump" arrangement shown in Fig. 21(a). For purposes of differential hygrometry the push-pull circuit shown in Fig. 21(b) can be used, with or without amplification. In the latter form, the detection of differences on the order of 0.001 per cent RH is possible in principle.

Other methods of display employing more sophisticated circuit arrangements, such as the use of the element itself as a component in an oscillatory circuit or the use of an AC bridge followed by an amplifier, have been employed but, in the author's opinion, are not normally necessary.

APPLICATIONS

The applications of any electric hygrometer are manifold and mostly obvious, and no attempt will be made to give an exhaustive list for the instrument here described except to mention a few fields of special interest.

Owing to the very high capacitance of the aluminum oxide elements, humidity readings may be made with ease at great distances using simple unscreened flex. Apart from its

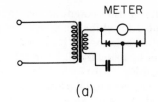

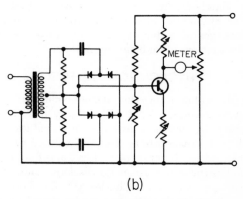

Fig. 21. (a) Diode pump arrangement for indicating relative humidity. (b) Push-pull arrangement for differential hygrometry. Capacitors indicated in both circuit diagrams represent hygrometer elements.

use at normal ambient temperatures, an element, being capable of rapid response and high sensitivity at subfreezing temperatures, can be used for the measurement and control of humidity in cold stores. Lightness and compactness are features of interest in high-altitude meteorological measurements so that the element can with advantage be incorporated in telemetry equipment.

Needle hygrometers have many possible applications, including the investigation of microclimates and of humidity or moisture gradients in solid materials.

Either by enclosing an element in a stirred atmosphere with a substance of unknown moisture-content or by inserting it into a hole in the substance itself, moisture content can be determined rapidly from the relative humidity isotherm for the substance.

The construction of humidity controllers is simple in the extreme. Using the diode pump arrangement shown in Fig. 21(a) and a sensitive relay in place of the meter to actuate either a humidifier or a dehumidifier, control within about ± 1 per cent RH is possible. Higher sensitivity can be achieved, either by backing-off the potential across a resistive load substituted for the meter and amplifying the out-of-balance EMF in order to operate a relay, or by using the differential arrangement shown in Fig. 21(b) by keeping one element in the atmosphere to be controlled and the other enclosed above an appropriate saturated salt solution.

Matched pairs of elements may be used in the differential arrangement to detect small leakages of water vapor in the presence of fluctuations of ambient humidity.

HYGROELECTRIC EFFECT

If an aluminum oxide element is charged to a certain voltage V, it will initially discharge itself by internal leakage. For values of $V > 1$ V, the rate of decay of voltage dV/dt plotted as a function of V (Fig. 22) is found to follow the same form as the discharge current-voltage curves of Charlesby[14] for barrier oxide layers. Since the current i is given by the relationship $dV/dt = -i/C_2$, Charlesby's equation

$$i = A_+ \exp (B_+ F) + A_- \sinh (B_- F)$$

may be fitted to the results. The first term refers to ion current and the second to electron current, and F is the field across the dielectric. This relationship has been used by Booker and Wood[15] to give an estimate of the pore base thickness which, for a commonly used anodizing current density of 40 mA cm^{-2}, is 85 Å.

The rate of decay of voltage in Fig. 22 falls off very sharply below 1 V, and the voltage itself is found to be asymptotic to a finite value.

Oscillograph traces of ballistic discharge current and voltage obtained by J. MacDowall (1953, private communication) showed a long "tail" which was attributed to a polarization current since the time constant $C_p G$ (G = galvanometer resistance) was considerably less than the length of the tail. However, the form of the discharge curves, including the tail, can in each case be described analytically in terms of the equivalent circuit of Fig. 6. The full expression for the voltage across an element discharged through a resistance G is

$$V = \frac{V_o}{(m_2 - m_1) C_o G}$$
$$\{(1 + m_2 C_o G) e^{m_1 t} - (1 + m_1 C_o G) e^{m_2 t}\} \quad (5)$$

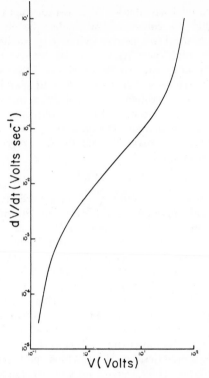

FIG. 22. Rate of decay of voltage as a function of voltage across an element of area 235 cm^2 initially charged to 72 V, aluminum base positive. Temperature 20°C; 45 per cent relative humidity.

$$m_1 = -b + \sqrt{b^2 - a^2}; \quad m_2 = -b - \sqrt{b^2 - a^2}$$

where

$$b = \frac{1}{2}\left\{\frac{1}{C_2}\left(\frac{1}{R_1} + \frac{1}{R_2}\right) + \frac{1}{C_o}\left(\frac{1}{G} + \frac{1}{R_1}\right)\right\}$$

and

$$a^2 = \frac{1}{C_o C_2}\left\{\left(\frac{1}{R_1} + \frac{1}{R_2}\right)\left(\frac{1}{G} + \frac{1}{R_1}\right) - \frac{1}{R^2}\right\}$$

if $G \ll R_1$, R_2 m_1 approximates to $-1/C_2 R_2$ and m_2 to $-1/C_o G$, and the former corresponds to the long tail in the discharge curves.

The oscillograph traces also showed a rapid recovery of voltage immediately after the ballistic discharge, the duration of which was ~5 msec. For such short periods of time, the subsequent recovery can be explained by the charging of C_o by C_2 through R_1. However, it has been found that after a period of shorting of as much as 15 hours there is still an immediate rise of voltage which cannot be so explained. The EMF measured on open circuit reaches an asymptotic value and, even in the absence of prior charging (except during the process of anodizing), is always in evidence. The magnitude of the EMF varies with relative humidity as shown in Fig. 23 and the following features are displayed.

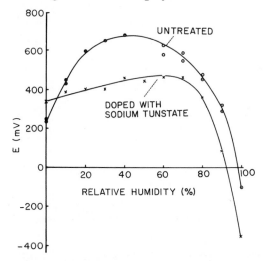

FIG. 23. Open circuit EMF as a function of relative humidity at 25°C generated by an untreated element and an element doped with sodium tungstate.

(1) Except at high relative humidity the shank is always positive with respect to the outer electrode.

(2) At zero relative humidity the EMF is finite.

(3) The EMF reaches a peak value of about 650 mV at between 40 and 50 per cent RH.

(4) As the humidity is increased beyond 50 per cent RH the EMF declines.

(5) As the saturated condition is approached the polarity of the EMF reverses.

By analogy with the properties of a thermocouple this behavior is termed the "hygroelectric effect."

It has been found that elements doped with lithium tungstate or thallium sulfate are little affected in their characteristics, though the effect of doping with sodium tungstate is to reduce the EMF by about 150 mV at most values of relative humidity. It is of interest to note that sodium tungstate is the only salt so far examined that confers stability on the capacitance and resistance characteristics of elements, but this may have no significance. The sensitivity of EMF to temperature is small

under normal ambient conditions but falls off appreciably as 0°C is approached.

It is difficult to account for these observations in terms of conventional electrolytic effects, particularly because the very existence of an EMF at all in a system in which the electrodes are composed of aluminum is inexplicable. To add to this difficulty is the observed reversal of EMF at high values of relative humidity.

Among several possible mechanisms that have been proposed may be listed

(a) Photoelectric emission at the surface of the aluminum oxide.

(b) Asymmetrical charge distribution in the oxide layer due to a high density of electron accepting Al^{+++} ions within the Al_2O_3 crystallite structure in the region close to the aluminum base.

(c) Electret formation during the process of anodizing.

Of these, mechanism (a) can easily be shown to be absent by screening the element from light. Mechanism (b) cannot be entirely ruled out, particularly because there is low electron mobility and charge trapping in the crystallite; but unless the migration of water into the crystallite both confers charge and in some way negates its effect at high values of relative humidity, other more substantial evidence will have to be evinced before the hypothesis can be accepted. Low charge mobility and charge trapping also favor mechanism (c) but, although the polarity of such an electret conforms to the imposed polarity during the anodizing process, the same difficulty prevails of explaining the role of water in modifying the EMF.

Although the actual mechanism of charge generation is not understood, certain phenomena help to indicate the location of the source of EMF. In Fig. 24 the variation of the difference in EMF on reducing the humidity of the environment of an element from 90 to 50 per cent RH is plotted as a function of time. In the example shown, the curve is exponential in form (with a time constant τ of 63 minutes) after about one-third of the change of EMF has been accomplished. This is comparable with the rate of desorption of water shown in Fig. 18, but it is to be noted that this is considerably slower than the fast response to similar changes of relative humidity displayed

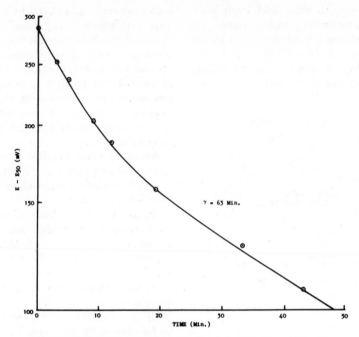

FIG. 24. Difference in EMF on reducing humidity from 90 to 50 per cent RH, $E - E_{50}$, as a function of time.

in Fig. 19. While the former is believed to involve bulk absorption (since surface adsorption tends to equilibrate in a few seconds[11]), the latter is a consequence of adsorption on the pore surfaces. It is suggested therefore that the source of EMF is located within the crystallite structure.

If then, water migrates into the crystallite structure and confers the effects described, its diffusion coefficient D is obtained from the time constant τ, since

$$D = b^2/\pi^2\tau$$

where b is the effective thickness of the absorber. Evidence, presented below, suggests that the pore base is the region of interest so that putting $b = 85$ Å and $\tau = 3780$ sec, $D = 1.9 \times 10^{-17}$ cm^2 sec^{-1}.

As a basis for discussion, it is proposed that the equivalent circuit of the element shown in Fig. 6 be slightly modified by introducing a source of EMF E in series with R_2 (Fig. 25). This circuit may be analyzed to give the recovery characteristics of the EMF of the element after being shorted ($G = 0$) for a period of time t_s. The full expression for the voltage appearing across the terminals under open circuit conditions ($G = \infty$), at time $t > t_s$ is

$$V = \frac{1}{m_1 - m_2} \frac{V_2}{C_o R_1}$$
$$\{\exp[m_1(t - t_s)] - \exp[m_2(t - t_s)]\}$$
$$+ E\left\{1 + \frac{1}{m_1 - m_2}\{m_2 \exp[m_1(t - t_s)] - m_1 \exp[m_2(t - t_s)]\}\right\} \quad (6)$$

V_2 is the voltage across C_2 at time $t = t_s$ and is given by

$$V_2 = \frac{ER_1}{R_1 + R_2}$$
$$\left\{1 + \frac{R_2}{R_1} \exp\left(-\frac{R_1 + R_2}{C_2 R_1 R_2} t_s\right)\right\} \quad (7)$$

Now, in general, since $R_1 \gg R_2$ and $C_o R_1 \gg C_2 R_2$, then $m_2 \gg m_1$, thus $m_1 = -1/C_o R_1$; $m_2 = -1/C_2 R_2$.

It may be shown that for $t - t_s \lesssim C_2 R_2$

$$E - V \propto E \exp\left(-\frac{t - t_s}{C_2 R_2}\right) \quad (8)$$

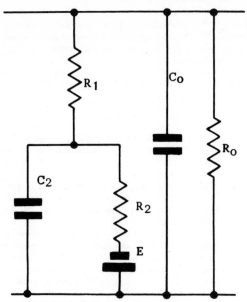

FIG. 25. Modified equivalent circuit of single pore.

and for $t - t_s \gtrsim C_2 R_2$

$$E - V \propto E \exp\left(-\frac{t - t_s}{C_o R_1}\right) \qquad (9)$$

so that these considerations, based on the proposed circuit, predict that if log $(E - V)$ is plotted as a function of $t - t_s$ there will be two distinct linear portions of the curve with slopes $-1/C_2 R_2$ and $-1/C_o R_1$. Figure 26, a typical example of such a plot, confirms the general form of Eq. (6) and clearly illustrates the existence of two straight lines of slope $1/1000$ sec^{-1} and $1/8000$ sec^{-1}. However, the implication that $C_2 R_2 = 1000$ seconds and $C_o R_1 = 8000$ seconds is difficult to interpret since for an element of this type $C_o \sim 10^{-3}\mu\text{f}$; $C_2 \sim 1 \mu\text{f}$; $R_1 \sim 10^5 \ \Omega$ at 50 per cent RH;

$R_2 \sim 2000 \ \Omega$ measured at 1000 cps. A suggested explanation is that under quasi-DC conditions charge transfer is by thermally activated ions or protons normally trapped in the crystallite structure or on its surface, but that under AC conditions the contribution to the measured conduction is largely derived from losses attributable to dipole relaxation.

Support for this explanation is given in Table 3 which shows the results of measurements, made under DC conditions at various temperatures and relative humidities, of the

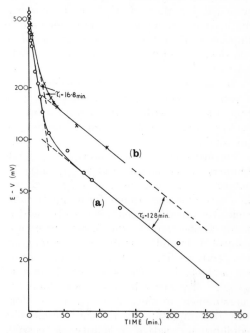

FIG. 26. Recovery of EMF of element short-circuited (a) for 1 minute (b) for 5 minutes, showing log $(E - V)$ as a function of $t - t_s$ at 25°C and 50 per cent relative humidity.

TABLE 3. VALUES OF R_i MEASURED AT VARIOUS TEMPERATURES AND RELATIVE HUMIDITIES, COMPARED WITH R_p MEASURED AT 25°C

Code: C = control; T = thallium sulfate; L = lithium tungstate; S = sodium tungstate

RH (%)	Temp. (°C)	R_1 (MΩ)				R_p (MΩ)			
		C	T	L	S	C	T	L	S
0	0	2090	9800	6550	453	—	—	—	—
	25	1650	5150	3750	368	1.67	1.45	2.18	0.092
	35	580	1650	1020	112	—	—	—	—
40	0	307	572	398	—	—	—	—	—
	25	—	—	—	—	0.235	0.104	0.041	4.3×10^{-4}
50	25	350	350	343	266	0.099	0.045	0.014	3.3×10^{-4}
90	25	28.0	3.1	2.55	4.35	6.0×10^{-4}	2.8×10^{-4}	3.4×10^{-4}	1.9×10^{-4}

internal resistance R_1 of normal and doped elements compared with corresponding values of R_p measured at a frequency of 1592 cps and at a temperature of 25°C. It is evident that the ratio of R_1 to R_p varies from about 10^3 to 1 at 0 per cent RH to about 10^4 to 1 at 100 per cent RH.

CONCLUSIONS

The theory of the aluminum oxide hygrometer based on its physical structure offers a satisfactory account of its behavior under AC conditions, and points to the causes of its principal limitation, that of long term aging. Methods of overcoming this limitation involve improvements in the physical construction of the element and doping the oxide layer with heavy ions.

Among other practical considerations, cheapness of construction together with good reproducibility within batches are features of interest from the standpoint of large-scale production.

The instrument has a rapid response, a low temperature coefficient and is not normally subject to hysteresis effects unless maintained in a saturated atmosphere for an appreciable time. Its versatility enables it to be used in many applications in the measurement and control of humidity within a wide range of temperatures. The construction of elements of small physical size makes possible the investigation of microclimates and humidity measurement in inaccessible locations. Moisture determination by the measurement of equilibrium relative humidity is possible either by enclosing an element with the substance in a container or by inserting it into a small hole in the substance itself.

The generation of a humidity-dependent EMF by an aluminum oxide element, termed the "hygroelectric effect," is not satisfactorily explained by conventional electrolytic mechanisms. An equivalent circuit, put forward to account for the general behavior of an element, qualitatively explains some of its features, though not very satisfactorily, and the subject merits further investigation.

Acknowledgments. The author wishes to thank Dr. C. J. L. Booker for supplying Figs. 3, 4 and 5 and Dr. J. L. Wood for many stimulating discussions. The measurement of the sorption properties of the anodic layer by Mr. A. G. Day and the provision of oscilloscope records of transient effects by Mr. Macdowall were both invaluable and are gratefully acknowledged. Mr. A. Lees proposed certain improvements in the design of the hygrometer elements and constructed them.

The work described in this paper was carried out as part of the program of the Department of Scientific and Industrial Research.

References

1. Ansbacher, F., "The Experimental Investigation of the Effect of Electron Bombardment on the Conductivity of Insulators," Ph.D. thesis University of London, 1949.
2. Ansbacher, F., and Ehrenberg, W., "Electron Bombardment Conductivity of Dielectric Films," *Proc. Phys. Soc. London Ser. A*, **64**, 362–379 (1951).
3. Ansbacher, F., and Jason, A. C., "Effects of Water Vapour on the Electrical Properties of Anodized Aluminium," *Nature*, **171**, 177 (1953).
4. Jason, A. C., and Wood, J. L., "Some Electrical Effects of the Adsorption of Water Vapour by Anodized Aluminium," *Proc. Phys. Soc. London Ser. B*, **63**, 1105–1116 (1955).
5. Cutting, C. L., Jason, A. C., and Wood, J. L., "A Capacitance-resistance Hygrometer," *Brit. J. Appl. Phys.*, **32**, 425–341 (1955).
6. Koller, L. R., "An Electrical Hygrometer," U.S. Patent 2237006 (April 1, 1941).
7. Booker, C. J. L., and Wood, J. L., "Electron Micrographs from Thick Oxide Layers on Aluminium," *Brit. J. Appl. Phys.*, **8**, 347–352 (1957).
8. Booker, C. J. L., "The Structure and Some Electrical Properties of Anodic Oxide Layers on Aluminium," Ph.D. thesis, University of London, 1958.
9. Wood, J. L., "Dielectric Properties of Water/Alumina," *Brit. J. Appl. Phys.*, **10**, 404–406 (1959).
10. Booker, C. J. L., and Wood, J. L., "Further Electrical Effects of the Adsorption of Water Vapour by Anodized Aluminium," *Proc. Phys. Soc.*, **76**, 721–731 (1960).
11. De Boer, J. H., "The Dynamical Character of Adsorption," p. 30, London, Oxford University Press, 1952.
12. Day, A. G., "A Vacuum Microbalance for Measuring Sorption on Dielectrics," *J. Sci. Instr.*, **30**, 260–263 (1953).
13. Jason, A. C., "The Use of High-speed Electromagnetic Relays in the Measurement of Capacitance and Frequency," *Lab. Pract.*, **3**, 25–27 (1954).
14. Charlesby, A., "Ionic Current and Film Growth of Thin Oxide Layers on Aluminium," *Proc. Phys. Soc. London, Ser. B*, **66**, 317–329 (1953); "Electron Currents in Thin Oxide Films on Aluminium," *Proc. Phys. Soc. London Ser. B*, 533–541 (1953).
15. Booker, C. J. L., and Wood, J. L., "Determination of Barrier Layer Thickness of Anodic Oxide Coatings," *J. Electrochem. Soc.*, **102**, 357–358 (1955).

40. A Hygrometer Which Utilizes an Anodic Oxide Film of Aluminum

Akira Miyata

Japan Steel and Tube Corp., Kawasaki, Japan

AND

Hiroshi Watari

Rikagaku Kenkyusho, Tokyo, Japan

ABSTRACT

A porous anodic film of aluminum is used as the sensor of a new type hygrometer. The remarkable change in resistance and capacitance of the sensor with humidity variation is explained by using a simple model based on the fibrous pore structure of the film. This model also accounts for the dependence of these changes on frequency. The moisture content of unhulled rice can be determined with satisfactory accuracy merely by inserting the sensor probe into a package containing the rice. This method requires no special sample so that sampling difficulties are eliminated. Handiness in measurement simplifies even the troublesome estimation of the moisture distribution in packages of cereals. The small moisture capacity of this hygrometer enables one to detect water vapor released from walls and floors and to test the adsorption and desorption characteristics of plate materials.

INTRODUCTION

The fact that a porous anodic film is apt to absorb moisture from the ambient atmosphere which alters its dielectric behavior is now well known. Jason *et al.*[1] described such an hygrometer, but we have developed a new type of hygrometer, entirely independent of theirs. Our hygrometer has many excellent features including less moisture absorption from the atmosphere and faster response than others. The field of moisture measurement has been so far advanced that ordinary psychrometers, dew-point hygrometers, or hair hygrometers cannot compete with these instruments. In this paper, we give a general idea of this hygrometer and some of its interesting applications.

THE SENSOR

Preparation of the Sensor

Simply, the sensor is made of a piece of anodized aluminum sheet, covered with a metallic coat which freely permits the sorption and desorption of deposited moisture. The authors used a gold film deposited by vacuum sputtering on a surface which previously had been roughened with sawtooth serrations. Thus when a second electrode of gold is applied on the anodized layer, the small vertical sawteeth remain free of gold and give access to moisture in the air.

As a typical example, we give the data of our test specimen. A rectangular piece of aluminum was cut from a sheet (99.99 per cent purity) 1 mm thick, 3 mm wide, and 40 mm long. One-half of the length, or 20 mm, was roughened with sawtooth serrations on its surface; this piece was annealed at 400°C for an hour; then it was chemically cleaned and polished and anodized in 3 per cent oxalic acid solution at 20°C for an hour with a current density of 1 A/dm². Then it was again reformed in a 1 per cent ammonium borate solution at 20°C for some time with 100 volts; after applying gold sputtering, some suitable lead wires were attached to both the upper coat of gold and the aluminum base metal.

Equivalent Circuit of the Sensor

In a recent electron microscope study[2] of anodic aluminum films, the author asserts that the porous film layer has a fibrous structure with cells packed together closely all over the surface. Each fibrous cell has a pore inside of it running vertically through the film surface reaching the extremely thin nonporous barrier layer at the bottom. In the case of our sensor, this barrier layer subsequently is made intentionally thicker by treating it in an ammonium borate solution with appreciable high voltage. Hereafter, for the sake of convenience, we will designate as the "first anodizing" the initial process of making the porous film, and the "second anodizing" the process of thickening the barrier layer.

Now assume that our sensor has an equivalent circuit something like that shown in Fig. 1, where R is the resistance of the inner surface of the pore absorbing moisture, r_0 and C_0 are respectively the resistance and the capacitance of the basic film material, and r_a and C_a are respectively the resistance and the capacitance of the barrier layer. Taking these all into account, we have as the total impedance of the sensor

$$\dot{z} = \frac{1}{1/R + (1/r_0 - j(1/\omega C_0))} + r_a - j\frac{1}{\omega C_a} \quad (1)$$

where ω is the circular frequency.

Rationalizing the denominator, we get as the series equivalent resistance of the sensor R_s

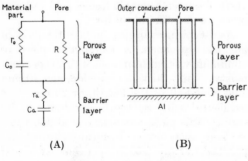

(A)   (B)

FIG. 1. (A) Equivalent circuit. (B) Model of sensor.

$$R_s = \frac{Rr_0(R + r_0) + (R/\omega^2 C_0^2)}{(R + r_0)^2 + (1/\omega C_0)^2} + r_a \quad (2)$$

and as its series equivalent capacitance C_s

$$\frac{1}{C_s} = \frac{R^2}{C_0} \cdot \frac{1}{(R + r_0)^2 + (1/\omega C_0)^2} + \frac{1}{C_a} \quad (3)$$

We now make the following assumptions for our case:

(1) The dielectric properties of the basic film material, whether it exists in the porous film or in the barrier layer, are constant throughout the material, and are independent of humidity.

(2) All we have to consider as affected by humidity is the resistance R of the inside absorbing layer of the pore, and this preserves its value whatever the frequency.

It has been shown[3] that the following relations hold for the oxide film of the metal.

$$\frac{d(1/C)}{d\ln\omega} = \frac{2}{\pi}r \cdot \omega \quad (4)$$

$$r \cdot \omega = k \quad (5)$$

where C and r are the equivalent series capacitance and resistance of oxide film of unit area and unit length, and k is a constant.

Now we will introduce a kind of structural factor N, which can be defined as follows:

$$N = \{A/(A - a)\}\,(d/D)$$

where A is the total film surface of the sensor, a is the sum of part of the pore areas, d is the thickness of the porous layer, and D is the thickness of the barrier layer. We can obtain by simple reasoning the following:

$$C_a = C_0 \cdot N \quad (6)$$

$$r_0 = r_a \cdot N = \frac{K}{\omega}N \quad (7)$$

where $K = kD/A$.
From Eqs. (2), (3), (4), (5), (6), (7), we have

$$R_s = \frac{R^2 KN\omega + RK^2 N^2 + (R/C_0^2)}{R^2\omega^2 + 2RKN\omega + K^2 N^2 + (1/C_0^2)}$$
$$+ \frac{K}{\omega} \quad (8)$$

$$C_s =$$

$$\frac{NC_0\{R^2\omega^2 + 2RKN\omega + K^2 N^2 + (1/C_0^2)\}}{(1 + N)R^2\omega^2 + 2RKN\omega + K^2 N^2 + (1/C_0^2)} \quad (9)$$

In the extreme condition when the sensor is thoroughly dried, we may take R to be infinite, and we have

$$(1/C_s)_{R \to \infty} = (1/C_a) + (1/C_0) \doteq (1/C_0) \quad (10)$$

for $1/C_a$ can be assumed negligible compared with $1/C_0$. Combining this with the general relations given in (4) and (5), we get

$$\left(\frac{1}{C_s} \right)_{R \to \infty} = \frac{2}{\pi} k \frac{d}{A-a} \ln \omega + \alpha$$

$$= \text{const.} \frac{d}{A-a} \log f + \alpha \quad (11)$$

where α is the integration constant, and f is frequency.

This equation shows that for an entirely dried condition, the relation between the reciprocal of C_s and $\log f$ must be linear, and if the porosity and the area of the sensor are held constant, the tangent of the angle which this linear line makes with horizontal line must be proportional to the thickness of the oxide film. The reciprocal values of C_s measured on the fully dried sensors anodized for 30, 60, 90 minutes with a current density of 1 A/dm^2, over the frequency range of 30 cps to 100 kc, are presented in the Fig. 2. It is seen that the reciprocal values of C_s are perfectly proportional to $\log f$. The ratio $(1/C_s)/\log f$ is proportional to the thickness of the oxide film as shown in Fig. 3, which is expected from Eq. (11). The capacitance variation is as small as 4 per cent in the range of the experiment. Thus we assume that the capacitance changes little.

The Variation of R_s with Frequency in the Fully Dried Condition

From Eq. (2), letting R go to infinity, we have

$$(R_s)_{R \to \infty} = r_0 \quad (12)$$

where r_a is ignored, being small as compared with r_0.

From Eqs. (5) and (12) we can derive

$$(R_s \cdot \omega)_{R \to \infty} = k \frac{d}{A-a} \quad (13)$$

Equation (13) shows that in the fully dried condition the product of R_s and frequency is constant, and for the case where the area and the porosity are taken constant as in our sensor, this product must be proportional to the thickness of the oxide. Figure 4 shows R_s

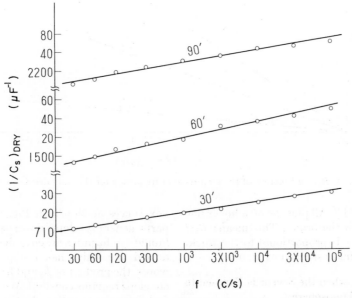

FIG. 2. Reciprocal values of C_s as a function of frequency for the fully dried sensor. Lines are labelled with the time employed for "first anodizing" with the current density of 1 A/sq dm.

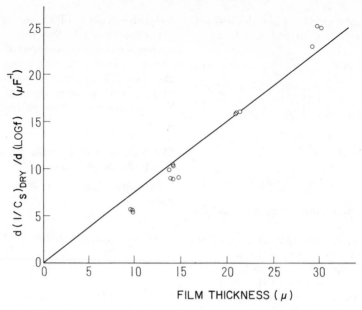

FIG. 3. The slope of $(1/C_s)_{dry}$ *vs* $\log f$ as a function of film thickness.

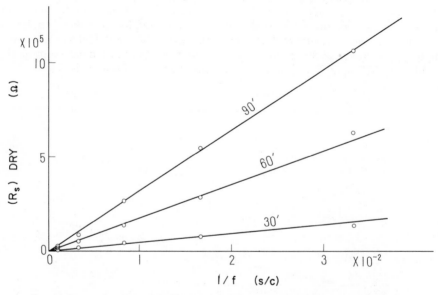

FIG. 4. R_s as a function of the reciprocal of frequency for the fully dried sensor.

as a function of $1/f$. All plots lie on a linear line passing through the origin. This means $R_s \cdot f$ is constant. $R_s \omega$ is proportional to the thickness of oxide film as shown in Fig. 5.

Variation of R_s when the Sensor is Exposed to a Humid Atmosphere

If we plot the relation between R_s and frequency on a logarithmic scale, we get con-vex curves as shown in Fig. 6. The convex parts generally slope down with increasing humidity, forming an envelope as shown by dotted line which has a slope -1; in other words, the product of R_s and frequency on this envelope remains constant. We will derive this fact from our equation. In Eq. (8), we regard R as the parameter, then as a result we have Eq. (14) as the envelope line,

$$(R_s \cdot \omega)_{\text{env}} = \frac{1}{2} (1 + K^2 N^2 C_0^2) \frac{1}{C_0} + K \quad (14)$$

where the notation $(R_s \cdot \omega)_{\text{env}}$ means the product of R_s and ω on the envelope line. Here we recognize that KNC_0 is equal to $\omega r_a C_a$ which is the tan δ of the barrier layer, having the

value of order 0.01. We therefore can neglect $K^2 N^2 C_0^2$ as compared with unity. It can also be shown easily that K is negligible in comparison with $1/(2C_0)$, remembering that N is large. Then we have

$$(R_s \cdot \omega)_{\text{env}} \doteqdot 1/(2C_0) \quad (15)$$

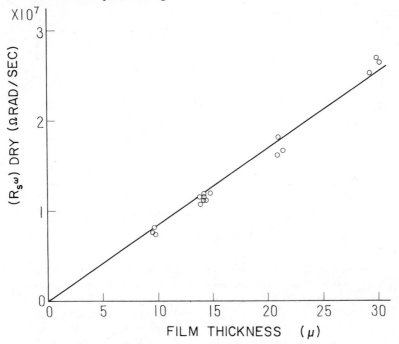

FIG. 5. $(R_s\omega)_{\text{dry}}$ as a function of film thickness.

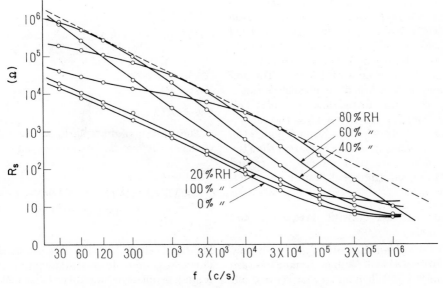

FIG. 6. R_s as a function of frequency at various humidities.

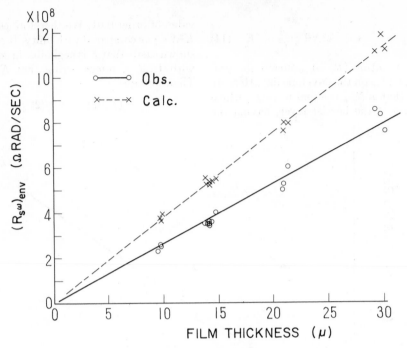

FIG. 7. $(R_s\omega)_{\text{env}}$ *vs* film thickness.

Since C_0 is approximately independent of frequency, the right side of Eq. (15) becomes constant. In other words, R_s times ω on the envelope line is constant. Moreover, $1/(2C_0)$ is proportional to the film thickness when the porosity of the oxide film and the area of the sensor are held constant [$(R_s \cdot \omega)_{\text{env}}$ *vs* film thickness is shown in Fig. 7]. The plots in this Figure come from sensors which were made from 99.99 per cent sheet aluminum anodized in a 3 per cent oxalic acid bath at 20°C with a DC current density of 1 A/dm², and having a moisture sensitive area of 1.5 cm². The full line shows a plot based on measured thicknesses, while the dotted line is a plot calculated from Eq. (15). Here C_0 is the capacitance of the fully dried condition. Though the calculated values are somewhat larger than the corresponding observed values, we regard them as in good agreement despite our rough assumptions.

Variation of tan δ with Frequency and Humidity

The values of tan δ as a function of frequency (30 ~ 10⁶ cps) for various humidities are shown in Fig. 8. When the sensor is dried off, the value of tan δ is 0.005 ~ 0.008 and scarcely changes with frequency but when air becomes humid, tan δ increases with increasing frequency region. At least it shows a maximum value, and the maximum moves to a higher frequency range with a humidity increase.

From Eqs. (8) and (9), we have as tan δ, $\tan\delta = \omega R_s C_s$

$$\tan\delta =$$

$$\frac{\omega R N C_0(a\omega+b)+K N C_0(R^2\omega^2+2a\omega+b)}{(1+N)R^2\omega^2+2a\omega+b} \quad (16)$$

where

$$a = RKN$$

$$b = K^2N^2 + (1/C_0)^2.$$

The solution of the equation $d(\tan\delta)/d\omega = 0$ yields as the maximum value of tan δ

$$(\tan\delta)_{\text{max}} =$$

$$\frac{C_0(2KNb+Nb\sqrt{b/(1+N)}+2K^2N^2\sqrt{b/(1+N)})}{2b+2KN\sqrt{b/(1+N)}} \quad (17)$$

The right side of Eq. (17) does not include R. This means that the maximum values of tan δ are independent of humidity. This must prove true as derived from the theory. In actual

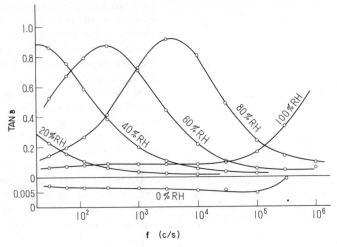

Fɪɢ. 8. Tan δ as a function of frequency at various relative humidities.

experiments sometimes this maximum value of tan δ differed from one sensor to another even though they had been manufactured under the same conditions. For a particular sensor, the maximum values of tan δ differed only on the average by 10 per cent. Therefore, we think we would be able to say that our theory is good qualitatively.

Admittance Change with Humidity Variation

In practice, when we want to measure humidity with our sensor, we have commonly used the variation of admittance. Figure 9 shows influence of humidity and second anodization voltage on the variation of admittance. When the sensor absorbs ample moisture, we may regard it as an electrolytic condenser having the capacitance derived from the second anodizing voltage and the area of sensor plate. This capacitance is C_a. In the Figure, the points marked with double circles on the ordinate line at 100 per cent RH give these capacitances. In the range of relative humidity less than 40 per cent, we cannot observe any dependence on the second anodizing voltage. At higher relative humidities, there appear marked differences and every curve points to the electrolytic condenser value. Therefore, in this way, we can get desirable humidity characteristics in the hygrometer, especially at higher relative humidities.

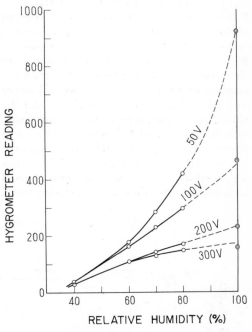

Fɪɢ. 9. Influence of the "second anodizing" voltages on the hygrometer reading (proportional to admittance) *vs* relative humidity. Curves are labelled with the "second anodizing" voltages.

Aging

The calibration curve of the sensor of this hygrometer gradually changes during the first few months after preparation, and then settles down. To investigate the aging effect of the environment upon the sensor, we exposed it

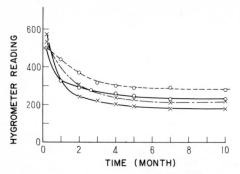

Fig. 10. Aging effect on the hygrometer reading at 80 per cent relative humidity after exposure to moist air of 75 per cent RH (solid line); desiccated air (dashed line); and ordinary atmosphere (chain line).

down. In Fig. 11(a), is shown the responding velocity α of the sensor. The responding velocity is the percentage of the variation of indication 2 minutes after an abrupt humidity change compared to that 4 minutes after the abrupt humidity change, as shown in Fig. 11(b). Therefore, when the rate of change is so slow that the reading after 4 minutes can still be regarded as varying linearly with time, α is 50 per cent, and when the rate of change is so fast that the reading after 2 minutes attains its final value, α is 100 per cent. What is shown in Fig. 11(a) is the variation of responding velocity, based on an abrupt change of 0 to 30 per cent RH air, after exposure to various environments. As seen in the Figure, 75 per cent RH air has the least deleterious effect on the responding velocity. The initial value of α is about 95 per cent, it becomes almost 99 per cent after one month, and remains 100 per cent thereafter. On the other hand, a sensor kept in desiccated air, deteriorates rapidly as time elapses, until after 10 months α has decreased to 50 per cent. From these results, we conclude that our sensor should be aged in air of 75 per cent RH for at least half a year, and always kept in this air when it is not used. With some sensors, though completely aged in this manner, the responding velocity decreases in case they are left carelessly in ordinary room air, and they often show much hysteresis or undesirable long-time drift.

to the following environments: (1) ordinary atmosphere, (2) moist air of 75 per cent RH, and (3) desiccated air of 0 per cent RH (over P_2O_5). All of the environments were at room temperature. Once a month, each sensor was taken out of the test air and examined at 35°C. Each sensor was usually put first in dried air (0 per cent RH) for 20 minutes, then the ambient air was adjusted to 30, 50, and 80 per cent RH in turn every four minutes, and the indication of the sensor was continuously recorded. In Fig. 10 is shown the behavior of the sensor at 80 per cent RH. After exposure to the above environments, all readings decreased sharply during the first 2 to 3 months, but after that they generally slowed

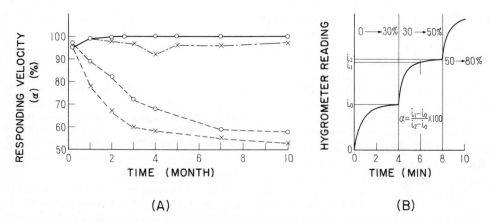

(A)   (B)

Fig. 11. A. Aging effect on the responding velocity after exposure of the sensor to moist air of 75 per cent RH (solid line); desiccated air (dashed line); and ordinary atmosphere (chain line). B. Illustrative figure of responding velocity.

Isotherms

In Fig. 12 examples of typical isotherms are shown. The value plotted on the ordinate is nearly proportional to the admittance of the sensor or the current at 1 V and 50 cps. The arrow in the Figure shows the direction of humidity change. We performed our test by subjecting the hygrometer first to the lower relative humidities, then increasing the relative humidity to 85 per cent. Then we repeated the test in the reverse direction, starting from the higher humidities. The returning curve does not coincide with the increasing curve, giving rise to a hysteresis loop. It took about 2 minutes to take a measurement at each relative humidity. Even if we take a reading at each humidity test point after exposure of a few hours, we can by no means get rid of the loop. Fortunately, the error caused by this hysteresis loop would not go over 1.5 per cent RH reading.

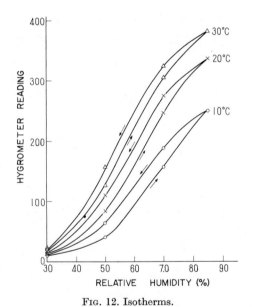

FIG. 12. Isotherms.

SOME APPLICATIONS

Moisture Distribution in the Aggregate of Unhulled Rice Grain

We housed the sensor in a long tubular rod probe (Fig. 13) suited for direct insertion from the outside of a bale (through hemp mat) into the interior of rice and cereals. The air in the

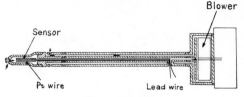

FIG. 13. Probe.

intergranular space and near the place where the measurement is carried out is forced to circulate, by a minute blower mounted at the rear end of the probe, in the direction shown by small arrow marks in the Figure. A very thin platinum wire, used as a resistance thermometer, is also fitted parallel to the sensor to measure the temperature of grain at the same time.

As an example of a study of moisture distribution, let us cite the humidity measurements in straw bag packages of unhulled rice. This example is a part of the work which has been done to check the dehydrating effect of artificially dried air on the piles of rare unhulled rice when they have to be deposited in the warehouse. The bag was made of two sheets of square straw mat sewed together at their edges, and contained 60 kg of unhulled rice. Figure 14 shows the moisture distribution at the vertical section at the center of one column of the cubic pile of bags. Humidities were measured by the long rod probe at 12 points for each bag, as shown with dots in the Figure. Distance of the adjacent measured points was 5 cm in the vertical direction and 15 cm in the horizontal direction. The time spent for measurement for each point was within 1 minute.

The moisture distribution in the lowest bag evidently shows that the drying action is very strong at the bottom. This corresponds to the fact that the dry air was forced into the cubic heap consisting of 2,000 bags from the underside. The bags other than those at bottom are generally drying uniformly from the outer surface of the bag, indicating the highest humid points almost at the center of the bags. The fifth bag from the bottom showed extremely high humidity. The humidity was too high to be measured with our hygrometer at those points marked >94 in the bag. When we picked up the rice grains of this bag, we found they had gone moldy.

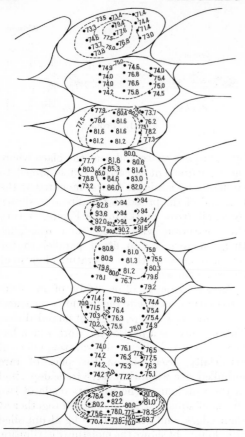

FIG. 14. Moisture distribution in the straw bag packages containing unhulled rice. Dots: measured points; dashed lines: equihumid line.

Figure 15 shows the entire distribution of relative humidity in one of the bags located on upper side of the cubic heap. The top Figure shows the state in the square size horizontal section, and the other three show the states in the vertical sections. We found an extremely high humid part in the bag. We picked up the rice of this particular part and saw that it had recently become very moldy. This might be attributed to the initial high content of moisture in rice grain, so high as to gather mold, and as soon as the mold developed, the moisture increased from the physiological excretion of water from the mold.

The Estimation of Moisture Content of Unhulled Rice

The equilibrium relation between the moisture content of unhulled rice and water vapor tension of ambient air that exists in

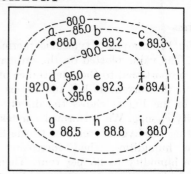

HORIZONTAL SECTION AT 15 CM FROM THE UPPER SURFACE

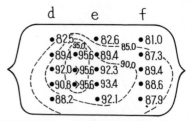

VERTICAL SECTION AT A–B–C

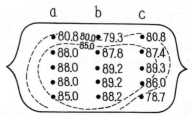

VERTICAL SECTION AT D–E–F

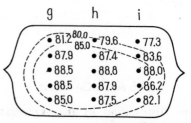

VERTICAL SECTION AT G–H–I

FIG. 15. Moisture distribution in one straw bag package containing unhulled rice. Dots: measured points; dashed lines: equihumid line.

intergranular space is shown in Fig. 16. We cannot differentiate between the curves plotted at three different temperatures such as 10, 20, and 30°C. Therefore, only by knowing the relative humidity of the ambient air in the intergranular space, can we estimate the grain's moisture content. Moisture content of unhulled rice, for the practical purpose of grading, preserving, etc., is generally in the range of 13 ∼ 18 per cent, corresponding to the relative humidity of 60 ∼ 87 per cent of the ambient air. By use of our hygrometer, an unknown humidity can be determined by comparison. After the sensor is inserted in a standard humidity bottle containing a sulfuric acid solution of a definite concentration, or a saturated solution of some salt, it is brought into the atmosphere of unknown relative humidity. When there is a difference, we can read an abrupt change, and make sure whether or not the unknown relative humidity is higher than the standard humidity. It takes only a few seconds for one determination, and if we prepare several standard bottles, we can get rid of the error due to the hysteresis of the sensor. This method is very convenient for determining whether the moisture content of a cereal is higher or lower than the desired one. In this way it is easy to determine an unknown humidity with the accuracy of 0.1 per

cent RH, providing a series of humidity standards at appropriate humidity intervals are used.

Data of the moisture determination of rice and some cereals estimated by this comparison method and those obtained from the ordinary weight loss methods by drying are given in the following table.

Material		Inter-granular Humidity (%)	Moisture Content (%)	
			Comparison Method	Dry Wt. Method
Unhulled rice	A	62.0–65.0	13.0–13.5	13.30
	B	75.5–79.0	15.0–15.5	15.17
	C	75.5–79.0	15.0–15.5	15.27
Wheat		65.0–66.5	(13.5–13.7)	13.59
Barley		66.5–69.5	(13.7–14.1)	9.90

In this experiment a series of sulfuric acid solutions which give various moisture contents differing 0.5 per cent from each other were used. For unhulled rice, both values agree well. For wheat and barley, their moisture content values were estimated from the same relation established for the unhulled rice and were shown in the brackets. As to the barley, this value apparently differs from the value obtained from the weight loss method. This means that the relation cannot be applied for barley.

Emission and Absorption of Water Vapor from Floors, Walls, etc.

The water vapor emission and absorption capacity of floors, walls, etc., is very important in ordinary residences for regulating air humidity, especially in rooms or store houses which must be kept air-conditioned. We contrived a simple method to measure this capacity for the plane samples. We introduce air of definite humidity into a bell-jar of known volume, put the bell-jar over the material to be tested, and let the inner air have direct contact with the material surface. The material surface emits or absorbs moisture to or from the surrounding air in the bell-jar according to the difference of vapor pressure in the air and at the surface; then the humidity of the air in the bell-jar gradually changes accordingly. Let the vapor pressure of the inner air be p and that of the material surface

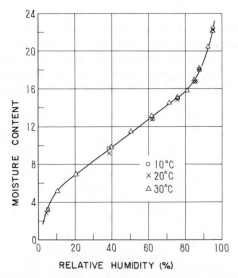

FIG. 16. Equilibrium relation between moisture content and relative humidity of ambient air for unhulled rice.

be P, the velocity with which the surface absorbs moisture becomes,

$$\frac{dp}{dt} = \alpha(P - p) \qquad (18)$$

where α is a proportionality constant. As hygroscopic materials generally have a greater humidity capacity than air, it makes little difference in P, even though some quantity of moisture is removed or added to it. By taking account of this fact, we can solve the upper equation as follows,

$$p = A + B \exp(-\alpha t) \qquad (19)$$

where A and B are integration constants.

Differentiating Eq. (19), we get

$$\frac{dp}{dt} = -\alpha B \exp(-\alpha t)$$

or

$$\ln \frac{dp}{dt} = \ln(-\alpha B) - \alpha t$$

When temperature is kept constant, p can be expressed by the relative humidity H; and we get

$$\ln \frac{dH}{dt} = \ln(-\alpha B') - \alpha t \qquad (20)$$

Thus, as long as P is assumed constant, the curve of $\ln dH/dt$ vs time will be a straight line, and the inclination of that straight line will give the value α. Then taking the volume of the bell-jar vessel to be V, the surface area of the material in the vessel to be S, the value $\gamma \equiv \alpha \cdot V/S$ becomes the moisture absorbing coefficient of the material to be tested, and the larger γ is, the quicker the moisture absorption becomes.

As the appropriate vessel for testing, we made use of the cover of the Scheibler-type desiccator, its inner diameter being about 17 cm. The general construction is shown in Fig. 17. Two glass tubes serve to introduce the air of given humidity into the vessel before starting the measurement. After the desired air is supplied, the vessel may be sealed with polyethylene tube and closed glass tubing; polyethylene sheet is inserted between the vessel and the material to avoid leaks; and a perforated circular mouth 16 cm in diameter, at the middle of the polyethylene sheet, defines the area of active surface of the material. To detect the least variation of humidity brought about by the moisture transference in this small vessel, both the size of the sensor, and the moisture retaining capacity of the sensor must be very small. In our experiment, we were able to make the moisture retaining capacity as small as 1.04×10^{-6} g H_2O/per cent RH, at 20°C in the range of relative humidity of 27 to 70 per cent. A volume of air of 5.9 cc at 20°C will have the same capacity, and this can be quite negligible compared with the 910 cc of the vessel volume.

Figures 18 and 19 give the examples of tests with familiar materials; when there are two curves for the material of the same kind, one is for the first measurement made after rather moistened air had been supplied for 30 minutes and the other is for the second measurement made after rather dry air had been supplied for 30 minutes. No difference of readings were observed for glass sheet and polyethylene sheet during the 30 minutes. The same proved true with air of far different

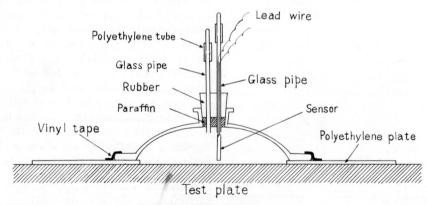

FIG. 17. Testing apparatus.

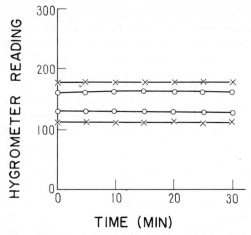

FIG. 18. Humidity change on plates. Glass plate (plotted with circle points); polyethylene plate (Plotted with cross points).

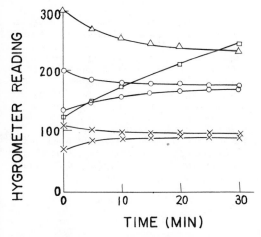

FIG. 19. Humidity change on plates. Acrylic acid plate (plotted with circle points); concrete floor (plotted with cross points); veneer plate (plotted with triangle points); concrete floor painted with vinyl laquer (plotted with square points).

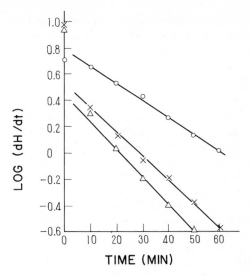

FIG. 20. Log (dH/dt) *vs* time. Concrete floor painted with vinyl lacquer (plotted with circle points); concrete floor (plotted with cross points); veneer plate (plotted with triangle points).

value for γ, we have 0.37 (15°C) for veneer plate, 0.30 (11°C) for concrete floor, and 0.19 (7°C) for concrete floor painted with vinyl lacquer, their unit being 10^{-6} g H_2O/cm² min. mm Hg.

Drying Phenomena of Wet Concrete Floor

Utilizing the above apparatus, we put the bell-jar over a wet concrete floor, and waited until the reading settled down; this gave the average moisture of the concrete surface. A jet of water was sprayed over a part of the concrete floor. As shown in Fig. 21, the measured values for both wet and dry parts got nearer to each other day after day, though there were some fluctuations. There was some

humidity. Thus these materials are concluded to have little capacity of moisture absorption; acrylic acid resin plate, concrete floor, and veneer plate were found to have appreciable capacity; concrete floor painted with vinyl lacquer, though small compared with bare concrete, still had considerable capacity. In Fig. 20 log (dH/dt) is plotted as a function of time. For vinyl paints, concrete surface, and veneer plate, we have almost straight lines except for 5 minutes after the beginning of the experiment. As the numerical

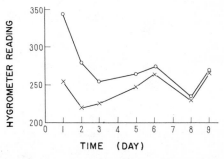

FIG. 21. Drying sequence of concrete floor. Water sprayed part (plotted with circle points); not sprayed part (plotted with cross points).

difference after 9 days, though both had nearly the same appearance not permitting visual distinction.

Moisture Loss from Plastered Wall

Here we consider the inside wall of a constant temperature and constant humidity room. It was prepared with a waterproof treatment, that is, it was finished with mortar and plaster, which was made about 3 cm thick. With the room kept at 52 per cent RH, the bell-jar was placed against the wall, and a moisture measurement was carried out; the result is shown in Fig. 22. At first, a humidity of 52 per cent was recorded as expected, but it rapidly increased to 60 per cent after about 17 hours, then slackened down until, after several hundred hours, 76 per cent was

attained. The sensitivity of the sensor was assured to be the same after the experiment as at the beginning. This experiment was begun 3 months after the room was finished; the room had been continuously used for the purpose of drying; and at the time of our experiment, the room was kept about 50 per cent RH. From this experiment, we may conclude that the wall still remained wet though it had been dried for 3 months with 50 per cent RH air. The wall had an average moisture of 50 per cent RH on the surface, and 76 per cent RH in the interior. The fact that there gradually appeared cracks and fissures on the wall as time elapsed, and that these increased in amount after about half a year, confirmed the experimental results.

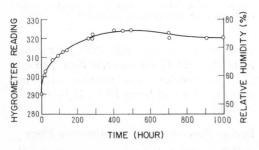

FIG. 22. Moisture emitted from the plastered wall which has been dried for three months.

References

1. Cutting, C. L., Jason, A. C., and Wood, J. L., "A Capacitance-resistance Hygrometer," *J. Sci. Instr.*, **32**, 425 (1955).
2. Akahori, H., "Electron Microscopic Study on the Growth Mechanism of Almite," *J. Metal Finishing Soc. Japan*, **13**, 154 (1962).
3. Miyata, A., and Furuichi, A., "Frequency Characteristics of Anodized Film Formed on Several Metals," *Sci. Papers Inst. Phys. Chem. Res. Tokyo*, **54**, 184 (1960).
4. Parts of this paper have been published in the following: *Rep. Inst. Phy. Chem. Res.*, **36**, 239 (1960); *ibid.*, **38**, 288 (1962); *ibid.*, **38**, 621 (1962).
5. Miyata, A., A.P. No. 2884593.

41. A Partial Evaluation of the Performance of an Aluminum Oxide Humidity Element

DAVID CHLECK AND FREDERICK J. BROUSAIDES

Parametrics Inc., Waltham, Massachusetts

ABSTRACT

The performance of aluminum oxide humidity elements is described. Elements were examined using a bridge circuit having an impedance related readout. Sensitivity to water vapor concentrations ranging from ambient conditions to dew points as low as $-90°C$ was found. The element senses absolute vapor concentration and the steady-state response is independent of the total gas pressure. Within experimental error, no temperature correction was found necessary over the range of $+25$ to $-80°C$. The time response of the element is rapid. The $1 - 1/e$ (63 per cent) change was found to occur within $2\frac{1}{2}$ seconds. The common air pollutants, ozone, nitrogen dioxide and sulfur dioxide, have no effect upon element response. Elements re-examined after periods up to a month have not drifted out of calibration. Long-term stability and aging characteristics have yet to be determined.

INTRODUCTION

A program has been initiated to investigate and develop the aluminum oxide element for water vapor analysis. Elements used in this study are of the Stover[1] type and consist basically of an anodized aluminum substrate onto which is evaporated a thin layer of gold. The aluminum substrate and the gold film act as the detector cell electrodes. Figure 1 is a sketch of cell construction. Details of cell construction and manufacture are amply described in the Stover article.

Changes in ambient water vapor concentra-

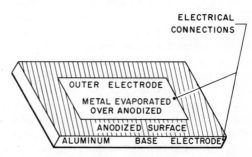

FIG. 1. Mechanical construction (after Stover[1]).

tion effect changes in the amount of water adsorbed by the oxide structure, and these, in turn, produce corresponding changes in cell impedance (resistive and capacitive).

The electrical characteristic selected as a water vapor correlative will depend upon the intended use of the hygrometer, the desired sensitivity, and the range of water vapor concentration to be covered.

In this study, development work was directed toward the application of the element to meteorological moisture sensing. Areas to be investigated include: (1) the practical operating range of the element, (2) element time response, (3) reproducibility and long-term stability, and (4) temperature and pressure effects.

CALIBRATION APPARATUS

For element calibration two basic methods were used to obtain "standard" atmospheres of known water vapor content: saturated salt solutions (static tests) and chemical desiccants (dynamic method).

Saturated salt solutions permit the establishment of high vapor concentrations (2,000 to 20,000 μg H$_2$O/l). In these tests, elements were sealed in bottles containing appropriate salt solutions. The bottles were then kept in a thermostatted water bath for at least several hours before the first measurements were taken. When two successive measurements, spaced approximately 15 minutes apart, showed no drift it was assumed that the vapor concentration within the jar was substantially at equilibrium. The values for vapor concentration above these salt solutions as reported by Wexler and Hasegawa[2] were accepted as valid.

For lower concentrations of water vapor, a modification of the use of chemical desiccants as reported by Trusell and Diehl[3] was adopted. In this method a moist gas stream is passed through a chemical desiccant bed where it is dried to a value characteristic of the desiccant used. The procedure has the advantage of being dynamic, and at constant temperature the vapor content of the stream is independent of the flow rate. Very high flow rates, however, can result in moisture breakthrough and must be avoided. In our study, the chemical desiccants selected permitted the establishment of vapor concentrations covering the range between 1.5 and 599 μg H$_2$O/l.

Trusell's apparatus was modified to include a bank of desiccant tubes covering the range of interest. By the manipulation of appropriately placed stopcocks the gas stream could be diverted through the desired desiccant. This eliminated the need to continually dismantle the train to change desiccants. The entire dessicant train was kept in a water bath thermostatted to 25°C. Figure 2 shows a diagram of the system.

To further increase the flexibility of the apparatus, the chamber containing the element was connected to a vacuum pump to allow establishment of reduced pressures. In this manner, a range of vapor concentrations could be established by feeding the output of a desiccant stream into the element chamber at reduced pressures. The water vapor concentration within the chamber was then calculated to be that of the input concentration multiplied by the chamber pressure expressed in atmospheres.

Element readout was performed with a circuit designed for this series of experiments (one of a variety that could be used). It was essentially an impedance bridge circuit in which the Al$_2$O$_3$ element comprised the test leg balancing capacitor and resistor decades. The bridge was first nulled at some very low dew point, generally below −90°C. When the element was exposed to water vapor, the bridge became unbalanced and the degree of

A. HUMIDIFIER, MgSO$_4$ · 7 H$_2$O

B. DRIERITE

C. DESICCANT TUBES

D. ELEMENT CHAMBER

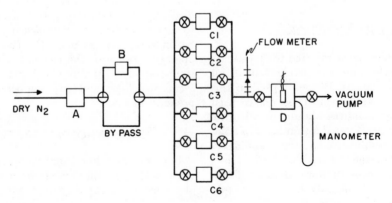

FIG. 2. Apparatus for water vapor concentration establishment using chemical desiccants.

unbalance was measured with a sensitive microammeter. Readout precision was increased by providing three decade stages of amplification of the unbalance signal covering a range of 0 to 15,000 meter units. It must be emphasized that these values are completely arbitrary and have no absolute significance in terms of element characteristics.

Response to Vapor Concentration

In these calibration studies, in order to utilize the pressure reduction technique in conjunction with the dynamic chemical desiccant method, it was necessary first to establish that the element was responsive to the partial pressure of water and independent of total pressure. Accepting as valid the desiccant efficiencies as reported by Trusell, if the element response is independent of total pressure we would expect to obtain the same response for dissimilar desiccants, if a pressure adjustment is made to compensate for water vapor output differences. This independence of pressure was indeed observed. The fact that general agreement between desiccants was found is also strong evidence of the probable correctness of Trusell's data.

In early experiments, the element properties of capacity and resistance were examined as possible indices of water vapor concentration. Figures 3 and 4 are graphs of this data for typical elements. Measurements were taken with a General Radio impedance bridge Type

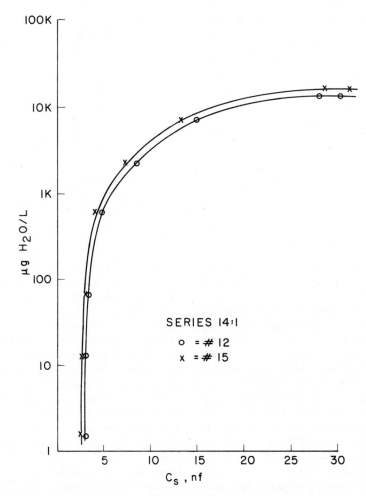

FIG. 3. Variation of capacitance with water vapor concentration.

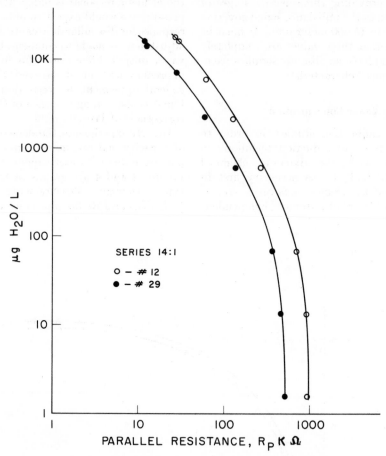

Fɪɢ. 4. Variation of resistance with water vapor concentration.

1650 A at 1 kc. Later, it was found more convenient to use impedance as the property measured.

With the bridge circuit designed for this study, a series of calibration curves was generated. Both static and dynamic measurements were taken. Figures 5 and 6 are plots for typical elements. The method used to produce vapor concentrations is indicated in Fig. 5, it may be noted that the points obtained through pressure reduction fall well within the general scatter of points taken at one atmosphere. Significantly, the range of water vapor concentration covered was greater than five orders of magnitude.

For the four elements shown, the calibration curves are almost superimposable. Though this condition is not always observed, different elements generally display curves of the same shape with displaced coordinates.

An everpresent difficulty in element calibration at very low vapor concentrations is the effect of the walls of the experimental apparatus. Regardless of the material used in making the system, the amount of residually sorbed water, when working at dew points below −50°C, becomes a major problem. Glass, as would be expected is particularly objectionable. Many hours of system operation have often been required before there was reasonable assurance of steady-state conditions. Conversely, a thoroughly dry system, achieved through extensive pumping or heating, is an excellent sink for moisture. Thus, sufficient time must be allowed to reach steady state when coming up from low dew points.

Temperature Dependence

A preliminary examination of element response to temperature variation was made. These studies indicate that the temperature coefficient is low and smaller than present experimental error.

In one test, an element, previously calibrated by the chemical desiccant method at +25°C, was contained in an isolated metal chamber. The chamber was in turn put into a well-insulated "Styrofoam" box packed with "Styrofoam" chips. Liquid nitrogen was poured into the box until a sufficiently low chamber temperature was achieved. The temperature within the box was monitored with a rod thermistor of the standard Weather Bureau type.

At temperatures below 0°C, vapor pressures of water are limited by the frost-point temperature (neglecting conditions of supersaturation). Thus, if an initially high vapor concentration was present within the chamber, at any given temperature a corresponding frost point will fix the vapor concentration. It must be emphasized that the humidity element is also being maintained at the same temperature as the measured frost point. Thus, the element is monitoring water vapor concentration continuously at conditions of saturation, i.e., 100 per cent RH.

Figure 7 shows a plot of the data taken in this manner. Since vapor concentrations were established using a "sliding scale" of temperature conditions, if a temperature coefficient exists, we would have expected to find a curve of different slope than that obtained by constant-temperature calibration. Deviation from the calibration curve taken at +25°C was found to be random and may be explained as arising from temperature differences between the walls of the chamber and the thermistor. In addition, since the test was performed statically, mixing rates within the chamber were not ideal. Experiments performed under more closely controlled condi-

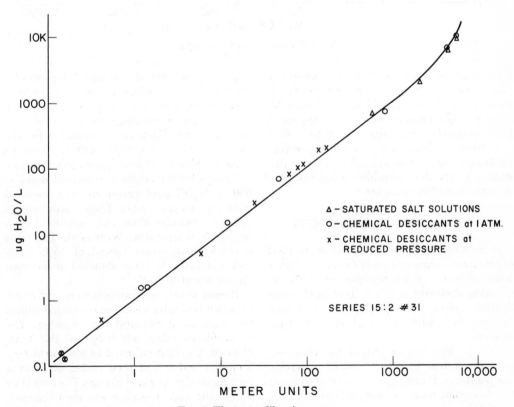

FIG. 5. Element calibration curve.

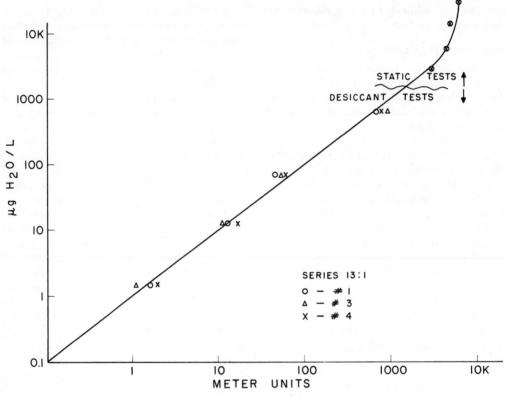

FIG. 6. Element calibration curves.

tions must be made in order to define the temperature coefficient more accurately. If there is a correction, it will be a second-order effect since no pronounced changes appear to have occurred over a range of -20 to $-90°C$.

Further evidence for a low-temperature coefficient may be found below in the discussion of the data obtained using the two-pressure humidity chamber.

TWO-PRESSURE CHAMBER TESTS

A chamber using the two-pressure method of generating a known humidity was used for a series of tests for intercomparison with the chemical desiccant method. Test port modifications allow for step-function humidity changes for examination of element time response.

Due to the time required for the two-pressure system to attain desired operating temperatures, four days were needed to cover the dew-point range of interest (100 to 22,000 μg H_2O/l).

Insufficient time was available for examining very low dew points. Figure 8 is a graph of data obtained during this period along with the values found using chemical desiccants and salt solutions. Each point indicated for the two-pressure system represents the average value for all runs at that vapor concentration.

Except for the chemical desiccant point at 600 μg H_2O/l good agreement was observed over the entire range. These data supply further evidence that the element has a negligible temperature coefficient. The tests cover a temperature spread of 45°C while still matching the data obtained in our own laboratory at $+25°C$.

Response time experiments were performed using an isolatable chamber contained within the main environmental test chamber. The isolatable chamber, which housed the Al_2O_3 element, was first adjusted to some arbitrary humidity value and then sealed off with a pneumatically operated closure. The humidity within the main chamber was then changed, and after a suitable equilibration period, the element was abruptly exposed to the new condition.

The response of the element was then followed as a function of time at a constant temperature of $+25°C$.

Two typical runs are shown in Table 1.

The electronic circuit used for element readout is highly damped and hence is not well suited for response time measurements. Notwithstanding this difficulty, the data appear to be in substantial agreement with data taken later at Parametrics. In both runs, the time to read a $1-1/e$ (63 per cent) change was less than five seconds and a 90 per cent change, less than ten seconds.

The elements tested during this period and previously calibrated at Parametrics demonstrated the required stability for operational use. No difficulty was found in reproducing response when identical conditions of system operation were established.

At steady-state no drift of the element response was observed. To assist in this evaluation, a standard carbon element (ML-

TABLE 1

Elapsed Time	Meter Reading	Meter Reading
0	1350	3100
5	2800	4500
10	3100	4750
15		4800
20		
25		
30		
35		
40		
45		
50		
55		
60		
75		4850
90		
105		
120	3100	4850
	$11\% \rightarrow 50\%$ RH	$50\% \rightarrow 95\%$ RH

418/AMT-4) was put into the chamber along with the Al_2O_3 sensor. The sole purpose of the carbon element (uncalibrated) was to substantiate the fact that changes in Al_2O_3

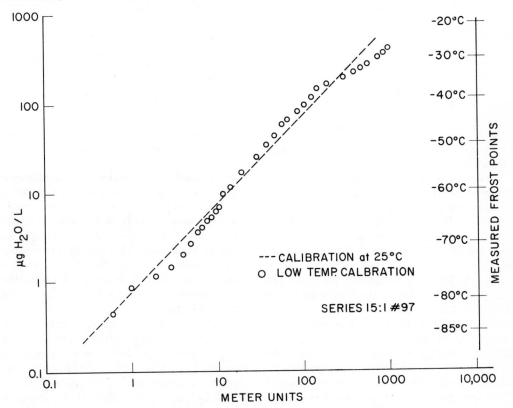

FIG. 7. Effect of temperature upon element calibration.

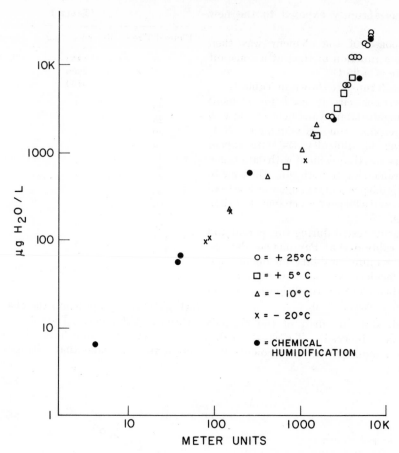

Fig. 8. Comparison of data taken with the two-pressure system and chemical desiccants.

element response reflected vapor concentration changes that occurred within the system.

Response drifts of the Al₂O₃ element were always accompanied by similar changes in carbon element response and in the expected direction. Unfortunately, the range of the carbon element was not great enough to be of use for this purpose at the lower dew points.

No evidence of element hysteresis was found. Slight differences of response that were seen were attributed to the fact that steady-state conditions within the chamber had not been attained. Generally, in this study, conditions within the two-pressure system were maintained 10 or 15 minutes between readings. Further slight changes would occur if sufficient time were permitted to reach a true steady state.

TIME RESPONSE

A chamber was designed having a diaphragm which could be punctured to provide for a rapid step-function change. Normal room humidity conditions initially present within the chamber were reduced by at least an order of magnitude by partially evacuating the chamber. Puncturing the diaphragm provided the humidity step-function by restoring the originally higher ambient water vapor concentration.

Impedance changes in the element accompanying humidity changes were displayed on an oscilloscope fitted with a camera attachment. When the diaphragm was ruptured, the sweep of the scope was simultaneously triggered. The time response characteristics of the element can readily be analyzed from the resultant scope picture.

When a step-function change was imposed upon the element (initial condition of 240 μg H_2O/l to a final condition of 5900 μg H_2O/l), it was observed that a 63 per cent change occurred in about 2½ seconds. This is in qualitative agreement with data obtained using the two-pressure system.

PERTINENT DATA

A program has been initiated to determine stability and aging characteristics. Stability under storage conditions of high and low humidity as well as with temperature variation will be examined. It is as yet too early to assess long-term stability. However, no changes in element calibration have been noted over periods of several weeks.

The effect upon element response to three common air pollutants, sulfur dioxide, nitrogen dioxide, and ozone, was examined.

Element behavior was observed with water vapor concentrations from ambient room conditions down to 60 μg H_2O/l. No effect upon element response was found with the following very high concentrations of pollutant: (1) SO_2 at concentrations of 100 ppm, (2) NO_2 at concentrations in excess of 200 ppm, and (3) O_3 at a concentration of 10 μg O_3/l.

Field Tests

Very early in this program several radiosonde balloon flights were performed at Hanscom Field, in Bedford, Massachusetts.

At this time uncalibrated humidity elements were incorporated into standard sonde circuitry of the AN/AMT-4 type.

The purpose of these flights was to obtain qualitative information with respect to element performance under operational conditions. Data from a flight to 25,000 ft is recorded in Fig. 9. No significance should be attached to meter readings except that they

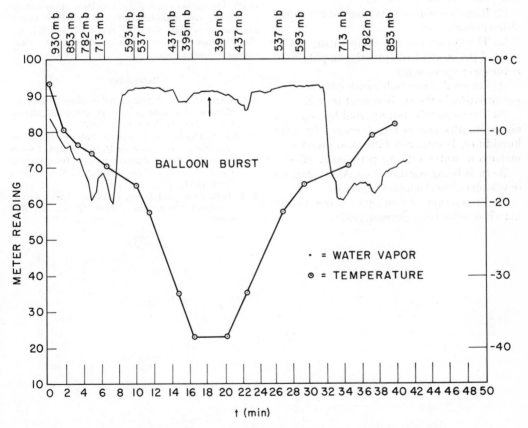

FIG. 9. Element performance during a radiosonde balloon flight to 22,500 ft.

bear some relation to water vapor concentration. High meter readings indicate low vapor concentration. The plateau section reflects the insensitivity of the circuit at dry conditions. It is important to observe that the response during ascent and descent is similar. In spite of the lack of circuit sensitivity, there was considerable fine structure.

These tests were encouraging in that the element behaved as was expected by displaying rapid time response and sensitivity to vapor concentration fluctuations.

SUMMARY AND FUTURE WORK

The aluminum oxide humidity element shows expectations of fulfilling the stringent requirements for meteorological sensors.

(1) Response is related to absolute water vapor concentration and is independent of the total pressure. The range covered is large, encompassing ambient ground conditions to dew points as low as $-90°C$.

(2) Response is rapid making possible good altitude definition.

(3) The apparently low temperature coefficient of the element will greatly simplify data reduction requirements.

(4) Its small mass will cause only a small perturbation in the environment tested.

(5) The element is not affected by common air pollutants and is not damaged by high humidities. It can even withstand direct submersion in water without permanent effect.

Work is being continued on Al_2O_3 element development in the following areas:

(1) Production of elements having closely matched calibration characteristics,

(2) Means for rapid calibration curve generation,

(3) Long-term stability and aging studies,

(4) The design of circuitry amenable to standard weather sonde instrumentation.

Though continued development is needed in the areas described above, the aluminum oxide element can find immediate application as a research tool in meteorological studies. All the requirements for balloon-carried humidity sensors (sensitivity, time response, and stability, etc.) have been demonstrated. It must be emphasized that element stability is more than adequate for flight requirements. It is presently known that these elements maintain calibration for at least several weeks. Future evaluation will determine the full extent of element stability.

Acknowledgment. This work was carried out under contract from the Direct Sensing Techniques Branch of the Aerospace Instrumentation Laboratory AFCRL. Initial support for the early stages of this work was received from the Geophysics Branch, ONR. The authors wish to express their appreciation to the above organizations and to Mr. James Morrissey and Mr. Bernard Weiss of AFCRL for their technical assistance in conducting the two-pressure system tests.

References

1. Stover, C. M., "Aluminum Oxide Humidity Element for Radiosonde Weather Measuring Use," *RSI*, **34**, No. 6, 632 (1963).
2. Wexler, Arnold, and Hasegawa, Saburo, "Relative Humidity—Temperature Relationships of Some Saturated Salt Solutions in the Temperature Range 0° to 50°C," *Natl. Bur. Std. Res. Papers*, (July 1954).
3. Trusell, Fred, and Diehl, Harvey, "Efficiency of Chemical Desiccants," *Anal. Chem.*, **35**, 674 (1963).

SPECTROSCOPIC HYGROMETRY

42. The Absorption of Radiation by Water Vapor

J. W. C. JOHNS

National Research Council of Canada, Division of Pure Physics, Ottawa, Canada

ABSTRACT

Molecular spectra can conveniently be classified into three separate types: (1) spectra due to rotation alone which occur in the infrared and microwave regions, (2) spectra due to vibration with rotation which occur in the infrared and occasionally as far as the visible, and (3) spectra due to electronic changes together with vibration and rotation which commonly occur in the visible, ultraviolet and Schuman regions of the spectrum.

In each of these broad general regions water vapor absorbs. The general features of the spectra are described and information which can be obtained on the water molecule is discussed.

Some recent examples of the use of spectroscopic methods applied to the determination of water vapor concentrations are mentioned.

INTRODUCTION

The purpose of this paper is to present a short account of the spectrum of water vapor. It is not intended to be a complete review of work carried out up to the present time, but it is hoped that it will give workers in the field of humidity some idea of what information is contained in the spectrum and perhaps give some ideas of possible uses to which the absorption spectrum may be put.

To a first approximation, it is possible to regard the energy of a given molecular state as the sum of the rotational, vibrational and electronic energies. Transitions between two states give rise to the emission or absorption of radiation equal in energy to the energy difference between the two states. Spectra arising from changes in rotational energy only, occur in the microwave and far infrared regions. Spectra arising from vibrational changes (together with rotation) occur in the infrared region and occasionally as far as the visible. Spectra arising from electronic changes (together with vibration and rotation) can occur in any region but are usually found in the visible, ultraviolet and vacuum ultraviolet regions. The following presentation is thus divided into three sections according to the region being discussed.

Beer's law, on which all spectroscopic determinations of concentrations must be based, can be stated in the form $I/I_0 = e^{-kx}$, where I is the light intensity after passing through the sample, I_0 is the incident intensity, x is the path length reduced to some absolute standard (usually NTP) and k is the absorption coefficient. A knowledge of this absorption coefficient at a given wavelength would thus seem sufficient for the determination of vapor concentrations. However the situation is complicated by the presence of other gases, which may also absorb in the region of interest and which, if the total pressure is high, will contribute to the broadening of the lines and thus cause apparent changes in absorption coefficients. Furthermore Beer's law will not be obeyed if the instrumental resolution is insufficient to resolve any fine structure in the spectrum. Brief mention is made in passing to measurements of absorption coefficients and to methods which take account of foreign gas effects.

PURE ROTATION SPECTRUM

Pure rotation spectra commonly occur in the microwave region of the spectrum, but the moments of inertia of the water molecule are small enough to make the spectrum extend, at normal temperatures, as far as 18 μ in the infrared. Only one transition has been found in the microwave region, and it was responsible, so the story goes, for considerable difficulties in the development of X-band radar.

Since all the three moments of inertia of water are different, the energy levels are those of an asymmetric top and consequently show a complex pattern. The energy levels of a rigid asymmetric rotor can be expressed in the form

$$F(J_\tau) = \frac{A + C}{2} J(J + 1) + \frac{A - C}{2} E_\tau^J(\kappa) \ (1)$$

where J is the quantum number of the total angular momentum, τ is a label denoting the $2J + 1$ sub-levels and κ is the asymmetry parameter which is given by

$$\kappa = \frac{2B - (A + C)}{A - C} \qquad (2)$$

The rotational constants A, B and C are inversely proportional to the corresponding moments of inertia I_A, I_B and I_C and by convention $I_A \leqslant I_B \leqslant I_C$. Values of $E_\tau^J(\kappa)$ have been given by Turner, Hicks, and Reitwiesener[40] as a function of κ (for a review of other derivations of rigid asymmetric rotor energies see Herzberg[17]). Not only is the pattern of energy levels of an asymmetric rotor complex, but in the case of H_2O, account must be taken of large centrifugal distortion effects if the spectrum is to be fully understood. The contribution of the centrifugal distortion terms can amount to several hundred cm^{-1} even at moderate values of J.

The symmetries of the rotational levels can be classified according to the behavior of the wave function, which can remain unchanged or change in sign, to a rotation of 180 degrees about two of the three axes (c and a, corresponding to the moments of inertia I_C and I_A, are usually chosen). There are thus four symmetry types which can be distinguished namely $++$, $+-$, $-+$, and $--$. The selection rules which govern transitions be-

tween rotational levels can be summarized (for the special case of water, in which the permanent dipole is parallel to the b axis)

$$\Delta J = 0, \pm 1$$
$$++ \leftrightarrow --$$
$$+- \leftrightarrow -+$$

Table 1 shows the observed energies of H_2O together with the symmetries of the levels taken from Randall, Dennison, Ginsburg, and Weber[37] who were able to assign most of the observed lines between 18 and 75 μ on the basis of the theory outlined above. Note that the microwave line, at 22237 Mc/sec, which has been assigned to the transition $6_{-5} \leftarrow 5_{-1}$ obeys the above selection rules. This microwave line has been measured by Becker and Autler,[3] and by Townes and Merritt,[39] and was first predicted by King, Hainer, and Cross.[25, 26]

King *et al.* also predicted three other long-wavelength lines. One of these, $3_{-2} \leftarrow 2_2$, at 6.15 cm^{-1} ($\equiv$ 183311.30 Mc/sec $\equiv$ 1630 μ) has been observed both optically by Iaroslavskii and Stanevich[22] and by microwave techniques by King and Gordy.[27]

Palmer[31-33] has investigated the transmission of radiation through water vapor under simulated atmospheric conditions throughout the range of the pure rotation spectrum. He has found quite good agreement with a model due to Benedict[4] based on actual line positions and intensities, provided the interval over which the transmission function is measured is large enough (about 50 cm^{-1}).

It is interesting to note that Becker and Autler[3] made their measurements at a total pressure of one atmosphere but at various partial pressures of water vapor. Consequently the measured line was very broad. They found that the line shape was fairly well represented by the theory developed by Van Vleck and Weisskopf[42] (see also Ref. 41).

VIBRATION-ROTATION SPECTRUM

When changes in vibrational energy take place simultaneously with changes in rotational energy, absorption (or emission) of radiation takes place in the infrared region of the spectrum.

The water molecule belongs to the C_{2v} symmetry group which has four disitnct

TABLE 1. PURE ROTATION ENERGIES IN THE GROUND STATE OF H_2O

	J_τ	W		J_τ	W		J_τ	W		J_τ	W
+ +	0_0	0	+ +	6_2	757.84	+ −	9_9	2226.41	+ −	11_{11}	3218.55
			− +	6_1	756.90	− −	9_8	2226.41	− −	11_{10}	3218.55
+ −	1_1	42.30	− −	6_0	661.63	− +	9_7	2010.67	− +	11_9	2974.88
− −	1_0	37.06	+ −	6_{-1}	649.11	+ +	9_6	2010.67	+ +	11_8	2974.88
− +	1_{-1}	23.78	+ +	6_{-2}	602.78	+ −	9_5	1811.18	+ −	11_7	2741.42
			− +	6_{-3}	553.00	− −	9_4	1811.18	− −	11_6	2741.42
+ +	2_2	136.10	− −	6_{-4}	542.80	− +	9_3	1631.95	− +	11_5	2523.08
− +	2_1	134.81	+ −	6_{-5}	447.20	+ +	9_2	1631.81	+ +	11_4	2523.08
− −	2_0	95.04	+ +	6_{-6}	446.69	+ −	9_1	1477.78	+ −	11_3	2322.82
+ −	2_{-1}	79.38				− −	9_0	1475.46	− −	11_2	2322.77
+ +	2_{-2}	70.03	+ −	7_7	1395.26	− +	9_{-1}	1360.85	− +	11_1	2145.17
			− −	7_6	1395.26	+ +	9_{-2}	1340.98	+ +	11_0	2144.06
+ −	3_3	285.45	− +	7_5	1216.63	+ −	9_{-3}	1283.29	+ −	11_{-1}	2000.71
− −	3_2	285.26	+ +	7_4	1216.63	− −	9_{-4}	1216.62	− −	11_{-2}	1984.20
− +	3_1	212.07	+ −	7_3	1060.07	− +	9_{-5}	1202.28	− +	11_{-3}	1898.56
+ +	3_0	206.25	− −	7_2	1059.88	+ +	9_{-6}	1080.72	+ +	11_{-4}	1840.14
+ −	3_{-1}	173.33	− +	7_1	931.50	+ −	9_{-7}	1079.41	+ −	11_{-5}	1811.21
− −	3_{-2}	142.17	+ +	7_0	927.92	− −	9_{-8}	920.41	− −	11_{-6}	1694.71
− +	3_{-3}	136.74	+ −	7_{-1}	842.65	− +	9_{-9}	920.41	− +	11_{-7}	1691.13
			− −	7_{-2}	816.78				+ +	11_{-8}	1525.65
+ +	4_4	488.24	− +	7_{-3}	782.54	+ +	10_{10}	2703.28	+ −	11_{-9}	1525.36
− +	4_3	488.24	+ +	7_{-4}	709.54	− +	10_9	2703.28	− −	11_{-10}	1327.58
− −	4_2	383.90	+ −	7_{-5}	704.40	− −	10_8	2472.44	− +	11_{-11}	1327.58
+ −	4_1	382.49	− −	7_{-6}	586.53	+ −	10_7	2472.44			
+ +	4_0	315.66	− +	7_{-7}	586.32	+ +	10_6	2255.08	− −	12_6	3033.78
− +	4_{-1}	300.33				− +	10_5	2255.08	+ −	12_5	3033.78
− −	4_{-2}	275.21	+ +	8_8	1789.77	− −	10_4	2055.04	− +	12_{-9}	1775.26
+ −	4_{-3}	224.74	− +	8_7	1789.77	+ −	10_3	2055.04	− −	12_{-10}	1775.26
+ +	4_{-4}	221.90	− −	8_6	1591.47	+ +	10_2	1876.16	+ −	12_{-11}	1558.42
			+ −	8_5	1591.47	− +	10_1	1875.68	+ +	12_{-12}	1558.42
+ −	5_5	742.30	+ +	8_4	1411.89	− −	10_0	1726.23			
− −	5_4	742.30	− +	8_3	1411.89	+ −	10_{-1}	1719.75	+ +	13_{-10}	2042.99
− +	5_3	610.42	− −	8_2	1256.24	+ +	10_{-2}	1614.43	+ −	13_{-11}	2042.99
+ +	5_2	610.21	+ −	8_1	1255.45	− +	10_{-3}	1581.88	− −	13_{-12}	1807.36
+ −	5_1	508.86	+ +	8_0	1132.10	− −	10_{-4}	1538.65	− +	13_{-13}	1807.36
− −	5_0	503.94	− +	8_{-1}	1123.11	+ −	10_{-5}	1446.68			
− +	5_{-1}	446.52	− −	8_{-2}	1052.92	+ +	10_{-6}	1438.50	+ −	14_{-13}	2074.30
+ +	5_{-2}	416.02	+ −	8_{-3}	1006.38	− +	10_{-7}	1294.07	+ +	14_{-14}	2074.30
+ −	5_{-3}	399.45	+ +	8_{-4}	983.22	− −	10_{-8}	1293.49			
− −	5_{-4}	326.49	− +	8_{-5}	885.84	+ −	10_{-9}	1114.91			
− +	5_{-5}	325.23	− −	8_{-6}	883.12	+ +	10_{-10}	1114.91			
+ +	6_6	1045.34	+ −	8_{-7}	744.31						
− +	6_5	1045.34	+ +	8_{-8}	744.24						
− −	6_4	888.89									
+ −	6_3	888.85									

species. Figure 1 shows the water molecule with the three principal axes a, b and c corresponding to the three moments of inertia I_A, I_B and I_C. The four symmetry operations (not to be confused with the symmetry species) are (1) rotation of 180 degrees about the b axis, denoted by $C_2(b)$, (2) reflection at the bc plane, denoted by $\sigma_v(bc)$, reflection at the ab plane, denoted by $\sigma_v(ab)$ and the identity operation, denoted by I. The wave function (which can be vibrational, electronic or vibronic) either remains unchanged or changes in sign under the influence of the symmetry operations. The four possible symmetry species and their relation to the symmetry operations are shown in Table 2.

There are three normal vibrations of the water molecule, which can be described as symmetrical OH bond stretching (ν_1), bond bending (ν_2) and antisymmetrical OH bond

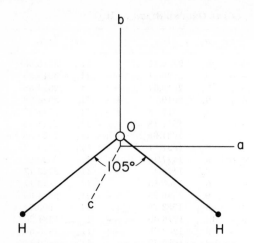

FIG. 1. Principal axes of the water molecule. The c axis is perpendicular to the plane of the paper.

TABLE 2. SPECIES TABLE FOR SYMMETRY C_{2v}*

	I	$C_2(b)$	$\sigma_v(bc)$	$\sigma_v(ab)$
A_1	+	+	+	+
A_2	+	+	−	−
B_1	+	−	+	−
B_2	+	−	−	+

* The + sign indicates that the wave function remains unchanged and the − sign indicates that the wave function changes sign.

stretching (ν_3). The first two are of A_1 symmetry while the third is of B_2 symmetry. Clearly no vibration can be antisymmetric with respect to the plane of the molecule, and thus vibrational at levels of the species A_2 and B_1 cannot exist. Such energy levels can only exist if the molecule is electronically excited, as will be described in the next section.

Herzberg and Teller[18] have shown that transitions are allowed if the product of the symmetries of the combining states have the symmetry species of a component of the dipole moment along one of the principal axes. These components M_a, M_b and M_c can readily be seen to have the species B_2, A_1 and B_1 respectively.

The lowest level of H_2O is symmetric with respect to all the operations of C_{2v} and is thus of A_1 symmetry. It can be seen that transitions from the ground state to vibrationally excited states of both A_1 and B_2 symmetries are allowed. In the former case, the alternating dipole moment is parallel to the axis of the

intermediate moment of inertia and the resulting band is said to be of type B. In the latter case the alternating dipole moment is parallel to the axis of the smallest moment of inertia and the resulting band is said to be of type A. In the case of a B_1 upper state, which is possible with electronic excitation, a type C band results. The selection rules for these, the only three types of allowed transitions, are summarized in Table 3.

TABLE 3. SELECTION RULES FOR ASYMMETRIC-TOP BANDS

$\Delta J = 0, \pm 1$, but $J = 0 \longleftrightarrow J = 0$		
Type A	Type B	Type C
$++\longleftrightarrow-+$	$++\longleftrightarrow--$	$++\longleftrightarrow+-$
$+-\longleftrightarrow--$	$+-\longleftrightarrow-+$	$-+\longleftrightarrow--$

From the point of view of the appearance of the spectrum, the relative line intensities are as important as the line positions. As in the case of the energy levels, the theory is complex and will not be dealt with here. Cross, Hainer and King[7] have given a table of line strengths, which can be used in conjunction with Boltzman factors to obtain relative line intensities. An additional complication in the case of water is due to the nuclear spin of the two identical hydrogen nuclei, which gives rise to a three-to-one intensity alternation between lines involving even and odd τ sublevels.

A large amount of work has been done on the infrared spectrum of water vapor, and no attempt will be made to review it here. Herzberg[17] has fully discussed the earlier work, particularly that of Mecke and his co-workers. More recent high-resolution studies have been made by Benedict and Plyler,[6] Benedict, Claasen and Shaw,[5] and Dalby and Nielsen[8] among others. It is from high-resolution studies of this type that the geometry of the ground state of water is derived. The infrared spectrum also gives information on the vibrational levels of the molecule. Apart from the three fundamentals at 1595 cm^{-1} (6.3 μ), 3652 cm^{-1} (2.7 μ) and 3756 cm^{-1} (2.7 μ), there are a large number of overtone and combination bands extending as far as the visible region of the spectrum. Some of these bands have been used for the experimental determination of atmospheric water vapor contents. For example, Kiseleva, Neporent and Fursenkov[28] flew a high-resolution spectrometer by balloon and studied the 1.4, 1.9, and 2.7 μ bands against the continuous radiation of the sun. Reviews of studies on the infrared transmission of the atmosphere have been given by Howard[20] and by Howard and Garing.[21]

ELECTRONIC SPECTRUM

Theoretical Expectations

The electronic ground state of water arises from the electron configuration

$$(1a_1)^2(2a_1)^2(1b_2)^2(3a_1)^2(1b_1)^2 \ldots \ldots {}^1A_1$$

The orbitals have been labeled according to their symmetry species (see Table 2) and have been numbered in the manner adopted by Ellison and Shull.[12] This number should not be confused with n, the principal quantum number, referred to below. All the low-lying orbitals derived from $n \leqslant 2$ atomic orbitals are filled, and as a consequence, there are no low-lying electronic states of the water molecule. In agreement with this there is no absorption of water in the visible or near ultraviolet regions of the spectrum. In order to obtain an excited electron configuration, it is necessary to promote an electron to an orbital with principal quantum number, n, greater than two, that is to a Rydberg orbital. Table 4

TABLE 4. ELECTRON CONFIGURATIONS OF SOME RYDBERG STATES OF H_2O

$(1a_1)^2(2a_1)^2(1b_2)^2(3a_1)^2(1b_1)(nsa_1)$				$\ldots {}^{3,1}B_1 \ldots$	1
,,	,,	,,	(npa_1)	$\ldots {}^{3,1}B_1 \ldots$	2
,,	,,	,,	(npb_1)	$\ldots {}^{3,1}A_1 \ldots$	3
,,	,,	,,	(npb_2)	$\ldots {}^{3,1}A_2 \ldots$	4
,,	,,	,,	(nda_2)	$\ldots {}^{3,1}B_2 \ldots$	5
,,	,,	,,	(ndb_2)	$\ldots {}^{3,1}A_2 \ldots$	6
,,	,,	,,	(ndb_1)	$\ldots {}^{3,1}A_1 \ldots$	7
,,	,,	,,	(nda_1)	$\ldots {}^{3,1}B_1 \ldots$	8
,,	,,	,,	(nda_1)	$\ldots {}^{3,1}B_1 \ldots$	9

Note. The $(1b_1)$ orbital may be regarded as the $(2p_x)$ orbital of the oxygen atom where the x axis (the c axis of Fig. 1) is perpendicular to the plane of the molecule.

lists the possible states obtained by exciting an electron from the outermost orbital of the ground configuration to s, p, and d Rydberg orbitals. States derived using nf orbitals have

not been considered, since transitions involving such states and the ground state should be weak because they correspond to the forbidden $F \leftarrow P$ transitions of the united atom. Each configuration listed does of course represent a Rydberg series of states whose energies can be represented by the usual formula

$$T = I - R/(n - \delta)^2 \qquad (3)$$

where T is the energy of the state, I is the ionization potential of the molecule, R is the Rydberg constant and δ is the quantum defect. Walsh[44] has pointed out that the quantum defect will have values close to 1.0, 0.6 and 0.1 for s, p and d orbitals respectively, thus providing a way to identify Rydberg series.

Fortunately the spectrum will be somewhat simpler than the above discussion of states might indicate since not all of them can be expected to be observed in absorption from the ground state. $A_2 \leftarrow A_1$ transitions are forbidden, as was implied in the discussion of rotation-vibration spectra, and singlet-triplet transitions are fairly strongly forbidden in a molecule as light as water. Thus there is a total of seven Rydberg series of singlet states leading to the formation of the H_2O^+ ion in its ${}^2B_1$ ground state which can be expected to be observed in absorption from the ground state. The spectrum will be further simplified under moderate resolution if it is remembered that groups of states represented by np or nd are degenerate in the united atom approximation. The five nd states and the three np states will be grouped more and more closely together as n increases and the orbital angular momentum, l, of the electron becomes uncoupled from the nuclear framework leading to the formation of single states, which may be called "d or p complexes".[10] However, if such bands are observed under high resolution, the rotational structure will be exceedingly complex. La Paglia[29] has shown that the symmetry-induced splitting of the np states should decrease exponentially with increasing n.

Further Rydberg series of states are of course expected if successive *inner* electrons are excited, and these series will lead to the various excited states of the H_2O^+ ion. Ionization potentials corresponding to the loss of an electron from each of the orbitals of the ground configuration have been calculated theoretically by Mulliken[30] and by Ellison and Shull,[12] and these agree very well with values obtained spectroscopically by Henning,[16] Price,[35] and Astoin, Johannin-Gilles and Vodar[2] and with values obtained from electron impact data by Price and Sugden[36] and by Frost and McDowell.[13] These results are summarized in Table 5. It may be noted

TABLE 5. IONIZATION POTENTIALS OF H_2O IN EV

Spectroscopic* Rydberg Limits	Electron Impact	Theoretical	State of H_2O^+
12.62 ± 0.02[35]	12.6 ± 0.01[13]	11.8[12]	$^2B_1$
	12.6 ± 0.1[36]		
	14.35 ± 0.03[13]	13.2[12]	$^2A_1$
	14.5 ± 0.3[36]	17[30]	
16.5[16]	16.34 ± 0.06[13]	18.6[12]	$^2B_2$
	16.2 ± 0.3[36]	18[30]	
33.5[2]		36.2[12]	$^2A_1$
		32[30]	
		557.3[12]	$^2A_1$

* Spectroscopic values have been corrected, where necessary, assuming 1 cm^{-1} = 1.239767×10^{-4}EV.

that there is no spectroscopic value corresponding to the loss of an electron from the $(3a_1)$ orbital. Walsh[43] has shown that this orbital is involved in the bending of the molecule; therefore, the loss of an electron from it must result in a change in shape. The Franck-Condon principle tells us that well marked Rydberg series will not be formed in such a case. In all probability the first excited state of H_2O^+ is linear as has been shown to be the case in the isoelectronic NH_2 radical by Dressler and Ramsay.[11]

One last point concerns the appearance of the spectrum. All the electronic levels just discussed lie above the dissociation energy of water. Consequently there is a possibility that the excited electronic states may be pre-dissociated, with the result that the observed bands will be diffuse, unlike spectra in the infrared region which must be sharp. Many of the bands in the vacuum ultraviolet region are found to be diffuse, a fact which can be of great importance in the measurement of water vapor concentrations using instruments of limited resolving power.

The Observed Spectrum

The first electronic absorption of water vapor is a broad continuous band stretching from about 1850 to 1500 Å. Even at this time there is some confusion regarding the exact nature of this absorption. Rathenau[38] measured some diffuse bands with a spacing of about 1300 cm^{-1}, and Wilkinson and Johnston[46] reported three peaks in the absorption at 1608, 1648 and 1718 Å. Still more recently Johannin-Gilles[23] found what seem to be the same peaks together with a few weaker ones as shown in Fig. 2. No convincing

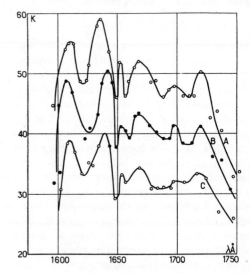

FIG. 2. Absorption of water vapor in the region 1750 to 1575 Å (after Johannin-Gilles[23]).

analysis of these peaks has been given so far, but Johannin-Gilles has given some evidence that they are shifted slightly in heavy water. On the other hand Harrison *et al.*[15] and Watanabe and Zelikoff[45] found no evidence of any structure as is shown in Fig. 3. It is interesting to note that the workers who found structure in the continuum also found that Beer's law was not obeyed. If this is correct, then it is possible that there is some still unresolved fine structure associated with the bands which would be revealed by studies at higher resolution. The upper electronic state involved is the first one listed in Table 4, an assignment first given by Mulliken.[30] Any interpretation of the peaks noted by some workers must await conclusive proof that they

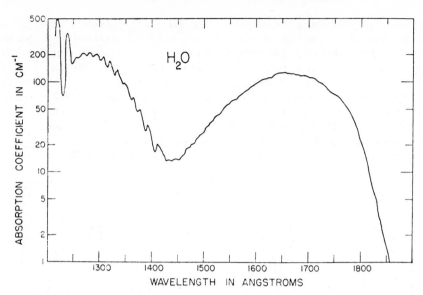

Fɪɢ. 3. Absorption of water vapor in the region 1900 to 1200 Å (after Watanabe and Zelikoff[45]).

are due to water and not to some impurity as suggested by Harrison *et al.*[15] (quoted by Watanabe and Zelikoff[45]).

The second absorption of water occurs at about 1300 Å and has been recorded by Rathenau,[38] Hopfield,[19] and Watanabe and Zelikoff.[45] It consists of a progression of diffuse bands which have been listed in Table 6 and may be seen clearly in Fig. 3. The frequency difference is about 785 cm^{-1} which is clearly too low for a bent water molecule of roughly the same dimensions as those of the ground state which has frequencies of 3652, 1595, and 3756 respectively for ν_1, ν_2 and ν_3. Watanabe and Zelikoff pointed out that the difference could conceivably be due to two superimposed progressions with 1600 cm^{-1} differences. However if that were the case, according to the Franck-Condon principle, we would not expect to see a long progression of bands. It seems much more reasonable to assign the bands as arising from absorption to a *linear* upper state of the water molecule which could have the electron configuration

$$(1a_1)^2(2a_1)^2(1b_2)^2(3a_1)(1b_1)^2 \ldots (3sa_1) \ldots \ldots {}^{3,1}A_1$$

and would be expected to have a low bending frequency since the "core" configuration is that of the first excited state of the NH_2 radical which is known to be linear and has a bending frequency of about 600 cm^{-1} (see

TABLE 6. H_2O Bands in the Region 1250 to 1450 Å

Rathenau (1933)[38]	Watanabe and Zelikoff (1953)[45]		
λ_{vac}	λ_{vac}	ν_{vac}	$\Delta\nu$
	1411	70870	
			920
	1393	71790	
			780
	1378	72570	
			740
1367	1364	73310	
			870
1352	1348	74180	
			720
1337	1335	74910	
			800
1320	1321	75700	
			750
1308	1308	76450	
			770
1294	1295	77220	
			840
1282	1281	78060	
			740
1268	1269	78800	
			820
1255	1256	79620	

Ref. 11). This state is thus analogous to that causing the 1700 Å absorption, except that instead of being the first member of a Rydberg series leading to the ground state of the H_2O^+ ion ($^2B_1$) it is the first member of a series leading to the first excited state of the ion ($^2A_1$). In

support of this, it may be noted that the two absorption maxima are separated by about 1.8 EV, which is very close to the difference in the corresponding ionization potentials.

Starting at 1240 Å the spectrum becomes comparatively sharp, and it is possible to see individual bands and in some cases even rotational fine structure. The region from 1250 to 1060 Å is shown in Fig. 4 which has been taken from Watanabe and Zelikoff,[45] and

Fig. 5 shows the rotational fine structure of the band at 1240 Å observed by the author.[24] Six bands have been observed in the region from 1240 to 1133 Å, and they may be arranged in two short progressions of the symmetric stretching frequencies of the upper states involved. These band systems have been identified as the first members of the two allowed np Rydberg series (2 and 3 in Table 4). The upper state of the 1240 Å band has been

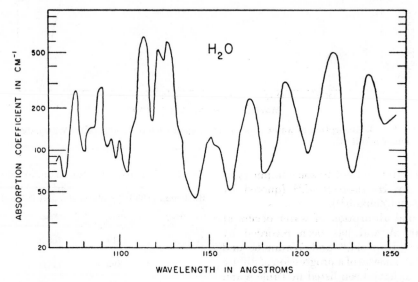

FIG. 4. Absorption of water vapor in the region 1250 to 1060 Å (after Watanabe and Zelikoff[45]).

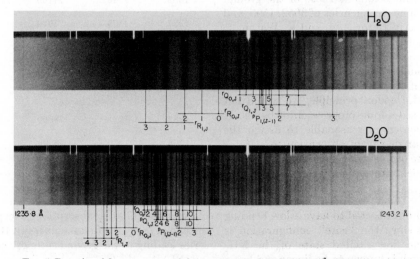

FIG. 5. Rotational fine structure of the water vapor band at 1240 Å. The top spectrogram is that of H_2O and the bottom one is of D_2O. Part of the analysis is indicated.

shown to be of $^1B_1$ symmetry,[24] so that the upper state of the 1220 Å band must be of $^1A_1$ symmetry. Rathenau's measurements of these bands[38] are included in Table 7 together with

TABLE 7. THE $3p$ BAND SYSTEMS OF H_2O*

$v_1'v_2'v_3'$			$^1B_1$	$\Delta\nu$	$^1A_1$	$\Delta\nu$
0	0	0	80684 (1239.4)		82030 (1219.0)	
				3180		3185
1	0	0	83864 (1192.4)		85215 (1173.5)	
				3069		3015
2	0	0	86933 (1150.3)		88230† (1133.4)	
(0	0	2)?				

* These measurements have been taken from one author (Rathenau[38]) for the sake of internal consistency. Figures in parentheses are wavelengths in Å units.

† Overlapped by $3d$ states.

the proposed analysis. The somewhat broad appearance of the band at 1152 Å may be due to a contribution from $2\nu_3$ (ν_3 is the antisymmetric stretching frequency) which could share some of the intensity of $2\nu_1$ by Fermi resonance, in a manner similar to that known to be important in the ground state.[9] Selection rules, based on arguments similar to those indicated in the discussion of vibration-rotation spectra, prevent a similar interaction taking place when only one quantum of these vibrations is excited.

The 0,0,0–0,0,0 bands of these systems can be fitted to the Rydberg formula with the known ionization potential, with $n = 3$ and with quantum defects of 0.72 and 0.66 respectively, thus confirming that the states are the $3p$ states. Price[35] has measured two further members of these series, but the intensity falls off very rapidly with increasing n thus preventing an accurate extrapolation to the series limit. This is because the transitions correspond to the forbidden $P—P$ transitions of the united atom.

The remainder of the spectrum between 1133 and 982 Å consists of two very strong Rydberg series which lead to the first ionization potential at 12.62 EV.[35] They are the nd and ns series, which, since the quantum defects are about 0.1 and 1.0 respectively, fall very close to each other. The first member of the nd

series and the second member of the ns series are shown clearly in Fig. 4 where it can be seen that the long-wavelength member of the pair is somewhat broader and seems to have some structure. Thus, contrary to a view expressed earlier, the author now feels that the long-wavelength component corresponds to the $3d$ group of states and the short wavelength component to the $4s$ state.

Henning[16] has observed the spectrum in the region from 600 to 900 Å from which he was able to deduce the rather rough, third ionization potential. Absorption coefficients have been measured by Astoin[1] and by Astoin, Johannin-Gilles and Vodar[2] in the region from 1000 to 160 Å. The results of Astoin are shown in Fig. 6. There are many sharp bands in the region and also several underlying continua. A discontinuity in the continuum at about 370 Å has been attributed to the increased probability of ionization at this energy and corresponds to the fourth ionization potential listed in Table 5.

Highly precise data seem to be lacking on the water vapor spectrum at wavelengths shorter than about 1200 Å indicating that useful further work could be done. Even at the longer wavelengths around 1700 Å, there is still some doubt as to the nature of the spectrum.

Intensity Measurements and Discussion

Both Watanabe and Zelikoff[45] and Wilkinson and Johnston[46] have measured the absorption coefficients in the 1700 Å absorption of water vapor. Johannin-Gilles[23] gives the absorption coefficient as a function of the pressure. Even though these workers do not agree as to the exact nature of the absorption, the results do agree to about 20 per cent. Watanabe and Zelikoff have also measured absorption coefficients as far as 1060 Å. Their results agree with that of Preston[34] who gives a single value at 1215 Å. At shorter wavelengths, measurements have been made by Astoin[1] (160 to 1000 Å) and by Astoin et al.[2] (200 to 500 Å).

The band at 1220 Å stands out as a particularly useful absorption for the measurement of water vapor concentrations. In the first place, the "wing" at the short wavelength side of this band overlaps the very strong Lyman α line of

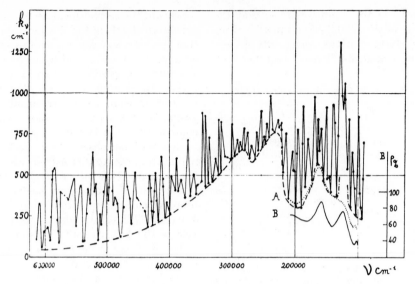

Fig. 6. Absorption of water vapor in the region 1000 to 160 Å (after Astoin[1]).

atomic hydrogen at 1215.67 Å. At this wavelength the absorption is strong ($k = 390$ cm^{-1}). In the second place, the band is diffuse and there will be no complications due to apparent changes in absorption coefficient if instruments of modest resolving power are used. Furthermore, the atmosphere is comparatively transparent at this wavelength so that only small corrections will have to be made for the presence of oxygen and nitrogen, etc. An instrument using the absorption of Lyman α by water vapor has been described by Garton, Webb and Wildy[14] who claimed a sensitivity of the order of 1 ppm in the detection of water vapor in samples of nitrogen at a path length of about 100 cm.

References

1. Astoin, N., *C.R. Acad. Sci.*, **242**, 2327 (1956).
2. Astoin, N., Johannin-Gilles, A. and Vodar, B., *C.R. Acad. Sci.*, **237**, 558 (1953).
3. Becker, G. E., and Autler, S. H., *Phys. Rev.*, **70**, 300 (1946).
4. Benedict, W. S., *J. Opt. Soc. Am.*, **47**, 1056 (1957).
5. Benedict, W. S., Claasen, H. H., and Shaw, J. H., *J. Res. Natl. Bur. Std.*, **49**, 91 (1952).
6. Benedict, W. S., and Plyler, E. K., *J. Res. Natl. Bur. Std.*, **46**, 246 (1951).
7. Cross, P. C., Hainer, R. M., and King, G. W., *J. Chem. Phys.*, **12**, 210 (1944).
8. Dalby, F. W., and Nielsen, H. H., *J. Chem. Phys.*, **25**, 934 (1956).
9. Darling, B. T., and Dennison, D. M., *Phys. Rev.*, **57**, 128 (1940).
10. Dieke, G. H., *Z. Physik.*, **57**, 71 (1929).
11. Dressler, K., and Ramsay, D. A., *Phil. Trans. Roy. Soc. London*, **251**, 553 (1959).
12. Ellison, F. O., and Shull, H., *J. Chem. Phys.*, **23**, 2348 (1955).
13. Frost, D. C., and McDowell, C. A., *Can. J. Chem.*, **36**, 39 (1958).
14. Garton, W. R. S., Webb, M. S. W., and Wildy, P. C., *J. Sci. Instr.*, **34**, 496 (1957).
15. Harrison, A. J., Cederholm, B. J., and Coffin, E. M., ONR Final Report, Mount Holyoke College, 1951.
16. Henning, H. J., *Ann. Physik.*, **13**, 599 (1932).
17. Herzberg, G., "Infra Red and Ramon Spectra," New York, D. Van Nostrand Co., 1945.
18. Herzberg, G., and Teller, E., *Z. Physik. Chem.*, **B21**, 410 (1933).
19. Hopfield, J. J., *Phys. Rev.*, **77**, 560 (1950).
20. Howard, J. N., *Proc. I.R.E.*, **47**, 1451 (1959).
21. Howard, J. N., and Garing, J. S., *Infrared Phys.*, **2**, 155 (1962).
22. Iaroslavskii, N. G., and Stanevich, A. E., *Opt. Spectr.*, **6**, 521 (1959).
23. Johannin-Gilles, A., *J. Rech. Centre Natl. Rech. Sci.*, **6**, 205 (1955).
24. Johns, J. W. C., *Can. J. Phys.*, **41**, 209 (1963).
25. King, G. W., Hainer, R. M., and Cross, P. C., *Phys. Rev.*, **70**, 108 (1946).
26. King, G. W., Hainer, R. M., and Cross, P. C., *Phys. Rev.*, **71**, 433 (1947).
27. King, W. C., and Gordy, W., *Phys. Rev.*, **93**, 407 (1954).
28. Kiseleva, M. S., Neporent, B. S., and Fursenkov, V. A., *Opt. Spectr.*, **6**, 522 (1959).
29. La Paglia, S. R., *J. Mol. Spectry.*, **10**, 240 (1963).
30. Mulliken, R. S., *J. Chem. Phys.*, **3**, 506 (1935).
31. Palmer, C. H., *J. Opt. Soc. Am.*, **47**, 367, 1024, 1028 (1957).

32. Palmer, C. H., *J. Opt. Soc. Am.*, **49**, 1139 (1959).
33. Palmer, C. H., *J. Opt. Soc. Am.*, **50**, 1232 (1960).
34. Preston, W. M., *Phys. Rev.*, **57**, 887 (1940).
35. Price, W. C., *J. Chem. Phys.*, **4**, 147 (1936).
36. Price, W. C., and Sugden, T. M., *Trans. Faraday Soc.*, **44**, 108 (1948).
37. Randall, H. M., Dennison, D. M., Ginsburg, M., and Weber, L. R., *Phys. Rev.*, **52**, 160 (1937).
38. Rathenau, G., *Z. Physik.*, **87**, 32 (1933).
39. Townes, C. H., and Merritt, F. R., *Phys. Rev.*, **70**, 558 (1946).
40. Turner, T. E., Hicks, B. L., and Reitwiesner, G., Asymmetric Rotor Eigenvalue Table, Ballistic Research Laboratories Report No. 878. Aberdeen Proving Ground, Maryland, 1953.
41. Van Vleck, J. H., *Phys. Rev.*, **71**, 425 (1947).
42. Van Vleck, J. H., and Weisskopf, V. F., *Rev. Mod. Phys.*, **17**, 227 (1945).
43. Walsh, A. D., *J. Chem. Soc.*, 2260 (1953).
44. Walsh, A. D., *J. phys. radium*, **15**, 501 (1954).
45. Watanabe, K., and Zelikoff, M., *J. Opt. Soc. Am.*, **43**, 753 (1953).
46. Wilkinson, P. G., and Johnston, H. L., *J. Chem. Phys.*, **18**, 190 (1950).

43. Water Vapor Density Measurements Utilizing the Absorption of Vacuum Ultraviolet and Infrared Radiation*

JAMES E. TILLMAN

Massachusetts Institute of Technology, Round Hill Field Station, South Dartmouth, Massachusetts

ABSTRACT

This paper discusses the measurement of water vapor density by measuring the absorption of vacuum-ultraviolet radiation and of infrared radiation. The vacuum-ultraviolet system requires path lengths of 0.069 to 55 cm to cover the saturation vapor pressure range of 30 to 0.038 g/m³ respectively and is capable of providing response times of 0.001 to 1.0 second along with accuracies of ±1.0 to 0.1 per cent of full scale, the exact values depending on the system. The problems of source stability, intensity, spectrum and life are discussed, and several techniques of improving these factors are considered. More research on the spectra of mixtures of hydrogen and inert gases is indicated. The errors due to "background" absorbing gases are quantitatively considered, and automatic compensating techniques are discussed. Deterioration of the system's windows is discussed along with methods of decreasing this deterioration. Various systems are discussed for different applications. A particular configuration of an infrared absorption hygrometer is presented which is capable of being used for short and long path measurements or both simultaneously. Stability and noise measurements on a system possessing inferior characteristics are presented to indicate the expected performance of the configuration discussed. Techniques are considered whereby simultaneous long path measurements can be obtained using several sources and a common detector. An all-electronic system is described which will utilize solid-state light sources being developed.

INTRODUCTION

The major portion of this paper is devoted to a study of the theory of and the practical problems associated with the measurement of water vapor density utilizing absorption techniques in the vacuum ultraviolet portion of the spectrum. Several important practical problems are discussed in detail, and data is presented on several components. One section is devoted to the consideration of systems for several applications and the performance of these systems is predicted. Although it is of secondary importance to this problem, a similar technique of O_2 density measurement in the lower 60 km of the atmosphere is discussed. The last section covers some of the advantages of a certain type of infrared absorption hygrometer and considers a new type of system that will utilize some solid-state light sources recently developed.

THEORY

With reference to Fig. 1, if it is assumed that a collimated monochromatic photon source is available, then the energy remaining after traversing a distance x is

* This work was supported in part by the Meterology Department, U.S. Army Research and Development Activity, Fort Huachuca, Arizona.

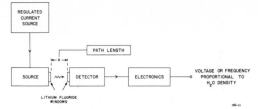

FIG. 1. Single-beam photon absorption water vapor density measuring system.

$$I = I_0 \exp$$

$$-\left(\frac{k_1\rho_1}{\rho_{1_0}} + \frac{k_2\rho_2}{\rho_{2_0}} + \frac{k_3\rho_3}{\rho_{3_0}} + \frac{k_4\rho_4}{\rho_{4_0}} + \ldots\right)x \quad (1)$$

where

I = energy at wavelength λ incident on surface $x_j = x_1$

I_0 = energy at wavelength λ incident on surface $x_j = 0$

k_i = absorption coefficient of ith gas in cm^{-1} at wavelength referred to (STP)[1]

ρ_i = density of ith gas

ρ_{i_0} = density of ith gas at STP (which may be fictitious in some cases)

i = subscript identifying gas

   $1 \to H_2O$, $k_1 = 387$

   $2 \to O_2$, $\;\; k_2 = 0.34$ (slightly pressure sensitive)

   $3 \to CO_2$, $k_3 = 1.97$

   $4 \to O_3$, $\;\; k_4 = 640$

   etc.   for any other gases

x = path length in cm.

For this equation to hold, it is assumed that the processes producing the absorption are such that the k_i are independent of pressure and the presence of other gases. If the source is not monochromatic and emits energy at various wavelengths, Eq. (1) still may be used to determine the absorption due to several gases if the detector's region of wavelength sensitivity encompasses only one of the emitted wavelengths. If there are several wavelengths or if a continuum of wavelengths is emitted by the source, absorbed by the gases, and detected by the detector, then the equation governing the process becomes

$$I = \int_{\lambda_1}^{\lambda_2} I_0(\lambda)\left\{\exp - \left(\frac{k_1(\lambda)\rho_1}{\rho_{1_0}} + \frac{k_2(\lambda)\rho_2}{\rho_{2_0}}\right.\right.$$

$$\left.\left. + \frac{k_3(\lambda)\rho_3}{\rho_{3_0}} + \frac{k_4(\lambda)\rho_4}{\rho_{4_0}} + \ldots\right)x\right\}d\lambda \quad (2)$$

where (λ) indicates that the function is now a function of wavelength, the interval from λ_1 to λ_2 is that wavelength interval in which both emission and detection occur, and I is now the total energy at all wavelengths. The previous assumptions are still necessary, especially the restriction that the $k_i(\lambda)$ are independent of pressure and composition; if the $k_i(\lambda)$ are a function of pressure, then the problem becomes even more complex. To determine the response at the output of the detector, an additional term, the detector's response as a function of wavelength, must be included inside the integral of Eq. (2). In the following discussion, the sole use of (2) will be to qualitatively explore the effects of a non-monochromatic source and of absorption coefficients which vary with wavelength and to determine the degree of accuracy to which Eq. (1) may be employed when the source is not monochromatic. Alternatively, if a given degree of accuracy is desired, Eq. (2) may be used to determine the requisite "spectral purity."

To determine the ease with which the density of a particular gas, ρ_i, may be measured, Eq. (2) should be consulted. As an important example consider the measurement of water vapor for which $i = 1$. First assume that an essentially monochromatic source can be obtained at any wavelength. Then the problem is to determine the wavelength at which

$$\frac{k_1(\lambda)}{k_i(\lambda)} \frac{\rho_1}{\rho_i} \frac{\rho_{i_0}}{\rho_{1_0}}$$

hereafter called the "absolute discrimination ratio" (ADR) is a maximum considering the range of ρ_i over which ρ_1 is to be measured. The value of a system operating at this wavelength will then be determined by the minimum value of the ADR, which is dictated by the minimum ρ_1 and/or the maximum ρ_i. If the ADR is very large for all combinations of ρ_1 and the ρ_i in the range in which ρ_1 is to be measured then the system is essentially sensitive to H_2O alone; however if the ADR is on the order of 100 or less for some combination of ρ_1 and the ρ_i, then the ρ_i must be considered. In measuring H_2O density in the "vacuum ultraviolet" portion of the spectrum,* molecular oxygen, O_2, is the main

* Roughly the region below 3500 Å where 10,000 Å = 1 μ or 10 Å = 1 mμ.

"background" gas affecting the measurement due to its relative density and to its wide range of absorption coefficient, $k_2(\lambda)$; this is illustrated in Fig. 2.[1] Figure 3 shows a plot of $k_1(\lambda)/k_2(\lambda)$, the "relative discrimination ratio" (RDR) *vs* wavelength. The ADR is simply equal to the RDR multiplied by $\rho_1\rho_{2_0}/\rho_2\rho_{1_0}$ and consequently is a maximum at the same wavelength for which the RDR is a maximum.

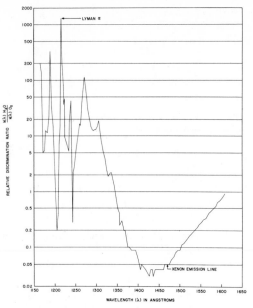

FIG. 3. Relative discrimination ratio *vs* wavelength —abscissa, wavelength, λ; ordinate, RDR.

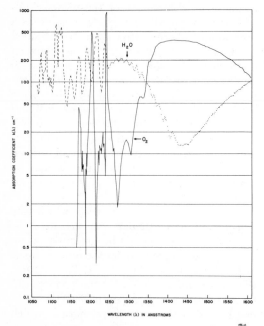

FIG. 2. Absorption coefficients of O_2 and H_2O *vs* wavelength referred to STP, cm^{-1}—abscissa, wavelength in angstroms, (λ); ordinate, absorption coefficient, cm^{-1}, $k(\lambda)$.

Notice that the RDR possesses several maxima, the highest being at 1215.6 Å. Also note that the RDR varies by more than four orders of magnitude in the region shown and that around 1450 Å, it is such that any absorption system would be essentially sensitive to O_2 rather than to H_2O due to the large value of $\rho_2\rho_{1_0}/\rho_1\rho_{2_0}$. This point will be considered later in more detail.

Returning to the immediate practical problem of the measurement of H_2O density, it is a pleasant coincidence that the RDR is maximum at approximately 1215.6 Å since this also happens to be the Lyman α emission line of atomic hydrogen. Another useful fact is that all other members of the Lyman series

(electronic transitions from the orbits of $n = 3$ or higher to the $n = 1$ ground state) are below the short-wavelength cutoff of lithium fluoride, LiF, the only material transparent enough to be used for "windows" in the source and detector.* The next closest emission lines of atomic hydrogen are the Balmer lines (electronic transitions from the orbits $n = 3$ or higher to the $n = 2$ orbit) whose short wavelength limit is 3647 Å. It is quite easy to select a detector whose efficiency essentially drops to zero for wavelengths above 3500 Å or less and whose short-wavelength cutoff is determined by a LiF window. Such detectors will be discussed in detail in later sections. Therefore, it would seem possible to construct a water vapor density measuring device by using a hydrogen discharge tube to produce the hydrogen atomic spectrum and by selecting an appropriate path length and detector. Since at first glance such a system would be sensitive only at Lyman α, its value should be determined by the ADR of the various gases at Lyman α. In the troposphere below 10 km, the ADR suggests that O_2 is the main background gas due to its large density even though its

* Other materials such as CaF_2, MgF_2, Al_2O_3, SiO_2, are transparent only when used in thin films on the order of 1000 Å thick or less.

absorption coefficient is small; the other gases producing even higher ADR's. Furthermore, the effect of O_2 and the other background gases can be reduced either automatically or by a simple correction based on a relatively inaccurate density measurement. Although this will be discussed later in greater detail, it should be mentioned that a total density measurement accurate to ± 10 per cent of sea level density would provide a water vapor density accuracy of ± 0.02 g/m³ (equivalent to a $-55°C$ dew point) as far as background gases are concerned.

SOURCE CHARACTERISTICS

The practical realization of an H_2O density measuring system operating in the vacuum ultraviolet portion of the spectrum is not quite as simple as is suggested by the atomic emission spectrum of hydrogen which is almost the ideal spectrum for such a system. The reason is that when the atomic hydrogen emission spectrum is obtained from a hydrogen glow discharge, additional energy is obtained at adjacent wavelengths due to molecular electronic transitions. Figure 4 illustrates a spectrum which might be considered typical of a pure hydrogen glow discharge or a hydrogen discharge with a small amount of neon present. Figure 5 shows the same source operated at a much higher hydrogen pressure. The pressure is proportional to the flow since this is a windowless discharge operating from a tank of hydrogen and discharging into a vacuum system. The wavelength is given in angstrom units, and to obtain the actual intensity incident on the

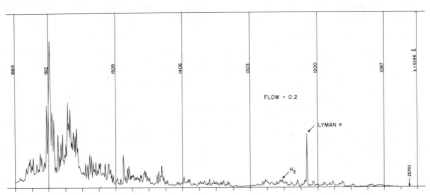

Fig. 4. Spectrum of low-pressure hydrogen glow discharge—abscissa, wavelength, λ; ordinate, relative intensity.

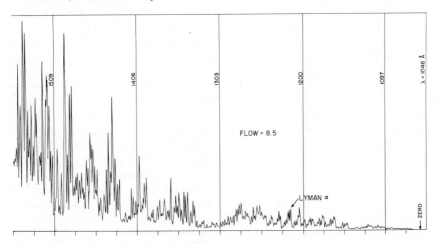

Fig. 5. Spectrum of high-pressure hydrogen glow discharge—abscissa, wavelength, λ; ordinate, relative intensity.

detector, a correction must be made for the decreasing transmission with decreasing wavelength of a lithium fluoride window which preceeds the detector. Note the significant increase in the atomic emission relative to the molecular electronic emission with decreasing pressure. This is due to an increase in electron and/or gas temperature, thereby increasing the percentage of the dissociated hydrogen in the discharge. The temperature is increased since the gas density was reduced while keeping the discharge power essentially constant. Further reduction in pressure would continue to improve the spectrum until the electron and/or ion mean free paths approach the dimensions of the electrodes and/or the minimum internal source tube dimensions. These effects will not be discussed since the relevant information is available in several books on glow discharge processes [2, 10, 11] and because there are other simple methods of obtaining the desired spectrum.

Since the undesirable emission is produced by hydrogen molecular electronic transitions while the desired emission is due to an atomic transition, an increase in the atomic to molecular hydrogen ratio should improve the spectrum. There are several methods of increasing this ratio such as thermally heating the discharge, increasing the power density and using buffer gases. Thermal heating of the discharge with a cathode has several distinct advantages over the other techniques if it is possible to produce the required ratio of atomic to molecular hydrogen. One advantage is that higher hydrogen pressures can be used than in a pure hydrogen low discharge of similar atomic-to-molecular ratio, thereby decreasing the problems due to cleanup of the hydrogen in the source. Another advantage is that the voltages required to operate a thermally heated discharge generally are an order of magnitude or more lower than those required for an unheated glow discharge. A disadvantage is that the addition of a filament and cathode would further complicate the structure of the source, and it is also possible that the operation of a filament in hydrogen at the temperatures necessary to produce a high degree of dissociation (80 per cent at 2800°K and approximately 2 mm Hg) may prove difficult.

Increasing the power density to increase the ratio of atomic to molecular hydrogen would eventually result in the source operating in the abnormal glow or arc discharge modes. There are various reasons why these modes are undesirable such as a decrease in the short- and long-term stability, higher operating temperatures and sputtering of the electrode materials.

It would appear that with two possible exceptions, a buffered glow discharge consisting of hydrogen and an inert buffer gas is the simplest method of producing an essentially pure atomic emission spectrum. Figure 6 shows the emission spectrum of a tank of commercial grade argon using a source which is essentially the same as that used to produce the previous hydrogen spectra. The discharge power was probably within 20 per cent of that in the case of hydrogen, and the pressure was within the range illustrated in the two previous spectra. The emission lines are identified by element, argon, nitrogen, oxygen and hydrogen being the only elements observed. Since the latter three elements were only impurities in the argon, it should be safe to assume that they constitute 1 per cent or less of the total gas. Other tanks of argon have produced similar spectra. Note the almost complete absence of the H_2 emission spectrum, there being a few lines which cannot be positively identified and which therefore could be H_2. However, these lines are almost three orders of magnitude less intense than Lyman α. To allow the Lyman α line to remain on the chart, the sensitivity of the electronics was reduced 30 times in the region surrounding Lyman α. This is indicated by the full scale photomultiplier current, i, shown at the top of the chart, which is 3×10^{-8} for the Lyman α region and 0.1×10^{-8} A for the rest of the region above 1066 Å. The intensities of several lines are indicated, and there are no lithium fluoride windows in the light beam. Note the two argon lines at 1048 and 1066 Å. Using the same power, it has been observed that the intensity of the buffered discharge is equal to or greater than that of a pure hydrogen discharge at Lyman α. Some argon buffered discharges have produced an order of magnitude of more intensity in the Lyman α line than a pure hydrogen discharge operating under similar conditions.

The first reason for this spectrum is that the relatively low density of hydrogen implies

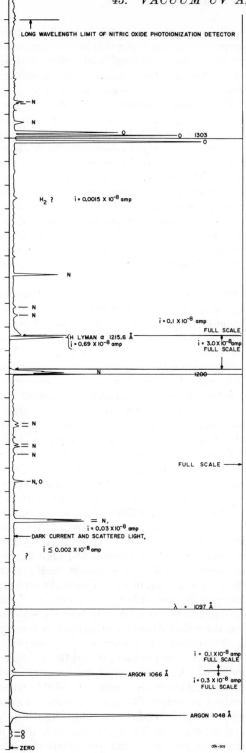

FIG. 6. Spectrum of argon-hydrogen, oxygen, nitrogen glow discharge — abscissa, intensity; ordinate, wavelength, λ.

that most collisions of hydrogen atoms will be with the inert gas and not with another hydrogen atom; therefore, once the molecule has dissociated, the probability of recombination is small. A second reason for the spectrum is that argon possesses metastable energy states which release their energy upon colliding with a hydrogen molecule.[2] This energy is adequate to dissociate a hydrogen molecule but inadequate to ionize either a hydrogen atom or molecule. Therefore, the molecular hydrogen is readily dissociated, and once dissociation has occurred, it is quite difficult for recombination to take place. Other inert gases have metastable states, but no quantitative information is available on the spectra there. A cylinder of neon was also tried but the H_2 emission spectrum was quite readily observed in this discharge. It must be emphasized that the proper combination of gases and pressure is yet to be determined which will provide the most efficient Lyman α source while removing the undesirable lines. The hydrogen-argon spectrum shown is quite satisfactory with the exception of the line at 1066 Å. Because the absorption coefficient of oxygen is 81 at this wavelength, at atmospheric pressure this line would be reduced by two or more orders of magnitude when the path length is long enough for measurements below 9.4 g/m^3 (saturation at $+10°C$) and when typical lithium fluoride windows are used.* However, for higher water vapor densities where shorter paths should be used, other techniques may be required to eliminate this line. Some of these techniques will be discussed in the section on windows and filters. If neon proves to be as effective as argon as a buffer gas, then the problem is solved since it has no emission lines in the wavelength region of interest. In a radio-frequency excited discharge, helium was used as a buffer gas almost completely suppressing the molecular spectrum.[3] However, it is necessary to determine the intensity of two He II lines at 1215.09 and 1215.17 Å before the value of helium as a buffer gas can be determined, since the absorption coefficient at 1215.0 Å is approximately twice the value at 1215.67 Å.[4] The intensity of these lines should be low since singly ionized emission lines should rarely appear in a glow discharge due to its low

* The transmission of LiF will be covered later.

temperature. In the case of oxygen and nitrogen, the un-ionized lines are quite strong while no singly ionized lines have been observed. Other evidence would support this conjecture, but a spectographic study is in order. It should be mentioned that various glasses are fairly permeable to helium as are some metals with respect to hydrogen.

The previously mentioned radio-frequency discharge has an advantage over other discharges in that it allows a source to be constructed without any internal electrodes; consequently the problems associated with electrode sputtering, contamination and cathode work function variation are eliminated. However, it is more difficult to regulate the intensity of a radio-frequency discharge. The radio-frequency discharge in the aforementioned paper produced an intensity at Lyman α of at least 10^{15} photons/sec.

The second major criticism of the buffered discharge is that it probably would operate at a lower hydrogen pressure and consequently have a shorter life due to "cleanup" of the hydrogen. To offset this effect, an increased buffer gas pressure and/or a more carefully constructed source may be required. However, the importance of this problem cannot be determined until quantitative data is obtained on the spectral purity vs buffer gas composition and relative density.

The problem of hydrogen "cleanup" may be solved by using a mixture of uranium and uranium hydride as a hydrogen source.* This mixture has the property of providing a constant hydrogen pressure at a constant temperature which is essentially independent of composition over a wide range of composition.[5] An additional advantage is that the free uranium reacts with any non-inert gas in the source thereby removing impurities from the source. The main disadvantage of such a source is that some method of heating the U-UH$_3$ mixture must be provided. The degree of temperature regulation of the heater required to produce a given intensity stability remains to be determined. However, a dual beam technique to be described later is capable of removing these variations as long as the power applied to the source remains within the

limits in which the source will operate properly. It should be possible to compensate for pressure variations and other factors which would otherwise cause the source intensity to vary by at least a factor of five.

One major assumption in the preceding sections is that the beam emerging from the source is collimated. The degree of collimation determines the degree of accuracy with which Beer's law predicts the absorption vs density and path length. Unfortunately, little is known about the degree of collimation of the present sources and whether or not they can be collimated with the proper optics. None of the sources previously used have possessed the required spectral purity to determine how well they followed Beer's law by absorption measurements, and no known measurements have been made on the distribution of intensity vs angle of the sources. In a single-beam system, the degree of collimation is not important if an empirical calibration or a function more complex than Beer's law incorporating the angular intensity distribution is satisfactory. However, there remains a question as to how appropriate some of the dual-beam techniques (to be described later) are when the source is not well collimated. An important reason for striving for a well-collimated source is that such a source of the required spectral purity can be used to construct an instrument that could easily be the best secondary standard of humidity measurements since its operation is based on a simple mathematical formula requiring only the knowledge of several physical constants. These constants have been measured to a fair degree of accuracy, and the instrument itself allows the determination of these constants with an accuracy limited only by the accuracy of the system and the primary standard. Once these constants are known, the absorption vs density is determined by a simple zero absorption calibration, the path length and the measurement of any background gas density and pressure, if the latter is necessary to obtain the desired accuracy. The zero absorption measurement can be made by flushing the path with dry nitrogen which is transparent for all practical purposes, and the relatively low absorption by background gases simplifies the measurement of these gases. It should be mentioned that the absorption coefficient of

---

* Such sources were constructed by Dr. H. E. Hinteregger of Air Force Cambridge Research Laboratories until 1956.

O_2 is slightly pressure-sensitive, thereby requiring the measurement of density and pressure or correcting for this effect.[4] In a later section, a technique will be discussed which may be capable of automatically compensating for the background gases encountered in the lower troposphere. Collimation can be accomplished by restricting the aperture of the detector if the intensity loss is permissible. Such a system, provided with a small removable aperture is capable of self-calibration when there is a question as to how well Beer's law applies using the maximum aperture. Calibration would be accomplished by measuring the intensity with the aperture inserted and with it removed for each value of dry air and/or water vapor density including a zero absorption value provided by an atmosphere of dry nitrogen. In the small aperture case, the absorption should be accurately predicted given the dry air density and water vapor density. If the system works well in both cases, the I/I_0 should be identical at each value of air and water vapor density.

WINDOWS AND FILTERS

The previous discussions assume that there are no problems such as the formation of a thin film of water and/or other material on the surface of the window. However, it is quite obvious that some surface reaction takes place when the transmission of various lithium fluoride windows is investigated with respect to surface treatment and exposure to the atmosphere. Uchida, Kato, and Matsui have shown that at Lyman α the transmission of a freshly cleaved sample of LiF dropped from 78 per cent to 48 per cent after a ten-day exposure to the atmosphere and to 43 per cent after an additional 12-day exposure.[6] Additional information may be obtained by studying the data in Table 1 which were obtained by the author and Dr. W. J. Scouler of M.I.T. Lincoln Laboratory; all measurements are at Lyman α. Note that the transmission is increased by approximately 20 per cent by heating to 550 or 600°C. Tests on other crystals from the same batch have produced similar results as long as the temperature exceeded 500°C. However, notice the maximum transmission *vs* temperature as shown in Table 2. The results might be explained by the presence of a film of lithium hydroxide: melting point

TABLE 1. HISTORY OF WINDOW SAMPLE No. 11; SIZE ½″ × ½″ BY APPROXIMATELY 2 MM THICK

	Transmission	Date
Removed from package about 2 years after purchase	.559	4/9/63
Heated to approximately 550°C in air, placed in vacuum system within 30 min.	.766	4/17/63
30 min. later under vacuum	.759	
Removed from vacuum and placed in desiccator		
Possibly exposed to high humidity while being used as a control sample along with other crystals which were being coated with thin films	.584	5/7/63
Approximately 1 hour later under vacuum	.568	
Removed from desiccator	.557	5/13/63
Still under vacuum	.549	5/14/63
Heated to 600°C, ½ hour in air	.758	5/14/63
In vacuum, liquid nitrogen trapped	.749	5/15/63
Desiccator 10 days later	.591	5/25/63

510°C. If the film were adsorbed water, it might be expected that temperatures on the order of two to three hundred degrees centigrade essentially would remove most of the water, although it is possible that the bonding energy of the adsorbed water film might be high enough to require temperatures on the order of 500°C or above for its removal. The fact that the transmission dropped significantly when the crystal was in a desiccator at a fairly low pressure is probably due to pump oil vapor or other contaminants.

TABLE 2. TRANSMISSION CHANGE OF SAMPLES *vs* TEMPERATURE

Sample No.	10	11	12	13	16
Temperature, °C	500	550	520	460	600
Time		several hours			½ hour
Before heating	.459	.559	.586	.476	.487
After heating	.678	.766	.776	.613	.755

Another disturbing possibility is that the thickness of any adsorbed water vapor film might fluctuate as the humidity fluctuates around 100 per cent RH at temperatures on the order of 0 to 20°C. First, this could cause the system response to deviate from the theoretically predicted absorption, and second, it could increase the response time to the time required by the film to reach equilibrium. The latter could be the dominant factor in the response time, since the limitations imposed by the source intensity, detector efficiency and the electronics suggest that the time required to provide a measurement accurate to within 1.0 per cent is on the order of 0.03 to 0.001 second. Therefore, a careful investigation of the nature of any surface films and techniques for reducing them and/or their detrimental effects is in order. Such experiments are planned since the equipment constructed to measure the crystal transmission can also be used to determine these surface effects by the admission of various mixtures of water vapor density and dry air density.* However, precautions must be taken so that the surface effects on the cell windows are not misinterpreted as surface effects on the window samples being studied. The actual quantitative effects of the variable window transmission may not be as large as has been implied and possibly may not be important in many applications if zero checks can be carried out every hour or so. The fact that the percentage transmission change seems to decrease with time may be considered favorable in that the transmission may approach some minimum or at least drop logarithmically thereby requiring less frequent calibration with increasing time. In addition, if the aging is identical for various windows, a dual beam technique to be described later can compensate for this effect.

It is possible that many of the window problems may be solved by coating the lithium fluoride with a thin film of some other material. Some of the possible advantages of using coated windows are: (1) a reduction in the hydrolysis of the window, (2) a decrease in the adsorption of water, (3) a mechanically tougher and more stable surface capable of being cleaned, and (4) high differential transmission ratios at 1215.6 and 1066 Å. Because other materials of 1-mm thickness are essentially opaque at Lyman α, the coatings must be quite thin (on the order of 20 to 1000 Å thick) and the short wavelength transmission limit must be as low as possible. Some of the materials that may be satisfactory are CaF_2,

MgF_2, Al_2O_3, MgO and SiO_2. Films of CaF_2, MgF_2 and Al_2O_3 have been deposited on LiF windows, and their transmissions have been measured, producing values of 15 to 35 per cent at Lyman α, while in some cases reducing the transmission at 1066 Å (the aforementioned argon emission line) by a factor of 20. Because no data has been obtained on water adsorption properties and because the exact nature of the surface film and any contaminants is unknown, none of the data obtained is presented. However, it is expected that higher transmission can be obtained with Al_2O_3 and MgF_2 since the set of crystals coated with CaF_2 at the same time as the above coatings produced a much lower transmission than previous crystals coated with CaF_2. Also, sample No. 11 was used as a control when the crystals were removed from the laboratory to be coated by a commercial firm, and its transmission dropped 20 per cent in the process. The main objective of these coatings was to determine if any of these materials could be deposited and if the transmission was adequate to merit further investigation. Considering the relevant factors, all of the materials look promising, and additional work is planned in an effort to obtain the maximum transmission and surface stability.

There is one additional problem concerning the long-term stability of any window and/or coatings; it is the reduction of transmission in the ultraviolet by the "solarization" of the windows due to the ultraviolet radiation and by exposure to an electron beam and/or glow discharge.[3, 7] The transmission loss is proportional to the total flux and is related to wavelength. A drastic decrease in transmission is usually accompanied by a visible change in the color, a good crystal appearing colorless. At the present, the exact mechanism is open to question and could be due to either impurities and/or a change in the crystal structure. In the case of radiation-induced changes, the original transmission can be restored by heating while the same does not always hold for glow-discharge-induced changes. Consequently, it is advisable to keep the discharge away from the window. Similar problems might be expected for any thin coatings applied to the LiF windows.

In several places, the ratio of transmission at 1215.6 Å to that at 1066 Å (an argon emis-

* The system excluding the absorption cells and window transmission measuring portions were designed by Dr. Scouler and have proven capable of maintaining an intensity stability of ± 0.2 per cent or better for periods of a half hour or greater.

sion line) has been mentioned. If argon is to be used in the source as a buffer gas, it is obvious that this ratio should be as large as possible so that either the window and/or the oxygen would essentially eliminate the line. As previously mentioned, the proper choice of window coating and thickness might provide a high ratio. It is desirable to eliminate as much of the background radiation as possible before it reaches the absorption path where it may cause the concentration of products of photochemical reactions to reach undesirably high values when the flow is zero. Another method is to use some other filter such as a gas or combination of gases. Oxygen is a first obvious choice since it could easily reduce the 1066 Å line by many orders of magnitude while only reducing the Lyman α line by a few per cent. However, the main trouble with this technique is that the photodecomposition of O_2 and the possible formation of O_3 may also reduce the efficiency of such a process. The addition of other transparent "buffer" gases to the filter may reduce the O_3 formation, but the actual value of O_2 as a filter remains to be determined. In a laboratory system where dry air could be continually flowing through the filter, photochemical reactions may be ignored. Another possible filter gas is argon. If the 1066 Å line is the result of a transition from a high energy level to a stable state, then the gas should also absorb this line. Although this technique is quite effective in this region for some inert gases, its value in the case of argon remains to be determined. Other filter gases may be used, but these are also susceptible to photochemical reactions in this portion of the spectrum.

DETECTORS

The detector problem, excluding the window, essentially has been solved since several satisfactory detectors are commercially available which previously were laboratory and/or specially modified commercial items. The simplest detector is the nitric oxide, NO, photoionization chamber previously developed by the Naval Research Laboratory. These devices are sensitive from 1050 Å (limited by the LiF window) to 1353 Å (the long-wavelength limit of photoionization in NO)

and possess typical quantum efficiencies* of from 0.1 to 0.5 at lyman α. The response time of this detector is presently unknown but probably is on the order of 0.001 seconds. The only equipment required to utilize these detectors is a bias supply (a small battery is excellent) of 10 to 50 V and a current measuring system; the current measuring system generally would be an electrometer due to the low currents to be measured (10^{-7} to 10^{-12}A). Several electrometers are commercially available which are quite adequate for most applications; some of these units are capable of producing a logarithmic function of the input.** If the optimum response time and/or ruggedness are desired, the work of Praglin and Nichols should be consulted.[8] They suggest that a response time of 0.1 to 0.03 can be obtained with a sensitivity of 10^{-12}A.

Photomultipliers sensitive only in the vacuum ultraviolet also make excellent detectors in some applications. Some devices have been prepared with quantum efficiencies of 10 to 30 per cent at Lyman α and 10^{-4} to 10^{-8} at 2500 Å or higher.[9] This paper also presents data on the quantum efficiency and the spectral response of photodiodes, which should also apply to photomultipliers, with photocathodes of the same material. The photomultiplier output can be measured by measuring the current at the anode (providing an analog output) or by measuring the output pulses due to individual photoelectrons (providing a digital output). The former method requires a carefully regulated power supply since the photomultiplier gain is proportional to a high power of the power supply voltage, while the latter method would require a high-speed counter if it is desirable to obtain rapid response and accuracy simultaneously. An advantage of the analog output of the photomultiplier is that currents on the order of μA to 1mA (as opposed to $\mu\mu$A for the NO detector) can be obtained thereby eliminating the need for an electrometer-type current measuring device. The advantage of the digital technique is that a dynamic range of 10^4 could be covered with an accuracy of 1 to

* The quantum efficiency of a device is defined as the number of photoelectrons produced per incident photon; it ranges from 0.0 to 1.0.

** For example, Keithley Instruments Inc., 12415 Euclid Ave., Cleveland 6, Ohio.

0.01 per cent using a measuring time of 1.0 second; various compromises can be made in the dynamic range, accuracy and measuring time depending on the applications. The accuracy of the digital system following the detector generally is ± 1 part in 10^6 to 10^9 per day ± 1 count. The maximum counting rate is limited by the counters available (10^8/sec) and the transit time of the photomultiplier (10^{-6} to 10^{-9} second depending on construction and voltage).

Because of the high work function of the photocathode materials used in these devices, the "dark current" (in the analog mode) or the noise pulses (in the digital mode), produced by thermal electrons, cosmic rays, radioactive contaminants in the device and other similar "noise" sources, are equivalent to an input flux of 5 to 50 photons/sec. Such background noise can be ignored in most applications since typical sources produce a Lyman α flux of 10^8 to 10^{10} photons/sec depending on the gases used, power level, source construction and system geometry.

SCATTERING

An examination of the error due to scattering by aerosols and/or liquid water drops shows that it always is less than 2 per cent and generally would be from one to two orders of magnitude less. The 2 per cent figure assumes a path length of 8 cm, (a length appropriate for measurements of dew points of $-30°C$ or less)* a particle diameter of 10^{-5} cm (Aitken nuclei), and a density of 4×10^6 particles cm^{-3} (an extremely high value in any location). Since such a concentration rarely would occur except in a heavily industrialized area at or near the ground, it is highly unlikely that such a low dew point would be observed in the same place at the same time. A path length of 0.8 cm (appropriate for a dew point of $-10°C$) would reduce the effect to 0.2 per cent. Fog with a liquid water content of 0.3 g/m^3 and a drop size of 1 to 10 μ would produce an error of 0.004 per cent or less on a system with 0.4-cm path length (appropriate length for dew points of 0°C or higher). Smaller drop radii are highly unlikely. Consequently, it is evident that scattering (particulate absorption is con-

* The appropriate path length *vs* density will be covered later.

sidered as a part of the scattering loss) can be ignored in most applications. Scattering may become significant in the measurement of small variations in a relatively high water vapor density; such measurements are often important in the study of turbulence in the atmospheric boundary layer and in the propagation of electromagnetic radiation.

SYSTEMS

Considering the present state of the art in vacuum-ultraviolet technology, it does not appear reasonable to expect that one type of system can be constructed which is the optimum system for all applications. For example, a dual-beam system consisting of a reference path and a measuring path probably would be superior to any single-beam system except when size, weight and cost were major factors. Also, the particular application would determine whether or not some simple operational procedure and a relatively simple system could be substituted for a more complex automatic system. For example, if a dry air reference sample periodically could be introduced in the sampling path, a single-beam system might well be more desirable than a more complex dual-beam system. Also, if the system need not operate for more than an hour or two (as in a radiosonde application), then a significant reduction in size, weight and cost may be possible. As a general rule, the cost should be directly related to the accuracy, reliability and response time required and the range of variables encountered, while it should be related inversely to the size, weight, and calibration frequency. The selection of a good or the optimum system for a given application requires a detailed set of requirements and an intimate knowledge of all of the factors concerning the system. Although the present state of the art does not provide adequate information to construct the optimum system for a given application, it is possible to outline systems that will be adequate in many applications. Enough information is available so that no major unforeseen problems should arise. Further insight into the problems may be gained by considering the construction of a single-beam system. In the follwing discussions, it will be assumed that the total emission at wavelengths other then Lyman α is less than 0.1 per cent of that at Lyman α.

First, the influence of the path length on the measurements should be considered. Table 3

TABLE 3

T(°C)	P(mb)	ρ(g/m³)	x(cm)	$\dfrac{k_1\rho_1}{\rho_{1_0}}$	$\dfrac{k_2\rho_2}{\rho_{2_0}}$
Saturated over Water					
+40	73.78	51.19	0.0407	24.6	0.0619
+30	42.43	30.38	0.069	14.6	0.0640
+20	23.37	17.30	0.121	8.32	0.0662
+10	12.27	9.40	0.221	4.52	0.0686
0	6.11	4.85	0.429	2.33	0.0711
−10	2.86	2.36	0.885	1.33	0.0738
−20	1.25	1.07	1.94	.515	0.0767
Saturated over ice					
−10	2.60	2.14	0.971	1.03	0.0738
−20	1.03	0.884	2.35	0.425	0.0767
−30	0.38	0.338	6.21	0.162	0.0798
−40	0.128	0.119	18.20	0.057	0.083
−50	0.039	0.038	55.5	0.018	0.087

lists the saturation vapor pressure and saturation density *vs* temperature along with the path length necessary to reduce the light intensity by $1/e$ due to water vapor absorption alone at saturation. The columns headed $k_1\rho_1/\rho_{1_0}$ and $k_2\rho_2/\rho_{2_0}$ indicate how much of the absorption is due to water vapor and oxygen, respectively, assuming a dry air pressure of 760 mm Hg and computing the dry air density at STP (760 mm and 0°C). Note that the two absorptions are equivalent at about −35°C. If the range of water vapor density is relatively small and the maximum signal-to-noise ratio and response time are desired, then an appropriate path length is the value indicated. Longer path lengths would drastically decrease the signal since the absorption is an exponential function of density, while shorter path lengths would require exceptional source stability due to the reduced intensity change per unit density change. With a slight compromise, it should be possible to satisfy most requirements by providing two or three automatically selected path lengths. If a wide range must be covered with few or no changes in path length, then a logarithmic amplifier (in an analog system) and a reasonable compromise in path length may suffice. Generally, this combination sacrifices response time or accuracy, or it necessitates a much more intense source. In an attended ground installation, where the path

length could be changed when necessary and a dry air sample can be periodically inserted, a system consisting of a single beam source, nitric oxide detector and electrometer should be satisfactory. If the source is well collimated (which should be possible since any intensity loss necessary could be counteracted by decreasing the response time) and the optimum path length is chosen, the error should be less than 0.25 per cent of full scale 99 per cent of the time, assuming (1) a source intensity of 2×10^7 photons/sec (many orders of magnitude below the maximum obtainable), (2) that the noise is due exclusively to the random photon generation process,* (3) a detector quantum efficiency of 0.2, (4) $1/e$ absorption due to water vapor, (5) O_2 absorption corrected, and (6) a response time of one second. For a random photon generation process, the noise is inversely proportional to the square root of time. Although many other types of single-beam systems can be constructed using logarithmic electronics or a digital type readout, more intense sources, etc, the rest of the discussion will center on the dual-beam system.

Figure 7 shows a particular type dual-beam system in which the output of the reference detector is part of a feed back loop which regulates the source intensity.** If it is assumed that the path lengths are identical, the detectors and current standard are stable, the intensities of the two beams remain identical with changes, the feedback loop gain is 10^5 or more, and the measuring amplifier is stable, then it can be shown that the system compensates for source intensity changes, variation in the feedback amplifier gain, and variations in the dry air absorption if the

* It has been observed that the source constructed for spectrographic use is limited by random photon noise when it is operating properly.

** As far as is known, Dr. H. E. Hinteregger and others of Air Force Cambridge Research Laboratories constructed the first ultraviolet dual-beam sources. This information was obtained from other members of the laboratory, and a copy of an unpublished paper was obtained from Dr. Hinteregger. This paper contains much excellent information on the techniques of vacuum-ultraviolet water vapor measurements, and it would appear that components of the quality constructed by this group have not since been duplicated. As is often the case, the aforementioned report was not obtained until these investigations had been in progress for several years.

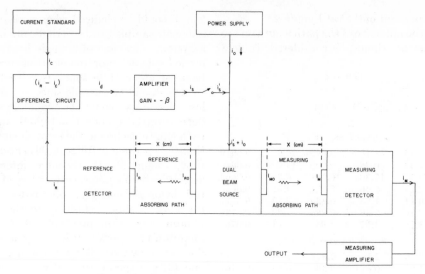

Fig. 7. Dual-beam absorption measuring system.

reference path is filled with dry air of the same density as that of the measuring path.* Although it has been completed, the proof of this statement will not be given since it would occupy too much space with equations; however, a qualitative explanation is in order: i_0 supples the main source current and i'_s (or i_s when the feedback loop is closed) supplies a correction current. If the source tries to increase in intensity, the difference circuit generates a signal which is amplified and which tends to reduce the current to the source. Similarly, a decrease in source intensity would be compensated for by an increase in i'_s. The same action takes place if the reference path transmission or the detector sensitivity varies As long as the amplifier gain, β, is high, variations in it have little effect. Therefore, this system can be used to compensate for dry air absorption and source instability. If a dry air correction is obtained in some other manner and if the reference path is open to the atmosphere and is made much shorter than the measuring path, then this system can compensate for window adsorption assuming that the effects are similar on all of the windows. If a reasonably intense source is constructed (e.g., 10^{10} photons/sec), it should be possible to construct a system with a response time of 0.001 second and a peak to peak noise level of

* In actual practice the reference path may contain dry air with a density equal to the total air density without producing a significant error.

1 per cent or less of full scale assuming that the path length has been optimized. If a slower response is acceptable, a longer path and/or greater accuracy may be obtained.

DENSITY CORRECTION AND MEASUREMENT

Previously, the necessity of some form of density measurement has been mentioned so that a correction for the absorption by O_2 can be made when measuring low water vapor densities. This section describes an absorption measuring system which is capable of satisfying the above requirement and, in addition, is capable of measuring O_2 density from the surface to 60 km (above which the path length becomes excessive) with little or no absorption by background gases. The components for this system are much easier to construct than those for the Lyman α measurements and probably can be purchased commercially. Returning to Fig. 3, notice that the RDR at 1469.6 Å (an emission line of xenon) is appropriate for the measurement of O_2. In addition either the coefficients and/or the densities of the following "background" gases are such that they may be ignored below 80 km: these gases are N_2, CO_2, H_2O, NO, N_2O, O_3, O, and N. The absorption coefficient of NO_2 is approximately 300, while its density is unavailable and the coefficient of xenon is unknown; it is doubtful that either would contribute any significant absorption.

For this system, the source would be a xenon glow discharge tube and the detector would be an ethylene sulphide photoionization cell.[12] The rest of the system would be similar to those used to measure water vapor. The source should be much more predictable and reliable since the only gas would be xenon and a uranium "getter" could be used. It is hoped that the details of this device can be published later since it can essentially be built from commercially available components.

Summary

The relevant physics and some of the technical problems associated with water vapor measurements in the vacuum ultraviolet have been considered in detail. The use of single- and dual-beam systems has been considered, and some suggestions have been made as to the components that may be appropriate in various applications. The major problems have been considered in detail and several possible solutions have been suggested. Work is continuing on these problems as time permits, and it is expected that a detailed report of this work will be published incorporating many of the techniques suggested herein.

AN INFRARED ABSORPTION HYGROMETER CAPABLE OF CLOSED-PATH, OPEN-PATH OR SEVERAL SIMULTANEOUS OPEN-PATH MEASUREMENTS

The purpose of this section is to point out several major advantages inherent in a specific configuration of an infrared absorption hygrometer. No general discussion of these devices will be given since the fundamentals are covered by other papers in this volume although certain limitations of these devices will be mentioned. Also, some advanced systems will be outlined which depend on recent advances in the field of solid-state photon sources.

Figure 8 shows schematically the major features of the device to be described. This design evolved from the desire to eliminate the problems associated with the wobbling filter and the segmented filter type hygrometers. It is assumed that a collimated light source is available, the degree of collimation determining the maximum path length for a given source intensity, accuracy, and response time. The beam is divided into two almost equal-intensity beams by a beam splitter and

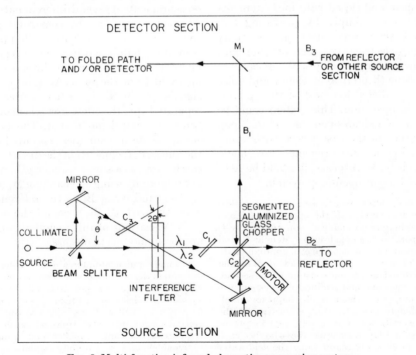

FIG. 8. Multi-function infrared absorption measuring system.

passes through the interference filter at normal incidence and at angle θ. (C_1, C_2 and C_3 should be ignored since they are only used for visual alignment.) The output wavelengths λ_1 and λ_2 are determined by the nature of the interference filter and the angle θ. Next, the two beams are directed to the segmented aluminized glass chopper wheel driven by a synchronous motor. The chopper consists of alternating wedges of aluminized glass and clear glass, and the beams are adjusted so that they coincide at the chopper disc. If an aluminum segment is in the beam, then λ_1 is reflected along beam B_1 and λ_2 is reflected along beam B_2. Conversely, if a clear glass segment is in the beam, then λ_1 passes through it and along B_2 and λ_2 also passes through and along B_1. (A portion of each wavelength also is reflected from the glass, and if this signal proves troublesome, an all metal chopper could be used.) If a closed-path measurement is desired, then B_1 is used and mirror M_1 is inserted. If an open-path measurement is desired, the B_2 is used along with a corner reflector and M_1 is removed to allow the reflected beam B_3 to enter the detector. Alternatively, the detector could be removed to the other end of the path. Finally, simultaneous open- and closed-path measurements can be obtained simply by providing two detectors. If the beam splitter has essentially zero loss (a dielectric type), then either or both measurements can be made with this system with the same theoretical efficiency and noise level as is predicted for most of the systems presently in operation. This system could be operated as either an open- or a closed-loop system except in the case where both open- and closed-path measurements are made simultaneously. In this case, it would have to be operated as an open-loop system.*

* A wobbling filter system with many practical deficiencies associated with the optical layout and wobbling technique (mechanical cam and follower) has been operated as an open-loop system at Round Hill with a peak-to-peak noise level of approximately 0.18 g/m³ of water vapor (independent of actual density measured) and a time constant of one second. When the machine and calibration system are operating properly (which rarely happens simultaneously mainly due to the calibration system), the stability generally is approximately ± 0.05 g/m³ for periods up to one day. Longer tests have not been run due to the problems in maintaining the acid-water bath at a constant water vapor density and due to

This system has several advantages that are not found in most other systems used for water vapor measurement. Probably the major advantage of this system is that it can be used for long open- or closed-path measurements or for both simultaneously. Second, the wavelength deviation can be made large enough so that one wavelength is in the band center and the other is out of the band. In the wobbling filter system, this is difficult to accomplish reliably and with a high frequency. However, this criticism in not very important in a closed-loop system if the noise level is adequately low. The fact that this system uses one filter as opposed to two or more in the segmented filter wheel type of instrument may be an advantage. However, additional optics are required for this system. Third, the response time of this open-loop system is limited only by the chopping frequency and/or the system noise level whereas the closed-loop systems have either thermally or mechanically limited response times. With the proper source and a closed-path system, a time constant of 0.05 second should be obtainable with a peak-to-peak noise of 0.1 g/m³ or less. The final advantage that will be mentioned is that this system can be modified to make simultaneous measurements at several different path lengths. This is accomplished by constructing several source sections, each with a chopper wheel containing a different number of segments. If all of the motors are synchronous and are operated from the same AC power, then the signals produced by each source can be separated in the detector electronics and synchronously demodulated. The number of simultaneous measurements is only limited by the number of segments in the disc. The system can be used as a single-wavelength, dual-path instrument by using λ_1, changing M_1 to a beam splitter, and using B_1 as the reference signal while the path B_2, B_3 becomes the measuring path. Variations of this technique and others are too numerous to discuss.

occasional component failures in the system (batteries are used in the present all solid-state amplifiers). This should illustrate the potential of the open-loop system which has several advantages over the closed-loop system such as faster response time and/or a constant light intensity. However, such a system requires a constant amplifier gain (quite easily obtainable) and a carefully stabilized detector sensitivity (i.e. temperature).

One of the major problems of the infrared is associated with the source intensity. The life of any black-body radiator limits the energy per unit area obtainable by increasing the temperature. Consequently, the only other method of increasing the available energy is to increase the area of the black body or to increase the angular aperture of the source collimator. If the source area is increased, the collimation suffers. If the collimator lens or mirror area is increased, the beam becomes larger and more difficult to process. Obviously, what is needed is a source which has a greater intensity per unit area than a black body. At the present, the only such device available is a gallium arsenide solid-state photodiode. This diode emits a narrow band of frequencies with a power density per unit wavelength which is greater than the hottest practical black body. Its efficiency and wavelength are a function of temperature, and at room temperature its wavelength is approximately 0.9 μ. However, it has been suggested that any wavelength between 0.9 and 3.0 μ may be obtained by alloying the proper materials, and such devices have been constructed. Furthermore, the intensity of these devices can be electronically modulated at rates of zero to 10^8 cps. Since the sources can be designed for different wavelengths, a system can be designed using two different wavelength devices at the focus of a small optical system. Modulation would then be accomplished by alternately energizing each diode. This system can be extended to multiple path length simultaneous measurements simply by providing several sources modulated at different frequencies and synchronously detected. The source wavelength can be selected to utilize an absorption band suitable for the path-length and density to be measured. In closing, it should be stated that a prototype of the first system is under construction and that a system utilizing the photodiodes will be constructed as soon as they become available.

Acknowledgment. The author wishes to express his appreciation to D. L. Randall and others at the Naval Research Laboratory for their kindness in supplying some components for the vacuum-ultraviolet portion of this work. Thanks are due to Professor D. P. Keily of the Massachusetts Institute of Technology, Meteorology Department, for his advice and encouragement on this problem, to Dr. William Scouler of Lincoln Laboratory for the generous use of the spectrograph without which this work would have suffered immeasurably, to Mr. J. H. Meyer of M.I.T. Lincoln Laboratory for his part in the experimental work and to Mr. J. R. Bauer and other members of Group 34 for their support. Also, thanks go to Dr. H. E. Cramer, Dr. F. A. Record, G. Fontes, H. Geary, J. Luby, and J. Peers of Round Hill Field Station for their assistance.

References

1. Watanabe, K., Zelikoff, M., and Inn, E. C., "Absorption Coefficients of Several Atmospheric Gases," Air Force Cambridge Research Center Technical Report No. 52–23, Geophysical Research Papers, No. 21, June 1953.
2. Action, J. R., and Swift, J. D., "Cold Cathode Discharge Tubes," New York, Academic Press, 1963.
3. Warneck, P., "A Microwave-Powered Hydrogen Lamp for Vacuum Ultraviolet Photochemical Research," *Appl. Opt.*, 1, 721–726 (1963).
4. Watanabe, K., Sakai, H., Motti, J., and Nakayama, T., "Absorption Cross Section of O_2, NO and NO_2 with an Improved Photoelectric Method," Air Force Cambridge Research Center, Technical Note 58–658, Scientific Report No. 4, December, 1958.
5. Spedding, F. H., Newton, A. S., Warf, J. C., Johnson, O., Nottory, R. W., Johns, I. B. and Daane, A. H., *Nucleonics*, 4, 4 (1949).
6. Uchida, Y., Kato, R., and Matcui, E., "Optical Properties of Some Solids in the Vacuum-Ultraviolet," *J. Quant. Spectry. Radiative Transfer*, 2, 589–598 (1962).
7. Schneider, E. G., "The Effects of Irradiation on the Transmission of Lithium Fluoride," *J. Opt. Soc. Am.*, 27, 72–74 (1934).
8. Praglin, T., and Nichols, W. A., "High-speed Electrometers for Rocket and Satellite Experiments," *Proc. Inst. Radio Engrs.*, 48, 771–779 (1960).
9. Dunkelman, L., Fowler, W. B., and Hennes, J., "Spectrally Selective Photodetectors for the Middle and Vacuum Ultraviolet," *Appl. Opt.*, 1, 695–700 (1962).
10. Loeb, L. B., "Basic Processes of Gaseous Electronics," Berkeley and Los Angeles, Calif., University of California Press, 1960.
11. Brown, S. C., "Basic Data of Plasma Physics," Cambridge, Mass., Technology Press, 1959.
12. Hennes, J. P., Scolnik, R., and Stober, A. K., *J. Opt. Soc. Am.*, 51, 1461 A (1961).

44. The NRL Lyman-Alpha Humidiometer

D. L. RANDALL, T. E. HANLEY, AND O. K. LARISON

U.S. Naval Research Laboratory, Washington, D.C.

ABSTRACT

The NRL Lyman-Alpha Humidiometer is an instrument which uses the selective absorption of electromagnetic radiation at 1215.6 Å by water vapor for measuring the humidity content of air. This radiation from a hydrogen lamp is emitted through a lithium fluoride window across a measuring path and through a lithium fluoride window in a nitric oxide gas detector tube. By photoionization, this radiation causes a current to flow in the metering circuit associated with the nitric oxide gas tube, and this current is a function of the water vapor density in the measuring path. The humidiometer has been under development at Naval Research Laboratory, and some of the procedures for making long-life hydrogen lamps and for using the humidiometer for airborne measurements are shown. This passive method of instantaneously measuring water vapor density without disturbing the air sample promises many new opportunities in the fields of meteorology, physics and chemistry.

INTRODUCTION

The NRL Lyman-Alpha Humidiometer is a new instrument which uses the absorption of electromagnetic radiation at 1215.6 Å by water vapor for measuring the water vapor density of the air. This instrument is simple in construction, is light, can be put in small packages, is sensitive to small amounts of water vapor, has a rapid time response, can be operated at any temperature, and can be used at any atmospheric pressure where the air has the same composition as at the surface.

By using the principle of absorption of Lyman-α radiation by water vapor, the air sample is not changed as it is in the dew-point hygrometer, lithium chloride strip hygrometer, or a wet- and dry-bulb thermometer. Furthermore, this instrument measures water vapor density below freezing and avoids the ambiguity of the vapor pressure being sampled over ice or supercooled water. This passive method of measuring water vapor density without disturbing the air sample promises many new opportunities for water vapor determination in the fields of meteorology, physics, and chemistry.

DISCUSSION

The objects of this paper are:

a. To explain the physical principles used by the humidiometer.

b. To describe the present model of the humidiometer.

c. To discuss the sensitivity of the humidiometer to water vapor.

d. To present methods for calibrating the instrument.

e. To review the development of the NRL Lyman-Alpha Humidiometer.

f. To point out possible applications of this new device.

Physical Principles of the Humidiometer

The NRL Lyman-Alpha Humidiometer consists of two major components as shown in Fig. 1. An energized hydrogen lamp radiates across a sampling path to a nitric oxide detector with its associated metering circuit. The light from the hydrogen lamp is emitted

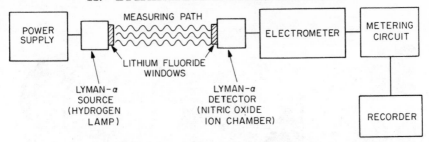

FIG. 1. The NRL Lyman-Alpha Humidiometer (block diagram).

through a lithium fluoride window across a measuring path and through the lithium fluoride window of the nitric oxide gas detector tube. By photo-ionization this radiation causes a current I to flow in the nitric oxide ion chamber which is connected to the electrometer, the metering circuit, and the recorder.

On the assumption that the current I is linearly proportional to the number of photons per second entering the ion chamber, we have by Beer's Law

$$I = I_0 e^{-k(\rho/\rho_0)x} \qquad (1)$$

where

I_0 = the current for vacuum conditions in the path.

k = the absorption coefficient for water vapor.

ρ_0 = the water vapor density at STP

ρ = the water vapor density under ambient conditions.

x = the length of the measuring path.

At Lyman-α (1215.6 Å) the coefficient[1] k for water vapor is about 387 cm^{-1} in an "oxygen window" centered on Lyman-α, where k for oxygen is 0.3 cm^{-1}. On either side of this window, the coefficient for oxygen is higher. The absorption coefficient of O_2 at 1205 Å is 500 cm^{-1} and at 1244 Å is 940 cm^{-1}. Nitrogen and other gases in a normal atmosphere have coefficients which are negligibly small. The absorption coefficient for ozone is quite high, about 500 cm^{-1}, but the concentrations of ozone at low levels in the atmosphere at normal temperature and pressure are negligibly small (less than 1 ppm) in comparison to the concentration of water (1.5 to 2 parts per hundred).

Description of Humidiometer

The components of the humidiometer shown in Fig. 1 are further illustrated in Figs. 2, 3,

and 4. Figure 2 shows two humidiometer probes mounted on the side of the WV-2 aircraft radome. Figure 3 is a close-up of the humidiometer probe. Figure 4 shows the internal parts of the probe.

Figure 5 is a schematic diagram of the logarithmic[2] airborne humidiometer. The power supply consists of a half-wave rectifier with a maximum output voltage of about 2200 V; it drops to about 1600 V during operation. The output current to the hydrogen lamp, V5, is regulated to a maximum value of 100 μA by controlling the cathode bias of the tube V7. The power supply is located in a rack on the instrument panel, but the hydrogen lamp is exposed outside the aircraft in a probe.

Tube V4 is the nitric oxide ion chamber, and this together with the cathode follower electrometer, and the 4.7×10^9 Ω drop resistor compose a compact potted unit. This unit is also mounted in the probe opposite the measuring path from the hydrogen lamp. The metering circuit, consisting of the Zener diodes and the logarithmic amplifier, is located in the instrument panel rack. The output of the humidiometer is connected to a "Visicorder."

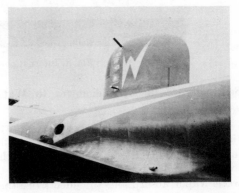

FIG. 2. Humidiometer probes mounted on side of the radome.

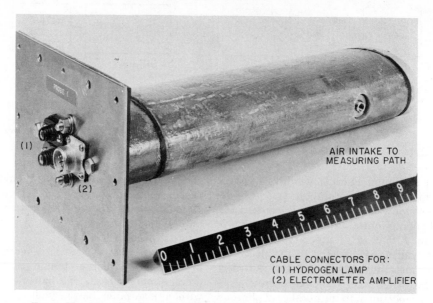

FIG. 3. Humidiometer Probe for mounting on side of the radome (assembled).

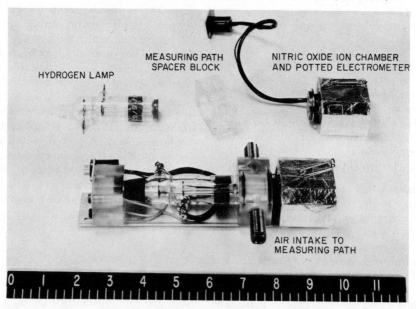

FIG. 4. Internal parts of humidiometer probe.

Sensitivity of the Humidiometer to Water Vapor

Although the consideration of the absorption coefficients previously given would indicate that the Lyman-α radiation of the hydrogen lamp would be sensitive only to water vapor absorption, the effects of other radiation frequencies need to be checked under practical conditions.

Practical considerations dictated the necessity of building a hydrogen lamp which would be easy to light and would have a long life. The factors which indicated that long tube life was the result of an abundance of hydrogen in the lamp were:

(1) The visual spectrograms of long-life tubes were those which showed a hydrogen continuum or higher pressure of hydrogen,

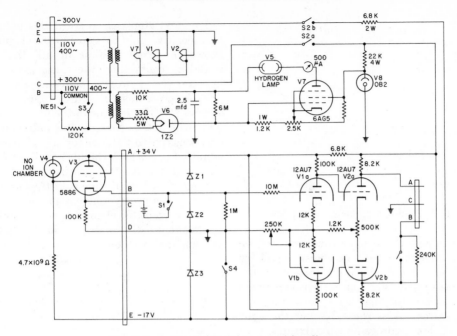

FIG. 5. Logarithmic humidiometer wiring diagram.

whereas the short-life tubes showed narrow spectral lines at lower hydrogen pressures (Figs. 6 and 7). Notice that three of the lamps in Fig. 7 are over a year old and that they show hydrogen continua.

(2) The number of flushings of tubes on the vacuum manifold indicated that the tube life increased with the number of times the tubes were flushed. This meant that hydrogen had been absorbed in the tube walls and did not decrease the pressure when the tube was sealed (Fig. 8).

The conditions which were favorable for easy lighting of the hydrogen lamp were:

(1) A relatively high hydrogen pressure in the lamp.

(2) A mixture of 90 per cent hydrogen with

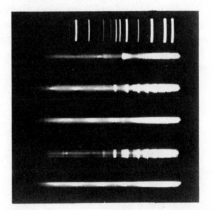

Plate 2		Exposure Time	Date Received from Tube Engineering Laboratory
Line 1	Mercury Reference	3 sec	—
2	Lamp P-6	12 min	6/30/60
3	Lamp T-7	12 min	6/30/60
4	Lamp S-4	12 min	6/30/60
5	Lamp K-15	12 min	8/2/61
6	Lamp K-4	12 min	11/18/60

The above pictures were made August 3, 1961

FIG. 7. Variation of hydrogen lamp spectra with age.

10 per cent neon was easier to excite than a tube filled at the same pressure with pure hydrogen.

A hydrogen tube analyzer was therefore built in which it was possible to fill the hydrogen lamp with any desired pressure of

FIG. 6. Comparison of a leaky hydrogen lamp spectrum and a tightly sealed hydrogen lamp spectrum. Line 1 is the mercury reference spectrum, line 2 is the tightly sealed hydrogen tube, and line 3 is the leaky hydrogen tube.

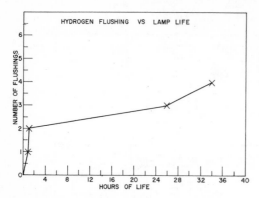

Fɪɢ. 8. Hydrogen flushings *vs* lamp life.

hydrogen and at the same time measure the sensitivity of the radiation to moist air and dry air. Figures 9 and 10 are illustrations of the apparatus used. Very crude measurements were made on the analyzer by observing the voltage drop across the tube and the light emitted. For hydrogen-neon mixtures with total pressures ranging from 0.2 to 2 mm of Hg, steady light and voltages were observed. From this test it appeared that the best gas pressure to use was 1.4 to 1.6 mm of Hg. This gas was a mixture of 9 parts hydrogen and 1 part neon.

The next step was to see if this radiation was sensitive only to water vapor. Figure 11 shows the results. First of all, the flush chamber containing the measuring path between the hydrogen lamp and the nitric oxide receiver was pumped to approximately 0 cm of Hg. The reading of the humidiometer was then noted. Now, if the radiation was only sensitive to water vapor, dry air could be admitted to the flush chamber without changing this deflection. Dry air was then admitted through a carbon dioxide cold trap until the pressure was nearly ambient pressure. There was no perceptible change in the humidiometer reading with the dry air in the chamber as compared with evacuated conditions. The

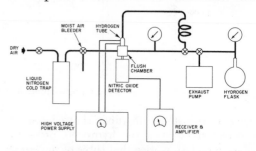

Fɪɢ. 10. Schematic diagram of hydrogen lamp analyzer.

Fɪɢ. 9. The hydrogen lamp analyzer. The absolute humidity calibration system consists of (A) the dry air source or tank, (B) the carbon dioxide-acetone cold trap, (C) the flush chamber through which light is radiated by (D) the hydrogen lamp, and detected by (E) the nitric oxide detector, (F) the pressure gauge, and the exhaust pump. Moist air is admitted to the system by the stopcock just before the flush chamber. A stopcock is rotated to connect the hydrogen lamp to the (G) hydrogen reservoir, and (H) manometer, or to the vacuum pump. (I) the DC power supply for the hydrogen lamp, and (J) the metering circuit amplifier are on the table.

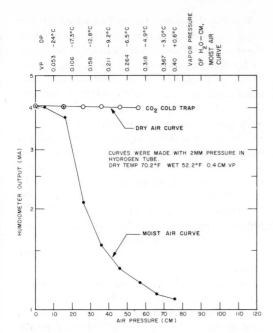

FIG. 11. Comparison of dry air and moist air humidiometer deflection curves.

flush chamber was then evacuated, and moist air of known water vapor pressure was admitted from the room. The flush chamber was then closed and evacuated. Notice that the radiation was sensitive to water vapor pressure and that at near 0 cm of Hg pressure the humidiometer deflection was the same as for the dry air curve.

This result was important because it showed that the hydrogen pressure of the tubes could be increased eight times over the pressure which was first used in making hydrogen lamps for the humidiometer and that radiation from this hydrogen-neon gas mixture was still sensitive to water vapor only. This meant longer tube life and easier lighting of the hydrogen lamps.

Now that the theoretical predictions and the practical applications of the humidiometer being sensitive to water vapor only are confirmed, further considerations of the humidiometer sensitivity are discussed. The response of the humidiometer to changes in moisture depends upon the ventilation speed of the sampling cavity, the time constant of the metering circuit, and the instrument sensitivity. The ventilation rate of the sensing cavity is nearly the same as the aircraft speed

since the unrestricted ventilation tube is $\frac{3}{8}$ in. i.d. and about 5 in. long. The time constant of the metering circuit is $\frac{1}{20}$ of a second. In the range between 2 and 14 mb of water vapor, the sensitivity of the instrument is .14 mb/μA. For this system there is no visible noise at the "Visicorder" galvanometer, since it is impossible to distinguish less than .075 μA or .01 mb on the "Visicorder" record.

However, when it was desired to change the packaging of the sensing head and the time response from 20 to 100 cps a basic noise limitation was encountered, namely, that the hydrogen tube oscillated. This oscillation was increased in frequency until it was above the frequency response of the recording circuits by removing tube V7 and placing approximately 20 megohms in series with and adjacent to the hydrogen lamp. The whole humidiometer has been repackaged in a smaller mount and the frequency response increased to about 100 cps by changing the resistor in series with the NO tube to $10^9\Omega$ (Fig. 5). The noise level limitation of the instrument circuit without the hydrogen lamp on is .01 mb for the instrument calibration using a $\frac{1}{2}$-in. measuring path. (This water vapor pressure corresponds to a dew-point temperature of $-77°C$).

Methods for Calibrating the Humidiometer

The humidiometer has been calibrated by a microwave refractometer technique, a flush chamber method, and checked at equilibrium humidities by a wet- and dry-bulb psychrometer procedure.

The Microwave Refractometer Method. The microwave refractometer method is especially useful for calibrating the humidiometer in flight. If both the humidiometer and the refractometer can be recorded on the same trace with the temperature and pressure, it is possible to calculate the water vapor density from the refractometer record and make a water vapor density *vs* humidiometer deflection scale. A calibrated refractometer indicates N, which is the sum of N_d, the dry air component of microwave refractive index, and N_w, the water vapor component of microwave refractive index. The dry air term is

$$N_d = 77.6 \, P/T \qquad (2)$$

and the water vapor term is

$$N_w = \frac{77.6\,(4810)}{T}\frac{e}{T} \qquad (3)$$

where

P = the total pressure measured in mb,

e = the water vapor pressure measured in mb

T = the temperature measured in degrees K.

The moist term, N_w, can now be found from the calibrated refractometer deflection and the computed dry air by the equation

$$N_w = N - N_d \qquad (4)$$

If we substitute from the equation of state for e/T with the gas constant R equal to 2.1662×10^{-4}, we obtain for the water vapor density ρ,

$$\rho = N_w\,(T)\,(2.16612)/77.6(4810 \times 10^4) \quad (5)$$

The disadvantages of this system are that the time responses of the temperature element, the refractometer, and the humidiometer are all different, and it is difficult to obtain typical deflections for the same sample of air. Furthermore, the water vapor density has to be computed from the refractive index formula. This is time consuming.

The Flush Chamber Method. In this system, the entrance and exit to the measuring path of the humidiometer sensing head are controlled by a flush chamber with stopcocks at the entrance and exit. On the intake side of the humidiometer flush chamber, the air sample is drawn into the chamber from a psychrometer chamber where the water vapor density of the sample is measured. The vapor pressure in the chamber is computed by the relation

$$e = (e_0/P_0)\,P \qquad (6)$$

where e is the water vapor pressure in the chamber, P is the total pressure in the chamber, e_0 is the ambient vapor pressure of the sample, and P_0 is the total ambient pressure of the sample. If the pressures in the flush chamber are lowered by a vacuum pump in arbitrary increments, say, of 100 mm of Hg for the desired calibration range, the water vapor density ρ in g/cc, can be computed from the equation of state where R is given the value of 2.88787×10^{-4}, and temperatures are measured in degrees K.

The Psychrometer Check Procedure. Before using the humidiometer, it is often desirable to check points on the calibration curve constructed by the methods described above. This is done by flushing air of constant humidity through the measuring cavity of the humidiometer and from thence into a wet- and dry-bulb psychrometer chamber. The stream of air should be moving about 5 to 10 miles per hour. A good source of dry air is a laboratory pressure tank. A good source of moist air is obtained by drawing air from the surface of a large bottle of water at room temperature. Intermediate values of humidity may be obtained by using a valve system to obtain mixtures of dry and moist air.

Several calibration curves are now shown. Figure 12 shows that the curves are spaced evenly and parallel as a function of hydrogen lamp current with a fixed measuring path length. Figure 13 shows that the slope of the calibration curve can be changed as a function of path length when the tube current is fixed. These results are in agreement with Beer's law.

The ability to shift the position of the calibration curve parallel to itself by changing the hydrogen lamp current or the path length makes it possible to make one calibration curve for a humidiometer and then to adjust the output of the instrument at some later time so as to always match the original calibration. Assume that the tube current is constant and the transmission of the lithium fluoride windows decreases as a function of time. This is because the windows become dirty and become etched with moisture. It is still possible to use this tube if two humidity check points are known since either the hydrogen lamp current or the path length may be varied to fit the original curve.

It is also possible to match the outputs of two humidiometers by this method. Figure 14 illustrates such an attempt.

However, these adjustments are for long-term operations. When the instrument is only used for 3 or 4 hours between calibrations these adjustments are not necessary. The zero drift of the electronic circuitry (without the hydrogen lamp on) after a 30-minute warm-up period is $1.7 \times 10^{-4}\,\mu$A in 1 hour. Sufficient experience has not been obtained to state how much the calibration curve changes with the etching of the lithium fluoride windows on

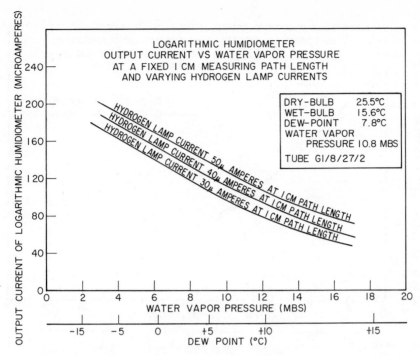

FIG. 12. Translation of humidiometer calibration curve by varying hydrogen lamp current.

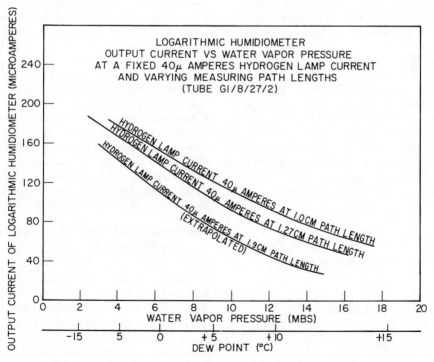

FIG. 13. Rotation of humidiometer calibration curve by varying path length.

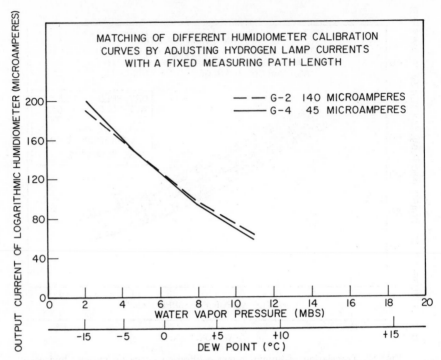

Fig. 14. Matching of two humidiometer calibration curves.

the hydrogen lamp and the ion chamber, although it is obvious that these windows become etched after several weeks exposure to the elements.

A Self-balancing Hydrogen Lamp. It is possible to eliminate errors due to hydrogen lamp tube current drift and to reduce the effects of errors caused by change in transmission properties of the lithium fluoride windows without frequent recalibrations. If the light from the hydrogen beam is viewed from two windows, through two receivers having different path lengths, then the following equations can be written

$$I' = I_0' \, e^{-k(\rho/\rho_0)x'} \text{ for path 1} \qquad (7)$$

and

$$I = I_0 e^{-k(\rho/\rho_0)x} \text{ for path 2} \qquad (8)$$

Paths 1 and 2 may be represented by

$$x = ax'$$

and

$$I_0 = cI_0'$$

Divide the first two equations and substitute for x and I_0 to obtain

$$\log (I/I') = \log c + k(\rho/\rho_0) \, x \, (1 - a) \qquad (9)$$

Since the same sample of air passes over both measuring paths, it is assumed that the windows on both measuring paths would be etched by water vapor the same amount, and the ratio c would remain the same. The constant a is one which relates the path lengths and remains fixed. This system eliminates drift due to changes in tube current since both paths see the same beam of light. The metering circuits, of course, must be checked, but two sources of error in measurement can be eliminated with the self-balancing hydrogen lamp, namely, hydrogen lamp tube current drift, and etching of the windows. Figure 15 shows this self-balancing hydrogen lamp.

Development of the NRL Lyman-Alpha Humidiometer Reviewed

The idea of using hydrogen Lyman-α radiation for measuring humidity was proposed by Dr. Herbert Friedman, Superintendent of the NRL Atmosphere and Astrophysics Division. The instrument as demonstrated by Dr. Friedman was simple and very light, and it had almost instantaneous time response. An instrument with these qualities had immediate

FIG. 15. Side view of self-balancing hydrogen lamp.

appeal to the Wave Propagation Branch of the Electronics Division as a device for use in connection with tropospheric scatter propagation studies where the micrometeorological structure of the atmosphere plays such an important role. The Wave Propagation Branch of NRL Electronics Division, began experiments with the humidiometer in 1957 with support from the Bureau of Naval Weapons, Meteorological Management Division. NRL published a report[5] describing the operation of the humidiometer, and reported on the instrumentation at the 1958 Spring Meeting of the International Scientific Radio Union (URSI).

However, all the problems for a good working instrument were not solved, chiefly because dependable hydrogen tubes could not be made. When the spectrograph and hydrogen tube analyzer were used in studying the tubes, a longer-life tube was produced. Of course, all of the problems in developing the humidiometer are not solved, but it is now possible as a result of work done at NRL to obtain the principal parts of the humidiometer, the hydrogen lamp and the nitric oxide ion chamber commercially.

CONCLUSION

The progress thus far in the development of the humidiometer seems to pave the way for the introduction of a new type of instrument to measure water vapor density. Some of the possible applications of this instrument are:

(1) *An Airborne Humidiometer:* NRL has had experience in this field and has found it to be practical. Figure 16 shows a humidiometer sounding record made on the "Visicorder." At present it is not possible to present any of our tape machine data.

(2) *Radiosonde Humidity Element:* The sensing elements of the humidiometer, the hydrogen lamp, and the nitric oxide ion chamber, are about the size of a pair of salt and pepper shakers and weigh 12 ounces. Because of its light weight, compactness, and capability of rapid time response, this system is being studied for possible use as a radiosonde device, and a low-altitude rocketsonde application.

(3) *A Basic Research Tool:* This instrument offers possibilities for measuring the pressure of water vapor below freezing. Most hygrometers have difficulties in this region, but the humidiometer measures the water vapor sample across the measuring path where the sample is always in the gaseous phase. The windows of the hydrogen lamp and the nitric oxide ion chamber, as well as the walls of the measuring path, should be above the temperature of the sample of air measured so that moisture deposits will not form within the instrument.

(4) *Microwave Radio Propagation Instrument:* NRL's interest in the humidiometer is for determining the presence of sharp refractive index gradients which cause anomalous propagation of electromagnetic energy at microwave frequencies and for detecting small cells of moisture which may produce scattering of electromagnetic energy at microwave frequencies.

References

1. Watanabe, K., Zelikoff, Murray, and Inn, Edward C. Y., "Absorption Coefficients of Several Atmospheric Gases," Geophysics Research Directorate, Air Force Cambridge Research Center, AFCRC Technical Report No. 53–23, June 1953.

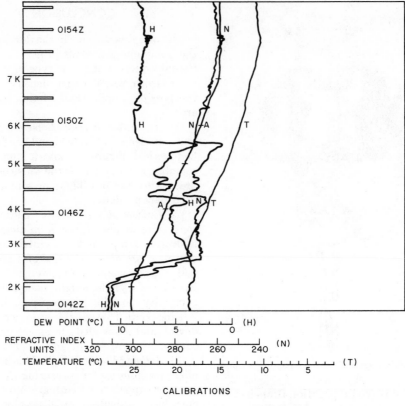

DEW POINT (°C)   10   5   0   (H)

REFRACTIVE INDEX   (N)
UNITS   320   300   280   260   240

TEMPERATURE (°C)   25   20   15   10   5   (T)

CALIBRATIONS

PRESSURE ALTITUDE (A)

TIME 0142Z
DATE 12 MARCH 1959
LATITUDE 8° 24' S
LONGITUDE 28° 28' W

FIG. 16. An airborne humidiometer sounding.

2. Ives, Walter J., "Logarithmic Scale Noise Meter," *Electronics*, **22**, 100–103 (August 1949).

3. Kreplin, R. W., Chubb, T. A., and Friedman, H., "X-Ray and Lyman-Alpha Emission from the Sun as Measured from the NRL-1 Satellite," *J. Geophys. Res.*, **67**, No. 6 (June 1962).

4. Smith, E. K. Jr., and Weintraub, S., "The Constants in the Equation for Atmospheric Refractive Index at Radio Frequencies," *Proc. IRE*, **41**, 1035–1037 (1953).

5. Bologna, J. M., Larison, O. K., Randall, D. L., and Ringwalt, D. L., "An Airborne Lyman-Alpha Humidiometer," NRL Report 5180, August 1958.

Note: The paper "The NRL Lyman-Alpha Humidiometer," will be published in a forthcoming issue of the *Report of NRL Progress.*

45. A Spectral Hygrometer for Measuring Total Precipitable Water

Norman B. Foster, David T. Volz and Laurence W. Foskett

U.S. Weather Bureau, Washington, D.C.

ABSTRACT

This paper describes a recording photo-electric spectral hygrometer developed by the U.S. Weather Bureau for determining the amount of water vapor in a vertical column of the atmosphere. Basically, the hygrometer monitors the relative radiant intensity of direct solar energy transmitted in a water vapor absorption band. A sensing path directed at the sun is maintained by means of a motor-driven equatorial mounting.

The intensity of the radiation in the selected region of absorption is compared to that of a nearby region having essentially no absorption. The region of absorption is centered at 0.935 μ and the reference region at 0.881 μ. Narrow-band-pass interference filters isolate the two spectral regions. Silicon solar cells are used as radiation detectors.

The instrument is designed so that the ratio of the photocurrents is proportional to the ratio of the transmitted radiant energies. Continuous ratio measurements are automatically obtained on a recording, self-balancing ratio bridge. Calibration depends on an empirical method involving simultaneous values of total precipitable water calculated from radiosonde observations.

Both laboratory tests and trial operation have demonstrated the dependability of the spectral hygrometer. Its stable design makes it suitable for use in the operational activities of meteorology as well as in research.

INTRODUCTION

Those interested in forecasting precipitation have for many years felt the need for a field instrument that would provide a continuous record from which the total precipitable water* could at any time be readily determined. It is possible to make an approximate computation of the total precipitable water from radiosonde observations, but this is a time-consuming procedure.

The absorption spectra method employed in the near-infrared region of the solar spectrum is, we believe, the most practical means of measuring total precipitable water. The fundamental technique was first described by Fowle.[7] The method with respect to this hygrometer consists of isolating two narrow regions of the solar spectrum: one in a suitable water vapor absorption band, the other in a nearby region where no absorption occurs. A ratio is established between the irradiance in these two regions. A change of water vapor concentration in the sensing path changes the ratio. However, when the radiant flux changes due to haze, smoke, mist, etc., the ratio remains essentially unaltered. Thus the ratio can be used as an index of the amount of water vapor in the sensing path. The latter quantity can then be divided by the appropriate optical air mass value in order to determine the

---

* The term, total precipitable water, is used in accordance with the definition given in the "Glossary of Meteorology," 1959.

vertical atmospheric water vapor content (total precipitable water).

PHYSICAL CONCEPTS

The water vapor absorption bands are identified with the vibrational and rotational motions of the water vapor molecules. Ascribed to the three normal modes of vibration of these molecules are three intense bands centered in the infrared near 6.27, 2.77, and 2.66 μ. The last two of these overlap considerably, thereby forming a broad region of absorption that is often referred to in the singular as the 2.7 μ band. A number of other bands, representing various multiples and combinations of the fundamental frequencies, occupy spectral positions from 3.17 to 0.57 μ The more prominent bands of this group are centered in the near infrared at approximately 1.88, 1.38, 1.14, and 0.93 μ (see Fig. 1). A detailed identification of the vibrational components of the water vapor spectrum can be found in a paper written by Adel and Lampland.[1] Molecular rotation also contributes to the formation of the bands described above. In a sense, rotational motions serve to shape these bands around the central wavelengths provided by the vibrational motions. Also contained in the water vapor spectrum is the strong and extensive band that lies in the far infrared beyond the so-called 10-μ window; this band is attributed solely to the effects of rotation. To conclude this brief description of

the water vapor spectrum, it seems appropriate to note that the bands diminish in strength more or less gradually toward the shorter wavelengths, with those in the visible region exhibiting relatively little absorption.

Care should be exercised in the selection of a band for use in measuring water vapor. A band should be chosen with an intermediate range of fractional absorption for the amount of water vapor likely to be contained in the sensing path. If the absorption is too strong, total absorption may occur when the water vapor content is high. If the absorption is too weak, the instrument will suffer in sensitivity and instrumental errors will tend to mask true values. The central region of the 0.93-μ band gives a satisfactory range of fractional absorption for the amount of water vapor usually encountered in the path of normal incidence to the sun through the earth's atmosphere.[6] A nearby region in the vicinity of 0.88 μ exhibits little or no absorption and therefore serves as an excellent region of reference.

In a spectral region of continuous absorption, the relationship between the absorption and the absorbing mass can be expressed as a simple exponential function. However, such a function does not accurately describe the absorption that occurs in the water vapor bands, since these are not of a continuous character. Actually these bands consist of numerous closely spaced lines; moreover, the line patterns are irregular in spacing and intensity. The absorption that occurs in a band

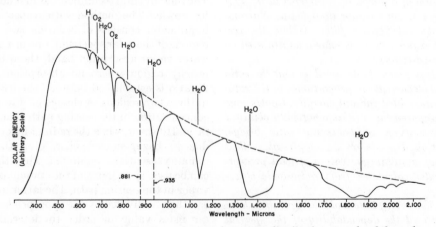

FIG. 1. Curve showing the approximate solar energy distribution at sea level through the visible and part of the near-infrared regions. Notation is made of the reference and absorption band centers. Some of the more prominent bands of absorption are indicated. Ordinates are in arbitrary units, not strictly to scale.

having such irregularities is actually a complicated process not precisely describable by a simple mathematical formula. Nevertheless, a relationship between the absorption and the absorbing mass does exist, and the curve approximating this relationship in a particular band, or subinterval thereof, can be established by empirical means. Furthermore, in most cases a relatively simple square-root expression closely describes this curve through a limited range of the fractional absorption.

Elsasser[2-5] formalized the square-root absorption law, which relates specifically to subintervals within the infrared water vapor bands. The square-root law states that the fractional absorption A which occurs in an atmospheric layer of finite thickness is directly proportional to the square root of the absorbing mass X and the square root of the atmospheric pressure P, and inversely proportional to the fourth root of the absolute temperature T. If isobaric and isothermal conditions prevail throughout the layer, then the equation

$$A = K(XP)^{1/2} \, T^{-1/4} \tag{1}$$

can be used as an expression of the square-root law. In this equation the factor K is a dimensional constant that depends on the units in which the variables are expressed as well as the spectral characteristics of the particular subinterval under consideration. Elsasser demonstrated that the square-root law closely describes the actual absorption curve in the range of relatively small to intermediate values of the fractional absorption. The reader is directed to the references cited above for further information concerning the limitations of the square-root law as well as for details pertaining to its formulation.

The equation presented above clearly indicates that the absorption spectra method, as it is implemented in this scheme of measuring total precipitable water, is marked by a degree of uncertainty due to the dependence of the absorption process on the pressures and temperatures through which the atmospheric water vapor is distributed. The approximate mean effects of the distributional relationships are obviously incorporated into the empirical calibration of the spectral hygrometer when radiosonde observations provide the comparative data for calibration. We are therefore basically concerned only with the relative errors arising from distributional variations. These errors are briefly discussed in the following paragraphs.

A simple consideration based on Eq. (1) shows that the absorption process is relatively insensitive to temperature in the range of temperatures through which the bulk of the atmospheric water vapor is distributed. This temperature range is small in an absolute sense, and the distributional profiles within this range are not excessively variant. Since the absorption varies only as the reciprocal of the fourth root of the absolute temperature, it becomes apparent that the relative errors introduced by the temperature effect are virtually insignificant.

A somewhat similar consideration, based on the same equation, shows that the pressure effect is not prohibitive. The bulk of the atmospheric water vapor normally appears in the lower troposphere. In other words, the vertical distributions of water vapor are weighted toward the higher pressures. Obviously, the absorption process is relatively less affected by incremental pressure variations at these pressures than at the lower atmospheric pressures. Soundings show that the vertical profiles of atmospheric water vapor distribution are not excessively variant. In most cases, therefore, the pressure effect does not introduce serious relative errors in this method of measuring total precipitable water.

Howard, Burch, and Williams[8] observed that the fractional absorption in the entire 0.93-μ band actually varies more nearly as the fourth root, rather than the square root, of the atmospheric pressure. The weaker pressure dependence in the observed case is attributed to overlapping of neighboring spectral lines. The spacing and intensity of the spectral lines—and hence, also the degree of overlapping—are variable in the water vapor spectrum. Each wavelength interval has its own characteristic fine structure. With this in mind, it seems reasonable to conclude that the pressure dependence of the absorption region of the spectral hygrometer, which monitors only a fraction of the wavelengths in the 0.93-μ band, should differ from that of the entire band. Theoretical considerations as well as some general experimental evidence given in the above-cited report lead us to believe that the actual pressure dependence of this particular absorption interval falls somewhere between the square-root and fourth-root relationships. Further research is obviously needed in this respect.

In their report, Howard, Burch, and Williams[8] suggest that the actual effect of temperature might also be smaller than indicated in the formal relationship represented by Eq. (1). They note that overlapping of neighboring spectral lines should be affected not only by pressure, but also by temperature, since both of these variables appear in the theoretical expression for the width of a spectral line. Thus the argument for ignoring the temperature effect gains even more support. At this point it seems appropriate to note that the slight uncertainties due to the temperature effect should merely serve to partially offset those due to the pressure effect. Since temperature as well as pressure decreases with altitude in normal atmospheric profiles, Eq. (1) clearly shows that the absorption is opposingly affected by pressure and temperature when a vertical displacement of water vapor occurs.

In view of the foregoing discussions, it appears that an empirical calibration of the spectral hygrometer should follow closely, through a limited range of fractional absorption, the simple equation

$$A = K'X^{1/2} \qquad (2)$$

Here, the new constant K' incorporates factors representing the integrated mean effects of temperature and pressure as well as the factors ascribed to the constant K in Eq. (1).

Thus far we have shown that the absorption spectra method can be expected to give fairly accurate relative measurements of total precipitable water. However, the dependence of absorption on pressure (and to a lesser degree, on temperature) implies that due consideration must be given to certain restrictions inherent to the application of this method:

(a) The spectral hygrometer should be operated at elevations close to that of the location where it is calibrated.

(b) Use of the instrument should be limited to a reasonable range of optical air mass values.

Obviously, the first restriction is relatively important. King and Parry[10] describe an

actual case, involving an experimental model of this instrument, which verifies this point. Independent calibrations for this instrument were obtained at two different elevations. A significant difference was observed between the two calibration curves, and an interesting relationship was found between the two curves. More research in this respect is highly desirable in order to determine whether an empirical relationship of this type is adaptable for general applications.

The second restriction is not operationally significant. Basically, it involves the question of whether the uncertainties due to the pressure effect are enhanced at any given fractional absorption when the latter is permitted to occur as a result of widely varying quantities of vertical water vapor content. A preliminary study, involving vertical atmospheric profiles (water vapor concentration *vs* pressure), shows that the variability in the slant-path profiles is not appreciably greater when these profiles result from a wide range of values of vertical water vapor content compared to a relatively narrow range. Indirect evidence resulting from the empirical calibration procedure and experimental use of the spectral hygrometer also indicates that the uncertainties due to the pressure effect are not selectively magnified by optical air mass variability.

The discussion in the foregoing paragraph does not take into account the inherent uncertainties attending very low solar elevation angles. These uncertainties are primarily related to the effects of refraction and excessive scattering and to possible timing errors associated with the rapidly changing long optical paths.

DESCRIPTION OF THE INSTRUMENT

The Optical Components

The two spectral regions of interest are isolated by first-order, narrow-band-pass interference filters. The filters are placed in the box housing in front of the photocells (see Fig. 2). In operation, the solar beam remains at normal incidence to the filters since the hygrometer is continuously aimed at the sun. The following data summarize the normal-incidence characteristics of these filters: The filter that isolates the region of absorption has its central wavelength at 0.935 μ, a peak trans-

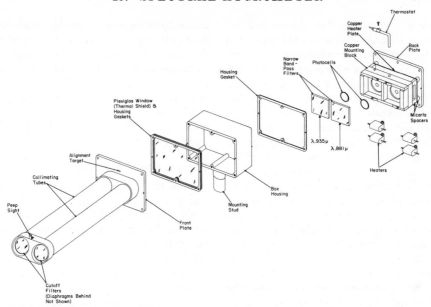

FIG. 2. Exploded view of the spectral hygrometer showing the relative orientation of the various components.

mittance of 43 per cent and a half-width of 13 mμ; the filter used for isolating the reference region has its central wavelength at 0.881 μ, a peak transmittance of 50 per cent, and a half-width of 13 mμ.

Parallel tubes of 12-in. length and 1⅞-in. i.d. are used for collimating the sunlight. Sharp-cutoff red filters, Corning C.S. No. 2-61 (transmittance <0.5 per cent at wavelengths below 0.590 μ), are installed at the forward ends of the collimating tubes to provide protection from the weather as well as to prevent the transmission of radiation through possible passbands of higher order. In order to minimize errors due to internal reflections, a diaphragm with 1⅜-in. i.d. is flush-mounted in the front end of each tube immediately behind the cutoff filter. A "Plexiglas" window is installed behind the collimating tube assembly, thereby isolating the box-housing chamber for more efficient thermostating of the photocells.

The Photocells

Silicon solar cells with 1-in.-diameter active surfaces are used as the radiation detectors. They are very fast in response (⩽20 μsec), and have exceptionally stable, long-life performance characteristics. A properly matched pair of these cells gives continuous ratios of the photocurrents in direct proportion to the ratios of the in-band to out-of-band solar energies. Laboratory tests verified the reliability of these cells.

Silicon solar cells exhibit a relatively high current response in the near-infrared region at which this hygrometer operates. The spectral response range of this type of photocell extends approximately from 0.35 to 1.15 μ, with a maximum response occurring near 0.75 μ. The photocells used have a nominal efficiency of about 10 per cent in the region of maximum response.

The response of these cells to incident light energy was found to be somewhat dependent on the ambient temperature. Temperature stability was achieved by thermostating the photocell mounting block at 100°F. This operating temperature also serves to prevent condensation from forming on the internal optical surfaces.

The current output of a silicon solar cell is directly proportional to the intensity of light incident upon its active surface when the load across the cell is small, approaching short circuit. Laboratory experiments were conducted to test the cells for linearity under increased external loads. The levels of illumination were adjusted so that the range of output current of each photocell was comparable to the range that it generates during normal operation of the spectral hygrometer. The results of these experiments indicate that under the simulated conditions of effective illumination the output current of this type of photocell begins to fall off very slightly from linearity as the external resistance is increased to values above about 10 Ω. This deviation was found to be relatively small even for resistances as high as 50 Ω. The deviation then increased more sharply for higher resistances. Although tests showed the nonlinearity to vary with different cells, it was found that by proper selection, pairs could be matched for similar deviations. By installing a pair of matched photocells in the hygrometer and keeping the external resistances fixed at specific values less than 50 Ω, it was possible to obtain ratios of output current proportional to the ratios of incident radiant energy. The error in the obtained ratios was always less than $\frac{1}{2}$ per cent regardless of the overall intensity of the incident beam.

Fluctuations in the overall intensity of the incident solar beam are related primarily to the processes of scattering and diffuse reflection by the atmospheric constituents. The effect of the gaseous constituents is slight, and that of the nongaseous constituents such as smoke, dust, and haze is somewhat greater; but, obviously, the greatest effect is that of clouds. However, these light-attenuating mechanisms are essentially nonselective in the near-infrared region within which the hygrometer operates. Therefore, since the hygrometer gives a linear ratio response with properly selected values for the fixed external resistances across the photocells, the ratio given by the hygrometer represents primarily a measure of the water vapor contained in the atmospheric sensing path regardless of the fluctuations in the overall intensity of the incident beam.

The foregoing statement is true only as long as the incident sunlight is sufficiently intense for the photocells to provide the minimum current necessary for the self-balancing ratio bridge* to find a balance point. In practice, when thin clouds appear in the path of the solar beam, a balance will occur only while the sun continues to cast relatively discernible shadows. In this case, the direct-beam

* This circuit employs a conventional potentiometric recorder which has been modified for use as a ratio bridge.

intensity corresponds roughly to about 15 per cent of that obtained with full sunlight. Below this level of illumination, the response of the recorder fails rapidly, and the scale error increases quite sharply. Future experimentation may show that increased amplification will permit this hygrometer to give valid readings even though the sunlight is obstructed by denser clouds.

The Equatorial Mounting

In order to get a continuous record of water vapor measurements, the hygrometer is placed on a motor-driven equatorial mounting (see Fig. 3) and trained on the sun. The mounting (also developed by the Weather Bureau) is weather-tight and capable of following the sun throughout the day without attention.

Fig. 3. Spectral hygrometer on an all-weather, solar-tracking equatorial mounting.

The Ratio-bridge Circuit

A schematic diagram of the self-balancing ratio-bridge circuit is shown in Fig. 4. The two photocurrents are fed into the bridge circuit. The ratio of the photocurrents is registered

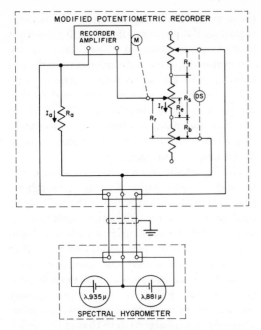

FIG. 4. Schematic diagram of the ratio bridge circuit. I_a—current from the absorption-band photocell; I_r—current from the reference-band photocell; R_a—40.0 Ω, the total resistance across the absorption-band photocell, which is also across the input of the recorder; $R_r = R_b + R_e$—the part of the resistance in the reference loop that is effective in the ratio bridge (i.e., the total resistance below the balance point); R_s—20.0 Ω, the entire resistance of the slide-wire; R_e—the part of the slidewire resistance below the balance point; R_b—zero suppression resistance, or the variable resistance below the slidewire which is used for shifting the ratio range of the recorder to match the operational ratio range of the hygrometer; R_t—compensating resistance, or the resistance above the slidewire which is varied simultaneously with R_b so that the external resistance across the photocell remains constant; DS—the 2-pole rotary selector switch which facilitates the simultaneous changing of R_b and R_t in equal amounts; M—the balancing motor.

directly on the recorder chart. The following discussion with reference to Fig. 4 explains the relationship of the photocurrents to the recorded ratios.

Several considerations led to the arbitrary choice of 40.0 Ω for R_a and 20.0 Ω for R_s. Among the factors considered were ratio-bridge sensitivity, recorder resolution, standardization of the recorder readings to the hygrometer ratios, and linearity of hygrometer ratios (see discussion on photocells). Further laboratory tests of this hygrometer indicated that the linearity consideration

requires a total of 36.0 Ω across the reference-band photocell when 40.0 Ω are placed across the absorption-band photocell. Consequently, the sum of R_b and R_t must be held constant at 16.0 Ω.

When a balance of the bridge occurs, the potential drop in one arm of the bridge equals that in the other. This is expressed by the equation $I_a R_a = I_r R_r$, from which we obtain the useful relationship $I_a/I_r = R_r/R_a$. The latter equation states that the ratio of the photocurrents varies inversely as the ratio of the resistances which are effective in the balancing process. This ratio of effective resistances is a direct function of the balance position of the bridge. Therefore the recorder gives a direct reading of the desired ratio of the photocurrents.

An example, in accordance with the designations in Fig. 4, clarifies the above relationship. As previously noted, R_a and R_s are fixed respectively at 40.0 Ω and 20.0 Ω. Assume in this case that R_b is set at zero and R_t at 16.0 Ω. (R_t is in the photocell loop, but never becomes part of the bridge circuit.) Now, if the recorder balances at half scale, R_e is 10.0 Ω and the ratio becomes $I_a/I_r = R_r/R_a = (R_b + R_e)/R_a = (0 + 10.0)/40.0 = .250$. Obviously these resistance values establish a ratio span of .000 to .500 across the recorder.

The hygrometer described normally operates in a range of ratios from .200 to .700, except with low solar elevations in very humid weather (see Fig. 5). The equation in the paragraph above reveals that the ratio span of the recorder is shifted to match the usual range of hygrometer ratios (.200 − .700) by simply setting R_b at 8.0 Ω. (R_t is then also set at 8.0 Ω.) In practice, R_b and R_t can be designed into the circuit so that corresponding increments (e.g., 4.0 Ω steps) can be simultaneously added and subtracted (or vice versa) by means of a 2-pole rotary selector switch. This step-resistance arrangement also facilitates the use of the recorder with any of several spectral hygrometers.*

* The ratio range of a particular hygrometer depends primarily on the combined effects of the respective characteristics of the narrow-band-pass filters, the corresponding responses of the photocells, the relative solar intensities in the respective wavelength intervals, and the fractional absorption coefficient for the specific wavelength interval of the absorption passband.

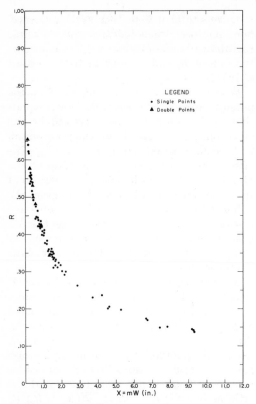

LEGEND
• Single Points
▲ Double Points

X = mW (in.)

FIG. 5. The tentative calibration of the spectral hygrometer. The curve represented by the plotted points gives the mass of water vapor X in the sensing path as a function of the hygrometer ratio R. The total precipitable water can be readily determined by means of the equality $W = X/m$, where m represents the optical air mass at the time of observation.

CALIBRATION

The calibration procedure consists of comparing the hygrometer ratios as shown by the recorder against the corresponding quantities of water vapor that exist in the respective sensing paths at the times of these comparisons. Usually the amount of water vapor in the sensing path is expressed in inches (or centimeters) of precipitable water. Experience shows that no simple method of calibration is available. A calibration using laboratory facilities is not feasible because of the excessive path lengths required to duplicate the typical quantities of water vapor that exist in the atmospheric paths of the solar beam. Furthermore, laboratory techniques can only yield constant-pressure calibration data. Since

theoretical and experimental knowledge regarding the pressure effect is still somewhat limited, adjustment of these data, in an attempt to approximate average conditions prevailing in the solar-inclined atmospheric paths, would, at this time, only add further complications and uncertainties. The decision was therefore made to obtain an approximate empirical calibration which makes use of radiosonde measurements.

The spectral hygrometer measures the amount of water vapor X in the atmospheric path of the solar beam, whereas the radiosonde measurement represents the approximate amount of water vapor W in a vertical column of the atmosphere. The calibration procedure therefore requires that the quantity determined from the radiosonde data must in each case be multiplied by a proportionality factor: the ratio of the length of the solar-inclined atmospheric path to that of the zenith atmospheric path. This ratio m, the optical air mass, is approximated by csc α, where α is the elevation angle of the sun. The optical air mass is expressed more precisely by Bemporad's formula*, particularly for solar elevations below 20 degrees. The solar elevation angle can be obtained from appropriate tables or curves, or it can be measured directly at the time of observation. The method used in determining this angle depends largely on the facilities available and on the number and frequency of the desired observations.

The tentative calibration shown in Fig. 5 consists of a plot of the recorded hygrometer ratios R versus appropriate optical air mass multiples mW of the corresponding radiosonde evaluations of total precipitable water. All plotted points in this calibration were obtained from simultaneous observations taken at the Observational Test and Development Center**, U.S. Weather Bureau, Washington, D.C., on favorable days from June, 1961 through April, 1962. A more precise calibration of this hygrometer is now being pursued.

* Bemporad's formula together with computations in terms of z, the complement of α, can be found in Table 137 of "Smithsonian Meteorological Tables", 6th rev. ed., 1951.

** Lat. 38° 59′ N, long. 77° 28′ W, elev. 276 ft MSL.

CONCLUDING REMARKS AND DISCUSSIONS

Instrumental Reliability

The following general statements are presented concerning the reliability of the spectral hygrometer:

(a) Laboratory tests have proved the stability and linearity of the instrumental equipment. These tests show that the accuracy of the hygrometer is not degraded by ambient temperature variations or by intensity fluctuation of the incident radiation.

(b) Experimental operation has provided strong evidence of the dependability and relative accuracy of the instrument. Changes in total precipitable water as detected by the spectral hygrometer were quite consistently comparable to those changes indicated by successive radiosonde measurements, regardless of the altitude, and hence the pressure, at which the changes occurred. Further confidence was established by means of another spectral hygrometer of the same design. The second instrument was operated simultaneously on an adjacent mounting during the calibration period. The records from the two instruments showed a striking agreement in relative measurements by consistently indicating identical changes in total precipitable water over both short and long periods of time.

(c) A preliminary study of an approximate nature was recently made in an effort to obtain a numerical appraisal of the pressure effect. The associated computations involved variations in the vertical distributional profiles of water vapor as shown in roughly 150 radiosonde records obtained during the calibration period. Results of this study indicate that the pressure-induced uncertainties in this method of measuring total precipitable water should normally not exceed .03 to .05 in. Extreme variations in the vertical profiles might cause occasional errors up to .10 in. Further studies of this type together with more thorough knowledge regarding the pressure effect are required before a more definite statement can be made in this respect.

Possible Applications

The availability of continuous measurements of total precipitable water suggests several distinct uses for the spectral hygrometer. Local correlation studies between total precipitable water and other meteorological variables become more feasible. These studies might include such factors as atmospheric stability, probability of precipitation or thunderstorms, amount of precipitation, or minimum temperature. An important application might be in the field of agricultural meteorology, especially with respect to the prediction of damaging frost. A suitable network of spectral hygrometers could provide important information regarding the movement and extent of moist tongues, which are of particular interest to the forecasters of severe weather. This type of network may also prove useful in conservation activities, particularly in the field of applied hydrology. Research in the realm of physical meteorology may offer further possibilities of instrumental application.

Acknowledgments. The authors wish to express their appreciation to Messrs. Elbert W. Atkins and Theodore Walters of the Observational Test and Development Center for providing technical assistance and facilities relevant to obtaining and analyzing the radiosonde data, to Dr. Earle K. Plyler of the National Bureau of Standards for his authoritative advice pertaining to water vapor absorption bands, and to Mr. Ralph Stair of the National Bureau of Standards for providing spectrophotometric analyses of the narrow-band-pass filters.

References

1. Adel, A., and Lampland, C. O., "A New Band in the Absorption Spectrum of the Earth's Atmosphere," *Astrophys. J.*, **87**, 198–203 (1938).
2. Elsasser, W. M., "On Some Properties of the Water-vapor Spectrum and Their Relations to Atmospheric Radiation," *Monthly Weather Rev.*, **65**, 323–326 (1937).
3. Elsasser, W. M., "New Values for the Infrared Absorption Coefficient of Atmospheric Water Vapor," *Monthly Weather Rev.*, **66**, 175–178 (1938).
4. Elsasser, W. M., "Heat Transfer by Infrared Radiation in the Atmosphere," *Harvard Meteorological Studies*, No. 6, 107 pp. (1942).
5. Elsasser, W. M., with Culbertson, M. F., "Atmospheric Radiation Tables," *Meteorol. Monographs*, **4**, No. 23, 43 pp. (1960).
6. Foster, N. B., and Foskett, L. W., "A Spectrophotometer for the Determination of the Water Vapor in a Vertical Column of the Atmosphere," *J. Opt. Soc. Am.*, **35**, 601–610 (1945).
7. Fowle, F. E., "The Spectroscopic Determination of Aqueous Vapor," *Astrophys. J.*, **35**, 149–162 (1912).

8. Howard, J. N., Burch, D. E., and Williams, D., "Near-infrared Transmission Through Synthetic Atmospheres," *Geophys. Res. Papers*, No. 40, 244 pp. (1955).

9. Huschke, R. E., ed., "Glossary of Meteorology," p. 437, Boston, American Meteorological Society, 1959.

10. King, R. L., and Parry, H. D., "Field Tests and Calibration of the Total Atmospheric Watervapor Hygrometer," Humidity and Moisture, Vol. 1, New York, Reinhold Pub. Corp., 1964.

11. List, R. J., ed., "Smithsonian Meteorological Tables," 6th rev. ed., p. 422, Washingon, D.C., Smithsonian Institution, 1951.

46. Infrared Absorption Hygrometer

Wayne F. Staats, Laurence W. Foskett, and Hans P. Jensen

Instrumental Engineering Division, U.S. Weather Bureau, Washington, D.C.

ABSTRACT

An optical hygrometer designed to measure the absolute humidity of the atmosphere by measuring the absorption effected in the 1.37 μ water vapor absorption band is described. Basically, the instrument comprises a 1-meter beam of radiant energy, a modulator, and a self-balancing servo system with detector photocell. Modulation and spectral isolation are obtained by means of an oscillating narrow-band interference filter. Through the use of this oscillating filter the energy in a spectral region of absorption is compared with that of a region of lesser absorption by changing the angle of incidence of the filter. A balance of energy is maintained in the two spectral regions by the servo system which automatically changes the lamp temperature and, hence, the energy distribution of the beam. Lamp temperature is monitored by a photocell, the output of which is an index of the water vapor. A calibration curve is given and the method of calibration is described. Moreover, preliminary calibration curves depicting the effect of pressure on the instrument are shown. Included is a brief discussion of stability and optimum design characteristics.

INTRODUCTION

Regions of water vapor absorption have long been known to exist in the visible and infrared spectrum. Langley, in 1884, while studying the absorption of solar heat by the earth's atmosphere, located four such regions in the solar spectrum.[1] These regions, or bands as he called them, lay in the near infrared between 0.9 and 1.9 μ, and although he was not sure at the time as to the nature of the bands, he concluded that they were of telluric origin since their intensity changed with the elevation of the observation stations. He referred to the bands as "cold bands," obviously because the bolometer saw them as cold when compared with the rest of the solar spectrum.

Later, when these "cold bands" were identified with water vapor absorption in the earth's atmosphere, Fowle undertook a study of certain of them with the aim of measuring the total amount of water between an observer and the sun.[2] Working in the 1.1- and 1.4-μ bands, he constructed and calibrated an infrared absorption hygrometer employing a prism spectroscope with a Nernst glower as an energy source and having an extreme optical path of more than 800 ft. From the absorption-vs-humidity data obtained with this instrument he was able to transfer calibration to other spectroscopes used in solar observations and thus measure the total water in the earth's atmosphere. It is interesting to note that Fowle's infrared absorption hygrometer was not constructed to measure water vapor at the earth's surface but rather to obtain data which would permit the measurement of the total precipitable water in the atmosphere overhead.

Since Fowle's work, scientists in the field of geophysics and hygrometry have developed infrared absorption hygrometers of varied design and operation, both for measuring atmospheric total precipitable water vapor overhead and for measuring water vapor at the earth's surface. Such instruments for the most part have been special-purpose instruments designed for research and not for general use.

More recently, because of the meteorologist's need for better instrumentation to measure water vapor in the atmosphere and because of certain intrinsic advantages offered by the infrared absorption method over other methods of measuring humidity, an effort has been made to develop a reliable general-purpose instrument of this type. Probably the most comprehensive and extensive work in the field has been carried out by Wood of General Mills, Ostergen of Beckman Instruments, and Foskett of the Instrumental Engineering Division, U.S. Weather Bureau.[3, 4, 5] This paper describes the present status of the work at the U.S. Weather Bureau.

HYGROMETER FUNDAMENTALS

Fundamentally, the infrared absorption hygrometer is an optical instrument designed to measure the absolute humidity of the atmosphere by measuring the absorption of radiant energy over a given optical path in the spectral region of an infrared water vapor absorption band. Basically such an instrument comprises an energy source, a beam of radiant energy, a radiant-energy detector, some means for isolating wavelengths in the spectral region of interest and a method for measuring the attenuation of radiant energy caused by the water vapor mass in the beam. The method usually employed in measuring the beam attenuation is the one first used by Fowle. It consists essentially of isolating the radiation in two regions of the spectrum (one in a water-sensitive absorption region and the other in a region close by where no appreciable absorption occurs) and of measuring the energy in each of these regions. The ratio of the energy intensities of these two regions can then be used as an index of the amount of water vapor in the optical path. This method of comparing the absorption band to that of the reference band permits the measurement of water vapor in the presence of transmission changes due to haze, smoke, or fog. This method may be used only if the measurements are made close enough in time and if the regions sampled are close enough spectrally that differential scattering by intervening particles in the beam does not become a first-order effect. It is not essential that the "out of band" measurement

be made in a spectral region completely free of water vapor absorption as long as the absorption coefficient is less than for the "in band" region. The instrument described later in this paper samples the "in band" and "out of band" regions sixty times per second. The spectral shift from region to region in this sampling is approximately 5 mμ, as shown in Fig. 1. It will be seen from the figure, which is a relatively high-resolution spectrogram of the 1.37-μ water vapor absorption band, that the spectra in such bands are not continuous but rather are characterized by numerous closely spaced lines, irregular both as to spacing and intensity. For this reason, the relation of absorption intensity to the absorbing water vapor mass cannot be expressed by the usual exponential function (Beers Law) as in the case where the region is one of continuous absorption. Considering the problem from a theoretical standpoint, Elsasser proposed that for a limited range of absorption the absorption can be expressed by the equation:

$$A = (P/P_0)^{1/2} (T_0 T)^{1/4} K(W)^{1/2} \qquad (1)$$

where A is the fractional absorption; T_0 and P_0 are standard temperature and pressure respectively; K is a constant depending on the spectral region of absorption; and W is the absorbing water mass or the "precipitable water" expressed in centimeters.[6, 7] (The expression precipitable water as used throughout this paper is defined as the depth of liquid water which if evaporated into a column of the same cross section, would produce the absorbing layer of gas.) More recently, Howard, in a comprehensive study of the absorption bands of water vapor and carbon dioxide, finds that the empirical equation

$$A = CW^{1/2} (P + p)^K \qquad (2)$$

fits experimental water vapor absorption data quite satisfactorily for weak absorptions.[8] In this equation, A is the total absorption, C is a constant dependent on the spectral region of observation and other factors, K is a constant approximately equal to 0.3 and p is the partial pressure of the water vapor. Other variables are as indicated for the equation proposed by Elsasser. Elsasser's equation indicates that the validity of an infrared-hygrometer calibration is dependent upon the temperature. The nature of this dependency,

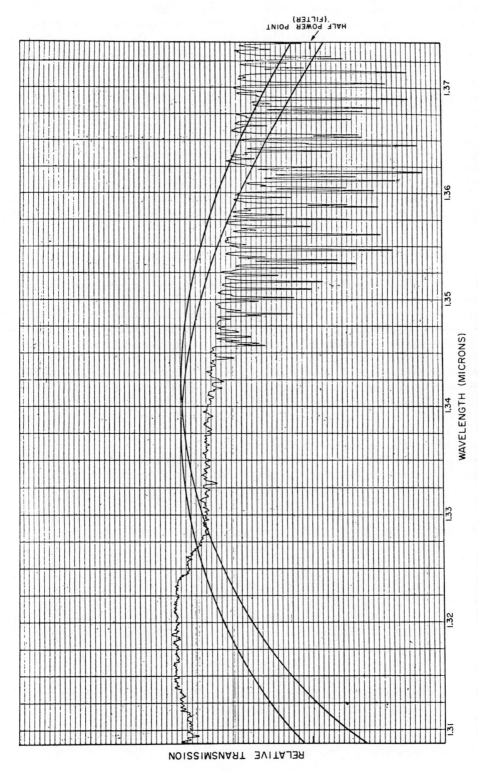

FIG. 1. Spectrogram with detail of the short-wavelength shoulder of the 1.37-μ water vapor absorption band. Arched curves show half-power spectral transmittance of oscillating filter in extreme positions.

however, is such as to make that effect a second-order one if the instrument is employed in making atmospheric measurements. The effect of pressure cannot be so treated. Both equations show a calibration dependency on pressure of such magnitude that it must be taken into account, if observations are made at elevations differing by a substantial amount. Both equations also show that the absorption increases linearly with the square root of the water mass. It is pointed out by Elsasser, however, that the relationship holds only for a limited range of absorptions.[6] For strong absorptions, the increase in absorption is less than the square root of the water mass.

The fact that the exact form of the water-mass-absorption function is not known, and probably cannot be expressed by a single equation, would appear to detract from the absorption-spectra method. This is not necessarily true, however, for while it would be desirable to know the exact relationship between water vapor mass and absorption, when effecting a calibration, it is not too important since an empirical relationship between absorption and absorbing mass, under different concentrations of water vapor, can be determined experimentally. Regardless of the exact form of the absorption function, it is well established that within limits, the rate of change of absorption increases with a decrease of water vapor concentration in the optical path. This behavior results in an increase of sensitivity in the infrared absorption hygrometer with a decrease in water

vapor absorption, a characteristic not common to many hygrometers.

Once the optical-path length and a method for measuring absorption have been tentatively agreed upon, the problem of arriving at a design for an infrared absorption hygrometer resolves itself mainly into selecting the water vapor absorption band which will be employed. Figure 2 is a low-resolution spectrogram showing the location and relative intensity of the water vapor absorption bands in the visible and near infrared.[9] The optical-path length in this case is 1,000 ft and the precipitable-water path is 5.7 mm. It will be observed from the spectrogram that the band intensity or coefficient of absorption, varies considerably from band to band, becoming progressively greater the farther the band is located in the infrared. This characteristic gives considerable latitude in the selection of a spectral region of observation for humidity measurements. It is apparent that for a long optical path and high humidities, a shallow band, such as the one at $0.93\,\mu$, should be used, while for a short optical path and low humidities, a deep band, such as the one at 2.7 microns, would be more desirable. Obviously, a band which will saturate or approach 100 per cent absorption for water vapor paths of interest is not satisfactory. Early work indicated that for best results the maximum absorption should be kept to 40 per cent or less.[5] Since water vapor concentrations generally encountered in the atmosphere at this latitude vary from a few tenths of a gram to more than 30

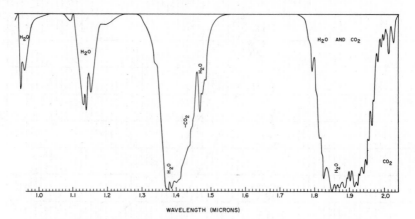

Fig. 2. Near-infrared spectrum in the neighborhood of the $1.37\text{-}\mu$ water vapor absorption band. Observations made over a 1000-ft atmospheric path at sea level with $5.7\text{-}m\mu$ precipitable water.

grams per cubic meter, the band selected should give not more than 40 per cent absorption for the optical path used at a water vapor concentration of 30 g/m³. It has been found that for optical paths of a meter or less, the 1.37-μ band meets this requirement. Moreover, this band, because of the steepness of its short-wavelength shoulder, offers another advantage, in the method of sampling or modulation employed, as will later be shown.

Of the points to be considered in the selection of a water vapor absorption band, last, but not the least in importance, is the question as to whether or not the spectral area under consideration contains absorption bands or lines as a result of the concentration of gases in the atmosphere other than water vapor. Figure 2 shows that such a situation exists in several of the near infrared water bands, where carbon dioxide absorption bands overlap the water vapor absorption bands. This figure also indicates that of the atmospheric gases that might give trouble in humidity measurements by the infrared absorption method, carbon dioxide is probably the most important to be dealt with. Obviously, the water vapor band employed must be so situated spectrally as to eliminate any possible effect of carbon dioxide. In using the 1.37-μ water vapor band, care has been taken to avoid the faint carbon dioxide absorption situated in that region by confining observations to the spectral area on the short-wavelength side of the band.

Salient Features of the Method

The infrared absorption hygrometer, designed to take advantage of the inherent qualities of the absorption-spectra method, has a number of features not common to other instruments for measuring humidity. The most outstanding of these features are:

(1) High sensitivity at low water vapor concentrations.

(2) Fast speed of response for all water vapor concentrations.

(3) Ability to effect an integrated humidity measurement over a short or long path without disturbing the sample.

(4) Ability to effect a humidity measurement without altering the sample concentration by either adding or subtracting water or changing the state of any part of the sample.

Feature (3) is not obtained if the humidity measurement is made over an enclosed path as in the case of the instrument described in this paper. Features (1) and (4) are obtained in all instruments of the absorption-spectra type, the limiting sensitivity under feature (1) being determined only by the path length for a given water vapor absorption band. Whether or not feature (2) is realized, is determined by the method employed in measuring the water vapor absorption. Since the instrument described in this paper employs a relatively slow servo system and an energy source with an appreciable time constant, its speed of response is about 1 second.

DEVELOPMENT OF THE HYGROMETER

Previous Work

A review of previous Weather Bureau work on the development of an infrared absorption type hygrometer is given in a report, dated September 1954.[10] In that report two experimental instruments, the outcome of the work at that time, are described in detail. These instruments are of essentially the same design, differing only in that one employs an open sensing path and the other a closed sensing path. The design utilized in the instruments makes use of the 1.37-μ absorption band and utilizes a reference wavelength of 1.24 μ. The sensing path is 1 meter in length. Basically, the design comprises (1) a tungsten-lamp energy source, (2) a lens-collimated beam of radiant energy, (3) a lead sulfide detector photocell, (4) a selenium monitor photocell, (5) a sector-wheel modulator or sampler, and (6) a servo system with amplifier. Spectral isolation is obtained by narrow band-pass interference filters contained in the sector wheel. The wheel is arranged so that alternate sectors pass bands of energy in the 1.38-μ and 1.24-μ spectral regions. The unique feature of the design is the method of measuring the water vapor in the sensing beam. This is done by chopping the beam with the sector wheel and thus effectively sampling the energy of the beam in the 1.24- and 1.37-μ spectral regions as the filters are alternately interposed. The sector wheel is rotated at such a speed that a sample is obtained for each region in 1/60 of a second. A servo-actuated self-balancing null system is employed whereby the energy in the 1.37-μ absorption band is kept equal to the energy in the 1.24-μ reference band at all times. Balance is maintained automatically by shifting the spectral energy distribution of the sensing beam. Shift is accomplished by varying the temperature of the lamp through a servo-operated variable transformer. The lamp temperature is then an index of the water vapor absorption in the beam. An index of the amount of water vapor in the beam is obtained by monitoring the energy of the lamp with a selenium photocell.

Instruments patterned after this design gave fairly satisfactory results over a limited water vapor range but their stability left a great deal to be desired. Moreover, the sector wheel, because of sharp transmission discontinuities between adjacent interference filters, introduced harmonics in the servo-system amplifier which presented electronic design problems and tended also to reduce sensitivity. The development in this area presently being carried out at the Weather Bureau is slanted to a similar design but with emphasis on elimination of the faults of the first instruments, particularly in regard to lack of long-time stability which is a first requirement for a meteorological instrument.

Later Work

A close study of the behavior of the first experimental instruments indicated that the basic measuring method employed in their design was satisfactory, and that better performance would be realized if an improved energy source and monitor photocell could be found. Moreover, it also seemed desirable, because of the aforementioned difficulties with the sector wheel, to investigate the possibility of replacing the wheel by devising some improved method for modulating or sampling the sensing beam.

With these aims in mind, a number of lamps and lamp power supplies have been tested for possible energy-source use, and a new method of modulating the beam has been developed. In addition, numerous photocells have been tested and other measuring schemes tried for possible use in monitoring the lamp temperature. Utilizing the findings from these investigations and resulting developments, several instruments of varying design configurations have been fabricated and tested. Of these instruments the most promising, from the standpoint of general performance, is the instrument shown in Figs. 3 and 4. A

FIG. 3. The 1-meter folded-path infrared absorption hygrometer as a packaged unit.

FIG. 4. One-meter folded-path infrared absorption hygrometer with humidity chamber cover off and equipment drawer extended.

number of instruments patterned after the one shown have been fabricated and are being used by the Weather Bureau in hurricane and tornado reconnaissance planes and at special test sites. Salient features of the design employed in these instruments will be described later.

AN IMPROVED MODULATOR

The dependency of the spectral band-pass of a multilayer silver interference filter on the angle of incidence is well known to workers in the field of optics.[11] This characteristic is demonstrated in Fig. 5 which shows the relationship of wavelength of maximum transmittance to angle of incidence for a filter having a band-pass in the neighborhood of the 1.37-μ water vapor absorption band. To a person, faced with the problem of designing an improved modulator to replace the sector wheel used on the first experimental instruments, the possibility of making use of this modulation effect is intriguing. By oscillating the filter about an axis, the band-pass trans-

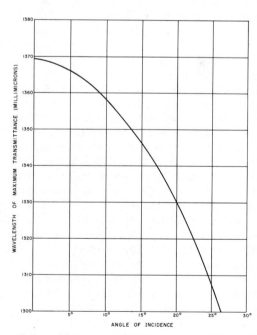

FIG. 5. Wavelength of maximum transmittance as a function of angle of incidence for a multilayer silver filter.

ition from one spectral region to another is smoother and without discontinuities (Fig. 5). From this it is apparent that modulation effected by such a method should, when viewed through an amplifier, be smooth, approach a sine wave, and be without pronounced harmonics. On first appraisal, the most important drawback to the method would appear to be the small shift in passband for a reasonable angle of oscillation. In designing the first experimental instruments, it was assumed that for best performance the reference spectral region should, if possible, be located completely out of the water vapor absorption band. For that particular design, therefore, a passband shift of approximately 130 mμ was required. A glance at Fig. 5 will show that for the spectral region under discussion such a shift by the oscillating-filter method is entirely out of the question. Selecting an oscillation swing of $\pm 2\frac{1}{2}$ degrees, which would appear to be realistic for a simple oscillating system, it will be seen (Fig. 5) that the maximum wavelength shift that can be obtained is approximately 16 mμ, about one-eighth that specified for the first design. In spite of this apparent deficiency, it was reasoned that the better performance, obtainable with an oscillating-filter-type modulator, might more than compensate for the reduction in sensitivity, due to the loss in spectral passband shift, by giving a better signal-to-noise ratio at the servo amplifier. This has proved to be the case. A number of modulators of this type have been designed and fabricated, and the results obtained with these units have been most gratifying. Figure 6 shows details of one of the first designs. It will be seen from this drawing that the modulator consists essentially of a filter-support ring, hinged to a sturdy frame by spring strap hinges, and an electromagnetic driver. Drive coupling is provided for the filter by a small permanent magnet carried on an arm extended from the filter support ring. This magnet swings in close proximity to the pole piece of the electromagnetic driver when the support ring is moved on its hinges. The hinges are not under longitudinal tension. Since the hygrometer employs a 60-cycle servo system, the electromagnetic driver is designed to operate from a 60-cycle source for oscillation of the filter. Optimum performance is obtained when the

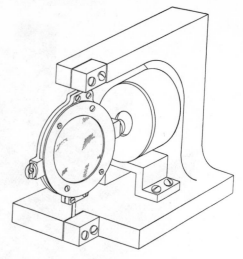

Fig. 6. Pictorial drawing of the oscillating-filter modulator.

stiffness and dimensions of the spring hinges are such as to give the system a natural period of about 80 cps. Figure 7 shows the relationship of oscillation amplitude to drive voltage for one of the modulators used.

ADVANTAGES OF THE OSCILLATING FILTER

The oscillating-filter method of modulation has exhibited desirable features not possessed by other methods. Of these the most outstanding are:

(1) The modulator is of exceedingly simple design requiring no rotating components.

(2) Modulation is accomplished without the occurrence of harmonics in the servo-system amplifier; i.e., the error signal, as detected by the amplifier, approaches a sine wave.

(3) The spectral region sampled can be brought as close to the reference spectral region as desired, consistent with adequate sensitivity, by changing the amplitude of oscillation.

(4) The spectral region sampled can be changed at will over a limited range (50 mμ in the 1.37-μ region) by changing the angle of incidence of the sensing beam, i.e., the rest-position angle of the modulating filter.

It was first thought that the dependence of the amplitude of spectral shift on filter-oscillation amplitude might lead to trouble in practice, as the amplitude of filter oscillation

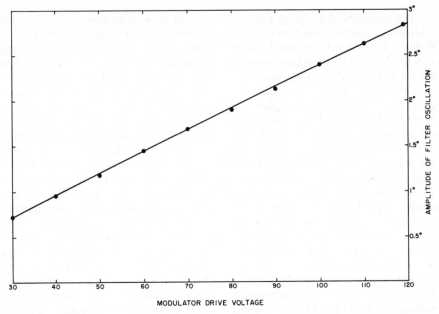

Fig. 7. Dependency of amplitude of filter oscillation on modulator drive voltage.

is directly dependent upon the magnitude of the 60-cycle line voltage. This has been found, in general, not to be the case since in most configurations tested, the amplitude of oscillation affects only the sensitivity of the servo loop over a wide range of modulator driving voltages. Some instrumental arrangements have shown that calibration has a slight dependency on amplitude of oscillation. This is believed to result from an abrupt change of slope of the absorption band contour in the observed region. The ability to change at will the spectral region of observation has important instrumental design implications, since by taking advantage of this characteristic one can begin to think of achieving a common calibration curve for all instruments of a given design.

Because of the improved performance and other outstanding advantages offered by this method of modulation, the latest infrared absorption hygrometer designs have centered around its use. When used, the design configuration is so arranged that (1) the peak transmission of the filter at the rest position is located directly over the shoulder of the water vapor absorption band, and (2) the modulator driving power is adjusted to give a minimum spectral sweep, consistent with adequate servo-system sensitivity. Figure 1

shows the approximate wavelength of the center of sweep and the amplitude of sweep employed in the modulators used in the latest hygrometer designs. In this Figure, the water vapor absorption spectra is depicted by the fine, unevenly spaced lines. The half-power spectral transmittance of the filter for the extreme positions of oscillation is illustrated by the arched curves. The curves show the transmittance to the same wavelength scale as the water vapor spectra. The Figure shows that the spectral sweep center is located at $1.34 \mu \pm 2.5 m\mu$. This places the wavelength of the maximum transmittance of the reference spectral region at 1.3375μ and that of the absorption spectral region at 1.3425μ. The ± 2.5-$m\mu$ spectral sweep amplitude represents a filter oscillation of approximately $1\frac{1}{2}$ degrees, which is quite small, and illustrates the extreme sensitivity of the oscillating-filter-modulation method.

FOLDED-PATH INSTRUMENT

The one-meter folded-path infrared absorption hygrometer, resulting from recent work in this field, is the latest instrumental design to have reasonable calibration stability over a period of time. For this reason, the instrument is described here in some detail.

Figure 3 is a photograph showing the one-meter folded-path infrared absorption hygrometer. Figure 4 is a second view of the same instrument. It shows the optical components of the instrument mounted under the cover with the electronic components occupying a drawer in the base. With the cover in place, the enclosure containing the optical train forms a gastight water vapor sensing chamber with vents on both ends to provide a sample flow path. The material used in fabrication of housing and mounting facilities is aluminum; retaining screws and fasteners are of corrosion-resistant steel. Switches on the front of the electronics drawer provide control for the various electrical components of the instrument. A connector on one end of the electronics enclosure connects the instrument to the 60-cycle powerline and the recorder. Power required for operation of the instrument is approximately 100 watts at 117V AC. Overall dimensions of the unit are approximately 25¾ in. long, 12½ in. wide, and 14⅜ in. high. Weight of the unit is about 70 pounds.

Figure 8 is a schematic showing the arrangement of the optical train and the general circuit configuration of electrical and electronic assemblies of the instrument. The major components of the optical train are a lamp, oscillating-filter modulator, mirror, lens, monitor photocell, and detector photocell with mixing cone. The major electrical and electronic components and assemblies are a servo motor, servo amplifier, lamp power supply and phase shift network. It should be noted that the optical train does not provide a well-collimated beam at the modulator. This arrangement of the optical train is used because it employs fewer optical components and gives less trouble from reflections than a two-lens configuration. In addition, a mixing cone is employed at the detector photocell. This device is used to make optical alignment less critical, and has been found to give better results than the diffusing plate used in the first experimental instruments. The lens is so positioned that a small image of the lamp filament is formed approximately one inch in front of the throat of the cone (Fig. 8). Except for the vibration filter which has been described the train is conventional.

As in the first experimental instruments, the electrical and electronic circuit configurations are designed to always give a null signal at the detector photocell. This null signal is obtained by automatically adjusting the lamp temperature, and hence the energy distribution of the beam to compensate for water vapor absorption losses in the absorption spectra of the beam. The monitor photocell output is an index of lamp temperature and an indication of the water vapor in the beam. The

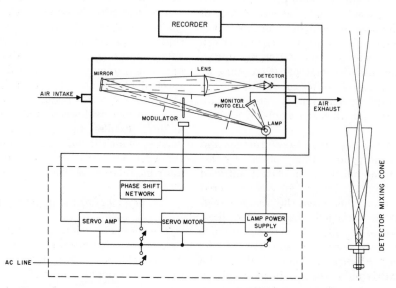

Fig. 8. Functional diagram showing general arrangement of optical and electrical components in 1-meter folded-path infrared absorption hygrometer.

servo amplifier and motor are conventional 60-cycle components originally designed by the Bristol Company for use in a self-balancing recording potentiometer. The amplifier is modified to reduce the input noise by changing the tube in the first stage from a 7F7 to a 7025, and by powering the first-stage filaments from unfiltered DC. The phase shift network consists of a stepdown transformer and a capacitor, so connected that the output of the transformer feeds the coil of the modulator electromagnet through the capacitor. The purpose of the network is to phase the modulator output so that the detector-error signals, as seen at the amplifier output, will be in quadrature with the 60-cycle line voltage and thus provide maximum driving torque at the two-phase servo motor which controls the lamp supply output voltage. The lamp supply is designed to furnish high-current low-voltage DC power for operation of the lamp. The first experimental instruments did not require a DC lamp supply since the lamp employed a massive coiled filament (20 A) which tended to smooth the 120-cycle powerline ripple seen by the detector photocell. The coiled-coil filament lamps, now used because they provide more blackbody radiation than the coiled filament type, have less massive filaments (2 to 4 A) and thus provide less ripple smoothing. To eliminate the possible loss of amplifier sensitivity, due to filament "hum," a well-filtered supply is required.

Data on the physical characteristics of the major components and assemblies used in the design of the folded-path instrument is given in the following list:

(1) Optical train

(a) Optical path length—1 meter

(b) Lamp—tubular bulb, coiled-coil filament, prefocus base, overall length $3\frac{1}{8}$ in., rated watts 28, rated volts 14.0, maximum operating volts 8.8 DC, time constant less than 1 second, life expectancy greater than 21,000 hours for continuous service.

(c) Filter—interference, narrow band-pass type, half-power band-pass 50 mμ, wavelength of maximum transmittance 1.376 μ, maximum transmittance 44 per cent.

(d) Modulator—angle of incidence of filter at rest position 17.0 degrees, spectral sweep 3.5 mμ, amplitude of filter sweep 1.3 degrees, electromagnetic drive voltage 92, 60-cycle AC.

(e) Mirror—front aluminized, with silicon monoxide protective coating.

(f) Lens—plano convex, white glass, focal length 6 in. diameter 2.4 in.

(g) Detector photocell—photoconductive, lead sulfide with special button-type holder and thin glass cover, sensitive area approximately $\frac{3}{16}$-in. diameter, dark resistance $\frac{1}{2}$ megohm, load resistance 1 megohm low noise, bias voltage 40 DC.

(h) Mixing cone—brass, gold plated, polished inside, cone angle 10 degrees, length $2\frac{3}{4}$ in.

(i) Monitor photocell—selenium, hermetically sealed, sensitive area $1\frac{1}{2}$ in. $\times$ $1\frac{1}{2}$ in.

(2) Electrical components and assemblies

(a) Amplifier—electronic, Bristol Type Cl, 120-V 60-cycle, 120-cycle suppression, band-pass 30 cps. Operating voltage gain approximately 1 million. Details of circuit design are shown in Fig. 9.

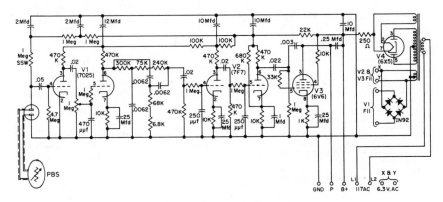

FIG. 9. Servo amplifier schematic wiring diagram.

(b) Servo motor—two phase, external gear train, 120-V, 60-cycle.

(c) Lamp power supply—direct current, ripple not to exceed 10 mV with 2-A load at 12 V. Details of circuit design are shown in Fig. 10.

In service, the output of the hygrometer is either read from a micro-ammeter or recorded on a millivolt potentiometric recorder. In either case, the total monitor photocell load is always kept equal to 111 Ω, a resistance at which the temperature sensitivity of the cell is small. In making surface observations, aspiration for the sensing chamber is obtained by drawing air through the chamber with an external motor-driven blower. Observations from an airplane are made by forcing air through the chamber with an airscoop.

CALIBRATION

A calibration curve for the folded-path unit, shown in Figs. 3 and 4, is given in Fig. 11. In effecting this calibration curve, the known relative humidities, resulting from saturated solutions of reagent-grade salts mixed with distilled water, are utilized. Figure 12 is a schematic of the calibrating apparatus used. In this apparatus, saturated salt solution B, is contained in a stainless-steel beaker. A metal housing, containing a circulating fan and intake and outlet connections, is fitted in the beaker opening. An "O" ring seal provides a gastight seal between the housing and the beaker. The hygrometer sensing chamber is connected in series with the intake and outlet connections of the fan assembly on the beaker. Coil F (stainless-steel tubing) is employed to keep the temperature of the circulating air entering the beaker equal to that within the beaker. The beaker is entirely submerged in a liquid temperature-controlled bath. At equilibrium, the saturation vapor pressure e_s is constant throughout the system. Forced-air circulation and vigorous stirring of the saturated salt solution, greatly lessens the time required to reach equilibrium.

In the beaker containing the salts, the saturation vapor pressure in millibars is

$$e_s = e_w (\text{RH}) \tag{3}$$

where e_w is the saturation vapor pressure of water at the temperature of the saturated salt solution (T_b) and RH is the per cent of relative humidity at (T_b) of the salt solution used.[12,13] The density of the water vapor P_w in g/m³ is

$$P_w = 216.7 \, e_s/T \tag{4}$$

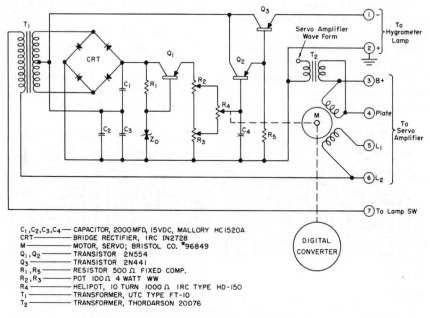

C₁,C₂,C₃,C₄ — CAPACITOR, 2000 MFD, 15 VDC, MALLORY HC1520A
CRT —————— BRIDGE RECTIFIER, IRC IN2728
M ——————— MOTOR, SERVO; BRISTOL CO. #96849
Q₁,Q₂ ————— TRANSISTOR 2N554
Q₃ ————————— TRANSISTOR 2N441
R₁,R₅ ————— RESISTOR 500 Ω FIXED COMP.
R₂,R₃ ————— POT 100 Ω 4 WATT WW
R₄ ————————— HELIPOT, 10 TURN 1000 Ω IRC TYPE HD-150
T₁ ————————— TRANSFORMER, UTC TYPE FT-10
T₂ ————————— TRANSFORMER, THORDARSON 20D76

Fig. 10. Lamp power supply schematic wiring diagram.

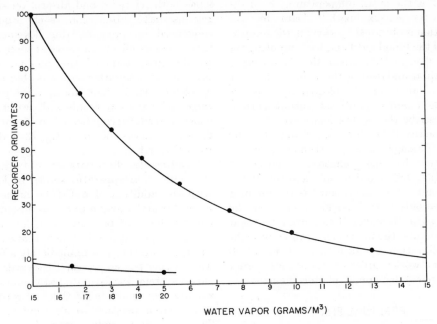

FIG. 11. Calibration curve for 1-meter folded-path infrared hygrometer.

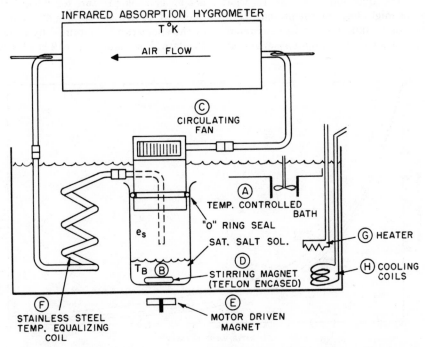

FIG. 12. Diagram showing arrangement of equipment employed in calibration of hygrometer.

where T is the mean temperature, °K of the hygrometer sensing path.[12] Data for the calibration is obtained by varying the temperature of the liquid bath and by computing the values of e_s and P_w upon the condition of equilibrium, and reading the monitor photocell output. Values of P_w plotted against the resulting monitor photocell output current then describe the calibration curve.

In practice it has been found that, barring serious damage to an instrument, once a calibration has been effected, a check on calibration drift requires only a check at the "dry point"; the "dry point" is the monitor photocell output with no water vapor in the sensing path. Moreover, it has been found that if drift occurs, the instrument can be brought into calibration by adjusting the photocell output network to give full scale at the recorder for the new "dry point" photocell current.

PRESSURE EFFECT

Since the oscillating-filter method of modulation compares a spectral region of water vapor absorption with a region of lesser absorption, rather than with a region of no absorption, the question arises as to what influence this might have on the pressure term of the absorption function for an instrument employing the device. One might assume that,

since both reference and absorption spectral regions have absorption, each would be influenced by pressure, thus lessening the total pressure effect. To arrive at some idea as to the magnitude of the pressure effect, preliminary calibration data was obtained, for a selected instrument, for a total pressure range of 200 to 1000 mb with water vapor concentration varying from 2 to 17 g/m³. The family of curves shown in Fig. 13 is derived from this data.

The pressure effect data was obtained with the calibration apparatus shown in Fig. 12, with the addition of a U-tube manometer, manostat and vacuum pump to measure and control the total pressure in the system. In using the apparatus, it is evident that changing the total pressure will immediately affect the water vapor partial pressure. However, in the closed system, the saturated salt solution will rapidly accommodate for this and return the water vapor pressure to its previous value. Thus, in effect, adding or removing air to change the total pressure alters only the partial pressure of dry air.

The most important conclusion that can be drawn from the curves of Fig. 13 is that there is a measurable pressure for the instrument in question. Moreover, an idea of the magnitude of the effect can be obtained by inspection of the data. For example, it will be observed that

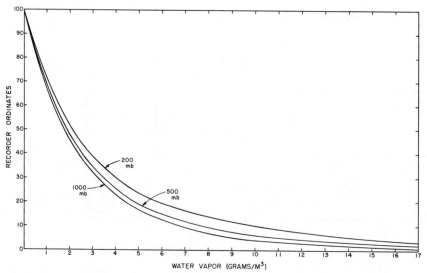

FIG. 13. Absolute humidity indications as a function of pressure for a selected 1-meter infrared absorption hygrometer.

for a recorder reading of 12.7, a 1000-mb calibration will indicate a water vapor concentration of 6.0 g/m³, whereas a 500-mb calibration will indicate a concentration of 6.8 g/m³. This, of course, means that if the instrument is calibrated at 1000 mb and this calibration is used in making observations at 500 mb, the indicated water vapor concentration will be too low and will be in error by approximately 12 per cent. Similar inspection shows an error of approximately 9 per cent for an indicated concentration of 4 g/m³ at 1000 mb. It is interesting to note that Wood's data for the pressure effect on an instrument designed to work in the 2.7-μ water vapor band shows errors of approximately 25 and 20 per cent, respectively, for the same water vapor concentrations.[3] This seems to indicate that if the pressure term of the absorption function follows the best-fit law by Howard, the $(P + p)$ exponent for the instrument in question is probably less than the 0.23 value found by Wood.

Work is now in process to repeat the pressure-effect data run and to determine, if possible, the exact form of the pressure term of the absorption function. The fact that the spectral regions sampled lie close together lends some hope to this being accomplished.

CONCLUSION

Several versions of a basic hygrometer, to measure water vapor by absorption in the 1.37-μ spectral region over relatively short paths, have been built. With a 1-meter absorption path it is possible to measure water concentration over a range from less than 10 ppm by volume to about 2500 ppm. The instrument is simple with a minimum of optical components, and except for a recorder, the only moving mechanism subject to deterioration from wear is a servo-voltage-balancing mechanism. Initial calibration is made using selective saturated-salt solutions at controlled temperatures, and calibration checks are accomplished by drying the chamber with a suitable desiccant. The sensitivity of the hygrometer varies from 1 or 2 ppm, by volume of water, at low humidities, to several parts per million at extremely high values. This humidity is resolved to an equivalent dew-point scale sensitivity ranging from two or three degrees at very low values to better than 0.5 degree at high humidities. In practice the sensitivity is generally limited to the recording or indicating device at about 0.1 per cent of the full-scale value. The short-term stability, up to one week, is excellent, and long-term stability, one month or more, varies considerably from instrument to instrument. The reason for this instability is still being investigated. Moreover, it is concluded that the full value of the method will not be achieved until a stable open-path instrument is developed in which the measurement is made in situ. The instrument is still classed as a special-purpose device and is not yet suitable for general field application.

Acknowledgment. The authors gratefully acknowledge the assistance of Messrs. Donald T. Acheson and Willard V. Compton of the Instrumental Engineering Division, U.S. Weather Bureau. Mr. Acheson designed the calibrating equipment and obtained the preliminary data showing the effect of pressure on the calibration. Mr. Compton has made the mechanical layout and design of the several instruments that have been built.

References

1. Langley, S. P., "Researches on Solar Heat and its Absorption by the Earth's Atmosphere," A report on the Mount Whitney Expedition, Professional Papers of the Signal Service No. XV, Government Printing Office, 1884.
2. Fowle, F. E., *Astrophys. J.*, **35**, 149 (1912).
3. Wood, R. C., "Improved Infrared Absorption Spectra Hygrometer," *Rev. Sci. Instr.*, **29**, 36–42 (1958).
4. Final Engineering Report, Measuring Set, Dewpoint AN/AMQ-14(XH-1), Item V, Contract AF 33 (600)-30790, Beckman Instruments, Inc.
5. Foskett, L. W., *et. al.*, "Infrared Absorption Hygrometer," *Monthly Weather Rev.*, **81**, 267–277 (1953).
6. Elsasser, W. M., "On Some Properties of the Water-Vapor Spectrum and Their Relation to Atmospheric Radiation," *Monthly Weather Rev.*, **65**, 323 (1937).
7. Elsasser, W. M., "New Values for the Infrared Absorption Coefficient of Atmospheric Water-Vapor," *Monthly Weather Rev.*, **66**, 175–178 (1938).
8. Howard, V. N., *et al.*, "Near Infrared Transmission Through Synthetic Atmosphere," Geophysical Research Paper No. 40, Geophysics Research Director, Air Force Cambridge Research Center, November 1955.

9. Yates, H. W., "The Absorption Spectrum from 0.5 to 25 Microns of a 1000-Ft. Atmospheric Path at Sea Level," Naval Research Laboratory Report No. 5033, September 27, 1957.

10. Wood, R. C., *et al.*, "Infrared Absorption Hygrometer—A Progress Report," Presented at First International Congress and Exposition of the Instrument Society of America, Philadelphia, Paper No. 54-36-1, September 1954.

11. Interference Filters, Transmission Type, 330 Millimicron—1200 Millimicron, Brochure No. D248, 11589, Bausch and Lomb Optical Company.

12. "Smithsonian Meteorological Tables," Washington, D.C., Smithsonian Institution, 6th ed (1951).

13. Wexler, A., and Hasegawa, S., *J. Res. Nat. Bur. Std.*, **53**, 19 (1954).

47. A Long-path Infrared Hygrometer

W. G. Tank and E. J. Wergin

The Boeing Company, Seattle, Washington

ABSTRACT

A recording infrared hygrometer which measures the total atmospheric water vapor content in a collimated beam of light is described. A beam of energy, propagated over a measured path, is collected at a receiver through a single aperture. Temperature-compensated lead sulfide cell detectors are used to sense the intensity of the collected energy in two bands of the infrared spectrum, one centered at a wavelength of 1.9 μ, the other at 2.2 μ. The former band is subject to attenuation by water vapor, the latter is not. The ratio of the received band energies is thus sensitive to the total amount of water vapor in the light path. Wavelength isolation is accomplished with narrow band-pass, germanium interference filters. The band energy ratio is effectively determined by passing the detector outputs through logarithmic signal converters and thence through a differential amplifier to a recorder.

Moderate amounts of haze or fog in the light path do not significantly affect system calibration. Changes in water vapor content of orders 0.5 per cent of the total amount sensed are readily detected, and system accuracy equals or exceeds that attained using conventional hygrometric techniques to measure total amounts of water vapor over long paths.

INTRODUCTION

The band structure of the near-infrared water vapor absorption spectrum provides the basis for measurement of atmospheric humidity by radiometric techniques.[3] The determination of the per cent transmission, over a measured path through the atmosphere,

of energy emitted in a specified water vapor absorption band by a precisely calibrated source, for example, can be related directly to the water vapor content of the atmosphere. A more tractable approach to such measurement, however, is one in which the intensities of energy received in two different but adjacent bands in the infrared spectrum are measured, one of which is attenuated by water vapor, the other not. A comparison of the two band energies then provides the required measurement.[2,12] Thanks to the development of two devices, the lead sulfide cell infrared detector and the narrow band-pass, interference filter, this type of differential absorption hygrometer, in many different configurations, is rapidly achieving operational status. Investigators are thereby being offered intriguing opportunities for atmospheric humidity research in a variety of problem areas difficult to investigate by conventional methods. The hygrometer to be described, for example, is designed specifically for studies in which the integrated value of the absolute humidity over extended paths through the atmosphere is the desired humidity parameter.

THE SENSING SYSTEM

The Reference and Sensing Bands

Basically, any differential absorption hygrometer requires a beam of radiant energy and some type of optical system to sense that beam at two prescribed wavelengths of the infrared spectrum. For the present case, the first requirement is readily attained by mounting an ordinary 6-V automobile headlight bulb, powered by a regulated DC power supply to

481

assure constant emission, at the focal point of a fast Schmidt-type optical system of 5-in. aperture. The tungsten filament source emits a continuous spectrum. Wavelength isolation at two wavelengths, one subject to attenuation by water vapor (the "sensing" band), the other not (the "reference" band), is accomplished by narrow band-pass, germanium interference filters.

The reference and sensing bands utilized are centered at wavelengths of 2.2 and 1.9 μ, respectively. This choice was made because (1) both wavelengths lie within the range of peak sensitivity of uncooled, lead sulfide cell detectors, (2) background radiation at such short wavelengths is practically nonexistent, and (3) ordinary glass transmits nearly 100 per cent of incident energy at these wavelengths, thus permitting the use of such glass in system optical components. The transmission curves of the filters actually used to isolate the selected bands are shown, along with the water vapor transmission curve, in Fig. 1. Note that

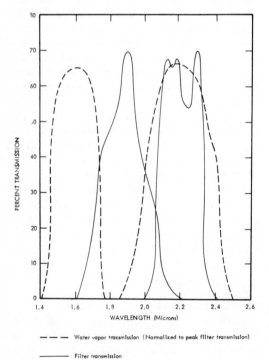

FIG. 1. The hygrometer reference and sensing narrow band-pass filter transmission curves (solid lines), and the normalized (to peak filter transmission) water vapor transmission curve (dashed line).

the sensing band is offset toward the long-wavelength side of the strong absorption band centered at 1.87 μ. Such offsetting serves to assure that the transmission in this sensing band over the range of optical depths of path lengths to be expected in operational use of the hygrometer will be approximately 20 per cent or greater, assuring, in turn, that a single absorption "law" will apply to all operational conditions.[5]

Receiver Optics

The optical system utilized to sense the emitted beam at the prescribed wavelengths is shown schematically in Fig. 2. The collimated beam is collected at the receiver through a single, 2.5-in. diameter aperture. A 180-degree prism beam splitter located behind the entrance aperture and collimating tube directs approximately half the incident energy through the 2.2-μ reference filter and half through the 1.9-μ sensing filter. Both arms of the split beam are then focused onto carefully matched (as to responsivity) lead sulfide cell infrared detectors. Focusing is accomplished by 2-in. diameter, ordinary glass, double convex lenses of 8-in. focal lengths located behind the secondary apertures. Opal glass diffusers are mounted immediately in front of the detectors to spread the focused beams over the entire sensitive areas of the detectors. This is done to eliminate shot noise that could be caused by inequalities in sensitivity at various spots on the detector surfaces.

The Instrument Package

The optical system just described is "packaged" as shown in Figs. 3 (exploded view) and 4 (assembled view). The interference

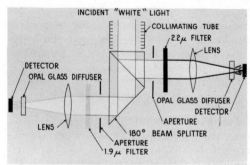

FIG. 2. Schematic diagram of the hygrometer receiver optics.

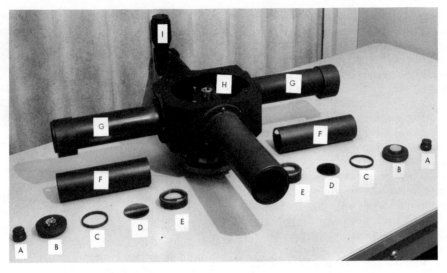

FIG. 3. Exploded view of the hygrometer receiver.

filters (D, Fig. 3) fit onto the collar mounts of the focusing lenses (E) and are held in place by the retaining rings (C). The lens-filter assemblies slide into the detector barrels (G) and are, in turn, held in place by the retaining sleeves (F). The detectors are mounted in threaded base plates (B) which screw into the detector barrels to hold all components rigidly in place.

Lead sulfide cells evidence a photoresistive effect. That is, a change in incident energy produces a change in cell resistance. Therefore, a DC bias voltage is applied, through appropriate load resistors, to the cells, and changes in incident energy are thereby manifested as changes in voltage outputs from the bias supply. The detectors used in the instrument are manufactured by the Eastman Kodak Company and are marketed under the trade name "Ektron" detectors. As is typical of all lead sulfide cell detectors, the dark resistances of these cells decrease at a rate of about 4 per cent per degree Centigrade increase in ambient temperature. Additional "Ektron" detectors, matched to the active cells and maintained at dark resistance, are therefore utilized as the load resistors in the bias supply circuitry in order to compensate for such temperature

FIG. 4. Assembled view of the hygrometer receiver.

effects. These temperature-compensating load resistors (A, Fig. 3), mounted in threaded plugs that screw into the underside of the detector barrels (Fig. 4,) are located as close as possible to the active cells in order to assure the greatest degree of temperature compensation.

Two other features of the receiver head: first, the prism beam splitter (H, Fig. 3) is mounted on a turntable base, controlled by the brass knob on the top plate of the receiver (Fig. 4). When the prism is rotated through 90 degrees in a clockwise direction, the source may be viewed through the receiver entrance aperture with the 2-power telescopic eyepiece (I, Fig. 3) for alignment purposes. Secondly, located at the secondary apertures of the detector barrels are iris diaphragms. These diaphragms are utilized to check the calibration of the system in a manner to be described later. The entire receiver head is attached to a standard $3\frac{1}{2} \times 8$ thread transit head mount for utilization on a standard surveyor's transit tripod.

THE READOUT SYSTEM

Any comparison of the two detector output signals would provide a measure of the water vapor content of the atmosphere within the beam of collected energy. A simple difference would suffice. However, the ratio between the two signals provides the much more reliable comparison because errors that could arise due to a decrease in the general level of sensed energy caused by the presence of haze or fog in the light beam would thereby be eliminated. That is, the ratio between the two signals reflects only their disproportionate, and not proportionate, changes. Hence, the ratio between the two signals is the comparison to be desired and is determined, effectively, as follows.

The high DC bias voltage applied to the cells would completely over-ride any signal sought on a straight DC readout system. The light beam is therefore chopped mechanically at the receiver aperture by a simple paddle-type chopper. The essentially AC carrier signals (Fig. 5) are then fed through capacitor-coupled (to eliminate the DC level) AC logarithmic converters. The converters rectify the AC signals and give DC outputs proportional to

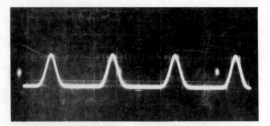

FIG. 5. Oscilloscope trace showing the shape of the chopped detector outputs.

the logarithm of the rms (root mean square) value of the input signals. These outputs in turn are fed into a DC differential amplifier to obtain the difference between the two logarithmic signals. The output from the differential amplifier, which is proportional, now, to the logarithm of the ratio of the band energies sensed, is then fed directly into an adjustable range, adjustable zero millivolt recorder. Schematically, the readout system is as shown in Fig. 6. Shown in Fig. 7 are all components of the complete system—source, chopper, receiver, and readout subsystem.

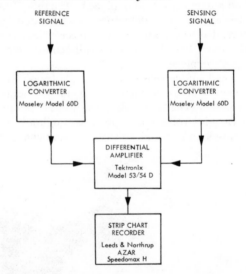

FIG. 6. Schematic representation of the hygrometer readout system. The recorded signal is proportional to the logarithm of the ratio of the input signals.

THE CALIBRATION

The calibration of the hygrometer proved quite predictable. Gates[5] demonstrated that throughout the spectral region of 0.87 to 2.54 μ, transmissions ranging between approx-

Fig. 7. The complete hygrometer system.

imately 20 and 80 per cent vary as the square root of the total amount of water vapor in the optical path according to:

$$\ln T = cw^{1/2} \tag{1}$$

where T represents transmittance, c a transmission coefficient, and w the total amount of water vapor expressed as precipitable millimeters. The recorded signal from the hygrometer may thus be expected to vary linearly with $(w)^{1/2}$. This is demonstrated in Fig. 8, the hygrometer calibration curve.

In arriving at Fig. 8, a calibration curve was first computed according to the square-root law, based on the measured values of the transmission coefficients for 1.9- and 2.2-μ wavelength radiation presented by Gates.[5] The validity of the computed curve was subsequently checked by comparing the water vapor content data obtained with the differential absorption hygrometer to similar data obtained using standard psychrometric techniques. A range of w values in this procedure was realized in two ways: (1) the normal variation in atmospheric water vapor content was monitored over a fixed path, and (2) the path was varied under conditions of constant water vapor concentrations. This procedure

permitted slight modification of the computed calibration curve such that the absorption hygrometer data conformed to the independently measured values of w.

Ordinate labels in Fig. 8 express recorder ordinates; abscissa values express the square root of precipitable millimeters of water vapor. The relationship between this latter quantity and absolute humidity is as follows:

$$w = \rho_w \cdot L \cdot 10^{-3} \tag{2}$$

where w is given in precipitable millimeters, ρ_w is absolute humidity in g/m^3, and L is path length expressed in meters. Hence, if the path length is known, ρ_w is readily recovered from measured values of $(w)^{1/2}$. The absolute value of ρ_w so obtained is interpreted as the average absolute humidity, or water vapor concentration, of the atmosphere between the source and receiver.

OPERATIONAL PROCEDURE

Use of the system in the field proceeds as follows. The propagation path is determined and the path length ascertained. The source and receiver are then aligned optically through use of the 2-power spotting telescopes with which both are equipped. Although instru-

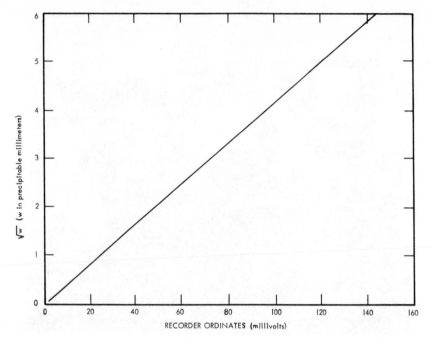

FIG. 8. The hygrometer calibration curve.

mental drift was found to be negligible, the zero reference is checked each operational run by replacing the 1.9-μ sensing filter with an additional 2.2-μ filter. The recorder should then read zero, equivalent to no water vapor in the path. Minor adjustments due to recorder or amplifier drift are made with the adjustable zero feature of the Leeds and Northrup "Speedomax H", "AZAR" recorder used to record the ratio signal.

Once the proper zero reference is established, the instrument is checked for insensitivity to general light-level changes in the following manner: iris diaphragms in the secondary apertures of the detector barrels permit partial closing of the secondary sensing aperture such that a finite signal is indicated on the recorder. The incident light intensity is then varied by means of a rheostat in the power line to the light source. If the recorder signal changes, further fine adjustments in the source-receiver alignment will correct the situation. Proper alignment is critical here because each detector must "see" the identical image of the source.

The above procedures serve (1) to establish the proper zero reference level and (2) to assure that system response to given signal ratios is proportionally the same from test run to test run. Once these procedures have been completed, the absorption filter is reintroduced into the sensing arm, and data collection is begun.

INSTRUMENT STABILITY

In evaluating the performance of the system, the apparatus was found to hold calibration well throughout a given test run and also from test to test. The "Ektron" detectors themselves are linear over a wide range of incident energy intensitities. Limits are imposed, however, by the ohmic heating of the cell films caused by too high incident energy intensities. A good rule of thumb to apply here is that linearity of response is assured so long as the output signal from a given cell does not exceed 10 mV per volt of applied bias. The only precautionary measure found necessary to assure overall system stability was that of allowing sufficient time (at least half an hour) for all electronic components of the readout system to attain stable operating conditions. Several factors that could contribute to erroneous data do, however, bear some comment, as do cursory tests made to determine their relative importance.

Temperature Effect

All cells used in the system, the active as well as the load resistor cells, are matched as to cell responsivity. This fact, plus the temperature compensating measure of using matched cells maintained at dark resistance as active cell load resistors, eliminates any adverse effect on system accuracy that could be caused by cell responsivity changes with changes in ambient temperature. And although energy absorption by water vapor between selected wavelength limits depends somewhat on ambient temperature, changes in ambient temperature of 20°C were found to have no measurable effects on the calibration.

Pressure Effects

Water vapor absorption of energy within a certain wavelength band is also dependant to some extent on atmospheric pressure. Although such effects become appreciable for drastic changes in ambient pressure (such as would be realized in airborne operations), the calibration curve established at a given pressure-altitude remains insensitive to pressure changes associated with the normal progression of "weather".

Scintillation Effects

Random inhomogeneities in the refractive index of the atmosphere caused by turbulence result in the twinkling or scintillation of remote light sources.[7] The atmospheric refractive index is expressible, for any radiation wavelength, as a complex number; the real part of this number expresses the effect of density on the refractive index, the imaginary part expresses the absorption effect. The real parts of the refractive index for 1.9- and 2.2-μ radiation are essentially equal, and only the former has an imaginary part different from zero. Therefore, insofar as the energy in both bands is viewed by the instrument through a *single entrance aperture*, the *density*-caused components of scintillation will be proportionally equal and will cancel out in the data readout system. The remaining *absorption*-caused scintillations as detected by the sensing detector, and as noted in the output of the readout system, therefore represent real fluctuations in atmospheric water vapor content.

Actually, scintillation acts, effectively, as additional "chopping" of the incident light. Insofar as the refractive index at 1.9 μ is slightly greater than that at 2.2 μ, it is conceivable that a greater degree of density-caused, in-phase scintillation could be evidenced at 1.9 μ than at 2.2 μ. This excess of "chopping" at 1.9 μ would be interpreted by the log converter as a higher DC output signal level, which, in turn, would result in a shift to the 'wet' side on the calibration. No such effect, however, was noticed during the course of field tests conducted to date.

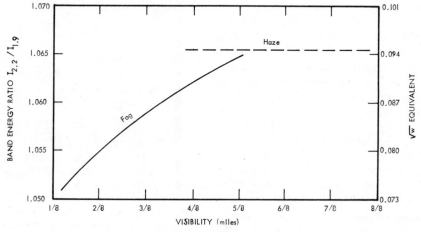

Fig. 9. Sensing and reference band energy ratios and equivalent water vapor content values established by differential scattering effects in fog and haze as functions of visual range.

Effect of Haze or Fog in the Beam

The introduction of particulate matter into a beam of light results in the scattering of light in all directions. This scattering process results in the perceptible attenuation of the beam as a whole. Relative to the sizes of typical fog and haze particles and to the radiation wavelengths utilized as the hygrometer sensing and reference bands, such scattering lies within the domain of Mie scattering, implying that the degree of scattering (and hence, attenuation) is wavelength dependent. Specifically, Mie scattering theory predicts that, for given particle size distributions, the shorter the wavelength, the more efficient is the scatter. Consequently, the radiation intensity perceived at 1.9 μ will be, to some extent, disproportionately less than that perceived at 2.2 μ. As a result, the system would indicate an atmosphere more "wet" than it actually would be.

Figure 9 presents estimates of the magnitude of this differential scattering effect. The curves are based on data on light transmission through fog obtained by Kurnick, Zitter, and Williams[9] and on similar data on light transmission through haze obtained by Gibbons.[6] Ordinate labels give visibility in miles. Abscissa values on the left side of this Figure express the band energy ratio established by the differential scattering effect; those on the right side indicate the water vapor content equivalent (relative to system sensitivity). These represent negative corrections, insofar as the water equivalent values express the apparent *excess* of water vapor content attributable purely to differential scattering effects.

Gibbons[6] found the scattering extinction coefficient in haze to exhibit a functional relationship with wavelength independent of visual range. In fog, however, the relationship between scattering coefficients at different wavelengths does change with changing visual ranges.[9] This effect comes about because of intrinsic differences in characteristic particle size distributions, and hence in scattering properties, between fogs of different opacities.[8]

According to the water equivalent values given in Fig. 9, how serious the effects of fog or haze in the beam of received radiation might be on system performance is largely a matter

of how much water vapor there is in the path to begin with. If the path lengths are long enough, or the atmosphere "wet" enough, such that the total amount of water vapor sensed is greater than, say, 0.5 precipitable mm, the error that could be caused by fog or haze in the path would probably be less than 2 per cent.

EXAMPLES

As examples of system performance under actual field-test conditions, consider Figs. 10, 11, and 12. Figure 10 shows a recorder trace obtained shortly after a rain shower on a partly cloudy day. The ground was wet, winds were moderate, and the path length between source and receiver was 400 meters, about 1.5

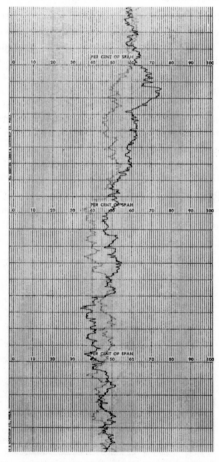

FIG. 10. A typical hygrometer recorder trace. Chart shows rapid changes in atmospheric water vapor content evidenced over wet ground on a partly cloudy day just after shower activity. The propagation path length was 400 meters.

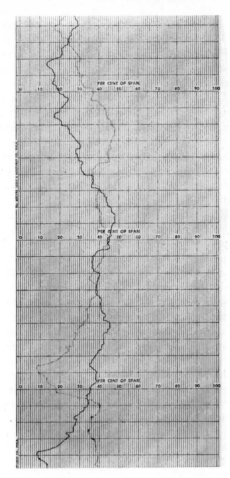

FIG. 11. Hygrometer record showing changes in atmospheric water vapor content associated with alternately on-shore and off-shore wind components. The propagation path length was 200 meters.

meters above the ground surface. The coordinates crosswise to the chart paper represent 30-second time coordinates. Only the darker traces are significant. The lighter traces are overprintings on the reverse side of the chart paper caused by the rolling up of the paper over the wet trace ink.

The most noticeable feature of Fig. 10 is the structure evidenced in the trace, implying very rapid fluctuations in atmospheric water vapor content. These rapid fluctuations undoubetdly reflect the dynamic evaporation processes active at the time the test run was made. They further point out one of the principle advantages the absorption hygrometer has to offer, namely, speed of response. The sensing "element" of such an hygrometer is a beam of

radiation. Consequently, speed of response is essentially that of the associated electronics that comprise the readout system, and to all intents and purposes, response to changes in atmospheric water content is therefore instantaneous.

The advantages of using the AZAR recorder in conjuction with a system such as that described here is demonstrated by Figs. 11 and 12. Shown in Fig. 11 is a recorder trace obtained on a sunny day when winds were light and variable. Source and receiver were 200 meters apart, and the propagation path was parallel to the shore of a small slough off Puget Sound, about 50 meters from the water's edge. The average absolute humidity was

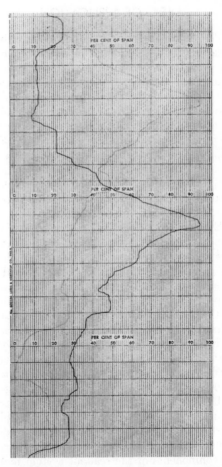

FIG. 12. Recorder trace obtained under conditions identical to those applicable to Fig. 11. Here, however, the zero reference is depressed, and the recorder scale factor is expanded to amplify the water vapor content fluctuations.

about 5 g/m³. The fluctuations in water vapor content were precisely correlated with wind direction, that is, when the wind was blowing off the water, pronounced increases in water vapor content were sensed. Conversely, when the wind direction changed to yield an off-shore component, the water content was observed to decrease.

Figure 12 is a recording obtained during the same test run. In this case, however, the recorder zero reference was depressed 30 units and the recorder scale factor increased by a factor of 10. Note how the variations in absolute humidity are amplified in Fig. 12. Again, the fluctuations were precisely correlated with wind direction.

AREAS OF APPLICATION

The infrared hygrometer just described measures the total amount of water vapor in the path through the atmosphere between source and receiver. Its greatest application will therefore be found in areas where such an integrating effect is desirable or where point checks of humidity are unrealizable from an operational or feasibility standpoint. For example, forest fire danger is a function of absolute humidity. The system described here would constitute a fire danger monitor when used to sense the total amount of water vapor in a path between two fire towers.

Evaporation from large reservoirs has become a problem of increasing importance in the dry regions of the western states. So much so that a great deal of effort has been devoted in recent years to devising methods to inhibit such evaporation, such as by use of surface coatings of the monomolecular type.[4] The long-path infrared hygrometer would be very useful here to monitor evaporation before and after the coating process, both to determine whether a need for the coating exists, and, *post factum*, to determine how effective such a coating is.

The simplicity and ruggedness of the system would lend itself well to airborne operations. Both source and receiver could be readily mounted on the exterior of the aircraft with all components of the readout system maintained inside. Too, as is typical of all infrared hygrometers, its sensitivity increases with decreasing water vapor concentrations. Therefore, the system would lend itself well to

humidity measurements in the typically "dry" regions of the upper atmosphere.

Finally, the system should lend itself well to studies in certain areas of micrometeorology and microclimatology. For example, the monitoring of evaporation over bodies of water or sublimation rates over snow surfaces would provide useful data to the research meteorologist. A very useful parameter in such studies is the total rate of evaporation *per unit of cross-wind length*.[11] Hygrometers of the type described would supply this information directly.

Relative to micrometeorological research, especially intriguing is the possibility of applying the instrument to investigate the equivalence (or lack thereof) of the eddy coefficients of heat and mass transfer. This could very easily be done by monitoring, simultaneously with the water vapor content recordings, the density scintillation as sensed by the 2.2-μ arm of the system. The "transfer functions" between scintillation and turbulence are well-known and are relatively easy to handle analytically.[1, 7, 10] Since as emphasized earlier, the system as a whole responds only to absorption-caused scintillation whereas the 2.2-μ arm responds only to density or, equivalently, temperature-caused scintillation, such a comparison of eddy transfer coefficients could readily be effected.

CONCLUSIONS

The catalog of humidity sensing devices is extensive. In spite of this, however, it is significant that no one technique or instrument can be singled out as representing the "standard" for humidity measurement. Each technique developed has its own place, determined as much by an intended sphere of application as by the degree of precision of measurement a particular device has to offer.

So it is in the present case. The infrared absorption hygrometer just described is designed specifically for use when the type of humidity data desired consists of an average or integrated value of absolute humidity over a prescribed path through the atmosphere. Several areas of application where such is the case have been pointed out. And when used for purposes for which designed, the hygrometer will yield results equaling or exceeding in accuracy those obtained using conventional techniques, and in a much more simple manner.

References

1. Bergmann, P. G., "Propagation of Radiation in a Medium with Random Inhomogeneities," *Phys. Rev.*, **70**, 486–492 (1946).
2. Foskett, L. W., Foster, N. B., Thickstun, W. R., and Wood, R. C., "Infrared Absorption Hygrometer," *Monthly Weather Rev.*, **81**, 267–277 (1953).
3. Fowle, F. E., "The Spectroscopic Determination of Aqueous Vapor," *Astrophys. J.*, **35**, 149–162 (1912).
4. Gartska, W. U., "Reservoir Evaporation and Its Reduction," *Proceedings of the 28th Annual Meeting of the Western Snow Conference*, pp. 39–43, Colorado State University, Fort Collins, Colorado, 1960.
5. Gates, D. M., "Near Infrared Atmospheric Transmission to Solar Radiation," *J. Opt. Soc. Am.*, **50**, 1299–1304 (1960).
6. Gibbons, M. G., "Wavelength Dependence of the Scattering Coefficient for Infrared Radiation in Natural Haze," *J. Opt. Soc. Am.*, **48**, 172–176 (1958).
7. Glenn, H. B., "Light Transmission Through an Apparently Clear Atmosphere," 36 pp., Raytheon Co., Santa Barbara Operations, Santa Barbara, California, 1960.
8. Junge, C., "The Size Distribution and Aging of Natural Aerosols as Determined from Electrical and Optical Data on the Atmosphere," *J. Meteorol.*, **12**, 13–25 (1955).
9. Kurnick, S. W., Zitter, R. N., and Williams, D. B., "Attenuation of Infrared Radiation by Fogs," *J. Opt. Soc. Am.*, **50**, 578–585 (1960).
10. Mintzer, D., "Wave Propagation in a Randomly Inhomogeneous Medium. III," *J. Acoust. Soc. Am.*, **26**, 186–190 (1954).
11. Sutton, O. G., "Micrometeorology," p. 306, New York, McGraw-Hill Book Co., Inc., 1953.
12. Wood, R. C., "Improved Infrared Absorption Hygrometer," *Rev. Sci. Instr.*, **29**, 36–42 (1958).

48. The Infrared Hygrometer — Its Application to Difficult Humidity Measurement Problems

R. C. Wood

Electronics Division, General Mills Aerospace Research, St. Paul, Minnesota*

ABSTRACT

The infrared absorption hygrometer offers attractive advantages in applications where sensitivity and high speed of response are important. In addition, it uses a method of measurement that does not alter sample concentration by adding or subtracting water or by changing the state of any part of the sample. A number of applications which utilize these advantages are described. Short-path infrared hygrometers are being used to monitor and control the humidity level in test chambers in connection with a program to determine the effect of humidity on the properties of various substances. Ranges covered vary from less than 0.5 to over 95 per cent RH. Vapor density within the test chambers is adjusted to any desired level in a matter of minutes. Another application described involves the measurement of water vapor diffusion through polyethylene films and other materials commonly used as vapor barriers in product packaging. Using a diffusion cell attachment to the infrared hygrometer, vapor permeability of standard area test specimens has been determined in a fraction of the time required by conventional gravimetric methods. Potential usefulness of the method in meteorological applications has been demonstrated in tests described in past reports. These are reviewed briefly, and a method for obtaining vertical humidity profiles along a tower is proposed. Calibration of the infrared hygrometer has involved use of a method essentially gravimetric in nature. This method is described in detail along with methods for checking calibration in the field.

INTRODUCTION

The infrared hygrometer has been developed to the point where it now offers attractive possibilities for experimentation and research in many areas. In addition to the meteorological field where challenging applications abound, other branches of science and industry present a host of opportunities as yet unexplored. In outlining a few of these, emphasis has been placed on particular applications where conventional methods fail or prove somewhat inadequate. Although the infrared approach can duplicate most of the routine functions of the more common hygrometers, it will be in similar special areas that the higher cost of an absorption spectra system will be justified.

THE ABSORPTION SPECTRA METHOD

Because the theory of the infrared hygrometer has been treated in several publications in the past[1-4] and was discussed in Paper 46 (see p. 465)[5] basic principles will be reviewed only briefly for the sake of completeness.

Molecules of a gas may be considered as behaving like tiny tuning forks in that they selectively absorb energy from frequencies which resonate with characteristic rotational and vibrational molecular motions. If, for example, radiation emitted from a hot filament

* This organization has been acquired by Litton Industries and is now known as: Applied Science Division, Litton Systems, Inc., 2295 Walnut St., St. Paul, 13, Minn.

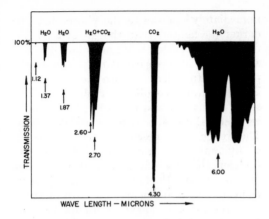

FIG. 1. Absorption bands of water vapor and carbon dioxide in the near infrared.

absorbed by atmospheric concentrations of water vapor and carbon dioxide. Even over short atmospheric paths of a few centimeters, strong bands centered near 1.38, 1.87, 2.7, 4.3 and 6.0 μ yield significant energy absorption. Figure 1 illustrates the relative intensity of these bands.

While individual approaches to humidity measurement by absorption spectra analysis have varied considerably (as determined mainly by the specific problems involved) they all utilize a radiation source, a means for isolating selected wavelengths of radiation, a sensing path, and a radiation detector. Energy measurements in one or more absorption bands are related to the concentration of absorbing gas in the sensing path.

is directed through the atmosphere to a suitable detector located some distance away, the energy received will not have the same distribution with wavelength as the energy emitted because various gases in the path will absorb energy from particular wavelengths. While the normal atmospheric constituents do absorb energy from visible wavelengths, these bands are weak, and energy attenuation cannot be detected by the unaided human eye. In the infrared, however, appreciable attenuation takes place. At certain wavelengths, for instance, 100 per cent of the sun's energy is

SYSTEM DESCRIPTION

The infrared hygrometer developed by General Mills, Inc., is shown in Fig. 2. It employs a 12-in. beam of infrared radiation. Energy attenuation in the 2.6-μ water vapor absorption band is related to the concentration of water vapor in the path. Design features are shown in the diagram, Fig. 3.

Basically the instrument consists of a radiation source, optical filters for isolating selected wavelengths of radiation, a sensing

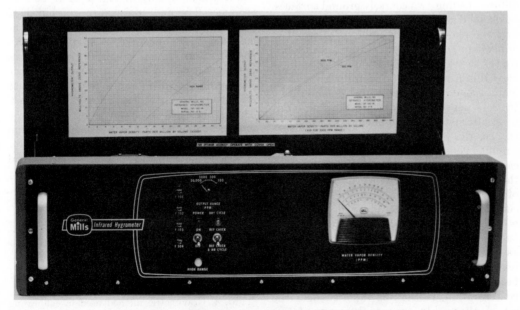

FIG. 2. General Mills short sensing path infrared hygrometer.

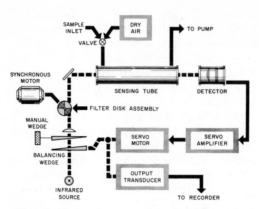

FIG. 3. Design features, General Mills infrared hygrometer.

path, a detector, a closed-loop servo- balancing system, and a standardizing method for drift correction.

A beam of light from a hot filament is brought into collimation by a simple plano-convex lens. This lens also serves as the limiting aperture of the system. A filter wheel rotating at 1800 rpm alternately interposes absorption (2.60 μ) and reference (2.45 μ) band-pass filters. After passing over the sensing path, the image of the limiting aperature is brought into focus on a glass diffusing plate by a plano-convex lens. A lead sulfide detector is located behind the diffusing plate. The diffuser, having two coarsely ground surfaces, tends to distribute the radiation uniformly over the photocell, thus nullifying any effect of point-to-point variation in photocell sensitivity. A wide band-pass interference filter located in front of the diffuser serves to eliminate second-order pass bands transmitted by the rotating sector disk. Since the disk interposes alternate filter sectors at a frequency of 60 cps, the photocell signal as seen by the amplifier consists of two 60-cycle components, each 180 electrical degrees out of phase with the other. When the light flux through each set of filter sectors is such that the two signal components are equal, one will cancel the other, and no signal will be observed. In this balanced condition the sector wheel appears, as far as the photocell is concerned, to be an homogeneous piece of glass, rotating in the beam but not modulating it. If, however, the concentration of absorbing vapor changes, the set of alternately spaced absorption filters

immediately appears to the photocell to be darker (or lighter) than the set of reference filters. The resulting beam modulation causes an error signal to appear at the output of the photocell. In order to return the system to a balanced (null) condition, a phase-sensitive servo mechanism controlled by the amplified error signal operates to move a glass wedge. The wedge is composed of a glass which has a differential in transmission at the two wavelengths. This differential is also a function of the wedge's thickness; thus a departure from an energy ratio of unity due to a variation of water vapor is quickly and automatically compensated by an appropriate change in position (thickness) of the glass wedge.

CALIBRATION OF THE IR HYGROMETER— A GRAVIMETRIC METHOD

Since the infrared hygrometer responds fundamentally to changes in absolute humidity (mass of water vapor per unit volume), this laboratory has resorted to a fundamental calibration method in which these parameters are measured directly.

In this method, atmospheres of known constant vapor density are produced by evaporating measured amounts of distilled water into a stream of dry air. This system is shown schematically in Fig. 4. Here two air streams, dry and moist, are combined to produce a calibration atmosphere having some constant level of water vapor density. Air entering the system is initially dried while passing through a bed of regenerated Linde "Molecular Sieve" to reduce its vapor density effectively to zero (less than 0.0001 g/m^3). This air is then divided into two streams, a moist stream and a dry one. The moist stream includes a small evaporator as the only source of water vapor in the system. Values V_1 and

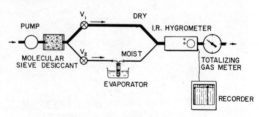

FIG. 4. Gravimetric method used in calibrating infrared hygrometers.

V_2 enable an operator to adjust the volume flows in the two branches and, correspondingly, the water vapor density in the combined stream entering the hygrometer. Although initially uncalibrated, the hygrometer acts as an indicator, enabling the operator to maintain a constant level of absolute humidity in the mixing tube. A totalizing gas meter at the system outlet measures volume accurately to within one per cent.

To illustrate how the gravimetric system is used, we will consider an example in which the operator desires to obtain a calibration point near a vapor density level of 0.1 g/m³ (−41°C frost point).   Initially, the entire system is flushed at a slow rate with dry gas until the hygrometer indicates that no water vapor is being desorbed from the copper duct tubing. At this point, the pump is stopped and approximately one gram of distilled water is added to the small evaporator. Valve V_2 is closed, the pump is restarted, and valve V_1 is adjusted for a flow of approximately 0.1 m³/min. by timing revolutions of the totalizing gas meter. At this point valve V_2 is opened slowly, permitting moist air from the evaporator to enter the mixing tube. The operator adjusts the flow of moist air until the hygrometer indicates a value of water vapor density near 0.1 g/m³. (Since the hygrometer is uncalibrated, this setting is an approximation based upon the operator's past experience with similar instruments.)

After the system has stabilized so that the selected recorder reading can be maintained with only minor adjustments of flow, the pump is stopped, and the evaporator is removed, weighed quickly on an analytical balance, and reinstalled. The gas meter is then read, and the flow is restarted. Flow continues for a period required to evaporate a weighable amount of water from the reservoir (for this case about 10 minutes).

At the end of the run the evaporator is weighed again, and the gas meter reading is noted. At this point we have obtained the following:

(1) Weight of water evaporated
(2) Volume into which the water has evaporated
(3) Observed hygrometer recorder reading.

Collectively this data defines one point on the hygrometer calibration curve. If, for example, 0.112 g of distilled water is evaporated during an interval in which 1.012 m³ of air pass through the system, the average vapor density is 0.111 g/m³. Since the operator maintains a constant density level during the run by observing the hygrometer and adjusting flows, this density and observed recorder reading yield a calibration point. Generally the operator will make two or three runs at each selected level to minimize the effect of weighing errors and to assure that absorption or desorption on duct walls is not affecting results. A typical (low-range) calibration of the General Mills short-path infrared hygrometer using the gravimetric calibration method is presented in Fig. 5.

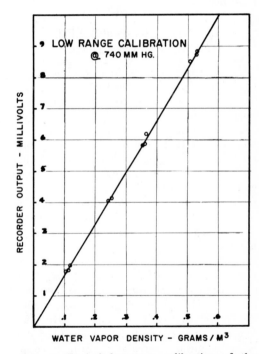

FIG. 5. Typical low-range calibration of the infrared hygrometer. The apparent linearity exhibited here is characteristic only of the low vapor density range.

SOME COMMENTS CONCERNING THE GRAVIMETRIC METHOD

The gravimetric approach is suitable for calibrating the infrared hygrometer because it deals with the fundamental parameters of interest directly without resorting to critical temperature baths, saturated solutions or other indirect techniques. Although the method does require a good analytical balance, the other hardware items used are commercially available at relatively low cost. The assembled system occupies very little laboratory space. At the present time, this author does not have much data showing how the gravimetric approach compares with other calibration methods, but tests with an infrared hygrometer previously calibrated with reference to saturated cold-temperature baths have revealed no important discrepancies. Similarly, a few comparisons with values obtained from a wet- and dry-bulb psychrometer in the dew-point range between 0 and 15°C have shown generally good agreement (± 1 deg C).

A SIMPLE ONE-POINT FIELD CALIBRATION CHECK

As described in detail in a previous paper[3] the GMI infrared hygrometer checks its own zero reading automatically every six hours by purging the sensing chamber with dry air. This normally allows correction for any instrumental drift that may be caused by temperature effects or aging of a component. Values at other points on the curve may also be compared with carefully taken psychrometric readings, but we have found that field personnel are frequently not skilled in the use of a psychrometer or sufficiently aware of the method's limitations. As a result, we have suggested the use of a simple, one-point check method that does not require an expensive setup or precise measurement of any physical quantity. This system utilizes an arrangement shown schematically in Fig. 6. Here the hygrometer is connected to a closed system whereby air is recirculated through copper coils cooled to 0°C in a bath of crushed ice. A wide-mouth thermos bottle available in most drug or hardware stores is an adequate

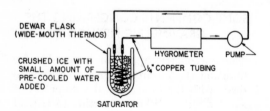

FIG. 6. Simple one-point field calibration check.

container for the crushed ice bath. A few drops of distilled water are added at the cooling coil inlet to assure that saturation will be reached at a temperature of 0°C. Then all hoses are connected, and the pump is adjusted for a moderate flow (approximately 0.1 cfm) through the system. If clean copper tubing is used and the line between the saturator and the hygrometer is kept short, a stable reading will be achieved within 10 minutes.

From the Smithsonian tables, air at 0°C in the cooling coils will have a vapor density W_s of 4.8 g/m³. It is necessary only to correct this value for temperature expansion to obtain the value of vapor density W in the hygrometer, and the following expression will serve.

$$W = W_s \times \frac{273}{273 + t} \qquad (1)$$

where t is the ambient temperature in degrees C at the hygrometer. If, for example, the ambient environment is 25°C, the calibration vapor density W will be

$$W = 4.8 \times \frac{273}{273 + 25} = 4.4 \text{ g/m}^3 \qquad (2)$$

The calibration point obtained in this way has been found to agree well (± 2 per cent) with the basic calibration obtained gravimetrically.

METEOROLOGICAL APPLICATIONS OF THE INFRARED HYGROMETER

The infrared hygrometer presents many advantages of interest to the meteorologist concerned with difficult humidity measurement problems. These arise mainly from the method's sensitivity to low vapor concentrations and from its high speed of response. An earlier paper by the author has discussed the hygrometer's application to meteorological problems. These are considered briefly here for the sake of completeness.

Use of a Duct System to Monitor Atmospheric Humidity

Because the first experimental infrared hygrometer had to be kept available for other tasks within the laboratory, it was never installed in a remote temperature shelter (the customary exposure for meteorological

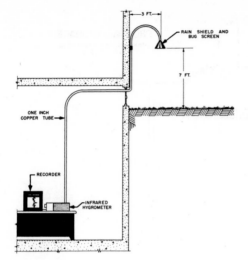

FIG. 7. Duct system for monitoring atmospheric humidity.

hygrometers). Instead, a duct system was used, which allows air to be pulled to the hygrometer from a shielded intake probe. This arrangement is shown in Fig. 7.

It consists of the hygrometer, an air pump, and approximately 40 ft of 1-in. copper tubing that connects the instrument to an intake probe outside the building. The intake end of the duct is protected from direct precipitation and from insects by an inverted cone and screen. The probe, extending 3 ft from the building and 7 ft above a grassy boulevard surface, draws in approximately 0.6 cfm of air. By meteorological standards, this exposure

leaves much to be desired, being subject to local influences, industrial contamination and automotive exhaust products. Nevertheless, it is felt that some of the data obtained will be of interest to meteorologists, suggesting future possible avenues of approach to difficult humidity measurement problems.

Figure 8 presents a portion of the recorder trace, showing a transition from a stable night time condition to typical daytime instability. As might be expected, the frequency of variation is found to be largely a function of wind velocity past the intake probe, whereas the amplitude appears to depend on factors involving moisture evaporation from local surfaces (grassy areas, lakes, etc.) that become heated by the sun. On overcast days, these variations are either absent or greatly reduced.

It may be pointed out that conventional wet- and dry-bulb measurements taken under conditions of similar instability cannot be relied upon to yield representative (average) values. Comparison checks performed by the author at the Instrument Division of the U.S. Weather Bureau in 1955 indicated that under these conditions wet- and dry-bulb-derived dew points will often depart as much as 6 to 8°F from the true average obtained from the infrared hygrometer trace. Such data could be misleading when taken on a routine basis and used for synoptic purposes.

The hygrometer has also proven to be a sensitive indicator with respect to humidity variations associated with air-mass changes.

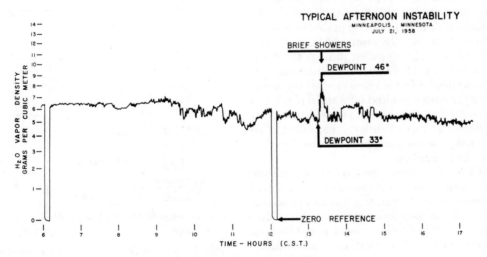

FIG. 8. Typical afternoon instability.

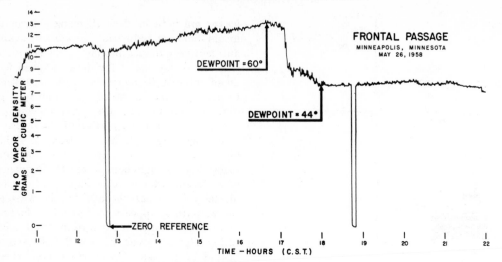

FIG. 9. Humidity variation with passage of a cold front.

Figure 9 shows a typical record obtained during the passage of a cold front at Minneapolis on May 26, 1958. On the basis of data collected over a period of nine months, humidity has frequently proven to be a more sensitive indicator of air mass change than temperature. Several frontal passages accompanied by negligible temperature drops have been identified with substantial and rapid shifts of the humidity trace.

Low-level Vertical Humidity Profiles

Our experience with a ducted sampling system has suggested another application, the measurement of low-level vertical humidity profiles from a tower or mast. This approach is illustrated in Fig. 10. Copper ducts $1\frac{1}{4}$ in. o.d. draw air from sampling probes located on a vertical mast. By means of a small centrifugal blower, air is pulled through the ducts at a velocity of 10 fps. An automatically-programmed selector valve enables the infrared hygrometer to bleed off a small portion of the total flow and make rapid determinations of the water vapor density in each duct. This method possesses a number of advantages that may be pointed out.

First, all measurements are made with the same instrument, an obvious asset where small differences in comparative values are important. Second, measurements are made rapidly; approximately 7 seconds are required for each determination. This includes the time required to purge the hygrometer's sensing chamber.

Third, accuracy and response are not affected by wind or temperature conditions. And finally, the intake probes furnish an excellent place to mount temperature sensors, because adequate forced ventilation minimizes radiation errors that may otherwise be a problem on calm, sunny days.

The inherent fast response of the infrared hygrometer is not greatly compromised by use of a duct system. We have found that use of a duct introduces a "delay," but relatively little "smoothing".

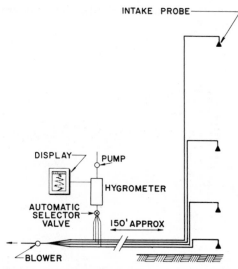

FIG. 10. Method of obtaining vertical humidity profiles from a tower or mast.

METHOD FOR CONTROLLING HUMIDITY LEVELS WITHIN SMALL CHAMBERS

One of the most useful applications of the infrared hygrometer has involved its use in the General Mills Materials Laboratory as a means for controlling the humidity levels in small environmental test chambers. In this work we are interested in the characteristics of different classes of powders as a function of the humidity environment.

Using a test arrangement like that shown in Fig. 11, we are able to create on short notice any chamber humidity level desired and to hold it precisely at the desired level within 1 or 2 per cent. At present, this is not an automatic system, although such a system would be easy to devise. The method now used involves a dry air stream, a moist air stream, valves for controlling each, and an infrared hygrometer monitor. The experimenter merely adjusts the flows in dry and moist streams until the proper humidity level, as indicated by the hygrometer, is reached. Chamber vapor densities from 0.1 to 19 g/m³ (0.5 to 95 per cent RH at 22°C) have been achieved easily and routinely. In principle, this method can be used with other types of hygrometer monitors, provided the hygrometer is (1) fast enough to detect humidity changes as they occur within the chamber, without appreciable lag, (2) sensitive to humidity levels as low as 0.1 g of water vapor per m³ (−42°C dew point) without loss of response speed, and (3) not appreciably affected by the presence of airborne powders which may be soluble in water or acids.

In our present powder studies, one infrared hygrometer is used in a manifold system to monitor sequentially experiments in six glove-box chambers.

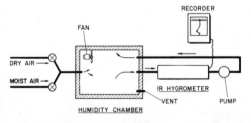

FIG. 11. Method for controlling humidity in a test chamber. In practice, one hygrometer may be connected to a manifold system in order to monitor the humidity levels in several chambers.

RAPID DETERMINATIONS OF THE WATER VAPOR PERMEABILITY OF PACKAGING MATERIALS AND COATED FABRICS

We originally became interested in the transmission of water vapor through films because of our parent organization's preoccupation with packaged dry cereals and their concern that the "Breakfast of Champions" be just as crunchy in Panama or London as it is in Minneapolis. From our packaging people we have learned that the testing of vapor-barrier materials is still an important part of quality control. We also learned that while most investigators use a gravimetric approach, there are as yet no accepted, industry-wide standard test conditions.

The testing of vapor barriers such as polyethylene, waxed glassine, and other films usually involves a laborious procedure in which the test sample is carefully sealed to the rim of a small dish filled with desiccant. The dish is weighed, placed in a humid atmosphere for a few days or weeks, and then reweighed, periodically. Water vapor transmission is subsequently expressed in terms of weight per unit area per unit of time.

The most serious objections to the gravimetric method arise from the handling required and from the excessive time needed for each determination. Because of its high response, speed and sensitivity at low vapor concentrations, it was felt that the infrared hygrometer could offer a better approach to the problem of measuring water vapor transmission through barrier films. We are currently exploring this idea using an experimental arrangement shown schematically in Fig. 12. Sample specimens 5½ in. in diameter are clamped in a stainless steel diffusion cell. Dry air is passed at a measured rate past one side of the sample, then into the infrared hygrometer. Initially the other (wet) side is also exposed to dry air so that a "zero" diffusion level can be obtained. After a steady-state zero reading is achieved (indicating that the sample is reasonably dry), moist air (95 to 100 per cent at 23°C) is recirculated through the "wet" half of the diffusion cell. Vapor diffusing through the test specimen into the "dry" side is detected by the hygrometer, and a time-concentration curve to an equilibrium value is obtained. This equilibrium value (g

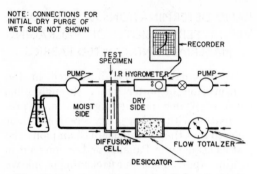

FIG. 12. Arrangement for determining the water vapor permeability of plastic films and coated fabrics using a diffusion cell-infrared hygrometer combination.

In this test, water vapor penetrating through the film raised the equilibrium vapor density of the dry side to 0.11 g/m³ (as indicated by the infrared hygrometer). Since the measured air flow past the dry side was at a rate equivalent to 0.945 m³ per day, the diffusion rate through the sample was 0.104 g/day. Taking into account the sample area (1.55×10^{-2} m²), this is equivalent to 6.7 g/day/m².

In a similar manner, we were able to measure the transmission rates through a number of films and coated fabrics kindly supplied by Mr. Charles F. Macy of the U.S. Army Quartermaster R and E Command.

In Table 1, values are compared with gravimetric determinations performed in Quartermaster laboratories. All values have been adjusted to equivalent test conditions as used by the Army—100 per cent RH wet side, 50 per cent RH dry side.

The two sets of data are in reasonable agreement considering the fact that they represent two different methods performed in two different laboratories on samples that are not necessarily identical. The important fact is that in no case did it take longer than one hour to make a determination using the IR hygrometer and diffusion cell. In most instances the time required was appreciably less.

As a result of this initial investigation, we

water vapor per m³ of air) is a function of the diffusion rate and the rate at which dry air is pulled past the sample. To maintain a relatively constant vapor gradient across the test specimen, high flow rates are used with more permeable samples. In all cases the air pressure across the sample is maintained at zero to avoid any possibility of moist air being forced through.

In Fig. 13, a portion of the recorder chart from a test of an 8-mil vinyl sample is reproduced. It is of interest to note that it took approximately four minutes for water vapor to penetrate through to the dry side after initial exposure.

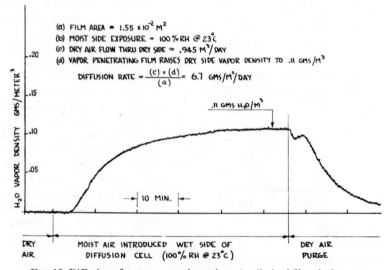

FIG. 13. Diffusion of water vapor through an 8-mil vinyl film. A characteristic recorder trace obtained with the infrared hygrometer and diffusion cell combination shown in Fig. 12.

TABLE 1. WATER VAPOR PERMEABILITY
MEASUREMENTS OBTAINED BY TWO EVALUATORS
USING DIFFERENT METHODS

Sample	Equilibrium Transmission Rate (g/m²/day)	
	Gravimetric Method*	IR Hygrometer Method†
Poly, 1 mil	3.0	2.9 (No. 1) 2.0 (No. 2)
Vinyl, 8 mil	6.2	3.4
Reevair fabric	554	435 (No. 1) 520 (No. 2)
Uncoated, 50% Fortreal 50% Avril	949	1100
Cotton poplin	840	1250
Kaycel paper	1047	1150

* Gravimetric determinations were made at U.S. Army Quartermaster R & E Center, Natick.

† IR hygrometer determinations were made at General Mills Aerospace Research, St. Paul.

feel that the infrared hygrometer-diffusion cell combination offers very attractive advantages to those groups concerned with the transmission of water vapor through films and coated fabrics. The system is fast, and no special skill is required of the operator. Because the hygrometer's response speed is not a function of vapor concentration or temperature, the graphic time-transmission curves obtained represent a picture of the diffusion process unbiased by sensor lag.

AN EXPERIMENTAL, LONG-PATH INFRARED HYGROMETER

One advantage unique to the absorption spectra method is its ability to obtain an integrated value of humidity over very long paths. Theoretically the sensing beam may be hundreds or even thousands of meters long. Because of this advantage, the method should prove useful in applications where space-integration is desirable and where it is difficult to obtain a truly representative value of humidity (e.g. above the surface of a large reservoir or over a growing crop).

In the Arctic, where measurement of humidity is usually a difficult and inaccurate process, long sensing paths will be a means for main-

taining measurable absorption in the face of prevailing low water vapor densities.

The measurement of low-level vertical profiles is also theoretically possible, using a method in which the sensing beam is directed alternately to a number of infrared sources or mirrors located at intervals along a tower.

Finally, the method does not "handle" the sample. Measurements are made through the free, unconfined atmosphere without influencing any natural meteorological process.

In 1959 the author designed an experimental long-path infrared hygrometer which utilized the 2.6-μ water vapor absorption band and a reference wavelength at 2.35 μ. For six months in 1960, this unit obtained continuous measurements of humidity, integrated over a 290-ft path above a General Mills parking lot at Minneapolis. Results of this work were reported in a paper presented at the Third Conference on Agricultural Meteorology, Kansas City, May 1960.[6]

System Description—Long-path Approach.

The experimental model long-path hygrometer is illustrated schematically in Fig. 14. Radiation from a 30-watt sealed-beam spotlight is directed over an unconfined sensing path to the receiver located at the other end of the base line. A portion of this radiation is collected by a 2-in. diameter, $f4$ meniscus lens. This lens also serves as the limiting aperture of the system. Two narrow band-pass interference filters are mounted side by side on a sliding holder behind the lens and depending upon the slide position will transmit absorbed (2.60 μ) or unabsorbed (2.35 μ) wavelengths of radiation. The image of the distant source is focused on a 1 × 1 mm uncooled lead

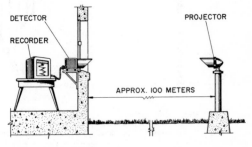

FIG. 14. Experimental long-path hygrometer system.

sulfide photocell. In order to provide a modulated signal for amplification, the light beam is interrupted at a frequency of 120 cycles by a motor-driven chopper. Although the chopper is located in the receiver, there is no significant contribution from background modulation.

In operation, a mechanical actuator (not shown) positions the two interference filters so that the detector is alternately exposed to 2.6-μ and 2.35-μ radiation from the distant source. The two resulting signals (E_a E_r) are amplified and displayed on a single-channel potentiometer recorder (time shared).

Since the 2.6-μ radiation is subject to attenuation by water vapor while the reference wavelength is relatively unaffected, the voltage ratio R obtained from recorded data,

$$R = \frac{E_a \ (2.60 \ \mu)}{E_r \ (2.35 \ \mu)} \tag{3}$$

is a function of the total precipitable water vapor in the path (or the average vapor density, assuming a constant path length). Neutral attenuators over the 2.35-μ filter keep this ratio from becoming disproportionately small in the face of large absorber concentrations and act as a limited range-changing adjustment.

The experimental unit was initially calibrated through a limited range in an 80-ft dark tunnel using reflectors to achieve a 140-ft path and psychrometic measurements as a comparison standard. After installing the instrument in its outdoor location, check measurements were within 3 per cent of the dark-tunnel calibration after the increase in path length had been taken into account. The calibration was subsequently extended to lower values (equivalent to –29°C dew point) by comparison with a point-sampling infrared hygrometer installed at one end of the base line.

In the outdoor test installation the 290-ft sensing beam of the long path hygrometer was approximately 25-ft above the ground surface and oriented in an east-west direction. The short sensing path infrared hygrometer installed at the east end of the base line provided a point-sampling standard of comparison. Both instruments were calibrated in terms of absolute humidity (g water vapor per m³) and had similar time constants of approximately three seconds.

A typical long-path recorder record is shown in Fig. 15. The irregular trace represents the fluctuation of transmitted energy at the 2.60-μ absorption-sensitive band due to variations of

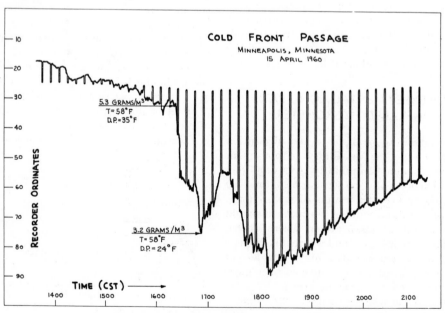

FIG. 15. Cold front passage as recorded by long-path infrared hygrometer at Minneapolis, Minnesota on April 15, 1960.

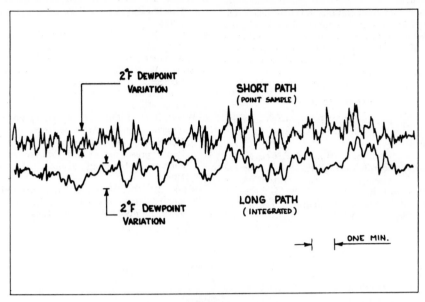

FIG. 16. Comparison of simultaneous traces from long-path and short-path hygrometers. Although the similarity is striking and larger features are common to both records, it is evident that space-integration has yielded a degree of smoothing.

water vapor in the path. Periodic one-minute reference traces show the relative insensitivity of the 2.35-μ band to these variations. As previously pointed out, the absorption/reference ratio is used in extracting vapor-density values from the calibration curve. This particular record may be of interest to meteorologists in that it shows the transition from moist to dry air with the passage of a typical cold front.

One of the principal advantages of the long-path approach is in obtaining more representative data through space-integration. Unfortunately, the experimental arrangement was not ideally situated for demonstrating this advantage because the sensing elements were located 25 ft above the ground and appreciable mixing could occur by the time moisture cells reached the level of the measuring system.

In Fig. 16, however, comparison of long- and short-path hygrometer traces does reveal an effect of smoothing due to space integration. This difference would be appreciably more apparent for systems operating just above a moist, growing crop on a hot summer afternoon.

Future Work—Long-path Systems

This has been a preliminary look at long-path infrared as a possible approach to atmospheric humidity measurements. Results are promising and appear to justify further work aimed at development of practical designs suitable for operational field use. One attractive approach to such a system has been developed by Tank[7]. He has chosen to use the water vapor absorption band centered near 1.9 μ and a method whereby the ratio of transmitted band energies is recorded directly. Other workers may find advantages in using the 1.37-μ absorption band and a different optical arrangement. Many variations of the long-path approach are possible.

Obviously, future long-path work should involve more than a development program aimed at the design and fabrication of reliable hardware. Limitations imposed by atmospheric scintillation and particle scattering present important basic questions yet to be answered satisfactorily.

Acknowledgments. The author gratefully acknowledges the helpful assistance of Mr. C. F. Macy who furnished samples for the material permeability tests and contributed the comparative gravimetric data. Mr. John Nash designed and tested the diffusion cell, and R. W. Barrett was instrumental in developing the gravimetric calibration technique. Special thanks are due to Mr. H. L. Demorest for his support and technical assistance during the development and testing of the infrared hygrometer.

References

1. Foskett, L. W., *et al.*, "Infrared Absorption Hygrometer," *Monthly Weather Rev.*, 81, 267–77 (1953).
2. Wood, R. C., Foskett, L. W., and Foster, N. B., "Infrared Absorption Hygrometer—A Progress Report," Presented at First International Congress and Exposition of the Instrument Society of America, Philadelphia, Paper No. 54-36-1, September 1954.
3. Wood, R. C., "Improved Infrared Absorption Spectra Hygrometer," *Rev. Sci. Instr.*, 29, 36–42 (1958).
4. Wood, R. C., "The Infrared Hygrometer as a Potential Meteorological Aid," *Bull. Am. Meteorol. Soc.*, 40, 280–84 (1959).
5. Staats, W. F., Foskett, L. W., and Jensen, H. P., "Infrared Absorption Hygrometer," Humidity and Moisture, Vol 1, New York, Reinhold Pub. Corp., 1964.
6. Wood, R. C., Johnson, C. B., "Long-path Infrared Hygrometer—An Approach to Space Integrated Measurements of Atmospheric Water Vapor," Paper presented at 3rd Conference on Agricultural Meteorology, Kansas City, Mo., May 1960.
7. Tank, W. G., "A Long Path Infrared Hygrometer," Humidity and Moisture Vol. 1, New York, Reinhold Pub. Corp., 1964.

SECTION V

COULOMETRIC HYGROMETRY

49. Additional Performance Data on a New Electrolytic Hygrometer Cell

R. H. Jones and Arne Petersen

Beckman Instruments, Inc., Fullerton, California

ABSTRACT

An electrolytic cell for a hygrometer has been developed using rhodium electrodes instead of platinum. The objective of this design was to produce a cell with greater usefulness in terms of operating time than was achieved with cells using platinum electrodes. A second objective was to eliminate or reduce to negligible proportions the errors inherent in moisture measurement in streams of high hydrogen content.

Experimental results show cells of the new design to have minimum useful life of about four to six times that of cells with platinum electrodes on similar service.

Reformation of water due to the catalytic recombination of electrolytically produced oxygen with hydrogen was shown to be minimized, and background currents in cells were shown to be negligible when measuring hydrogen as well as other gases.

INTRODUCTION

The theory and application of the electrolytic hygrometer has been the subject of a number of excellent papers [1] and need not be reiterated here. Since the introduction of commercially available hygrometers, electrolytic cells have used (with some modifications) the basic materials, geometry, and construction described in Keidel's original paper.[1] Czuha *et al.*[2] describe the use of glass as the confining substrate for the electrodes instead of "Teflon" (as used by Keidel) and explain that advantage is taken of the better wetting properties of glass to deposit a very thin coating of P_2O_5 in the interelectrode spaces. Mention of cells of different geometry, materials, and construction (and, therefore, different performance characteristics) was made at the 1962 Pittsburgh Conference on Analytical Chemistry and Applied Spectroscopy by Reeds and Petersen.[3] It is the intent of this paper to present additional performance data on these electrolytic cells. The cells of concern in this discussion were constructed with rhodium electrodes instead of the traditional platinum.

In considering changes in the parameters of cell design, the goal of the cell refinements was directed toward overcoming or alleviating two severest application problems: (1) high moisture levels resulting in short operational life of cells and (2) the so-called hydrogen recombination resulting in inaccuracies of moisture measurement in streams where hydrogen is the major component.

Consider first the problem of high moisture levels and short life of electrolysis cells operating in such applications. It has been found that cell failure in such applications results from a shorting caused by one electrode contacting the other. This has been characterized by the formation of black deposits in the interelectrode space. These black deposits were caused by what was essentially an electroplating process; the platinum anode slowly dissolved and plated out on the cathode. When the deposited platinum bridged from the cathode to the anode, the cell suddenly shorted out. The rate at which platinum is deposited

507

has been determined experimentally to be roughly proportional to the total water which the cell has electrolyzed and hence to the water level in the sample stream.

The second problem involved the so-called "hydrogen recombination" in which the electrolytically generated oxygen reacted with hydrogen to form additional water. This phenomenon was observed in streams where the major constituent of the gas was hydrogen. Apparently this reaction was catalyzed by the platinum of the electrodes. Czuha *et al.*[2] suggest several mechanisms by which this recombination may take place.

EXPERIMENTAL

A brief description of the experimental equipment used in collecting data is in order and is shown in Fig. 1. The test rig as shown permitted running of cells in parallel gas streams and also making of series measurements, i.e., the measuring of moisture by an electrolytic process downstream of a cell where the same electrolytic process had already taken place. This arrangement made possible simple testing of cell efficiency and also provided a ready means for testing for "hydrogen recombination."

With the apparatus as shown, it was possible to continuously make up samples of relatively high water content. A reasonably close approximation of water concentration could be calculated from the measurement of

gas pressure and temperature along with vapor pressure data on water. In addition to this rig, a number of standard production electrolytic hygrometers were used to gather experimental data.

The first concern was cell efficiency. We define cell efficiency as that amount of moisture absorbed and electrolyzed by the hygrometer cell divided by the total moisture present in the sample. If a cell was 100 per cent efficient, it should remove all moisture from the sample gas, and the effluent from the cell should be bone dry. If this effluent was directed to a second electrolytic cell, this cell should indicate zero moisture if the cell ahead of it was truly 100 per cent efficient. This assumes no background current in the cell, a subject which will be discussed presently. To check cell efficiency, wet nitrogen was used as the sample gas. Representative results are shown in Table 1.

We now make this assumption; if a cell measuring moisture in a hydrogen stream shows "hydrogen recombination," the first cell in the series arrangement would indicate water vapor present plus recombination water. The second cell in the series arrangement would indicate primarily recombination water. The difference in the two readings is roughly the water vapor present in the sample stream.

If the second cell in the series arrangement shows no recombination, then apparently the first cell of the same design must not perform any recombination either. In testing this

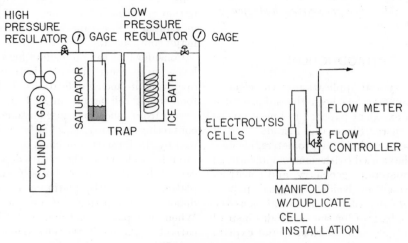

FIG. 1. Experimental apparatus.

TABLE 1. EFFICIENCY OF RHODIUM CELLS ON WET NITROGEN GAS

Indicated Moisture First Cell in Series (ppm)	Indicated Moisture Second Cell in Series (ppm)	% Moisture Electrolyzed in First Cell (cell efficiency)
Cell No. 1 672	Cell No. 2 1.7	99.8
No. 3 739	No. 4 3.3	99.5
No. 5 712	No. 6 7.2	99.0
No. 7 712	No. 8 0.4	99.9+

assumption, the same experiment was again performed except that wet hydrogen was the sample gas instead of wet nitrogen. Representative results are shown in Table 2.

TABLE 2. EFFICIENCY OF RHODIUM CELLS ON WET HYDROGEN GAS

Indicated Moisture First Cell in Series (ppm)	Indicated Moisture Second Cell in Series (ppm)	% Moisture Electrolyzed in First Cell (cell efficiency)
Cell No. 1 378	Cell No. 2 3.2	99.2
No. 3 500	No. 4 4.5	99.0
No. 5 454	No. 6 4.0	99.0
No. 7 470	No. 8 1.5	99.7

The average value obtained in the nitrogen run was 99.5 per cent moisture indication in the first cell of the series arrangement. With wet hydrogen as the sample stream, the average value of first cell indication dropped only to 99.2 per cent. From this we conclude that there is either no hydrogen recombination or that it is negligible except perhaps for extremely low level measurement.

The effects of hydrogen recombination on the accuracy of measurement of water in hydrogen is well known. A glance at data obtained with standard platinum electrolysis cells with 26-in. element lengths shows the magnitude of recombination error. Table 3

TABLE 3. HYDROGEN RECOMBINATION ERROR ON PLATINUM CELLS WITH 26-IN. ELEMENT LENGTH (PARALLEL ARRANGEMENT)

Gas	Condition	Indicated Moisture Cell No. 1 (ppm)	Cell No. 2 (ppm)
Dry N_2	No flow	<3	<3
Dry N_2	100 cc/min.	<3	<3
Dry H_2*	No flow	37	22
Dry H_2*	100 cc/min.	60	40

* Cylinder hydrogen.

shows representative data for hydrogen and nitrogen samples under flow and no flow conditions.

Table 4 shows comparative data taken on an electrolytic hygrometer using alternately a platinum cell and a rhodium cell. Theoretical moisture levels shown in Table 4 were calculated from gas pressure on the saturator.

TABLE 4. COMPARATIVE RESULTS OF MOISTURE MEASUREMENT IN HYDROGEN AND NITROGEN WITH PLATINUM AND RHODIUM ELECTROLYTIC CELLS

Gas	Theoretical Moisture* (ppm)	Indicated Moisture (Pt cell) (ppm)	Indicated Moisture (Rh cell) (ppm)
Nitrogen	520	580	—
Hydrogen	520	800	—
Nitrogen	540	—	530
Hydrogen	540	—	535

* Calculated from pressure and temperature on saturator.

As previously mentioned, it has been established that there are background currents in electrolytic cells due to residual conduction of the cells. Baumann[4] states that these background currents can be responsible for large errors, particularly below the 10-ppm measurement level. He states further that these background currents can be evaluated in three ways:

(1) By passing a dry gas through the cell for a period of time to dry the cell completely;

(2) By blocking the flow and allowing the system to dry by electrolysis;

(3) By measuring the electrolysis current at two flow rates.

Cells were tested under the first two of these conditions. Data for a representative cell is shown in Table 5.

The third method of evaluating background current was by measuring the electrolysis

TABLE 5. BACKGROUND CURRENT IN ELECTROLYSIS CELL

Gas	Condition	Moisture Indication* (ppm)
Dry N_2	Flow 100 cc/min.	0.8
Dry N_2	No flow	0.4
Dry H_2	Flow 100 cc/min.	1.8
Dry H_2	No flow	1.9

* Background current divided by 13.2 μA/ppm.

current at various flow rates. Figure 2 shows indicated readings for a cylinder hydrogen stream which was passed through a P_2O_5 drier and then by-passed the drier. Flows were measured with a "bubble flowmeter."

Figure 3 shows the results of a run made on the same cell with wet nitrogen.

The conclusion we draw from these data is that errors resulting from the so-called hydrogen recombination are of little or no significance to the measurement of moisture in hydrogen streams. We attribute this to the use of rhodium electrodes in place of platinum and suggest that this is due to the lesser degree of catalytic activity of the rhodium as compared to platinum.

As previously noted, a second problem has occasionally arisen from the use of platinum electrodes in electrolysis cells. This has been the relatively short life of cells in applications involving moisture measurement at relatively high levels. We have mentioned the cause of this short life to be a bridging of the inter-electrode space by the deposition of platinum plating on the cathodic electrode. With platinum cells, shorting occurs at the inlet end of cells after some service time. This time depends on moisture level in the sample. Also, this tends to indicate that most of the water in the sample is absorbed and, consequently, electrolyzed in the first few inches of cell element. It has been determined by spectrographic analysis that the black deposits in the interelectrode space contained a high platinum content.

Failure of cells with rhodium electrodes has resulted from shorting between wires in a manner similar to cells constructed with platinum windings. However, such failures, on an average, have occurred after service life four to six times longer than was the case with platinum electrode cells. It should be emphasized in this discussion that the data gathered was for the purpose of determining the life of cells as related to moisture level. We express cell life in terms of "part per million hours." (Example: a cell running on a 100 ppm sample for 100 hours would accumulate 10,000 ppm-hours.) The life of cells tested in the preparation of this paper has averaged about 250,000 ppm-hours. Average life of platinum eletrode cells is on the order of 50,000 ppm-hours.

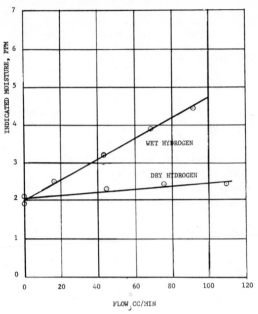

Fig. 2. Measurement of low-level moisture in hydrogen gas.

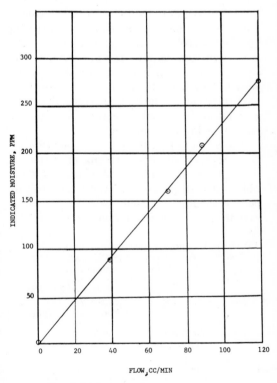

Fig. 3. Moisture *vs* flow rate, wet N_2.

CONCLUSIONS

We would like at this point, to comment on some of the various causes of electrolytic cell failure. One common cause is neutralization of the P_2O_5 desiccant by alkaline gases such as ammonia or certain amines. The symptom of such failure is the inability of the cell to detect moisture. In effect, the cell becomes an open circuit. A second cause of failure is due to coating of electrodes with oils or liquids contained in the sample. Still another cause of failure is plugging of cells due to polymerization in applications involving moisture measurement in unsaturates. It is quite obvious that the materials of the electrodes in electrolysis cells will not alleviate any of these causes of failure, although it is conceivable that cell life in some polymerizable streams may be improved because of the lesser catalytic properties of rhodium.

In summary, we feel that the use of rhodium in electrolysis cells is an advancement in the art of low level moisture measurement for two reasons: (1) the increased life of cells as related to moisture content of the sample stream, and (2) the reduction, if not the virtual elimination of errors due to the reformation of water when measurement is made in streams with high hydrogen concentration.

References

1. Keidel, F. A., Pittsburgh Conference on Analytical Chemistry and Applied Spectroscopy, February 1956.
2. Czuha, M., Gardner, K. W., and Sawyer, D. T., *J. Electroanal. Chem.*, **4**, 51 (1962).
3. Reeds, J., and Petersen, A., Pittsburgh Conference on Analytical Chemistry and Applied Spectroscopy, February 1962.
4. Baumann, F., *Anal. Chem.*, **34**, 1665 (1962).

50. Mixing Ratio Indicator

Paul B. MacCready, Jr., and John A. K. Lake

Meteorology Research, Inc., Altadena, California

ABSTRACT

A mixing ratio indicator has been developed for atmospheric measurements which indicates grams of water vapor per kilogram of air, independent of temperature and pressure variations. It features a short time constant (sometimes under one second), a wide operating range (from a few thousandths of a gram per kilogram to more than 30 g/kg), small size, and low power consumption.

The unit utilizes a phosphorous pentoxide electrolyzing cell in series with a battery. The cell permits a flow of current which is exactly proportional to the rate of water vapor entering it. The mixing ratio indicator system requires that the rate of mass flow of air through the cell be kept constant so that the current can be interpreted directly as the mixing ratio. The mass flow is controlled at the prescribed value by means of a mass flow sensor which, through a servo amplifier, controls the pump drive. The mass flow sensor is based on the hot wire mass flow heat transfer principle, and automatically compensates for variations in ambient pressure and temperature, and, to a considerable extent, for variations in the constituents of the gas being sampled.

Design concepts and details are given, various versions and applications are detailed, and the design of a unit for measurement in the low densities and low mixing ratio values expected in the Mars atmosphere is described. Although the mixing ratio indicator system is still in a continuing developmental stage, the system has demonstrated excellent operation over a broad variety of configurations and uses and has been employed on various research programs.

INTRODUCTION

The Meteorology Research, Inc., mixing ratio indicator utilizes a water vapor sensor which absorbs all the water vapor from the air or gas which is drawn through a tube and, by an electrolyzing process, permits a current to flow which is exactly proportional to the rate of water vapor absorption. The complete meteorological instrument uses this sensor, together with means for causing a constant mass flow of air through the cell. Thus the instrument can directly indicate mixing ratio independent of ambient temperature and pressure.

Since the first version of the mixing ratio indicator was developed in 1959, various models have been developed and used for a variety of purposes. The devices have some features which make them especially valuable for certain uses:

(a) The time constant can be as short as 1 second.

(b) One instrument can cover a broad range of mixing ratio, even exceeding $10^4 : 1$.

(c) The system constitutes an absolute measurement technique, with calibration depending primarily on the calibration of the mass flow sensor at one mass flow rate. Sensors may be replaced without recalibration.

(d) The output is electric current, and is essentially linear with mixing ratio. Large output voltages are readily obtainable. The value of voltage used in the indicator circuit is not critical.

(e) One system works over a broad range of ambient temperature and pressure conditions.

(f) Mixing ratio measurements can be

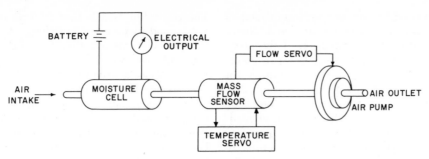

FIG. 1. Mixing ratio indicator (MRI).

made at below freezing temperatures and also at very high temperatures.

(g) The system can be small, and may conveniently be battery powered.

(h) The sensor is very tiny, and samples air at a very low rate.

These virtues must be balanced against the relative complexity of the device and the fact that there are still some unknown characteristics of the sensor.

The device can be considered developmental, but various operational uses have been made of it. Ruskin[6] describes some features of the method. This paper details some of the versions and describes some of the applications.

Figure 1 illustrates the complete mixing ratio indicator system. The air pump, usually operating in the range of 5 to 10 cc/min. of STP air, continually draws the air through the moisture cell. The electrolyzing moisture cell acts as a current regulating device. For any fixed battery voltage, it yields a current directly proportional to the rate at which water vapor enters the cell (conversion, 93.5 μg of water per coulomb). The mass flow sensor monitors the mass flow rate and, through the flow servo, causes the pump to keep the mass flow constant in spite of variations of ambient conditions. The temperature servo maintains

FIG. 3. Breadboard version of mixing ratio indicator to check feasibility as a Mars atmosphere probe.

the calibration of the mass flow sensor and, to some extent, automatically compensates for the type of gas if it is other than air.

Figures 2 and 3 show representative versions of the system. Figure 2 is the MRI Model 901 unit. It is battery operated and weighs 16 pounds with batteries for 200 hours of operation. The full-scale ranges are from 30 to 0.03 g/kg mixing ratio. Figure 3 shows

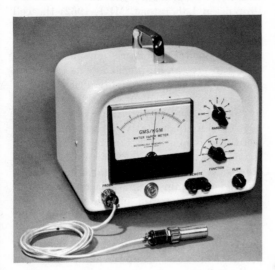

FIG. 2. The MRI Model 901 mixing ratio indicator.

a miniaturized breadboard version developed for the National Aeronautics and Space Administration-Jet Propulsion Laboratory (Meteorology Research, Inc., 1962) to determine the feasibility of the technique for possible measurements from a capsule descending through the atmosphere of Mars. The unit weighs 11 ounces, with a nonlinear readout system but without the batteries (approximately 1 watt required). Some details of these and other units will be given later in this paper.

THE MOISTURE CELL

The electrolyzing water vapor sensor cell principle was developed by duPont.[4] The duPont Company holds the original patent, No. 2,830,945, dated April 15, 1958, and has licensed several companies to build and sell the cells. Certain of the licensees have made improvements in the cell construction. The primary use of the cells has been in the process industry field. Long time constants can be tolerated there, and hand-adjusted flow systems are feasible. The MRI mixing ratio system incorporates a short, fast-response version of the cell in a flexible system which is practical for meteorological measurements.

The phosphorous pentoxide moisture sensor is, in theory, a chemical moisture trap and electrolytic cell. The trapping agent, P_2O_5, maintains a very low water vapor pressure and equilibrates quite rapidly. The electrolytic cell has two platinum electrodes wound as a very tight double helix on the inside of a small glass tube. The electrolyte, the $P_2O_5 \cdot x\, H_2O$, is introduced as a 10 per cent solution in acetone. When the acetone has evaporated, a potential is applied across the two electrodes to drive off the moisture which is present in the hydrate. The sensor is then prepared to pick up moisture from the atmosphere, electrolyze it, and pass the current necessary to read. Since all the moisture trapped is immediately electrolyzed and the drying agent is itself always dry as a result of the electrolysis, it performs at a continual optimum. The overall chemistry of this system is:

$$P_2O_5 + x\, H_2O \rightarrow P_2O_5 \cdot x\, H_2O$$

$$P_2O_5 \cdot x\, H_2O \rightarrow P_2O_5 + x\, H_2 + \frac{x}{2} O_2 +$$

$$\text{current}$$

The cell calibration is that 93.5 μg of water correspond to 1 coulomb of charge passed by the cell. It turns out that for STP air at a constant flow rate of 4.5 cc/min., 1 ppm of water vapor (a mixing ratio of 0.001 g/kg) corresponds to a current of 1 μA.

The fundamentals of cell operation are complex and not yet perfectly understood. Sometimes a slight water regeneration has been detected, and the cell can be rendered inoperative by certain uncommon contaminants. Further details on such cell factors are given by Czuha,[1] Jones and Peterson[3] and Finley and Shaffer[2]. The evidence gathered so far leads to the conclusion that the cell is appropriate for normal meteorological applications.

The range of normal operation of the cell which has been verified for meteorological measurements is from about 30 to 0.01 g/kg. Above 30 g/kg the current through the cell, usually over 30 mA, heats the cell. Although the cell can withstand considerable heat, the heating will cause an upper limit to the range of usefulness. Lowering the voltage across the cell will reduce the heat dissipated. The cell limit will depend strongly on the flow rate used through the sensor; a very low flow would be appropriate if the unit were being employed primarily for high mixing ratio values. The real limit at the low end of the range is not known because of the difficulty of performing any calibration at values below about 0.01 g/kg. During the study for the Jet Propulsion Laboratory (MRI, 1962) the cell seemed to give reasonable results to about 0.003 g/kg; however, the calibration procedure at such low values is questionable. The cell itself can give an output as low as two parts per billion when thoroughly dried, and it would seem, in agreement with the supposition by Keidel,[4] that a practical system can be developed for quantitative measurements well below the 1-ppm level. For measurements at these low levels, a greater flow rate can profitably be used. The cell design must be carefully tailored to eliminate spurious readings. The tube length upstream of the moisture cell must be an absolute minimum, all moisture sources must be removed, and a moisture barrier downstream of the cell is indicated to prevent vapor moving up the pumping system to the cell.

In the field the meteorological version of the cell has been used at temperatures well below freezing. From flight tests there seems to be no problem in cell operation at $-20°C$. In virtually any cold-weather application, the tiny cell can readily be heated should this prove necessary. It is possible that the time constant is slowed by cold temperatures, but the effect has not been apparent during flight investigations.

Some brief tests of the time constant of the meteorological cell have been conducted. With some cells the time constant has turned out to be shorter than 1 second. Longer time constants have been found with other cells, even up to 10 seconds. It appears that the cell coating thickness may play a dominant role in determining the time constant and that the cell wire size is also important.

If the cell is harmed by contaminants or if the coating gets washed off by some liquid water, it can be cleaned and recoated and will then be usable again. If it picks up a water droplet which effectively shorts the cell, this moisture can be slowly removed by the electrolyzing principle if the current is limited so as to avoid excessive heating. When the instrument is started after sitting in a normal atmosphere, there will be a period of about one minute during which the extra accumulated water vapor in the phosphorous pentoxide is being electrolyzed, so the unit will indicate too high a mixing ratio value during this starting transient. In practice, a light bulb is put in the cell circuit as a voltage limiter; it simultaneously gives a warning of a shorted cell while limiting the voltage across the cell.

THE MASS FLOW SENSOR

It is the mass flow sensor which makes the meteorological mixing ratio indicator feasible. To obtain mixing ratio from the cell current, the air mass flow rate must be known. To make the mass flow rate measurement as accurate as possible during wide variations in ambient conditions it is most convenient to servo-control the mass flow rate to be constant, so that the flow sensor is always operating at one point. This has the added feature of permitting the cell meter to be calibrated directly in terms of mixing ratio.

The hot wire principle is used for mass flow measurement, with heated thermistors employed instead of wires because of the convenience afforded by their good sensitivity and high voltage level. A heated thermistor bead placed in the gas stream is cooled by the stream, and when placed in a Wheatstone bridge arrangement, it will give an output as a function of mass flow. The flow sensor is greatly stabilized against temperature changes if a second thermistor constitutes one of the other legs of the bridge, being positioned in a chamber where the gas flow is slow compared to the point where the first thermistor is located. The bridge is so designed that both thermistors are at about the same temperature, and the pump servo system is designed so that the desired mass flow rate is found at zero bridge output.

Even with the two-thermistor setup, there will be a change of calibration with large temperature changes of the flow sensor housing. Therefore it is desirable to temperature-control this housing (which also temperature-controls the gas entering the flow sensor, because the heat transfer to the slow moving gas from the walls of the small entrance tube is fast). The small mass flow sensor is observable in Fig. 3, the breadboard unit for JPL. The heater is actually a transistor, and the thermistor beads are mounted in a small extension on the transistor cap.

For special applications, it has proven advantageous to adjust the housing temperature to keep the compensating thermistor at a given temperature, rather than keeping the housing and gas at a given temperature.

The advantage of controlling the block (and gas) temperature with respect to the compensating thermistor, instead of keeping it constant as with a thermostat, is that the temperature of both beads is maintained constant in face of changing gas conductivity and specific heat as well as changing ambient temperature. This causes the mass flow to vary to a predictable and fairly small extent with conductivity and specific heat. With thermostat type control the mass flow would vary to a greater extent, and this variation would also depend on the temperature/resistance characteristics of the individual thermistors used. The reasons for this are as follows: Using

W_a, W_c = power dissipated in "active" and in "compensating" beads

$s = C_p$ = gas specific heat at constant pressure

k = gas thermal conductivity

ρ = gas density

a = bead radius

V = velocity of gas past bead

m = mass flow of gas

A = area of gas channel near "active" bead

T_a, T_c = temperature of "active" and "compensating" beads

t = temperature of gas near beads (= block temperature)

King's Law can be applied to the power dissipation of the active bead if it is assumed that the bead approximates a cylinder of radius a and length $2a$:

$$W_a = 2a(k + 2\sqrt{ksa\rho V})(T_a - t) \quad (1)$$

and

$$W_c = 4\pi ka(T_c - t) \quad (2)$$

ignoring convection in both expressions. Therefore,

$$W_a = 2a(k + 2\sqrt{ks\,a/A\,m})(T - t) \quad (3)$$

In the moisture meter, the sensor is operated in a servo loop with a pump, which varies such that $T_c = T_a$ (i.e., the thermistor bridge balances at all times). So we have by combining the expressions for W_a and W_c:

$$\frac{W_a}{2a(k + 2\sqrt{ks\,a/A\,m})} = \frac{W_c}{4\pi ka} \quad (4)$$

or

$$m = \frac{A}{a}\left(\pi\frac{W_a}{W_c} - \frac{1}{2}\right)^2 \cdot \frac{k}{s} \quad (5)$$

This relation applies whether or not the sensor is temperature controlled. If it is not, variation in ambient temperature has a large effect on the ratio W_a/W_c and a smaller effect on the gas "constants" s and k. If the block temperature is simply fixed, by a thermostat-heated arrangement, effects of change in ambient temperature are, of course, eliminated. However, changes in s and k due to variation in the chemical composition of the gas will not only affect the ratio k/s, but also change the temperature of the beads with the result that W_a and W_c will both vary according to the temperature/resistance characteristics of the beads. The consequent variation in W_a/W_c, and hence m, is large.

Now if heater feedback is applied to the block such that T_c, rather than t, is kept constant, both W_a and W_c remain constant despite changes in k and s, as well as in ambient temperature. We can now write for any gas or mixture of gases, at any temperature within the controlling range of the feedback loop

$$m = (\text{constant}) \times \frac{k}{s} \quad (6)$$

The ratio k/s varies much less than either k or s individually, among common gases not too near their boiling point.

TABLE 1. SPECIFIC HEAT (AT CONSTANT PRESSURE) AND CONDUCTIVITY FOR A FEW GASES

	Air	N_2	O_2	H_2	He	CO_2	NH_3
$k \times 10^4$	.57	.52	.56	3.63	3.4	.31	.45
$s(=C_p)$	.24	.25	.22	3.38	1.25	.19	.52
$ks \times 10^4$	.14	.13	.12	12.3	4.2	.06	.23
$k/s \times 10^4$	2.4	2.1	2.5	1.08	2.7	1.63	.88

As the moisture cell processes moist air, it produces gaseous hydrogen and oxygen. When mixing ratios greater than a few grams of water vapor per kilogram of air are encountered, this hydrogen must be considered in calculating the mass flow sensor sensitivity. Thus the mixing ratio indication* calibration must take into consideration the type of mass

* The mixing ratio indicator can be considered to show mixing ratio (the mass of water vapor per mass of dry air) or specific humidity (the mass of water vapor per total mass of air). For low moisture values (say less than a few g/kg) the two terms are identical for all practical purposes. Mixing ratio indicator was chosen as the instrument title primarily because of the agreement with the Company initials. The details of the calibration factor at higher moisture levels depend on which moisture variable is to be shown and on the type of design used in the mass flow sensor. If the moisture sensor housing temperature is controlled to keep the compensating thermistor at constant temperature, as shown above, the mass flow rate will depend only on the gas constituents, not the thermistor characteristics. Then the exact moisture cell current vs mixing ratio or vs specific humidity can be calculated even for very moist air. For ordinary purposes, rather than using a slightly nonlinear scale for the high moisture values, it is adequate to use linear scales and adjust the scale sensitivity slightly on the 10 g/kg and 30 g/kg scales to make the meter reading satisfactorily close to the specific humidity or the mixing ratio, whichever is desired.

flow meter and how it varies with the gaseous constituents.

The flow sensor takes about 80 milliwatts. For initial warm-up the heater requires about 300 milliwatts for 10 to 20 seconds; thereafter, it consumes low continuous wattage, the amount depending on the insulation (110 milliwatts if uninsulated at ordinary ambient conditions).

The flow sensor as designed can sense a flow change of less than 0.05 cc/min. for flows between 1 and 40 cc/min. of STP air. Tests during the JPL program showed the flow sensor would operate down to pressures of 0.01 atm. At somewhat lower pressures, in the micron and submicron range, the heated thermistor starts acting similarly to a Pirani or thermocouple vacuum gage, and then is affected by the pressure.

THE PUMP SYSTEM

For typical uses the pump must be a long-life device taking little electric power and pumping in the range of perhaps 5 to 20 cc/min. of STP air across a pressure drop of 4 in. of water or more. It need not maintain accuracy, because the servo control which powers it keeps adjusting it. An ordinary AC powered aquarium pump of the vibrating diaphragm type is adequate for typical meteorological needs. The MRI Model 901 unit and several airborne versions use a radial whirling rod on a DC motor which pulls air in through the center axis because of centrifugal force and aerodynamic effects at the rod tips.

For the JPL breadboard, various alternatives were considered to give smaller size, lower power consumption, operation at pressures of 0.1 to 0.01 atm, low magnetic field, and adaptability to sterilization at 145°C. The pump shown in Fig. 3 is a diaphragm type meeting most of the requirements. Additional tests implied that refinements such as size changes and proper acoustical and mechanical tuning could permit the unit to meet all the requirements.

For aircraft versions, the pump must be capable of powering the flow across the pressure drop of the cell and tubing, and also against the pressure difference between moisture cell inlet and the pump outlet. With the low-power centrifugal pump, it was necessary to position the moisture cell and pump outlet so that the pressure difference between them was not great. Usually the moisture cell is positioned so outside air blows smoothly past it, but the pressure around the cell is approximately cockpit static pressure. For pressurized installations, all the system components pertaining to flow can be positioned at ambient conditions, separate from the electronics.

SOME APPLICATIONS

This section reviews a few of the meteorological uses to which this mixing ratio indicator has been put. The main point demonstrated is the versatility of the device; all the measurements were handled with versions of the Model 901 unit. Although the cases do not show anything particularly unexpected meteorologically, the applications are interesting and each shows some special feature of the measurement technique.

Case 1—Pressurized High Altitude Flight

The Model 901 was installed on a B-47 flight for contrail investigation. The instrument was placed in the forward observer position with the probe in the cabin air inlet, and operated by an observer with no previous experience with the instrument. The flight took place April 21, 1960, from Edwards Air Force Base, California, in conjunction with a contrail study by MRI for AFCRC.

The instrument was turned on after regular contrail runs were completed, but the B-47 was still in the contrail and cirrus layer (247 mb). The aircraft flew at this altitude for several minutes noting the mixing ratio varied between 0.06 and 0.08 g/kg. The B-47 then descended taking readings on the way down.

The readings of moisture fluctuated up to 100 per cent humidity at the contrail level, and it agreed well with the radiosonde data below 650 mb where the radiosonde started providing data. Of course the MRI unit showed more microstructure than the radiosonde because more points were taken.

The outside air came through a compressor, a refrigerator (turned off), and about 20 ft of tubing before reaching the sensor, and this introduced some lag in the readings because of the way water vapor is absorbed by the walls. From various flights, it appears that the effect is very small during flight into increasing amounts of water vapor (usually during descent), but larger when the water vapor is decreasing. The obvious solution is to have the sensor situated in ambient conditions, but for many applications the performance gain would not be worth the extra installation trouble.

Case 2—Unpressurized High Altitude Jet Flight

Figure 4 is a summary of measurements made by the Model 901 on a flight August 26, 1960, at Flagstaff, Arizona, with a T-37 Cessna Jet Trainer of the USAF. The difference

between "up" and "down" lags introduced by the length of tubing between the sensor and ambient air is shown. The unpressurized air passed through a turned-off refrigerator and probably 15 ft of tubing. Above 22,000 ft, climb averaged 500 fpm, and descent 1800 fpm.

The main equipment and meteorological points from the flight and from Fig. 4 are:

(a) The pump servo would handle the required mass flow even at 30,000 ft (laboratory studies have indicated a 35,000 ft limit with the present low-efficiency pump).

(b) The mixing ratio increased sharply above 20,000 ft.

(c) The measurement inside the clouds seemed correct.

(d) Above cloud tops, traverses and sound-

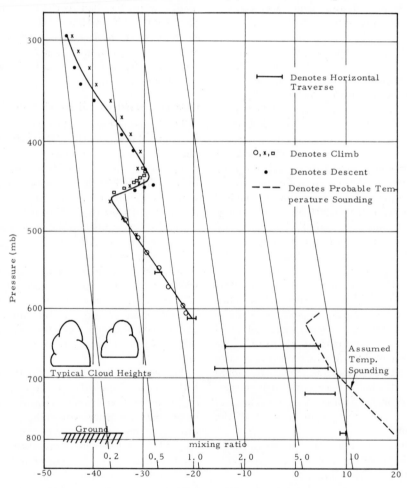

FIG. 4. T-37 flight.

ings gave the same mixing ratio values, and showed very dry air.

(e) Below cloud top level, traverses showed huge variations in mixing ratio; this is the region of mixing between the moist surface air and the dry environment air. High values invariably were associated with clouds, hence with air raised from lower elevations.

(f) The mixing ratio variations are greatest at cloud level. The low end of the mixing range logically increased with decreasing height. Because of mixing, the maximum values decreased slightly with altitudes.

Figure 4 graphically illustrates the convective transport of moisture upward from lower, relatively moist air. It points out that in this region a single sounding is not necessarily significant, while a single sounding is meaningful above this mixing layer. Obviously the mixing ratio indicator is a useful tool for detailed studies of convective motions, especially because it can identify air "labeled" by moisture before that air is "labeled" by the presence of a cloud.

Case 3—Measurements in Supercooled Cloud at −24°C

The technique of measurement of freezing nuclei which Meteorology Research, Inc., and the affiliated Atmospheric Research Group have adopted for the past few years involves introducing an air sample into the chamber of a cold box with glycerined walls, humidifying

the chamber by a breath, which creates a supercooled cloud, and counting the crystals which appear on a supercooled sugar solution at the bottom of the chamber in 60 and 120 seconds. Two chambers are used simultaneously, one at −20°C, the other at −24°C. To evaluate this measurement technique, it was necessary to ascertain when the air in the box was saturated with respect to water and with respect to ice, because this determines droplet and crystal growth. It was noted that the visible cloud disappeared in the −24°C chamber in about 60 to 70 seconds.

Figure 5 gives the results of the tests in the chamber at −24°C. When breath of about 1/30th of the chamber volume is blown into the chamber, the temperature as shown by a thermistor rises to −21.5°C, cools to −23°C at 30 seconds, and is essentially back at −24°C after 80 seconds. The box is practically isothermal throughout its depth. The water vapor is initially 1.3 g/kg for the amount of breath humidifying; it decreases as water vapor is removed by the glycerine of the walls. The rate of removal will depend somewhat on the amount already in the glycerine.

Figure 5 shows the decrease of water vapor measured by the mixing ratio indicator with the probe in the cold chamber. Also shown are the calculated values for saturation with respect to water and with respect to ice. The shaded area must refer to the amount of water contained in the form of liquid. This

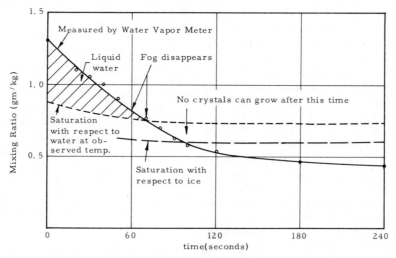

Fig. 5. Water vapor change at −24°C in chamber with glycerined walls.

amount is zero at about the time the visible fog disappears. Apparently after 100 seconds, the box is unsaturated with respect to ice and no new crystals could form.

Up to 70 seconds, the indicator is evidently measuring both the water vapor and the supercooled liquid water. It would be expected that the water in tiny droplets would enter the sensor, turn to vapor as the air surrounding it is dried by the sensor, and be included in the measurement. Since the flow velocity up into the vertically oriented sensor is on the order of 10 to 20 cm/sec. this would include virtually all the droplets comprising a typical newly formed cloud, and the meter reading would be practically total moisture.

Case 4—Micrometeorological Study

On August 25, 1960 at Flagstaff, a brief micrometeorological investigation was made from 1800 to 2100 MST in a small volcanic crater (450-ft diameter of flat grass-covered area, in 1000-ft diameter cup, having walls 50 to 120 ft, situated at 8000 ft). This period covered the time of rapid ground cooling from 18 to 2°C, and the onset of gentle drainage winds.

The complete results of time variation of the wind, temperature, and water vapor are too complex to present here, but the pertinent results relating to the water vapor are worth summarizing.

The air from above the grass up to 10 ft above the ground had a mixing ratio of 6.8 to 8.2 g/kg, averaging around 7.3 g/kg and being rather constant in time and altitude. Occasionally a stratified layer could be detected by having say, 0.3 g/kg more moisture than the air a few inches lower.

The interesting variations were within the layer of matted grass and up to a few inches above the grass. At 1800 the mixing ratio measured at the grass level varied from 10.0 to 15.0 g/kg. At 2000, values between 6.4 and 9.0 g/kg were noted. At 2100, with the air above one foot being 6.8 to 7.0 g/kg, the air immediately above the grass was around 5.8 to 6.5 g/kg, and 5.6 to 15 g/kg within the grass layer. The ground air temperature averaged about 2°C, which would permit a mixing ratio of only 5.9 g/kg. The temperature probe verified that within the grass layer, local very warm and cold spots existed, at which temperature the observed mixing ratios would presumably not be above saturation. Ground cooling made the adjacent air saturated and thus removed water vapor as condensation or dew, while the insulating effect of the grass (some of which was dry straw) permitted some warm, moist pockets. The fast response of the water vapor probe, and its small size, made it especially useful for this study.

Case 5—In-cloud Study

On August 27, 1962, on an NSF program* at Flagstaff, a Cessna 180 equipped with the aircraft version of the Model 901 spiraled up in the strongly rising core of a developing thunderstorm from the base at 12,500 ft to a height of 19,300 ft. The mixing ratio indicator functioned appropriately inside this cloud and showed mixing ratios corresponding to practically 100 per cent RH at all heights. On several occasions during the upward spiral, the aircraft got in the turbulent edge of the ascending column where dry outside air was being mixed in, and the mixing ratio momentarily decreased. The sensor housing tended to exclude droplets.

CONCLUSIONS

The mixing ratio system has a versatility which makes it appropriate for a variety of meteorological tasks, from probing at stratospheric heights to measuring around leaves and blades of grass. The complete system is somewhat complex, but it is nevertheless far simpler than some of the alternatives presently available. More development is still required to obtain a complete understanding and utilization of the phosphorous pentoxide electrolyzing cell for meteorological applications. Some major mechanical redesign of the cell is indicated for special applications. If the cell is deemed satisfactory for any given purpose, then the rest of the system can be considered straightforward engineering development. With development, the technique seems suitable for operational application at extremely low and extremely high mixing ratio values in a wide range of situations.

* National Science Foundation Grant NSF G11969, Atmospheric Sciences Program.

Acknowledgments. The permission of Jet Propulsion Laboratory to include results from the MRI study (MRI, 1962) is gratefully acknowledged. This work was performed for the Jet Propulsion Laboratory, California Institute of Technology, under Contract No. 950207, a subcontract under NASA Contract NAS 7-100.

Mr. Peter Davey handled the basic development of the mass flow sensor, including the technique of compensating for unknown gas constituents. Mr. Kenneth Beesmer performed time constant tests on the cell. Mr. Harold Hutchinson and Mr. William Gregge helped substantially with the pump development on the JPL project, and Dr. Harner Selvidge has been invaluable on many aspects of the program. Consolidated Electrodynamics Corp. personnel have been most helpful throughout the program, especially Mr. Michael Czuha, Jr. Mr. Arthur Rosenthal was most helpful in studying the very low moisture level chemistry of the cell, and Mr. Lawrence Bockhold assisted ably in developing the apparatus to supply dry atmospheres.

References

1. Czuha, Jr., M., "Adaptation of the Electrolytic Moisture Detector To Atmospheric Humidity Measurement," Humidity and Moisture, Vol 1, New York, N.Y., Reinhold Pub. Corp, 1964

2. Finley, C. M., and Shaffer, J., "The Detection of Parts per Million Moisture in Refrigerants," Humidity and Moisture, Vol 1, New York, N.Y., Reinhold Pub. Corp., 1964.

3. Jones, R. H., and Petersen, A., "Additional Performance Data on a New Electrolytic Hygrometer Cell," Humidity and Moisture, Vol. 1, New York, N.Y., Reinhold Pub. Corp., 1964.

4. Keidel, F. A., "Determination of Water by Direct Amperometric Measurement," *J. Anal. Chem.*, **31**, 2043–8 (1959).

5. Meteorology Research, Inc., "A Moisture Analyzer for Martian Atmosphere," Final Report, NASA-JPL Contract No. 950207, Sept. 10, 1962.

6. Ruskin, R. E., "The Measurement of Humidity in Meteorology," *Weatherwise*, **16**, No. 2 (1963).

51. Adaptation of the Electrolytic Moisture Detector to Atmospheric Humidity Measurement

MICHAEL CZUHA, JR.

Bell & Howell Research Center, Pasadena, California

ABSTRACT

The principle of electrolysis of water in the Pt-P_2O_5-H_2O system and the state of the art are reviewed. Two approaches have been considered in adapting the electrolysis cell to atmospheric humidity measurements: (1) control of the mass rate of air input by means of a mass flow meter-pump servo system and (2) diffusion of moisture through a porous hydrophobic barrier.

The first method utilizes a small pump in conjunction with a bead thermistor mass flow indicator. The thermistor bridge output controls the pump speed in a transistorized circuit.

In the second method, a porous "Teflon" barrier isolates the electrode matrix from the atmosphere. The mass rate of water input is governed by the difference in partial pressure of water vapor across the barrier. An ideal condition for diffusion exists since the concentration of water vapor on the electrode side of the barrier is always near zero.

Temperature has a measurable effect on the diffusion cell. The rate of flow of air past the cell has a slight effect which may involve pumping through the barrier. The response rate of the diffusion cell is not as high as in the forced-air system.

A combination of the two techniques might result in linear operation over a wide range of humidity.

INTRODUCTION

The electrolytic moisture cell first introduced by Keidel[1] in 1956 differs from the usual electric hygrometers in that the conducting film is electrolyzed continuously by an applied DC voltage and the cell current, rather than the cell resistance, is measured as a function of the moisture content. A thin film of polyphosphoric anhydride is hydrolyzed to phosphoric acid which is electrically dissociated into hydrogen, oxygen, and the original anhydride.[2] The net effect of this mechanism is the conversion of water to its elements with the passage of a current given by Faraday's Law of electrochemical equivalence. The Pt-P_2O_5-H_2O system is unique in its regenerative behavior and in providing an accurate measure of absolute humidity in gases. Figure 1 shows an exposed view of the tubular electrolytic cell presently used in commercial instruments.

Numerous applications have been made of the electrolytic moisture cell in determining water in gases,[3] liquids,[4, 5] solids,[6, 7] and in the products of combustion in carbon-hydrogen microanalysis.[8, 9] Less extensive work has been reported on the use of the cell in meteorology. An early study was made for the Air Force with a balloon-borne electrolytic hygrometer at altitudes up to 50,000 ft.[10] The report indicated the feasibility of the method; however, an excessive pressure drop within the sensing element prevented pumping a sufficiently large sample volume for satisfactory instrument response at pressures lower than 100 mb.

Studies in this laboratory have shown additional limitations on the tubular element involving high moisture levels and extreme temperatures.[11] To attain adequate performance over a wide dynamic range of humidity,

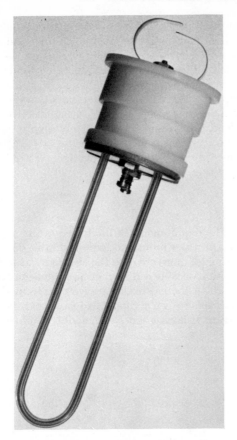

Fig. 1. CEC electrolytic moisture cell.

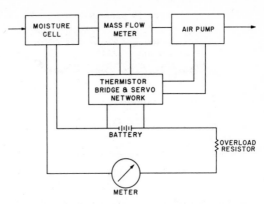

Fig. 2. Circuit diagram for servo control of mass rate of air through a moisture cell.

pressure, and temperature, modifications in cell design, as well as in the sampling system, were obviously necessary.

This paper describes two approaches taken in adapting the electrolytic cell to atmospheric humidity measurements: (1) control of the mass rate of air input at low flow rates in a short cell using a servo-controlled pumping system, and (2) diffusion of moisture through a porous hydrophobic barrier in a radically modified cell. The feasibility of combining the two techniques is also considered.

SERVO-CONTROLLED AIR PUMP

Since the electrolytic cell responds linearly to the mass rate of water intake, a fixed known rate of flow of air into the element is all that is needed for direct conversion of the electrolysis current to absolute humidity. Under temperate conditions, and for moderate changes in atmospheric pressure, the flow control system,

shown schematically in Fig. 2, operates satisfactorily in maintaining a constant mass rate of air flow through the cell.

Air drawn through a moisture element by a small DC operated pump cools one of two thermistor beads connected to a resistance bridge comprising a mass flow meter. The resulting bridge unbalance controls the speed of the pump by means of a transistorized feedback network. A battery supplies the bridge current, pump power, and electrolysis current. A milliammeter, in series with the moisture cell, is graduated in terms of absolute humidity units. Recent developments at Meteorology Research Inc.,[12] enable this

Fig. 3. Short segment of electrolytic moisture cell.

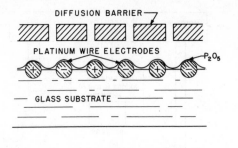

FIG. 4. Cross section of a moisture diffusion cell.

system to operate at extremes of temperature and pressure by the use of temperature compensating thermistors and a refined servo-pumping system.

At the low flow rates (5 to 10 cc/min.) normally used with the servo-controlled pumping system, a short element, 1 or 2 in. in length (see Fig. 3), is efficient in electrolyzing all of the incoming moisture. However, there are limitations to the use of the narrow tubular cell at high moisture levels. The inlet end of the element can become overheated as a result of excessive current, and an attendant increase in activity of the P_2O_5 may cause cell failure.[11] An extreme condition of overload can occur in airborne tests during traverse of cloud formations. The relatively high intake velocity of the small cell can cause particulate moisture to impinge on the electrodes, resulting in shorting failure.

DIFFUSION CELL

The requirements of limitation of the mass rate of water input and more favorable distribution of moisture over the electrodes at high humidity levels can be met in a diffusion cell in which the electrodes are isolated from the atmosphere by a porous hydrophobic barrier.[13] Figure 4 shows a cross section of the diffusion

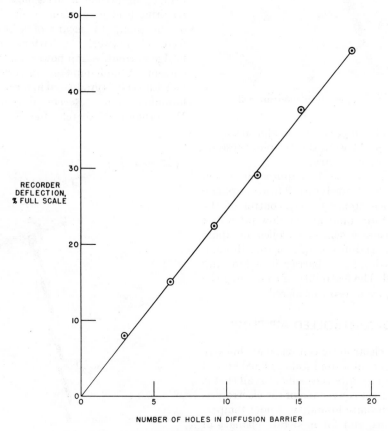

FIG. 5. Dependence of diffusion cell current on porosity.

cell. Drilled, or otherwise porous, "Teflon" serves as a good diffusion barrier. The electrode structure is similar to that previously described ; i.e., it consists of platinum wires closely spaced on a glass substrate which is coated with a thin layer of P_2O_5. The assembly is preferably cylindrical with the electrodes wound in bifilar fashion around the outside of the glass cylinder or rod. This geometry also affords a relatively large diffusion area in a compact cell.

Moisture diffuses through the barrier and is electrolyzed. A gradient of moisture concentration, which functions as the diffusion driving force, exists across the barrier. An ideal condition for diffusion exists because there is always virtually zero partial pressure of water vapor at the electrode matrix surface.

The rate of mass transfer of moisture through the "Teflon" has been found to be directly proportional to the porosity of the barrier. Figure 5 shows the response of a diffusion cell, as a function of the number of holes (.010-in. diameter) in a barrier made of $\frac{1}{4}$-in. "Teflon" tubing, 1 in. long with $\frac{1}{16}$-in. wall. The tests were made with nitrogen containing approximately 3000 ppm moisture.

In a true diffusion process, the mass rate of water vapor entering the cell would be independent of the air velocity. The effect of air velocity across the diffusion cell was determined by placing the cell and a velocity probe within a blower duct. A 10 per cent increase in cell current was observed as the velocity was increased from 0 to 750 fpm. The air flow was not rigidly controlled from an aerodynamic standpoint. Turbulence and pulsations in pressure may have caused some pumping of air through the pores of the barrier.

The diffusion cell responds linearly to moisture content as shown in Fig. 6. The tests were made on a drilled "Teflon" sleeve. The moisture levels were checked against a conventional high-range Moisture Monitor operating at 20 cc/min. on the same stream. Linearity extends to very low moisture levels, as shown in Fig. 7, in tests made with a highly porous sintered "Teflon" sleeve. However, the speed of response drops considerably at the lower moisture levels. Figure 8 shows the 63 per cent response time of the diffusion cell as a function of moisture level compared with similar data on the conventional tubular cell utilizing forced flow.

The effect of temperature on the response speed of the diffusion cell was also determined. The response speed increases with increasing

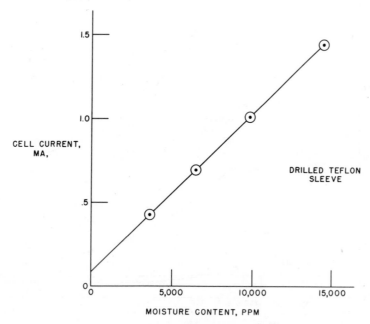

FIG. 6. Linearity of a high-range moisture diffusion cell.

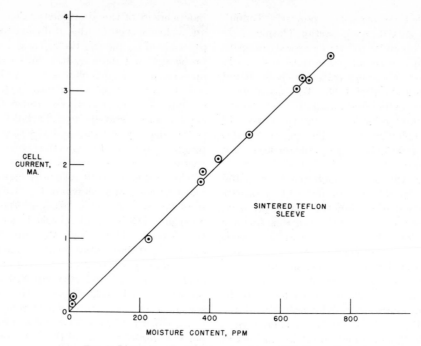

FIG. 7. Linearity of a low-range moisture diffusion cell.

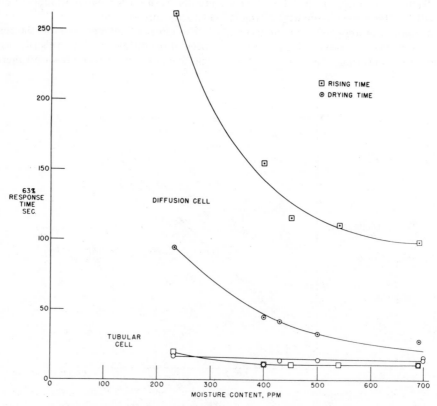

FIG. 8. Comparison of the response speeds of forced flow and diffusion cells.

temperature. However, no quantitative determination of the temperature coefficient of diffusion was made because of self-heating in the element and the difficulty of measuring the temperature of the barrier. An interesting phenomenon was observed at temperatures appreciably below room temperature. Figure 9 shows a cycling behavior of the cell current for the sintered "Teflon" cell at $-30°C$, resembling chromatograph peaks, with a marked decrease in intensity of electrolysis between peaks. The dotted line shows the steady-state response at room temperature. The cell coating apparently accumulated water during the relatively inactive period as a result of a drop in the rate of hydrolysis of P_2O_5 with decreasing temperature. As the heat of reaction warmed the coating, the rate of hydrolysis increased causing an increase in cell conductance. The sharp rise in the electrolysis current was accompanied by additional IR heating. As the absorbed water was consumed, drying out the coating, the cell cooled off again and the process was repeated. The cycling pattern was highly reproducible and continued indefinitely or until the cell was brought back to room temperature. The integral of peak area over one cycle was identical with the integral at constant current at room temperature over the same period, indicating 100 per cent absorption and electrolysis of the water in spite of the cycling behaviour.

CONCLUSION

Use of the electrolytic moisture cell in meteorological applications, particularly at high humidity, requires control of the mass rate of water input into the cell by operating at flow rates of air far below the normal rates used in conventional gas applications. The concept of diffusion across a porous hydrophobic barrier, corresponding to the condition of zero flow rate, can be utilized at moisture levels approaching that of saturated air.

The diffusion barrier permits operation at high moisture levels by providing more favorable distribution of the water vapor over the electrode matrix, thereby eliminating the overload problems of the tubular cell. Since linear response is obtained in both instances, it should be possible within a single cell to switch from diffusion to forced flow as the moisture level drops below the region for optimum response by diffusion. The forced flow feature would be, in effect, a built-in calibration system for the diffusion cell.

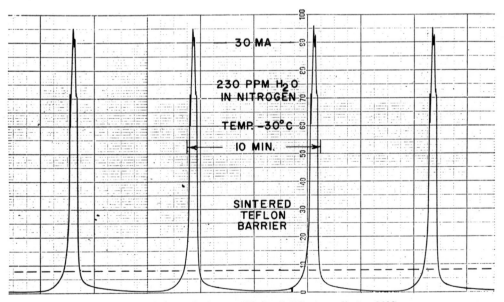

FIG. 9. Behavior of a porous "Teflon" diffusion cell at $-30°C$.

References

1. Keidel, F. A., "Determination of Water by Direct Amperometric Measurement," *Anal. Chem.*, **31**, 2043 (1959).
2. Czuha, M., Jr., Gardiner, K. W., and Sawyer, D. T., "The Electrochemical Behavior and Analytical Applications of the Pt-P_2O_5-H_2O System," *J. Electroanal. Chem.*, **4**, 51 (1962).
3. Taylor, E. S., "A New Instrument for the Moisture Analysis of Freon Fluorinated Hydrocarbons," *Refrig. Eng.*, **64**, 41 (1956).
4. Keidel, F. A., "Electrolytic Hygrometer," Proceedings of Ninth Annual Symposium on Process Fluid Analyzers, 1957.
5. Cole, L. G., Czuha, M., Jr., Mosley, R., and Sawyer, D. T., "Continuous Coulometric Determination of Parts per Million of Moisture in Organic Liquids," *Anal. Chem.*, **31**, 2048 (1959).
6. Armstrong, R. G., Gardiner, K. W., and Adams, F. W., "Electrolytic Determination of Microgram Quantities of Water in Paper," *Anal. Chem.*, **32**, 752 (1960).
7. Bagger, J. B., Marsh, R. F., and Finley, C. M., "Microcoulometric Measurement of Moisture in Solids," 12th Pittsburgh Conference on Analytical Chemistry and Applied Spectroscopy, 1961.
8. Haber, H. S., and Gardiner, K. W., "A Rapid Instrumental Method for the Microdetermination of Carbon and Hydrogen in Organic Compounds," *Microchem. J.*, **6**, 83 (1962).
9. Olson, E. C., Houtman, R. L., and Struck, W. A., "Rapid Micromethods of Elemental Analysis. III. Precise Coulometric Determination of Hydrogen in Organic Compounds," *Microchem. J.*, **5**, 611 (1961).
10. Waters, J. L., "Adaptation of an Electrolytic Water Vapor Detector for Balloon Measurement of Water Content of the Atmosphere," Air Force Cambridge Research Center, Technical Report No. 60-245-II, 1960.
11. Czuha, M., Jr., "Efficiency and Heat Effects in Electrolytic Moisture Cells," 14th Pittsburgh Conference on Analytical Chemistry and Applied Spectroscopy, 1963.
12. Lake, J., Private communication from Meteorology Research Inc., Altadena, California. "This work was performed for the Jet Propulsion Laboratory, California Institute of Technology, sponsored by the National Aeronautics and Space Administration under Contract NASA 7-100," September 1962.
13. Czuha, M., Jr. (to Consolidated Electrodynamics Corporation), U.S. Patent 3,001,918 (September 26, 1961).

52. The Detection of Parts Per Million Moisture in Refrigerants

C. M. FINLEY AND JOHN SHAFFER

Consolidated Electrodynamics Corporation, Analytical and Control Division,
Pasadena, California

ABSTRACT

This paper describes one analytical technique usable for trace water determination, the electrolytic cell of Keidel. After explaining its theoretical operation, original difficulties encountered with its application to refrigerants are described. Later improvements in cell design are described which allow much greater efficiencies.

Application of these newer cells to refrigerants is examined, and the improved efficency at varying moisture levels is shown. The effect of varying flow rate is also examined and results tabulated.

The conclusions to be drawn from these data show that newer cell design improvements allow the use of electrolytic cells without efficiency calibration curves on varied refrigerant gases.

INTRODUCTION

The electrolytic moisture cell was first described by Keidel[1] of duPont, and has since found widespread use in the laboratory as well as in process instrumentation. Several companies are currently producing devices which are licensed from duPont to use this electrolytic cell.

Briefly, the cell consists of a small glass capillary, around the inside circumference of which is wound a double helix of electrode wires coated with a thin desiccant film. As a gas containing moisture passes through the cell, the moisture is absorbed by the desiccant. The applied voltage on the cell electrolyzes the water to hydrogen and oxygen, regenerating the desiccant. The electrolysis current is a direct and linear function of the mass flow rate of water into the cell.

Application of this principle has been quite broad and by suitable extraction techniques, its use has been extended to liquids[2] and solids.[3]

In June of 1956, work was reported by E. S. Taylor[4] of duPont on the application of the electrolytic moisture cell to refrigerants. In this report, difficulties encountered with cell efficiency were described. As a result of these difficulties it was concluded that calibration of any given cell was necessary in order to obtain accuracy when the device was used with fluorinated hydrocarbon refrigerants. With such calibration, however, Taylor concluded that the electrolytic cell was a more reliable measuring device than other commonly used methods of instrumentation.

Although the cells in use at the time of Taylor's work definitely exhibited an inability to extract quantitatively the water from a refrigerant stream, later improvements in cell design have brought about a reexamination of this problem. Specifically, it appears that the use of glass as the cell substrate material, taken together with improvements in desiccant coating techniques,[5] has produced a cell that offers much greater efficiency. Early cells used TFE as the substrate, upon which the aqueous coating solution tended to form droplets or puddles. This resulted in a reduced desiccant surface area which led to reduced efficiency and response. A glass substrate, coated with an acetone-based coating solution

TABLE 1. FLUORINATED REFRIGERANTS USED AS TEST COMPOUNDS

COMPOUND	MOLECULAR WEIGHT	BOILING POINT	VAPOR PRESSURE AT ROOM TEMPERATURE	PURITY OF SAMPLE
CCl_3F	137.4	24 °C	~ 0 psig	99.9
CCl_2F_2	120.9	−30 °C	85 psig	99.0
CF_4	88.0	−128 °C	500 psig	95.0
$CHClF_2$	86.5	−41 °C	123 psig	99.9
$C_2Cl_2F_4$	170.9	3.5 °C	14 psig	95.0

produces a continuous thin film with a large surface area. Significant improvement in efficiency and response with such a cell was demonstrated, and this led to a reconsideration of the fluorinated refrigerant application·

The refrigerant materials selected for this study are shown in Table 1. While this by no means covers the entire range of compounds, it was felt to be sufficiently representative.

EXPERIMENTAL METHOD

The apparatus assembled for the experimental work is schematically shown in Fig. 1. The instruments used were standard in every respect but flow control. Because the sample gas passed through the instruments consecutively, the flow controllers in the first two were bypassed, allowing the third instrument to establish the flow rate for the three. A series arrangement was used so that any sample water vapor that escaped the first cell would be detected in the second cell. Any water escaping from the second cell would be detected by the third. This technique is often used to establish cell efficiency due to its sensitivity and accuracy.

The sample passed from the magnesium perchlorate dryer, through a plastic line selected by the multiport valve, to the first cell. The plastic lines were used to add moisture

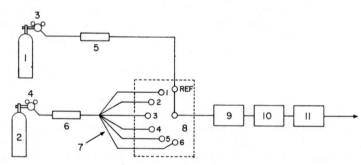

1. DRY N_2
2. SAMPLE
3,4-PRESSURE REGULATORS
5,6-CHEMICAL $\left[Mg(ClO_4)_2 \right]$ DRYERS
7. VARIOUS LENGTHS OF PLASTIC TUBING
8. MULTIPORT VALVE
9,10-CEC TYPE 26–303 MOISTURE MONITORS, MODIFIED SO THAT THE FLOW CONTROLLERS WERE BYPASSED, AND EQUIPPED WITH STANDARD MOISTURE CELLS.
11. UNMODIFIED 26–303, EQUIPPED WITH STANDARD MOISTURE CELL.

FIG. 1. Schematic diagram of test apparatus.

on a continuous basis to the dry gas stream passing through them. Most elastomeric and plastic materials are slightly permeable to water, and the rate of water migration through a specific material is a function of the difference in water vapor pressure across the wall, the wall thickness, the surface area and the temperature. The equilibrium level in a dry flowing stream is, therefore, a function of these parameters plus the gaseous sample flow rate and the ratio of pressure across the barrier. It is independent of the composition of the sample gas.

With the exception of these lengths of plastic tubing, inserted in the system to allow a predictable influx of moisture, all of the sample system was clean, dry stainless steel.

However, in all "dry" systems (those having moisture levels of 1 ppm or less), some residual moisture is always present in the gas stream due to desorption of water from the surfaces contacting the sample gas. In order to measure true changes in water vapor level from other sources, the background levels of the connecting stainless steel tubing had to be established. This was done by allowing dry N_2 to flow through the system for an extended period of time. Once this had been done, the indicated "background" level was noted. All the measurements thereafter made at higher input levels of moisture were corrected to compensate for these residual levels. Table 2 shows these values for nitrogen, which was used as a reference.

TABLE 2. EXPERIMENTAL DATA FOR NITROGEN SAMPLE, SHOWING THE METHOD USED FOR BACKGROUND CORRECTION. MOISTURE LEVEL EXPRESSED AS P.P.M. BY VOLUME

SAMPLE — NITROGEN

PRESSURE — 20 psig

FLOW RATE — 100 ml/min

VALVE POSITION	CELL #1			CELL #2			CELL #3			NET SUM
	GROSS	BACKGROUND	NET	GROSS	BACKGROUND	NET	GROSS	BACKGROUND	NET	
REF.		0.9 ppm			0.2 ppm			0.6 ppm		—
1	4.2	− 0.9	= 3.3	0.2	− 0.2	= 0	0.6	− 0.6	= 0	3.3
2	10	− 0.9	= 9.1	0.2	− 0.2	= 0	0.6	− 0.6	= 0	9.1
3	22	− 0.9	= 21.1	0.2	− 0.2	= 0	0.6	− 0.6	= 0	21.1
4	47	− 0.9	= 46	0.2	− 0.2	= 0	0.6	− 0.6	= 0	46
5	78	− 0.9	= 77	0.2	− 0.2	= 0	0.6	− 0.6	= 0	77
6	190	− 0.9	= 189	0.2	− 0.2	= 0	0.6	− 0.6	= 0	189

TABLE 3. EXPERIMENTAL DATA FOR CCl_3F, EXPRESSED AS P.P.M. BY VOLUME

SAMPLE — C CL_3 F

PRESSURE — 0 psig (sampled with vacuum pump)

FLOW RATE — 100 ml/min

1ppm by weight = 7.6 ppm by volume

CELL #1	CELL #2	CELL #3	TOTAL	% EFFICIENCY
13.1ppm	0 ppm	0.2ppm	13.3ppm	98.5
17.1	0	0.2	17.3	98.8
47.1	0	0.2	47.3	99.6
92.1	0.1	0.4	92.6	99.5
369	0.4	0.2	369.6	99.8

TABLE 4. EXPERIMENTAL DATA FOR CCl_2F_2, EXPRESSED AS P.P.M. BY VOLUME

SAMPLE — C CL 2 F2

PRESSURE — 20 psig

FLOW RATE — 100 ml/min

1 ppm by weight = 6.7 ppm by volume

CELL # 1	CELL # 2	CELL # 3	TOTAL	% EFFICIENCY
3.1 ppm	0 ppm	0 ppm	3.1	100
7.7	0	0	7.7	100
31	0	0	31	100
52	0	0	52	100
73	0	0	73	100

TABLE 5. EXPERIMENTAL DATA FOR CF_4, EXPRESSED AS P.P.M. BY VOLUME

SAMPLE — C F4

PRESSURE — 20 psig

FLOW RATE — 100 ml/min

1 ppm by weight = 4.9 ppm by volume

CELL # 1	CELL # 2	CELL # 3	TOTAL	% EFFICIENCY
3.6 ppm	0 ppm	0 ppm	3.6 ppm	100
12.6	0	0	12.6	100
24.1	0	0	24.1	100
56	0	0	56	100
204	0	0	204	100

RESULTS

All of the sample materials examined except $CHClF_2$ are listed in Tables 3 to 6. Because $CHClF_2$ behaved in an anomalous manner it will be discussed later. These Tables present all of the data gathered during the course of the experimental work. The practical significance of this data can be seen more clearly in Fig. 2. This Figure relates the moisture level indicated by the first cell to the true moisture level in the gas. In all cases (except $CHClF_2$), the points describe a line extremely close to the theoretical line of 100 per cent

efficiency, which is the dotted line shown. Within the experimental error, a practical efficiency of 100 per cent is achieved.

Data for $CHClF_2$ are presented in Table 7, along with an average computed from data for N_2, CCl_2F_2 and CF_4. This tabulation of average results is included as a means of estimating what the true moisture level in the gas is for the various valve positions. These three were chosen because sample pressures were the same as for $CHClF_2$, and thus the experimental conditions were as nearly identical as possible.

TABLE 6. EXPERIMENTAL DATA FOR $C_2Cl_2F_4$, EXPRESSED AS P.P.M. BY VOLUME

SAMPLE — C2 CL2 F4

PRESSURE — 14 psig

FLOW RATE — 100 ml/min

1 ppm by weight = 9.5 ppm by volume

CELL # 1	CELL # 2	CELL #3	TOTAL	% EFFICIENCY
1.7 ppm	0 ppm	0 ppm	1.7 ppm	100
4.3	0	0	4.3	100
15.3	0.1	0	15.4	99.4
29.1	0.1	0	29.2	99.7
49	0.1	0	49.1	99.8
124	0.2	0	124.2	99.8

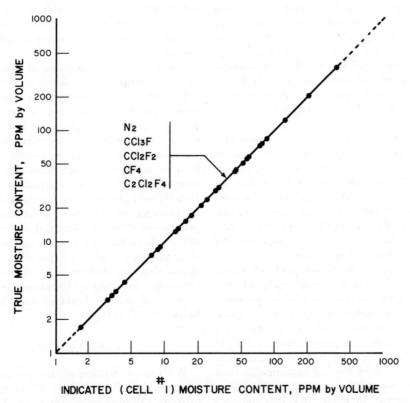

FIG. 2. Indicated moisture content versus true moisture content, for all compounds except $CHClF_2$. The dashed line represents the theoretical one-to-one relationship.

TABLE 7. DATA FOR $CHClF_2$ AND AVERAGED DATA FOR N_2, CCl_2F_2 AND CF_4; ALL EXPERIMENTAL CONDITIONS WERE IDENTICAL. MOISTURE CONTENTS EXPRESSED AS P.P.M. BY VOLUME

PRESSURE — 20 psig

FLOW RATE — 100 ml/min

SAMPLE — AVERAGE RESULTS
FOR N_2, CCl_2F_2, CF_4

SAMPLE — CH Cl F2

1 ppm by weight = 4.8 ppm by volume

CELL #1	CELL #2	CELL #3	APPROX. TRUE H2O	VALVE POSITION	CELL #1	CELL #2	CELL #3	INDICATED TOTAL H2O
3.3 ppm	0 ppm	0 ppm	3.3 ppm	1	3.3 ppm	0 ppm	0 ppm	3.3 ppm
9.8	0	0	10	2	8.7	0.1	0	8.8
25.4	0	0	25	3	35.1	1.0	0.2	36.3
51	0	0	50	4	77	1.6	0.2	79
75	0	0	75	5	113	10.6	1.4	125

It may be seen that as the moisture level in the $CHClF_2$ stream increased, a signal appeared first in cell No. 2 and then in cell No. 3. These signals were quite significant in magnitude and appeared to be slowly increasing with time. Furthermore, with one exception, both the total indicated water content and the level indicated by the first cell exceeded the level expected. In the worst case, the expected level was exceeded by 50 to 60 per cent.

Marked changes in cell characteristics also occurred. Both the first two cells became sluggish in response and refused to dry out on the dry N_2 stream. One cell eventually appeared to short out. Considerable "noise" appeared in all the cells as time passed, and all three were finally replaced. Immediately thereafter the entire system appeared to return to normal on the N_2 stream.

This is strong evidence to suspect a chemical reaction between the desiccant, P_2O_5, and the $CHClF_2$, apparently enhanced by the presence of water. The behavior observed is quite similar to that seen when an amine or a strongly corrosive compound, such as HF, is present. One additional bit of evidence was obtained from the following experiment: Into each of two identical glass-stoppered bottles, a small quantity of white, dry P_2O_5 powder was placed. One bottle was flushed out gently with N_2, the other with $CHClF_2$. Within a few days, the P_2O_5 in contact with the $CHClF_2$ had assumed a brownish-purple hue. The other sample showed no sign of discoloration at all. An attempt to extract the colored material with $CHCl_3$ and study it with infrared was unsuccessful.

One tentative explanation of this phenomenon is proposed as follows: $CHClF_2$ by virtue of its unsymmetrical nature, would tend to have a labile proton. A chemisorption product, or even a true addition product, could be subject to degradation at the electrode surfaces. Such an occurrence might lead to formation of an organophosphorous compound or carbonaceous residue. In addition HF or F_2 might be released. Any of these phenomena would lead to at least semi-permanent effects detrimental to the function of the cell. In particular, noise, inefficiency and poor response could be expected as a result. While this explanation is by no means conclusively supported by the facts at hand, it is offered as one explanation for the erratic behavior of $CHClF_2$.

CONCLUSIONS

With the exception of this one refrigerant compound, all fluorinated hydrocarbons examined showed good response and excellent reproducibility. In all cases except $CHClF_2$, the electrolytic cell displayed about the same efficiency with the representative refrigerant gases as has been previously noted with inert gases. This is sharply in contrast with the phenomena observed by Taylor[1] and others several years ago. It is, therefore, reasonable to assume that the changes in cell design as well as improvements in coating techniques have yielded a much-improved electrolytic cell for the detection of parts per million water.

References

1. Keidel, F. A., "Determination of Water by Direct Amperometric Measurement," Reported at the Pittsburgh Conference on Analytical Chemistry and Applied Spectroscopy, February 1956.
2. Cole, L. G., Czuha, M., Jr., Mosley, R., and Sawyer, D. T., "Continuous Coulometric Determination of Parts Per Million of Moisture in Organic Liquids," *Anal. Chem.*, **31**, 2048 (1959).
3. Shaffer, J. A., and Finley, C. M., "Design Criteria of a New Moisture Monitor for Solids," Reported at the Instrument Society of America Fall Instrument-Automation Conference, New York, September 1960.
4. Taylor, E. S., "A New Instrument for the Moisture Analysis of 'Freon' Fluorinated Hydrocarbon Refrigerants," Reported at the American Society for Heating, Refrigerating, and Air-Conditioning Engineers Meeting, Cincinnati, June 1956.
5. Czuha, M., U.S. Patents 3072556 and 3014858.

MISCELLANEOUS METHODS

53. Thermal Conductivity Gas Analysis in Hygrometric Applications

R. H. Cherry

Leeds & Northrup Company, North Wales, Pennsylvania

ABSTRACT

Even though the first successful use of the thermal conductivity method for measuring the humidity of air was reported some forty years ago, and various aspects of its hygrometric application have been investigated, a study of the literature leads one to the conclusion that this form of hygrometry has not received the level of use warranted by its capabilities and its simplicity.

The first part of this paper presents a state-of-the-art survey of the theory, apparatus and application of thermal conductivity gas analysis. In so doing, the unique capabilities as well as the limitations of the method are examined with particular emphasis on hygrometry. In the opinion of the author, factors which have deterred hygrometric applications are the requirement for empirical calibration of thermal conductivity analyzers, and lack of appreciation of the relatively minor limitations imposed by virtue of thermal conductivity maxima which occur when water vapor is added to certain nonpolar dry gas mixtures. The paper includes a discussion of hygrometric calibration techniques which are suitable for use with thermal conductivity gas analyzers.

The second part of this paper presents data, heretofore unpublished, on the influence of water vapor on the thermal conductivities of a variety of gas mixtures, covering a wide range of thermal conductivity of the dry background gas. Included are data for mixtures of water vapor, air and carbon dioxide which yielded unexpected values. The theoretical implications and practical significance of these data are discussed. It is demonstrated that the observed behavior can be explained by the molecular association of water vapor and CO_2 in the gas phase.

STATE-OF-THE-ART SURVEY

Introduction

Although no detailed description of his method is reported in the literature, Leon Somzee is thought to have first suggested use of the thermal conductivity method for gas analysis in about 1880. A hiatus of about thirty years occurred before practical instrumentation based upon this method began to evolve. In the period 1910 to 1920, thermal conductivity gas analyzers were introduced, first by the Siemens and Halske Company in Germany, and later the Sperry Gyroscope Company in the U.S. and Cambridge Instrument Company in Britain. Leeds & Northrup, as well as a few other companies, entered the field in the 1920's.

For the past three or more decades, this method has enjoyed wide use in certain areas of industrial gas analysis. Its simplicity and reliability recommend its use whenever it is applicable. In recent years, thermal conductivity detectors have found wide use in gas chromatography where the conditions of application are nearly ideal. This is mentioned because chromatography is a method that should not be overlooked for determining trace to moderate quantities of water vapor.

Thermal Conductivity Gas Analysis and Hygrometry

Thermal conductivity gas analysis commonly is of the "hot-wire" type or its equivalent. An electrically heated wire, or in some cases a thermistor, serves the dual function of heat source and temperature sensor. As the composition of gas in the cell cavity changes, so does its thermal conductivity. For each particular gas composition the hot-wire attains thermal equilibrium with its surroundings when the electrical heat input is balanced by all the heat losses from the hot-wire. By proper cell design, and by limiting the operating temperature of the hot-wire, the heat loss due to thermal conduction through the supports for the hot-wire, as well as the radiation and convection losses from the

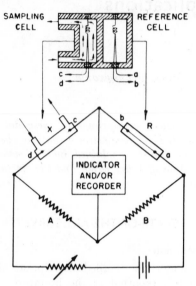

Thermal conductivity bridge for single-pass analysis

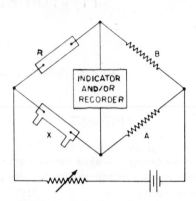

Alternate form of thermal conductivity bridge for single-pass analysis

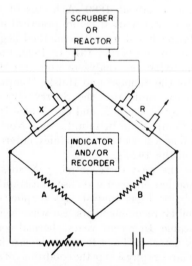

Thermal conductivity bridge for double-pass analysis

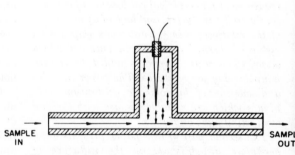

Thermal conductivity cell; diffusion-exchange type

FIG. 1. Thermal conductivity bridge configurations and cell types. (*Courtesy of Process Instruments & Controls Handbook*).

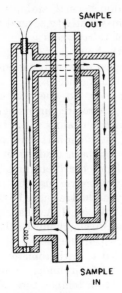

Thermal conductivity cell;
convection-exchange type

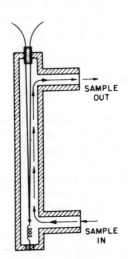

Thermal conductivity cell;
direct flow type

FIG. 1—*continued*. Thermal conductivity bridge configurations and cell types. (*Courtesy of Process Instruments & Controls Handbook*).

surface of the wire, are minimized. In a well-designed thermal conductivity cell, more than 90 per cent of the total heat loss is accounted for by gaseous conduction from the hot-wire to the cooler walls of the cell cavity. Most hot-wire cells are designed to have, or to approximate, cylindrical symmetry with the thermal element axially located in the cell cavity. It is not necessary for the purposes of this paper to dwell upon details of cell design or upon the theory of heat transfer applicable to thermal conductivity cells.

Commonly used circuit and gas analysis cell arrangements are shown in Fig. 1. The upper portion shows Wheatstone Bridge arrangements used in thermal conductivity gas analyzers. There are many variants of these basic bridge types depending upon application requirements. The lower portion shows cell types classified in relation to the means employed for introducing sample gas into the cell. Three sampling configurations are depicted schematically showing (1) diffusion-exchange, (2) convection-exchange and (3) direct flow types. For the diffusion and convection exchange arrangements, the effect of variations in flow rate of the main sample

stream can be made negligible. In the direct flow type, it is essential to maintain a constant rate of flow of the sample gas. The diffusion-exchange type is unique from another point of view; if its cell geometry and dimensions are correctly executed, the response of this type of cell is substantially independent of pressure over a wide range—which is in accord with kinetic theory if the cell responds only to thermal conductivity of the gas within the cell. Pressure dependence of the thermal conductivities of gases and vapors are discussed comprehensively by Vines[1] and Bennett and Vines.[2,3] They conclude that pressure coefficients are relatively small except for mixtures of polar and nonpolar vapors when the proportion of polar component is greater than about 75 per cent.

The important characteristics of thermal conductivity as a method of gas analysis are reviewed briefly below.

First, it is a quantitative technique which relies completely upon empirical calibration. This is partly because of the lack of precise and comprehensive knowledge of the thermal conductivities of gases and, additionally, of the exact relationship between thermal conductivity and composition of a complex gas mixture. Furthermore, even if such information were available, it would be both time-consuming and of questionable value to attempt to compute the precise repsonse of a particular thermal conductivity bridge. Such computations are useful only in a general way in predicting approximate sensitivity and in selecting operating conditions to maximize performance.

Second, thermal conductivity is a physical property which, of itself, does not provide qualitative identification of a particular gaseous component. One must have knowledge of the qualitative content of a gas mixture before serious consideration can be given to applying the thermal conductivity method. In complex gas mixtures of higher than binary order, one must have knowledge of the relationships among the several components as their relative concentrations vary in the total mixture.

Thus, application of the thermal conductivity method of quantitative gas analysis is limited to binary gas mixtures, both components of which are known or to the equivalent of a simple binary mixture. This may have discouraged broader application of thermal conductivity gas analysis, even though those familiar with this field know that a surprisingly large number of industrial gas analysis problems turn out to involve the equivalent of simple binary mixtures. This frequently is the result of judicious analysis of the problem and design of the analyzer system. Nevertheless, it is worth repeating that the two unavoidable requirements that no amount of judicious handling can sidestep are:

(1) The need for empirical calibration, and

(2) The requirement that the qualitative composition and the variations in concentration of the several components remain within the tolerable limits for which the analyzer is designed.

The state-of-the-art related to thermal conductivity gas analysis may be summarized as follows:

(1) The applicable kinetic and thermal theory, measurement technique and overall methodology are well understood.

(2) Materials of construction and manufacturing techniques are available for producing cells having excellent corrosion resistance and dimensional stability, and with measurement sensitivity several times better than possible thirty years ago.

In short, the know-how and equipment now available appear to be amply adequate to meet present application needs.

Referring now to thermal conductivity hygrometry, there are surprisingly few literature references dealing with this type of application, although it is quite possible that broader use has been made than is apparent from a study of the literature. The earliest practical hygrometric use of the thermal conductivity method seems to be that reported in 1920 by Professor G. A. Shakespear[4] of the University of Birmingham, England. At that time he described the use of his apparatus, which he called a "katharometer" to measure the humidity of air under laboratory conditions down to a temperature of $-11°C$. In 1930, Rosecrans[5] described a thermal conductivity absolute humidity analyzer subsequently used for recording relative humidity at constant temperature. This instrument was calibrated by the method of Walker and Ernst.[6]

It is understandable why, up to about 25 years ago the thermal conductivity method did not receive more attention in hygrometry. Cell design and materials of construction were not adequate to withstand industrial usage including continuous exposure to moist gases, without the occurrence of significant calibration shifts. In the mid-thirties, cells which were rugged and fully capable of withstanding exposure to highly corrosive atmospheres became commercially available. Accordingly, there is no basis today for attributing the apparently limited use of thermal conductivity hygrometry to lack of adequate equipment. The reasons must be sought elsewhere.

A very specific factor, which perhaps has unduly discouraged the application of thermal conductivity hygrometry, is the well-known occurrence of a thermal conductivity maximum for water vapor in mixtures of air and in several other nonpolar background gases. This, in fact, is not a substantial limitation in many applications. For example, for water vapor in air, the thermal conductivity maximum only precludes operation in the dew-point range of about 50°C (122°F) to 80°C (176°F), corresponding to about 12 to 47 per cent water vapor by volume at atmospheric pressure. Within this range, either low sensitivity or ambiguity of interpretation may be problems. Actually there are many hygrometric applications which lie either above or below this middle range.

A second region of limited application is at the lower temperatures. The practical limit of detection of this method for water vapor in air is about 0.001 per cent by volume (equivalent to a dew-point of about $-70°C$). This sensitivity is five to ten times better than the overall stability and reliability of calibration and measurement. It is reasonable, therefore, to state that there is no bar to making reliable measurements to 0.01 per cent water vapor, which is equivalent to gas having a dew point of $-40°C$. Thus, if a measurement of water vapor reliable to about one part in sixty is satisfactory, a thermal conductivity hygrometer may be calibrated to have a full scale dew point equal to 0°C (0.61 per cent H_2O by volume) at atmospheric pressure. If one part in twenty-five is adequate, the full scale dew point would be about $-10°C$.

Another possible reason which may have a bearing on limited hygrometric application is that the output of a thermal conductivity bridge is responsive to volume concentration, rather than to units commonly used in hygrometry, such as per cent relative humidity and dew point. In earlier work done by the author,[7] a ratio measurement was devised which permitted a direct read-out in per cent RH. This scheme which requires the use of two identical thermal conductivity bridges is illustrated in Fig. 2. The right-hand bridge is the reference bridge. It is continuously supplied with gas saturated at the sample gas temperature. The left-hand or sample bridge is continuously exposed to the influence of the sample gas at its prevailing water vapor content. Consequently, the output of the reference bridge increases and decreases as the saturated water vapor concentration of the reference gas varies in response to changes in the sample gas temperature. This variable voltage output of the reference bridge energizes the slidewire against which the output of the sample bridge is compared. The net result is a measurement of the ratio of actual aqueous partial pressure to the partial pressure at saturation. Due to the approximately

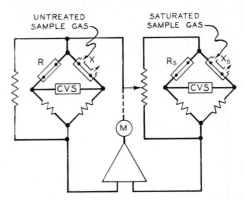

FIG. 2. Schematic of thermal conductivity type relative humidity measuring system.

parabolic shape of the per cent water vapor *vs* thermal conductivity relationship, small errors occur in recorded RH—not exceeding 2 per cent RH for dry-bulb temperatures up to 45°C. The greatest errors occur between 30 and 50 per cent RH, depending upon the maximum saturation temperature for which the bridge is calibrated. The bridge outputs can be adjusted easily at the two humidity extremes simply by supplying first dry gas to both bridges for zero adjustment, then saturated gas at or near the desired maximum dry-bulb temperature for 100 per cent RH adjustment.

A tabulation of calibration units used and corrections required in thermal conductivity hygrometry is given in Table 1 taken from an earlier publication of the author.[8]

The most significant advantages of thermal conductivity hygrometry are:

(1) An analyzer system can be designed so that the addition or removal of moisture from the actual sample stream does not occur. This makes the method ideal for closed systems, especially those of small capacity. Furthermore, the analyzer itself need not occupy any of the available space in the conditioned zone.

(2) At saturation, for temperatures below the freezing point, the measurement is independent of the uncertainties associated with dry- and wet-bulb hygrometry. It measures the ratio of existing aqueous vapor pressure to total pressure without ambiguity as to equilibrium with ice or subcooled water.

(3) Its use in the higher range of dry-bulb temperatures can avoid the difficulties usually

TABLE 1. HUMIDITY CALIBRATION UNITS AND CORRECTIONS REQUIRED
(*Courtesy of Analytical Chemistry*)

CALIBRATION UNIT USED	CORRECTION REQUIRED
RATIO OF VAPOR PRESSURE TO TOTAL PRESSURE, OR MOLE FRACTION	NONE ⎫ WITHIN THE TEMP. AND
SPECIFIC HUMIDITY OR MIXING RATIO (WEIGHT OF WATER VAPOR PER UNIT WEIGHT OF DRY GAS)	NONE ⎭ PRESSURE RANGE IN WHICH "IDEAL" BEHAVIOR MAY BE EXPECTED
DEW POINT AT STANDARD PRESSURE	PRESSURE
ABSOLUTE HUMIDITY AT STANDARD TEMPERATURE AND PRESSURE (WEIGHT OF WATER VAPOR IN UNIT VOLUME OF MIXTURE)	TEMPERATURE AND PRESSURE
RELATIVE HUMIDITY AT STANDARD TEMPERATURE AND PRESSURE	TEMPERATURE AND PRESSURE

associated with wet- and dry-bulb psychrometry in this range.

(4) Response to composition changes is continuous and fast, maintenance is low, and reliability is excellent.

(5) Indicating, recording and controlling functions can be derived readily from a single analyzer.

It would be unrealistic not to call attention to relative economic factors. Thermal conductivity hygrometers are neither the least expensive nor are they the most expensive of those capable of fully automatic operation. As in most applications of measurement technology, one analyzes the economic as well as the technical factors before selecting the optimum approach. It is possible that the thermal conductivity method may not be receiving the overall consideration it deserves.

Moisture Calibration Techniques

As mentioned earlier, the thermal conductivity method requires empirical calibration. However, before discussing water vapor calibration procedures, it should be noted that the matter of field calibration checks can be handled rather simply, once a thermal conductivity bridge has been calibrated against appropriate water vapor/gas mixtures. It is only necessary to provide one or more

gas mixtures (usually stored compressed in metal cylinders) which have thermal conductivity values equal to those of the water vapor/gas mixtures at which calibration checks are to be made. For example, water vapor/air mixtures can readily be simulated by oxygen/air mixtures.[8] The oxygen/air mixtures are assigned equivalent water vapor values by passing them through the thermal conductivity bridge previously calibrated against actual water vapor/air mixtures. This gives the correct water vapor equivalent under the actual operating conditions of the bridge.

For calibrating thermal conductivity analyzers, it is most convenient to have a calibration standard that will deliver a substantial flow of conditioned gas over a fairly wide range of flow rates. In the author's earlier work on this problem the use of saturated salt solutions and sulfuric acid solutions was discarded because of the erratic results obtained. The Walker and Ernst[6] approach seemed too elaborate and has the disadvantage of dependence upon accurate measurement of flow ratio. Wexler's[9] apparatus, shown in Fig. 3, is patterned after that of Walker and Ernst, and was designed specifically for investigating the behavior of radiosonde hygrometers at low temperatures. Its limitation to saturation at the ice point makes it unsuitable for the range of dew point

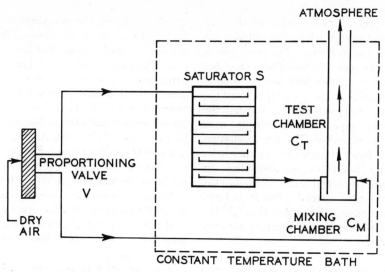

FIG. 3. Principle of operation of Wexler's humidity calibration apparatus.

that must be covered in many applications. In earlier work at subfreezing temperatures, the author used a labyrinth chamber similar to Wexler's trays of ice. This labyrinth chamber was made of brass to obtain isothermal conditions, and its function was that of a condenser maintained at freezing or subfreezing temperatures by submersion in "freezing mixtures." Gas saturated at approximately the ice-point was passed through the chamber in which excess water vapor was continuously deposited as a film of frost. The results of these experiments in the subfreezing range have been reported.[8] The conclusions reached were: For "condensing equilibrium" conditions, that is, when the influent dew point exceeds the condenser temperature and condensation of water vapor is occurring continuously, the observed dew point of the effluent gas corresponds to that of subcooled water. For "evaporating equilibrium" conditions, that is, when the influent gas has a dew point lower than the condenser temperature and ice is evaporating continuously, the observed dew point corresponds to that of ice. In the latter case, the condenser was previously "frosted-up" and allowed to come to thermal equilibrium at the desired temperature.

In work conducted by the author at dew points above freezing and up to about 45°C (113°F) the saturator shown in Fig. 4 was used. Performance data on this saturator have been published.[8] Its capabilities were tested for

flow rates as high as a liter of dry influent gas per minute. It delivers saturated gas over this range of flow believed to have a moisture content reliable to 0.01 per cent water vapor by volume, which is equivalent to $\pm$ 0.05°C dew point at 25°C and about $\pm$ 0.2°C dew point at 0°C. Referring to Fig. 4, the bottom

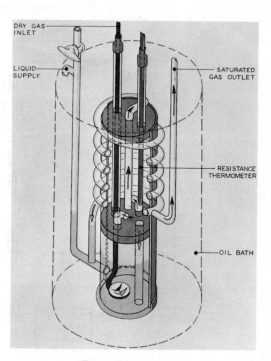

FIG. 4. Gas saturator.

chamber is about two-thirds filled with distilled water through which the influent gas is passed in fine bubbles. The wet gas is admitted to the upper (equilibrium) chamber through two ports in the floor and in tangential motion relative to the vertical walls of the chamber. Saturated gas is emitted through the central discharge pipe, entering this pipe near the floor of the chamber. The gas discharges by downward flow through the external helix in which any additional condensation or precipitation of entrained water returns to the water section via the water-leg. Saturated gas, free of entrainment, discharges through the vertical outlet tube to the thermal conductivity analyzer.

INFLUENCE OF WATER VAPOR ON THERMAL CONDUCTIVITIES OF GAS MIXTURES

The saturator was used in conjuction with the differential thermal conductivity bridge shown in Fig. 5. This four-cell bridge configuration is equipped with convenient arrange-

ments for drying the gas sample for zero check and with a drier interposed between the measuring cells (designated X) and reference cells (designated R). The advantages of this arrangement are that the dried sample gas is used as the flowing reference for comparison of thermal conductivity between the dry and humid states; and sample flow is substantially identical for all the cells. Average gas temperature in the cell cavities for these experiments was close to 200°C, with the cells located in an oil bath maintained at $60° \pm 0.05°C$.

Figure 6 shows the calibration data over the range 0 to 3 per cent water vapor by volume, and for a variety of gases and gas mixtures covering a wide range of thermal conductivity of the dry gas.

The curve for 18 per cent H_2 in N_2 clearly indicates a thermal conductivity maximum at about 1.1 per cent water vapor. All the other curves in the positive region above that for the 18 per cent H_2/N_2 mixture, with the exception of those for 100 per cent CO_2 and argon, would be expected to exhibit both maxima and reversal of bridge output at higher water

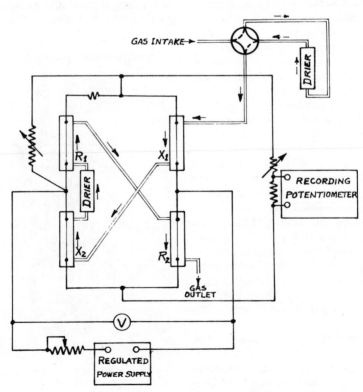

Fig. 5. Schematic of differential thermal conductivity bridge.

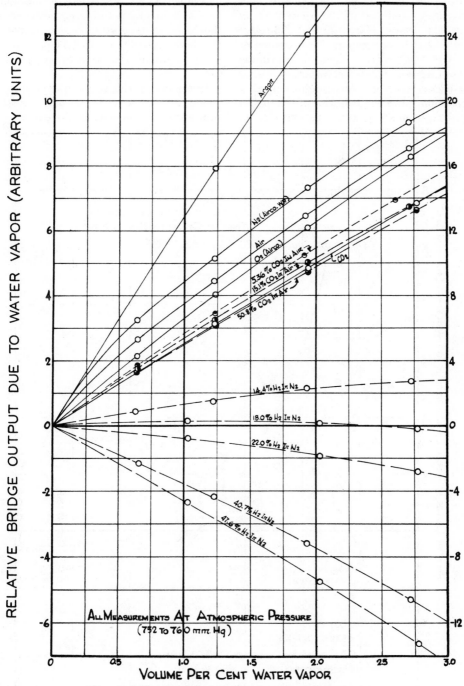

FIG. 6. Calibration data for water vapor in various gases.

vapor concentrations well beyond the range of this plot, since their dry thermal conductivities exceed that of 100 per cent water vapor. The data of Vargaftig and Timroth[10] indicate that water vapor/CO_2 mixtures at 65°C exhibit a thermal conductivity maximum at about 40 per cent water vapor. It also is probable that the water vapor/argon curve has a maximum, since the behavior of this polar/nonpolar gas mixture would be expected to

parallel that for methanol/argon demonstrated by Bennett and Vines[3] to have a maximum. In the cases of argon and CO_2, however, there should be no reversal of bridge output since the thermal conductivity of 100 per cent water vapor is greater than that of either argon or CO_2.

In setting up this series of experiments, in which all the dry background gases are substantially nonpolar, it was expected that

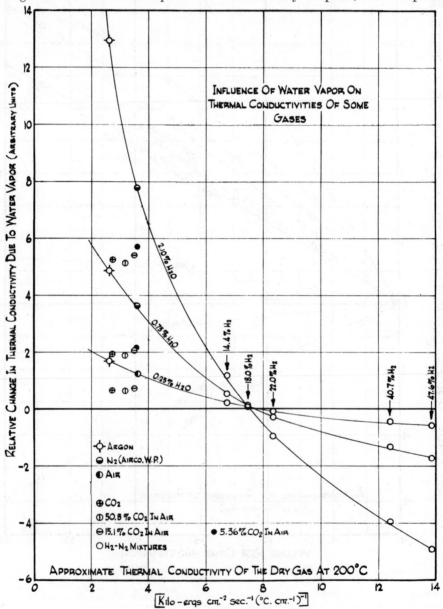

FIG. 7. Percent water vapor isograms for various gases.

a systematic correlation would be observed between change in thermal conductivity due to water vapor and thermal conductivity of the dry background gas. On this basis the curves for the CO_2/air mixtures and for pure CO_2 should have fallen between the curves for N_2 and argon. The unexpected results shown in Fig. 6 were cause for further investigation in search of an explanation.

Evaluation and Discussion of Experimental Observations

The volume per cent water vapor isograms of bridge output plotted against thermal conductivity of the dry gas in Fig. 7 are derived from the data in Fig. 6. If the original expectations had materialized the points for CO_2/air mixtures and for pure CO_2 would have fallen on, or close to, the smooth curves of bridge output obtained for other water vapor/gas mixtures. Each group of points for the CO_2/air mixtures should be associated with the smooth curve lying above it. It will be noted also that the isograms all intersect the abscissal axis at a thermal conductivity of about 7.5, whereas the computed thermal conductivity for steam at 200°C is about 2.85

kilo-ergs cm^{-2} $sec^{-1}(°C$ $cm^{-1})^{-1}$. The computed value of 2.85 is the "polar conductivity" for steam which should be much lower than the ideal or "nonpolar conductivity" for water vapor in low concentrations, as discussed by Bennett and Vines.[3] The nonpolar conductivity of water vapor from the experiments reported in this paper is about equal to that of dry 18 per cent hydrogen in nitrogen. These data were taken with convection-exchange cells, and there was the possibility that convection cooling might have a greater influence than expected. Accordingly, the experiments were repeated with a set of diffusion-exchange cells. Additional gases, including argon/nitrogen and helium/nitrogen mixtures, were included to provide additional data in the portion of the curve used to determine sensitivity ratio, that is, the ratio of the observed change in conductivity, to the change expected when water vapor is added to a dry gas having a particular thermal conductivity. Figure 8 shows only one set of these data at a water vapor level corresponding to a saturator temperature of about 10°C (50°F). This is slightly above midway between the extremes of the range of water vapor concentration

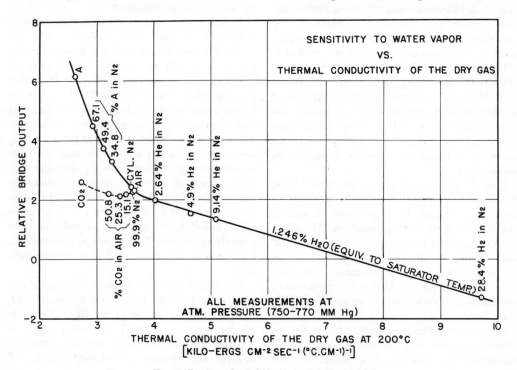

FIG. 8. Isogram for 1.246 per cent water vapor.

covered in Fig. 7. Also, in this plot the ratio of ordinate to abscissa constants was changed to give a more horizontal plot. The same phenomena were observed, and it was concluded that convection losses must play a very minor role, if any.

A possible explanation of the observed effects in the CO_2-bearing gases was reduction of the aqueous vapor pressure in the saturator effluent caused by solution of CO_2. In calculating the suppression of aqueous vapor pressure in the saturator effluent, published data on the solubility of CO_2 in water at various temperatures were used, and it was assumed that all the dissolved CO_2 forms a monohydrate in solution. On this basis, the computed suppression for a saturator temperature of 10°C was less than 1 per cent of the vapor pressure for pure water, or about equal to the reliability of the saturator at this temperature. Whereas, the apparent suppression observed from the thermal conductivity data for pure CO_2 is about 60 per cent. It is well known that CO_2 is at least partially hydrated in water solution. Schilfarth[11] estimates that 38 per cent of the CO_2 dissolved in water at 0°C and atmospheric pressure is hydrated. Claussen[12] has proposed two structures involving water/gas hydrates. He suggests that the CO_2 hydrate probably involves $5\frac{3}{4}$ molecules of water per molecule of CO_2. A more generally accepted structure is $CO_2.6H_2O$. However, even if this form of hydration could occur under the conditions of the experiments reported in this paper, the hexahydrate would only account for a 6 per cent reduction in aqueous vapor pressure, or about one-tenth of the observed reduction in sensitivity.

Considering now the gas phase, Kunz[13] and Wagner[14] have reported evidence of agglomerations of CO_2 in the atmosphere bound on nuclei of condensation or reaction. The equilibrium between the normal gaseous CO_2 and that bound to nuclei was reported to be affected by radiation, temperature gradient, and size of the nuclei. Also, small amounts of organic aerosols were said to enhance agglomeration.

In the experimental apparatus used to obtain the data just presented, it appeared reasonable to assume that radiation and organic contamination could be ruled out. On the other hand, a substantial temperature gradient exists in any thermal conductivity cell between the hot wire and the wall of the cell cavity. There also was the possiblity—even though it seemed quite remote in view of the saturator design—that entrainment and carry-over in the effluent gas might provide suitable nuclei for agglomeration sites. Of all the parameters mentioned by Kunz and Wagner, the temperature gradient in the cell appeared to be the best prospect. In addition, it is well known that gases of different molecular weight tend to separate in a thermal field. In this case, it would be expected that any CO_2 agglomerates formed would tend to concentrate near the cavity walls, with a middle annular layer rich in CO_2 and the layer adjacent to the hot-wire rich in water vapor. Such a stratification would be expected to cause deviations from normal behavior of the thermal conductivity cell. However, even this possibility was not accepted with much confidence as an explanation of the observed effects in view of the great similarity of data obtained with both convection-exchange and diffusion-exchange cells. In convection-exchange cells the stratification effects should be much less pronounced.

It was finally postulated that the observed reduction in sensitivity probably was the result of formation of carbonic hydrate in the gas phase which molecularly bound some of the water vapor and prevented it from displaying what one might call "its expected thermal conductivity" behavior. The simplest case of a monohydrate association equilibrium was assumed. The data for 100 per cent CO_2 were used to compute a constant for this association equilibrium. The equilibrium constant was then used to compute sensitivity ratios for the lower concentrations of CO_2 in air—specifically 50.8, 25.3 and 15.1 per cent CO_2. Table 2 shows the observed and computed sensitivity ratios. The greatest deviation is less than 4 per cent, which is surprisingly close.

Finally, in order to get an additional check on the probability of the formation of CO_2 hydrates in the vapor phase, limited experiments were conducted in which volume changes were measured at constant pressure, and pressure changes at constant volume, all at room temperature. These experiments

TABLE 2. COMPARISON OF OBSERVED AND COMPUTED SENSITIVITY RATIO

VOL. % CO_2 IN AIR (DRY GAS)	SENSITIVITY RATIO (SATURATOR TEMP. EQUIV. TO 1.246 VOL. % H_2O)	
	OBSERVED	COMPUTED
100.0	0.48_2	———
50.8	0.62_9	0.64_7
25.3	0.76_1	0.78_6
15.1	0.84_6	0.86_0

appeared to confirm at least qualitatively, that some form of association of water vapor and CO_2 occurs in the vapor phase.

These investigations were not extended to other gases, but by inference one might expect similar behavior for SO_2 and other gaseous anhydrides which may be present in a sample.

Conclusions

Whatever the mechanism it is concluded that, when CO_2 in significant concentrations is present in a gas mixture, there is a reduction in the thermal conductivity effects one might expect to observe upon the addition of water vapor. The data strongly suggest an association equilibrium between water vapor and CO_2 to form $H_2O.CO_2$. The practical significance of this conclusion is to suggest caution in applying thermal conductivity hygrometry in applications involving gas mixtures containing significant concentrations of CO_2, and possibly for similar gaseous anhydrides. This effect does not represent a bar to hygrometry in air. Finally, it is probable that there are many situations involving industrial gas mixtures where the hydrate complication can be "calibrated out" of the end result.

Acknowledgment. The author wishes to acknowledge the valuable assistance of his associates, Messrs. J. F. Spear and F. C. Snowden, who participated in the experimental studies conducted some time ago, the data for which are published here for the first time. More recently, the assistance of Dr. Edgar L. Eckfeldt has been most helpful both in bringing the literature search up to date and in providing constructive comments.

References

1. Vines, R. G., "The Thermal Conductivity of Organic Vapors: The Influence of Molecular Interaction," *Australian J. Chem.*, **6**, 1 (1953).
2. Bennett, L. A., and Vines, R. G., "The Thermal Conductivity of Organic Vapors. The Relationship Between Thermal Conductivity and Viscosity, and the Significance of the Eucken Factor," *J. Chem. Phys.*, **22**, 360 (1954).
3. Bennett, L. A., and Vines, R. J., "Thermal Conductivities of Organic Vapor Mixtures," *J. Chem. Phys.*, **23**, 1587 (1955).
4. Shakespear, G. A., "A Discussion on Hygrometry," *Proc. Phys. Soc. London*, **34**, lxxxviii (1921).
5. Rosecrans, C. Z., "A High Sensitivity Absolute-Humidity Recorder," *Ind. Eng. Chem. Anal. Ed.*, **2**, 129 (1930).
6. Walker, A. C., and Ernst, E. J., "Preparation of Air of Known Humidity and Its Application to the Calibration of an Absolute-Humidity Recorder," *Ind. Eng. Chem. Anal. Ed.*, **2**, 134 (1930).
7. Cherry, R. H., "Relative Humidity Measuring System," U.S. Patent 2,501,377 (March 21, 1950).
8. Cherry, R. H., "Determination of Water Vapor—Thermal Conductivity Methods," *Anal. Chem.*, **20**, 958 (1948).
9. Wexler, Arnold, "Divided Flow, Low Temperature Humidity Test Apparatus," *J. Res. Natl. Bur. Std.*, **40**, 479 (1948).
10. Vargaftig, N. B., and Timroth, D. L., Transactions of the Fourth World Power Conference, Vol. 3, p. 1642, London, Lund-Humphries, 1952. See also Fig. 8 of Ref. (3).
11. Schilfarth, H., "The Solubility and Absorption of Carbon Dioxide in Water and Beer," *Brauerei Wiss. Beil.*, **4**, 96 (1951).
12. Claussen, W. F., "A Second Water Structure for Inert Gas Hydrates," *J. Chem. Phys.*, **19**, 1425 (1951).
13. Kunz, Josef, "The Formation and Destruction of Agglomerations and Accumulations of Carbon Dioxide in the Atmosphere," *Monatsh.*, **83**, 946 (1952).
14. Wagner, G., "Analytical Investigations of the Carbon Dioxide Content of the Atmospheric Air," *Oesterr. Chem. Z.*, **54**, 133 (1953).

54. Continuous-absorption Hygrometry with a Pneumatic Bridge Utilizing Critical Flow

WILLIAM A. WILDHACK, THOMAS A. PERLS,* CHARLES W. KISSINGER**
AND JOHN W. HAYES†

National Bureau of Standards, Washington, D.C.

ABSTRACT

Design considerations and calculated performance and test results are presented for a continuous-absorption hygrometer consisting of a pneumatic critical-flow bridge in which the humidity is measured by the change which occurs in the pressure between two critical-flow nozzles in series when the water vapor is absorbed by a desiccant. Data are presented on the flow characteristics of small nozzles, and on the factors influencing the time constant of critical-flow bridges. Several possible bridge arrangements are discussed, and performance is calculated for the most suitable of these, assuming (1) pressure-proportional flow through the downstream nozzles and (2) no dependence of flow through the upstream nozzles on the pressure changes between critical-flow nozzles in series. Consideration is also given to the operation of bridges in which condition (1) is not fulfilled. Several points of design are considered, and a working model of a pneumatic critical-flow hygrometer is described. The humidity computed from readings of these instruments agreed with "standard" humidities generated by a pressure-humidity apparatus developed at NBS within an average of 0.3 per cent RH (0.65 per cent maximum difference). The discrepancies were smaller than the estimated uncertainty of the humidities developed by pressure-humidity apparatus.

* Now at Lockheed Missiles and Space Company, Houston, Tex.

** Now at Naval Ordnance Laboratory, White Oak, Md.

† No longer at NBS.

INTRODUCTION

"Critical" flow occurs in nozzles of proper shape and size (but not in sharp-edged orifices) over a certain range of ratios of downstream to upstream pressures; for variations of downstream pressures in this range, the flow does not vary. For ideal gases over certain ranges of pressures, the mass flow under this condition is proportional to the absolute upstream (inlet) pressure and independent of the exact value of the downstream pressures.

The use for instrumentation applications of the laws controlling the flow of fluids through orifices is not new. A patent[1] was issued as early as 1893 on a pyrometer based on the measurement of the change in pressure between two "apertures" in series. Careful measurements of the flow of air through nozzles of various shapes, all having a throat diameter near 20 mm (0.79 in.), were made by Bachmann in 1911 and reported in a dissertation,[2] with the purpose of investigating discharge coefficients and the onset of "critical" flow for application to accurate flow measurement instrumentation. Another application of critical-flow nozzles in instrumentation appeared in 1927, when a patent[3] was issued on "Apparatus for Measuring the Flow of Gases," consisting of two restrictions in series, the first a capillary tube ("constricted tubular inlet"), the second a critical-flow nozzle with which "use may be advantageously made of the known principle of maximum flow." One of the present authors devised a critical-flow pressure control apparatus in 1943, and later extended the double-nozzle system for various applications: for pressure division, thermometry, and gas analysis, of which hygrometry is a special case. The flow of fluids through constrictions in series was further investigated for water and steam[4, 5] in this country from 1936 to 1944 and for gases[6] in Sweden, in 1949. Further improvements in dynamic gas thermometry were described during the 1948 Annual Meeting of the Institute of the Aeronautical Sciences.[7] A number of other patents relate to applications of critical flow.[8] The use of various simple means for obtaining critical-flow nozzles was investigated in this country[9] and in Sweden,[10] and studied for their application to the accurate measurement of gas flow.

The research described in this report is a continuation of the work in this field by one of the authors,[11] and covers the design, calculation of performance and tests of an "absolute" critical-flow hygrometer, i.e., one for which the performance can be calculated from nozzle dimensions or pressure ratios and the known properties of gases. The hygrometer design makes use of the fact that, in principle, the intermediate pressure between two nozzles in series, both operating under conditions of critical flow, should change by the amount of the vapor pressure of water in the incoming gas, if the gas is passed through a desiccator in the intermediate region. A similar flow line, but without desiccator, permits a more precise differential measurement of the intermediate pressure with and without desiccation, hence the pneumatic-bridge arrangement is desirable. It should be noted that the intermediate pressure is governed by the size of the downstream nozzle, and may be well below the minimum required to obtain critical flow through the upstream nozzle, particularly if the upstream nozzle has a properly designed divergent exit. Therefore, within these limits, pressure drop across the desiccant, *with dry air*, will have no effect on the intermediate pressure as measured at the entrance to the downstream nozzle.

Since it is clearly desirable that any pneumatic device operate with as little pumping as possible, it is desirable to use small nozzles and also to have as much pressure regain as possible in the divergent exit regions.

To determine under what conditions the theoretical operation could be attained and how small the flows could be, investigations were made of the flow characteristics of small nozzles, the time constants associated with gas analysis by absorption methods based on critical flow, and several possible arrangements for critical-flow bridges designed for this purpose.

CHARACTERISTICS OF FLOW THROUGH SMALL NOZZLES

For critical flow in a nozzle:

(1) The flow through the nozzle must be independent of downstream pressure.

(2) The mass flow through the nozzle must be proportional to the entrance pressure.

These two conditions, together with several associated parameters, were investigated for small nozzles. Results of these investigations are summarized below.

Independence of Flow with Respect to Downstream Pressure, and Pressure Recovery

(1) Independence of flow with respect to downstream pressure was found for all nozzles of .003-in. diameter, or larger, at pressure ratios very near the theoretical value $r_c = 0.528$ for air. The "critical pressure ratio," r_c, is defined as the ratio of throat pressure to upstream pressure for critical flow.

(2) No significant pressure recovery was obtained with nozzles or orifices less than 0.010 in. in diameter, irrespective of entrance shape and length and angle of expansion cone.

(3) Independence of flow with respect to downstream pressure was attained with throat lengths as small as a small fraction of the throat diameter, although the experimental value of the pressure ratio at which this occurs decreases below the critical value at very short throat lengths.

(4) The opposing effects of frictional losses and pressure regain in expansion nozzles result in an optimum combination of angle and length of expansion cone, and this combination varies with throat diameter. In general, the optimum angle for small nozzles is considerably smaller than for large nozzles, and appears to have a value near 2 degrees (total angle) for a 0.025-in. nozzle. Because of frictional losses, there is also an optimum expansion ratio (ratio of cross-sectional areas at the two ends of the expansion cone) which decreases with nozzle diameter.

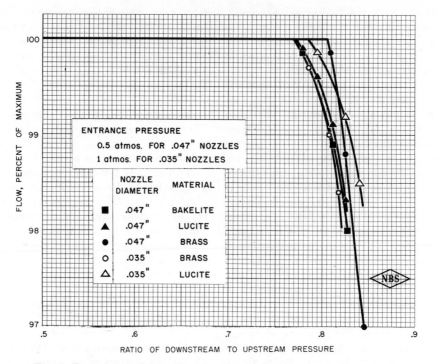

Fig. 1. Dependence of flow through convergent-divergent nozzles on ratio of downstream to upstream pressure.

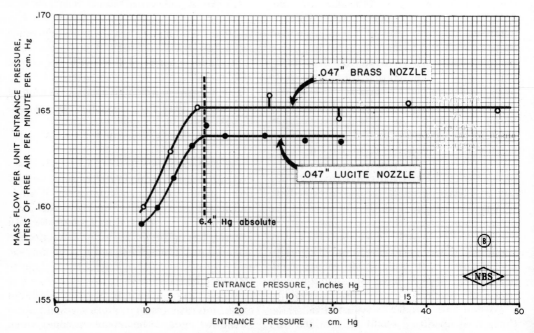

Fig. 2. Variation of discharge coefficient with entrance pressure for two 0.047 in. nozzles.

(5) The maximum attainable downstream-to-upstream pressure ratio for independence of flow from downstream pressure (with optimum expansion cone) is about 0.73 for .025-in. nozzles, and 0.80 for .040-in. nozzles.

(6) With nozzles of .035- and .047-in. throat diameter, having expansion cones with a total angle of 2 degrees and a length of 2 in., independence of flow with respect to downstream pressure is attained at downstream-to-upstream pressure ratios of $0.78 \pm .03$, when the entrance pressure is 1 atm. Similar values are obtained with 0.047-in. nozzles at $\frac{1}{2}$ atm. Typical curves of flow, on a very expanded scale, *vs* downstream-to-upstream pressure ratio are shown in Fig. 1.

Pressure-Proportional Flow

The variation of the discharge coefficient of small nozzles was investigated as a function of entrance pressure and nozzle size. Typical curves for nozzles of 0.047-in. diameter are shown in Fig. 2 in which the ordinate, "mass flow per unit entrance pressure," is proportional to discharge coefficient. These data, together with similar data obtained for other nozzles, are replotted in Fig. 3(a) and 3(b) *vs* nominal Reynolds Number. The *actual* Reynolds Number at the throat of the nozzle is smaller by a factor equal to the discharge coefficient, since the average velocity of the gas at the throat of the nozzle is less than the sonic velocity by this factor. Subsidiary tests obtained with different test gases verified that the change in discharge coefficient is a Reynolds Number effect (see p. 562).

Factors Influencing Time Constant of Instrument Systems Involving Critical-Flow Nozzles

One of the important characteristics of an instrument is its response to a sudden change in value of the quantity being measured. In the case of critical-flow nozzles arranged in the form of a bridge, and with a desiccator in one branch (see Fig. 4), the approach to an equilibrium value for the indication following a change in humidity is not as simple to compute as for pressure equilibrium in a two-nozzle flow circuit.

Depending on the volume and geometry of the flow line between the two nozzles, upstream of the desiccator, there will be some time lag in response after a change of incoming humidity, simply because of the time required for the gas of differing humidity to sweep out this volume. For a flow rate of 25 lpm ($\sim$400 cc/sec) and a line volume of 10 to 20 cc, plus void volume in spent desiccant of 0 to 100 cc, this "sampling time" may be from a few hundredths to a few tenths of a second. After the gas of changed humidity encounters the active desiccant, the change in P_2 begins. The rate of approach to a new equilibrium or steady state value of $P_1 - P_2$ depends on the flow rate, F_2, the total volume of the line plus desiccant voids between the nozzles, and also on the variable volume of the differential pressure gauge or manometer. It is further complicated by the transient disturbance of P_1 caused by the coupling through the differential pressure gauge.

Neglecting the transient in P_1 we may derive a "time constant" as follows:

Let F_2 be the characteristic critical volume flow of the downstream nozzle, as measured at P_2 and T_2 (the temperature at the entrance to the downstream nozzle), V_2 the total fixed intermediate volume (line plus voids), and $(dV/dP)_g$ the volume-pressure compliance of the differential pressure gauge.

Assume that P_2 differs by $(\Delta P_2)_0$ from its equilibrium value, then the excess mass flow rate (in or out) is:

$$\Delta M = \frac{(\Delta P_2)_0}{P_2} F_2 \rho_2 = (\Delta P_2)_0 F_2 \frac{\rho_0}{P_0} \quad (1)$$

The corresponding time rate for change of ΔP_2 (or of P_2) in volume V_e is

$$\frac{d(\Delta P_2)_0}{dt} = \frac{\Delta M}{V_e} \frac{P_0}{\rho} \quad (2)$$

where the effective volume $V_e = V_2 + P_2 (dV/dP)_g$.

The factor P_2 enters with the gauge compliance because the volume change in the gauge must be newly filled with gas at pressure P_2, whereas the fixed volume needs only an increment of additional gas corresponding to the incremental change in P_2. (For sensitive gauges or oil manometers, the effect of the "live" volume of the gauge may be equivalent to several hundred cubic centimeters of fixed or "dead" volume.)

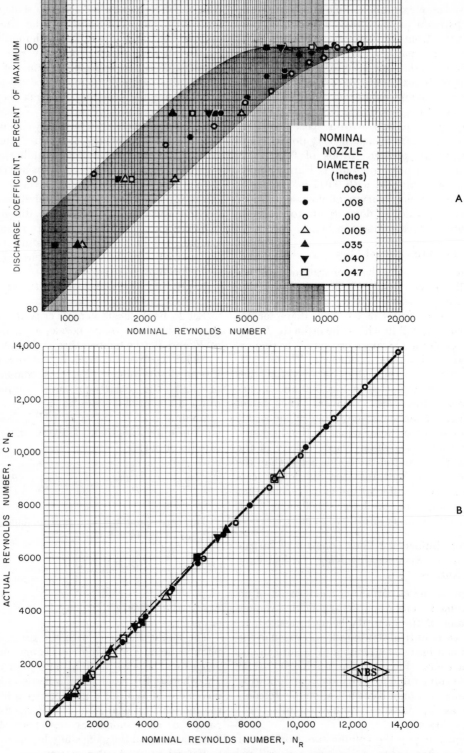

FIG. 3. Dependence of discharge coefficient on Reynolds Number for nozzles 0.006 in. to 0.047 in. in diameter. (a) Discharge coefficient *vs* nominal Reynolds Number. (b) Actual Reynolds Number *vs* nominal Reynolds Number, N_R. (The actual Reynolds Number is equal to the product of the nominal Reynolds Number and the discharge coefficient.)

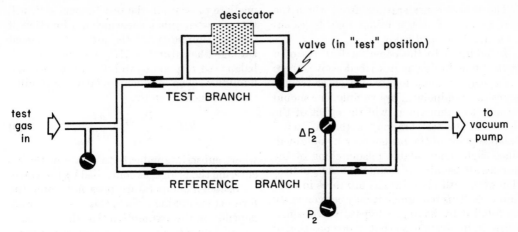

FIG. 4. Critical-flow bridge having two arms in test branch. This arrangement was used in the final design of the critical-flow hygrometer.

Combining,

$$\frac{d(\Delta P_2)_0}{dt} = \frac{(\Delta P_2)_0 \, F_2 \, \rho_0/P_0 \, P_0/\rho_0}{V_e} \quad (3)$$

or

$$\frac{d(\Delta P_2)}{\Delta P_2} = \frac{F_2 \, dt}{V_e} \quad (4)$$

Integrating:

$$\Delta P_2 = (\Delta P_2)_0 \left[1 - e^{\frac{-F_2 t}{V_2 + P(dV/dP)_g}} \right] \quad (5)$$

The approximate "time constant" τ is thus

$$\tau = \left(\frac{V_2 + P(dV/dP)_g}{F_2} \right) \quad (5a)$$

Measurements of response time (to 0.65 of total change) were made with various volumes, nozzles, and gauges, indicating that the effect of these factors was approximately as computed.

It is clear that a rapid response is not consistent with small flow rates and sensitive indicators—both of which are desirable design features. For this instrument, we chose to make the flow as small as consistent with critical flow. With line volume of about 100 cc, and a gauge having a compliance of about 1.5 cc/in. of water column, the time required for equilibrium within the accuracy of reading was about 10 seconds ("time constant" about 3 seconds). Obviously this response time could be shortened fairly easily if this were an important design goal. By using a mechanically stiff gauge, with sensitive electronic sensors and appropriate amplification, and a small desiccant container (at the cost of more frequent changes!) the response time could probably be reduced by a factor of ten.

Alternative Flow Circuits for a Critical-Flow Bridge Hygrometer

In a critical-flow bridge, four nozzles are arranged in two parallel branches, each branch containing two nozzles in series. In principle, the concentration of one component of a mixture of gases which is passed through such a bridge may then be determined in the following way. A device which absorbs the component in question (or perhaps increases concentration to a saturation value) is placed between the upstream and downstream nozzles of one branch (called the test branch; in the case of a hygrometer, this device would be a desiccator, or a saturator). Since mass flow rate through the downstream nozzle is proportional to its upstream pressure (i.e., the intermediate pressure), the change in mass flow introduced by the device between the nozzles affects the intermediate pressure in the test branch. The intermediate pressure in the test branch is then compared with that in the other (reference) branch by means of the differential manometer, ΔP_2. From this measurement, together with the absolute value of P_2, the change in concentration produced by the device in the test branch may be deduced.

Theoretical considerations from which the performance of such a bridge may be calculated are developed below.

In addition to the essential features of a critical-flow bridge as described above, there are other considerations which enter from a practical standpoint. For example, one should be able to eliminate at will the effect of the device in the test branch, so that a "zero" balance point of the bridge may be obtained, since slight unavoidable mismatching of the nozzles almost always results in a ΔP_2 indication even with identical gas mixtures in both branches. This requirement may conveniently be fulfilled by having a bypass valve somewhere in the system, so that in one position of this valve the gas flowing through the two branches is the same (i.e., the device is either out of the system, or the composition of the gas is made such that the device in the test branch produces no further change).

In the design of a hygrometer, many arrangements of saturators, desiccators, and valves are possible. A few of these will be discussed, and the more important features of each pointed out.

In the arrangement shown in Fig. 5, a desiccator is permanently connected into the test branch. Room air is drawn into the instrument through any one of three paths, as controlled by a three-way valve. If the room air is passed through the desiccator before entering the bridge, the desiccator in the test branch has no further effect, and the ΔP_2 manometer merely measures the unbalance due to mismatching of nozzles in the bridge. If the room air passes directly into the bridge, the desiccator in the test branch will remove water vapor, thus decreasing the mass flow rate through the downstream test branch nozzle, which therefore also reduces the inter-

mediate pressure in the test branch. ΔP_2 will then show an unbalance which is a function of ambient humidity. If the air is first passed through the saturator, ΔP_2 will show an unbalance corresponding to 100 per cent relative humidity. The ambient relative humidity (RH) is then given by:

$$RH = \frac{P_{2_{\text{room}}} - \Delta P_{2_{\text{des.}}}}{P_{2_{\text{sat.}}} - \Delta P_{2_{\text{des.}}}} \tag{6}$$

where subscripts indicate the state of the air entering the bridge, as controlled by the valve.

Although temperature does not enter the formula for mixing ratio in this case, accuracy depends on the assumption that the saturator completely saturates the incoming air at room temperature, which is seldom true.

Another source of error is introduced into this arrangement if the resistance to flow offered by the three alternative paths is different, so that in effect the entrance pressure to the bridge is changed by switching the valve. This may be seen by considering the dependence of that part of ΔP_2 which is due to nozzle unbalance, upon entrance pressure. For a simple bridge in which unprimed quantities refer to conditions between nozzles in one branch, and primed quantities to conditions in the other branch:

$$M = K_1 P_1 = K_2 P_2$$
$$M' = K_1' P_1 = K_2' P_2' \tag{7}$$

$$\Delta P_2 = P_2 - P_2' = \frac{K_1 P_1}{K_2} - \frac{K_1' P_1}{K_2'}$$

$$= P_1\left(\frac{K_1}{K_2} - \frac{K_1'}{K_2'}\right) \tag{8}$$

where

M = mass flow rate through individual branches

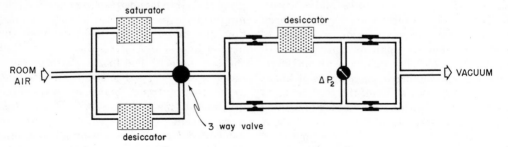

Fig. 5. Critical-flow bridge with desiccator permanently connected in test branch.

K = constants

P = pressure as indicated by subscript.

This shows that the part of ΔP_2 which is due to nozzle mismatching is proportional to P_1. A similar analysis will show that the part of ΔP_2 which is produced by absorption in one branch of the bridge will also be proportional to P_1. Therefore any variation of P_1 with valve position will give rise to error in Eq. (6), where the differences in ΔP_2 are assumed to be due to differences in absorption only.

In practice, two precautions will generally serve to reduce these effects to a negligible level. First, the ΔP_2 "zero" unbalance should be made as small as possible, since any change in the "zero" ΔP_2 due to change in P_1 upon switching will be superimposed on the simultaneous change in ΔP_2 due to absorption. Second, the resistance to flow through the three alternative paths of the arrangement shown in Fig. 5 may be adjusted to very nearly the same value by means of suitable constrictions.

In the arrangement shown in Fig. 6, the valve and alternate paths are placed in the intermediate region of the test branch. By means of the three-way valve, ΔP_2 may be measured with saturated air, dry air, or room air entering the downstream nozzle of the test branch. In this case ambient relative humidity is given by:

$$RH = \frac{P_1}{P_2'} \cdot \frac{\Delta P_{2_{\text{des.}}} - \Delta P_{2_{\text{room}}}}{\Delta P_{2_{\text{des.}}} - \Delta P_{2_{\text{sat.}}}} \qquad (9)$$

where subscripts indicate the condition of the gas entering the downstream nozzle of the test branch, as controlled by the valve, and P_2' is the intermediate pressure in the test branch with the valve in the "zero" position. This arrangement has several advantages over that shown in Fig. 5. One less desiccator is required, and also, the desiccator and saturator are in the test branch where they carry only one-half the total flow through the bridge. A disadvantage is that the desiccator and saturator volumes are in the test branch where they act directly to increase the time constant of the bridge.

In the arrangement shown in Fig. 4, there are only two alternative paths in the test branch. This reduces the volume and thereby also reduces the time constant. It will be noted that this bridge has no "internal calibration" for RH i.e. the RH is not given directly by observations taken solely with the bridge as is the case for the arrangements shown in Figs. 5 and 6. Either a calculated or an experimental calibration of the bridge must be used. Temperature must be observed, and a correction for variation of entrance pressure P_1, must be made. (See below.)

In principle, either a saturator or desiccator could equally well be used in the test branch, since it is only necessary to provide a known specific humidity with which to compare the specific humidity of room air. Expressions for the changes in differential pressure reading with relative humidity (RH) for the cases of

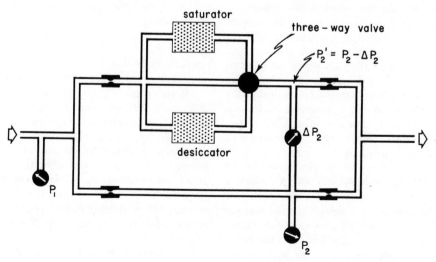

FIG. 6. Critical-flow bridge having three arms in test branch.

(a) a saturator and (b) a desiccator in the test branch are

(a) $(\Delta P_{2_{sat.}} - \Delta P_{2_{room}}) \propto 1 - (RH)\dfrac{P_2}{P_1}$ (10)

(b) $(\Delta P_{2_{room}} - \Delta P_{2_{des.}}) \propto \quad (RH)\dfrac{P_2}{P_1}$ (11)

It may be seen that in both cases the magnitude of the sensitivity of the instrument (i.e., change in differential-pressure reading per unit change in relative humidity) is the same, although there is a reversal of sign. Also, in the case of a saturator, the magnitude of the change in differential-pressure reading is greater, requiring a gauge of higher range, which, in the typical case of $P_2/P_1 = 0.5$ would be operated in only the upper half of its range for a change in relative humidity from 0 to 100 per cent.

The difficulties encountered with saturators, when used in any of the bridge designs discussed above, arise in the following way. If the saturator were ideal, i.e., if it produced complete saturation, and the temperature at which this saturation was produced could be accurately measured, then the specific humidity of the saturated air would be a known quantity. However, saturators generally do not produce complete saturation, and the accurate determination of temperature is made difficult by the cooling effect associated with vaporization. Inaccuracy due to incomplete saturation can be reduced to a negligible amount by placing several saturators in series. The requirement of an accurate temperature measurement is fundamentally more difficult to meet, since saturation temperature must be very accurately measured in order to determine specific humidity to the same accuracy which is obtained when a desiccator is used. For example, a common desiccant, anhydrous $CaSO_4$, removes about 99.98 per cent of the water vapor from saturated air at 30°C. For equivalent accuracy using a saturator, temperature would have to be measured to approximately .003°C. Such a measurement obviously would be difficult.

Another practical consideration which arises in the design of a bridge concerns the location of the valve in the system, first from the point of view of trapping entrained gas, and also for the case of liquid absorbers or saturators. As a typical example, let us consider two alternative locations of the valve in the bridge of Fig. 4, viz., at the upstream or downstream tee of the test-branch bypass. Consider what happens when the valve is located at the downstream tee as shown in Fig. 4 and a solid desiccant is used in the test branch.

In the "test" position, all air entering the downstream nozzle must pass through the desiccator, i.e., there are no volumes from which blocked gas might diffuse into the stream. On the other hand, in the "zero" position, the tube leading to the desiccator is open to the gas stream, so that there may be some diffusion of dry gas into the stream. If the valve is placed at the upstream tee, then in the "test" position it may be seen that room air blocked in the bypass can diffuse into the stream of dry air coming from the desiccator. In the "zero" position of the valve, dry gas from the desiccator might also diffuse into the stream of room air flowing through the bypass. Therefore the downstream location of the valve is preferable from this standpoint, since the possibility of diffusion is eliminated in the "test" position.

Analysis of a typical arrangement will serve to illustrate the difficulties involved and the necessary precautions. Let the valve be at the downstream tee, and assume that the pressure drop through the bypass is less than through the bubbler. Switching the valve from the "zero" to "test" position gives rise to no difficulties, since the upstream pressure immediately bubbles gas through the bubbler. In switching from the "test" to the "zero" position it is important that the valve make the new connection before breaking off the old one, otherwise flow would be momentarily cut off and pressure built up in the bubbler, so that when the bypass path was opened, the gas trapped on the downstream side of the bubbler would force liquid into the system through the upstream tee. This feature of the valve is also necessary, regardless of whether a liquid or dry reagent is used in the test branch, in order to avoid large pressure surges due to momentary stoppage of flow. These surges would appear on the ΔP_2 manometer, and could easily be many times the maximum equilibrium values of ΔP_2.

Consideration must also be given to what happens to liquid saturators when flow through the bridge is started or stopped. It is assumed that the entire system is at atmospheric pressure when inoperative, and that the equilibrium value of P_2 when operating is less than atmospheric pressure. Under these conditions, the valve must be in the "test" position when the bridge is started, otherwise the air trapped at atmospheric pressure on the downstream side of the bubbler will force liquid into the system. When stopping the bridge, however, the valve may be in either the "zero" or "test" position.

As is seen by the examples given in the preceding discussion, many bridge arrangements are possible. The arrangement shown in Fig. 4 was used in the design of the pneumatic critical-flow hygrometer, and it is this arrangement which will be referred to in the theoretical considerations which follow.

CALCULATED PERFORMANCE OF CRITICAL-FLOW BRIDGE

In this section theoretical considerations will be developed giving the calculated performance of a critical-flow bridge, first without regard to possible Reynolds Number effects, and then taking into account experimental data on the variation of the discharge coefficient as a function of Reynolds Number.

Performance may be calculated for a critical-flow absorption bridge as shown in Fig. 4. The basic expression for the mass flow rate, M, through a critical-flow nozzle[9] (using cgs units) is

$$M = C A P \cdot \left[\frac{m}{R} \gamma \left(\frac{2}{\gamma+1} \right) \frac{\gamma+1}{\gamma-1} \right]^{1/2} \cdot T_e^{-1/2} \quad (12)$$

where

C = discharge coefficient
A = throat area of nozzle
P = entrance pressure
m = molecular weight of the gas
R = gas constant
γ = ratio of specific heats
T_e = entrance temperature.

Let m' be the molecular weight of the test gas, m the molecular weight of the gas after absorption of the unknown component; also, let

$$f'(\gamma) = \gamma' \left(\frac{2}{\gamma'+1} \right)^{(\gamma'+1)/(\gamma'-1)}$$

for the test gas, and $f(\gamma)$ the corresponding function for the gas remaining after absorption. Let P_2' = the entrance pressure of the downstream nozzle in the test branch with the valve in the "zero" position (test gas); P_2'' = the corresponding pressure with the valve in the "test" position (gas remaining after absorption); M' = the mass flow rate for the test gas; M = the mass flow rate for the gas remaining after absorption.

Then

$$M = K[mf(\gamma)]^{1/2} P_2'' \quad (13)$$

$$M' = K[m'f'(\gamma)]^{1/2} P_2' \quad (13a)$$

where

$$K = CA(RT_e)^{-1/2} \quad (14)$$

Up to this point, it has only been assumed that the flow through the upstream nozzle is independent of the insertion of the absorption reagent, and that the mass flow through the downstream nozzle is directly proportional to the entrance pressure of this nozzle.

For the bridge hygrometer of Fig. 4,

$$\frac{P_2' - P_2''}{P_2'} = \frac{M'/[m'f'(\gamma)]^{1/2} - M/[mf(\gamma)]^{1/2}}{M'/[m'f'(\gamma)]^{1/2}}$$

$$= 1 - \frac{[m'f'(\gamma)/mf(\gamma)]^{1/2} M}{M'} \quad (15)$$

The general interpretation of this equation is rather cumbersome, especially since it is not known how $f(\gamma)$ should be averaged in the case of a mixture of gases with different values of γ. Since this paper is concerned with the application of the critical flow bridge to hygrometry, the remainder of the discussion will make use of certain approximations allowed by this particular application.

Let

$$r = \text{Mixing Ratio} = \frac{\text{Mass } H_2O}{\text{Mass Dry Air}}$$

$$= \frac{M' - M}{M} = \frac{M'}{M} - 1 \quad (16)$$

therefore,

$$\frac{M}{M'} = \frac{1}{1 + r}$$

$$\frac{P_2' - P_2''}{P_2'} = 1 - \left[\frac{m'f'(\gamma)}{mf(\gamma)} \right]^{1/2} \frac{1}{1 + r} \quad (17)$$

which may also be written

$$r = \left[\frac{m'f'(\gamma)}{mf(\gamma)} \right]^{1/2} \frac{1}{1 - (P_2' - P_2'')/P_2'} - 1 \quad (18)$$

The quantity $P_2' - P_2''$ is the difference between the two values of ΔP_2 in the "zero" and "test" positions of the valve (see Fig. 4).

Let us consider first the factor which depends on γ. We can calculate $f'(\gamma)$, for moist air, in two ways: (1) by taking a weighted average of the values of γ for air and water vapor and constructing $f'(\gamma)$ from this average, or (2) by calculating $f(\gamma)$ for both air and water vapor and taking a weighted average of these values of $f(\gamma)$. At a mixing ratio as high as 4 per cent (100 per cent RH at 97.8°F), the factor

$$\left[\frac{f'(\gamma)}{f(\gamma)}\right]^{1/2}$$

calculated by these two methods is equal to 0.99915 or 0.99935, respectively, and the difference between either of these and unity may therefore be neglected for our purposes. This is rather fortunate since there is some question as to whether this factor should be included at all, as the times involved in the flow through the throat section of the nozzles are short enough so that relaxation phenomena should be taken into consideration in evaluating an effective γ for the test gas. (With a refinement of measurement techniques to the order of 0.01 per cent, it should be possible to use the critical flow device to obtain information on the effective values of γ for various mixtures.)

We may now write

$$r = \frac{(m'/m)^{1/2}}{1 - (P_2' - P_2'')/P_2'} - 1 \quad (19)$$

or

$$r = \left(\frac{m'}{m}\right)^{1/2}\left[1 + \frac{P_2' - P_2''}{P_2'} + \left(\frac{P_2' - P_2''}{P_2'}\right)^2 + \ldots\right] - 1 \quad (20)$$

At a mixing ratio of 4 per cent, $(m'/m)^{1/2} = 0.9886$, and, as a first order approximation, $(P_2' - P_2'')/P_2' = 0.05$. The second-order term may therefore be as large as 5 per cent of the first-order term, and may not be neglected. The third order term is in practice never larger than 0.25 per cent and will be neglected here.

Since M'/M is itself a function of r, it is possible to tabulate values of r against the corresponding values of $(P_2' - P_2'')/P_2'$ as computed from Eq. (19). The tabulated values, when plotted as in Fig. 7, provide coefficients in the approximate formula

$$r = 0.767_4\left(\frac{P_2' - P_2''}{P_2'}\right) +$$

$$0.86\left(\frac{P_2' - P_2''}{P_2'}\right)^2 \quad (21)$$

For a given r, the instrument indication depends somewhat on temperature and pressure, but only to a negligible degree in practice. Thus a 5 per cent change in atmospheric pressure affects the factor by 0.06 per cent in the worst case, and a change in temperature of ±5 degC (from 25°C) affects this factor by up to 0.3 per cent. For greater temperature excursions, a family of correction curves can be computed and drawn.

In many cases, it is desired to know relative humidity rather than mixing ratio. At 760 mm Hg and 25°C, we can calculate the relative humidity corresponding to the mixing ratio previously determined. At different entrance pressures, the saturation mixing ratio varies inversely as the pressure, and the relative humidity varies directly as the pressure for a given measured r. The expression for r must therefore be multiplied by a factor proportional to entrance pressure to yield the relative humidity. Since the expression for r already contains P_2' (proportional to entrance pressure) in the denominator, it is possible to determine experimentally the ratio of P_2' to entrance pressure and to calculate a relationship between $(P_2' - P_2'')$ and relative humidity which is independent of atmospheric pressure to the same degree as the previous determination of mixing ratio. (See below.)

Departure of Bridge from Calculated Performance as a Function of Reynolds Number of Downstream Nozzles

The calculated performance of a critical-flow bridge as developed above assumes that the discharge coefficient C of the downstream nozzle remains constant with pressure. This assumption is true only for sufficiently high values of Reynolds Number. The dependence of discharge coefficient on Reynolds Number

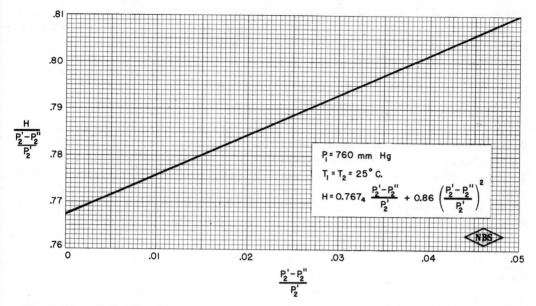

FIG. 7. Theoretical calibration curve for critical-flow pneumatic hygrometer with downstream nozzles operated at nominal N_R 9000.

has the general form shown in Fig. 3. (See also p. 151, Fig. 10.6 of Ref. 12.)

Therefore one might expect results which do not agree with calculated performance when the bridge is operated at Reynolds Number N_R in the range where C varies. The magnitude of the effect may be calculated by considering the way in which C enters the formula for $(P_2' - P_2'')/P_2'$. This may be done by considering C a variable in the derivation of Eq. (15), which then takes the form:

$$\frac{P_2' - P_2''}{P_2'} = 1 - \frac{C'[m'f'(\gamma)]^{1/2}M}{C[mf(\gamma)]^{1/2}M'}$$

$$= 1 - \frac{C'}{C} K' \quad (22)$$

where the quantity $K' = [m'f'(\gamma)]^{1/2}M/[mf(\gamma)]^{1/2}M'$ varies with humidity over the range from unity down to 0.95, corresponding to mixing ratios from zero to 4 per cent, respectively. The response of the hygrometer bridge, in percent of the response calculated from Eq. (15), is given by:

$$\text{Per Cent Response} = \frac{1 - C'/C K'}{1 - K'} \times 100 \quad (23)$$

Since the discharge coefficient C' corresponds to the intermediate pressure P_2' (test gas), and

C corresponds to P_2'' (gas after absorption), C'/C is greater than unity, and the response given by Eq. (23) will be less than 100 per cent.

Equation (22) may also be written in a form in which C' is expressed in terms of the variation of C with nominal Reynolds Number, N_R:

Per Cent Response

$$= \frac{1}{1 + (K'/C N_R dc/dN_R)} \times 100 \quad (24)$$

The behavior of C as a function of N_R is not known with sufficient accuracy at present to permit an accurate calculation of corrections to humidity readings *vs* N_R by means of Eq. (24). [See Fig. 3(a) in which the uncertainty in C *vs* N_R is indicated by the shaded area.] A correction based on the available data is in the right direction, however, and at least of the correct order of magnitude.

Effects of Varying Gas, Nozzle Diameter, and Intermediate Pressure

The Reynolds Number was varied experimentally by changing one or more of several parameters such as pressure, nozzle diameter, and gas (i.e., viscosity and density). Pressure at the entrance to the downstream nozzles was reduced by the use of a small upstream nozzle or a restriction at the entrance of the bridge. Downstream nozzles as small as 0.006-in. diameter were used, and the bridge was operated with H_2 and He as well as with air. In this manner, Reynolds Numbers from 30 to about 9000 at the downstream nozzles were obtained.

Design Requirements for Hygrometer Bridge

In designing a critical-flow hygrometer bridge to perform as calculated in the preceding section, it is necessary to avoid several effects which might result in extraneous pressure changes at the measuring instruments. Such pressure changes may be caused by poor alignment or roughness at the pressure taps, and by condensation at the throat of the nozzles, by frictional heating, or by the heat developed by absorption in the desiccator.

Pressure-tap Errors. Tests were conducted on various "tees" to determine the magnitude of the errors in pressure readings due to the flow past the pressure taps. In each test, two different tees were connected, in series, to a vacuum pump with the flow controlled by a critical-flow nozzle with a throat diameter of 0.047 in. (This was the downstream-nozzle size used in the final design of the pneumatic critical-flow hygrometer, see below.) The pressure difference between the two taps was measured with a water manometer, and the pressure drop in the short line between the taps was compensated for in the data by taking successive observations with the flow in opposite directions. Tests on different sizes of tees showed differences in readings up to 1 cm H_2O, depending on both the size of the "through" tube and the size of the tap opening. It was found, however, that the pressure at a $\frac{1}{4}$-in. smooth tee differed from the pressure in a large chamber by only 0.3 cm H_2O. This is negligible with respect to the intermediate pressure, P_2, but not with respect to the differential pressure ΔP_2. It was thus important to use identical tees at the pressure taps for ΔP_2.

Throat-temperature Effects. Condensation or ice formation in the throat of critical-flow nozzles was suspected to be the cause of several types of anomalous behavior shown by small nozzles (diameter $<.009$ in.).

For example, small nozzles had abnormally low flow rates when operated on moist air, as compared to dry air. The decrease in mass flow rate in going from dry to saturated air can be calculated from Eqs. (13) and (13a) and should be 0.6 per cent for air which contains 2 per cent H_2O vapor by weight. This decrease was verified within experimental error for a 0.009-in. nozzle, but the corresponding decrease for a 0.004-in. nozzle was about 2.5 per cent. Also, when two nozzles of 0.004- and 0.010-in. diameter were operated in series, P_2 exhibited both rapid fluctuations and slow drifts accompanied by sharp recovery.

Similar instability was also present in an experimental bridge using 0.004- and 0.006-in. nozzles, appearing as fluctuations in ΔP_2 even while the test-branch valve was in the "zero" position. In this case it was found that the effect was eliminated by placing a fine fritted-glass filter ahead of the intake to the bridge.

In order to determine whether the thermal conductivity of the nozzle material had an appreciable effect on the slow drifts observed with even large nozzles, stability tests were conducted with several 0.035- and 0.047-in. diameter nozzles made of brass, "Lucite," and "Bakelite." No difference in behavior was observed in these nozzles, either individually or when used in a hygrometer bridge.

In an attempt to observe condensation of water vapor, several "Lucite" nozzles having both round and rectangular cross sections and various expansion cones were constructed. The nozzles were observed under a low-power microscope while moist air was being drawn through them. Droplets of water were seen to form at the throat and to blow away as they grew in size. It was found that the angle of the expansion cone influenced condensation, with greater angles in general producing condensation more readily. Cigarette smoke introduced into the air produced great quantities of condensation, of both water and volatile tars. Fritted-glass or glass-fiber filters placed ahead of the nozzle eliminated the increase in condensation due to smoke, but did not completely stop all condensation.

In view of this evidence, it seems reasonable to assume that the instabilities observed above were caused by condensation forming on the walls at the throat of the nozzles and blowing away, thus changing the area of the nozzle, or the discharge coefficient, or both. Naturally, the effect was more noticeable in small nozzles.

The effect of the filter in reducing visible condensation, and also instability, can be attributed to the removal of condensation nuclei from the incoming air.

The relatively small amount of remaining condensation and instability is presumably due either to particles not removed by the filter, or to other possible condensation nuclei, such as CO_2 molecules and agglomerations of water molecules, as suggested in Ref. 13 and 14.

Temperature Effect. As noted above, the entrance pressure to each downstream nozzle in a critical-flow bridge is proportional to the square root of the absolute temperature of the gas. For a typical mixing ratio, $r = 0.02$, the relative difference between the entrance pressures of the two downstream nozzles in a hygrometer bridge is about 2.6 per cent, so that a 1 per cent error in the determination of r could be caused by an extraneous pressure change, in one of the branches, of 0.026 per cent, requiring a difference in absolute temperature of only about 0.05 per cent, or 0.15°C at room temperature. It is therefore necessary to insure that the gas entering the downstream nozzles be at the same temperature in the two branches, within 0.1°C or better. Effects tending to change the temperatures of the gas include expansion cooling at

the upstream nozzles (nearly equal in both branches) and the heat of absorption in the desiccant, plus effects in the connecting tubing, the largest of which is heat conduction of the tubing itself, partly to the ambient air. It was found experimentally that very good temperature equilibrium could be insured by means of a heat-exchange coil made of three feet of copper tubing in each branch curved in a double-helix and soldered together.

FINAL DESIGN OF PNEUMATIC HYGROMETER

In constructing an "absolute" hygrometer, i.e., one which would have the performance calculated above, it was necessary to use nozzles with a sufficiently large diameter so that corrections for Reynolds Number, N_R, would not be required. This condition is satisfied provided $N_R \geqslant 9000$ (Fig. 8). For air at approximately ½ atm, this requires downstream nozzles with a throat diameter $D = 0.047$ in. From pressure-recovery data given above, it was estimated that the intermediate pressure in the bridge could be made 0.7 atm or more if the upstream nozzles were 0.035 in. in diameter and had an expansion cone with a total angle of 2 degrees and a diameter ratio of 3:1. (This requires a total

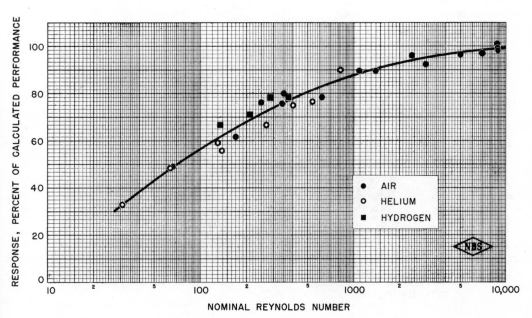

FIG. 8. Response of critical-flow hygrometer *vs* nominal Reynolds Number of downstream nozzles.

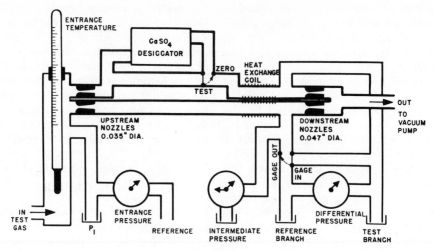

Fig. 9. Diagram of critical-flow pneumatic hygrometer. (See photograph, Fig. 10.)

length of 2 in.) With an entrance pressure of 30 in. Hg, this choice of upstream nozzles allowed for a pressure drop up to 4.5 in. Hg in absorbers or saturators introduced between nozzles. The 0.047-in. downstream nozzles were also provided with a 2 degree, 2-in. expansion cone to insure good pressure recovery and reduce the demands on the pumping system. A diagram of the complete critical-flow hygrometer is shown in Fig. 9, and a photograph of the instrument is shown in Fig. 10. Pressure taps are provided in parallel with all gauges to provide for connection to external gauges either for increased accuracy or for purposes of obtaining a permanent record of the pressures.

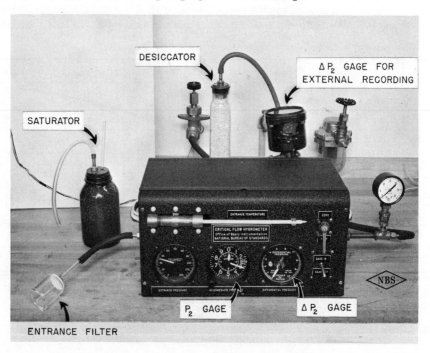

Fig. 10. Critical-flow pneumatic hygrometer. (See diagram, Fig. 9.)

Experimental Calibration with Standard Humidity Apparatus

A pressure-humidity apparatus[15] developed at the National Bureau of Standards was used to provide an experimental calibration of the critical-flow pneumatic hygrometer. The results of this calibration are shown in Table 1 and Fig. 11. It is seen that the experimental calibrations of the pneumatic hygrometer agree with the computed performance within 0.65 per cent RH and with an average variation of ± 0.3 per cent RH. It should be noted that this variation is smaller than the estimated uncertainty of the pressure-humidity apparatus.

Stability and Reproducibility

Tests were conducted with atmospheric air and also at higher humidities provided by bubbling atmospheric air through saturators filled with small glass balls. Small instabilities were traced to condensation phenomena (see p. 564), and these were greatly reduced by means of an entrance filter consisting of a "coarse" fritted glass disk. The remaining instability was of the order of 0.01 in. H_2O,

TABLE 1. CALIBRATION OF CRITICAL-FLOW PNEUMATIC HYGROMETER AGAINST NBS STANDARD PRESSURE-HUMIDITY APPARATUS

| | | *Relative Humidity Calculated from* | | |
Test No.	Entrance Temp. to Hygro-meter (°C)	Pressure Humidity Apparatus Data (%)	Pneuma-tic Hygro-meter Data (%)	Dis-crepancy Between Calculated RH (%)
1	25.95	86.3	86.4	−0.1
2	26.2	81.85	81.8	+0.05
3	26.5	75.0	75.0	0.0
4	26.3	68.3	68.2	+0.1
5	26.25	61.85	61.2	+0.65
6	26.25	53.5	53.4	+0.1
7	26.3	44.5	43.9	+0.6
8	26.4	35.9	35.6	+0.3
9	26.35	27.3	26.7	+0.6
10	26.4	21.52	22.1	−0.58
11	26.48	15.3	14.8	+0.5
12	26.78	12.98	13.5	−0.52
13	27.0	43.4	43.5	−0.1
			Avg.	± 0.3

corresponding to less than 0.2 per cent RH at 25°C.

The reproducibility of the hygrometer was difficult to evaluate because of the limitations

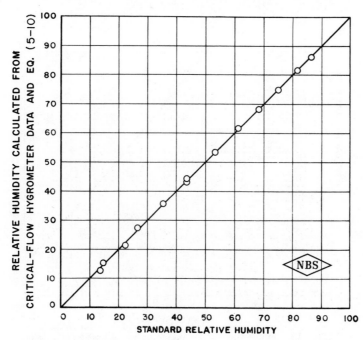

FIG. 11. Calibration of critical-flow pneumatic hygrometer shown in Fig. 9 and Fig. 10.

of equipment to provide known humidities. The tests conducted with the pressure-humidity apparatus (see above) showed that the reproducibility is certainly better than ± 0.5 per cent RH.

Readings of Relative Humidity from the Critical-Flow Hygrometer

In many applications, it may be desirable to obtain readings of relative humidity directly from the hygrometer. For a given mixing ratio, the ratio $(P_2' - P_2'')/P_2'$ is a constant [see Eq. (17)] so that the difference in readings of the differential pressure gauge, yielding a value of $(P_2' - P_2'')$, will be proportional to mixing ratio, provided the intermediate pressure P_2 (and hence the entrance pressure) is kept constant. There is no atmospheric-pressure correction to relative humidity, how-ever, since RH = mixing ratio/saturated mixing ratio, and both these factors are inversely proportional to the atmospheric pressure. At a fixed temperature, say 25°C, the differential pressure gauge is thus readily calibrated in terms of relative humidity. The nonlinearity of this calibration is sufficiently small for a reasonable range of atmospheric pressures (± 5 per cent), so that a linear calibration may be used with a maximum error of less than ± 0.5 per cent RH.

In the present instrument, this approximate linear calibration is 1 in. $H_2O = 18.27$ per cent RH at the entrance to the upstream nozzles (± 0.47 per cent RH maximum error). Because of the presence of an entrance filter, the air entering the upstream nozzles has already been expanded to a slight degree, and atmospheric relative humidity is therefore obtained by

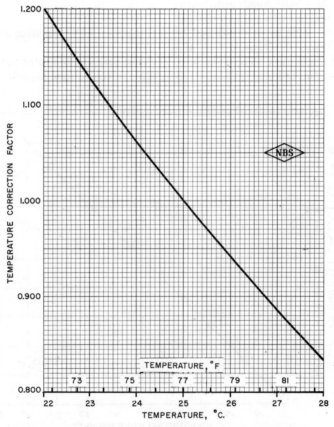

Fig. 12. Temperature correction factor for calibration of critical-flow pneumatic hygrometer in per cent RH per inch H_2O change in differential pressure.

multiplying the RH at the entrance to the upstream nozzles by a factor equal to the ratio of atmospheric pressure to the pressure at the entrance of the upstream nozzles. With a typical pressure drop, through the entrance filter and connecting tubing, of 8.3 in. H_2O, this ratio is 1.020, so that the approximate linear calibration at 25°C, becomes 1 in. H_2O = 18.63 per cent RH. The correction factors by which this number (18.63 per cent) must be multiplied at different temperatures are given in Table 2 and Fig. 12.

TABLE 2. TEMPERATURE CORRECTION FACTORS

t (°C)	Correction Factor
15	1.88_3
20	1.37_5
22	1.19_9
23	1.12_6
24	1.06_2
25	1.00_0
26	0.94_2
27	0.88_8
28	0.83_3
30	0.74_0
35	0.54_8

Appendix A

Data for Calculation of Reynolds Number at the Throat of a Critical-Flow Nozzle

Tabulated quantities are:

γ = ratio of specific heats

r_c = the critical ratio of throat pressure to entrance pressure of a critical-flow nozzle;

$$r_c = \left(\frac{2}{\gamma + 1}\right)^{\gamma/(\gamma - 1)}$$

T_2 = the temperature at the throat, in °K; $T_2 = 2T_1/(\gamma + 1)$

ρ = the gas density, at (r_c atm, T_2), in g/cm³, calculated from data for (1 atm, 0°C) in "Handbook of Chemistry and Physics" (Chem. Rubber Pub. Co., Cleveland, Ohio)

μ_{T_2} = the gas viscosity, in poises, at the temperature T_2, by interpolation from data in "Handbook of Chemistry and Physics"

V_{T_2} = the gas velocity, in cm/sec, calculated from data for $V_{0°C}$ in "Smithsonian Physical Tables," and

$\rho V/\mu = N_R/D$ = the Reynolds Number per unit diameter, at the nozzle throat (r_c atm, T_2).

The values are approximate, since a correction is needed for the change in the velocity of sound with diameter of the nozzle.

TABLE 3. CRITICAL RATIO AND ADIABATIC COOLING AT THROAT OF CRITICAL-FLOW NOZZLE, FOR VARIOUS GASES

Gas	γ	r_c	T_2 (for $T_1 = 300$°K)	Adiabatic Cooling at Throat °C	°F
CO_2	1.30	.550	261	39	70
N_2, air O_2, H_2	1.40	.528	250	50	90
He, A	1.67	.487	225	75	135

Acknowledgment. L. Honea and D. S. Goalwin assisted in construction and testing of critical-flow nozzles in the early part of the critical-flow investigations. A. S. Iberall[16] investigated the possible variation in γ. Calibration of flow-measuring apparatus and some of the tests on critical-flow nozzles were conducted with the help of H. H. Allion. A. Wexler provided and operated the standard pressure-humidity apparatus used for checking the computed calibration of the critical-flow hygrometer.

TABLE 4. DENSITY, VISCOSITY AND VELOCITY OF SOUND AT THROAT OF CRITICAL FLOW NOZZLE, FOR SEVERAL GASES

Gas	$\rho(r_c$ atm, $T_2)$	μ_{T_2}	V_{T_2}	$\frac{\rho V}{\mu}$ (at r_c atm, T_2)
H_2	0.0519×10^{-3}	$.79 \times 10^{-4}$	12.1×10^4	7.95×10^4
He	0.1053×10^{-3}	1.66×10^{-4}	8.82×10^4	5.60×10^4
N_2	0.722×10^{-3}	1.55×10^{-4}	3.24×10^4	15.1×10^4
Air	0.745×10^{-3}	1.59×10^{-4}	3.18×10^4	14.9×10^4
O_2	0.824×10^{-3}	1.73×10^{-4}	3.04×10^4	14.5×10^4
A	1.053×10^{-3}	1.81×10^{-4}	2.80×10^4	16.3×10^4
CO_2	1.137×10^{-3}	1.31×10^{-4}	2.52×10^4	21.9×10^4

References

1. Uehling, E. A., and Steinbart, A., U.S. Patent 503,337 (August 15, 1893).
2. Bachmann, H., Dissertation, Heidelberg, Press of Carl Pfeffer, 1912.
3. Tate, K. L., U.S. Patent 1,630,318 (May 31, 1927).
4. Stuart, M. C., and Yarnall, D. R., "Fluid Flow Through Two Orifices in Series," *Mech. Eng.*, **58**, 479 (August 1936) with discussion **58**, 744 (November 1936).
5. Stuart, M. C., and Yarnall, D. R., "Fluid Flow Through Two Orifices in Series-II," *ASME Trans.*, **66**, 387 (July 1944).
6. Langefors, B., *Teknisk Tidsk.*, **79**, 399 (1949).
7. Moore, D. W., Jr., "A Pneumatic Method for Measuring High-Temperature Gases," *Aeron. Eng. Rev.*, **7**, 30 (1948).
8. French Patent 782,791 (1935); U.S. Patents 2,523,564; 2,549,621; 2,549,622; 2,549,623; and 2,703,013, etc.
9. Andersen, J. W., and Friedman, R., "An Accurate Gas Metering System for Laminar Flow Studies," *Rev. Sci. Inst.*, **20**, 61 (1949).
10. Vestin, R., Olsson, O., and Somersalo, A., Instruments and Measurements Conference, p. 297, The Royal Swedish Academy of Engineering Sciences, Stockholm, 1949.
11. Wildhack, W. A., "A Versatile Pneumatic Instrument Based on Critical Flow," *Rev. Sci. Inst.* **21**, 25 (January 1950).
12. Hall, Newman A., "Thermodynamics of Fluid Flow," New York, Prentice-Hall, Inc., 1951.
13. Dryden, Hugh L., "The Role of Physics in Aeronautical Development," *Phys. Today*, **5**, 14 (May 1952).
14. Head, Richard M., "Investigation of Spontaneous Condensation Phenomena," Guggenheim Aeronautical Laboratory, California Institute of Technology, 1949 (Thesis).
15. Wexler, A., and Daniels, R. D., Jr., "Pressure-Humidity Apparatus," Res. Paper 2312, *J. Res. Natl. Bur. Std.*, **48**, 269 (April 1952).
16. Iberall, A. S., "The Effective 'Gamma' for Isentropic Expansions of Real Gases," *J. App. Physics*, **19**, 11, pp. 997–9 (November 1948).

55. Hair Humidity Elements

Frederick K. Davey

The Bendix Corporation, Friez Instrument Division, Baltimore, Maryland

ABSTRACT

The use of human hair as a humidity sensor is discussed in relation to sensitivity, accuracy, and speed of response. Some effects of mechanical loading are noted and the problem of hysteresis is discussed. The advantages and disadvantages of rolled hair relative to normal hair are indicated.

The expansion and contraction of human hair has been used to measure relative humidity for nearly two centuries. Despite the availability of other materials and of newer, more sophisticated and more accurate techniques, hundreds of thousands of hair-actuated humidity measuring and control devices are made every year. The reasons for the continued popularity of hair-actuated devices are simple and readily apparent. Hair is strong enough and the changes of length caused by changes in relative humidity are large enough to drive recorder pens or electrical switches either directly or with motion amplified by levers. Hair is cheap and the devices are usually simple and inexpensive. Despite the availability of more accurate and faster responding instruments, it is likely that hair-actuated devices will be in use for many years, and it is desirable that the users of these instruments be aware of their limitation.

Figure 1 shows a typical curve of hair elongation as a function of relative humidity. The exact curve for any given hair is variable depending on the source and treatment used to remove fats and oil. The curve is not linear, but simple mechanical linkages can produce a high degree of linearity.

A most advantageous property of hair is that this curve is only very slightly affected by temperature despite the fact that the partial pressure of water vapor associated with a given value of relative humidity varies by more than a factor of 20 over the range of temperature where hair is useful. The differences observed at different temperatures are mostly associated with thermal expansion and can be compensated by the design of the device.

The curve of Fig. 1 was made with a load of 1 gram on each hair which represents a stress of about 500 psi. Higher stress will produce a slightly different curve. This is fairly typical of the loading of hair elements though loads 10 times this value have been used. At higher stresses, long-term drift becomes a problem, causing permanent changes of length and altering the calibration curve.

One of the most troublesome characteristics of hair humidity elements is the effect of humidity exposure on the calibration curve. This is shown in Fig. 2. The hair, stored for a number of days at very low humidity, exhibited what is known as the "dry" curve when tested at increasing humidities, but after exposure to very high humidity, it exhibited a different calibration curve which we call the "wet" curve. This effect is apparently due to the complex structure of hair, which consists of different layers.

The practical effect of these two-calibration curves depends on the use to which a hair hygrometer is put. Usually the wet curve is used and the hairs are wetted with water before calibration. Transition from the "wet" to "dry" curve is exceedingly slow at relative

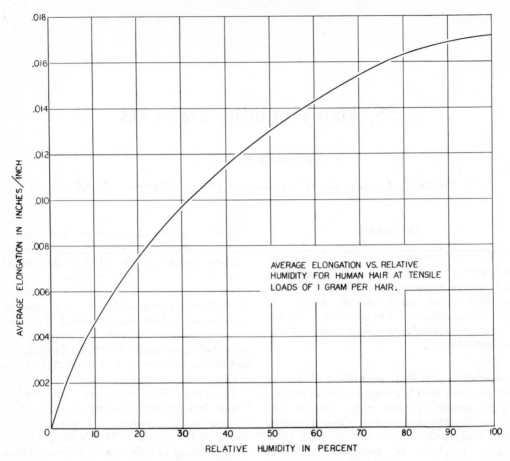

FIG. 1. The elongation of hair as a function of relative humidity.

humidities above 50 per cent and will cause little change in indication. At lower humidities the change is more rapid, but the difference in indication between the two curves is less. However, a device calibrated on the "wet" curve and subsequently stored at low humidity before measuring 50 per cent RH air will read too high by 20 per cent. While proper operation can be restored by wetting the hair or by exposure to saturated air, this effect does impose a limitation on the use of the device.

In practice, for most homes and most meteorological surface measurements, the normal ranges of humidity and normal variation in humidity keep the errors due to this "wet-dry" effect within acceptable limits. However, for many scientific or industrial applications this poses an unacceptable limitation.

The speed of response of hair to changes in humidity depends on temperature, stress on the hair, and the relative humidity and direction of the change.

Hair under light loading and adequate ventilation will have a time constant of approximately three minutes at room temperatures. The time constant gets longer the lower the temperature, and for all practical purposes hair no longer responds at −40°C. Response is faster if the hair is under higher stress and is somewhat faster for increasing humidity than for decreasing humidity. Response is markedly slower at low relative humidity than at high relative humidity.

All of the above discussion is applicable to human hair which has been simply treated to remove fats and oils. A further treatment, rolling the hair, was first investigated by Dr.

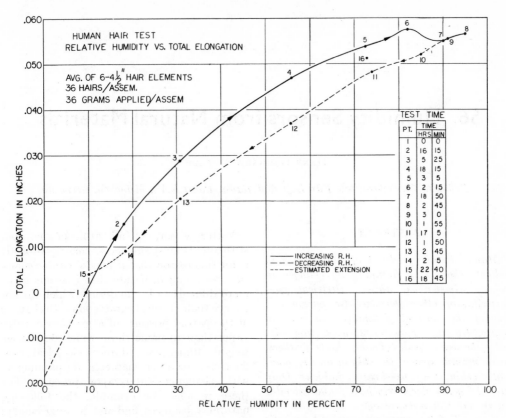

Fig. 2. Effect of previous humidity exposure on calibration curve.

E. Frankenberger in Germany. In this treatment the hair is passed between two rollers which change the essentially circular cross section of the hair to an elliptical cross section. The changes in performance of the hair are generally greater for higher rolling pressures exerted.

Rolled hair responds much faster than normal hair, the response time being reduced by a factor of 5 to 10 depending on the rolling pressure used. The shift from wet to dry curve is much faster with rolled hair, for example four hours at about 25 per cent RH, and for applications measuring slow changes in humidity this allows complete equilibrium.

The advantages are obtained in rolled hair with the sacrifice of strength. Rolled hair generally has only 20 per cent or less breaking stength than normal hair and great care must be taken in design of devices employing it.

This brief summary of some of the properties of hair shows that, as may be expected, a device used for almost two centuries cannot approach the accuracy, sensitivity, and speed of response of more recent devices such as infrared hygrometer or mass spectrometers. However, hair-actuated devices have a useful place in many applications and, since they are relatively inexpensive, will be with us for quite a few more years.

56. Humidity Sensors from Natural Materials*

HANS GERHARD MÜLLER

Deütsche Versüchsanstalt Für Lüft-ünd Raüm Fahrt E.V., München, Germany

ABSTRACT

Many organic products of natural origin indicate changes of humidity by changes in weight, dimensions, duress, electrical conductivity, or other characteristic parameters. Among the natural substances in use in hygrometry are cotton fibers, wool, raw silk, linen, the seed capsules of some plants, feathers, hairs, natural sponge, the skin of an egg, goldbeater's skin, straw, wood chips, and horn. Only hair and goldbeater's skin have found extended use in scientific meteorology.

Hair with fatty materials removed by caustic soda, ethyl ether, or alcohol, is in wide use on radiosondes in Europe.

Rolling hairs to an elliptical cross section with a 1:4 ratio of dimensions increases the expansion coefficient of the hair by 50 per cent over that of the natural product. Rolled hairs have a more linear relation between expansion and relative humidity and have considerably improved response rates as compared to natural hairs. Permissible loading is reduced from 0.8 to 0.3 gram by the rolling process, but the high-humidity performance is greatly improved.

Organic products of natural origin have played a significant role in the determination of the water vapor content of the air. With progress in technology, however, they are losing their importance, mainly for their lack of reproducibility and their frequently only superficially known mode of operation. Some of these methods, however, show advantageous features which justify, though in a more limited sense, their continued use.

* Translated by Reinhold M. Marchgraber.

Water vapor, of all atmospheric constituents, is most subject to condensation. It is for this reason that it reacts with so many surfaces found in nature that it seems to be more difficult to list materials which do not change their physical parameters with changes of the partial pressure of atmospheric water vapor than to name those which do change weight, dimensions, duress, electrical conductivity, or other characteristic parameters with changing water-vapor pressure. For these reasons, for example, the following natural substances find use in hygrometry: cotton fibers, wool, raw silk, linen, the seed capsules of some plants, feathers, hairs, natural sponge, the skin of an egg, goldbeater's skin, straw, wood chips, horn, and many more. Only hair and goldbeater's skin, however, have found extended use in scientific meteorology.

Hair hygrometers are frequently used in meteorological networks in the form of recording hygrographs whenever accuracy is not too important and where their performance can be monitored from time to time using psychrometric techniques. Hair and goldbeater's skin hygrometers further find use in radiosondes, which readily allow a transformation of the expansion of the humidity sensor to characteristic signals of the radiosonde's telemetry. (German radiosonde H50, the Finnish radiosonde, the British Mark 2B model, and many others may serve as examples.)

Immaculate cleanliness of the sensing surfaces, especially removal of all traces of fatty substances, is an important criterion for successful operation. This is obtained through the use of solvents such as a solution of caustic soda or ethyl ether.

The use of the hair as a hygrometric substance goes back to H. B. deSaussure, who investigated its behavior. Gay-Lussac established the functional relation between relative humidity and hair expansion, and an early theory was given by B. Sresnewsky.

The interaction between hair and water vapor is rather complex. The outer membrane of the hair contains cells that show cavities that connect with the air if one removes the fatty layer enclosing the bare hair. J. R. Katz performed experiments with cellulose and hydrocellulose fibers which lead to the assumption that water deposited between the intermediate cells of the fiber material enlarges their spacing. It is to be noted that the hair hygrometer is capable of indicating over-saturation.[5]

For natural hair, a nonlinear relation between the change of length and relative humidity is found:[2]

TABLE 1

Relative Humidity	Change in Length of the Natural Hair Expressed in Per Cent of the Total Change
0	0.0
10	20.9
20	38.8
30	52.8
40	63.7
50	72.8
60	79.2
70	85.2
80	90.5
90	95.4
100	100.0

The total change of length over the range 0 to 100 per cent RH is found to be about 25×10^{-3}. The thermal coefficient of expansion is much smaller (34×10^{-6} per °C) or, if mounted in brass or aluminum supports, about 15×10^{-6} per °C. The value given seems to be well established at low values of relative humidity. For medium and large RH values, the values given by different authors differ considerably.

The sensitivity of the hair hygrometer is severely reduced if its exposure allows contamination by dust or condensing vapors. Precautions must be taken to keep the sensor surface extremely clean. In cases where short lag time is of secondary importance, a thin protective enclosure of water vapor permeable plastic (cellophane) can give an advantageous protection against contamination.

The transformation into a readout of the length of the hair which represents the water vapor to be measured has to be accomplished without extensive load on the hair. The loading which can be tolerated depends somewhat on the thickness of the hair; it should, however, not exceed about 0.8 gram.[10]

Hair hygrometers employing hair bundles are not particularly advantageous, since the expansion coefficient differs from hair to hair, and the sensitivity of the bundle is hence determined by the lowest coefficient present. In addition, the use of a bundle increases the lag time of the instrument. For this reason, modern instrument technology uses single hairs or, by means of special mounting, well-balanced groups of two or three hairs as sensors. Full exposure of the sensor surfaces to the environment must be insured.

The process of obtaining equilibrium between hair and water vapor environment depends on several factors: the amount of water vapor which is transferred in unit time from the air to the surface of the hair, the diffusion of the sorbed water within the hair, and the removal of the heat of condensation generated by the sorption process. G. Hofmann[7] has found theoretically and in good agreement with the experimental data of Frankenberger[8] that the dominating parameter controlling the lag above -10°C is the hair, and below -20°C, the transport of the water vapor through the air. This explains the increase of lag with decreasing temperature as well as with decreasing relative humidity. (See Table 2.) The considerable lag of the natural hair is a strong handicap for its use in aerological instrumentation.

It was therefore a big improvement when a technique of mechanical and chemical treatment resulted in considerable reduction of lag. E. Frankenberger[8] started with the concept that the lag would become shorter if the surface-to-volume ratio of the hair could be increased. He pressed the hair, immersed in oil, between a set of highly polished steel cylinders and removed its fatty substances in a bath of alcohol. Under this procedure the length of the hair increases about 5 per cent; the cross section becomes elliptical with a 1:4

ratio of the main axis, and its elasticity and tensile strength decrease. According to Lang,[6] such a "rolled" hair should not be loaded by more than 0.3 gram maximum if its calibration is to be maintained. The expansion coefficient of the rolled hair is about 50 per cent larger than that of the natural product. A nearly linear relation between expansion and relative humidity replaces the function of Gay-Lussac; hence a significant improvement is obtained, especially in the most interesting region of high relative humidities.

The most important improvement of the Frankenberger hair, however, is its significantly improved lag characteristic. The calibration curves are remarkably stable. W. Schulze[9] studied the lag coefficients of various types of humidity sensors by evaluating radiosonde flights. If one exposes a hair to a step function change of water vapor concentration in the air, the response of the element is described by the equation

$$U_a - U_h = \Delta U = \alpha \frac{dU_h}{dt} \qquad (1)$$

where

$U_a =$ the humidity of the air
$U_h =$ the humidity indicated by the hygrometer
$t =$ the time
$\alpha =$ the lag coefficient.

For a step change in the humidity of the air, one obtains

$$\Delta U = \Delta U_0 e^{-t/\alpha} \qquad (2)$$

Hence, an exponential law describes the transient period before a new equilibrium is reached.

Schulze determined α as a function of the absolute water vapor content of the air for from 9.0 to 0.02 gram of water per cubic meter and over a temperature range of from $+10$ to $-60°C$. He found α, in the first approximation, independent of the direction of the changes experienced by the sensor.

The rolled hair proved to be by far superior to other humidity sensors. The lag coefficient for humidities above 0.05 g/m^3 is nearly constant and is found to be about 10 seconds, thus matching the lag coefficient of the bimetal thermometer used in the German radiosonde. The lag coefficient of the natural, untreated hair is, under identical operating conditions,

approximately 600 seconds, and that of a sensor made from goldbeater's skin, is about 300 seconds. Table 2 shows the increase of the lag for 100 per cent RH with decrease of temperature.

TABLE 2

		α	
	60 sec	100 sec	200 sec
Occurs for			
Natural hair	$-2°C$	$-10°C$	$-15°C$
Goldbeater skin	$-12°C$	$-18°C$	$-24°C$
Rolled hair (Frankenberger)	$-53°C$	$-60°C$	below $-60°C$

At the noted temperatures (in °C).

The results obtained by W. Schulze led to the conclusion that in aerological probing of the atmosphere the natural hair fails to give useful data below $-10°C$, and goldbeater's skin, below $-20°C$. The Frankenberger hair shows a lag for the environmental temperatures, that is, for temperatures above 0°C, about equal to that of the bimetal thermometer. For temperatures between 0 and $-20°C$, a correction for lag is necessary below approximately 40 per cent RH. Below $-55°C$ the rolled hair becomes useless. According to W. Schulze as well as L. Raab, the rolled hair yields useful humidity profiles in the stratosphere for relative humidity values below about 20 per cent. Changes in structure which lead to similar effects as the rolling process used by Frankenberger may be obtained by chemical treatment. Proposals of this kind include treatment of the hair with extracts of Koratine (J. Jakobi[11]) and with Phenolic (A. Lang[6]).

A. Lang investigated hairs from mummies of various ages (400-year-old Peruvian hair preserved by sodium chloride and 3000-year-old hair from Egypt) and found a behavior very similar to that of the rolled hair. It cannot, however, be determined how much of this similarity is due to the chemical treatment and how much is due to an aging process which changed the structure of the hair.

It was mentioned before that the behavior of the hygrometer depends strongly on the transport of the water molecules through the air to the surface of the sensor as well as on the distribution of the water within the structure of the hair. Practical use requires consideration of these factors. For example: exposure of the sensor to a "dry" environment for a longer time affects its behavior. A regeneration by exposure to high environmental humidities is necessary before the sensor can be used reliably. There is also a small dependence on the "history" of the element. The measurement of changes in environmental humidity after an element has reached water vapor saturation may yield values which can be 6 to 8 per cent too high. These effects were studied extensively by E. Frankenberger and W. Schulze.

In summing up, one may state that the characteristic properties of the hair hygrometer are well known and that the role of the hair in the instrument of humidity is still a significant one. Besides hair, goldbeater's skin is still in use. It is inferior in sensitivity and lag characteristic to the rolled hair. Studies of the characteristic properties of goldbeater's skin were made by P. Gondet and M. Petit.

References

1. de Saussure, H. B., "Essais sur l'Hygrometrie," Neuchatel, 1783; "Defence de l'Hygromètre à cheveux," Genf, 1788.
2. Kleinschmidt, E., *Beitr. Phys. Atm.*, **2**, 99 (1908).
3. Sresnewsky, B. J., *Met. Z.*, **13**, 145 (1896).
4. Katz, J. R., Akad. Wetensch., Amsterdam (1924).
5. Weber, A., Inauguraldissertation, Marburg, 1912.
6. Lang, A., *Ann. Meteorol.*, **6**, 164 (1953/4).
7. Hofmann, G., *Ann. Meteorol.*, **6**, 77 (1953/4).
8. Frankenberger, E., *Forsch. u. Erf. Ber. Dt. Wetterdienst A Nr.*, 26 (1944).
9. Schulze, W., *Ann. Meteorol.*, **5**, 223 (1952).
10. Raab, L., *Tellus*, **6**, 405 (1954).
11. Jakobi, J., German Patent 886,820, Wiesbaden (1953)

57. The Piezoelectric Sorption Hygrometer

W. H. KING, JR.

Analytical Research Division, Esso Research and Engineering Company, Linden, New Jersey

ABSTRACT

A water analyzer was developed employing a novel means of indicating selective sorption. The sensing element is a radio-frequency quartz crystal coated with a hygroscopic material. In a simple circuit using such a crystal, the frequency of oscillation is decreased when the crystal gains weight due to water sorption on the coating. Since frequency changes can be measured accurately and rapidly, this results in an accurate and simple moisture analyzer.

The performance characteristics of the sorption hygrometer can be changed by the choice of the hygroscopic coating. The most sensitive detectors are made using molecular sieves. Polar liquids are the most rapid and linear but least sensitive. Hygroscopic polymers offer wide range of nonlinear response and high selectivity.

Typical data obtained on an instrument using this principle of measurement are as follows: Range: 0.1 to 33,000 ppm; Speed: 99 per cent dry-down in one minute; Minimum Detectable: ± 0.1 ppm; Selectivity: hydrogen, hydrocarbons, olefins, alcohols, acid gases and chlorinated solvent vapors cause only negligible interference. These performance data are unequaled by any other hygrometer. The simplicity of radio-remote reading should have important radiosonde applications.

INTRODUCTION

Piezoelectric quartz crystals are used in great numbers for the controlling of frequencies in radio transmitters and receivers. Quartz crystals are also widely used as selective filters in electrical networks. Their use in ultrasonic generation and detection is widely practiced.[1] Other uses of quartz crystals are less familiar. These include the measurement of temperature,[2] thickness of evaporated metal films,[3] the dew point of gases,[4] and the adsorption of gases on quartz.[5] The sensitivity of crystals to metal film deposition is very high. Warner and Stockbridge[6] report detecting about 10^{-11} g/cm².

This paper presents information on water detectors made by coating quartz crystals and then measuring changes in vibration due to changes in the coating.

THE DETECTOR CRYSTAL

There are many sizes, shapes, and frequencies of quartz crystals available commercially which can function effectively as weight detectors. The type of crystal chosen for this work is shown in Fig. 1. The choice was based on convenience. The crystals are small, rugged and inexpensive. A frequency of around 9 Mc was chosen as a compromise between sensitivity and durability. The designation recognized by all crystal manufacturers is plated electrode, 9 Mc, AT cut, HC6/U holder. The quartz discs are commonly about 12 mm in diameter and about 0.2 mm thick. The area covered by an electrode is normally between 0.3 and 0.5 cm². The AT cut crystal is almost insensitive to temperature fluctuations (0.5 cps/°F. Examination of many crystals of this type showed the linear relationship between mass added to the crystal surface and the frequency change. This is consistent with the results obtained by other observers.[3-6]

FIG. 1. The unit at the right is a sealed crystal commonly used for frequency control in electronic circuits. The unit at left shows the metal plated electrodes on the quartz disc. Frequency of these units is 9×10^6 cps.

Defining terms:

ΔF = Frequency change in cycles per second (cps)

ΔM = Total mass change in grams

K = 2.3×10^8 cps/g for a typical 9-Mc unit

$$\Delta F = K \Delta M \qquad (1)$$

The constant K and its linearity were determined by quantitative electroplating experiments where the metal deposit was accurately determined by Faraday's law. The piezoelectric quartz crystal is therefore a very sensitive millimicrobalance with linear and quantitative response. Further, most crystals are made to withstand extremes of thermal and vibrational shock. By choosing materials of construction, they can be made chemically inert.

To make a water detector, the crystal is coated with a hygroscopic material, placed in an oscillator circuit, and provided with gas conduits to hold the gas to be analyzed. Many other types of detectors are, of course, possible using this principle.

The signal from the detector crystal oscillator is a radio frequency which can be measured with very high precision in a variety of ways. The greatest precision is obtained from digital frequency counters which are available from many manufacturers. These units can measure the signal directly to $\pm$ 0.1 cps. Analog audio-frequency meters are much cheaper and can also be employed effectively. The audio frequency can be obtained by heterodyning a second or reference crystal oscillator with the detector oscillator. Remote reading of the signal is also possible by employing transistor oscillators and using a radio to pick up and heterodyne the signals. Specific circuits will not be given in this paper because of the wide variety available commercially. Circuits are not critical to the art of detection, and oscillator and mixing circuits are well known in the field of electronics.[7]

DETECTOR CHARACTERISTIC DETERMINED BY COATING

It is possible to relate quantitatively the detector signal to the absorption isotherms of a hygroscopic coating. The following equations are helpful in this regard.

Defining terms:

ΔF_0 = Frequency change due to dry coating

ΔW_0 = Weight of dry coating

ΔF = Frequency change due to water absorbed (signal)

ΔW = Weight increase due to water absorbed

and substituting them in Eq. (1)

$$\Delta F_0 = K \Delta W_0 \qquad (2)$$

Dividing Eq. (1) by Eq. (2)

$$\frac{\Delta F}{\Delta F_0} = \frac{\Delta W}{\Delta W_0} \qquad (3)$$

Rearranging Eq. (3)

$$\Delta F = \frac{\Delta W}{\Delta W_0} \Delta F_0 \qquad (4)$$

Equation (3) shows that the fractional frequency change equals the fractional weight gain of the coating. Since the weight gain of a hygroscopic adsorbent is a function of the water partial pressure, the sorption detector signal (ΔF) is a function of partial pressure. Equation (4) may be used to get an idea of the detector's absolute sensitivity with a partic-

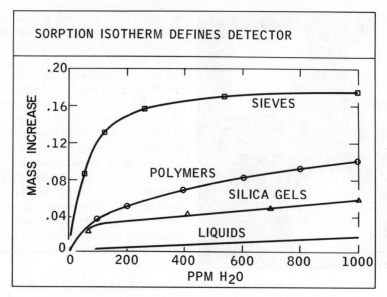

FIG. 2. Adsorption isotherms measured with coated crystals.

ular coating. Coatings from $\Delta F_0 = 1$ to 120 kc can readily be obtained with various materials.

Typical adsorption isotherms measured with coated quartz crystals are shown in Fig. 2. The zeolite-type materials such as molecular sieves make the most sensitive water detectors in the low partial pressure range. Polar liquids like polyethylene glycol make very rapid and linear detectors. However, liquids are not as permanent or as selective as solid absorbents. A compromise on linearity, sensitivity, and operating range is available by using a wide variety of hygroscopic polymers and natural resins. Many kinds of glue, cellulose products, thickening agents, and similar products are easily coated on crystals and make good water detectors.

PERFORMANCE OF A TYPICAL DETECTOR

Range

The nonlinear adsorption isotherm of a hygroscopic polymer makes it possible to use a single detector to cover an exceptionally wide range of humidities. The data shown in Table 1 were obtained on a single unit. The noise level was about 0.5 cps corresponding to a minimum detectable amount of 0.1 ppm. It is observed that there is adequate signal to make measurements at 100 per cent RH (30,000 ppm).

TABLE 1

Water Concentration (ppm)	Signal (cps)
0.1	0.5
1.0	7.8
10.0	66.0
100	310
1,000	950
10,000	2,550
30,000	3,900

Speed

The new water detector has exceptionally fast response speed because water pickup and release by the absorbent is fast. This was demonstrated by the following test. A commercially available electrolytic hygrometer which is in popular use was compared to a prototype instrument using the new crystal detector. Both instruments sampled the same gas at the same time during dry-down conditions and the results were simultaneously recorded. Table 2 shows the exceptionally high speed of indication of the new detector. The electrolytic took 30 minutes to indicate 98 per cent change while the crystal required only 1.5 minutes.

TABLE 2

Time on Dry Gas (min.)	H₂O (ppm) by	
	Crystal	Electrolytic
0	430	460
0.5	90	220
1.5	7	125
30	0.36	7.2
60	0.16	3.7

Interference

The measurement of water vapor in many types of gas streams is possible with the new detector. Interference from changing gas composition can come from two main sources: (1) absorption of the interfering gas that produces a "water signal," and (2) absorption of the interfering gas thereby causing a change in the water absorbing ability of the coating. The first problem can be eliminated by measuring a signal on the unknown wet gas and comparing it to the signal obtained when the same gas is passed through a suitable dryer. The second problem is minimized by using highly selective adsorbents. If the adsorption is small, the co-adsorption interference will also be small. Table 3 shows the results of a critical test of a prototype water analyzer* using the new detector. A drying tube was first connected in front of the analyzer so that all gases were dried to the same extent before entering the analyzer. The data are shown as equivalent water concentration when the test gas is substituted for air.

TABLE 3. INTERFERENCE FROM GASES

Test Gas	Gas Response Relative to Air in Equivalent H₂O (ppm)	Test Gas	Gas Response Relative to Air in Equivalent H₂O (ppm)
100% Hydrogen	2.6	100% Carbon Dioxide	44.0
100% Methane	1.7	100% Carbon Monoxide	0.7
100% Ethylene	1.3	100% N₂	0.0
100% Butane	2.6	100% O₂	0.0
9% Benzene	10		
4% Heptane	10	8% HCl	16.0
		8% H₂S	6.8
100% "Freon" 12	7.0	1% SO₂	1.0
100% "Freon" 22	5.5	1% Ethanol	1.0
3% Perchloro-ethylene	8	12% Methanol	150

* Gilbert and Barker Manufacturing Company, West Springfield, Mass.

FIG. 3. The parallel gas conduits preheat the sample gas. The sealed reference crystal provides temperature compensation. In this case the signal is the frequency difference between detector crystal and reference crystal. This is one of many possible modes of use.

The interference data show that the adsorption of gases and vapors is very low and can be neglected because most gas streams do not change as widely as shown in this test.

Gas Flow, Temperature and Pressure

The detector senses the partial pressure of water by adsorption and, therefore, will be sensitive to temperature and total pressure. Fairly constant pressure is realized by venting the detector to the atmosphere through a length of tubing to minimize back diffusion of atmospheric water. Flow rates are chosen to minimize effects on temperature and pressure of the detector. Rates from 50 cc/min. to 1000 cc/min. are often used. Temperature can be controlled accurately by the use of many types of commercially available crystal ovens that are made for this purpose. Figure 3 is a photograph of a detector crystal and a sealed reference crystal in a crystal oven*. Gas enters and leaves the top of the crystal cover through

* Crystal oven model HO-9, International Crystal Manufacturing Co.

parallel $\frac{1}{8}$-in. tubing which also preheats the gas before it enters the detector. The oven is normally covered with insulation that was removed for the photograph.

Operation of the detector at pressures other than atmospheric pressure is possible, if desired. Below atmospheric pressure, leaks of atmospheric water into the detector can be a problem. Working above atmospheric pressure yields the advantage of higher sensitivity. The ability to operate at different total pressures is indicated in Fig. 4. Here a detector was calibrated with three different gas streams at pressures ranging from 50 to 1520 mm Hg.

Durability and Life

Experience with many polymer coated crystals over $1\frac{1}{2}$ years showed that they can be made very durable. Calibrations have been shown to hold for over 7 months. With ordinary care, dirt and dust do not seem to stick to the crystal. On some occasions, detectors and gas feed lines become fouled with oil condensate. When this happens the oil is

removed by flushing the system with alcohol. Detectors are not affected by this cleaning procedure.

A cycling test of 10 detectors with different coatings was made to see if the coatings would flake off. The detectors were exposed to dry air for one minute and then 10,000 ppm (33 per cent RH) air for one minute for many weeks. In this test the loss of 0.02 per cent of coating was detectable. This would correspond to the same percentage change in the calibration factor. After 70,000 cycles (50 days) most of the detectors showed about 0.05 per cent loss of coating while some showed 0.05 per cent gain in weight. The loss or gain observed would not have changed the detector's calibration significantly.

CONCLUDING REMARKS

We have shown that coated piezoelectric crystals can be used as sensitive sorption detectors. The detectors are rugged, sensitive, and fast, and they can be used in a wide variety of gas streams. Very high precision of

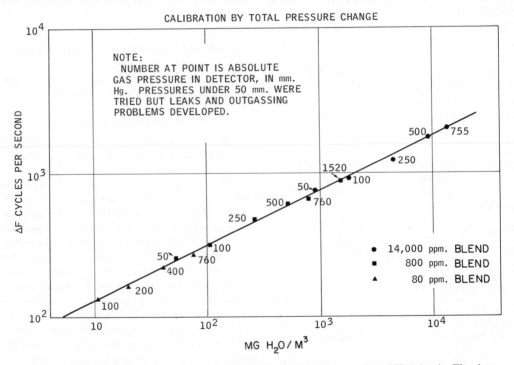

FIG. 4. This calibration curve was obtained with three standard samples of H_2O in air. The data were obtained by lowering the total sample pressure in the detector and keeping the temperature and feed gas compositions constant.

reading can be obtained because the signal is a frequency which lends itself readily to digital readout techniques.

Remote indication of water content is facilitated because the original signal is a radio frequency. Applications of the new detector are expected to cover a wide spectrum from radiosonde balloon measurements to precision laboratory determinations.

Acknowledgment. The writer wishes to thank the many members of the Esso Research and Engineering Company who contributed to this work. My special thanks to A. B. Dean who made the many detectors and measurements summarized in this paper.

References

1. Mason, W. P., "Piezoelectric Crystals and Their Application to Ultrasonics," Princeton, N.J., D. Van Nostrand Company, 1950.

2. Flynn, T. M., Hinnah, H., and Newell, D. E., "An Improved Cryogenic Thermometer," Paper F-2, 1962 Cryogenic Engineering Conference, 1962.

3. Oberg, P., and Longensjo, J., "Crystal Film Thickness Monitor," *Rev. Sci. Instr.*, **30**, No. 11, 1053 (1959).

4. Van Dyke, K. S., "Dew Point Hygrometer," US Patent No. 2,571,171 (Oct. 16, 1951) (Filed July 4, 1945).

5. Slutsky, L. J., and Wade, W. H., "Adsorption of Gases on Quartz Single Crystals," *J. Chem. Phys.*, **36**, No. 10, 2688–2692 (1962).

6. Warner, A. W., and Stockbridge, C. D., "The Measurement of Mass Using Quartz Crystal Resonators," Symposium on Vacuum Microbalance Techniques, Los Angeles, California, 1962.

7. Landee, Robert W., *et al.*, "Electronic Designer's Handbook," New York, McGraw-Hill Book Company, Inc., 1957.

58. A Sensitive Heat-of-Adsorption Water Vapor Recorder

Gene C. Flumerfelt

Mine Safety Appliances Company, Pittsburgh, Pennsylvania

ABSTRACT

A sensitive water vapor recorder using the heats of adsorption and desorption is discussed. A Wheatstone bridge containing thermistors imbedded in two small driers is used as the thermal to electric transducer. The driers are alternately exposed to wet sample and to pre-dried sample portions. The signal is presented as an oscillating recorder trace whose amplitude varies as the water concentration. The response is linear in concentrations up to 500 ppm. The sample input requires a minimum of 10 psig and 6 l/min.

Sensitivity to water vapor in air is 240 μV/ ppm and varies with specific heat for water in other gas streams.

The method is applicable to most process streams, except those containing high concentrations of H_2S or strong acid gases.

INTRODUCTION

The need for continuous and accurate measurement of low concentrations of water vapor in gases is of increasing importance.

Gases which are transported for long distances must be maintained at low water content to prevent blocking of transmission lines by condensation or hydrate formation.

Many catalysts in the petrochemical industry are damaged by traces of water in the process stream. Drying columns can be maintained at highest efficiency if the effluent streams are monitored and regeneration is applied just before or at the instant of breakthrough.

In addition to the need to control water vapor concentration at established limits in process streams, the accumulation of accurate and reliable data is required to establish similar limits for other processes.

Many methods for determination of water concentration are in use. The hair hygrometer, the wet-and-dry-bulb humidity indicator, the dew-point determination and its variations,[1] and the electrolytic hygrometer[2] are familiar tools. Each of these methods has its advantages and its limitations.

After evaluating the existing methods, it seemed desirable to investigate another method which would overcome some of the limitations inherent in the existing moisture monitors.

PRINCIPLE OF OPERATION

The method to be discussed in this paper was first published by Strange and Skarstrom in 1955.[3] The detection and measurement of water vapor in gases is based upon the principle that energy in the form of heat is released when a gas or vapor is adsorbed upon a suitable solid. This energy, the heat of adsorption, varies with such factors as the nature of the adsorbate gas or vapor, the nature of the adsorbent solid, the temperature of adsorption, and the ratio of the gas adsorbed to the gas present in the adsorbent.

The energy change with which this paper deals must also be limited to the purely physical state of change. No chemical reaction, as in chemisorption, must occur. The phenomenon must be reversible.

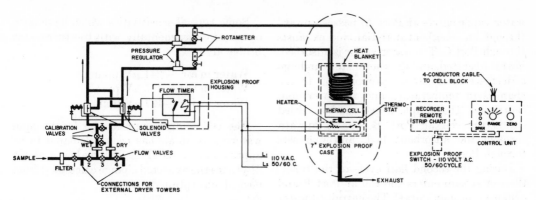

FIG. 1. Schematic flow diagram, water vapor analyzer.

The main part of the heat of adsorption, Q, of vapors, as distinguished from gases, appears to be the heat of liquification L. There is a close similarity between the heat of adsorption of water on materials such as alumina, charcoal, bleached cotton and silica gel, and the heat of liquification of water. For very small concentrations, Q may be $1\frac{1}{2}$ times the value of L, but it approaches L as the concentration increases.[4]

Figure 1 is a schematic diagram of the analyzer designed to measure the concentration of water vapor in gases using the principle of heat of adsorption.

The sample enters at the left through a sintered metal filter and a shutoff valve (Valve 1). The sample is divided into two separate streams. One half passes through Valve 2 and a filter into the "wet" section of the analyzer. The other half of the sample is passed through a suitable dryer and back to the "dry" section of the analyzer through

Valve 4. Both streams then flow through solenoid valves to pressure regulators which are designed to maintain a constant flow at a preset value. Flow indicators and needle valves are provided for flow adjustment.

A timer operates the solenoid valves on a 3-minute cycle alternating the exhaust ports of both solenoid valves at 90-second intervals, Thus, both sample lines to the cell housing contain alternately wet and dry sample.

In the cell housing, the two sample lines are wound together on an aluminum heat exchanger so that both samples achieve identical temperatures before entering the sensing cell. The heat exchanger and the sensing cell are thermostatted at 100 to 120°F.

Figure 2 is a sketch of the sensing cell which contains two adsorbent beds, each connected to one of the two sample lines. In each adsorbent bed, there are two thermistors encased in a glass envelope. During one half cycle of the flow timer, a sample containing

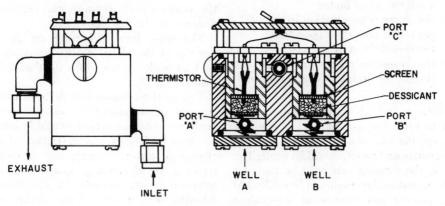

FIG. 2. Sensing cell.

water vapor enters at Port A, passes upward through an adsorbent material, and exhausts through Port C. The water vapor is adsorbed, heat is liberated, and the thermistors undergo a decrease in resistance proportional to the changes in temperature and in water concentration. The sample which has been dried enters the cell at Port B, passes upward through the adsorbent bed, and exhausts through Port C.

During the second half cycle of the timer, the wet stream enters the cell at Port B and exhausts through Port C. The entrained water is adsorbed, heat is liberated, and the thermistor resistance changes as above. At the same time, the dry sample enters the cell at Port A, passes through the adsorbent and exhausts through Port C. Because the principle of adsorption in this application is physical, not chemical, and therefore reversible, the dry sample removes the water deposited during the first half of the cycle. The advantage is twofold. First, the adsorbent is regenerated and prepared for the next wet sample, and secondly, the removal of water causes cooling to occur, and the temperature difference between the thermistors in the two wells is twice that which would be expected if only the heat of adsorption were measured.

The general formula for estimating the output of the cell for known concentrations of water in specific gases is:

$$E = k \times \frac{CL}{C_p} \times T_b \qquad (1)$$

where

E = the peak to peak EMF generated by the cell

k = a cell efficiency factor

C = the water concentration in grams

L = the latent heat of evaporation

C_p = the specific heat of the gas

T_b = the response characteristic of the thermistor bridge to changes in temperature.

As the formula indicates, the response will be dependent upon the specific heat of the gas, but the specific heat of a process gas does not change greatly and its effect will be negligible. However, the formula can only be used for estimation, and analyzers should be calibrated on the process gas stream or equivalent sample.

Some typical sensitivities which have been obtained experimentally with the thermistor bridge are:

Water in air —241 μV/ppm
Water in CO_2—175 μV/ppm
Water in He —427 μV/ppm

The cell temperature change for 10 ppm water vapor in air has been calculated to be approximately 0.041°C. This value is about $2\frac{1}{2}$ times the expected change calculated from heat of adsorption data.

INSTRUMENTATION

Water Indication

The four thermistors of the sensing cell are electrically connected in a typical Wheatstone Bridge arrangement. A remote-control unit contains a power supply, zero adjustment, and four separate span controls. The output of the Wheatstone Bridge is fed to a recording potentiometer through the span resistors. Figure 3 shows a typical recorder presentation of the output of the cell. The recorder is a —1 to +1 mV recorder with a midscale zero. The cell output was adjusted for a full scale deflection of 10 ppm. The chart speed was 2 in./hour, each horizontal line corresponding to 15 minutes.

The envelopes which are caused by the reversing signal from the sensing cell correspond to water concentrations of 7.0, 4.8, and 2.0 ppm water vapor in air reading from bottom to top in the direction of recorder travel.

Figure 3 illustrates that the determination of water concentration is made by measuring the peak-to-peak distance and relating that distance to the full chart range.

The noise level illustrated on the upper portion of the chart is approximately 8 per cent of scale or the equivalent of 0.8 ppm water.

This method cannot strictly be called a continuous measurement of water vapor, but peaks are obtained with the rapidity necessary for most processes. An indication of a step change in water concentration in either increasing or decreasing quantities can be obtained in 90 seconds. In the first three minutes, 50 per cent of the change will be indicated, and in fifteen minutes, more than

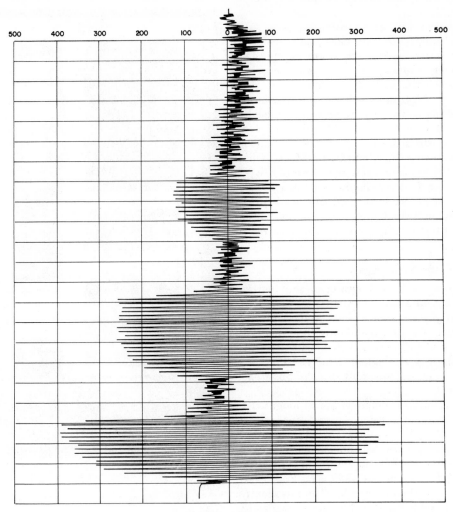

Fig. 3. Recorder trace.

80 per cent of the change will be recorded.

The presentation of water concentration as an oscillating signal with an envelope varying in amplitude with changes in water concentration is adequate for most applications. The signal output has been connected to storage capacitor networks and to peak-to-peak double slide wire recorders in an effort to present the water concentration as a straight line or step-line function. These networks so far have proved inadequate or too costly. Studies are being continued to obtain the straight-line representation of water concentration at a reasonable cost.

Dryers

A dryer was not shown in Fig. 1. As may be assumed, the basic principle of operation depends upon the selection of a dryer suitable for the application. The following are the requirements for a dryer.

(1) It must completely remove the water vapor present in the sample.

(2) It must not remove any sample component which may develope a significant heat of adsorption in the sensing cell.

(3) It must not chemically change any sample component to a compound which may develop a significant heat of adsorption in the

cell or which may block or foul the sample lines.

A regenerative dryer with alumina or silica gel is satisfactory for most applications in which heavy hydrocarbons are not present. However, alumina will remove some of the hydrocarbons, and interference from their heats of adsorption will cause a significant interference. In this application, a zeolite material such as a molecular sieve of 3- to 4-Å pore size is used.

If the sample components tend to polymerize at the regeneration temperature of a dryer, a replaceable dryer should be used. For these applications, we have used calcium hydride, magnesium perchlorate, phosphorous pentoxide, and preconditioned molecular sieves or alumina.

MSA Water Vapor Analyzer

Figure 4 is a photograph of the analyzer built by Mine Safety Appliances Company. The dryer has not been installed on this analyzer. All components are mounted on a steel rack 71 in. high and 28 in. wide. The rack is supported by channel iron feet 26 in. long. The completed assembly weighs about 350 pounds.

All electrical components are mounted in explosionproof housings suitable for installation in Class I, Division I, Group D hazardous atmospheres.[5] The cell and heat exchanger are enclosed in the housing on the upper right of the rack. The solenoid timer is enclosed in the housing on the lower right. The flow control system and solenoid valves are shown at the lower left part of the rack. The area at the upper left side of the rack is occupied by a regenerative dryer or two replaceable dryers.

Not shown on the photograph are the control unit and the indicating recorder which are usually located remotely in a control room or nonhazardous area.

CALIBRATION

Calibration of an analyzer in the 10- to 100-ppm water vapor range is difficult. In the factory, we have developed a calibrator which blends a stream of gas saturated with water at high pressures at 32°F with a stream which has been dried through towers containing, suc-

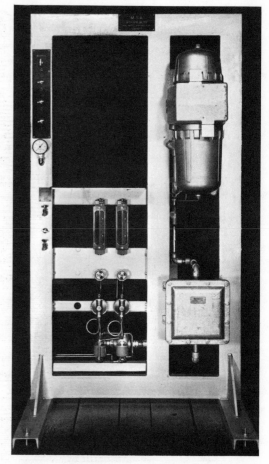

FIG. 4. MSA water vapor analyzer (dryer not shown).

cessively, calcium chloride, calcium sulfate, and phosphorus pentoxide. Flow control regulators on each stream maintain constant flow rates. Reproducibility and accuracy of the preset concentrations fall within 1 per cent.

A reliable and universal field calibrator has not yet been achieved although an approximate calibration can be made.

Figure 1 shows a series of three "calibration valves" on the "wet" section of the analyzer. They can be used as follows: If Valve 2 is closed and Valve 3 is opened, dry gas will be admitted to both sides of the sensing cell, and a zero signal will result. If the center calibration valve is closed and the other two valves are opened, the sample gas can be led through tubing connected to the outlets of these valves to a refrigerated chamber containing a source of water, preferably in the form of ice cubes, and back to the wet section of the analyzer. The water concentration can be calculated by the formula:

$$C = \frac{e_s}{P \times 10^{-6}} \qquad (2)$$

where

C = water concentration in ppm

e_s = vapor pressure of ice at saturation chamber pressure

P = absolute gas pressure.

One range can be calibrated at the known concentration and the other ranges can be calibrated at lower ranges by comparison to the standard range.

EVALUATION OF THE METHOD

Advantages

The use of the described method affords many advantages:

The analyzer can be rugged and relatively maintenance free.

All materials in contact with the sample stream are type 316 stainless steel, "Teflon," nylon, and glass except for the adsorbent. Therefore, corrosion is not often a problem.

The sensing cell is small and is self-regenerating. If a process malfunction should cause exposure of the cell to extremely high moisture conditions even condensation in the cell, the analyzer can be restored to operation within 4 to 6 hours' purging with the normal sample gas. Disassembly is not usually required.

The analyzer has been designed to operate in the ranges from 0 to 10 ppm to 0 to 1000 ppm. However, it can easily be used to determine water concentrations in the range of relative humidities.

The response for concentrations up to 500 ppm is essentially linear. For concentrations above 500 ppm, some nonlinearity occurs as a result of the Wheatstone bridge characteristics.

The analyzer is specific for water vapor when suitably chosen desiccants are used. Gases usually adsorbed by desiccants have low molar heats of adsorbtion in comparison to that of water. Gases which are not adsorbed by the dryer appear equally on both sides of the cell and their effects tend to cancel.

Limitations

The method has been successfully used for most applications. However, it has not been found suitable for determining the water content of sample streams containing large amounts of hydrogen sulfide or the strong acid gases such as chlorine and hydrogen chloride. Hydrogen sulfide is readily adsorbed by most desiccant materials and has a molar heat of adsorption equal to nearly half of that of water. The acid gases tend to destroy, by chemical erosion, the adsorbents commonly used.

The flow rates of the two halves of the sample stream must be kept constant with respect to each other. The flow control regulators, which are an integral part of the system, must be maintained in good operating condition. The flow regulators require a minimum of 6-psig input pressure for operation. The minimum sample flow rate is 6 l/min. If a regenerative dryer is used, the rate of flow will be correspondingly higher.

SUMMARY

I have described a method of measuring the water content in gases. The principle of measurement is based upon relating concentration to heats of adsorption and desorption. I have discussed the advantages and the limitations of the method, and have shown in some detail the means by which the principle of measurement has been reduced to practice to obtain a rugged, reliable, and specific tool for process use.

Acknowledgments. I wish to express my appreciation to the many persons who have aided in the development of the instrument reported here. Among these, I would expressly like to mention the aid of Mr. F. J. Schirm and Mr. J. P. Strange of Mine Safety Appliances Company.

References

1. Jury, S. H., and Light, W. Jr., "Automatic Frost Point Hygrometer," *Anal. Chem.*, **22**, 1536–40 (1950).
2. Crawshaw, J. K., and Davidson, F. G., "Electrolytic Hygrometers for Measurements in Gases Down to a Few Parts Per Million," *J. Sci. Instr.*, **36**, 121–5 (1959).
3. Strange, J. P., and Skarstron, C. W., "A Sensitive Thermoelectric Water Vapor Recorder," 10th Annual Instrumentation Conference, Instrument Society of America, Los Angeles, California, September 1955.
4. Bikerman, J. J., "Surface Chemistry," p. 214, New York, Academic Press, Inc.
5. Bulletin No. 70, National Board of Fire Underwriters, Section 500, 1960.

59. The Interaction of Water Vapor with a Thin Liquid Layer: Applications to Gas Chromatography and Hygrometry*

R. J. CHARLSON

Department of Atmospheric Sciences, University of Washington, Seattle, Washington

ABSTRACT

Adsorption hygrometers can utilize either a solid or liquid material for interaction with water vapor. The use of the former usually leads to unpredictable behavior. The latter, however, offers a reversible sorption process that can be analyzed by the application of Raoult's Law. Two experimental devices will be described which depend on a gas-liquid system:

(1) A gas chromatograph modified to yield absolute humidity data. The currently available sensitivity is on the order of 1 to 5 ppm with a 10-cc sample.

(2) A capacitive detector that utilizes a chromatograph packing as the dielectric of a capacitor. At equilibrium, the dielectric constant of a mixture of a hygroscopic liquid and an inert solid can be related to the humidity of the gas flow. A theoretical description of the device as well as experimental data are presented. The detection limit is on the order of 10 ppm and could be extended to perhaps 0.1 ppm.

INTRODUCTION

The ideal adsorption hygrometer must exhibit a completely reversible adsorption-desorption cycle, preferably one which can be described by a suitable physical chemical theory. Typical gas-solid instruments

* The research reported in this paper was sponsored by the Air Force Cambridge Research Laboratories, Office of Aerospace Research, under contract AF 19 (628) 303.

generally seem to fail in this respect and consequently suffer from hysteresis, poor repeatability, slow response, and poor behavior at low humidities.[1] The use of a gas-liquid system has merit for alleviating at least some of these difficulties.

Two experimental arrangements which depend on such a gas-liquid system have been utilized:

(1) A gas chromatograph modified to provide data on the humidity of gaseous samples,

(2) A detector that utilizes a chromatograph packing as the dielectric of a capacitor.

GAS CHROMATOGRAPHY

Gas liquid partition chromatography has been an important tool in analytical chemistry for almost a decade.[2, 3] Basically, the technique involves the separation of substances in the gas phase according to their affinity for the liquid coating of a solid substrate. The measured sample of a mixture of air and water vapor is injected into the adsorbing column which is a tube packed with small solid particles which are coated with a hygroscopic liquid. Following adsorption, helium is passed through the column to elute the sample. The thermal conductivity of the effluent stream is measured by a four-element hot wire Wheatstone bridge, and the air and water vapor peaks are then recorded. Figure 1 shows a typical chromatogram for an air-water separation. Because the hot wire detectors must be

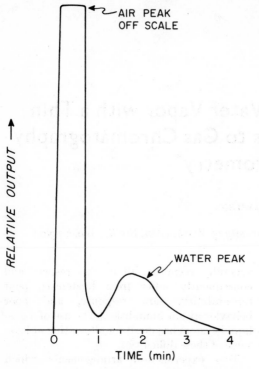

FIG. 1. Typical chromatogram, air-water separation.

operated at high temperature to obtain high sensitivity, it is necessary to prevent contact with oxygen in the air peak. In addition to showing a bypass arrangement that prevents detector damage by air oxidation, Fig. 2 also illustrates the configuration of the entire instrument.

Perhaps the most important facet of the chromatograph is the packing material itself. For water analyses, the substrate material must exhibit an absolute minimum affinity for water; i.e., it should be non polar. The substrate should also have a large surface area-to-mass ratio so that a reasonable amount of the liquid phase can be dispersed into a thin layer over the surface of the solid. Specially prepared fluorocarbon chromatographic substrates which fulfill these requirements are commercially available.* The choice of a liquid is also somewhat critical. The two main requirements for the liquid used in water vapor determinations are:

(1) A very low vapor pressure at the operating temperature of the instrument,

* Such a fluorocarbon is marketed as "Fluoropak 80" by the Fluorocarbon Co., 1206 East Ash Avenue, Fullerton, California.

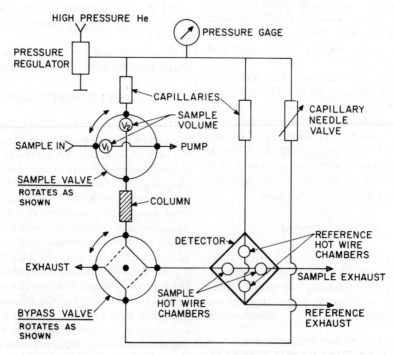

FIG. 2. Bypass valve flow scheme as installed in Beckman GC2-A gas chromatograph.

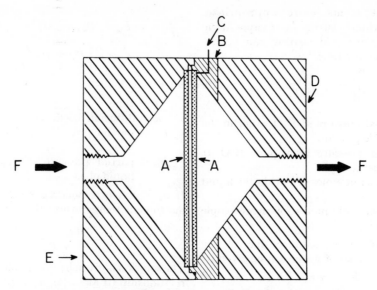

FIG. 3. Cross section of Hygrometer: Liquid Film (HYLIF). A, parallel porous stainless steel plates between which the packing is contained; 8.5-cm diameter, 1-mm separation. B, "Teflon" insulator. C, electrical connection to underground capacitor plate. D and E, stainless steel clamp blocks. F, airflow.

(2) An affinity for water without permanent retention or chemical binding; i.e., a polar liquid.

Typical liquids that can be used are polyethylene glycol, triethylene glycol dimethyl ether, tetraethylene glycol dimethyl ether, and at lower temperatures, glycerol. Since the substrate has a large surface area-to-mass ratio, it is possible to use up to 20 per cent liquid phase (by weight) without bleeding or flowing of the liquid. The thickness of the liquid film on the substrate granules is typically on the order of 2500 Å.

The chromatograph is capable of detecting water vapor concentrations as low as 50 ppm (frost point approximately −50°C) at 1-atm pressure with a 7.5 × 0.5 cm column with a 1-cc sample and a 30-second elution time. The column packing consists of "Fluoropak 80" coated with 20 per cent by weight "Carbowax 400".* By increasing the sample to 10 cc and making modifications on the column, it is anticipated that the detection limit will be extended to 1 to 5 ppm with a slightly longer elution time.

* "Carbowax" 400 is a Union Carbide Chemicals Company trademark for polyethylene glycol.

THE HYGROMETER: LIQUID FILM[4, 5]

As part of some experiments with the chromatograph, an apparatus was devised for measuring the dielectric constant of the solid-liquid mixture as a function of the ambient water vapor concentration. Further experiments have indicated that such a technique is in itself a sensitive method for measuring humidity. Figure 3 shows the configuration of the porous capacitor that is used for the measurement of humidity as a function of the dielectirc properties of the heterogeneous liquid-solid packing material. The device will be herein referred to as the Hygrometer: Liquid Film (HYLIF). This device depends on the equilibrium established between water vapor in the sample flow and the liquid coating of the packing material. A capacitance difference will be realized upon changing the relative humidity of the gas stream because of the different number of dipolar water molecules contained in the liquid portion of the packing. The dependence of the electrical resistivity of the packing material on humidity can be used instead of the capacitance measurement. However, the theoretical treatment is not as accurate, and the capacitance measurement seems more appropriate.

The equilibrium between water vapor in the gas flow and the liquid coating can be described by Raoult's Law:

$$\frac{P_w}{P_T} = \frac{n_w}{n_w + n_s} \qquad (1)$$

where

P_w = partial pressure of H_2O vapor in the sample gas flow

P_T = vapor pressure over pure H_2O at temperature T

n_w = number of moles of H_2O in the liquid film

n_s = number of moles of hygroscopic liquid.

The change in capacitance due to the addition of n_w moles of water can be given by

$$\Delta C = k\, n_w \qquad (2)$$

where

ΔC = change in capacitance due to the addition of n_w moles of water to the packing material, $\Delta C = 0$ at $n_w = 0$.

k = proportionality constant including geometry of the capacitor and dielectric properites of H_2O.

And finally, the relative humidity is related to the capacitance:

$$\frac{P_w}{P_T} = RH = \frac{\Delta C/k}{\Delta C/k + n_s} \qquad (3)$$

where

RH = relative humidity.

Since n_s is constant, this reduces to

$$\frac{P_w}{P_T} = \frac{A\Delta C}{A\Delta C + 1} \qquad (4)$$

where

$A = 1/kn_s$.

If the relative humidity is small, i.e., $P_w/P_T \ll 1$, then

$$\frac{P_w}{P_T} = A\Delta C \qquad (5)$$

A possible form of the time response of this device to a step increase of humidity with temperature constant also can be calculated. The rate of change of n_w with respect to time can be given (assuming uniform composition in the liquid layer and no substantial depletion of the air stream):

$$\frac{dn_w}{dt} = \kappa\,(P_w - P_w)$$

$$= \kappa \left[P_w - P_T \left(\frac{n_w}{n_w + n_s} \right) \right] \qquad (6)$$

where

t = time

κ = diffusion coefficient

P_w = partial pressure of H_2O in the gas flow

P'_w = partial pressure of H_2O over the liquid phase.

If $n_w \ll n_s$ (corresponding to $P_w/P_T \ll 1$ at instrument temperature) this reduces to

$$\frac{n_s dn_w}{P_w n_s - n_w P_T} = \kappa dt \qquad (7)$$

The solution is given by the simple exponential relationship (if at $t = 0$, $n_w = 0$):

$$n_w = \frac{P_w n_s}{P_T} \left[1 - \exp\!\left(\frac{-\kappa P_T}{n_s} t \right) \right] \qquad (8)$$

Or, in terms of capacitance via the sensitivity equation [Eq. (5)],

$$\Delta C = \frac{P_w}{P_T A} \left[1 - \exp\!\left(-\frac{\kappa P_T}{n_s} t \right) \right] \qquad (9)$$

Thus the capacitance should be an exponential function of time at low humidities with κ, P_T and n_s each having an effect on the response time. In particular, the response time can be shortened by decreasing n_s at the cost of decreased sensitivity. If this theory is correct, the time response should be independent of the sample flow humidity.

The temperature dependence of the device also can be obtained by assuming that the main effect of temperature lies in P_T; i.e., that A for a first estimate is independent of T. From eq. (5), (with a fixed P_w),

$$-\frac{1}{P_T} \frac{dP_T}{dT} = \frac{1}{\Delta C} \frac{d\Delta C}{dT} \qquad (10)$$

where T = temperature.

But $(1/P_T)(dP_T/dT)$ can be given by the Clausius-Clapeyron equation:

$$\frac{1}{P_T} \frac{dP_T}{dT} = \frac{\Delta H_{\text{vap}}}{RT^2} = \frac{-1}{\Delta C} \frac{d\Delta C}{dT} \qquad (11)$$

where

ΔH_{vap} = heat of vaporization of H_2O

R = gas constant.

At 300°K, the heat of vaporization of water is about 575 cal/g and $(1/\Delta C)(d\Delta C/dT)$ is thus about 6 per cent per degree. Hence, control or knowledge of the temperature of the packing to about 0.1 deg C seems necessary for an inaccuracy of 0.6 per cent of capacitance change, ΔC.

DATA

Data have been obtained on the sensitivity and time response equations of HYLIF; however, the temperature dependence experiments are still pending. The capacitance of the hygrometer as pictured in Fig. 3 is measured with a Tektronix type 130-LC meter modified for recorder readout. The capacitance (dry) is 125 pF (picofarad). The packing is 20 per cent "Carbowax 400" on "Fluoropak 80".

Figure 4 shows a tracing of the recorder output for three different humidity "square" pulses. The relative humidity remained below 5 per cent at 24°C so that the approximations in the preceding discussion are valid, i.e., $P_w/P_T = A\Delta C$. For these data, the sensitivity coefficient is $4.25 \times 10^{-2}\ (pF)^{-1}$. The signal-to-noise ratio for the largest step (2.0 per cent RH at 24°C) is about 60/1 and for the smallest (0.28 per cent RH at 24°C) about 10/1. Other data have been taken at higher humidities and show similar agreement with sensitivity equation [Eq. (4)]. The criterion for choice of packing is the same as that described for the chromatograph.

Four features of the time response can also be obtained from these data. First, to show that the form of the time response equation [Eq. (9)] agrees with the measured curve, the data are plotted in the semilog plot of Fig. 5. The near linearity of these points indicates the exponential nature of the response. Second, since both increasing and decreasing humidity plots have nearly the same slope, the response time is the same in both directions. Third, the lack of hysteresis can be observed in the repeated return to $\Delta C = 0$ in Fig. 4. Fourth, the response time is independent of the humidity in this low humidity regime.

The data of Fig. 4 were taken at an instrument flow rate of approximately 15 l/min. The response time dependence on flow rate can be evaluated by observation of the time for half response at different flow rates. At 5 l/min. this $t_{1/2}$ is about 17 seconds and at 17 l/min. this half time is reduced to approximately 11 seconds.

CONCLUSIONS

Three different configurations can be used which depend on the principle of HYLIF:

(1) The instrument can be operated at a fixed temperature so that P_T in Eq. (4) is fixed. The measured parameter is thus P_w.

(2) The instrument can be built with a small thermal inertia so that it is in thermal equilibrium with the surroundings. In this case, the device is a relative humidity sensor.

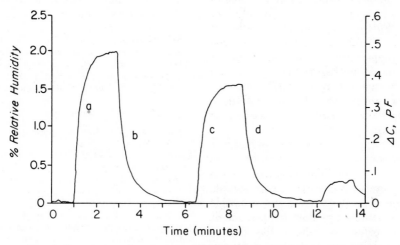

Fig. 4. Capacitance-time data for HYLIF. The letters refer to the plots in Fig. 5. $T = 24°C$.

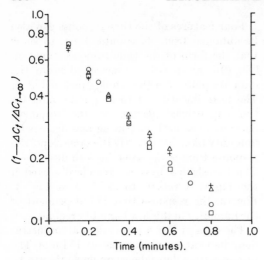

FIG. 5. Semilog plot of $(1 - \Delta C_t/\Delta C_{t\to\infty})$ *vs* time for the data in Fig. 4. Four separate responses are plotted; ○ corresponds to the portion of the curve marked "a," △ to "b," □ to "c" and + to "d." ΔC_t is the change of capacitance evaluated at time t; $\Delta C_{t\to\infty}$ is the equilibrium value.

(3) If HYLIF is operated at a constant capacitance by varying the temperature to bring the device into vapor pressure equilibrium with the sample gas flow, a record of capacitor temperature suffices to determine the humidity. Of these three, only the first has been built and operated; however, plans call for testing the other two.

The use of HYLIF for the measurement of humidity has already shown advantages in the realm of uniform response time for both increasing and decreasing humidity, a lack of hysterisis, and sensitivity to relatively low humidities. Further applications include the measurement of relative humidity over 100 per cent by operation of the instrument at a higher temperature than ambient. [Equation (1) indicates that the ratio P_w/P_T must be kept below unity to prevent n_w from approaching values resulting in bleeding of the liquid phase.]

Finally, it is apparently possible to measure total water content of two- or three-phase systems since it is possible to run the instrument at temperatures above that of the sample intake. For such measurements, it is desirable to bring the sample gas flow to instrument temperature before it enters the porous capacitor. Further, to obtain higher sensitivity in the electronics, temperature-stabilized

circuitry is necessary. To this end, a constant-temperature integrated unit is being built to include a heat exchanger, the capacitor and the electronics.

Another interesting feature of the principle of HYLIF is the dependence of the change in capacitance on the existence of a dipole moment in the detected molecule. Water is not unique in this respect, and it may be possible to detect other polar molecules such as H_2S, HCN, SO_2 and CO under appropriately controlled experimental conditions. All but one molecular species would have to be eliminated prior to its detection by the capacitor. It seems possible to detect hydrocarbons by bringing the desiccated sample gas flow to a high temperature with air to oxidize the organic materials to CO_2 and H_2O. Detection of H_2O then suffices for the determination of combustible organics.

The tentative applications of HYLIF in this laboratory are predominantly meteorological and will include:

(1) The measurement of stratospheric humidity.

(2) The humidity in clouds and in arctic ice fog, both including and excluding solid and liquid water by the use of an electrostatic separator.

(3) The supersaturation at low temperatures upstream from forming cirrus and lenticularis clouds which occurs due to the long formation times of ice particles in such conditions.

(4) Bioclimatological measurements such as the water vapor budget of human beings.

Acknowledgment. Thanks are extended to Professor Buettner and other members of the Atmospheric Sciences Department staff for many helpful discussions and suggestions and to Mr. Sam Antion for his help in the fabrication of apparatus.

References

1. Rigby, Malcolm, *Meteorol. & Geoastrophys. Abstr.*, **13**, 3622 (Dec. 1962).
2. James, A. T., and Martin, A. J. P., *Analyst*, **77**, 915–932 (1952).
3. Pecsok, R. L., ed., "Principles and Practices of Gas Chromatography," New York, John Wiley & Sons, Inc., 1961.
4. Buettner, K. J. K., and Charlson, R. J. *U.S. Patent Application No. 342,381*, February 4, 1964.
5. Charlson, R. J., *Liquid Film Hygrometry*, Doctoral Dissertation, University of Washington, Seattle, June 4, 1964.

60. A Relative Humidity Sensor Based on the Capacitance Variations of a Plastics Film Condenser

David E. Nelson and Elias J. Amdur

Honeywell Inc., Minneapolis, Minnesota

ABSTRACT

The impedance of a condenser to AC may change as a function of its moisture content and temperature. In thin film condensers suitable for use as RH sensors, the impedance variations observed are due to two factors which affect the capacitance of the sensor:

1. Physical changes in thickness or area of the film

2. A change in the dielectric constant of the film.

An RH sensor has been developed which consists of a thin plastic film with evaporated gold electrodes on the faces. The gold electrodes are conductive but quite porous. A number of materials have been investigated in order to determine their suitability for use as the dielectric of this hygrometric system.

Sensors have been produced which are usable from 10 to 100 per cent RH over a temperature range from −35 to 80°C. They show satisfactory stability with time and are not injured by contact with water or certain common contaminants. These sensors show a substantial variation of capacitance with temperature as well as with RH, but this appears to yield to compensation in associated circuitry.

Electronic humidity transducers depend on a change in an electrical parameter of some material as a function of the moisture content and temperature of the space surrounding the transducer. Most of the commercially important transducers utilize surface or volume resistivity. Humidity sensors of this type may be adversely affected by contaminants that increase or inhibit the natural conductivity of the sensor. We believe that this tendency of humidity sensors to change their characteristics with time is one of the most important problems in the field today. Because of this, we feel that any stable sensing system, regardless of complexity, would be an important contribution to the art of humidity measurement and control. We have found one such system which may be used as a capacitive hygrometer.

Capacitive hygrometry is not new. However, it has never been successfully applied on a commercial scale. This is probably due to the lack of a suitable humidity sensitive dielectric and the problems of instrumentation.

The dielectric constant of atmospheric air and of many solid materials is a function of its moisture content and temperature. A simple humidity sensor is an ordinary air dielectric condenser where the capacitance of the condenser is a function of the water content and temperature of the air between the plates. The main disadvantage of this sensor is the relatively small change in capacitance with a change in humidity. One way of increasing this change is to displace the air with a material that will pick up an increased amount of water. There is a wide selection of materials that will work in this manner with varying degrees of success. Nylon was the first material to be tested in our laboratory. The dielectric constant was found to change by a factor of 10 as the RH was increased from 10 to 90 per cent at 25°C. It was also noted that nylon became conductive at the high relative humidities. In other words, the impedance of the condenser developed a large resistive component as the nylon absorbed water. This is undesirable because it complicates the instrumentation and increases the possibility of contamination. In addition, the nylon absorbed a relatively large quantity of water which caused the condenser to respond slowly to changes in humidity.

At this point of our program we were able to list the properties desired for the plastic dielectric and to choose from the available plastic films the material that would give us the best results. These properties are:

(1) Low water absorption, approximately 0.5 per cent equilibrium water absorption for 100 per cent RH. This we determined would cause about a 10 per cent change in dielectric constant which is adequate for instrumentation, but not enough to unduly lengthen the response time.

(2) High water vapor permeability is necessary to insure a rapid response to a change in humidity.

(3) Good strength, resilience, stiffness and resistance to creep in order that the base capacity of the sensor will be stable.

(4) High resistance to chemical attack and a low permeability to contaminating materials.

(5) High volume resistance so that the dissipation factor of the condenser will stay at a low level for all temperature-humidity conditions we wish to sense.

(6) The ability to maintain these properties over a wide range of temperature and humidity.

On comparing this list of ideal characteristics with the literature on available plastics, it soon became apparent that there was one plastic that seemed to best meet our requirements. That plastic is "Delrin",* an acetal resin, which is a crystalline form of highly polymerized formaldehyde.

"Delrin" has the desired level of water absorption and a relatively high permeability to polar compounds such as water. Its crystalline structure makes it a hard material with good resistance to creep. Its chemical and electrical properties are nearly ideal for a sensor of this type. Few chemicals affect it, and it has a high electrical resistance at high levels of temperature and humidity.

Prototype sensors were constructed by in-

* Trademark for E. I. duPont de Nemours & Company.

FIG. 1. Prototype capacitive sensor.

serting a disk of "Delrin" film of approximate one-mil thickness in a mask suitable for gold evaporation. Both sides of the film were then flashed with a layer of gold about 50 Å thick. Gold in this thickness forms a conductive surface, but remains pervious to water vapor. The two layers of gold are the condenser plates. The dielectric is the "Delrin" plastic. Figure 1 is a photograph of a prototype sensor. The "Delrin" film is held between the two cup-shaped halves of the sensor. Electric contact to the film is made at a center post. Three contacts are provided for three-terminal capacitance determinations. The base capacity of the sensor depends on both the thickness of the film and the area of the plates. The physical dimensions of the film are affected by both the amount of water absorbed and the ambient temperature. As a first approximation, the coefficient of linear expansion due to either absorbed water or temperature can be considered to be the same in all three dimensions.

The capacity of a condenser is directly proportional to the area of the plates and inversely proportional to their spacing. Since area increases as the square of the linear expansion and the thickness increases directly with the linear expansion, it is apparent that the capacity of the sensors will increase directly with their linear expansion.

"Delrin" will increase in length by about

.4 per cent at 25°C when subjected to a change in relative humidity of 10 to 90 per cent. An element with a base capacitance of 500 pF would therefore change 2 pF due to the linear expansion caused by the water absorption.

The coefficient of linear thermal expansion of "Delrin" is about 8×10^{-5} per °C. An element with a base capacitance of 500 pF would therefore change 2 pF due to the thermal expansion caused by a temperature change of 50°C.

The dielectric constant of water is much higher than that of dry "Delrin." As "Delrin" absorbs water, its dielectric constant increases. "Delrin," like most materials, absorbs an amount of water that is a function of the ambient relative humidity and temperature. The dielectric constant of "Delrin" as a function of humidity and temperature is presented as Fig. 2. Here it is shown that the dielectric constant varies from about 3.5 at low humidity and temperature to about 4.7 at high humidity and temperature. From this data one can construct the capacitance *vs* relative humidity characteristic for any base capacitance desired. Consider a sensor having a base capacitance of 500 pF. Its 25°C capacitance characteristic as obtained from Fig. 2 is presented as Fig. 3. It is observed that a

change of 10 to 90 per cent in RH causes a change in capacitance of 59 pF. The capacitance change due to the dielectric constant is thus far greater than that caused by dimensional change, and should be considered the primary variable in this type of sensor. The dissipation factor (1000 cycles) for dry "Delrin" is near zero and rises to about 2 per cent at high temperatures and humidities.

A sensor is of practical value only if it is possible to make a number of them with the same characteristic. In pilot production, it has been possible to make groups of four or five sensors at a time that have capacitance characteristics that lie within 2 per cent RH of each other.

The "Delrin" capacitive sensor does not show measurable hysteresis when calibrated at constant temperature. If a sensor is subjected to an increasing and then decreasing RH in 10 per cent steps allowing 20 minutes for stabilization at each point, the decreasing curve will repeat the increasing curve within ½ per cent RH.

The relative humidity time constant is defined as the time required for the sensor to indicate 63 per cent of a step change in relative humidity. The time constant of the capacitive sensor as a function of temperature is pre-

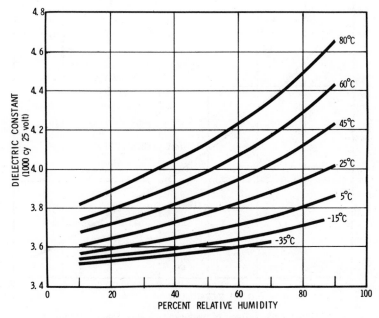

FIG. 2. Characteristic isotherms.

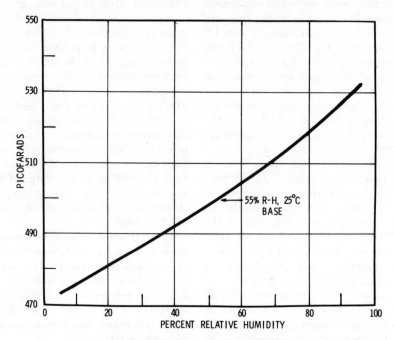

Fig. 3. Characteristic for a 500-picofarad base sensor.

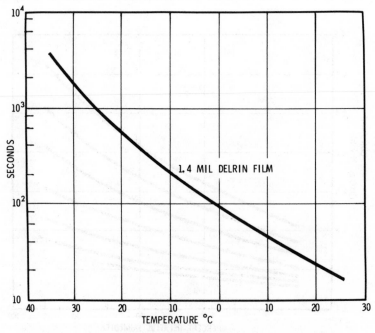

Fig. 4. Time for 63 per cent of response to a step change in humidity.

sented as Figure 4. This data is for a sensor of about 1½ mils thickness. The time constant is about 15 seconds at room temperature and increases to about one hour at −35°C. The response time could be reduced by using a thinner film. Due to the small mass and large area of this sensor, it has a fast response to temperature changes which enables it to follow quite closely a changing ambient condition.

The maximum and minimum operating temperature limits for this sensor have not been determined precisely. Sensors have been calibrated at temperatures as high as 80°C.

Some have been exposed to temperatures as high as 125°C for short periods of time without detrimental effect. While these sensors have less change in capacity for a given change in humidity and are much slower in response at low temperatures, they have been calibrated as low as −35°C.

The capacitive sensor is still in the development stage. The associated readout instrumentation and control devices are being developed. We anticipate that this sensor will take its place among the important transducers in the field of humidity sensing.

61. Properties and Uses of Color Change Humidity Indicators

Bruce G. Blinn

Humidial Company, Colton, California

ABSTRACT

A chemical-type color change relative humidity indicator, that was inexpensive and not easily damaged, proved to be the solution of the problem of indicating dangerous humidity conditions in the storage of critical military inventories.

These indicators, using cobaltous chloride as the basic ingredient, impregnated in blotting paper, are not easily damaged, are stored easily, are a simple go-no-go gauge for simplified reading and are versatile in regard to the many possible variations. Humidity indications from 8 to 80 per cent are possible.

The indicators are placed in, or on, the container that must be observed. When the humidity indicator states that the humidity is dangerous, the container must then be protected further by reactivation of the drying agent, usually a desiccant of the silica gel or dehydrated clay types.

A color guide, used as a color comparison can be printed next to the various indicating color spots for easy reading.

The indicators have a temperature-caused error of 2½ per cent RH for each 10° F away from a base of 75° F. Excessive humidity will damage the indicating color spots by causing the spots to expand.

Even before the second World War there was a need for inexpensive, easily read relative humidity indicators, that could not be damaged by vibration and were not susceptible to loss of calibration. This need was brought to a head during the war, when much damage was caused to our equipment and supplies. Metallic, organic and synthetic materials quickly deteriorated at the high relative humidities in the Pacific and the tropics. There was even fungus damage, which begins at about 65 per cent RH.

We found that the dehydrated package was the most satisfactory protection. We needed an indicator to determine whether the package was sufficiently dehydrated, as it was not a simple matter to prevent leaks in a container or package and the entrance of damaging water vapor, especially in coastal and semi-tropical areas of high humidity.

Changes in atmospheric pressure, as well as expansion and contraction of trapped air within a rigid container, due to the normal day and night temperature cycles, will cause any semi-tight package to breathe. For this reason, a leaky tank stored outdoors will soon reach 100 per cent RH within and will completely saturate any desiccant, unless protective measures are taken.

Today we find improved containers, some of flexible types, with low moisture vapor transmission rates. The amount of dehydrating desiccant needed is computed by a formula, which depends upon the volume of air, the materials packaged, and the MVTR of the barrier.

Although there was an indicating silica gel desiccant in use in the past, it had definite drawbacks since the indicator was not reversible. Once the indicator showed unsafe

602

condition it could only become useful again if the silica gel was reconditioned (by heat or otherwise).

After the war, the color change chemical indicator was developed, which used blotting paper as the vehicle. Using cobalt chloride solutions, with additives, we developed a wide range of humidity indications. The range is as low as 8 per cent and as high as 80 per cent. These indicators can be placed in a package and observed through windows built in the container, or they can be externally viewed by placing the indicator in a metal housing and placing the metal housing in the shell of the container, using gaskets and a locknut or a threaded boss. This is quite a simple matter and it only takes a few seconds to install this plug into the storage container.

These indicators are usually a simple "go-no-go" gauge, such as a "blue color means safe and a pink color means unsafe." In this case, 40 per cent RH is the usual calibration

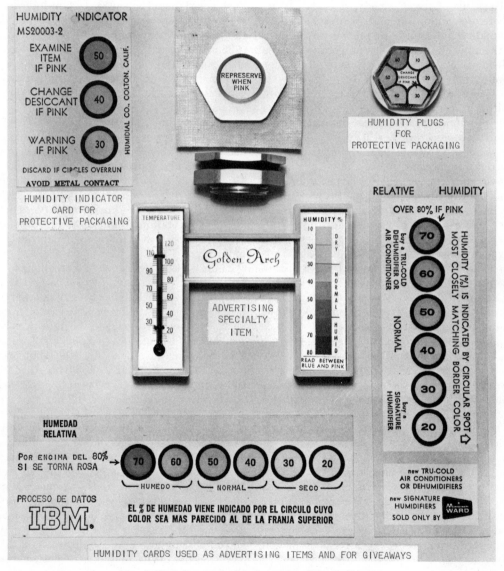

FIG. 1. Varied uses of color change humidity indicators.

indicated. When the humidity is actually 40 per cent the color is lavender, midway between the blue and pink.

Some users, of course, wish other humidities shown and, therefore, these indicators contain several indicating spots that change colors at different humidities.

Since containers which are only semi-tight breathe in cool, damp night air and expel drier air during the heat of the day, we find that the atmospheric condition of the interior of a container can soon reach nearly 100 per cent RH and can easily saturate any desiccant in places like Cape Kennedy, Florida. It is, therefore, quite imperative that accurate humidity indicators are present to indicate dangerous humidities. The properties of these chemical indicators make them suitable for this purpose.

They can be manufactured to be accurate within a 5 per cent RH range. They do not lose their calibration, are as fast acting as usual hair-type indicators, are easily portable, small in size and can be stored indefinitely in airtight containers. All of these advantages have proved the color change humidity indicator, using blotting paper as its vehicle, to be a better packaging indicator than the gel, direct reading or electrical type. Of particular note is the fast-acting aspect of this type of indicator *vs* the gel type. The gel type must become partially saturated with moisture before the indicator will turn pink. This may take many days in a tightly closed package of still air. The card type must only absorb the moisture in the blotting paper.

As regards the reading of the indicator, we again note that when the humidity is below the stated calibration of the particular spot we are observing, the spot will be a distinct blue. When the humidity is higher than this calibration, the spot will be a distinct pink. The bluer the color, the drier is the air, and vice versa.

It takes about a 10 per cent RH range for any spot to turn from a distinct blue to a distinct pink (in between it is lavender). However, with a little practice, an observer may judge the humidity within a 5 per cent range. This accuracy is as great as can be expected, even using expensive hair or coil hygrometers.

Sometimes a permanent color guide is provided with the indicators, so that all a person has to do is match a color with the guide to determine the humidity. The chemical color change type of indicator has several weaknesses, however. If the chemical is placed on the blotting paper so as to form a circular spot, it should not be exposed to over 80 per cent RH for a long period of time, since the chemical will absorb so much water that it will cause the spots to expand and, therefore, cause the calibration to change somewhat. This condition is easily noticed because the spot will expand over its black ink borders. Such a card should be replaced. If the indicator is the fully impregnated type, e.g., covers all the paper and therefore has no place for the chemical solution to expand, then this weakness can be avoided. There is no damage at extremely low humidities. Direct contact with water will damage the spots by leaching out the chemicals.

The indicators, if exposed to extreme heat, prolonged exposure to the sun, and normal outside conditions for six months or over, will turn from a blue indication to a greenish-blue. This, of course, is caused by the yellowing of the blotter paper combining with the blue color of the chemical. This, however, does not affect its calibration. Ammonia and Hydrazine are the only known gases that will damage the indicators.

There is also a temperature correction, as is common with most humidity indicators. This temperature correction has been calculated to be $2\frac{1}{2}$ per cent RH for each 10° away from 75°F. In other words, should the indicators be read at 55°F there will be a 5 per cent error in the indication of the spot. The spot will appear to be pinker than it should be. At 95°F, the indicator will register a 5 per cent error and will be bluer than the spot would be.

There appear to be many more applications of the color change humidity indicator than the simple storage indicator. We have already noted that the indicators may be placed in a metal plug, thereby eliminating the need of installing a window in the container, or of opening a container to look inside at the card. This plug may also be designed to hold desiccant, thus this one piece of hardware may act as a dehydrator and indicator. In this case, the indicating plug can be designed so that it can indicate both the relative humidity of the air within the container and the condition of the desiccant. Both of these indications may be viewed from outside the container.

These plugs may also be designed so that they can be used as a free breather to equalize pressures caused by changes in atmospheric pressure when the container is flown from location to location. (Air passes through the desiccant.)

It must be noted here that the humidity indicator should be located in a shaded position in the lower or middle portion of any container, since the humidity within a container will vary from top to bottom when exposed to the sun or heat.

This type of indicator can also have commercial uses, where inexpensive humidity indicators are effective as an advertising specialty giveaway, such as showing the need for the purchase of a humidifier or dehumidifier. Wherever humidity is important, these indicators are an inexpensive, and yet accurate answer, within 5 per cent humidity.

There have been many instances where these indicators have been used with thermometers to provide useful home weather instruments. The uses are as varied as the imagination.

62. Accurate Hygrometry with Ionic Single Crystals

R. G. WYLIE

National Standards Laboratory, C.S.I.R.O., Sydney, Australia

ABSTRACT

An outline is given of a method of hygrometry utilizing ionic single crystals, the physical basis of which was described by the author in 1957. The main problems involved in the design of the apparatus are considered, and three forms which have been used, including that now being produced commercially, are described. The evolution and characteristics of the control system by which the apparatus is operated automatically are considered briefly. In appendices, the use of carbon dioxide to provide continuous low levels of cooling, and the use of tapered solid sections to achieve a more rapid propagation of temperature changes in parts of the apparatus, are outlined.

Examples are given of recorded changes in humidity. One shows the response of the instrument to small step changes, and another the temperature dependence of the evolution of water vapor from the wall of a rubber tube.

INTRODUCTION

In 1957 the author described a new type of hygrometer utilizing ionic single crystals.* In two papers,[1,2] the general features of the method have been described, and the observed behavior of single crystals of potassium chloride has been reported in some detail. However, no account has been given of the

---

* The term "electrolytic condensation hygrometer" was originally proposed; at the National Standards Laboratory the hygrometer is usually referred to as the E.C.H. The commercial version is known by the name of the author.

apparatus or techniques which have been used, or of the design of the hygrometer developed for commercial production. Some details of these aspects are included in the present outline.

The following sections deal with the relevant properties of ionic single crystals, the forms of the hygrometers which have been developed and the design of the control system by which they are operated automatically, as well as some aspects of the performance. The use of carbon dioxide for continuous cooling and the characteristics of tapered solid sections as regards the propagation of temperature disturbances, both of which are exploited in some designs of the hygrometer, are considered in appendices.

SOME PROPERTIES OF IONIC SINGLE CRYSTALS

Ideally, the surface of an ionic single crystal begins to dissolve in water taken from the surrounding gas if the vapor pressure of the water in that gas is raised above the equilibrium vapor pressure of a saturated solution of the crystal substance at the particular temperature. At this critical vapor pressure, a thin layer of saturated solution can remain quiescent on the crystal surface. At higher vapor pressures it grows, and at lower pressures it diminishes, in thickness. Essentially the same phenomena occur if the pressure of the surrounding vapor is constant and the temperature is varied, and this is essentially what happens in the hygrometer.

It is more convenient to think in terms of

relative humidity, and the principle can be re-stated as follows. The equilibrium relative humidities of the saturated solutions of suitable crystal substances do not depend greatly on temperature, but the relative humidity of a vapor of constant pressure can be adjusted to any desired value simply by adjusting the temperature. Thus, when the crystal is surrounded by a gas of constant water vapor pressure, an equilibrium temperature T_e can be found at which a thin layer of saturated solution, formed on the surface, will be of unchanging thickness. Changes in the thickness can be detected by observing the electrical conductance of the layer. In the hygrometer, the temperature is adjusted until the electrical resistance of the crystal surface is constant, and in the automatic hygrometer the temperature is continuously varied to keep this resistance constant. As the vapor pressure of a gas passing over the crystal is varied over a considerable range, the equilibrium temperature T_e varies over a considerable range, and for any observed value of T_e, a corresponding dew-point temperature can be derived.

A striking demonstration of the speed with which the conducting layer forms can be given by supporting a crystal of 1- or 2-mm size by spring pressure between electrode strips connected to a resistance indicator. When the crystal (say, of photographers' hypo) is introduced through the neck of a flask into the air space over a water surface, the resistance falls in a second or two to less than one megohm (MΩ) and continues to fall rapidly. The demonstration works best if the edges of the crystal parallel to the electrodes are coated as described in the next paragraph.

A detailed account of the properties of potassium chloride crystal elements has been given earlier,[2] but an outline of the principal properties is desirable here. Workable layer thicknesses lie between a value of about 100 Å, for which the detailed structure of the surface begins to play a dominant role, and a value of several thousand angstroms, for which gravity and surface tension forces drain the layer from the surface at a significant rate. If the layer is too thin (i.e., the electrical resistance maintained is too high), the local curvature of the liquid, which is then in the form of tiny fillets located at steps which inevitably exist on the surface, leads to errors by causing a lowering

of the equilibrium vapor pressure, and the equilibrium temperature is too high. If the layer is too thick, then a steady dissolution of the crystal occurs in order to replenish the loss due to drainage and due to flow under surface tension forces, and the apparent equilibrium temperature is too low. For accurate work, continuity of the layer across the edges of the crystal cannot be assumed, and the edges are provided with a thin coating of gold or other conducting material, which contacts the supporting electrodes.

Unless the crystal is substantially contaminated with water-soluble matter or the crystal surface is insufficiently flat, the equilibrium temperature is substantially independent of layer thickness over about a decade variation in thickness. When steady conditions have been achieved for a layer thickness (or electrical resistance) in the desirable working range, then for equilibrium temperatures not much below 0°C, an absolute accuracy of 0.01°C can be obtained, and the automatic instrument can accommodate small changes in humidity in a matter of seconds.

Figure 1 shows the recorded temperature of a system consisting of a crystal of potassium chloride in a gas of constant dew point 0°C, for a succession of step changes in resistance. In this case a resistance of 1 MΩ corresponds approximately to a layer thickness of 180 Å. For resistances below about 1 MΩ, the temperature has come to the true equilibrium value within 0.01°C. For the lower resistances, the time required to achieve conditions steady to 0.01°C, after switching from one resistance setting to a substantially different setting, bears little relationship to the response time of the hygrometer for variations in humidity. The former is determined by the speed with which the surface layer takes up a stable distribution under the influence of surface tension forces, while the latter, which is accompanied only by rapid transient changes in resistance, is much more a matter of the dynamics of the control system.

One of the features of the method is the degree of freedom represented by the free choice of the operating level of electrical resistance. Proof of correct operation is given by the observation that substantially the same equilibrium temperature T_e is obtained for each of two or more resistance values. It has

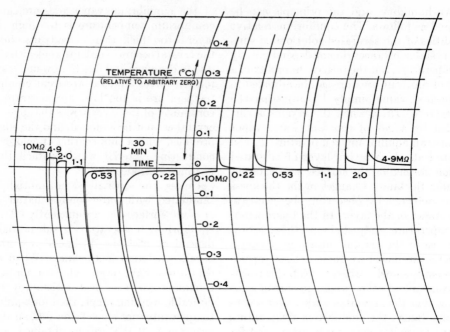

Fig. 1. A record of the temperature of a system comprising a crystal of potassium chloride and a surrounding gas of constant dew-point 0°C, when the surface resistance of the crystal is caused to take the sequence of values shown, by the imposition of temperature changes. A resistance of 1 MΩ corresponds to a surface layer of saturated solution approximately 180 Å thick.

been found that when an excessive amount of soluble contaminant is present, the observed equilibrium temperature, obtained for three or more resistances, can be extrapolated to zero resistance to give the true T_e with reasonable accuracy, zero resistance corresponding to infinite dilution of the impurity. Surface contaminants, like oleic acid, are practically without effect in small quantities.

It will be clear that to take full advantage of the method an automatic instrument must be used, but even with manual balancing the method is superior to the dew-point method.

THE DESIGN OF THE HYGROMETER

Some General Considerations

The hygrometer must accommodate the crystal in a flow of gas under isothermal conditions in such a way that the temperature can be varied automatically in response to deviations of the crystal resistance from a set value. A number of design problems are involved, especially if the instrument is to be of rapid response. To achieve the most rapid response,

use has been made of tapered sections to speed the propagation of temperature disturbances in a solid component, an innovation which is outlined in Appendix II.

The problems involved in obtaining a satisfactory steady-state temperature distribution and those associated with the dynamical behavior are in two distinct groups. A steady flux of heat through the parts of the instrument can result in differences in temperature between the crystal, the gas flowing over it, and the thermometer. A compact copper or, more usually, silver body about 3 cm in size has been used as the basis of the design. A steady flux of heat of the order of 1 watt must be exchanged between the heater and the cooling system, while the heater must be in very close relationship to the crystal and to certain parts of the body for dynamical reasons. A heat flux of 1 watt transmitted between opposite faces of a 3-cm silver cube produces a temperature difference of approximately 0.1°C, a result which shows that considerable care is necessary in determining the geometrical arrangement.

The requirements for a satisfactory steady-state temperature distribution and for dynamical properties compatible with stable and rapid automatic operation are somewhat in conflict. A consequence is that it is difficult to obtain a design for the metal body which will give a high performance and yet is easy to make, and in the three designs described below, performance is in inverse proportion to constructional difficulty.

The main dynamical considerations relate to the propagation of temperature disturbances in the body itself. Another consideration is the transient adsorption (or desorption) of water vapor at metal surfaces in the temperature equalizer passages, and elsewhere, which occurs with temperature change, transiently altering the concentration of the water vapor in the gas passing over the crystal. For this effect to be small, the metal surfaces must be clean.

The part of the apparatus envisaged in the preceding paragraphs has been termed the thermal unit. In addition, the hygrometer as a whole includes an electronic unit, which for automatic operation has usually been constructed to provide indication of the actual (as distinct from the set) crystal resistance and indication of the temperature, as well as automatic balancing.

Some Forms of the Thermal Unit

Three forms will be described: first, a relatively simple instrument suitable for manual and semi-automatic operation to about 0.1°C in the dew point; second, the instrument used to obtain the results published earlier (including those of Fig. 1), and finally the instrument which is being made commercially.

The manual instrument is shown in section in Fig. 2. A copper or silver body B, in the form of a solid of revolution, is set in foamed plastic thermal insulation TI and provides an isothermal enclosure for the crystal C, which, if a

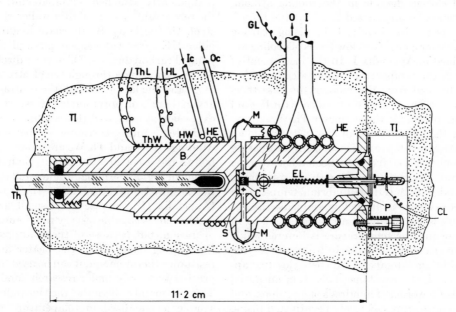

FIG. 2. Cross-sectional view of the thermal unit of a hygrometer suitable for manual operation.

B	copper or silver body		Ic	refrigerant inlet
C	crystal		M	distribution space (manifold)
CL	crystal electrode lead		O	gas sample outlet
EL	electrode assembly		Oc	refrigerant outlet
GL	ground lead		P	electrode plug
HE	temperature equalizer or heat exchanger		S	silver disc (if body is copper)
HL	heater winding leads		Th L	resistance thermometer leads
HW	heater winding		Th W	resistance thermometer winding
I	gas sample inlet		TI	thermal insulation

copper body is used, sits on a silver disc S soldered to the body. The gas sample flows in continuously at I and out at O, passing through the temperature equalizing coil HE, and the manifold comprising the space M and the small radial holes shown. The crystal is held in position by spring pressure of the electrode EL which is incorporated in the plug P. The plug is sealed by an O-ring and is itself held firmly in the body by spring fittings.

The body is cooled by passage of a refrigerant through the heat exchanger coil HE; it is heated electrically by means of the winding of fine, insulated copper wire HW. A somewhat similar winding, Th W, serves as a resistance thermometer. This can be used as the sensing element, when the temperature of the body is controlled automatically, to provide what may be termed semi-automatic operation. Carbon dioxide (gas or liquid) expanded from cylinder pressure is the most convenient refrigerant, and to prevent the formation of solid carbon dioxide in the cooling system, this must be pressurized to about 100 $lb/in.^2$. The principles involved in using carbon dioxide for continuous low levels of cooling are outlined in Appendix I. In the instrument of Fig. 2, the temperature, when steady, either can be read from the mercury-in-glass thermometer Th or can be obtained with the aid of the resistance thermometer Th W.

In the simplest use of the instrument, an electrical resistance indicator using alternating current at a low level is connected between the central electrode and the body, which is grounded (GL). If the equilibrium temperature T_e is assumed to be below ambient, the gas sample is set flowing at a rate of, say, 2 to 10 cc/sec, and the temperature is lowered while the resistance indicator is watched. As the equilibrium temperature is closely approached, the resistance falls from an initial level of the order of hundreds of megohms, and the temperature can easily be adjusted (using the CO_2 expansion value, or with this at a constant setting, using the heater) until the indicated resistance is in the desired range and constant. The temperature can then be read. For the best accuracy, the balance should be held until the initial small drift of the temperature (see Fig. 1) disappears.

These operations are rather similar to those performed in using a dew-point hygrometer, but there are two important differences. One is that a steady balance can be maintained with only small accidental deviations, and the other is that the resistance value which is held can be chosen by the operator. Subjectively, there is little comparison between the methods. The present instrument is pleasant to operate and induces little fatigue in the operator.

The penalties for the simplicity of the design of Fig. 2 are inaccuracies due to heat flow in the body and, of course, lack of suitability of the design for automatic operation.

The instrument shown in part sections in Fig. 3 is that with which the data of Fig. 1 were obtained. It has features analogous to those of the manual instrument, and in the Figure they are lettered correspondingly. The gas sample is introduced into a set of holes parallel to the axis, via a manifold unit M, the associated tubes of which push into the body, plug-in fashion. The tubes of this unit, and those of the permanently attached manifold unit Mc for the refrigerant gas, are of thin-walled stainless steel. In the body B, alternate longitudinal holes HE carry the gas sample and the expanded carbon dioxide. The former discharges to the atmosphere through the electrode plug at O, and the latter through the central space at Oc; there is no provision for pressurizing the expansion system, and this is a limitation.

Heater and resistance thermometer windings, HW and Th W, are wound on the body, and to a greater extent than in the design of Fig. 2, use is made of tapered sections to transmit temperature changes more rapidly (Appendix II). Because of its small size, the instrument is capable of very rapid automatic operation, but because of the relationship of the cooling channels to the heater and the resistance thermometer, it can be used for very precise work only under research conditions. This is mainly because the incoming gas sample is equalized in temperature with a section of the silver body not at the same temperature as the crystal bed or the resistance thermometer.

The effect is practically eliminated in the design of Fig. 4, which shows the instrument produced commercially. Again, the lettering has the same significance as in Fig. 2. The detail of the design is such that a purely local exchange of heat occurs between each section

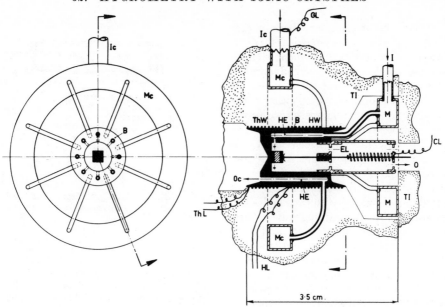

FIG. 3. The thermal unit used in the original investigational work with potassium chloride crystals. The symbols have the same meaning as in Fig. 2, but B is a silver body, and Mc is a coolant-gas manifold.

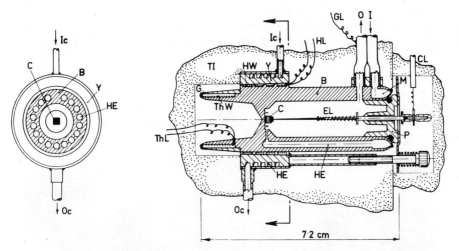

FIG. 4. The thermal unit of the instrument which is made commercially. The symbols have the same meaning as in Fig. 2, but B is a silver body and Y is a cooling yoke.

of the heater and the two ribs which border it. A further feature is the thermal guard ring G provided over the resistance-thermometer winding Th W. This is joined to the thermometer former at the end by an annular ring of insulating material, providing a gas space over the thermometer winding which can be sealed. The silver body B has tapered sections to speed the propagation of temperature changes.

It should be emphasized that the speed of response and the dynamical behavior of the instrument depend very largely on the distances separating the center of the heater, the crystal and the resistance thermometer, and on the shapes of the sections connecting these parts. In terms defined in Appendix II, in Fig. 4 the crystal is connected thermally to the region of the heater winding by a spherical taper, while the resistance thermometer winding is supported on a cylindrical taper.

The design not only has excellent steady-state properties but also good dynamical characteristics. Other properties which it possesses to a greater degree than either of the other designs are a low flow resistance to the gas sample (a pressure drop of 0.5-mm water gauge for a flow rate of 1 cc/sec), a low corrodibility of the gas-sample circuit, and easy access to the crystal.

Figure 5(a) shows the unit of Fig. 4 incorporated in its housing, with carbon dioxide expansion and pressure retaining valves V and PV, temperature equalizer ring and (not shown) provision for flushing out the top cavity with a slow flow of exhausted carbon dioxide to prevent the condensation of atmospheric moisture in the instrument. The complete unit of Fig. 5 is referred to as the thermal unit. The whole apparatus, comprising the thermal unit and the associated electronic unit, is shown in operation in Fig. 5(b). A potentiometric recorder is usually connected to the electronic unit, to provide, in effect, a continuous record of dew-point temperature; the recorder is not shown in the photograph.

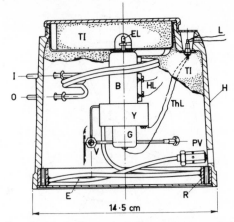

FIG. 5. (a) A diagram of the whole commercial thermal unit, complete with housing H, carbon dioxide expansion and pressure retaining valves V and PV, and temperature equalizer ring R to which the carbon dioxide exhaust line E is attached.

Automatic Operation and the Electronic Unit

Although constancy of the crystal resistance, and not the establishment of any particular value, is the primary criterion for equilibrium, this criterion is satisfied if the crystal resistance is brought to, and held, at a

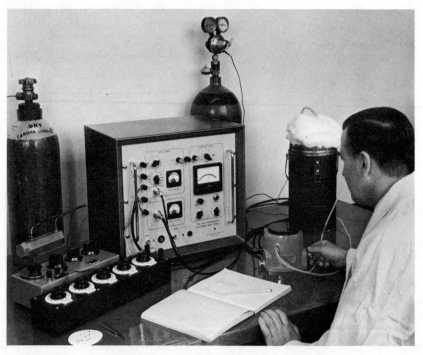

FIG. 5. (b) View of the hygrometer in operation.

more or less arbitrarily selected value. If the heater power is made proportional to the deviation of the actual crystal resistance from the set value, and if oscillation does not result, the temperature will come to the equilibrium value T_e. No "droop" or "load error" can exist, because the actual crystal conductance depends on the time-integral of the deviation of the temperature from T_e, so that even the smallest errors are corrected, in time.

The system just described can at best be made marginally stable. The hygrometer has been operated in that manner with the use of phase-lead sections in the control loop, but the resulting behavior is undesirable. The basic difficulty is that a sinusoidal disturbance is retarded in phase by almost $\pi/2$ in the step

Heater Input → Temperature Change
of the Body

while a further retardation of $\pi/2$ occurs in the integrating process

Change of Crystal Temperature
→ Change of Crystal Conductance.

The system approximates what is generally termed an inherently unstable servo system. This is overcome by greatly reducing the first of these phase retardations through use of what is, in effect, a negative feedback subsidiary loop. This must be electrothermal and not purely electrical in character. It is conveniently provided by making the heater power dependent on the temperature, as detected by the resistance thermometer, as well as on the crystal resistance.

The resulting system is shown as a block diagram in Fig. 6. Consideration of the system will show that the actual resistance of the crystal at balance depends on the balance temperature T_e itself (measured relative to the balance point of the resistance thermometer bridge). For technological reasons which cannot be given here, this results in a restriction of the dew-point range which can be covered automatically for any one setting of the controls. The restriction can be greatly relaxed if an electrical link, differentiating with respect to time, is introduced into the secondary control loop, a feature indicated in Fig. 6 as being an alternative. Unfortunately, this feature very considerably complicates the

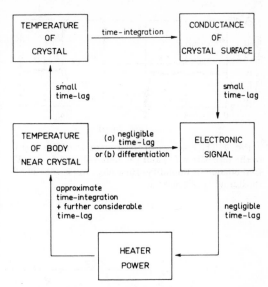

FIG. 6. Functional block diagram of the control system which provides rapid automatic balancing.

detail of the electronic unit. The actual crystal resistance at balance no longer depends on the balance temperature. Electronic units both with and without the feature are being made commercially; that shown in Fig. 5(b) is of the simpler form.

It is worth mentioning that the same type of secondary control loop could be used to stabilize automatic dew-point hygrometers, which present an at least nominally similar control problem. The heater power would be made dependent on both the photoelectric response and the temperature.

The use of the system of Fig. 6 with the present hygrometer gives not only stable but very rapid operation. Nyquist diagrams have been computed for the whole system by regarding the silver body of the thermal unit as being made up of sections for which calculation is feasible, and making other suitable approximations. The results are in general agreement with the observed behavior. In particular, two modes of instability of rather different frequency are predicted, and these have been observed in practice.

CONCLUSION

In conclusion, two examples of the recording of humidity changes with the apparatus will be given. In each case an apparatus of the

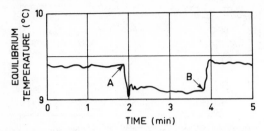

FIG. 7. The response of the apparatus of Fig. 5 (b) to the imposition (A) and the removal (B) of a small step change in humidity. Basically, the record is of the humidity of room air.

ment can follow small changes. A piece of ordinary rubber tube about a foot long was incorporated in a line carrying gas of dew point 0°C to the hygrometer. The flow rate was approximately 5 cc/sec. The more or less steady efflux of water vapor from the rubber has increased the reading from the level of the broken line. When the rubber tube is warmed by clasping with the hand (at points H), a rapid increase in the efflux of vapor from the rubber occurs, and recovery follows when the tube is released (at points R). Each recovery

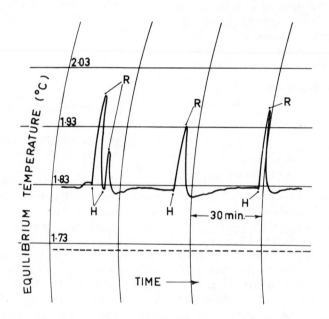

FIG. 8. The effect of warming a short length of rubber tube which is carrying gas of dew point 0°C to the apparatus. The apparent equilibrium temperature has been elevated from the level of the broken line by moisture emerging from the rubber. The tube was warmed in the hand at points H and released at points R. The gas flow rate was approximately 5 cc/sec.

type shown in Fig. 5(b) has been used, the crystals having been of potassium chloride.

Figure 7 shows the response of the hygrometer to the application of a step-function change in humidity and its removal. The change was produced by injecting a stream of dry nitrogen into a rapid flow of air from which the hygrometer was taking a sample.

Figure 8 shows a record obtained in a demonstration of the way in which the instru-

is followed by a transient period in which the efflux is at a lower rate. Obviously, the use of rubber tube in such a situation should normally be avoided.

References

1. Wylie, R. G., "A New Absolute Method of Hygrometry. I," *Australian J. Phys.*, **10**, 351 (1957).
2. Wylie, R. G., "A New Absolute Method of Hygrometry. II," *Australian J. Phys.*, **10**, 429 (1957).

Appendix I

Continuous Cooling Using Gaseous or Liquid Carbon Dioxide

The continuous expansion of carbon dioxide from commercial cylinders provides a convenient source of continuous cooling for the hygrometer described in the text. Below the critical temperature of approximately 31°C, gaseous and liquid phases are both present in the cylinder, the one being delivered with the cylinder in an erect position and the other if the cylinder is inverted. For a cooling power of the order of 1 watt, a very fine expansion valve is needed, especially when the liquid is used. The hygrometer has usually been used with a needle of included angle 7 degrees operating in a hole 0.5 mm in diameter, the spindle being provided with an 80 TPI thread. The kinetic energy imparted to the gas is negligible and the expansion occurs at constant enthalpy. To see the course which the expansion takes, and the need for a pressure-retaining valve downstream of the needle valve, reference may be made to Fig. 9.

The figure shows a thermodynamic diagram for carbon dioxide,[1] plotted with rectangular axes for temperature and entropy. Curvilinear coordinates are given for pressure and enthalpy. With an initial temperature of 20°C, for purposes of illustration, the liquid and gas in the cylinder are in states represented respectively by the points A and A′. Expansion of the liquid to atmospheric pressure is represented by the heavy broken line ABC. It is seen that the result is a mixture comprising 70 per cent gaseous and 30 per cent solid carbon dioxide at a temperature of approximately −78°C. Such an expansion is unsatisfactory because of the formation of solid, which causes blockages and an irregular flow. Even if gas is drawn from the cylinder, so that the line A′B′C′ is followed, a little solid is formed, and the flow is not reliable. If, on the other hand, the liquid is expanded to a pressure in excess of the triple-point pressure of approximately 5.3 atm, no solid can be formed. Thus, for approximately 8 atm the line AB is followed, and as heat is absorbed, the liquid sprayed through the valve is evaporated along the line BB′ and the gas is then heated along B′D. Likewise, for the same pressure, gas expansion follows the course A′B′D, the carbon dioxide expanded at the valve containing several per cent of liquid spray.

If the gas is exhausted from the hygrometer at 0°C, for example, then the cooling available per gram of carbon dioxide is approximately 55 calories if the liquid is used or 18 calories if the gas is used, the cylinder being at 20°C. The diagram shows that the expansion of the gas from 8 atm to 1 atm produces only a small additional cooling effect; of course, no effect at all would be obtained with a perfect gas.

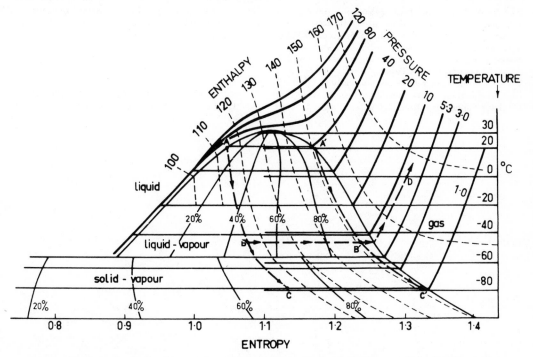

FIG. 9. A thermodynamic diagram for carbon dioxide, illustrating the use of the liquid or gas to provide continuous low levels of cooling. Basic diagram adapted from Plank and Kuprianoff.[1]

To obtain a smooth expansion, it is necessary for the carbon dioxide to be clean and extremely dry, especially if the liquid is used. Nominally dry carbon dioxide may be put through granulated calcium carbide before expansion, to remove traces of moisture.

Reference

1. Plank, R., and Kuprianoff, J., "Thermal Properties of Carbon Dioxide in the Gaseous, Liquid and Solid States," *Z. Ges. Kalte-Ind. Beihefte*, **1**, 1 (1929).

Appendix II

The Propagation of Temperature Disturbances Along Solids of Tapered Section

The propagation of a temperature disturbance along a solid of decreasing cross-sectional area occurs more rapidly than along a uniform bar. The rate depends on the way in which the cross-sectional area A varies with distance, and it is possible to show that, given a particular form, it is always possible to prescribe another form along which propagation is still more rapid. A practical limit is set once it is specified that at the end of the solid a given thermal load must be carried. The optimum form for the most rapid transmittance of a disturbance to a given load at a prescribed distance may not be known, but it will be obvious how large the load can be without greatly affecting the result.

Consider that the cross-sectional area A varies with distance x as

$$A = (-x)^m$$

The greater speed of propagation for more rapid tapers (greater m) can be illustrated with well-known results for $m = 0$, 1 and 2. The first case corresponds to a uniform bar, while the second and third include respectively a sector of a cylinder (wedge) and a sector of a sphere (cone). Tapers for which $m = 1$ and 2 may, therefore, be referred to generally as cylindrical and spherical tapers. Results for the propagation of disturbances resulting from an applied step-function change in temperature are given for the cylinder and the sphere by Carslaw and Jaeger.[1] Half the ultimate change occurs at the apex of a spherical taper in roughly one-third the time it takes to occur at the end of a uniform bar of the same length. The time for the cylindrical taper is intermediate and closer to the value for the spherical taper.

The transfer function, which expresses the change in amplitude and phase of a propagated sinusoidal temperature disturbance as a complex number, is in general expressible in terms of Bessel's functions of order $n = (m - 1)/2$ which have the complex argument $x(\omega/iD)^{1/2}$, where ω is the angular frequency and D is the thermal diffusivity. Tables of these functions are available for isolated values of n.

If the tapered section is itself a substantial load on another section, then, for purposes of deriving a Nyquist diagram, it becomes necessary to know the thermal impedances of the connecting ends, which are derivable after calculating the spatial derivatives of the transfer functions. The necessary functions are readily available for a uniform bar, a cylindrical taper, and a spherical taper.

Reference

1. Carslaw, H. S., and Jaeger, J. C., "Conduction of Heat in Solids," Oxford, Clarendon Press, 1959.

63. The Mode of Operation of Saturation Temperature Hygrometers Based on Electrical Detection of a Salt-solution Phase Transition

David E. Nelson and E. J. Amdur

Honeywell Inc., Minneapolis, Minnesota

ABSTRACT

When a salt crystal is exposed to water vapor at a relative humidity below that of its phase transition, the electrical resistance of its surface will be very high. As the relative humidity increases to that corresponding to the initiation of a liquid phase on the surface of the crystal, the electrical resistance will decrease rapidly. This resistance decrease may be reversed by heating to reduce the ambient relative humidity. Two forms of hygrometers which are based on this phenomenon are: (1) a form in which the resistance of a salt is held constant by heating or cooling the sample and salt by external means controlled from the measured resistance, and (2) a form in which a salt with a low phase transition relative humidity is used and AC electrical current is furnished to a bobbin covered with cloth containing the salt so that it and the air sample immediately in contact with it are brought to the phase transition by resistive heating and are maintained there by a self-regulatory mechanism. In each case, the temperature attained is related to the ambient vapor pressure or dew point.

The mode of operation of the self-regulating form of hygrometer is discussed in greater detail. A plot of relative humidity vs bobbin resistance is introduced and the effect of salt content is indicated. This basic curve is used to show how "droop," the variation of control point with load, varies with ambient temperature, air velocity, and pressure at constant ambient humidity.

Since lithium chloride is the most common salt used in self-heating phase transition hygrometers, the phase diagram of the water-lithium chloride system is introduced to explain peculiarities in the operation of these devices at certain ambient humidity levels.

INTRODUCTION

The equilibrium vapor pressure of water as a function of the temperature of a coexisting plane condensed phase under isothermal conditions is very accurately known over a wide range of temperature. This relationship has been used as the basis for the classical dew-point hygrometer which is essentially an experiment to determine the temperature at which the water vapor in a space will reach saturation on a cooling surface. Other methods of equal validity are based on the properties of hygroscopic salts, and it is the purpose of this paper to show that these methods are related to condensation procedures and to discuss the mode of operation and certain peculiarities of one form of dew-point hygrometer based on the electrical detection of a salt-solution phase transition.

VAPOR PRESSURE OF WATER-SALT SOLUTIONS

One effect of dissolving a salt in water is to depress the vapor pressure of the water. In very dilute solutions of highly ionized salts the resulting depression may be computed from Raoult's law by applying suitable activity coefficients. In very concentrated solutions, the effects become complex, but the depression of vapor pressure remains a function of the salt concentration. In systems where the solution, a solid phase of the salt, and water vapor coexist in isothermal equilibrium, the vapor pressure depression reaches its limit. Figure 1 shows the water vapor pressure-*vs*-temperature curves of saturated solutions of several salts. Because of the complexity of the theory of concentrated solutions, vapor pressure curves of saturated solutions must be experimentally determined.

THE BASIS OF SALT HYGROMETRY

Figure 2 shows the vapor pressure *vs* temperature curves of water and of saturated lithium chloride solution, maintained saturated by the presence of the solid phase. The condition at point A is selected for purposes of illustration. If the vapor pressure of the space is decreased to point B by pumping or flowing dry gas over the condensed phases, the water will evaporate and the dry phase will remain. If the vapor pressure is increased to point C by adding vapor or flowing high relative humidity gas over the condensed phases, moisture will condense into the solution, the solid salt will dissolve, and a solution will remain.

The condensed phases may be retained at equilibrium when the vapor pressure of the vapor phase is changed if the system is heated or cooled to the temperature which places the new vapor pressure on the equilibrium curve of Fig. 2 (points D and E). The temperature at which equilibrium is reestablished indicates the vapor pressure at the new vapor phase condition. This procedure is the basis for phase transition hygrometry and is completely analogous to cold mirror hygrometry in which the temperature corresponding to a predetermined moisture film condition is used as the basis for determination of the vapor pressure. In one case, the vapor pressure-temperature relationship of pure water is used for the computation and in the other case one uses the vapor pressure-temperature equilibrium of a saturated salt system. It is also apparent that the salt-solution transition temperature may be readily converted to the conventional "dew-point" temperature by proceeding on a constant vapor pressure line until intersecting the curve for pure water and

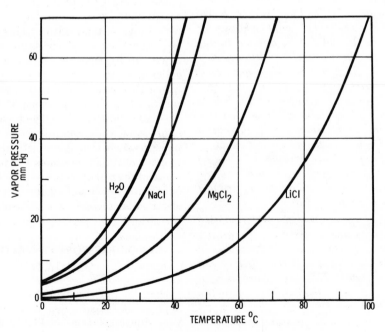

FIG. 1. Pressure-temperature curves.

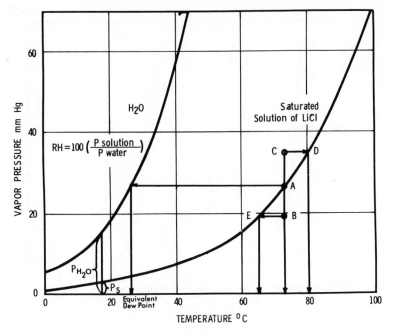

FIG. 2. Pressure-temperature diagram for H_2O and LiCl.

then proceeding down to the temperature axis. This is commonly done because the dew point is a generally recognized reporting form for humidity.

DETECTION OF TRANSITION EQUILIBRIUM

No simple method of determining the stability of the solid and liquid phases of a salt system exists when they are both present in massive form. However, it is relatively easy to detect when the solid dry salt is barely wetted by solution. The dry salt shows a high electrical resistance which falls rapidly when the solution begins to form. The equilibrium conditions which may be detected and maintained are therefore those which correspond to conveniently measured electrical resistance values between that of the dry salt and that of the solution formed when the salt dissolves completely.

Practical hygrometers based on this detection procedure are (1) those in which the salt is placed in a gas sampling chamber, the temperature of which may be externally controlled to maintain the desired equilibrium condition[1] and (2) the form in which the

equilibrium salt temperature is determined by self heating through the application of electrical current sufficient to maintain the salt temperature against heat losses to the surroundings.[2]

SELF-HEATING PHASE TRANSITION HYGROMETERS

Figure 2 reveals that the ratio of the vapor pressure over a saturated salt solution to that for pure water at the same temperature is the relative humidity of the vapor phase of a saturated solution-vapor system. This characteristic relative humidity of a saturated salt solution may be independent of temperature, or it may be some function of temperature.

Figure 3 shows typical curves of the change in resistance of salts with relative humidity, determined at constant temperature with the Honeywell two-pressure humidity atmosphere producer.[3] In these cases a drop of concentrated salt solution was allowed to evaporate between 2-mm diameter gold ball electrodes spaced about 1 mm apart, leaving an unoriented crystal mass. It will be seen that as the relative humidity of the surrounding air is increased to the phase transition of the salt,

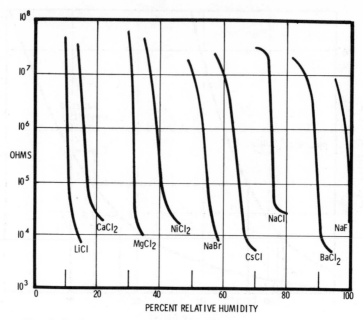

FIG. 3. Typical resistance characteristics for various salts (25°C).

the resistance falls through several decades in each case. Any of these salts may be used in hygrometers utilizing external temperature control to maintain the salt specimen at constant resistance, since either heating or cooling may be provided. Lithium chloride is the only salt widely used in self heating hygrometers because in these devices only heating is available and selection of a salt having a transition at a higher relative humidity results in a restricted range of usefulness. Lithium chloride permits the use of these instruments in atmospheres where the relative humidity exceeds approximately 11 per cent.

The bobbin of a lithium chloride self-heated hygrometer is shown in Fig. 4. Such bobbins are prepared by winding bifilar electrodes on an inert fabric sleeve over an inert bobbin. The fabric is subsequently treated with a salt solution and dried. The resistance is measured between the wire electrodes.

These bobbins are made by each manufacturer in standard sizes and of standardized materials and therefore in still air have defined heat transfer coefficients by convection and radiation to the surroundings. The amount of power necessary to maintain each design of bobbins at their equilibrium temperature in still air of a given vapor pressure is therefore fixed. At a given power level and applied voltage, the operating resistance of the bobbin is determined by these factors.

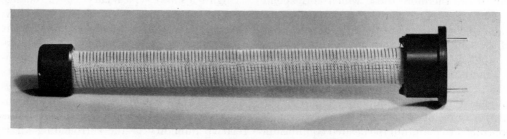

FIG. 4. Typical dew-probe bobbin.

Figure 5 shows that while the change in bobbin resistance is very great at the phase transition, the slope of the curve never becomes vertical, which has considerable effect on the behavior of self-heating hygrometers under practical operating conditions.

EFFECT OF SALT CONTENT ON BOBBIN TEMPERATURE

The bobbin of the self-heating hygrometer is treated with a lithium chloride solution which may be dried before insertion in the apparatus or after insertion by application of the operating current. The concentration of the treating solution may be varied over wide limits, and the amount of solution applied will vary somewhat with the application method. The amount of lithium chloride on the operating bobbin is therefore subject to wide variation. Figure 6 indicates schematically the effect of this variable. It will be seen that increasing the solution will lower the resistance curve while decreasing the salt content will raise it. The curves shown are those for a constant ambient temperature equal to the equilibrium temperature. Since the bobbin is at equilibrium only at one resistance value, it does not follow these curves precisely as it

approaches equilibrium, but the closer it approaches the equilibrium resistance value the more exactly these curves indicate the actual conditions. Since the bobbin configuration, the heat loss conditions, and the applied voltage are fixed the bobbin must operate at constant resistance regardless of salt concentration. The effect of varying the salt content of the bobbin sleeve is therefore to change the equilibrium relative humidity and, consequently, the bobbin temperature. Since a change in bobbin temperature changes the required bobbin resistance, these factors interact to produce a final bobbin temperature somewhat closer to the original than initial inspection of these curves might indicate.

In actuality, the amount of salt which is applied to a hygrometer bobbin must be kept within certain limits. If it is too high or too low, the bobbin cannot be operated in the steep portion of its resistance curve over a wide variety of conditions, and the equilibrium temperature at constant ambient humidity will be found to vary greatly with a variety of factors.

In practice, it is advisable to standardize on a given concentration of treating solution and to use a fixed treating procedure. If this is done, the equilibrium temperature under

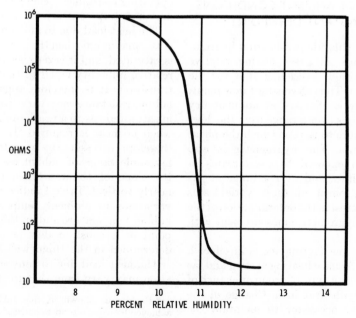

FIG. 5. Typical bobbin resistance.

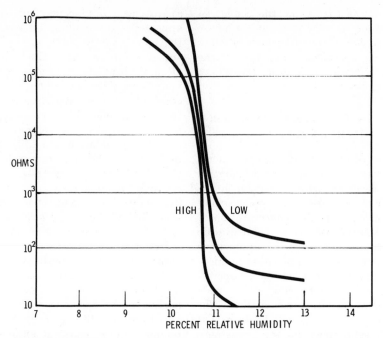

Fig. 6. Illustration of the effect of salt concentration on bobbin resistance characteristics (25°C).

constant conditions may be kept constant within $\pm$ 0.15 deg C, for a large number of similar bobbins.

THE EFFECT OF AMBIENT CONDITIONS AT CONSTANT DEW POINT

The lithium chloride self-heating hygrometer will operate in gases having relative humidity conditions exceeding that for the phase transition. Thus at constant dew point, the hygrometer is effective at ambient dry bulb temperatures over a range from the dewpoint temperature to that at which the phase transition occurs. The hygrometer is also operated when exposed to gas streams of differing velocities, and over a range of gas pressures. The effect of these variables is therefore of interest in the determination of the precision of a hygrometric measurement with these devices.

The self-heating hygrometer is in effect a miniature of a furnace heating system and, as such, is subject to a type of droop or change of control point with heat load. Change in the amount of heat necessary to maintain the bobbin at an equilibrium temperature requires

the operation of the bobbin at a different resistance level. From Fig. 5 it can be seen that the slope of the resistance curve results in a change in equilibrium temperature when the operating resistance is changed. This "droop" may be interpreted as instrument error.

The heat load due to ambient temperature is at a maximum when the gas being measured is saturated, and it is zero when the gas has a relative humidity equal to that of the phase transition. It is therefore apparent that the bobbin resistance may vary from a low value in saturated gas to a nearly infinite resistance when no heat is required. In practice, it is therefore necessary to operate in the most favorable range of bobbin resistance, where the slope of the resistance curve is most nearly vertical. Table 1 indicates the effect of variations in ambient temperature on the bobbin temperature and on the observed dew point at a constant dew point of 10°C, as determined in the Honeywell laboratory.*

The heat load due to convection and radiation may vary from that in still air to that

* Results as shown in this table can only be achieved by using a proper choice of materials for the substrate and electrodes.

TABLE 1

Actual Dew Point (°C)	Ambient Temp. (°C)	RH (%)	Bobbin Temperature (°C)	Dew Point from Bobbin Temperature (°C)	Deviation from Saturation Value (°C)
10	10.38	97.5	47.81	9.94	−0.06
10	17.86	60.0	47.88	9.99	−0.01
10	26.72	35.0	47.89	10.00	0.00
10	34.45	22.5	47.90	10.01	+0.01
10	41.95	15.0	47.91	10.02	+0.02

in high winds. Approximately 3 to 4 times the still air heat loss may occur as the air velocity is increased. This range of heat loss does not in itself appear to introduce a great error, since it is proportionately much less than the range caused by variation of dry bulb temperature. However, the self-heating hygrometer has a rather slow response to changes of ambient conditions* and tends to over- and under-shoot considerably before coming into equilibrium after a step change in conditions. Gusty air flow conditions therefore introduce large errors. It is common to utilize draft shields when the gas velocity impinging on the bobbin exceeds 10 m/min.

Ordinary atmospheric pressure changes do not greatly affect the bobbin temperature

* The most rapidly responding sensor of this type which is commercially available has a time constant (to 63 per cent of a step change) of 90 seconds.

attained at constant dew point, but they become important when the total pressure changes become larger.* The effect of this parameter has not been experimentally investigated in our laboratory. Theoretical considerations indicate that the heat loss by convection will vary as the square root of the gas density, while the heat loss by radiation will remain constant:

$$g_T = g_r + \frac{\rho_2^{1/2}}{\rho_1^{1/2}} \times g_{c_1} \qquad (1)$$

As the indifferent gas is removed from the system, the limiting heat loss is that by radiation, which should be 25 to 50 per cent of

* This must not be confused with the effect of total pressure changes on dew point which result from an increase in vapor pressure with total pressure. In the case considered in the text, the vapor pressure is held constant but the total pressure is varied.

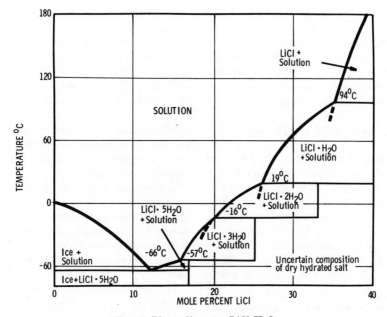

FIG. 7. Phase diagram, LiCl-H$_2$O.

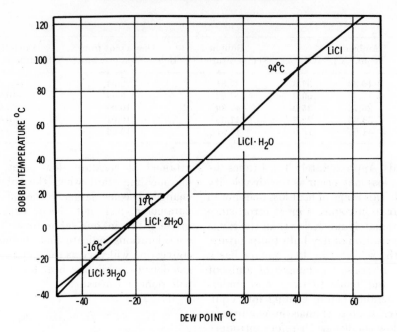

F<small>IG</small>. 8. Dew-probe characteristic temperature.

the heat loss at 1 atm, depending on bobbin temperature. In some cases, particularly in the petroleum industry, self-heating phase transition hygrometers are used at pressures as high as 3500 psig. This would result in a heat loss which would be about seven times as great as at one atmosphere. Pressure changes should therefore induce errors of the same order as those caused by changes in the ambient temperature.* Since high pressure conditions introduce the greatest errors, special calibration may be used to eliminate this source of error if the gas pressure is expected to be relatively constant.

REPRODUCIBILITY OF HYGROMETERS

The foregoing discussion of the effect of ambient conditions on the accuracy of the self-heating hygrometer does not indicate the basic reproducibility of these devices when operated under constant ambient conditions. Quality control inspection of Honeywell production bobbins indicates that in still air at atmospheric pressure, with an ambient temperature of 25°C and a dew point of 8.5°C,

* This statement does not consider the change in saturation vapor pressure caused by the high total pressure of the gas sample.

the maximum deviation of several hundred bobbins was within $\pm$ 0.15°C. This deviation includes the error of test instrumentation.

THE EFFECT OF HYDRATE FORM ON EQUILIBRIUM TEMPERATURE

Few salts pass from an anhydrous form to a saturated solution over all possible conditions without passing through hydrate phases. The more hygroscopic salts have several possible hydrate phases. Lithium chloride has hydrates with one, two, three and five molecules of water per molecule of salt. The phase diagram of this salt is shown in Fig. 7. Inspection of this diagram helps to explain several peculiarities observed in the calibration curves of lithium chloride phase transition hygrometers.

While the recorded hydrate transition temperatures indicate the limits of stable phase equilibrium, it is possible for neighboring hydrates to exist beyond these limits in a metastable condition as "supercooled" phases. These are shown in Fig. 7 as dotted lines.

Figure 8 shows a plot of the bobbin temperature *vs* the ambient dew-point temperature as determined in the Honeywell humidity standard, using typical self-heating lithium chloride hygrometers. Three hydrate transition points may be recognized, occurring as in Fig. 7 at 41, -12 and $-34°C$ dew point.

If a hygrometer is started in an atmosphere of greater humidity than a hydrate transition dew point and the humidity is then reduced below the transition point, the bobbin temperature appears to fall on an extension of the curve in effect above the transition point. If the bobbin is started in an atmosphere of low humidity and then subjected to higher humidity air, the bobbin temperature values follow a lower curve. In certain dew-point regions, therefore, two bobbin temperatures are possible, depending on the direction of approach to the hydrate transition point. Bobbins operating on the upper temperature are remarkably resistant to changeover to operation on the lower curve, but bobbins operating on the lower curve will spontaneously "break" over to operation on the upper curve some degrees before the hydrate transition point is reached.

The ambiguity caused by possible operation at two bobbin temperatures in a single air sample has a practical effect on the utilization of these hygrometers because it appears as a source of error. Below the $41°C$ dew-point hydrate transition, this phenomenon is noticeable down to about $34°C$, where the ambiguity appears to reach $1\frac{1}{2}°C$. A more serious condition exists below the $-12°C$ dew-point hydrate transition. In this region, it has been found that careful laboratory manipulation can extend operation on the upper temperature curve down to $-35°C$ dew point. In practice, as determined from observations of a meteorological installation, the lowest limit appears to approximate $-23°C$ dew point. The ambiguity which results from the two temperature phenomenon in this region reaches $3\frac{1}{2}°C$.

The third hydrate phase transition, that between the di- and trihydrate phases, occurs at $-33°C$ dew point. In this region the bobbin will operate on the upper or dihydrate line. If the unpowered bobbin is placed in an atmosphere at a condition to the left of the trihydrate curve of Fig. 8 and is then powered, no heating will occur unless the dew point is raised to a position on the trihydrate line. Almost immediately, however, the bobbin

temperature will rise further to a position on the dihydrate line.

A tentative mechanism has been evolved to explain these phenomena. For example, a bobbin operating on the monohydrate curve near the $41°C$ transition will give up one molecule of water of hydration per molecule of salt, and will begin to operate on the anhydrous salt curve if the dew point equal to the transition is exceeded. It is able to do this because loss of hydrate water requires heat, and this tends to cool the bobbin to the anhydride curve which would lie below the monohydrate curve above the transition. On the same basis, if a bobbin operating on the anhydride curve is subjected to a reduction in ambient dew point, when conditions pass the transition point the anhydrous salt should take up water. This requires the release of heat which helps maintain the system on the upper line. Further, when a bobbin operating on the monohydrate line is subjected to a rising dew-point condition until it approaches the vicinity of the hydrate transition point, it may suddenly begin operating on the upper curve. The heat for this transition may come from the electric current which is applied in the operation of the bobbin. No mechanism has been evolved to explain why the bobbin does not follow the anhydride curve at all temperatures instead of following the monohydrate curve exclusively below about $34°C$ dew point.

PRECISION OF THE SELF-HEATING HYGROMETER

An instrument based on the salt-solution phase transition must operate on a definite curve and cannot recognize the possible existence of two bobbin temperatures in some regions of dew point. The best procedure is therefore to determine a calibration curve which reduces the ambiguity to a minimum. Figure 9 shows the residual error after such a curve is drawn. Obviously the lithium chloride self-heating hygrometer is best suited for operation in the regions from -12 to $+34°C$, and again above $41.0°C$. The error caused by temperature ambiguity must be evaluated for each application at dew-point values where this phenomenon is possible.

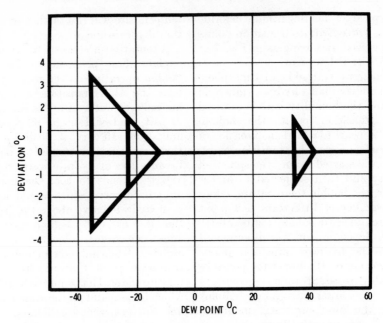

FIG. 9. Uncertainty of indicated dew point caused by phase transition instability.

CONCLUSION

The self-heating lithium chloride dew-point hygrometer is a very precise instrument ($\pm$ .15°C) when suitable care is taken in the installation. The regions of highest precision are between -12 and $+34$°C, and above 41°C dew point. In regions of phase ambiguity the errors introduced by this phenomenon must be considered. For many industrial uses the errors introduced by ignoring this ambiguity do not affect the usefulness of the instrument, considering the simplicity and relatively low cost of such installations.

References

1. Wylie, R. G., *Australian J. Phys.*, **10**, 341, 429 (1957).
2. Allen, A., and Cushman, R. W., U.S. Patent 2,343,878 (1944).
3. Amdur, E. J., Research Center Report GR2998-R1, Minneapolis-Honeywell Regulator Company, Minneapolis, 1956.

64. An Investigation of the Accuracy and Response Rate of a Lithium Chloride Heated Electrical Hygrometer*

C. P. HEDLIN

National Research Council, Division of Building Research, Saskatchewan, Canada

AND

F. N. TROFIMENKOFF

Department of Electrical Engineering, University of Saskatchewan

ABSTRACT

The operation of these hygrometers depends on the fact that the electrical resistance of a salt film changes rapidly in the region near to the critical point. The application of a constant voltage across the salt film results in heating of the system to a temperature which is characteristic of the ambient dew-point temperature.

To assess the accuracy of these hygrometers, a series of measurements was made in the laboratory in the dew-point temperature range from -30 to $80°F$. A straight line equation relating dew-point temperature and sensor temperature was obtained by using the method of least squares. The standard error was $0.4°F$ for the region above $32°F$.

In further experiments, the dependence of sensor temperature on temperature differential and on applied voltage was investigated. In the latter case, voltages were varied in the range from 0 to 120 V, and the corresponding temperatures and resistances were measured in the presence of fixed psychrometric conditions.

In experiments to assess the response time under normal operating conditions, at room temperature, it was found that after a step change of $25°F$ in the dew-point temperature, equilibrium was reestablished in 10 to 15 minutes.

INTRODUCTION

For a number of years lithium-chloride heated electrical hygrometers have been used at the Prairie Regional Station of the Division of Building Research for recording weather data and for other research work. This instrument has several desirable features. It can be used over a wide range of humidity; the result is given in terms of temperature which can easily be converted to a humidity value; and little maintenance is required.

An investigation of this unit has been carried out as part of a humidity instrumentation program, using a two-temperature recirculating atmosphere producer[1] as a calibrating standard. The initial calibration work was carried out by the second author as part of a graduate thesis program.

DESCRIPTION OF SENSOR

In addition to commercial units, a number of smaller sensors were constructed at the laboratory for use in locations where space

* This paper is a contribution from the Division of Building Research, National Research Council, and is published with the approval of the Director of the Division.

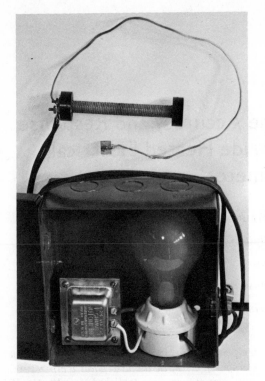

FIG. 1. Laboratory-built sensor and auxiliary equipment.

was limited. This type of sensor and associated power supply are shown in Fig. 1. In one group of these sensors, the substrate consisted of a stainless steel tube, $\frac{1}{4}$-in. o.d., and $3\frac{1}{2}$ in. long. The tube was treated with an insulating varnish, and wound with a layer of glass-fiber tape. A bifilar coil of 0.025-in. silver wire was wound over the tape, the spacing between the wires being approximately 0.05 in. A thermocouple, having good thermal contact with the walls, was placed in the geometrical center of the tube.

OPERATION

To put a sensor into operation, a dilute solution of lithium chloride is applied to the glass-fiber wick. A ballast lamp (50-watt, 32-V) is connected in series with the sensor, and 24 V are applied across the combination. The ballast lamp serves to limit the current to about 1.3 A during the start-up period, when the film is very moist and its resistance is low. As heat is generated, the film dries and its resistance increases markedly. After about 10

minutes, the resistance of the film becomes the limiting resistance of the circuit.

This hygrometer operates on the principle that the temperature of the salt film is regulated so that the vapor pressure of the water it contains will be equal to the water vapor pressure in the surrounding air. In most systems, the temperature of the sensor is higher than that of the surroundings, but it could be used at temperatures below ambient by employing a cooling system. For operations at any temperature above ambient, the usual method of supplying the necessary heat is to use the salt film as an electrical conductor, whose resistance R varies in accordance with the heat requirement by exchanging moisture with the surrounding air. A constant AC voltage E is applied to electrodes in contact with the salt film. Since the load is almost a pure resistance, the wattage dissipated as heat is $W = E^2/R$. In Fig. 2, the variation of heat loss with temperature differential is shown for a commercial sensor.

RESPONSE RATE

A measure of the rate of response to a step change in humidity was made by using the atmosphere producer to provide one set of conditions and the room air for another. In the

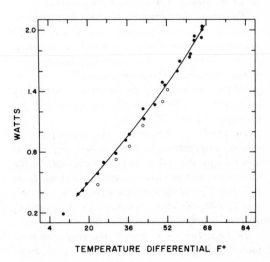

FIG. 2. Heat loss plotted against sensor air temperature difference. Air movement varied from still to roughly 100 fpm. Sensor was approximately 4 in. long and $\frac{5}{16}$ in. in diameter; axis was horizontal. Solid dots—no shield; open circles—shield in place.

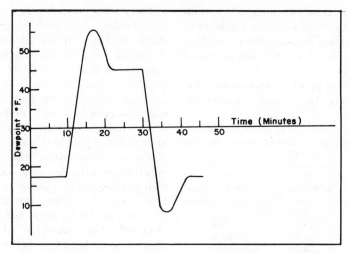

FIG. 3. Response of a sensor to a step change in dew-point temperature. In the first run, the dew-point temperature was increased; in the second, it was decreased.

first, the dry-bulb temperature was 60°F and the dew-point temperature was 17°F. In the room, the dry-bulb temperature was 72°F and the dew-point temperature was 45°F. The step change was arranged by the simple expedient of rapidly withdrawing or inserting the sensor into the atmosphere producer. Its behavior is illustrated in Fig. 3. The response time for such a change was found to be about 15 minutes, both for increasing and decreasing dew points.

CALIBRATION

In the first phase of calibration work, four of the laboratory-built sensors were investigated in the atmosphere producer. These were placed in the calibrating chamber in pairs since this was all that the space would conveniently hold. Electrical and thermocouple connections were provided in the cover of the calibration chamber. The sensor temperatures were measured using copper-constantan thermocouples. A precision potentiometer was used to measure the EMF, and an ice bath was used as a reference junction. The temperature measurements may be regarded as accurate to within ± 0.2 Fahrenheit degree. A series of sensor temperatures was obtained for dew-point temperatures ranging from 0 to 80°F.

Conover[2] observed an abrupt change in the temperature indicated by this hygrometer

when the dew-point temperature was raised above 10°F after remaining below that value for some time. He attributed this behavior to the change of the salt from the dihydrate to the monohydrate state. Conover gave a temperature of 55°F for this transition point, while Mellor[3] gives two possible values, 54.5°F and 70.7°F. At the NRC Division of Building Research, Ottawa, a sudden drop in sensor temperature was observed to occur after it had been exposed to a fixed dew-point temperature of $-15°F$ for about 6 hours. A new equilibrium temperature was eventually reached about 5 Fahrenheit degrees below that which existed before the change. A reverse transition occurred at a dew-point temperature of about 6°F.

A number of transitions have been noted in routine operation of a cell set up to measure atmospheric dew point at the Prairie Regional Station. Several hydration transitions occurred at a sensor temperature of about 50°F (dew point = 0°F) 6 or 7 hours after having crossed the 65°F temperature line. Several dehydrations were found to have occurred at a temperature between 60 and 65°F. Where the temperature is continuously recorded, such transitions may be fairly readily identified. When the temperature is recorded periodically, however, the transitions may be mistaken for change in air condition.

To investigate this phenomenon in more

detail, a commercial heated electrical hygrometer was placed in the atmosphere producer at
the Prairie Regional Station and calibration
was carried out for dew-point temperatures
in the range from $+18$ to $-24.5°F$.

When the dew-point temperature was
lowered by steps, the sensor temperature

TABLE 1. VALUES OBTAINED FROM EXPERIMENTAL
DATA IN THE DEW-POINT TEMPERATURE REGION
BELOW 12°F

Dew Point	t_c (dihydrate)	t_c (monohydrate)
−24	7.8	
−22	10.2	19.8
−20	13.6	22.2
−18	16.1	24.7
−16	18.9	27.5
−14	21.9	30.1
−12	24.9	32.8
−10	27.9	35.2
−8	31.0	38.3
−6	34.2	40.8
−4	37.4	43.7
−2	40.5	46.4
0	44.0	49.3
2	47.4	51.8
4	51.0	54.5
6	54.6	57.4
8	58.4	60
10	62.2	63
11.5	65	65

followed the monohydrate line, reaching
equilibrium after each change and giving
stable readings. When the transition to the
dihydrate level occurred, however, the temperature dropped rapidly to a level 6 or 8
degrees below the final value and then
gradually rose to it [Fig. 4(a)]. Such transitions
were observed to occur at dew-point temperatures ranging downward from 0°F. Most of the
attention was paid to the relationship between
the sensor temperature and dew-point temperature, and the dew-point temperature was
changed frequently. Consequently, the time
that elapsed before transition was not
observed in detail. From the data that were
obtained, the transition appeared to be
dependent on both time and temperature. On
one occasion, the sensor operated for 18 hours
at a dew-point temperature of −6°F. At the
lowest temperatures, some difficulty was experienced in obtaining a reading before the
transition occurred. The sensor was "started"
several times at an ambient dew-point
temperature of −15.3°F. On each occasion,
equilibrium was reached on the dihydrate
curve [Fig. 4(c)].

In these experiments, the sensor operated
on the dihydrate curve until its temperature
was raised to a critical value, at which time
the reverse transition occurred. In this case,

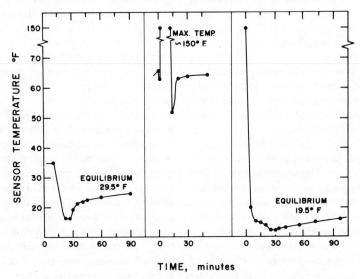

FIG. 4. (a) Sensor temperature *vs* time during transition from the
monohydrate to the dihydrate level. (b) Temperature *vs* time during
the transition to the monohydrate level. (c) Temperature *vs* time
during a "start-up."

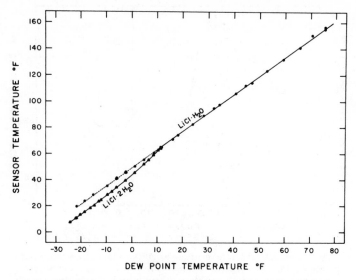

Fɪɢ. 5. Calibration curves for lithium chloride heated electrical hygrometer. The line through the monohydrate data is represented by the equation $t_c = 49.3 + 1.404 t_d$.

the appearance was similar to that of a normal start-up [Fig. 4(b)]. The sensor resistance dropped to a low value and its temperature rose as a result of the release of moisture due to the transition to the monohydrate form. In the work at the Prairie Regional Station, this transition occurred at about 65°F, but the sensor operated in a stable manner until that temperature was reached.

A second quadruple point exists for the monohydrate and the anhydrous salt in the region of 210°F. This region was traversed by raising the dew-point temperature, but no transition was observed.

An equation to relate the sensor temperature, t_c, and dew-point temperature, t_d,

$$t_c = 49.3 + 1.404 t_d$$

was obtained by fitting a straight line to the data between 32°F dew point and 80°F dew point. The standard error was about 0.4 deg F (Fig. 5).*

There appears to be a slight curvature in the data, with the result that some error exists. For example, the equation predicts a sensor temperature that is too low by roughly 1 Fahrenheit degree at the lower end of the curve. One would expect a break to occur at

* Only representative points are shown above 32°F dew point.

32°F, since the dew-point temperatures are referred to ice. When the data for the monohydrate below 32°F dew point were included, however, very nearly the same result was obtained. Thus, with quite good accuracy, this equation applies for the monohydrate for dew-point temperatures from 80°F down to the lowest values that were investigated. Data for the region below 12°F dew point are given in Table 1.

VARIATION OF SENSOR TEMPERATURE AT FIXED DEW-POINT TEMPERATURE

The vapor pressure exerted by the salt film on this type of hygrometer is sometimes assumed to be equal to that of a saturated solution of the salt at the same temperature. Practical experience indicates that this assumption is substantially correct. If the vapor pressure and temperature characteristics of the two do coincide, however, the sensor temperature should vary only with the dew-point temperature and should be independent of limited variations in the applied voltage, and of the ambient temperature as long as it is below that of the sensor.

In one series of experiments, a sensor was "started" with fixed dew-point and ambient temperatures, but the voltage was varied. The

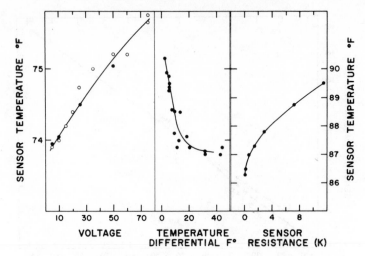

FIG. 6. (a) Sensor temperature *vs* applied voltage. Dew-point temperature, 18.0°F; ambient temperature, 50.5°F. (b) Variation in sensor temperature with variation in sensor-ambient air temperature difference. (c) Sensor temperature *vs* sensor resistance. Sensor was not operated; the temperature of the air was varied. Dew-point temperature, 26.5°F.

sensor was allowed to drive off the moisture in the usual manner, but at about the time it reached the maximum temperature in the start-up process, the applied voltage was set at the desired value and the sensor was then allowed to come to an equilibrium temperature. The sensor was carefully washed between each "start." The excess water was removed, and a solution of the salt was poured over it, preparatory to the next observation. The equilibrium temperatures and voltages are shown in Fig. 6(a). From measurement of the current flow, sensor resistance was also found.

In a second series of experiments, a sensor was operated in the usual manner. The dew-point temperature was held constant at 17.5°F, and the ambient temperature varied in the range from 19.5 to 72.7°F [Fig. 6(b)].

In another experiment, with a constant dew point of −26.5°F, a temperature-resistance relationship was obtained by raising the ambient temperature above the normal value for the sensor and measuring the sensor resistance as the temperature was lowered by steps [Fig. 6(c)]. In this case, the normal voltage was not applied to the sensor; a small AC voltage was applied briefly for each resistance measurement.

All three of these experiments indicated that small variations in sensor temperature may occur independently of the dew-point temperature, introducing errors up to roughly 1½ deg F.

To obtain an approximate measure of the usual departure of the salt on the hygrometer from the critical condition, a laboratory-built

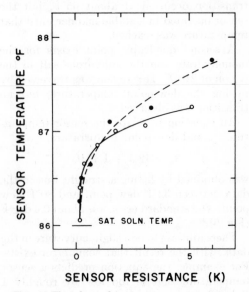

FIG. 7. The plots of sensor temperature *vs* sensor resistance. Sensors were operated over a saturated solution of lithium chloride which was at 86.0°F. Sensor resistance was varied by changing the applied voltage.

sensor was operated in a sealed flask over a saturated solution of lithium chloride. The voltage was varied by steps and resistance of the sensor was measured at each point. In general, operating sensor resistance will probably be in the range from 200 to 5000 Ω. In Fig. 7, this corresponds to a temperature range of about $\frac{1}{2}$ to $1\frac{1}{2}$ Fahrenheit degrees above that of the saturated solution.

Following small decrements in voltage, equilibrium was usually reached within an hour. Following small increments of voltage, however, particularly in the low-temperature portions of the curves, approach to equilibrium was exceedingly slow.

A more direct method of observing this difference is that of comparing data for the saturated liquid with the sensor calibration curve (Fig. 8). It is apparent here also that the temperature of an operating sensor generally exceeds that of a saturated solution which is at the same dew-point temperature.

These experiments indicate that this hygrometer operates at a temperature somewhat higher than it would if the lithium chloride was at the critical condition. Through variation in temperature differential, it is apparent that the sensor temperature may vary by as much as 1 Fahrenheit degree under normal operating conditions. From operation of the sensor over a saturated solution of lithium chloride, it appears that the operating range may be $\frac{1}{2}$ to $1\frac{1}{2}$ Fahrenheit degrees above that of the saturated solution.

CONCLUSION

The lithium chloride heated electrical hygrometer normally operates at a higher temperature than it would if the salt were in the condition of a saturated solution. Because of the relationship between sensor temperature and sensor resistance, it will probably operate in a temperature range whose extreme limits during normal operations are approximately $\frac{1}{2}$ to $1\frac{1}{2}$ Fahrenheit degrees above that of a saturated solution. As a result of this variability, a small inherent error exists.

A more important error may occur in the dew-point temperature region immediately below 11.5°F. In this region, two hydrate levels occur and the sensor may operate on either one. The dew-point temperature indicated by the two hydrate levels is the same at a dew-point temperature of 11.5°F; it differs by approximately 3 Fahrenheit degrees at 0°F dew-point temperature. Because the difference is greater at lower temperatures, it is necessary to exercise caution when measurements are made in this region. Under the con-

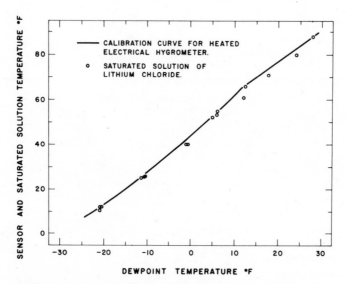

FIG. 8. Comparison of the calibration curve for a lithium chloride heated electrical hygrometer with the corresponding data for saturated lithium chloride solutions.

trolled conditions in an atmosphere producer, operation on the monohydrate line was observed at dew-point temperatures down to −22°F. A limited number of observations on an outdoor installation, however, suggest that transition to the dihydrate level often occurs in the region of 0°F dew point in the practical case. The reverse transition occurred at approximately 11.5°F dew point in the atmosphere producer and in the region between 8 and 11°F dew point in the outdoor installation.

Calibration of the lithium chloride heated electrical hygrometer has shown that the relationship between the sensor temperature and the dew-point temperature is nearly linear for the monohydrate level over much of the normal operating range when the dew-point temperatures below 32°F are referred to ice. Within the dew-point temperature range from −20 to +70°F, the calibration curve does not deviate from the best fitting straight line by more than about 1 Fahrenheit degree dew point.

References

1. Till, C. E., and Handegord, G. O., "Proposed Humidity Standard," *Trans. ASHRAE*, **66**, 288–308 (1960).
2. Conover, J. H., "Tests and Adaptation of the Foxboro Dewpoint Recorder for Weather Observatory Use," *Bull. Am. Meteorol. Soc.*, **31**, 13–22 (1950).
3. Mellor, J. W., "A Comprehensive Treatise on Inorganic and Theoretical Chemistry," Vol. 2, p. 542, New York, Longmans, Green & Co., 1927.

65. Improvements in Dew-point Measurements of Gases by the Use of Peltier Devices

Otto J. Leone

Consulting Engineer, West Newton, Pennsylvania

ABSTRACT

In dew-point hygrometry which depends on the cooling or heating of a dew-spot surface as part of the measuring operation, there has been a need for better means for cooling and controlling the operation. Past methods have involved the inconvenience, bulk and other limitations accompanying the use of refrigerating liquids, gases and other cooling equipment. Developments in thermoelectric Peltier cooling and heating in recent years have made it possible to have fast and positive cooling or heating of surfaces, dew-spot moisture films or of saturated salt solutions in dew-point measurement, over a wide range of temperatures and with comparatively simple equipment. The application of Peltier devices to several types of hygrometers is considered, including a description of equipment used, performance, and a comparison of ranges, advantages and limitations of each type.

INTRODUCTION

Heating and cooling operations are utilized in several types of hygrometers to measure the dew point of gas-moisture mixtures. In some instruments a surface is cooled to temperatures below ambient to form a dew deposit by condensing water vapor from the gas. Another class of sensors uses temperature-controlled saturated-salt principles in which the temperature and electrical conductance or resistivity of the solution are related to the dew point: the salt solution may require heating and cooling operations above and below the ambient temperature. Cooling of sensors below ambient temperatures with refrigerant liquids and gases has been cumbersome, often messy, slow and usually difficult to control in a simple manner. Mechanical refrigerators that use compression and expansion of gases and liquids must be maintained at temperatures substantially lower than the lowest dew-point or salt-solution temperature to be measured. In saturated-salt methods, if only the heat loss to the atmosphere is available for cooling the solution, the lowest dew points that can be measured are limited; the use of artificial refrigeration by older methods is not only cumbersome but quite costly and complicated. When only natural cooling is used, and if the solution equilibrium temperature corresponding to a measured dew point is close to the ambient temperature, the cooling and the measuring operations may have very slow response to dew-point changes.

The need for an artificial cooling means which is more simple, less bulky and faster than conventional refrigeration is apparent. The method to be selected for cooling and heating should be fast, easy to control, and of suitably small size for use in a dew-point instrument. Consideration of the characteristics of Peltier coolers indicates that they are suitable for the requirements of this application.

PELTIER COOLING

Although Peltier discovered about 130 years ago that junctions of dissimilar electrical conductors will become heated or cooled by passing direct current through them, and that the effect varies with changes in the quantity and polarity of the direct current flowing through the junction, it is only in recent years that Peltier devices have been available to provide the heat-pumping capacities at low current and power consumption, for a wide range of temperatures, to satisfy the requirements of a dew-point instrument.

Improvements in the performance of Peltier coolers has been made possible by the development of better semiconductors, which will provide better cooling than is possible with metal junctions. Also, better techniques in designing and making Peltier coolers by optimizing the volume, lengths and cross-sectional area dimensions of the legs in each Peltier couple, and by cascading and the use of multistage combinations of Peltier couples have served to improve cooler performance. At the sacrifice of some heat-pumping capacity, Peltier coolers for dew-point applications to temperatures of $-50°C$ or lower can operate on as little as 3 or 4 A of current or about 3 watts of power, in cooling from about $+27°C$. Other designs may require up to 30 A or about 30 watts of power for similar performance, but their heat-pumping capacity may also be greater.

As stated before, the type of cooler-heater system to be selected should be easily adaptable to manual or automatic control for heating or cooling of the dew spot. The amount of current or power to be controlled in the Peltier devices is small enough for the use of standard electronic control components for the operation of magnetic amplifiers or of silicon-controlled rectifiers in relatively small packages. Much greater flexibility, stability and speed of control are available by the use of such control components to cool the dew spot with Peltier coolers than by older methods of cooling as mentioned before, and with considerably less control hardware.

The requirement for fast cooling and heating can be met easily by the use of Peltier coolers. The time required to cool or heat will vary according to the design, but can be made very fast. For example, three-stage coolers can be made to cool a dew-spot surface from room temperature of $+70°F$ to $-60°F$ in less than a minute. If the current is cut off at $-60°F$, the dew spot will return to $+70°F$ in less than

two minutes, or very much faster if current of reversed polarity is applied to the module. It is inconceivable that conventional refrigeration could match such performance. For this reason, conventional refrigerators have been operated at fixed low temperatures, and a means for countering the cooling effect with a heating effect has generally been used. While such operation is also possible with Peltier coolers, alternatively, the refrigerated temperature using the Peltier cooler can be controlled directly on a proportional control basis by controlled regulation of the current to the cooler.

SURFACE RESISTIVITY

Peltier coolers may be used with visual-optical or photoelectric dew-spot sensors, or with the saturated-salt solution sensor that has already been mentioned. The cooler may also be used with a dew-spot sensor based on the measurement of the electrical resistivity or conductance of the dew-layer deposit. While all of these sensors have their limitations, the author's experience with the last type based on changes in surface resistivity indicates that it has some advantages that should be examined.

In making dew-point measurements with a fogged mirror by visual-optical or light reflectance methods, and simultaneously measuring the electrical resistivity of the dew-spot surface between two spaced conductors on the dew spot, it was noted by the author that the surface resistivity measurement is not only more sensitive than light reflectance methods, but that it provides a reliable indication of changes in the thickness of the dew layer. A measurement of the thickness of the moisture film between the two spaced probes is equivalent to a measurement of the mass of the dew deposit. At temperatures above the dew point, the surface resistivity method indicated the presence of a dew layer which was not observable by the light reflectance methods. The resistivity method also indicated changes in the thickness as the dew spot surface temperature was heated or cooled at temperatures above the dew point at constant absolute humidity or dew point, or if the surface temperature was held constant above the dew-point temperature and the absolute humidity or dew point of the measured sample was changed. The changes in surface resistivity were the result of the changes in the dew-layer thickness; resistivity changes caused by the variations of the surface temperature as compared to changes resulting from variations in dew-layer thickness were negligible, if there was any contribution due to the temperature changes alone. With the visual or photoelectric optical sensor methods there appeared to be a threshold below which they were not as sensitive as the surface resistivity method.

In the region of sensitivity in which visual or photoelectric optical methods are capable of measuring the dew layer, there appears to be a limit to the accuracy of determining· the thickness of the dew layer when certain physical characteristics of the moisture change. This limitation has been attributed to variations in size, sphericity and number of globules of moisture which form the dew layer and which affect scatter and light reflectance properties of optical methods. Any such effects or limitations from these variations have not been noticeable with surface resistivity measurements.

Surfaces of materials such as the mirror already referred to, and other dielectric surfaces tend to sorb and desorb water vapor as the humidity and dew point change. At surface temperatures higher than the dew point of the atmosphere in contact with the surface, the moisture film adhering to it can be made thicker or thinner by cooling or heating the surface. As the film thickness changes, there will be a corresponding change in the electrical surface resistance, which can be related to the surface temperature and to the dew point.

The relation between surface resistivity and surface temperature for various levels of dew point or absolute humidity may be represented by plotting curves as in Fig. 1. Actual surface resistance values are not shown, but only a generalized relation is plotted for various dew-point or absolute humidity levels T_1, T_2, T_3, etc., for which the higher subscript numerals represent higher moisture and dew-point levels. For each moisture level, if a surface temperature which is initially higher than the dew point is cooled and surface resistance measurements are noted at various temperatures above and below the dew point, a family of curves generally similar to Fig. 1 can be

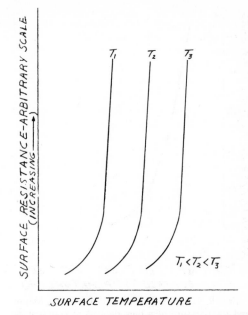

FIG. 1. Curve shows changes of surface resistivity as temperature of surface changes at several dew-point levels, T_1, T_2, and T_3.

plotted. It will be noted that the surface resistivity is reduced sharply as the dew-point temperature is approached. The relation between resistivity, surface temperature and adsorbed moisture is a fundamental characteristic for each surface material.

In tests previously referred to the author connected an electronic amplifier with high impedance input between two probes attached to the surface of the mirror (also mentioned before) and measured the amplifier output current at various dew-point levels as the dew-spot temperature was cooled by a Peltier cooler or was allowed to become heated. For each dew-point level a curve similar to that of Fig. 2 was plotted to show the changes in amplifier current output as the surface temperature between the probes was changed near or above the dew point. The circuit arrangement was such that an AC signal was impressed across the surface between the probes; the amplified output was a rectified current signal. The reason for using alternating current between the probes was to prevent possible polarization in other tests when a saturated salt solution was tested between the spaced probes.

The curve in Fig. 2 of an actual test is

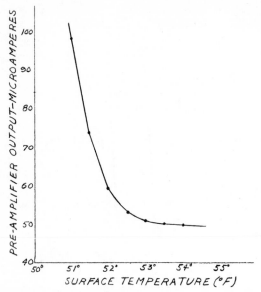

FIG. 2. Relation between electrical conductance and temperature of a dew deposit at constant dew point.

typical of the relation between the amplifier current output as the dew-spot temperature between the two probes is varied. The atmosphere being tested was controlled at 72°F dry bulb temperature and showed a dew point of 36°F as measured by other methods. The curve shows that the amplifier output current decreased as the dew-spot surface was heated, and finally reached a limiting low value at the higher surface temperatures. The relation represented by the curve in Fig. 2 is the reciprocal of that represented by Fig. 1. The current output of the amplifier may be calibrated in terms of the surface resistivity or the electrical impedance between the measuring probes. While the slope of the curve in Fig. 1 is fixed for a given material, the slope of Fig. 2 for the same material may be changed by adjusting the amplifier gain or other parameters. This latter feature is useful in adapting the amplifier to control components that may be used for closed-loop control of heating and cooling of the dew-spot surface to maintain the surface resistivity at a fixed reference value when performing the dew-point measurement operation.

The curve in Fig. 2 does not extend to the dew point of the tested sample which was 36°F. If it had been extended, the amplifier current

output at 36°F would have shown as much as several milliamperes of output signal, the actual value depending on the gain or other adjustments made to the amplifier.

Calibration of the amplifier output to the surface temperature is most easily made by heating or cooling the dew spot between the probes until the surface temperature equals the known dew point of a sampled atmosphere that has been measured by other means; the amplifier current output for any desired gain setting is then noted, which value may be used as the reference standard. If the dew point is increased, or if the dew-spot temperature at constant dew point is cooled below the dew point, the surface resistivity will change in a direction to increase the amplifier current output above the reference standard. Conversely, the current value will be less than the reference value if the surface temperature of the dew spot is heated above the dew point or if the dew point is increased. By manually or automatically cooling or heating the dew spot as required to maintain the amplifier current output at a reference value, a measure of the dew-spot surface temperature will provide an indication of the dew point of the atmosphere being tested.

The dew-spot temperature corresponding to any amplifier current output selected as a reference standard may be the same as the dew point, or the calibration may be such that the indicated surface temperatures will be higher than the dew point by some constant, which may be calibrated to be any value from 0 to 15°F or more. In the latter case, the actual dew point is always equal to the measured surface temperature minus a constant. An advantage of operating at surface temperatures higher than the actual dew point is that the moisture film is thinner than it would be at the dew point. Since less mass transfer of moisture must be interchanged at the gas-liquid interface when the dew point changes, faster measuring response is available. It would be expected that less heat transfer should be required on the thinner films to change the vapor pressure balance relative to the atmospheric vapor pressure as the dew point changes. This type of operation may be useful for such applications as measuring dew-point gradients through a cloud formation, for example. The response of the sensor when

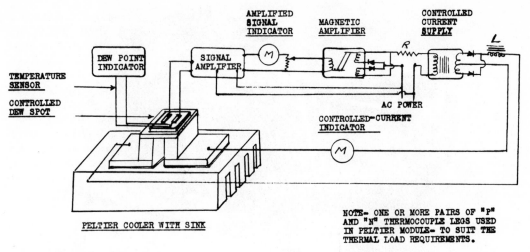

FIG. 3. Schematic diagram of dew-point indicator system using a surface resistivity sensor and Peltier cooling at dew spot.

subjected to fast short blasts of gas of higher and lower dew points is fast enough that the amplifier current output is also pulsed. A sensitive and fast means for measuring any simultaneous changes of surface temperature is also required to follow the fast changes in dew point.

DEW-POINT INDICATORS

Figure 3 shows a schematic diagram which utilizes the surface resistivity sensor to operate a magnetic amplifier and rectifier circuit for closed-loop control of current input to a Peltier cooler module. Although a single Peltier couple is shown, multiple units or cascaded stages of couples may also be used. The controlled dew spot comprises a flat thin dielectric surface for which glass, plastics and various other materials have been used. Two spaced sensor probes are mounted on the dielectric surface; in some cases, spaced point contacts have been used. The size and thickness of the dielectric plate, and the length and spacing of the probes are not critical if the amplifier includes means for adjusting gain or sensitivity. Dielectric plates as small as .12 in. × .22 in. × .020 in. thick, to .50 in. × .50 in. × .125 in. thick have been used with the same amplifier system.

If the atmosphere in contact with the dew spot of the system of Fig. 3 changes, the magnetic amplifier and current supply change the current input to the Peltier cooler in a proportional manner so as to increase or decrease the cooling effect at the dew spot, as necessary to maintain the surface electrical leakage of the dew spot at a reference standard value. The reference value is set by a zener diode reference source which is either incorporated in the circuit either after the amplifier or used as a biasing control for the magnetic reactor; the reference circuit is not shown in the Fig. 3. The current supply to the Peltier cooler is filtered to provide a rectified current having not more than 10 per cent ripple. With the closed-loop control maintaining the surface electrical leakage of the dew spot at a reference value, the corresponding surface temperature of the dew spot will be an indication of the dew point. A surface thermocouple, thermistor or resistance temperature transducer and indicator are shown in Fig. 3 for this measurement.

In Fig. 3, heating of the dew spot is accomplished by reducing current input to the Peltier module and by natural heat loss to the atmosphere. Alternatively, faster heating may be obtained by using means to reverse the polarity of the direct current to the Peltier module or by incorporating a small electrical resistance heater element close to the dew spot surface.

Figure 4 shows a photograph of the electrical components for an industrial dew-point hygrometer based on the circuit of Fig. 3. The

FIG. 4. Dew-point analyzer chassis based on circuit of Fig. 3.

equipment is housed in a transmitter cabinet, with remote transmission by means of thermocouple leads to an electronic recorder which may be located up to a few hundred feet away. Figure 5 shows one version of a complete hygrometer which also uses the circuit in Fig. 3 and magnetic amplifier components in Fig. 4. The larger indicator to the right is a temperature indicator which operates from a surface type thermocouple which measures the dew-spot temperature. A thermistor or a resistance-type temperature transducer may also be used. The indicating meter at the top left of the front panel indicates the amplifier current output and may serve to indicate null balance conditions with respect to the surface resistivity of the dew spot relative to a reference standard value. The small meter in the lower left corner of the panel indicates the amperes of rectified and filtered direct current which is put into the Peltier cooler. Two Peltier coolers are shown on top of the cabinet; they are mounted on heat sinks arranged for natural cooling. The Peltier coolers use "N" and "P" types of bismuth telluride materials that are doped with some impurities. The cooler on the left can cool the dew spot to $-20°C$ in air from room temperatures of about $25°C$, and at maximum current of 3.5 A of direct current at .85 V. The cooler uses eight couples in a single stage.

The cooler on the right side of the cabinet top of Fig. 5 has two stages of couples, and can cool from a room temperature of $72°F$ to about $-35°F$ in air, at 25 A current flow, at approximately 1 V. Forced-air convective cooling is also used for lower dew-point measurements. Both of the Peltier devices in Fig. 5 are equipped with a controlled dew-spot sensor of dielectric material, two spaced probes, and

FIG. 5. Dew-point indicator with surface resistivity sensor and Peltier cooling of dew spot, with thermocouple surface temperature meter. Two sensors shown on cabinet with heat sinks for natural cooling.

Fɪɢ. 6. Dew-point sensor for industrial gas sampling, using three-stages of Peltier cooling and heat sink with blower for forced convection cooling.

means for measuring the surface temperature for dew points above freezing. They have also been adapted for use with lithium salt between the probes using a glass fiber or plastic tape to hold the salt solution.

Figure 6 shows another Peltier cooler that is equipped with a three-stage cooler module, arranged for use with a pressure-type enclosure for sampling industrial gas under pressure. It is mounted on a heat sink to which is attached a blower to cool the Peltier cooler. A small dew-spot sensor is mounted on the topmost stage of the cooler; the dielectric surface is metallized at three points on the top. Two spaced probes and a fine thermocouple are soldered to these points and wired to electrical pressure-type feed-throughs located in the base plate. Figure 4 shows an installed view of the blower and Peltier assembly with the pressure-type enclosure housing the cooler. The three-stage cooler is capable of cooling an air sample from 72°F to −60°F at maximum direct current of 8.5 A at about 1 V. Nitrogen gas with up to 30 per cent hydrogen can be cooled to about −55°C. Depending upon the application and dew-point range, the sensor may be operated with or without lithium salt on it.

Figure 7 shows a hygrometer indicator which uses a control system similar to Fig. 3,

Fɪɢ. 7. Disassembled dew-point indicator based on circuit of Fig. 3, except that a SCR control is used instead of a magnetic amplifier.

except that the magnetic amplifier is replaced with a silicon-controlled rectifier. The signal amplifier and controlled current supply are of the same types as in Fig. 3. The advantage of this control system over the magnetic amplifier is that it is much smaller and lighter. The unit in Fig. 7 can easily handle currents to 25 or 30 A at the low voltages required for operation of Peltier coolers. It is arranged for bias and gain adjustments of the SCR control unit.

It should be mentioned that the controlled dew-spot sensor in Fig. 3 may also be adapted to use a saturated salt solution between the probes, such as a lithium chloride solution, with adjustments to handle the lower resistance when using salt between the probes. This method appears to have some advantages over conventional salt-solution measuring cells. The long winding of the spaced conductors is not required; in fact, spaced point contacts may be used. This means considerably less opportunity is present for shorting between contacts or spaced conductors if reasonable spacing is used between them. The salt solution may be self-heated and controlled by passing electric current through it in the conventional manner, or it may be both heated and cooled from external sources. This type of operation is possible in the circuit of Fig. 3, which makes it possible to use a very small "chemical dew spot" area for faster heat transfer and measuring response than is now available. By passing only weak currents through the solution to measure the moisture in it, sensor failure from high current surges, as occurs in cells adapted for self-heating, is eliminated, since only microamperes or several milliamperes of current at most passes through the solution and between the spaced conductors.

The principal advantage of using a saturated salt as compared to the moisture or dew layer only on the dew spot surface is that for any given dew point, the salt method will operate at higher temperature levels. However, it cannot cover a measuring range to as high a temperature as the surface resistivity method using a dew layer of moisture only between the sensor probes. There is also the inconvenience of replenishing the salt periodically.

The effect of dirt and other contaminants on the surface resistivity method has not been fully determined, particularly for the more difficult industrial applications. The advantages of using short probe lengths or spaced point contacts has been mentioned as a means to reduce possible shorting between the conductors by dirt. A resistivity sensor using a dew layer only for the dew spot has been operated continuously for over nine months in ordinary atmosphere without any attention or noticeable change in calibration.

The surface resistivity sensor will operate satisfactorily in still air or in air or gas streams. It is recommended that gas velocities be limited to as low a value as possible, because excessive velocities require more cooling capacity for the dew-spot operations. The speed of response for measuring dew-point changes is faster at higher velocities, because the mass transfer of moisture between the dew layer and the gas in contact with it is increased with increasing velocity.

Measuring accuracy of the surface resistivity sensor is usually limited to the accuracy available in the temperature measuring system, and particularly the indicator, which is about ± 1 deg C as higher dew points checked against wet and dry bulb or dew cup methods. While experience below freezing is limited so far, less accuracy is to be expected at very low dew points as is the case with most hygrometers. The accuracy possible with the surface resistivity sensor under best conditions has not been determined, but there is reason to believe that potentially accuracy to within ± 1 deg F or better is possible at higher dew points.

The dew-point range over which Peltier coolers may be used has not been determined, but in the present state of the art, ranges from -100 to $+200°F$ seem possible with bismuth tellurides. It is possible that lead tellurides may be used for coolers at higher temperatures, even though they are not as satisfactory for cooling as the bismuth telluride materials.

CONCLUSION

Limitations in cooling and heating operations for dew-point measurement have been discussed. It has been shown that the use of Peltier devices can improve measuring operations in certain types of dew-point hygrometers.

Reference

U.S. Patent 2,979,950.

66. Hygrometer Developments at the U.S. Naval Research Laboratory*

R. E. Ruskin

U.S. Naval Research Laboratory, Washington, D.C.

ABSTRACT

Development of hygrometers at NRL has included, for operational aircraft use, an aerograph probe which automatically corrects the humidity measurements for aircraft speed effects of dynamic heating and provides simple corrections for pressure changes. An adaptation of this instrument permits micrometeorological sounding in the undisturbed air beneath a helicopter. A dew-point hygrometer with thermoelectric cooling of the condensation mirror is housed in an aircraft probe for external fuselage mounting. A fast-response adjunct to the dew-point sensor is an ultraviolet absorption detector in the same probe housing. A heated-air inlet provides evaporation of cloud liquid water to permit measurement of total water content.

Balloon-borne frost-point hygrometer development has emphasized reducing moisture contamination when used for measurements in the stratosphere. A dew-point hygrometer for arctic use employs Ranque-Hilsch vortex cooling of the condensation mirror without use of other coolants. Two types of electronic psychrometers prevent freezing of the wet bulb wick by preheating the air sample without changing the resultant reading of water vapor pressure.

Other research and developments in the humidity field are described.

* The research and development described herein was supported by the Bureau of Naval Weapons, Advance Research Projects Agency (ARPA) and the Office of Naval Research.

INTRODUCTION

While assisting the United States Navy in providing humidity instrumentation for its various types of application, the Naval Research Laboratory has developed several methods of humidity measurement and, in cooperation with the National Bureau of Standards, has evaluated for Navy application most of the promising methods which have become available from other groups.

AIRPLANE AND HELICOPTER AEROGRAPH

For aircraft obtaining weather or hurricane data on extended operational flights, Aerographs AN/AMQ-8 and AN/AMQ-17 provide a digital indication of humidity along with free-air temperature and atmospheric pressure at flight altitude.

The humidity sensor is of the carbon type [discussed in this volume by Stine (p. 316) and by Marchgraber and Grote (p. 331)] fabricated in a cylindrical shape to permit use in an axial-flow vortex thermometer probe, shown as an exploded view in Fig. 1. In flight the ram pressure of the air entering the probe from the right produces a vortex whose center is cooled by the Ranque[1] effect to produce a temperature at the humidity and temperature sensors equal to that of the free air, thus eliminating the requirement for calculating the dynamic heating normally produced in flight.[2, 3] Since

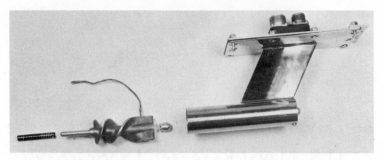

FIG. 1. Humidity and temperature probe for mounting on the outside of airplane fuselage.

the air pressure at the surface of the sensor varies slightly with flight speed, the calibration charts require adjustment to allow for this effect. The vapor pressure of humidity in the air sample is varied as the ratio of absolute pressure is varied in passing through the probe. The pressure change produces an equivalent dew-point change of $\frac{1}{2}$ to $1\frac{1}{2}$ deg C for flight speeds of 140 to 330 mph true air speed. The dew-point curves were plotted with a 1 deg C offset so that they might be used directly for most propeller aircraft flights. Between 330 and 440 mph, 1 deg C of dew point is added, the correction increasing with air speed as indicated in the curves of Ref. 4.

For micrometeorological measurements, e.g., to determine possible radar beam refraction by thin moisture layers in the atmosphere, the same types of sensors were mounted in an aspirated housing designed to be suspended 40 ft below a helicopter as shown in Fig. 2. This method of exposure permits the sensors to be located in air which has not been disturbed by the downward wash from the helicopter rotor blades, provided a forward speed of at least 15 knots is maintained. The seemingly simple requirement to measure humidity from a helicopter contains several nonobvious hazards (which can easily be fatal) if the sonde unit does not have correct aerodynamics, density, balance, and cable-reeling provisions.

The data from the aircraft vortex thermometer probe and from the helicopter suspended sonde is cabled into a servo-driven recorder[5] where it is recorded in printed digits together with a superimposed graph of the data in another color over each column of digital data. This type of record permits an approximation of data trends, yet provides a readout accuracy which is available only with digital recording.

WATER CONTENT OF CLOUDS

An aircraft probe is under development to provide an absolute measurement of total- and liquid-water content in clouds and of the humidity of the air outside and inside of clouds. The principle of operation of this instrument is the evaporation of liquid water or ice of the cloud and the measurement of humidity of the sample to determine the total-

FIG. 2. Helicopter sonde suspended in flight.

water content. This humidity measurement may be read out either in terms of mass of water vapor per unit volume of air or the dew point of the sample or, as in our case, in both units. The cloud sample passes continuously and rapidly through an electric evaporative heater, then is measured by an ultraviolet spectral absorption hygrometer using the hydrogen Lyman-alpha spectral line as discussed in this volume by Tillman (p. 428) and by Randall *et al.* (p. 444). This sensor is capable of providing about .01 second time response to moisture changes appearing in the sampling path of the hydrogen-Lyman-alpha light beam.

The overall time response of the instrument depends not only on the Lyman-alpha sensor response but also on the time required for the sample to pass through the evaporator. With a 1-cm diameter entry and a plane speed of 150 knots, a heater power of 500 watts can heat the sample sufficiently to achieve evaporation in about .01 second for passage from entry to detector. If a limited amount of power is available on the plane, a smaller heater entry must be used with correspondingly slower time response of the overall instrument. A larger diameter of entry improves the probability of intercepting a representative sample of the various droplet sizes, particularly the larger drops which may be present in quite small numbers per unit of cloud volume, yet contribute a major portion of the liquid-water content. The present developmental model incorporates an entry diameter of one centimeter which permits sampling one liter of air in approximately 12 meters of flight path if the flow through the entry is isokinetic. Achieving isokinetic flow is important in order to prevent a variable collection efficiency for the various sizes of droplets entering the probe. In order to avoid diverting small droplets around the entry by ram pressure buildup ahead of the entry, the flow must be relatively unrestricted through the evaporator and the Lyman-alpha sampling space; furthermore, a negative pressure must be applied at the discharge point of the air sample leaving the probe. This suction is provided aerodynamically by discharging the sample at a point just aft of the maximum thickness portion of the probe.

While the Lyman-alpha detector has the advantage of extremely fast time response in measuring humidity, it has the disadvantage of being somewhat unstable in terms of calibration drift. In order to provide an absolute calibration of the total water probe, the Lyman-alpha indication is almost continuously compared with that of a dew-point hygrometer sampling a parallel humidity sample. Readings of the two sensors should be identical during flight through clear air. The dew-point-hygrometer sample, however, enters the probe at a point near the trailing edge of the probe such that liquid water is not present at the inlet since centrifuging occurs as the air flows over the probe. The water-vapor content indicated by the dew-point sensor during flight through a cloud will deviate from that of the Lyman-alpha sensor by an amount equal to the liquid-water content per unit volume of the cloud.

The developmental model probe shown in Fig. 3 incorporated a dew-point sensor of the design previously used in the NRL balloon-borne frost-point hygrometer of the type discussed in this volume by Nathan (p. 155). Instead of the liquid refrigerant used for balloon flights, the same condensation mirror was cooled by a thermoelectric Peltier cooler. Mirror surface temperature was automatically maintained at the dew-point temperature by an induction heater whose oscillator current was controlled by the optical balance of photo detectors located .to be sensitive to changes from a preset level of dew or frost deposit on the mirror surface. The air inlet near the center of the probe in Figs. 3(a) and (b) was used to admit air for cooling the thermoelectric cooler heat sink fins. The Lyman-alpha source tube is visible at the upper left in Fig. 3(b). This probe was mounted on a circular plate which was used in place of a standard window in a "Superconstellation" plane during flight tests. A later model probe is designed to incorporate a commercially available thermo-electric dew-point sensor such as that described in this volume by Paine and Farrah (p. 174).

BALLOON-BORNE FROST-POINT HYGROMETER

The basic balloon-borne dew-point/frost-point sensor mentioned above (as applied to aircraft use for cloud water content) has been

A

B

Fig. 4) to duct the sample to the mirror from about $1\frac{1}{2}$ ft away from the instrument body, which also may be permeated with moisture adsorbed at ground level. When taking stratospheric data during the descent portion of balloon flights (to avoid moisture from the flight train) frost-point values as low as $-95°C$ have been measured as discussed by Mastenbrook.[6]

VORTEX DEW-POINT HYGROMETER

Before the availability of thermoelectrically cooled dew-point hygrometers, a need existed for an automatic dew-point instrument with self-contained cooling, particularly for arctic use. Research[4] on Ranque-Hilsch vortex cooling led to a working model dew-point hygrometer in which the condensation mirror could be cooled 45 deg C below ambient temperature by means of a self-contained air compressor which pumped the sample air under pressure through a small heat exchanger to remove a portion of the heat of compression. The sample then entered tangentially into a vortex cooling

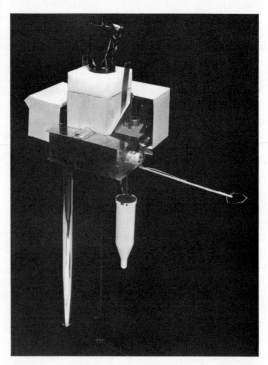

FIG. 4. Balloon-borne frost point sonde; stainless steel inlet duct extends below. On other models inlet extends to side.

FIG. 3. A. Developmental model of cloud water content probe for mounting on plane. Air discharge holes are visible beneath probe. Hole in end cap is temporary observation hole normally closed. B. Probe with cover removed showing heater inlet at top of figure, Lyman-alpha source tube behind heater; dew-point sensor enclosed. Pressure lines are for experimental pressure measurements at various points during flight.

refined for stratospheric balloon flights (Fig. 4) using liquid "Freon-13" for coolant instead of a thermoelectric cooler. Emphasis has been placed on reducing the amount of adsorbed moisture from ground level gaining access to the sensor during stratospheric measurements where the moisture level is of the order of one-millionth of that at ground level. Stainless steel is used (visible extending downward in tube. Hot air (above inlet temperature) was discharged from one end of this tube and cold air was discharged from a hole in the center of the other end. The amount of temperature difference was dependent on the pressure at the inlet, the fraction of cold *vs* hot air discharged, and by several factors in the design of the vortex tube. In general, designs which generate a large temperature drop require high inlet pressures and deliver a small percentage (of the order of 5 per cent) of cold air *vs* hot air. Tubes designed for smaller temperature drop can deliver up to one-third of the total air from the cold side.

The dew-point hygrometer incorporated a vortex tube designed to operate from a built-in ½-hp air compressor and provide 45 deg C of cooling with 35-psi inlet pressure. An amount of cooled air sample was provided sufficient to cool a small mirror whose stem extended into the cold air discharge hole of the vortex tube. The cold air temperature could be changed instantaneously by changing the throttling of the hot discharge end of the vortex tube. Balanced photodetectors maintained the dew deposit on the mirror at a preset size by servo controlling a small valve which simultaneously controlled the hot air discharge and the air pressure at the inlet to the vortex tube. Since the air sample temperature at the mirror was within a few degrees above dew point, temperature gradients in the mirror were small enough to permit the use of a fine wire resistance thermometer as well as a thermocouple for monitoring mirror temperature.

During development of the vortex dew-point hygrometer, a series of interesting experiments were conducted to determine the feasibility of monitoring condensation of fog in a continuous sample being cooled by the vortex tube with the temperature controlled by the servo valve. The temperature of the sample at the beginning of visible condensation was found to be unreliable as a measure of dew point, particularly below freezing. Liquid water condensing out of the sample reduced the vapor density (whereas, when the condensate is collected on a mirror surface the amount of condensate is held at an equilibrium level such that no further moisture is removed from the sample). The number and size of fog particles varied according to the number and nature of condensation nuclei present in the

sample. Use of a radioactive source did not provide a significant increase in the number of condensation centers which would be active at low supersaturations. At lower temperatures the fog was sometimes still invisible until the temperature was lowered well below the dew point of the sample.

HEATED AIR PSYCHROMETER

Several types of electric wet-bulb psychrometers were developed to indicate the vapor pressure of the air independently of preheating of the sample.[7] By heating the sample, the temperature of the wet bulb could be maintained above freezing without changing the psychrometer indication of vapor pressure.

The basic principle of operation of all of the types is to provide an electrical signal proportional to the saturation vapor pressure at the temperature of the wet bulb, then subtract therefrom another electrical signal which is proportional to the product of barometric pressure and wet-to-dry bulb difference in accordance with the Ferrel equation:[8]

$$e = e' - 0.000367 \, P(t - t') \left[1 + \left(\frac{t' - 32}{1571} \right) \right]$$

where

$e =$ pressure of water vapor at temperature t

$e' =$ saturation pressure of water vapor at temperature t'

$t =$ temperature of dry bulb

$t' =$ temperature of wet bulb

$p =$ barometric pressure expressed in same units as e and e'.

Since the wet bulb temperature is never permitted to be below 32°F, the factor $1 + (t' - 32)/1571$ may be considered to be unity with insignificant reduction of accuracy.

Using a simple Wheatstone bridge circuit such as is shown in Fig. 5, temperature of the wet bulb can be measured electrically by use of a linear resistance thermometer element[9] (labeled EL) with its resistance balanced against that of a fixed resistance S by adjusting a potentiometer (labeled Temp. Bal. Pot) geared directly to an indicator. A and B are equal fixed resistors, and the value of S may be chosen equal to the resistance of the element at the midpoint of the temperature range desired. The calibration trimmer can be omitted, or 1 or 2Ω can be used for convenience in adjusting for deviation of the various components from their nominal values. In practice, an adjustable shunt resistor is connected across the potentiometer to adjust for inaccuracy of the nominal slope or span of the element and potentiometer. The same type of bridge can be used to measure the difference in temperature between the wet-and dry-bulb temperatures if the fixed resistor S is replaced by a second resistance-thermometer element and both elements are linear.

In one type of heated air psychrometer, the wet bulb temperature was measured by a bridge using a resistance thermometer element whose resistance varied nonlinearly in a manner to cause the bridge-balancing potentiometer to indicate directly the saturation vapor pressure at the wet-bulb temperature. The difference-bridge-balancing potentiometer was shunted with a variable resistance which was adjusted according to independently measured barometric pressure and thus changed the proportionality constant of the difference - bridge - balancing potentiometer. The shaft of this potentiometer was inter-

connected with the saturation-vapor-pressure potentiometer through a mechanical subtracting linkage to provide an indication of ambient vapor pressure. The main problem in quantity duplication of this type of instrument was the technical competence required in properly padding a thermistor with nickel resistance thermometer wire and a fixed resistor to provide the proper resistance-temperature curve to provide a bridge indication of saturation vapor pressure.

In another type of heated air psychrometer, the bridge of Fig. 5 was used to measure the wet-bulb temperature, but instead of simply indicating the value of wet-bulb temperature, the indicator was geared to drive another potentiometer which was wound nonlinearly with the resistance proportional to the saturation vapor pressure of water at each temperature indicated. In Fig. 6, this vapor-pressure-function potentiometer is shown in the lower right corner. The vapor-pressure balance potentiometer in the small bridge in the lower right of Fig. 6 automatically followed the resistance of the vapor-pressure-function potentiometer and read out saturation vapor pressure on its indicator if the wet- and dry-

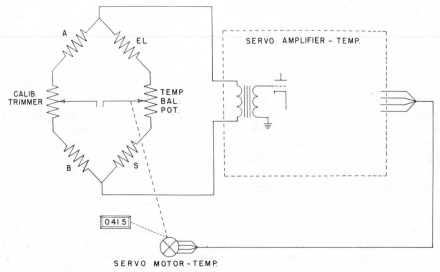

Fig. 5. Schematic diagram of Wheatstone bridge for resistance-thermometer measurement of ambient or wet-bulb temperature.

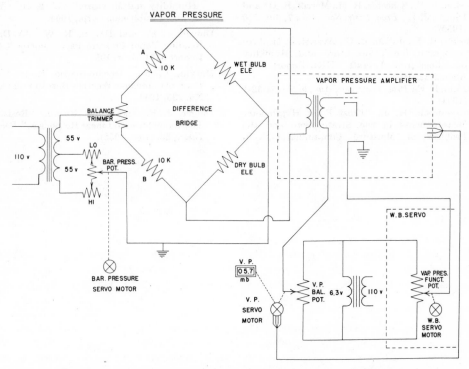

FIG. 6. Schematic circuit of vapor pressure bridges for heated air psychrometer.

bulb temperatures were equal so that no signal came out of the difference bridge in the upper center of Fig. 6. If the wet bulb was cooler than the dry bulb, then the difference bridge applied a signal in the input transformer of the vapor pressure amplifier, shifting the null point of this servo to a point corresponding to the difference between the original voltage and that from the difference bridge. This latter voltage was modified slightly by the barometric pressure to complete the requirements for following the Ferrell equation to indicate the vapor pressure of the air sample. The inlet heater power was controlled automatically by the wet-bulb servo such as to maintain the wet bulb slightly above freezing.

SUMMARY

The requirements for humidity measurements vary considerably for the various applications within the Navy. In addition to the instruments discussed above, a need exists for improved shipboard instrumentation, particularly to improve fog forecasting by

better accuracy for nearly-saturated conditions. Contamination by salt spray complicates the problem. Attempts are underway to adapt a commercially available dew-point hygrometer such as that described in this volume by Francisco and Beaubien (p. 165) to reduce the effects of salt-spray contamination on shipboard.

For most Navy applications emphasis must be placed on ease of operation and maintenance by relatively untrained personnel in the fleet. Frequently the usual criteria for determining the feasibility of an instrument are secondary to problems created by the specific type of application to which the instrument will be subjected in Naval operations.

References

1. Ranque, M. G., *J. Phys. Radium*, **4**, 112–115 (1933).
2. Ruskin, R. E., Schecter, R. M., Dinger, J. E., and Merrill, R. D., "Development of the NRL Axial-Flow Vortex Thermometer," NRL Report 4008, Sept. 1952.

3. Ruskin, R. E., Schecter, R. M., Merrill, R. D., and Dinger, J. E., *Proc. Instr. Soc. Am.*, **7**, 308–310 (1952).

4. Ruskin, R. E., Julian, B. G., Averitt, J. M., "An Aerograph for Temperature and Humidity Soundings from Aircraft," NRL Report 5166, August 22, 1958.

5. Ruskin, R. E., *Proc. Instr. Soc. Am.*, **9**, No. 54-32-1 (1954).

6. Mastenbrook, H. J., "Frost Point Hygrometer Measurements in the Stratosphere and the Problem of Moisture Contamination," in "Humidity and Moisture," Vol. 2, New York, Reinhold Publishing Corp., 1964.

7. Dinger, J. E., and Brown, R. W., "A Direct-Reading Vapor-Pressure Psychrometer," NRL Report 3731, Sept. 1950.

8. Marvin, C. F., "Psychrometric Tables," U.S. Dept. of Commerce Weather Bureau Publication No. 235, 1941.

9. Dinger, J. E., and R. E. Ruskin, "Resistance Thermometer with Linear Responses," *Rev. Sci. Instr.*, **23**, (Dec. 1952).

67. A Technique for the Continuous Indication of Medium-Low Water Vapor Pressures

R. G. Wylie, W. A. Caw and N. W. Bryant

National Standards Laboratory, C.S.I.R.O., Sydney, Australia

ABSTRACT

A hygrometer suitable for recording water vapor pressures in the range of dew points from 0 to −50°C is described. The water vapor in a stream of air is converted into a combustible gas by passing it through a bed of solid reactant. The quantity of combustible gas so produced is then measured by burning it catalytically at the surface of a platinum wire and recording the temperature difference between the wire and a similar reference wire in the air upstream of the reactant.

INTRODUCTION

Over the last decade there has been a considerable increase in the importance of hygrometry at low humidities. This has occurred particularly in the compressed gas industry, in furnace atmosphere control, in nuclear engineering and in the chemical industry. In some cases dew points as low as −70°C are involved, where the problems of measurement are very difficult and for which special methods have been developed, but long-standing problems still exist in the refrigeration industries in regard to dew points in the range of 0 to −50°C. There is a need for a simple method of recording humidity in this range, which includes the dew points encountered in cold storage and freezing rooms. The present paper describes a method which can meet this need in many cases.

The methods at present available for the measurement of dew points below 0°C depend on a remarkable variety of physical principles. The frost-point method is often used, but, in a form suitable for recording, the apparatus is not simple. The cloud-chamber method,[1] exemplified in the well-known "Alnor" hygrometer, is suitable for direct observations but cannot easily be adapted for recording. Again, the hygroscopic film comparator method, developed by Weaver and co-workers,[2] is unsuitable for recording, and in any case finds its main use in the very low dew-point range. The hygrometer most adaptable to recording low humidities is that due to Keidel,[3] which is becoming known as the coulometric hygrometer. It, too, is used mainly for the very low range, below −50°C, and by reason of its nature it is not suitable for dew points much closer to 0°C. The present method, which is particularly suitable for dew points in the range 0 to −30°C, is therefore attractive. It has a simple physicochemical basis, and its characteristics agree reasonably well with the theoretical expectations. It can provide an accuracy of better than 5 per cent in the vapor pressure for dew points not far below 0°C, and it has a response time of a few minutes. The apparatus involved is easy to make and has stable characteristics.

In the following, the essentials of the method are described and some results are given to indicate its capabilities. These results were obtained with a laboratory version of the apparatus. No attempt has been made to design a compact instrument.

651

THE METHOD

The basis of the method is to pass the gas sample continuously through a chemical reactant which converts the water vapor present into a more easily detectable gas. In the particular method used, a reactant in the form of a granulated solid converts the water vapor into a gas which can be burnt with oxygen, and this gas is detected by the heat which is liberated when it is oxidized catalytically at an electrically heated platinum wire.

Calcium hydride, sodamide and calcium carbide, which have been used as the solid reactant, produce respectively hydrogen, ammonia and acetylene, when acted upon by water vapor. Of these the calcium carbide has given the best results, as well as the greatest sensitivity. The reaction of calcium carbide with water has been used widely in the determination of the moisture in solids by batch methods.[4] The chemistry of the conversion process is only approximately described by the usual simple chemical equation, in which the products are acetylene and calcium hydroxide. One reason for this is that commercially available calcium carbide is only about 80 per cent pure, the main impurity being calcium oxide. The chemical reactions change substantially if the temperature is raised; indeed, if the calcium carbide reaction vessel is heated to 150°C, no combustible component and no water vapor is present in the issuing gas. At ordinary temperatures, roughly 20 per cent less acetylene is obtained than the expected mole per 2 moles of water vapor. Thus, to some extent the conversion process is an empirical one. It might be necessary to recalibrate the instrument at one point if a different supply of calcium carbide were used.

To detect the acetylene, two small platinum coils connected into adjacent arms of a simple wheatstone bridge are used. The general arrangement is shown in Fig. 1(a). The moist air (oxygen, etc.) enters a tube containing one of the platinum coils, and after passing over that coil, passes through the reactant and emerges with the water vapor replaced by acetylene. It then passes into the tube containing the second platinum coil. At this coil, heat is liberated by the combustion process, so that the temperature, and hence the electrical resistance, of the coil is changed. The resulting out-of-balance voltage of the bridge is recorded with a suitable instrument. The calibration depends on the rate of flow of the gas, which must, therefore, be held constant. The pressure drop in the reactant is negligible.

If no special measures are taken, the calcium hydrate formed in the granular reactant builds up on the inlet side, and the moist gas must pass through this product before reaching unreacted carbide. Because of adsorption of the water vapor in the very hydrophilic hydrate, eventually the speed of response to a change in water vapor pressure is greatly reduced and, even more important, the results become unreliable. It has been found that this

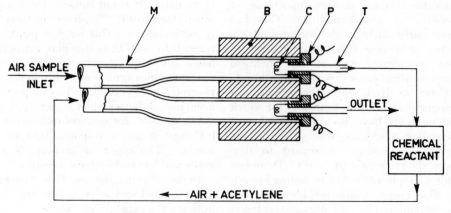

Fig. 1. (a) Section of catalytic detector.

M Copper tube   C Platinum coil
B Copper block   P Fiber plug
T Outlet tube

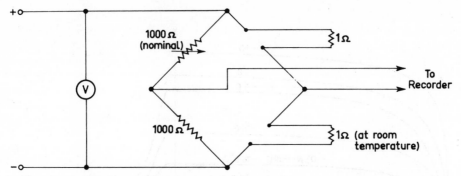

Fig. 1. (b) Electrical circuit (V = voltmeter). The 1-Ω resistors are the platinum coils. The 1000-Ω resistors are decade boxes.

undesirable feature can be removed if the bed of reactant is tapped regularly by a mechanical device, so that the hydrate formed largely falls out into a suitable trap. Actually, there is always a little hydrate in the bed, for some of it is firmly attached to the surface of each decomposing grain.

EXPERIMENTAL RESULTS

Many aspects of the technique have been investigated experimentally; some investigations are still in progress. No attempt will be made to report the work fully here, but two sets of experimental results will be given to show the value of the method. These results have been obtained with the experimental cell shown in Fig. 2. This cell comprises a vessel V, which contains the reactant, and a detachable bulb B which collects the calcium hydroxide released by the tapping action of the fiber hammer H. The cell is tapped about once per second, and with sufficient impulse to produce obvious movement of the grains of reactant. The cell is supported in a relatively elastic mounting. The capillary tube C, through which the falling hydrate passes, provides a diffusion resistance which ensures that the gas entering the cell is not affected appreciably by the hydrate in the bulb B.

The sensing head of the experimental instrument is as shown in Fig. 1(a). The copper tubes M, which are approximately 1 cm in bore, are soft-soldered together for about 20 cm, to assist in equalizing the temperatures of the gas streams reaching the platinum coils, and are soft-soldered into a cylindrical copper block B, with its axis

parallel to the tubes, to ensure that the coils have the same environmental temperature. A large annular cooling disc [not shown in Fig. 1(a)] ensures that the heat dissipated by the coils does not cause an excessive rise in the temperature of the block B.

The platinum coils (approximately 3 mm in diameter) are made from wire of 0.1-mm diameter. Each consists of 4 convolutions of wire, and is welded at its ends to 0.5-mm

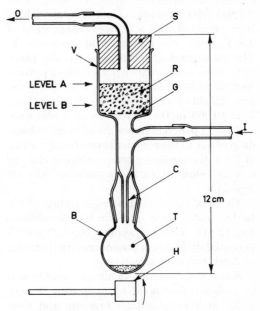

Fig. 2. Section of reactor vessel.

I inlet	G gauge
O outlet	C capillary tube
S stopper	T trap for calcium
R reactant calcium	hydrate
carbide	V vessel for reactant

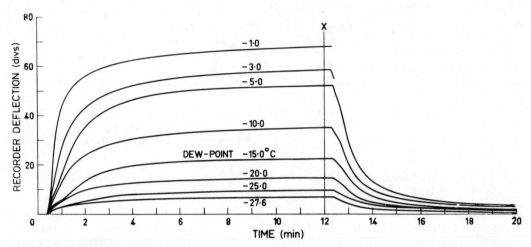

Fig. 3. Response of the hygrometer to step changes in water vapor pressure from very dry to the dew points shown, and back to very dry.

platinum wires, which pass through the fiber plugs P. The resistance of each coil at room temperature is about 1 Ω.

The simple Wheatstone bridge circuit is as shown in Fig. 1(b). It has usually been operated from a storage battery, but can equally be operated from a small, well-regulated power supply. The results given here were obtained with a bridge voltage drop of 3.5 V, which was indicated on the meter V. The corresponding temperature of the platinum wire, measured with an optical pyrometer, is 1100°C. Under these conditions the zero stability is remarkably good, being about 1 in 10,000 in the resistance of a platinum coil over a period of hours. At a bridge voltage drop of 4.5 V, the zero drifts noticeably, while at 2.5 V the operating temperature is close to a limit below which the sensitivity falls off rapidly.

The maximum out-of-balance voltage of the bridge under these experimental conditions was 12 mV. This was applied through a 6 : 1 potential divider to a potentiometric recorder of 2-mV full-scale sensitivity.

A continuous stream of air was conditioned to a chosen dew point by saturating it over water at a suitable high pressure and then expanding it through a needle valve to atmospheric pressure. It was then passed through the apparatus at a flow rate of 1 cc/sec. Figure 3 shows the recorded deflection for a step rise of humidity from zero to each of

several levels and a step return to zero humidity. It is seen that reasonably steady conditions are reached in 5 minutes. The response time is not a great deal longer at the lowest humidities as compared with the highest. The long tails of these curves are a feature associated with the use of gas of zero humidity.

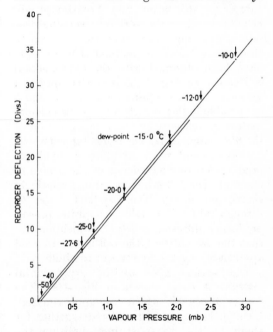

Fig. 4. Calibration of the hygrometer using a fresh bed, full points; and the same bed after a total of 320 hours at a dew point of −15°C, open circles. The level of the bed dropped from A to B in Fig. 2.

Steps between levels above zero result in a more rapid approach to a steady reading.

Figure 4 shows the results of calibrations of the apparatus and a measurement of the life of the reactant charge. The cell was filled with the carbide to the level A (Fig. 2). The apparatus was then operated at a gas flow rate of 1 cc/sec, and the calibration shown by black dots was obtained. Operation was then continued (with some interruptions) for a total period of 320 hours, using gas of dew point −15°C. At the end of this time, the carbide had fallen to the level B (Fig. 2). The calibration was then repeated, and the points shown as small open circles in Fig. 4 were obtained. The calibration has the same slope, within close limits, but is slightly displaced due to a small error in the zero setting. The response time to humidity changes was much the same in both calibrations. It is clear that the characteristics of the apparatus are little changed as the bed of carbide is consumed.

CONCLUSIONS

The method described is capable of recording the humidity of air for dew points down to −50°C. Its accuracy is about 0.1 mb (1 mb = ¾ mm Hg) in the water vapor pressure, and the response time is a few minutes. The apparatus is simple to construct and relatively rugged. Many possible applications of the method are to be found in investigations relating to the conditions in cold-storage rooms.

Scope exists for the more detailed study of the chemistry and physical chemistry of the conversion process which occurs in the bed of reactant. This process very largely determines the accuracy and speed of response of the instrument.

References

1. D.S.I.R. Food Investigations, Special Report No. 8, "The Measurement of Humidity in Closed Spaces," H.M. Stationery Office, Revised edition, 1933.
2. Weaver, E. R., Hughes, E. E., and Diniak. A. W., "Determination of Water Vapor from the Change in Electrical Resistance of a Hygroscopic Film," *J. Res. Natl. Bur. Std.*, **60**, 489 (1958).
3. Keidel, F. A., "Determination of Water by Direct Amperometric Measurements," *Anal. Chem.*, **31**, 2043 (1959).
4. Geary, P. J., "Determination of Moisture in Solids," B.S.I.R.A. Research Report M.24, 1956.

68. Detection and Measurement of Humidity and Moisture by the Hygrophotographic Technique

M. JOSEPH SIVADJIAN

Institut Pasteur, Paris, France

ABSTRACT

Among the different methods of detection and measurement of humidity which have been described, hygrophotography occupies a special place for different reasons. The principle, which is new and unknown for other chemical compounds, is the reversibility of a photochemical reaction accompanied by a change of coloration which disappears instantly under the action of a small quantity of water and of humidity.

It, therefore, permits the recording of the water emitted by a source of humidity at the place of its emission and associates, in this way, chemical sensibility with photographic precision.

The hygrophotographic plates or films composed of a complex salt of silver and mercuric proto-iodide, can be very easily calibrated and serve in the micro determination of small quantities of water discharged. They can be prepared either with the conventional photographic films or plates, or with colloidal silver and mercuric bi-iodide, made into an emulsion in a solution of gelatin at 5 per cent.

Also, because of the principle of the method, the hygrophotographic plates and films must be carefully exposed to daylight or an intense source of artificial light, and blackened before being used for the detection and the recording of humidity. Still owing to this principle, the hygrophotographic plates and films were able to be used with success in almost all the scientific and industrial domains covered by this Symposium.

Because the hygrophotographic material is very sensitive to atmospheric humidity, the results which are recorded must be definitely established with the printing on conventional photographic films and plates by the contact process. Disclosed and recorded, by the aid of this method, were traces of water in organic liquids such as alcohols, acetone, etc. The diffusion of water through organic liquids which are not miscible in water was studied, as well as the retardation of the evaporation by the monolayers. The study of the permeability to water and moisture of most of the sheets of commercial plastics materials has been possible, thanks to the aid of the European Research Office of the U.S. Department of Defense.

The moisture content and the distribution of humidity in foods (butter, margarine, sausage, etc.) was studied by the hygrophotographic method, which also permitted the measurement of the humidity of the soil and the determination of the wilting point in agriculture. In plant physiology, lengthy research was carried out on plant transpiration and its variations under the influence of different causes and factors. In human and animal physiology, the hygrophotographic method renders a very great service in the study of perspiration and the physiology of sweat glands. It permits the accurate recording of the topographic distribution of these glands and the dermatoglyphic identification of individuals by the aid of this recording. In pharmacology, the perspiration of the palm and sole of rats and mice may be studied, as well as the action of various drugs on this perspiration. In meteorology, different meteorologists have studied the distribution of rain drops by recording them on hygrophotographic plates.

INTRODUCTION

Among the different methods of detection and measurement of humidity which have been described, hygrophotography occupies a special place for several reasons. The principle, which is new and unknown for other chemical compounds, is the reversibility of a photochemical reaction accompanied by a change of coloration which disappears instantly under the action of a small quantity of water and of humidity.

In the same way as photography is the art of obtaining images by exposing a sensitive surface to light, hygrophotography is the name I have given to the process by which an image can be obtained on a sensitive surface by combined action of light and humidity.

It, therefore, permits the recording of the water emitted by a source of humidity at the place of its emission, and in this way, it associates chemical sensibility with photographic precision.

The sensitive surface of a hygrophotographic plate or film has the property of changing its color when exposed first to light and then to water or humidity. It can be prepared from an ordinary photographic plate by impregnating the emulsion with a double salt of mercury and silver iodide. The plate, coated in this way, is normally yellow, but when it is exposed to light, it changes color and becomes blackish-violet. Its most remarkable property after exposure is its great sensitivity to water, which restores it to its original yellow.

THE HYGROPHOTOGRAPHIC TECHNIQUE

The first method of preparing hygrophotographic plates with conventional photographic materials is the following.

The silver bromide plate or film (containing no coloring matter or sensitizer of any kind), after immersion in the developer solution (methol-hydroquinone) in the darkroom, is brought into daylight, fully developed, summarily washed and fixed in a hyposulfite solution with the object of removing any trace of unreduced bromide. Next, after careful washing, it is dipped in a 3 per cent solution of mercuric chloride in which it bleaches

completely. Then, for removal of excess mercuric chloride, it is immersed again for 15 to 20 minutes in a basin filled with water (not running water), and transferred to a solution of potassium iodide where the plate gradually turns a yellow color which, when uniform, is without trace of the white chloride or orange tint. This may be ascertained by examining the plate from the side of the backing. The plate is then removed from the bath, quickly rinsed in water, and allowed to dry.

These reactions take place according to the following formulas:

$$Ag + HgCl_2 = HgAgCl_2$$

$$HgAgCl_2 + 2KI = HgAgI_2 + 2KCl$$

The choice of concentration of the potassium iodide solution has a very important bearing on the success of the results. We first established it at 0.5 per cent, since the stronger concentrations brought about a total blackening of the hygrophotographic plates. However, from time to time a superficial blackening of the plates was observed even with this concentration; it caused no inconvenience, however, as long as quantitative measurements and calibration were not attempted. After applying the microdosage method of water with the aid of hygrophotographic plates, the determination of the most favorable concentration was once more attempted. We arrived at the conclusion that it depends on the nature and brand of the plate used, varying between 0.50 and 0.25 per cent. As an example, we discovered that with the orthochromatic plates, without any coloring matter, and especially with "Lactate" plates, 9 × 12 cm, the optimal concentration of potassium iodide was 0.25 per cent; the most dilute solutions are not of any use. On the other hand, with the films, the iodide solution at 0.50 per cent never gave any problems.

Our practice is to carry out this operation in two stages: after fixing and washing of the plates, they are put to dry. It is not until the next morning, when all the plates are completely dry, that they are put in the solution. of mercuric chloride for bleaching.

The plates are left to soak for a period of 15 to 20 minutes in fresh water to take out the excess of mercuric chloride which gives a red coloration in the presence of potassium iodide. (The plates should not be washed in running water.) They are then put into a liter of 0.25 per cent potassium iodide solution, and they are left there until the entire plate has become uniformly yellow; this is verified by an examination of the supporting side.

If, in spite of the washing, the plates become a little red at the surface, this can be removed by rubbing the red parts with the fingers.

When the toning is finished, the plates are quickly rinsed and put to dry. During the toning, it is necessary to shake the liquid from time to time in order to avoid the formation of streaks along the edges, which are visible in the proofs.

A liter of mercuric chloride solution may be used several times in bleaching, but a liter of potassium iodide solution at 0.25 per cent used for the toning of six 9×12 plates is rejected after use.

The second method is the following: An equimolecular mixture of colloidal silver and mercuric iodide is heated at 52 to 55°C for about three hours, with stirring, in a 6 per cent gelatin solution. The color of the solution gradually changes to yellow. During this heating process the silver reduces the mercuric iodide, and is itself converted to an iodide, which, in the presence of the reduced mercury salt, gives the same double mercurosilver iodide.

A mere pouring of the emulsion onto glass plates or any support provides hygrophotographic plates identical with those made with conventional photographic silver bromide.

The double salt of mercury and silver obtained within the emulsion in the course of these operations is highly stable and insoluble. It is sensitive to the action of light which causes a rapid change of color from yellow to a violet black. But its outstanding feature, after exposure, is its great sensitivity to water and atmospheric humidity which act in such a way as to convert it to its original yellow hue.

It is this new and valuable property, the ability to record images and patterns under the combined action of light, in the first place, and humidity, in the second place, which enabled me to achieve a practical method of investigation which I have called hygrophotography.

By consequence, the use of hygrophotographic plates and films requires their previous blackening by exposure either to daylight or to a source of intense artificial light. In quantitative experiments, it is even necessary to avoid the blackening of the edges on the supporting side by reflection, protecting the back of the plates during their exposure to light. This can be accomplished by placing them in a photographic pressing frame.

Since the blackening of the hygrophotographic plates under the action of the light is not irreversible, it disappears gradually when the plates are kept in darkness. This is a result of the action of the atmospheric humidity, which brings about, at the same time, the disappearance of the image recorded on the plate.

Therefore, to conserve the images obtained, copies must be made of them on ordinary photographic paper of silver bromide, or even better, on transparencies by the contact process, the hygrophotographic plate serving as negative.

USES OF THE METHOD

Plant Physiology—Studies on Foliar Transpiration

For the recording of the transpiration of the leaves of green plants by means of hygrophotographic plates, the leaf of the plant,

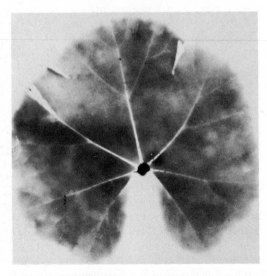

FIG. 1. Hygrophotograph showing the leaf transpiration.

detached or not, is placed between two hygrophotographic plates blackened in identical fashion and tightened very firmly with the aid of two clips.

When the hygrophotographic image obtained has enough detail, the exposure is stopped by removing the clips and separating the impressioned plates which will serve as ordinary negatives in the manner as explained above (Fig. 1).

The Humidity of the Soil

Since the relation between the plant and the soil on which it is grown is extremely close, the hygrophotographic plates were used to study the inequality in the distribution of humidity of the soil and to record this humidity at different depths.

To make this recording, following removal of a 23-mm wide strip (for the densitometric scale and calibration) from the 9×12-cm hygrophotographic plate, the remainder is wrapped in lightweight nylon material to protect the sensitive side against earth friction, and is sunk vertically into the earth as far as the black line showing the soil level. The plate is left there for a period of time which varies, according to the humidity of the soil, from one or two seconds to a few hours, after which it is joined to the calibrated fragments. The whole plate is then photographed by the contact process (Fig. 2).

The Sweat Glands and the Physiology of Perspiration

For the hygrophotographic study of the functioning of the sweat glands in the palm area and the sole of the feet, the subject puts his hand or his foot on a hygrophotographic film, previously blackened through exposure

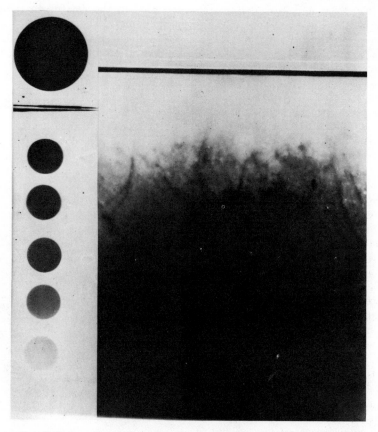

FIG. 2. Impression of the soil moisture content at a level of 3 cm under the surface.

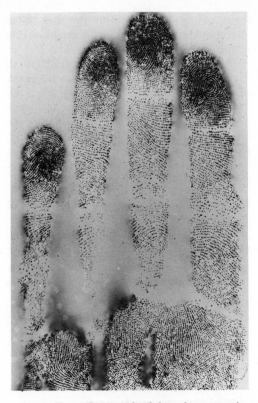

FIG. 3. Hygrophotograph of the palmar sweating.

a small piece of hygrophotographic film, previously blackened, is stuck to the sole of each of the two paws or to only one of them. The film is left in place for one minute, in the case of mice, and two minutes for rats. At the end of about two seconds, in the normal rat, the first specks of yellow begin to appear. After two minutes, the film is removed, and a copy is made of it by printing on a plate or a film for diapositives (Fig. 4).

Meteorology

A hygrophotographic plate, prepared and darkened as previously described, is coated on the darkened sensitive side with a thin layer of castor oil using a flat brush. It is necessary to wait a little while before exposing the slide to the rain or aerosol droplets, to allow the oil surface to become smooth. Then, having exposed the plate to the droplets, it is again necessary to wait a while, from a few seconds to a few minutes, to allow the droplets to be recorded in the gelatin on the hygrophotographic plate. The oil is then wiped off using a wad of cotton wool or rag, and, if necessary,

to light for a period which varies from a few seconds to a few minutes, according to the subject (Fig. 3).

Furthermore, the topographic study of the distribution of sweat glands is interesting because it makes possible personal identification by the examination of the dermatoglyphic patterns and certain characteristic sweat gland clusters on an outspread minimum of skin surface, not exceeding two square millimeters.

Pharmacology of the Skin

The hygrophotographic recording technique has further shown the manner in which the functioning of the sweat glands could be modified under the action of pharmacological agents.

To record the perspiration of the sole of the paws of rats and mice by hygrophotographic films, a fragment of film is applied to the bottom of the paw of the animal with the aid of a piece of adhesive tape. The animal is held by an assistant while, by means of tape,

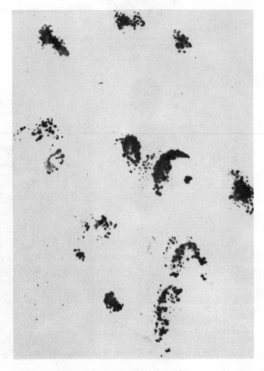

FIG. 4. Hygrophotograph, with 6X magnification, of the sole of the paw of a rat.

final traces of oil can be removed by washing the plate in chloroform. However, for obtaining a satisfactory contact print on the bromide paper or glass plate, cleaning with cotton wool is sufficient (Fig. 5).

Spider Web

When a prepared hygrophotographic plate is cautiously applied to a spider web of the Aranea genus, early in the morning when it is covered with dew or after a rain, a life-size image may be obtained of the web; such an image will reproduce the threads distended with dew or laden with drops of rain (Fig. 6).

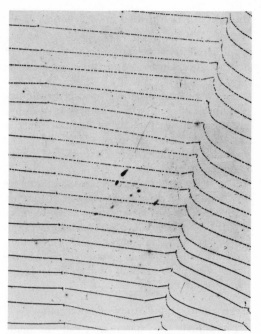

Fig. 6. Hygrophotograph of a spider's web wetted by morning dew.

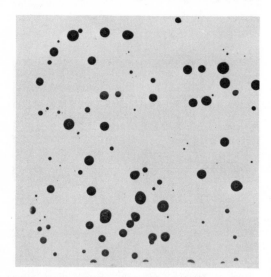

Fig. 5. Impression of drops obtained using a coating of castor oil on a hygrophotographic plate.

The Humidity of the Greasy Materials

When a hygrophotographic plate has been exposed to light and is ready for use, a section of a uniform and freshly made lump of butter or any other greasy solid material, such as margarine, having dimensions in proportion with those of the chosen plate, is then applied to the gelatin of the plate. The lump is held in place for 4 or 5 minutes, if butter is used, and longer for a product less rich in water; during this time a light pressure is exerted on it.

When the hygrophotographic image appears on the side of the support, the mass of greasy material is then taken off and the plate is cleaned carefully with a piece of cotton in order to eliminate the last portions of fatty material sticking to it. Then, a print is made by contact process on silver bromide paper or on transparencies, and the picture obtained of the distribution of the humidity in the greasy material is permanently attached (Fig. 7).

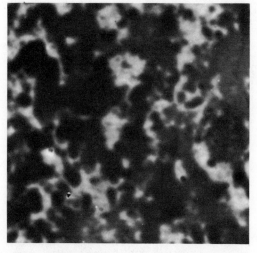

Fig. 7. Enlargement of a recording made with butter manufactured by the Fritz's continuous method (11X magnification).

Humidity in Dehydrated Food Products

Next, I have employed the hygrophotographic method to estimate the degree of hydration of sausages and other pork in the following manner. A slice of sausage 2 or 3 mm thick is pressed between two hygrophotographic plates and, after the preparation has been placed on a table, a suitable pressure is exerted on the superior plate until the appearance of the hygrophotographic image is sufficiently detailed.

The two plates are then removed and copies are made as described above, either on transparencies or on paper. To operate more rapidly, a copy is made on transparencies, and a negative of the transparencies is prepared on an identical plate which serves in turn to make prints on photographic paper or enlargements (Fig. 8).

Hygrophotographic Study of Detergency

I studied the detergency of nonionic surfactants in the following manner: two pieces of white cotton cloth are taken and soaked in melted vegetaline. They are then pressed between two sheets of filter paper, to take out the excess of grease, and are left to cool. The solution of the two surfactants whose detergent properties are to be com-

FIG. 9. Hygrophotograph showing the wetting activity of two detergents.

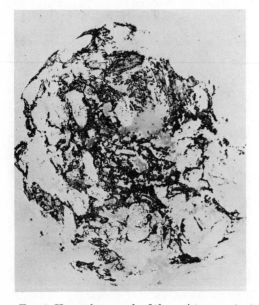

FIG. 8. Hygrophotograph of the moisture content of a pork sausage.

pared, are put into glass receptacles. These solutions are obtained by dissolving a gram of the product in 300 ml of distilled water. A cloth soaked in grease is then put into each of the solutions and stirred for a certain amount of time (twenty minutes, for example) by an agitator. These cloths are taken out after washing and rinsed in clear water, and the excess of water is removed by pressing them between two sheets of filter paper. This operation must be repeated, if necessary, in order to obtain a cloth which retains only the humidity in its fibers. This cloth is then pressed between a hygrophotographic plate and an ordinary transparent glass plate (obtained, for example, by scratching the gelatin of a used

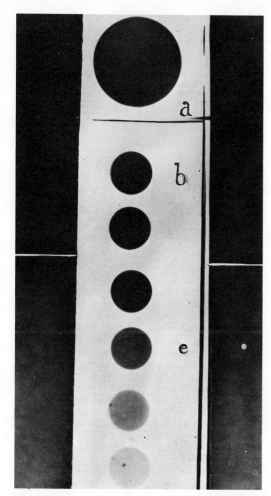

FIG. 10. Hygrophotographic recording of the water diffused through a packaging plastic sheet, with the densitometric scale for comparison.

photographic plate). When the hygrophotographic image is printed clearly enough, the usual photographic print is made (Fig. 9).

Permeability of Plastic Materials to Water and Moisture

I have also applied the hygrophotographic technique to the study of the permeability of packaging materials to water and moisture. In the particular domain of plastics, I have carried out very extensive research, thanks to the subsidy granted by the European Research Office of the U.S. Department of the Army, a grant which lasted for three years.

The technique consists of preparing bags of plastic material containing hygrophotographic

plates. These bags are hermetically sealed by fusion after creating a vacuum within them which is submitted to the action of a humidity source at temperatures varying from 25 to 95°C. Finally, the quantity of humidity which passes through the plastic bag is measured by comparison with a densitometric scale as shown in Fig. 10.

Analytical Applications—Detection of Minute Quantities of Water in the Organic Solvents

The hygrophotographic technique allows for the detection and measurement of trace amounts of water in organic solvents, such as absolute alcohol. If a drop of commercial absolute alcohol is placed on ash-free filter paper, and this paper, covered with a sheet of ordinary glass, is placed in a pressure frame directly against a hygrophotographic plate previously blackened by exposure, this drop of alcohol extends freely by absorption into the thickness of the paper. However, the very small quantity of water which must be present in the commercial alcohol passes from the paper into the gelatin on which it produces a yellow ring. This ring becomes black in the positive image and surrounds a gray area (Fig. 11).

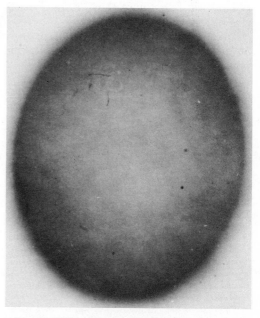

FIG. 11. Hygrophotographic image of the moisture contained in a drop of absolute alcohol.

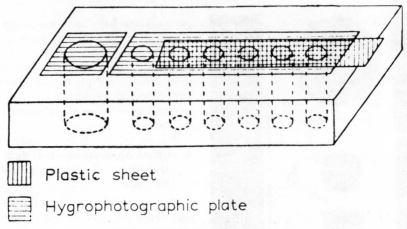

|||| Plastic sheet

▦ Hygrophotographic plate

FIG. 12. "Plexiglas" block for calibration.

CALIBRATION OF THE HYGROPHOTO-GRAPHIC PLATES AND DETERMINATION OF HUMIDITY

A circular recess, 0.748 in. in diameter (19.4 mm) and 0.472 in. deep (12 mm) is bored out of a "Perspex" ("Plexiglas") block 0.748 in. (19 mm) thick, 5.511 in. (140 mm) long, and 1.968 in. (50 mm) wide. A little farther on, six much smaller cavities, 0.356 in. (9 mm) in diameter and 0.472 in. (12 mm) deep, are also made. These cavities are filled with pure water at equal levels, in our arrangement 0.157 in. (4 mm) from the top of the "Perspex" block (Fig. 12).

To calibrate the hygrophotographic plate by means of this arrangement, the following procedure is used:

As described above (p. 659), a narrow strip 0.905 in. (23 mm) wide is cut from the 9 × 12 cm plate; then a small square is cut from one end of the strip. Another square piece of the same size (cut from an unserviceable hygrophotographic plate) is applied to the first square (on the gelatin side), and the two pieces are weighed in a microbalance. During this operation, they are joined by a clip provided with a ring for suspension to one scale of the balance. A counterweight, consisting of two identical pieces (unserviceable), is set on the other balance scale. Equilibrium is restored by adding the balance weights required.

The piece of plate to be calibrated, thus weighed, is then placed above the larger cavity of the "Perspex" block previously blocked off with a very thin, adequately rigid, transparent, and impervious plastic sheet. The diameter of this cavity and, therefore, its area are known.

The plate is held firmly in position by weights set on it for 2 minutes. Care should be taken to protect it against too strong a light and to cover it, if need be,

with black paper. Then the pressure is reduced, and the cavity is uncovered by cautiously removing the plastic material. This time, the plate is held in position for 12 minutes. The time mentioned may vary within broad limits according to room temperature. (At an average of 72°F (22 to 23°C), the "exposure" required 12 to 18 minutes, the time during which moisture absorption by the plate, as a function of time, retains its linear aspect.)

At this point in our experiments, a circular discolored area shows up on the plate. This is promptly removed from the block, and the gelatin surface of the plate to be calibrated is covered at once by the gelatin surface of the other piece. These are joined by means of the clip and reweighed. The difference between the two weighings is the quantity of water absorbed and fixed by the hygrophotographic plate. (The outer plate prevents the loss in weight of the plate to be calibrated through evaporation of its moisture at the time of the second weighing, the moisture so lost being absorbed by the outer plate.) Since the area of the discolored surface and the quantity of water absorbed by it are known, the quantity of water fixed per unit area is readily determined.

The remaining part of the narrow strip is then set on the "Perspex" portion that included the six identical cavities filled with pure water up to the above-mentioned level. (These cavities have also been previously blocked off with the impervious plastic sheet.) The strip is pressed against the "Perspex" block by means of a suitable weight. The pressure is held for exactly two minutes. Then the pressure is reduced, and the cavity is uncovered by removing the plastic material; the sensitized surface of the plate thus is in contact with the vapor given off by the sixth cavity. For this to be correctly done, a piece of paper is stuck underneath the transparent block; on this paper are equidistant black lines showing the points up to which the plastic sheet can be removed to uncover one cavity fully without uncovering the next one.

After two more minutes, the remaining cavities are uncovered in sequence every 2 minutes, until eventually, a number of rounded spots exhibit a range of steadily weaker discolorations, depending upon the effects of water vapor on the plate and the area. This is done for periods of 12, 10, 8, 6, 4 and 2 minutes for the six cavities. At one end is the rounded area showing the greatest discoloration, and at the other end, is that which shows the least discoloration. This narrow strip is then removed and, before being joined to the calibrated piece, it is covered with the gelatin surface of another unserviceable strip of the same size, during a time equal to that needed for the weighing.

Under these conditions, and provided that the requirements mentioned are duly met, maximum discoloration of this densitometric scale is found to be identical with that of the calibrated piece, since the exposures of both discolored portions are identical (12 minutes). With the achievement of this identity, the quantity of water absorbed by the portion of hygrophotographic plate set above the small cavity for 12 minutes shows that the plate has fixed, per unit of surface, a quantity of water equal to that fixed by the large circular reference area used for calibrating.

Since the diameter of this large reference area, which is pure yellow in the hygrophotographic plate and black in the positive (a, in Fig. 10) is 19.4 mm, its area is 295.5mm² and, if the quantity of water absorbed by the surface is 3690 μg, for example, the quantity of water fixed is therefore 12.49 μg/mm². The same applies, of course, to b in this Figure and

as absorption of water vapor by gelatin conforms to a linear law within limits of the period of time and temperature selected, the quantity of water fixed per unit of surface in the other portions of the densitometric scale can be readily determined, these portions being exposed for 10, 8, 6, 4 and 2 minutes. respectively.

Dividing 12.49 by the longest exposure (12 minutes) gives the quantity of water absorbed per square millimeter of area per minute, i.e., 1.04 μg/mm²/min.

In Fig. 13, the exposures of the various portions of the desitometric scale are shown as abscissas, while the ordinates show the densities of the blackening expressed by the logarithm of the ratio between the strength of the incident and transmitted light I/I_0. The density equating unity is that which will let through one-tenth of the incident light strength.

A linear plot is thus obtained, every division of which shows the quantity of water absorbed every minute per surface area equal to unity; in the present instance 1.04 μg. If the blackening due to the moisture percolating through the sheet of plastic material, for example, after remaining 80 hours in the water, is identical with that of e in the Fig. 10, obtained after 6-minutes exposure, the blackening

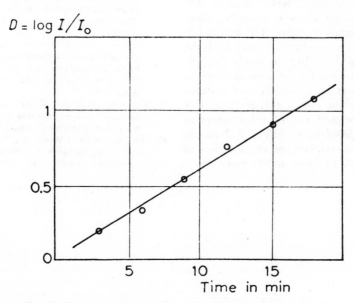

FIG. 13. Plot: every division shows the quantity of water absorbed per minute and per surface area equal to unity.

corresponds to an absorption of $6 \times 1.04 = 6.24 \ \mu g$ of water per square millimeter. Since this quantity of water is absorbed by the hygrophotographic plate after remaining 80 hours in the water at normal temperature, this represents a permeability of $0.07 \ \mu g/mm^2/$ hour.

SUMMARY

The hygrophotographic plates or films composed of a complex salt of silver and mercurous iodide can be easily calibrated and serve in the microdetermination of small quantities of water discharged by leaf transpiration in plant physiology. They permit the measurement of the humidity of the soil in agriculture. In human and animal physiology, the hygrophotographic technique renders great service in the study of perspiration and the physiology of sweat glands. It permits the accurate recording of the topographic distribution of these glands and the personal identification by the aid of these dermatoglyphic recordings. In pharmacology, since the perspiration of the sole of rats and mice can be recorded, the action of different drugs on this perspiration may be studied.

In meteorology, different meteorologists, including the author, have studied the distribution of rain drops by recording them on hygrophotographic plates. The author has also studied the moisture content and the distribution of humidity in foods (butter, margarine, sausages) by the same method, as well as the wetting properties of various detergents. By the aid of this method, this author has disclosed and recorded traces of water in organic solvents, such as alcohols and acetone, and has studied the permeability of plastic materials to water and to moisture.

References

1. Sivadjian, J., "Dix années d'hygrophotographie," *Année Biol.*, **36**, 199–214 (1960). Review of results obtained during the first decade, with a complete list of bibliography from the beginning until 1960 (52 references).
2. Sivadjian, J., "Physiology and Topography of Sweat Glands. Hygrophotographical Studies," *Dermatologica*, **122**, 460-467 (1961).
3. Sivadjian, J., "Hygrophotographic Measurement of Soil Moisture Following a Protracted Drought," *Soil Sci.*, **90**, 369–373 (1960).
4. Sivadjian, J., "Etude hygrophotographique du problème de l'eau chez les plantes croissant sur un rocher," *Bull. Soc. Botan. France*, **108**, 97–99 (1961).
5. Sivadjian, J., and Corral, F., "Determination of Minute Quantities of Water and Water Vapor by the Hygrophotographic Method," *Anal. Chim. Acta*, **26**, 185–190 (1962).
6. Sivadjian, J., and Corral, F., "Hygrophotographic Studies on the Permeability to Water and Moisture of Packaging Materials," *J. Appl. Polymer Sci.*, **6**, 561–570 (1962).
7. Sivadjian, J., "Hygrophotographical Recording Method for the Moisture Content of Foods and for the Permeability of Food Packaging Materials to Water and to Moisture," First International Congress of Food Science and Technology, London, 18th–21st September 1962 (Abstract of Papers, pp. 68–69).
8. Sivadjian, J., "Action de la chlorpromazine sur l'épilepsie expérimentale et sur la transpiration," *Arch. Intern. Pharmacodyn.*, **143**, 377–384 (1963).
9. Sivadjian, J., "La transpiration végétale. Mesure et enregistrement hygrophotographique," Colloque international sur la méthodologie de l'Eco-physiologie végétale, Montpellier, 7–12 Avril 1962.
10. Sivadjian, J., "L'humidité du sol. Mesure et enregistrement hygrophotographique," Colloque international sur la méthodologie de l'Eco-physiologie végétale, Montpellier, 7–12 Avril 1962.
11. Meszaros, E., and Wirth, E., "Distribution spectrale des gouttes des pluies tombant des nuages stratiformes," *Idöjàràs*, **64**, 82 (1960).
12. Meszaros, E., and Wirth, E., "Some Remarks on the Sivadjian Method of Measuring Rain-drop Spectrum," *Idöjàràs*, **63**, 329 (1959).

Author Index

667

Subject Index